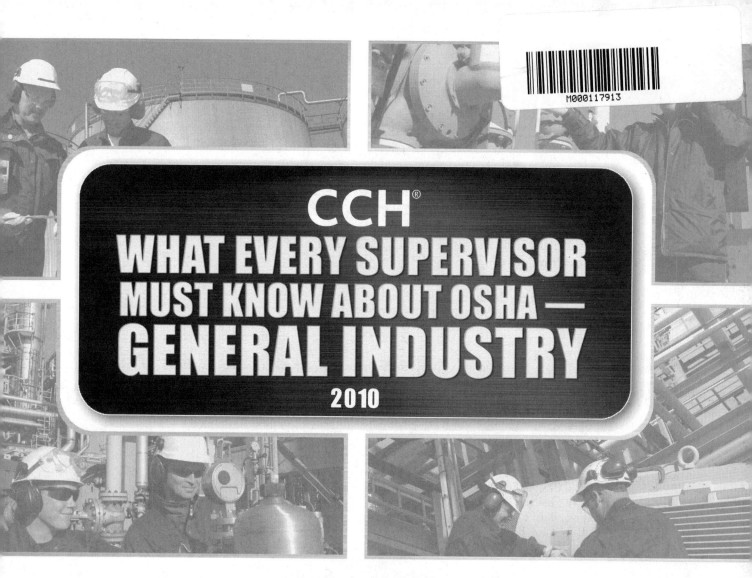

CCH®
WHAT EVERY SUPERVISOR MUST KNOW ABOUT OSHA — GENERAL INDUSTRY
2010

Joe Teeples

SUSTAINABLE FORESTRY INITIATIVE

Certified Fiber Sourcing
www.sfiprogram.org

®. Wolters Kluwer
Law & Business

Vice President, Business Compliance Unit: Paul Gibson, J.D.
Portfolio Managing Editor: Joy Waltemath, J.D.
Managing Editor: David Stephanides, J.D.
Coordinating Editor: Laurel Gershon, J.D., LL.M.
Production Coordinator: Daniel J. Dalaly
Cover Design: Craig Arritola
Interior Design: Craig Arritola
Layout: Kathie Tingson Luzod

ISBN 978-0-8080-2361-6
©2010 **CCH**. All Rights Reserved.
4025 W. Peterson Ave.
Chicago, IL 60646-6085
1 800 248 3248
hr.cch.com/safety

AUTHOR BIOGRAPHY

Author Joe Teeples has over 25 years in the field of occupational safety. He has served as the safety manager of a federal installation where he was instrumental in reducing lost time injuries by 66 percent. Teeples also served the government in the role of director of one of OSHA's Training Institute education centers. In his role as a "train the trainer" in OSHA's Outreach program for various educational centers, he has prepared written training materials, slides, movies, online courses and books for other trainers to use. His company has taught safety around the world in locations such as Saudi Arabia, Trinidad, Guam, Saipan and the Virgin Islands. In the United States, he has trained students on federal requirements from the East Coast to the West Coast, from Alaska to Hawaii.

Teeples holds an M.B.A. from the University of Wisconsin and is a certified member of the World Safety Organization that serves a consultative role to the United Nations. He is also a member of the American Society of Safety Engineers. As a measure of his dedication to safety, Teeples maintains a web site at www.wisafety.com with many useful items for safety professionals to download and use at no charge.

Benson

TABLE OF CONTENTS

(handwritten annotations: WK1, wk1, wk2, wk3, wk8)

Table of Contents

Chapter 5: Hazard Communication 141

Chapter 6: Personal Protective Equipment 165

Chapter 7: Hazardous Waste Operations and Process Safety Management ... 185

Chapter 8: Permit-Required Confined Spaces 197

WK8

WK 8

WK8

WK 8

Table of Contents

OCCUPATIONAL SAFETY AND HEALTH PRE-TEST
(See appendix for answers)

1. What are the two basic purposes of the OSH Act of 1970?
a. f and h
b. g and i
c. g and h
d. f and I
f. To eliminate or minimize occupational hazards in the workplace.
g. To provide a safe and healthful workplace.
h. To recognize, avoid and control hazards in the workplace.
i. To conserve human resources.

2. What is one important effect that Executive Order 12196 has on Federal Agencies?
a. Mandates compliance with all standards applicable to private industry, except where alternative standards are approved by the Secretary of Labor.
b. Mandates that Federal Agencies' programs be consistent with private industry.
c. Provides for OSHA response to reports of hazardous conditions from employees of any Federal Agency.
d. Mandates the establishment of Occupational Safety and Health Committees at the national and other appropriate levels.

3. A confined space supervisor must ensure the following before allowing entry into a confined space.
a. Employee's are trained and qualified
b. The atmosphere has been tested and is safe for entry
c. A standby attendant is present
d. All of the above

4. OSHA regulates the use of compressed air for cleaning purposes. What is the main reason for this and how is it regulated?
a. Compressed air can cause increased noise exposure, and this is controlled by the use of sound-dampening nozzles.
b. Air hoses can rupture causing the hose to "whip" and strike workers. Airlines must be equipped with pressure loss closure valves.
c. Compressed air blows particles and dust causing eye and pressure with guarding.
d. Gases in compressed air can be toxic. Filters and gas absorbents must be used on air compressors.

5. Air purifying respirators are:
a. Permitted in oxygen deficient atmospheres
b. Not permitted in oxygen deficient atmospheres
c. Worn with full beards if the employee will not shave
d. Designed to cool the respirator user

6. Arc welding refers to the use of an electrical current to produce the weld.
a. True
b. False

7. **What is the purpose of ring-testing abrasive grinding wheels?**
   a. A method of detecting cracks in the wheels.
   b. Checks the wheel diameter to assure proper size and mounting.
   c. Tests the rated capacity (in rpm) for the compatibility of the wheel and grinder.
   d. Checks the abrasive action to assure that older wheels are not overworked.

8. **The 29 CFR 19 10, Subpart N addresses storage and handling of materials. Which of the following does Subpart N not address?**
   a. Flammable storage
   b. Fork lift trucks
   c. Hoisting equipment
   d. Railroad cars

9. **Doors, passageways, and stairways, which are not a means of egress, shall be:**
   a. Clearly marked "NOT AN EXIT"
   b. Locked to prevent entry
   c. Removed to prevent confusion
   d. No action required

10. **The most important factor in the use of hearing protectors is:**
    a. The Noise Reduction Factor published by the vendor
    b. The case hardened shell
    c. The polymeric expanded foam adhesive
    d. The fitting to an employee

11. **The permissible exposure limit set by OSHA for lead is:**
    a. 200 ugh/m3
    b. 20 ugh/m3
    c. 50 ugh/m3
    d. 100 ugh/m3

12. **What is a safety can?**
    a. A tightly sealed metal container used to store corrosive material.
    b. A spring-loaded, self-closing container of 10 gallons or less which will not allow the escape of vapor when heated.
    c. A glass container used to store materials that are corrosive to metal containers.
    d. A spring-loaded, self-closing metal container, 5 gallons or less, that will allow the escape of vapor when heated.

13. **Rolling scaffolds must have guardrails at what height?**
    a. 4 feet
    b. 6 feet
    c. 10 feet
    d. 12 feet

14. **Flammable materials have a flash point of less than _____degrees F.**
    a. 200
    b. 110
    c. 160
    d. 100

15. **Guardrails must be 42" high with a midrail between the top rail and floor.**
    a. True
    b. False

16. **A spreader must be used whenever cross cutting stock.**
    a. True
    b. False

17. **High pressure compressed gas cylinders can be handled by their protective caps:**
    a. Anytime, that's what the caps are made for
    b. Only when lifting vertically
    c. During transportation and storage
    d. Never, the cap is only designed to protect the valve.

18. **Which of the following is not one of the storage requirement flammable and combustible liquids?**
    a. The quantity of material stored
    b. The types of containers
    c. The stacking and arrangement of containers
    d. Continuous monitoring for vapor concentration

19. **OSHA makes only three basic requirements of employers with regard to Medical and First Aid. What are they?**
    a. f, g, and h
    b. f, g, and j
    c. g, h, and j
    d. g, h, and I
    e. h, I, and j
    f. Availability of ambulance service
    g. First Aid
    h. Availability of medical personnel
    i. Availability of drenching & flushing
    j. Personal Protection Equipment

20. **A chemical with a skin designation indicates:**
    a. The chemical may be absorbed into the bloodstream through the skin, the mucous membranes, and/or the eye. This absorption contributes to overall exposure.
    b. Skin absorption is the only significant route of exposure; inhalation potential is minimal.
    c. All chemicals are readily absorbed through the skin; those chemicals with a skin designation are corrosive or irritating to the skin.
    d. All of the above

21. **Reverse polarity would be a serious OSHA citation.**
    a. True
    b. False

22. **A class "A" GFCI trips at 5 mA plus or minus 1 mA.**
    a. True
    b. False

23. **"Medical personnel" as defined by OSHA, may be physicians, nurses, or trained (Red Cross or equivalent) First Aid personnel.**
   a. True
   b. False

24. **Which of the following is not a function of foot protection?**
   a. Protect the foot from crushing
   b. Protect the sole of the foot from puncture by nails
   c. Electrical protection
   d. High visibility with reflective footwear

25. **A good disinfectant mixture is 1 part chlorine bleach to _ part(s) water:**
   a. 1
   b. 7
   c. 5
   d. 10

26. **A "Point of Operation" can be described as:**
   a. The area where a belt and pulley create a nip point
   b. The location where the operator stands.
   c. The point at which cutting, shaping, boring, or forming is accomplished upon the stock
   d. The area of the press where material is actually positioned and work is being performed during any process such as shearing, punching, forming, or assembling.

27. **Which of the following devices may be used for overcurrent protection?**
   a. Circuit Breaker
   b. Main Disconnect
   c. Fuse
   d. GFCI
   e. Both A and C

28. **Which of the following best describes the term egress as applied by OSHA?**
   a. The way to, through, and away from an exit.
   b. A specially designated exit or escape.
   c. A function of the fire protection requirements of a building.
   d. Non-portable fire protection, such as a sprinkling system.

29. **Water is a good extinguishing agent but should never be used on a Class___ fire.**
   a. A
   b. B
   c. C
   d. It can be used on all fires

30. **29 CFR 19 10, Subpart D, covers the safe use of walking and working surfaces. Which of the following is not considered under Subpart D?**
   a. Stairways
   b. Ladders
   c. Handrails
   d. Slippery floors
   e. Workbenches

31. Egress (emergency exiting) fundamentals include:
   a. Sufficient exits for occupant load
   b. Illuminated exit markings
   C. Exits not locked or obstructed
   d. All of the above

32. The Hazard Communication standard requires which of the following:
   a. Employees must be provided with a comprehensive medical examination.
   b. Employees must receive training on the hazardous chemicals in their work area.
   c. Each employee must be provided with his/her own set of MSDSs.
   d. All of the above

33. Tongue guards on bench grinders must be adjusted within:
   a. 1/8"
   b. 1/4"
   c. 3/8"
   d. 1/2"

34. Which of the following are not points of operation guards or devices
   a. Photoelectric light curtain
   b. Pullbacks
   c. Emergency pull cord
   d. Two hand controls

35. A worker is using a ladder improperly. Which of the following situations constitutes improper use of a ladder?
   a. An extension ladder is being used in place of a single ladder.
   b. An employee is using a ten-foot stepladder and standing on the next to-the-top step,
   c. A single ladder is leaning against a roof, extending one foot above the roof surface.
   d. An extension ladder is extended to a length of forty feet and the footing is about ten feet from the supporting wall.

COURSE OBJECTIVES

- Become familiar with the Occupational Safety and Health Act, 29 CFR 1910 and relevant interpretations and applications
- Identify common causes of accidents and fatalities in hazardous areas of industry
- Identify abatement strategies for hazards found in industry
- Understand basic instructional methods and techniques
- Be able to present 10 and 30 hour training programs using the OSHA regulations and guidelines

Note: This 2005 version of the course material has been revised based upon comments from instructors and students in the field. It was felt that the original material provided by the OSHA Training Institute in Illinois was of such high quality that the number of changes should be kept to a minimum. Wherever possible the original intent, text and artwork of the 1995 manual was retained in order to allow current instructors to remain familiar with the manual by maintaining the "look and feel" that they have been used to as well as to keep the material in the public domain.

It was felt that the material needed to be updated (the last complete update was in 1995) to:

- Create a flow of educational topics that tended to enhance the educational process as opposed to skipping from one section to another in the book. For example, following a discussion of Industrial Hygiene where the student learns about PEL's and TWA's, the discussion leads to asbestos, lead, hazard communication and hearing conservation programs to reinforce the use of those IH terms. Rewriting the class matrix and ensuring that the book followed the matrix accomplished this. The four day flow was designed to lead the student from a discovery of OSHA and its jurisdictions to specific regulations, and then cover how to train an adult population and finally how to use the OSHA Outreach program to its fullest.
- Update the manual to reflect changes made in Federal regulations since 1995.
- Reduce the number of pages and bulk of the overall book in order to make it more useable and less expensive to print, publish, distribute and ship.
- Include page numbers for easy reference.
- Include student activities (the pretest is printed in the book, along with a safety committee work activity and the answers.
- Sample PPE Assessment forms and Training forms have been included.
- OSHAs FIRM and Outreach Training Catalog have been included.
- Sections on Safety Committees, Office Safety, Training and Accident Investigation have been added.

What Every Supervisor Must Know About OSHA General Industry

Suggested Matrix

TIME	MONDAY	TUESDAY	WEDNESDAY	THURSDAY
8:00 8:50	Opening Remarks Bio Sheets Objectives	Bloodborne Pathogens Asbestos Update	Hazardous Materials	Welding
9:00 9:50	Pre test/review	Hazard Communication	Fire Protection	Vpp OSHA Outreach
10:00 10:50	Intro to OSHA, Inspections, Penalties Intro to Standards	Hazard Communication	Routes of Exit	Training Techniques
11:00 11:45	Standards Workshop	Personal Protective Equipment	Machine Guarding	Q & A OSHARep.
11:45 12:45	Lunch	Lunch	Lunch	Lunch
12:45 1:35	Record Keeping	Hazwoper And Process Safety Management	Lockout Tagout	Review for Exam
1:45 2:35	Record Keeping	Permit Required Confined Spaces	Hand and Power Tools	Exam
2:45 3:35	Walking and Working Surfaces	Power Generation and Electrical	Materials Handling	Exam and Course Evaluations
3:45 4:30	Introduction to Occupational Health	Electrical Concluded	Forklift	Certificate Awards Course Closes

INTRODUCTION TO OSHA

More than 90 million Americans spend their days on the job. They are our most valuable national resource. Yet, until 1970, no uniform, comprehensive provisions existed for their protection against workplace safety and health hazards.

In 1970, the U.S. Congress considered annual figures such as these:

- Job-related accidents accounted for more than 14,000 worker deaths;
- Ten times as many person-days were lost from job-related disabilities as from strikes;
- Estimated new cases of occupational diseases totaled 300,000; and
- Nearly 2½ million workers were disabled.

In terms of lost production and wages, medical expenses and disability compensation, the burden on the nation's commerce was staggering. Human cost was beyond calculation. Therefore, the Occupational Safety and Health Act of 1970 was passed by a bipartisan Congress *"to assure so far as possible every working man and woman in the Nation safe and healthful working conditions and to preserve our human resources."*

This Act requires employers to provide a safe and healthful work place.

General Health and Safety Section 5(a)

Each employer:

1) shall furnish to each of their employees employment and a place of employment which are free from recognized hazards that are causing or are likely to cause serious physical harm to their employees.

2) shall comply with occupational health standards promulgated under this act.

The Act also requires that employees follow the rules:

Section 5(b)

Each employee

1) shall comply with occupational safety and health standards and all rules, regulations, and orders issued pursuant to this act which are applicable to their own actions and conduct.

Under the Act, the Occupational Safety and Health Administration (OSHA) was created to:

- Encourage employers and employees to reduce workplace hazards and to implement new or improve existing safety and health programs;
- Provide for research in occupational safety and health to develop innovative ways of dealing with occupational safety and health problems;
- Establish "separate but dependent responsibilities and rights" for employers and employees for the achievement of better safety and health conditions;
- Maintain a reporting and recordkeeping system to monitor job-related injuries and illnesses;
- Establish training programs to increase the number and competence of occupational safety and health personnel;
- Develop mandatory job safety and health standards and enforce them effectively; and
- Provide for the development, analysis, evaluation and approval of state occupational safety and health programs.

While OSHA continually reviews and redefines specific standards and practices, its basic purposes remain constant. OSHA strives to implement its mandate fully and firmly with fairness to all concerned. In all of its procedures, from standards development through implementation and enforcement, OSHA guarantees employers and employees the right to be fully informed, to participate actively and to appeal actions.

The Act's Coverage

In general, coverage of the Act extends to all employers and their employees in the 50 states, the District of Columbia, Puerto Rico and all other territories under federal government jurisdiction. Coverage is provided either directly by federal OSHA or through an OSHA-approved state program (see section on OSHA-Approved State Programs).

As defined by the Act, an employer is any "person engaged in a business affecting commerce who has employees, but does not include the United States or any State or political subdivision of a State." Therefore, the Act applies to employ-

ers and employees in such varied fields as manufacturing, construction, long shoring, agriculture, law, medicine, charity, disaster relief, organized labor and private education. Such coverage includes religious groups to the extent that they employ workers for secular purposes.

The following are not covered under the Act:
- Self-employed persons;
- Farms at which only immediate members of the farm employer's family are employed; and
- Working conditions regulated by other federal agencies under other federal statutes.

However, when another federal agency is authorized to regulate safety and health working conditions in a particular industry, if it does not do so in specific areas, OSHA standards then apply.

As OSHA develops effective safety and health standards of its own, standards issued under the following laws administered by the Department of Labor are the Safety Act, the Arts and Humanities Act and the Longshoremen's and Harbor Workers' Compensation Act.

Origin of OSHA Standards
The OSHA standards were taken from three sources:
- Consensus standards;
- Proprietary standards; and
- Federal laws in effect when the Occupational Safety and Health Act became law.

Consensus standards are developed by industry-wide, standard-developing organizations and are discussed and substantially agreed upon through consensus by industry. OSHA has incorporated the standards of the two primary standards groups, the American National Standards Institute (ANSI) and the National Fire Protection Association (NFPA), into its set of standards.

For example, ANSI Standard B56.1-1969, Standard for Powered Industrial Trucks, covers the safety requirements relating to the elements of design, operation and maintenance of powered industrial trucks.

Another consensus standard source is the NFPA standards. NFPA No. 301969, Flammable and Combustible Liquids Code was the source standard for Part 1910, Section 106. It covers the storage and use of flammable and combustible liquids with flash points below 200°F.

Professional experts within specific industries, professional societies, and associations prepare proprietary standards. The proprietary standards are determined by a straight membership vote, not by consensus. An example of these would be the "Compressed Gas Association, Pamphlet P-1, Safe Handling of Compressed Gases." This proprietary standard covers requirements for safe handling, storage and use of compressed gas cylinders.

Some federal laws in effect before the OSH Act are enforced by OSHA, including the Federal Supply Contracts Act (Walsh-Healey); Federal Service Contracts Act (McNamara-O'Hara); Contract Work Hours and Safety Standards Act (Construction Safety Act); and the National Foundation on the Arts and Humanities Act.

Horizontal and Vertical Standards

Standards are sometimes referred to as being either "horizontal" or "vertical" in their application. Most standards are horizontal or "general," which means they apply to any employer in any industry. Standards relating to fire protection, working surfaces and first aid are examples of horizontal standards.

Some standards, however, are relevant only to a particular industry, and are called vertical, or "particular" standards. Examples are standards applying to the long shoring industry or the construction industry, and to the special industries covered in Subpart R.

OSHA is responsible for promulgating legally enforceable standards. OSHA standards may require conditions or the adoption or use of one or more practices, means, methods or processes reasonably necessary and appropriate to protect workers on the job. It is the responsibility of employers to become familiar with standards applicable to their establishments and to ensure that employees have and use personal protective equipment when required for safety.

Employees must comply with all rules and regulations that are applicable to their own actions and conduct. Where OSHA has not promulgated specific standards, employers are responsible for following the Act's general duty clause.

The general duty clause of the Act states that each employer "shall furnish ... a place of employment which is free from recognized hazards that are causing or are likely to cause death or serious physical harm to his employees."

States with OSHA-approved occupational safety and health programs must set standards that are at least as effective as the federal standards. Many state plan states adopt standards identical to their federal counterparts. OSHA standards fall into four categories: General industry, maritime, construction and agriculture.

Code of Federal Regulations

One of the most common complaints from people who must comply with the Part 1910 standards is "How do you wade through hundreds of pages of standards and make sense out of them?" From time to time you may have experienced this frustration and been tempted to toss the standards in the "round file."

The Code of Federal Regulations is a codification of the general and permanent rules published in the *Federal Register* by the executive departments and agencies of the federal government. The Code is divided into 50 titles that represent broad areas subject to federal regulation. Each title is divided into chapters that usually bear the name of the issuing agency. Each chapter is further subdivided into parts covering specific regulatory areas. Based on this breakdown, the Occupational Safety and Health Administration is designated Title 29 – Labor, Chapter XVII.

OSHA's regulations (Title 29) are issued as of July 1. The approximate revision date is printed on the cover of each volume. Each volume of the Code is revised at least once each calendar year and issued on a quarterly basis approximately as follows:

- Title 1 – Title 16 as of January 1
- Title 17 – Title 27 as of April 1
- Title 28 – Title 41 as of July 1
- Title 42 – Title 50 as of October I

The Code of Federal Regulations is kept up to date by individual issues of the *Federal Register*. These two publications (the CFR and the *Federal Register*) must be used together to determine the latest version of any given rule.

To determine whether there have been any amendments since the revision date of the Code volume in which the user is interested, the following two lists must be consulted: the "Cumulative List of CFR Sections Affected" issued monthly and the "Cumulative List of Parts Affected" which appears daily in the *Federal Register*. These two lists will refer you to the *Federal Register* page where you may find the latest amendment of any given rule. The pages in the *Federal Register* are numbered sequentially from January 1 to January 1 of the next year. The *Federal Register* is one of the best sources of information on standards, since all OSHA standards are published there when adopted, as are all amendments, corrections, insertions or deletions. Each year the Office of Federal Register publishes all current regulations and standards in the *Code of Federal Regulations* 29 (CFR), available at many libraries and from the Government Printing Office. OSHA's regulations are in Title 29, Part 1900 – 9999. The *Federal Register* is available in many public libraries. Annual subscriptions are available from the Superintendent of Documents, U.S. Government Printing Office, Washington, D.C. 20402.

Under Chapter XVII, the regulations are broken down into Parts. Part 1910, for example, is the standard you are all familiar with, "Occupational Safety and Health Standards," commonly known as the "General Industry Standards." Under each part, such as Part 1910, major blocks of information are broken down into Subparts.

Where to Obtain Copies of Standards

To assist the public in keeping current with OSHA standards, "OSHA Regulations, Documents and Technical Information on CD-ROM" was developed. This CD contains the full text of all OSHA regulations (standards), selected documents and technical information from the OSHA Computerized Information System (OCIS). The OSHA CD is available from the Superintendent of Documents. However, only the *Federal Register* can be used as the official source for OSHA regulations.

Major Subparts in the 1910 standards include:
- Subpart D, Walking-Working Surfaces;
- Subpart E, Exit Routes, Emergency Action Plans, and Fire Prevention Plans;
- Subpart F, Powered Platforms, Manlifts, and Vehicle-Mounted Platforms;
- Subpart G, Occupational Health and Environmental Control;
- Subpart H, Hazardous Materials;
- Subpart I , Personal Protective Equipment;
- Subpart J , General Environmental Controls;
- Subpart K , Medical and First Aid;
- Subpart L, Fire Protection;
- Subpart M, Compressed Gas and Compressed Air Equipment;
- Subpart N, Materials Handling and Storage;
- Subpart 0, Machinery and Machine Guarding;
- Subpart P, Hand/ Portable Powered Tools – Other Hand-Held Equipment;
- Subpart Q, Welding, Cutting and Brazing;
- Subpart R, Special Industries;
- Subpart S, Electrical; and
- Subpart Z, Toxic and Hazardous Substances.

Each Subpart is further broken down into sections. The index of Subpart D, Walking-Working Surfaces is shown below.
- 1910.21   Definitions.
- 1910.22   General requirements.
- 1910.23   Guarding floor and wall openings and holes.
- 1910.24   Fixed industrial stairs.
- 1910.25   Portable wood ladders.
- 1910.26   Portable metal ladders.
- 1910.27   Fixed ladders.
- 1910.28   Safety requirements for scaffolding.
- 1910.29   Manually propelled mobile ladder stands and scaffolds (towers).
- 1910.30   Other working surfaces.
- 1910.31   Sources of standards.
- 1910.32   Standards organizations.

Subpart D is broken down into sections. Section 21 (1910.21), called "Definitions," provides the user with definitions of terms used in each of the Subpart D sections. Section 22 covers general requirements, which include housekeeping, aisle marking, open pit protection and floor loading designation. Sections 23 through 30 give specific requirements for such things as floor openings, ladders, scaffolding, mobile ladder stands and dock boards. Section 31 and 32 provide the user with basic information on the source standard used to prepare each section and the standard organizations referenced in the subpart. Each subsequent subpart repeats these last two items (i.e., source of standard and standards organization).

Subparts E and L go together. All of the requirements for an exit, access to an exit, and exit discharge are contained in Subpart E. Employee emergency plans and fire prevention plans are also included in this subpart.

Subpart L, Fire Protection, contains requirements for fire brigades, whenever an employer establishes them, and provides standards relating to different types of fire extinguishing systems. These include portable and fixed fire-suppression equipment, as well as other fire protection systems, including fire detection and employee alarm systems.

Subpart F, Powered Platforms, Manlifts, and Vehicle Mounted Work Platforms, provides standards for devices used to lift personnel to elevated work positions.

Subparts G and Z go together as they are health related. Subpart G contains ventilation requirements and limitations for noise and radiation exposures. Subpart Z contains limitations for air contaminants as well as specific standards for certain toxic health hazards (e.g., asbestos, lead, inorganic arsenic and acrylonitrile). OSHA's "right-to-know" rule, titled "Hazard Communication," is also contained in Subpart Z.

Subpart H is titled "Hazardous Materials." This subpart has many sections common to all industry.

One of these sections is 101 and contains general requirements relating to handling, storage, and use of compressed gases. Section 106 is widely used because it gives requirements for storage of flammable liquids in portable tanks or other portable containers and safety standards for industrial operations and service station operations. Section 106 also addresses the design of flammable liquid storage cabinets and the interior design of flammable liquid storage rooms. Another commonly used section is 107, which discusses the basic requirements for the design, construction, electrical wiring, ventilation, illumination, operations and maintenance of paint spray booths.

Section 110 is applicable to any operation where liquefied petroleum gas is used to fuel forklifts or for other industrial purposes. The requirements for companies using anhydrous ammonia for any of its operations are detailed in Section 111. Standards for Hazardous Waste Operations and Emergency Response are contained in Section 120.

Subpart I contains requirements for the use of personal protective equipment. Requirements are set forth for protection of all parts of the body, including the eye, face, head and extremities. Section 132 also mentions use of protective clothing, shields and barriers. Section 134 contains requirements for the use of respiratory protection.

Subpart J, General Environmental Controls, contains requirements for sanitation, temporary labor camps and "non-water carriage disposal systems." Section 144 contains safety color-coding requirements for marking physical hazards, such as portable containers of flammable liquids. For example, in Section 106 where the standard discusses the use of approved cans, the color of that approved can is actually described in Section 144. Colors and specifications for signs, aisle marking, tags, machine controls and other items are in Section 144 and 145.

Section 147 covers the control of hazardous energy (lockout/tagout) during the servicing and maintenance of machines and equipment.

Subpart K contains requirements for first aid and consists of only three paragraphs. The first paragraph requires the ready availability of medical consultation on worker health. The second paragraph requires first aid-trained personnel when the company is not geographically close to a hospital. The third paragraph requires eyewashes and deluge showers to be in the work area where employees might be exposed to injurious corrosive materials.

Subpart M, "Compressed Gas and Compressed Air Equipment," sets forth the basic requirements for air receivers in Section 169. These include such things as an indicating gauge, a safety valve, and a drainpipe and valve.

Subpart N is titled "Materials Handling and Storage." Section 176 discusses general storage requirements. Section 178 covers powered industrial trucks used to transport, load, unload and stack these materials. Other materials handling devices, such as overhead cranes, derricks and helicopters, are also covered in Sections 179 through 183. Sling standards are in Section 184.

Subparts 0 and P go together. Basically, Subpart 0 contains the guarding requirements for larger pieces of machinery. Subpart P then contains guarding requirements for hand-held portable power tools. If you wanted to know the guarding requirements for a mechanical power press, you would use Subpart 0, Section 217. If you wanted to know the requirements for a hand-held circular saw, you would use Subpart P, Section 242.

Subpart Q is a specific standard on welding, cutting and brazing. Any welding operation should meet these standards. Specific types of operations covered by this standard include oxygen-fuel gas, arc and resistance welding.

Subpart R contains specific industry standards or "vertical" standards as we discussed earlier. For example, if a company's main business were in pulpwood logging, any hazards noted in those operations should be referenced to the vertical standard.

Subpart S is the electrical standard. These are among the most frequently cited general industry standards.

Paragraph Numbering System

The OSHA standards are easier to deal with once you become familiar with the paragraph numbering system in the *Federal Register*. For example, Part 1910, Section 110 will appear as:

29 CFR 1910.110

The first number, 29, stands for the Title, which in this case relates to Labor. Next, CFR, stands for Code of Federal Regulations. Next, 1910, is the Part number. After 1910 is a period, followed by an Arabic number. This is the Section number; in this case, the number is 110. If you followed this system to its place in the standards, you would find information on the storage and handling of liquefied petroleum gases.

After the Section level, there will be more numbers and letters within parentheses. These represent Subsections. The following example refers to a specific Subsection within the standard:

29 CFR 1910.110(b)(13)(ii)

Like Parts and Sections, Subsections appear in a specific order as well. As noted in the example above, the first level consists of lowercase letters. If the section has three major paragraphs of information in it, they will be numbered 110(a), 110(b) and 110(c). The letter b in the example above refers to the second paragraph or subsection in Section 110.

The next level of numbering involves Arabic numbers. If there are three paragraphs of information between subsections (a) and (b), they will be numbered (a)(1), (a)(2) and (a)(3). The number 13 appears in the example, representing the 13th paragraph or subsection in Subsection (b).

The next level uses the lowercase roman numeral. If there are three paragraphs of information between subsections (a)(1) and (a)(2), they will be numbered (a)(1)(i), (a)(1)(ii) and (a)(1)(iii). The lowercase Roman numeral ii appears in the example, representing the second paragraph or subsection in subsection (b)(13).

Fortunately, the system complexity ends here. If there are more than three levels of subsections, the three-paragraph numbering sequence will be repeated. The one difference is that they will appear in italics:

29 CFR 1910.110(b)(13)(ii)(*b*)(7)(*iii*)

It should be noted, however, that standards promulgated after 1979 may be identified differently when there are more than three levels of subsections. Rather than repeat and italicize the lowercase letter, a capital letter will be used in the fourth set of parentheses. The next subsections also will be Arabic and lowercase Roman numerals, but not italicized:

29 CFR 1910.304(f)(5)(iv)(F)(1)

Color Coding

To further simplify the reading of standards, it is suggested that you color code your standards book. For example, go through the book and find all the section numbers and highlight them in pink. Also highlight every section head full column width in pink. Then go through the book and highlight the subsections (i.e., lowercase letter, Arabic number, lowercase Roman numeral in parentheses) in yellow:

				PINK	**YELLOW**
	Code of				
Title	Fed. Reg.	Part	Section		Subsections
29	CFR	1910	.110		(b)(13)(ii)(*b*)(7)(*iii*)

Also note there is a subject index in the back of the standards book; this index can be very helpful when trying to locate specific standards based on a key word. If you try to locate information within the standards by using the Table of Contents, remember that the particular section number contained on each page is printed in the upper corner of that page.

Federal Employees

Under the Act, federal agency heads are responsible for providing safe and healthful working conditions for their employees. The Act requires agencies to comply standards consistent with those OSHA issues for private sector employers. OSHA conducts federal workplace inspections in response to employees' reports of hazards and as part of a special program that identifies federal workplaces with higher than average rates of injuries and illnesses.

Federal agency heads are required to operate comprehensive occupational safety and health programs that include recording and analyzing injury/illness data, providing training to all personnel and conducting self-inspections to ensure compliance with OSHA standards. OSHA conducts comprehensive evaluations of these programs to assess their effectiveness.

OSHA's federal sector authority is different from that in the private sector in several ways. The most significant difference is that OSHA cannot propose monetary penalties against another federal agency for failure to comply with OSHA standards. Instead, compliance issues unresolved at the local level are raised to higher organizational levels until resolved. Another significant difference is that OSHA does not have authority to protect federal employee "whistleblowers." However, the Whistleblower Protection Act of 1989 affords present and former federal employees (other than those in the U.S. Postal Service and certain intelligence agencies) an opportunity to file their reports using their internal Inspector General lines of communication.

Provisions for State and Local Governments

OSHA provisions do not apply to state and local governments in their role as employers. The Act does provide that any state desiring to gain OSH approval for its private sector occupa-

tional safety and health program (see section on State Plans) must provide a program that covers its state and local government workers and that is at least as effective as its program for private employees. State plans may also cover only public sector employees.

How New Standards are Developed

OSHA can begin standards-setting procedures on its own initiative or in response to petitions from other parties, including the Secretary of Health and Human Services (HHS), the National Institute for Occupational Safety and Health (NIOSH), state and local governments, any nationally recognized standards-producing organization, employer or labor representatives or any other interested person.

Advisory Committees

If OSHA determines that a specific standard is needed, any of several advisory committees may be called upon to develop specific recommendations. There are two standing committees, and ad hoc committees may be appointed to examine special areas of concern. All advisory committees, standing or ad hoc, must have members representing management, labor and state agencies, as well as one or more designees of the Secretary of HHS. The occupational safety and health professions and the general public also may be represented. The two standing advisory committees are the:

- National Advisory Committee on Occupational Safety and Health (NACOSH), which advises, consults with, and makes recommendations to the Secretary of HHS and to the Secretary of Labor on matters regarding administration of the Act; and
- Advisory Committee on Construction Safety and Health, which advises the Secretary of Labor on formulation of construction safety and health standards and other regulations.

NIOSH Recommendations

Recommendations for standards also may come from the National Institute for Occupational Safety and Health (NIOSH), established by the Act as an agency of the Department of HHS. NIOSH conducts research on various safety and health problems, provides technical assistance to OSHA and recommends standards for OSHA's adoption. While conducting its research, NIOSH may conduct workplace investigations, gather testimony from employers and employees and require that employers provide information to them. NIOSH also may require employers to provide medical examinations and tests to determine the incidence of occupational illness among employees. When such examinations and tests are required by NIOSH for research purposes, they may be paid for by NIOSH rather than the employer.

Standards Adoption

Once OSHA has developed plans to propose, amend or revoke a standard, it publishes these intentions in the *Federal Register* as a "Notice of Proposed Rulemaking" or often as an earlier "Advance Notice of Proposed Rulemaking."

An "Advance Notice" or a "Request for Information" is used, when necessary, to solicit information that can be used in drafting a proposal. The Notice of Proposed Rulemaking will include the terms of the new rule and provide a specific time (at least 30 days from the date of publication, usually 60 days or more) for the public to respond. Interested parties who submit written arguments and pertinent evidence may request a public hearing on the proposal when none has been announced in the notice. When such a hearing is requested, OSHA will schedule one and will publish, in advance, the time and place for it in the *Federal Register*.

After the close of the comment period and public hearing, if one is held, OSHA must publish in the *Federal Register* the full final text of any standard amended or adopted and the date it becomes effective, along with an explanation of the standard and the reasons for implementing it. OSHA may also publish a determination that no standard or amendment needs to be issued.

Emergency Temporary Standards

Under certain limited conditions, OSHA is authorized to set emergency temporary standards that take effect immediately. First, OSHA must determine that workers are in grave danger due to exposure to toxic substances or agents determined to be toxic or physically harmful or to new hazards. Then, if OSHA determines an emergency standard is needed, it will publish the emergency temporary standard in the *Federal Register*, where it also serves as a proposed permanent standard. It is then subject to the usual procedure for adopting a permanent standard, except that a final ruling must be made within six months. The validity of an emergency temporary standard may be challenged in an appropriate U.S. Court of Appeals.

Appealing a Standard

No decision on a permanent standard is ever reached without due consideration of the arguments and data received from the public in written submissions and at hearings. Any person who may be adversely affected by a final or emergency standard, however, may file a petition (within 60 days of the rule's promulgation) for judicial review of the standard with the U.S. Court of Appeals for the circuit in which the objector lives or has his or her principal place of business. Filing an appeals petition, however, will not delay the enforcement of a standard, unless the Court of Appeals specifically orders it.

Variances

Employers may ask OSHA for a variance from a standard or regulation if they cannot fully comply by the effective date, due to shortages of materials, equipment or professional or technical personnel or can prove their facilities or methods of operation provide employee protection "at least as effective." Employers located in states with their own occupational safety and health programs should apply to the state for a variance. If however, an employer operates facilities in states under federal OSHA jurisdiction and also in state-plan states, the employer may apply directly to federal OSHA for a single variance applicable to all the establishments in question. OSHA will then work with the state-plan states involved to determine if a variance can be granted that will satisfy state as well as federal OSHA requirements.

Temporary Variance

A temporary variance may be granted to an employer who cannot comply with a standard or regulation by its effective date due to unavailability of professional or technical personnel, materials or equipment, or because the necessary construction or alteration of facilities cannot be completed in time.

Employers must demonstrate to OSHA that they are taking all available steps to safeguard employees in the meantime and that they have put in force an effective program for coming into compliance with the standard or regulation as quickly as possible.

A temporary variance may be granted for the period needed to achieve compliance or for one year, whichever is shorter. It is renewable twice, each time for six months. An application for a temporary variance must identify the standard or portion of a standard from which the variance is requested and the reasons why the employer cannot comply with the standard. The employer must document those measures already taken and to be taken (including dates) to comply with the standard.

The employer must certify that workers have been informed of the variance application, that a copy has been given to the employees' authorized representative and that a summary of the application has been posted wherever notices are normally posted. Employees also must be informed that they have the right to request a hearing on the application. The temporary variance will not be granted to an employer who simply cannot afford to pay for the necessary alterations equipment or personnel.

Permanent Variance

A permanent variance (alternative to a particular requirement or standard) may be granted to employers who prove their conditions, practices, means, methods operations or processes provide a safe and healthful workplace as effectively as would compliance with the standard.

In making a determination, OSHA weighs the employer's evidence and arranges a variance inspection and hearing where appropriate. If OSHA finds the request valid, it prescribes a permanent variance detailing the employer's specific exceptions and responsibilities under the ruling. When applying for a permanent variance, the employer must inform employees of the application and of their right to request a hearing. Anytime after six months from the issuance of a permanent

variance, the employer or employees may petition OSHA to modify or revoke it. OSHA also may do this of its own accord.

Interim Order

So that employers may continue to operate under existing conditions until a variance decision is made, they may apply to OSHA for an interim order. Application for an interim order may be made either at the same time as, or after, application for a variance. Reasons why the order should be granted may be included in the interim order application. If OSHA denies the request, the employer will be notified of the reason for denial.

If the interim order is granted, the employer and other concerned parties will be informed of the order, and the terms of the order are published in the *Federal Register*. The employer must inform employees of the order by giving a copy to the authorized employee representative and by posting a copy wherever notices are normally posted.

Experimental Variance

If an employer is participating in an experiment to demonstrate or validate new job safety and health techniques, and that experiment has been approved by either the Secretary of Labor or the Secretary of HHS, a variance may be granted to permit the experiment. In addition to temporary, permanent and experimental variances, the Secretary of Labor also may find certain variances justified when the national defense is impaired. Variances are not retroactive. An employer who has been cited for a standards violation may not seek relief from that citation by applying for a variance. The fact that a citation is outstanding, however, does not prevent an employer from filing a variance application.

Public Petitions

OSHA continually reviews its standards to keep pace with developing and changing industrial technology. Therefore, employers and employees should be aware that just as they may petition OSHA for the development of standards, they may also petition OSHA for the modification or revocation of standards.

Recordkeeping and Reporting

Before the Act became effective, no centralized, systematic method existed for monitoring occupational safety and health problems. Statistics on job injuries and illnesses were collected by some states and by some private organizations; national figures were based on not-altogether-reliable projections. With OSHA came the first basis for consistent, nationwide procedures — a vital requirement for gauging problems and solving them.

Employers of 11 or more employees must maintain records of occupational injuries and illnesses as they occur. The purpose of keeping records is to permit survey material to be compiled, to help define high-hazard industries, and to inform employees of the status of their employer's record. Employers in state-plan states are required to keep the same records as employers in other states.

OSHA recordkeeping is not required for certain retail trades and some service industries. Exempt employers, like nonexempt employers, must comply with OSHA standards, display the OSHA poster and report to OSHA within eight hours of the occurrence of any accident that results in one or more fatalities or the hospitalization of three or more employees. If an on-the-job accident occurs that results in the death of an employee or in the hospitalization of three or more employees, all employers, regardless of the number of employees, must report the accident, in detail, to the nearest OSHA office within eight hours. In states with approved plans, employers report such accidents to the state agency responsible for safety and health programs.

Injury and Illness Records

Recordkeeping forms are maintained on a calendar-year basis. They are not sent to OSHA or any other agency. They must be maintained for five years at the place of business and must be available for inspection by representatives of OSHA, HHS or the designated state agency. Many specific OSHA standards have additional recordkeeping and reporting requirements. (See Chapter 20, Recordkeeping.)

Keeping Employees Informed

Employers are responsible for keeping employees informed about OSHA and the various safety and health matters with which they are involved. Federal OSHA and states with their own occupational safety and health programs require that each employer post certain materials at a prominent location in the workplace. These include:

- The Job Safety and Health Protection workplace poster (OSHA 2203 or state equivalent) informing employees of their rights and responsibilities under the Act. Any official edition of the poster is acceptable. In addition displaying the workplace poster, the employer must make available to employees, upon request, copies of the Act and copies of relevant OSHA rules and regulations.
- Summaries of petitions for variances from standards or recordkeeping procedures.
- Copies of all OSHA citations for violations of standards. These copies must remain posted at or near the location of alleged violations for three days or until the violations are corrected, whichever is longer.
- The Log and Summary of Occupational Injuries and Illnesses (OSHA No. 300). The log must be maintained and a summary (OSHA No. 300A) must be signed by an officer of the company and posted no later than February 1. It must remain in place until May 1.

All employees have the right to examine any records kept by their employers regarding their exposure to hazardous materials or the results of medical surveillance. Occasionally, OSHA standards or NIOSH research activities will require an employer to measure and record employee exposure to potentially harmful substances. Employees have the right (in person or through their authorized representative) to be present during the measuring as well as to examine records of the results.

Under these substance-specific requirements, each employee or former employee has the right to see his or her examination records, and must be told by the employer if his or her exposure has exceeded the levels set by OSHA. The employee must also be told what corrective measures are being taken.

In addition to having access to records, employees in manufacturing facilities must be provided with information about all of the hazardous chemicals in their work areas.

Employers are to provide this information via labels on containers, material safety data sheets and training programs.

Workplace Inspections

Authority to Inspect

To enforce its standards, OSHA representatives are authorized under the Act to conduct workplace inspections. Every establishment covered by the Act is subject to inspection by OSHA compliance safety and health officers, who are chosen for their knowledge and experience in the occupational safety and health field. Compliance officers are vigorously trained in OSHA standards and in recognition of safety and health hazards. Similarly, states with their own occupational safety and health programs conduct inspections using qualified compliance safety and health officers.

Under the Act, "upon presenting appropriate credentials to the owner, operator or agent in charge," an OSHA compliance officer is authorized to:

Enter without delay and at reasonable times any factory, plant, establishment, construction site or other areas, workplace, or environment where work is performed by an employee of an employer....

Inspect and investigate during regular working hours, and at other reasonable times, and within reasonable limits and in a reasonable manner, any such place of employment and all pertinent conditions, structures, machines, apparatus, devices, equipment and materials therein, and to question privately any such employer, owner, operator, agent or employee.

Inspections are conducted without advance notice. There are, however, special circumstances under which OSHA may indeed give notice to the employer, but even then, such a notice will be less than 24 hours. These special circumstances include:

- Imminent-danger situations that require correction as soon as possible;
- Inspections that must take place after regular business hours or that require special preparation;

- Cases where notice is required to ensure that the employer and employee representative or other personnel will be present; and
- Situations in which the OSHA area director determines that advance notice would produce a more thorough or effective inspection.

Employers receiving advance notice of an inspection must inform their employees' representative or arrange for OSHA to do so. If an employer refuses to admit an OSHA compliance officer or if an employer attempts to interfere with the inspection, the Act permits appropriate legal action to be taken.

Based on a 1978 Supreme Court ruling (Marshall v. Barlows, Inc.), OSHA may not conduct warrantless inspections without an employer's consent. It may however inspect after acquiring a judicially authorized search warrant based upon administrative probable cause or evidence of a violation.

Inspection Priorities

Obviously, not all 6 million workplaces covered by the Act can be inspected immediately. The worst situations need attention first. Therefore, OSHA has established a system of inspection priorities.

Imminent Danger

Imminent-danger situations are given top priority. An imminent danger is any condition where there is reasonable certainty that a danger exists that can be expected to cause death or serious physical harm immediately or before the danger can be eliminated through normal enforcement procedures.

Serious physical harm is any type of harm that could cause permanent or prolonged damage to the body or while not damaging the body on a prolonged basis, could cause such temporary disability as to require inpatient hospital treatment. OSHA considers that "permanent or prolonged damage" has occurred when, for example, a part of the body is crushed or severed; an arm, leg or finger is amputated; or sight in one or both eyes is lost. This kind of damage also includes that which renders a part of the body either functionally useless or substantially reduced in efficiency on or off the job. For example, bones in a limb shattered so severely that mobility or dexterity will be permanently reduced.

Temporary disability requiring in-patient hospital treatment includes injuries, such as simple fractures, concussions, burns, or wounds involving substantial loss of blood and requiring extensive suturing or other healing aids. Injuries or illnesses that are difficult to observe are classified as serious if they inhibit a person in performing normal functions, cause reduction in physical or mental efficiency or shorten life.

Health hazards may constitute imminent-danger situations when they present a serious and immediate threat to life or health. For a health hazard to be considered an imminent danger, there must be a reasonable expectation that toxic substances, such as dangerous fumes, dusts or gases are present and that exposure to them will cause immediate and irreversible harm to such a degree as to shorten-life or cause a reduction in physical or mental efficiency, even though the resulting harm is not immediately apparent.

Employees should inform the supervisor or employer immediately if they detect or even suspect an imminent-danger situation in the workplace. If the employer takes no action to eliminate the danger, an employee or an authorized employee representative may notify the nearest OSHA office and request an inspection. The request should identify the workplace location, detail the hazard or condition and include the employee's name, address and telephone number. Although the employer has the right to see a copy of the complaint if an inspection results, the name of the employee will be withheld if the employee so requests.

If a request for inspection is made, the OSHA area director will review the information and immediately determine whether there is a reasonable basis for the allegation. If it is decided the case has merit, the area director will assign a compliance officer to conduct an immediate inspection of the workplace.

Upon inspection, if an imminent danger situation is found, the compliance officer will ask the employer to voluntarily abate the hazard and to remove endangered employees from exposure. Should the employer fail to do

so OSHA, through the regional solicitor, may apply to the nearest federal district court for appropriate legal action to correct the situation. Before the OSHA inspector leaves the workplace, he or she will advise all affected employees of the hazard and post an imminent-danger notice; judicial action can produce a temporary restraining order (immediate shutdown) of the operation or section of the workplace where the imminent danger exists. Should OSHA "arbitrarily or capriciously" decline to bring court action, the affected employees may sue the Secretary of Labor to compel the Secretary to do so.

Walking off the job because of potentially unsafe workplace conditions is not ordinarily an employee right. To do so may result in disciplinary action by the employer. However, an employee does have the right to refuse (in good faith) to be exposed to an imminent danger. OSHA rules protect employees from discrimination if:

- Where possible, he or she asked the employer to eliminate the danger and the employer failed to do so;
- The danger is so imminent that there is not sufficient time to have the danger eliminated through normal enforcement procedures;
- The danger facing the employee is so grave that "a reasonable person" in the same situation would conclude there is a real danger of death or serious physical harm; or
- The employee has no reasonable alternative to refusing to work under such conditions (e.g., asking for reassignment to another area).

Catastrophes and Fatal Accidents
Second priority is given to investigation of fatalities and catastrophes resulting in hospitalization of three or more employees. The employer must report such situations to OSHA within eight hours of their occurrence. Investigations are made to determine if OSHA standards were violated and to avoid recurrence of similar accidents

Employee Complaints
Third priority is given to employee complaints of an alleged violation of standard or of unsafe or unhealthful working conditions. Also included in this category are serious referrals

of unsafe or unhealthful working conditions from other sources, such as local or state agencies or departments.

The Act gives each employee the right to request an OSHA inspection when the employee feels he or she is in imminent danger from a hazard or when he or she feels that there is a violation of an OSHA standard that threatens physical harm. OSHA will maintain confidentiality if requested, will inform the employee of any action it takes regarding the complaint and, if requested, will hold an informal review of any decision not to inspect. Just as in situations of imminent danger, the employee's name will be withheld from the employer, if the employee so requests.

Programmed High-Hazard Inspections

Next in priority are programmed, or planned, inspections aimed at specific high-hazard industries, occupations or health substances. Industries are selected for inspection on the basis of factors such as death, injury and illness incidence rates and employee exposure to toxic substances. Special emphasis may be regional or national in scope, depending on the distribution of the workplaces involved. States with their own occupational safety and health programs may use somewhat different systems to identify high-hazard industries for inspection.

Follow-up Inspections

A follow-up inspection determines whether previously cited violations have been corrected. If an employer has failed to abate a violation, the compliance officer informs the employer that he or she is subject to alleged "Notification of Failure to Abate" violations and may face additional proposed daily penalties while such failure or violations continues.

Inspection Process

Prior to inspection, the compliance officer will become familiar with as many relevant facts as possible about the workplace, taking into account such things as the history of the establishment, the nature of the business and the particular standards likely to apply. Preparing for the inspection also involves selecting appropriate equipment for detecting and measuring such things as fumes, gases, toxic substances and noise.

Inspector's Credentials

An inspection begins when the OSHA compliance officer arrives at the establishment. He or she will display official credentials and ask to meet an appropriate employer representative. Employers should always insist upon seeing the compliance officer's credentials. An OSHA compliance officer carries U.S. Department of Labor credentials bearing his or her photograph and a serial number that can be verified by phoning the nearest OSHA office. Anyone who tries to collect a penalty at the time of inspection or promotes the sale of a product or service at any time is not an OSHA compliance officer. Posing as a compliance officer is a violation of law; suspected impostors should be promptly reported to local law enforcement agencies.

Opening Conference

In the opening conference, the compliance officer (CSHO) will explain why the establishment was selected. The CSHO also will ascertain whether an OSHA-funded consultation program is in progress or whether the facility is pursuing or has received an inspection exemption; if programmed, the inspection is usually terminated. The employer will then be asked to select an employer representative to accompany the CSHO during the inspection.

The CSHO will explain the purpose of the visit, the scope of the inspection and the standards that apply. The employer will be given a copy of any employee complaint that may be involved.

An authorized employee representative also will be given the opportunity to attend the opening conference and to accompany the compliance officer during inspection. If a recognized bargaining representative represents the employees, the union ordinarily will designate the employee representative to accompany the compliance officer. Similarly, if there is a plant safety committee, the employee members of the committee will designate the employee representative (in the absence of a recognized bargaining representative). Where neither employee group exists, the employees themselves may select an employee representative or the compliance officer will determine if any employee suitably represents the interest of other employees. Under no circumstances may the employer select the employee representative for the walk-around.

The Act does not require that there be an employee representative for each inspection. Where there is no authorized employee representative, however, the compliance officer must consult with a reasonable number of employees concerning safety and health matters in the workplace; such consultations may be held privately.

Inspection Tour

After the opening conference, the compliance officer and accompanying representatives will proceed through the establishment, inspecting work areas for compliance with OSHA standards. The compliance officer will determine the route and duration of the inspection. When speaking with employees, the compliance officer will make every effort to minimize any work interruptions. The compliance officer will observe conditions, consult with employees, take instrument readings, examine records and possibly tale photos for record purposes.

Trade secrets observed by the compliance officer will be kept confidential. An inspector who releases confidential information without authorization is subject to a $1,000 fine and/or one year in jail. The employer may require that the employee representative have a security clearance for any area in question.

Employees will be consulted during the inspection tour. The compliance officer may stop and question workers in private about safety and health conditions and practices in their workplaces. Each employee is protected under the Act from discrimination for exercising their safety and health rights.

Posting and recordkeeping will be checked. The compliance officer will inspect records of deaths, injuries and illnesses that the employer is required to keep. He or she will check to see that a copy of the totals from the last page of OSHA No. 300 has been posted and that the OSHA workplace poster (OSHA 2203) is prominently displayed. Where records of employee exposure to toxic substances and harmful physical agents are required, they will be examined.

The CSHO also will explain the requirements of the Hazard Communication Standard, which requires employers to establish a written, comprehensive hazard communication program that includes provisions for container labeling, material safety data sheets and an employee-training program. The program must provide a list of the hazardous chemicals in each work area and the means the employer will use to inform employees of the hazards of non-routine tasks.

During the course of the inspection, the CSHO will point out to the employer any unsafe or unhealthful working conditions he or she observes. At the same time, the CSHO will discuss possible corrective action if the employer so desires. Some apparent violations detected by the compliance officer can be corrected immediately. However, even if immediately corrected the apparent violations may still serve as the basis for a citation and/or notice of proposed penalty. An inspection tour may cover part or all of an establishment, even if the inspection was in response to a specific complaint, accident or fatality.

Closing Conference

After the inspection tour, a closing conference will be held between the compliance officer and the employer or the employer representative. It is a time for free discussion of problems and needs — a time for frank questions and answers.

The compliance officer discusses with the employer all unsafe or unhealthful conditions observed on the inspection and indicates all apparent violations for which a citation may be issued or recommended. The employer is told of appeal rights. The compliance officer does not indicate any proposed penalties. Only the OSHA area director has that authority, and only after having received a full report.

During the closing conference, the employer may wish to produce records to show compliance efforts and to provide information that can help OSHA determine how much time may be needed to abate an alleged violation. When appropriate, more than one closing conference may be held. This is usually necessary when health hazards are being evaluated or when laboratory reports are required.

A closing discussion will be held with the employees, or their representative if requested, to discuss matters of direct interest to employees. The employees' representative may be present at the closing conference.

The CSHO will explain that OSHA area offices are full-service resource centers that provide a number of services, including guest speakers, handout materials that can be distributed to interested persons, and training and technical materials on safety and health matters.

Citations and Penalties

The OSHA area director issues citations. After the compliance officer reports his or her findings, the area director will determine what citations, if any, will be issued and what penalties, if any, will be proposed.

Citations inform the employer and employees of the regulations and standard alleged to have been violated and of the proposed length of time set for the abatement. The employer will receive citations and notices of propose penalties by certified mail. The employer must post a copy of each citation near the place the violation occurred for three days or until the violation is abated, whichever is longer.

Penalties

There are several types of violations that may be cited and penalties that may be proposed. Citation and penalty procedures may differ somewhat in states that administer their own occupational safety and health programs.

Other Than Serious Violation. A violation that has a dire relationship to job safety and health, but probably would not cause death or serious physical harm. A proposed penalty of up to $7,000 for each violation is discretionary.

A penalty for an other-than-serious violation may be adjusted downward by as much as 95 percent, depending on the employer's good faith (demonstrated efforts to comply with the Act), history of previous violations and business size. When the adjusted penalty amounts to less than $100, no penalty is proposed.

Serious Violation. A violation where there is substantial probability that death or serious physical harm could result and that the employer knew, or should have known, of the hazard.

A mandatory penalty of up to $7,000 for each violation is proposed. A penalty for a serious violation may be adjusted downward, based on the employer's good faith, history of previous violations, the gravity of the alleged violation, and size of business.

Willful Violation. A violation that the employer knowingly commits or commits with plain indifference to the law. The employer either knows that what it is doing constitutes a violation, or is aware that a hazardous condition existed and made no reasonable effort to eliminate it.

Penalties of up to $70,000 may be proposed for each willful violation, with a minimum penalty of $5,000 for each violation. A proposed penalty for a willful violation may be adjusted downward, depending on the size of the business and its history of previous violations. Usually, no credit is given for good faith.

If an employer is convicted of a willful violation of a standard that has resulted in the death of an employee, the offense is punishable by a court-imposed fine, imprisonment for up to six months, or both. A fine of up to $250,000 for an individual or $500,000 for a corporation may be imposed for a criminal conviction.

Repeated Violation. A violation of any standard, regulation, rule or order where, upon reinspection, is found to be substantially similar to a previous violation. A repeated violation brings a fine of up to $70,000. To be the basis of a repeated citation, the original citation must be final; a citation under contest may not serve as the basis for a subsequent repeated citation.

Failure to Abate Prior Violation. Failure to abate a prior violation may bring a civil penalty of up to $7,000 for each day the violation continues beyond the prescribed abatement date.

De Minimis Violation. De minimis violations are violations of standards that have no direct or immediate relationship to safety or health. When de minimis conditions are found during an inspection, they are documented in the same way as any other violation, but are not included on the citation.

Additional violations for which citations and proposed penalties may be issued upon conviction:

- Falsifying records, reports or applications can bring a fine of $10,000, up to six months in jail, or both.
- Violations of posting requirements can bring a civil penalty of up to $7,000.

- Assaulting a compliance officer or otherwise resisting, opposing, intimidating or interfering with a compliance officer while he or she is engaged in the performance of his or her duties is a criminal offense, subject to a fine of not more than $5,000 and imprisonment for not more than three years.

Table 1-1.
OSHA PENALTIES

Willful	
– Maximum	$70,000
– Minimum	$ 5,000
Repeated – Maximum	$70,000
Serious, Other-than-Serious, Other Specific Violations	
– Maximum	$7,000
Failure to Abate for each calendar day beyond abatement date	
– Maximum	$7,000
OSHA Notice	$1,000
Posting of OSHA Record Keeping Summary	$1,000
Posting of Citation	$3,000
Maintaining OSHA 300, OSHA Record Keeping	$1,000
Reporting Fatality/Catastrophe	$5,000
Access to Records under 1904	$1,000
Notification Requirements under 1903.6 (Advance Notice)	$2,000

Appeals Process

Appeals by Employees
If an inspection was initiated due to an employee complaint, the employee or authorized employee representative may request an informal review of any decision not to issue a citation.

Employees may not contest citations, amendments to citations, penalties or lack of penalties. They may contest the time in the citation for abatement of a hazardous condition. They also may contest an employer's Petition for Modification of Abatement (PMA), which requests an extension of the abatement period. Employees must contest the PMA within 10 working days of its posting or within 10 working days after an authorized employee representative has received a copy. Within 15 working days of the employer's receipt of the citation, the employee may submit a written objection to OSHA. The OSHA area director will forward the objection to the Occupational Safety and Health Review Commission, which operates independently of OSHA.

Employees may request an informal conference with OSHA to discuss any issues raised by an inspection, citation, and notice of proposed penalty or employer's notice of intention to contest.

Appeals by Employers
When issued a citation or notice of a proposed penalty, an employer may request an informal meeting with OSHA's area director to discuss the case. Employee representatives may be invited to attend the meeting. The area director is authorized to enter into settlement agreements that revise citations and penalties to avoid prolonged legal disputes.

Petition for Modification of Abatement
Upon receiving a citation, the employer must correct the cited hazard by the prescribed date unless it contests the citation or abatement date. Factors beyond the employer's reasonable control may prevent the completion of corrections by that date.

The written petition should specify all steps taken to achieve compliance, the additional time needed to achieve complete compliance, the reasons such additional time is needed, all temporary steps being taken to safeguard employees against the cited hazard during the intervening period, that a copy of the PMA was posted in a conspicuous place at or near each place where a violation occurred and that the employee representative (if there is one) received a copy of the petition.

Notice of Contest
If the employer decides to contest either the citation, the time set for abatement or the proposed penalty, it has 15 working days from the time the citation and proposed penalty are received in which to notify the OSHA area director in writing. An orally expressed disagreement will not suffice.

There is no specific format for the Notice of Contest; however, it must clearly identify the employer's basis for filing the citation, notice of proposed penalty, abatement period or notification of failure to correct violations.

A copy of the Notice of Contest must be given to the employees' authorized representative. If a recognized bargaining agent does not represent any affected employees, a copy of the notice must be posted in a prominent location in the workplace or personally served upon each unrepresented employee.

Review Procedure

If the written Notice of Contest has been filed within the required 15 working days, the OSHA Area Director will forward the case to the Occupational Safety and Health Review Commission. The commission is an independent agency not associated with OSHA or the Department of Labor. The commission will assign the case to an administrative law judge.

The judge may schedule a hearing in a public place near the employer's workplace or, if it is found to be legally invalid, disallow the contest. The employer and the employees have the right to participate in the hearing; the commission does not require that attorneys represent them. Once the administrative law judge has ruled, any party to the case may request a further review by OSHRC. Any of the three OSHRC commissioners also may, at his or her own motion, bring a case before the commission for review. Commission rulings may be appealed to the appropriate U.S. Court of Appeals.

Appeals in State-Plan States

States with their own occupational safety and health programs have a state system for review and appeal of citations, penalties and abatement periods. The procedures are generally similar to federal OSHA's, but a state review board or equivalent authority hears cases.

OSHA-Approved State Programs

The Act encourages states to develop and operate, under OSHA guidance, state job safety and health plans.

Once a state plan is approved, OSHA funds up to 50 percent of the program's operating costs. State plans are required to provide standards and enforcement programs, as well as voluntary compliance activities that are at least as effective as the federal program. State plans developed for the private sector also must, to the extent permitted by state law, provide coverage for state and local government employees. OSHA rules also permit states to develop plans limited in coverage for state and local government, or public schools, employees only; in such cases, private sector employment remains under federal jurisdiction.

To gain OSHA approval as a developmental plan, a state must have adequate legislative authority and must demonstrate that within three years it will provide standards-setting, enforcement and appeals procedures; public employee protection; a sufficient number of competent enforcement personnel; and training, education and technical assistance programs.

If, at any time during this period or later, it appears that the state is capable of enforcing standards in accordance with the above requirements, OSHA may enter into an operational status agreement with the state. OSHA generally limits its enforcement activity to areas not covered by the state in the agreement and suspends all concurrent federal enforcement.

Scheduled accident and complaint inspections generally become the primary responsibility of the state.

When all developmental steps concerning resources, procedures, and other requirements have been completed and approved, OSHA then certifies that a state has the legal, administrative, and enforcement means necessary to operate effectively. This action renders no judgment on how well or poorly a state is actually operating its program, but merely attests to the structural completeness of its program. After this certification, there is a period of at least one year to determine if a state is effectively providing safety and health protection.

Employers and employees should find out if their state operates an OSHA-approved state program and, if so, become familiar with it (See Exhibit 1-2.). State safety and health standards under approved plans must keep pace with federal standards, and state plans must guarantee employer and employee rights as does OSHA. If it is found that the state is operating at least as effectively as federal OSHA and other requirements including compliance staffing levels are met, final approval of the plan may be granted and federal authority will cease in those areas over which the state has jurisdiction.

Exhibit 1-2. State-plan states.
The following states and territories have OSHA-approved state plans:

Alaska	New Mexico
Arizona	New York*
California	North Carolina
Connecticut*	Oregon
Hawaii	Puerto Rico
Indiana	South Carolina
Iowa	Tennessee
Kentucky	Utah
Maryland	Vermont
Michigan	Virgin Islands*
Minnesota	Virginia
Nevada	Washington
New Jersey*	Wyoming

*Plans only cover public-sector employees.

Services Available

Consultation Assistance

Consultation assistance is available to employers who want help in establishing and maintaining a safe and healthful workplace. Largely funded by OSHA, this service is provided at no cost to the employer. No penalties are proposed or citations issued for hazards identified by the consultant. Consultation is provided to the employer with the assurance that his or her name and firm and any information about the workplace will not be routinely reported to the OSHA inspection staff.

Primarily developed for smaller employers with more hazardous operations, the consultation service is delivered by state government agencies or universities employing professional safety consultants and health consultants. When delivered at the worksite, consultation assistance includes an opening conference with the employer to explain the ground rules for consultation, a walk through the workplace to identify any specific hazards and to examine those aspects of the employer's safety and health program that relate to the scope of the visit, and a closing conference followed by a written report to the employer of the consultant's finding and recommendations.

This process begins with the employer's request for consultation and the commitment to correct any serious job safety and health hazards identified by the consultant. Possible violations of OSHA standards will not be reported to OSHA enforcement staff unless the employer fails or refuses to eliminate or control worker exposure to any identified serious hazard or imminent danger situation. In such unusual circumstances, OSHA may investigate and begin enforcement action.

Employers who receive a comprehensive consultation visit, correct all identified hazards, and demonstrate that an effective safety and health program is in operation may be exempted from OSHA programmed enforcement inspections (not complaint or accident investigations) for a period of one year. Comprehensive consultation assistance includes an appraisal of all mechanical, physical, work practice, and environmental hazards of the workplace and all aspects of the employer's present job safety and health program.

Voluntary Protection Programs

The voluntary protection programs (VPPs) represent one part of OSHA's effort to extend worker protection beyond the minimum required by OSHA standards. These programs as well as expanded onsite consultation services and full-service area offices are cooperative approaches that when coupled with an effective enforcement program, expand worker protection to help meet the goals of the Occupational Safety and Health Act of 1970.

The three VPPs-Star, Merit, and Demonstration-are designed to:
- Recognize outstanding achievement of those who have successfully incorporated comprehensive safety and health programs into their total management systems;
- Motivate others to achieve excellent safety and health results in the same outstanding way; and
- Establish a relationship between employers, employees, and OSHA that is based on cooperation rather than coercion.

Star Program. This program is the most demanding and the most prestigious. It is open to employers in any industry who have successfully managed a comprehensive safety and health program to reduce injury rates below the national average for that industry. Specific requirements for the program include:
- Management commitment and employee participation;
- A high quality worksite analysis program;

- Hazard prevention and control programs; and
- Comprehensive safety and health training for all employees.

These requirements must all be in place and operating effectively.

Merit Program. This program is primarily a stepping stone to Star Program. An employer with a basic safety and health program built around the Star requirement who is committed to improving the company's program and has the resources to do so within a specified period of time may work with OSHA to meet Star qualifications.

Demonstration Program. This program is for companies that provide Star-quality worker protection in industries where certain Star requirements may not be appropriate or effective. It allows OSHA both the opportunity to recognize outstanding safety and health programs that would otherwise be unreached by the VPP and to determine if general Star requirements can be changed to include these companies as Star participants.

OSHA reviews an employer's VPP application and conducts an on-site review to verify that the safety and health program described is in operation at the site. Evaluations are conducted on a regular basis: annually for Merit and Demonstration programs and triennially for Star. All participants must send their injury information annually to their OSHA regional office. Sites participating in the VPP are not scheduled for programmed inspection; however, any employee complaints, serious accidents or significant chemical releases that may occur are handled according to routine enforcement procedures.

An employer may make application for any VPP at the nearest OSHA regional office. Once OSHA is satisfied that, on paper, the employer qualifies for the program, an on-site review will be scheduled. The review team will present its findings in a written report for the company's review prior to submission to the Assistant Secretary of Labor, who heads OSHA. If approved, the employer will receive a letter from the Assistant Secretary informing the site of its participation in the VPP. A certificate of approval and flag are presented at a ceremony held at or near the approved worksite. Star sites receiving reapproval after each triennial evaluation receive plaques at similar ceremonies. The VPPs described are available in states under federal jurisdiction.

Training and Education

OSHA's area offices are full-service centers offering a variety of informational services, such as availability for speaking engagements, publication, audio-visual aids on workplace hazards and technical advice.

The OSHA Training Institute in Arlington Heights, Ill., provides basic and advanced training and education in safety and health for federal and state compliance officers; state consultants; other federal agency personnel; and private sector employers, employees and their representatives. Institute courses cover areas such as electrical hazards, machine guarding, ventilation and ergonomics. The Institute facility includes classrooms, laboratories, a library, and an audiovisual unit. The laboratories contain various demonstrations and equipment, such as power presses, woodworking and welding shops, a complete industrial ventilation unit and a sound demonstration laboratory.

OSHA also provides funds to nonprofit organizations to conduct workplace training and education in subjects where OSHA identifies areas of unmet needs for safety and health.

Current grant subjects include agricultural health and safety, and hazard communication programs for small businesses that do not have safety and health staff to assist them. Organizations awarded grants use funds to develop training and educational programs, reach out to workers and employers for whom their program is appropriate and provide these programs to workers and employers.

Grants are awarded annually, with a one-year renewal possible. Grant recipients are expected to contribute 20 percent of the total grant cost. Information on grants can be found at the OSHA web site at www.osha.gov. Look for the Susan Harwood Grants. These grants run annually from September to September with the submissions being due to the OSHA Training Institute in Arlington Heights, Ill. in June or July.

Employer Responsibilities and Rights

Employers have certain responsibilities and rights under the Occupational Safety and Health

Act of 1970. Employer responsibilities and rights in states with their own occupational safety and health programs are generally the same as in federal OSHA states. Employers must cooperate with the OSHA compliance officer by furnishing names of authorized employee representatives who may be asked to accompany the compliance officer during an inspection. If none, the compliance officer will consult with a reasonable number of employees concerning safety and health in the workplace.

All employers must:

- Meet the general duty responsibility to provide a workplace free from recognized hazards that are causing or are likely to cause death or serious physical harm to employees and comply with standards, rules and regulations issued under the Act.
- Be familiar with mandatory OSHA standards and make copies available to employees for review upon request.
- Inform all employees about OSHA.
- Examine workplace conditions to make sure they conform to applicable standards.
- Minimize or reduce hazards.
- Make sure employees have and use safe tools and equipment (including appropriate personal protective equipment) and that such equipment is properly maintained.
- Use color codes, posters, labels or signs when needed to warn employees of potential hazards.
- Establish or update operating procedures and communicate them so that employees follow safety and health requirements.
- Provide training required by OSHA standards (e.g., hazard communication, lead).
- Report to the nearest OSHA office within eight hours any fatal accident or one that results in the hospitalization of three or more employees.
- Keep OSHA-required records of work-related injuries and illnesses and post a copy of the OSHA 300A from February through April each year. (This applies to employers with 11 or more employees.)
- Post, at a prominent location within the workplace, the OSHA poster (OSHA 2203) informing employees of their rights and responsibilities.

- Provide employees, former employees and their representatives' access to the Log and Summary of Occupational Injuries and Illnesses (OSHA 300) at a reasonable time and in a reasonable manner.
- Provide access to employee medical records and exposure records to employees or their authorized representatives.
- Not discriminate against employees who properly exercise their rights under the Act.
- Post OSHA citations at or near the worksites involved. Each citation, or copy thereof, must remain posted until the violation has been abated or for three working days, whichever is longer.
- Abate cited violations within the prescribed period.

Employers have the right to:

- Seek advice and off-site consultation as needed by writing, calling or visiting the nearest OSHA office. (OSHA will not inspect merely because an employer requests assistance.)
- Be active in an industry association's job safety and health programs.
- Request and receive proper government-issued identification from OSHA compliance officers prior to inspections.
- Be advised of the reason for the inspection.
- Have an opening conference with the compliance officer.
- Accompany the compliance officer during the inspection.
- Have a closing conference at the end of the inspection.
- File a written Notice of Contest with the OSHA area director within 15 working days of the receipt of a notice of citation or a proposed penalty.
- Apply to OSHA for a temporary variance from a standard if unable to comply because of the unavailability of materials, equipment or personnel to make necessary changes within the required time.
- Apply to OSHA for a permanent variance from a standard if able to furnish proof its facilities or method of operation provide employee protection at least as effective as that required by the standard.
- Take an active role in developing safety and health standards through participation in

OSHA Standard Advisory Committees, nationally recognized standards-setting organizations, and evidence and views presented in writing or at hearings.

- Be assured of the confidentiality of any trade secrets observed by an OSHA compliance officer during an inspection.
- Submit a written request to NIOSH for information on whether any substance in its workplace has potentially toxic effects in the concentrations being used.

Employee Responsibilities and Rights

Although as a policy OSHA does not cite employees for violations of their responsibilities, each employee "shall comply with all occupational safety and health standards and all rules, regulations, and orders Issued under the Act" that are applicable. Employee responsibilities and rights in states with their own occupational safety and health programs are generally the same as for workers in federal OSHA states.

Employees must comply with all applicable OSHA standards. In addition, employers should:

- Read the OSHA poster at the job site.
- Follow all employer safety and health rules and regulations and wear or use prescribed protective equipment while engaged in work.
- Report hazardous conditions to the supervisor.
- Cooperate with the OSHA compliance officer conducting an inspection if he or she inquires about safety and health conditions in the workplace.

While the part of the law covering employee responsibilities is not considered the "general duty clause," it is an important part of the act. It means employees must follow the rules established by the employer. Employees must obey all safety rules and regulations and cannot pick and choose which ones to abide by.

11(c) Rights: Protection for Using Rights

Employees have a right to seek safety and health on the job without fear of punishment as described in Section 11(c) of the Act. The law says employers shall not punish or discriminate against workers for exercising rights such as:

- Complaining to an employer, union, OSHA or any other government agency about job safety and health hazards;

- Filing safety or health grievances;
- Participating on a workplace safety and health committee or in union activities concerning job safety and health; and
- Participating in OSHA inspections, conferences, hearings, or other OSHA-related activities.

If an employee is exercising these or other OSHA rights, the employer is not allowed to discriminate against that worker in any way, such as through firing, demotion, taking away seniority or other earned benefits, transferring the worker to an undesirable job or shift, or threatening or harassing the worker.

If the employer has knowingly allowed the employee to do something in the past (e.g., leaving work early), he or she may be violating the law by punishing the worker for doing the same thing following a protest of hazardous conditions. If the employer knows that a number of workers are doing the same thing wrong, it cannot legally single out for punishment the worker who has taken part in safety and health activities.

Workers believing they have been punished for exercising safety and health rights must contact the nearest OSHA office within 30 days of the time they learn of the alleged discrimination. A union representative can file a 11(c) complaint for a worker. The worker does not have to complete any forms. An OSHA staff member will complete the forms, asking what happened and who was involved.

Following an 11(c) complaint, OSHA will investigate. If an employee has been illegally punished for exercising safety and health rights, OSHA will ask the employer to restore that worker's job earning and benefits. If necessary, and if it can prove discrimination, OSHA will take the employer to court. In such cases, the worker does not pay any legal fees. If a state agency has an OSHA-approved state program, employees may file their complaint with either federal OSHA or a state agency under its laws.

Other Rights

Employees have the right to:
- Review copies of appropriate OSHA standards, rules, regulations and requirements that the employer should have available at the workplace.

- Request information from the employer on safety and health hazards in the area, precautions that may be taken and procedures to be followed if an employee is involved in an accident or is exposed to toxic substances.
- Receive adequate training and information on workplace safety and health hazards.
- Request the OSHA area director to investigate if you believe hazardous conditions or violations of standards exist in your workplace.
- Have your name withheld from your employer, upon request to OSHA, if you file a written and signed complaint.
- Be advised of OSHA actions regarding your complaint and have an informal review, if requested, of any decision not to inspect or to issue a citation.
- Have your authorized employee representative accompany the OSHA compliance officer during the inspection tour.
- Respond to questions from the OSHA compliance officer, particularly if there is no authorized employee representative accompanying the compliance officer.
- Observe any monitoring or measuring of hazardous materials and have the right to see these records and your medical records, as specified under the Act.
- Have your authorized representative, or yourself, review the Log and Summary of Occupational Injuries (OSHA 300) at a reasonable time and in a reasonable manner.

- Request a closing discussion with the compliance officer following an inspection.
- Submit a written request to NIOSH for information on whether any substance in your workplace has potentially toxic effects in the concentration being used and have your name withheld from your employer if you so request.
- Object to the abatement period set in the citation issued to your employer by writing to the OSHA area director within 15 working days of the issuance of the citation.
- Participate in hearings conducted by the Occupational Safety and Health Review Commission.
- Be notified by your employer if it applies for a variance from an OSHA standard and testify at a variance hearing and appeal the final decision.
- Submit information or comment to OSHA on the issuance, modification or revocation of OSHA standards and request a public hearing.

While OSHA normally does not issue fines and penalties to federal agencies, those agencies must recognize the financial cost of this type of enforcement action. Congress has been exploring the possibility of allowing OSHA to fine agencies of the federal government and has enacted the Postal Employee Safety Act. The U.S. Postal Service recently came under the auspices of OSHA and is now subject to penalties and fines that must come out of their operating budget.

Construction vs. General Industry

Because OSHA is responsible for ensuring the safety and health of workers in a variety of industries, it has developed regulations for each industry, such as maritime, construction and general industry (manufacturing). Often these regulations may seem to overlap and the worker must understand what regulation applies to his or her work. OSHA considers the work being performed as the key element to this "entry argument" into the regulations. So even though a worker has a job title of construction operator, he or she may fall under the general industry rules depending on the job that is being performed.

For example, OSHA defines "construction work" as "work for construction, alteration, and/or repair, including painting and decorating."

The General Industry Standard § 1910.23(c)(1) for fall protection starts at 4 ft. and requires a guardrail:

Every open-sided floor or platform 4 feet or more above adjacent floor or ground level shall be guarded by a standard railing (or the equivalent as specified in paragraph (e)(3) of this section) on all open sides except where there is entrance to a ramp, stairway, or fixed ladder. The railing shall be provided with a toeboard wherever, beneath the open sides, workers can pass.

The Construction Standard § 1926.501(b)(15) for fall protection starts at 6 ft. and allows for such protective devices as guardrails and personal fall arrest systems:

Each employee on a walking/working surface (horizontal and vertical surface) with an unprotected side or edge which is 6 feet (1.8 m) or more above a lower level shall be protected from falling by the use of guardrail systems, safety net systems, or personal fall arrest systems.

For example, a company has one maintenance worker who fixes heating and ventilation systems and a building with a roof that is 5 ft. tall. On Monday the worker goes to the rooftop to replace a bad motor. That work would be considered an alteration of the system, so it would fall under the construction standard. The rule that applies is the construction rules that takes effect at 6 ft. The worker needs no fall protection. Two weeks later, the same worker returns to the same heating unit to change filters. He is not altering, constructing, painting or decorating, he is performing routine maintenance. At this point, he must be protected by the general industry standard, which takes effect at 4 ft. Now he must be protected by a guardrail system. Same person, same roof, same heating system. Different rule.

Safety Committees

The principal function of committees shall be to consult and provide policy advice on and monitor the performance of the safety and health program.

Committees shall be established at establishments or groupings of establishments consistent with the mission, size and organization of the company and its collective bargaining configuration. The employer shall form committees at the lowest practicable local level. The principal function of the establishment (or local) committees is to monitor and assist in the execution of the employer's safety and health policies and program at the workplaces.

- Committee members should serve overlapping terms. Such terms should be of at least two years' duration, except when the committee is initially organized.
- The committee chairperson shall be nominated from among the committee's members and shall be elected by the committee members. Management and nonmanagement members should alternate in this position. Maximum service time as chairperson should be two consecutive years.
- Committees shall establish a regular schedule of meetings and special meetings shall be held as necessary.
- Adequate advance notice of committee meetings shall be furnished to employees and each meeting shall be conducted pursuant to a prepared agenda.
- Written minutes of each committee meeting shall be maintained and distributed to each committee member, and upon request, shall be made available to employees and to the Secretary.

- Employers shall provide all committee members appropriate training as required.
- The safety and health committee is an integral part of the safety and health program and helps ensure effective implementation of the program at the establishment level.
- Monitor and assist the safety and health program at establishments under its jurisdiction and make recommendations to the official in charge on the operation of the program;
- Monitor findings and reports of workplace inspections to confirm that appropriate corrective measures are implemented

Injured Workers May Sue Government

A construction worker injured on an Army installation after a contracting officer failed to enforce contractual safety standards may sue the government under the federal Tort Claims Act, a federal district court ruled June 4, 1999. In *Pelham v. U.S.* (No. 84-1395), the U.S. District Court for the District of New Jersey affirmed its earlier ruling that while a contracting officer's implementation of a safety inspection program is discretionary, once the officer suspects safety deficiency, he or she must act upon it.

The accident occurred when a forklift was used to lift a garbage dumpster in which Jerry Pelham was standing in order to attach cables to a 20-ft. roof-support suspension beam. When the forklift lurched, Pelham lost his balance and caught his hand between the forklift mast chain and pulley, amputating parts of three fingers and severely cutting a fourth.

Shortly before Pelham was injured, the contracting officer observed a worker in a metal container being hoisted by a forklift. The contracting officer testified that he "raised the issue" with the job superintendent, who told him that it was standard practice.

Under the terms of the contract, the contractor was required to take safety measures prescribed by the government's contracting officer. The contracting officer was required to notify the contractor of any non-compliance with safety provisions and had authority to issue a stop-work order if the contractor failed to comply promptly.

Discretionary Function Exception

Lawsuits against the United States for injuries caused by government employees in situations where a private person, would be liable are authorized by the FTCA. Under an exception to the act, the government is not liable for claims based on a discretionary function, whether or not the discretion involved is abused.

The court distinguished the Pelham case from two other Third Circuit decisions that applied the discretionary function exemption to the government's alleged failure to inspect a radioactive extraction facility and remove asbestos. Negligence in the development of safety provisions or a spot check program is not the kind of conduct at issue here the court stated, where the issue is "ministerial implementation of safety regulations" rather than "the discretionary authority to develop such provisions."

The contracting officer accepted the contractor's response rather than assume his ministerial responsibility under the contract to enforce compliance. The court found that under the contract "there is nothing discretionary about this responsibility." Once the contracting officer suspected a safety violation, his duty to check safety requirements was ministerial and not discretionary under the FTCA, the court ruled. Decisions made at the operational level, as distinguished from the planning level, are not protected by the exception, the court found.

Your Safety Committee

Name of the Committee (Be creative: for example — Safety Wizards/Lean Green Safety Team):

_____

Committee Motto (Safety is job one/No one left behind)**:**

_____

Measurable Goals For The Committee (20% reduction in lost time accidents/Develop a safety newsletter by June 1/Determine required training topics by December 1)**:**

_____

_____

_____

Elected Leader:

_____

Recorder:

_____

Name of members: _____

Name of members: _____

Name of members: _____

Name of members: _____

Name of members: _____

Name of members: _____

Name of members: _____

Name of members: _____

Most Frequently Cited Standards

Manufacturing Citations

Listed below are the standards which were cited by **Federal OSHA** for the specified SIC during the period October 2007 through September 2008.

Standard	Cited	Insp	Penalty ($)	Description
Total	38060	6082	38054020	
19100147	3469	1795	3488668	The control of hazardous energy (lockout/tagout).
19101200	2757	1494	789734	Hazard Communication.
19100212	2403	1954	3074319	General requirements for all machines.
19100134	2301	965	769938	Respiratory Protection.
19100305	2153	1271	1296022	Wiring methods, components, and equipment for general use.
19100178	1878	1224	1462565	Powered industrial trucks.
19100303	1643	1155	1108481	General requirements.
19100219	1640	890	1065985	Mechanical power-transmission apparatus.
19100215	1148	702	463726	Abrasive wheel machinery.
19100132	1005	756	598124	General requirements.
19100023	913	697	1185741	Guarding floor and wall openings and holes.
19100095	819	394	582507	Occupational noise exposure.
19100022	805	640	2221852	General requirements.
19100119	753	89	2852799	Process safety management of highly hazardous chemicals.
19100213	742	404	461846	Woodworking machinery requirements.
19100157	713	568	204579	Portable fire extinguishers.
19100179	595	258	493996	Overhead and gantry cranes.
19100217	594	225	656526	Mechanical power presses.
19100107	575	237	295865	Spray finishing using flammable and combustible materials.
19100037	547	431	261353	Maintenance, safeguards, and operational features for exit routes.
19040029	524	483	163403	Forms.
5A0001	508	412	1460288	
19100242	482	475	317540	Hand and portable powered tools and equipment, general.
19100304	458	386	326609	Wiring design and protection.
19100106	457	275	335601	Flammable and combustible liquids.
19100146	457	194	483432	Permit-required confined spaces
19100253	413	319	222827	Oxygen-fuel gas welding and cutting.
19100151	401	392	306304	Medical services and first aid.
19100133	354	335	294471	Eye and face protection.
19100266	342	79	148578	Logging operations.
19100184	338	182	236103	Slings.
19101025	319	96	347794	Lead.
19101000	282	138	248576	Air contaminants.
19040032	267	213	36567	Annual summary.
19100335	248	140	237748	Safeguards for personnel protection.
19101026	245	109	135969	
19100036	210	188	193973	Design and construction requirements for exit routes.
19100307	205	121	5697279	Hazardous (classified) locations.
19100252	197	161	150595	General requirements.
19101030	185	99	63462	Bloodborne pathogens.
19100334	183	156	91052	Use of equipment.
19100024	166	138	138073	Fixed industrial stairs.
19100176	162	151	175106	Handling materials - general.
19100333	160	137	190903	Selection and use of work practices
19100141	153	109	51083	Sanitation.
19100110	118	98	74801	Storage and handling of liquefied petroleum gases.
19101052	117	40	66673	Methylene Chloride.
19100138	115	110	50653	Hand Protection.
19100265	101	48	88708	Sawmills.
19100243	97	92	86124	Guarding of portable powered tools.
19100038	94	88	45008	Emergency action plans.
19100332	90	83	117020	Training
19100101	86	83	36522	Compressed gases (general requirements).
19100027	78	51	94262	Fixed ladders.
19101027	77	13	36814	Cadmium
19100120	71	41	84190	Hazardous waste operations and emergency response.
19101048	69	30	26698	Formaldehyde.
19100254	56	50	52137	Arc welding and cutting.
19100067	55	49	58208	Vehicle-mounted elevating and rotating work platforms.
19040007	53	38	12390	General recording criteria.
19040041	53	53	13820	
19100094	52	38	20353	Ventilation.
19100145	51	48	34940	Specifications for accident prevention signs and tags.

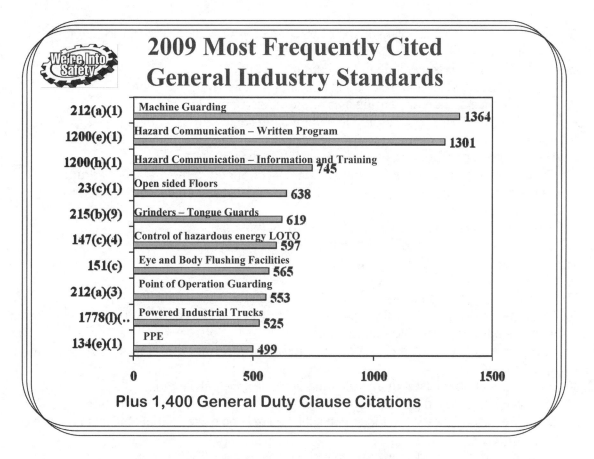

2009 Most Frequently Cited General Industry Standards

We're Into Safety

212(a)(1)	Machine Guarding	1364
1200(e)(1)	Hazard Communication – Written Program	1301
1200(h)(1)	Hazard Communication – Information and Training	745
23(c)(1)	Open sided Floors	638
215(b)(9)	Grinders – Tongue Guards	619
147(c)(4)	Control of hazardous energy LOTO	597
151(c)	Eye and Body Flushing Facilities	565
212(a)(3)	Point of Operation Guarding	553
1778(I)(..	Powered Industrial Trucks	525
134(e)(1)	PPE	499

Plus 1,400 General Duty Clause Citations

Hazard Violation Search Workshop #1
(See appendix for answers.)

Description of Hazard

1. Exit access blocked by pallet. Less than 20 in. width.
2. Fire extinguisher (charged) found lying on floor.
3. Type BC fire extinguisher used near bales of shredded paper – no type A available.
4. At some locations in large facility, directions of travel to exit are not apparent.
5. No portable fire extinguisher inspection/maintenance program.
6. Fixed carbon dioxide extinguishing system not being inspected and tested annually.
7. No exit signs anywhere in plant employing 50 employees.
8. Exit door blocked from outside.
9. Sprinkler heads in storage area blocked by stacked bags within 5 in. of heads.
10. Fire extinguishers obstructed by containers.
11. Exit access door swings against exit travel; considered high hazard occupancy room.
12. No eyewash facility in battery charging area — battery acid being used.
13. Employee observed smoking in a flammable liquid storage area.
14. Eye protection required — items being used do not meet ANSI requirements.
15. Respirators required — no training program for users.
16. Baseball caps being worn by maintenance employees replacing take-up roller bearing on conveyor while standing on a maintenance catwalk.
17. Equipment ground prong on portable electric drill broken off.
18. Forklift observed being used as a man lift using only standard pallet.
19. Permanent aisles in container storage area not marked.
20. Containers being used for storing flammable liquids — not of the approved type.
21. Paint spray booth with electric motor and fan placed inside exhaust duct.
22. End attachments on a wire rope sling are cracked and deformed.

23. General industrial plant: 150 gallons of toluene stored outside of an inside storage room (Flashpoint = 45°F, B.P. = 232°F).
24. Welding operation being done in paint spray booth.
25. Forklift purchased in 1966 performing high lifts without overhead guard.
26. LP gas service station dispensing area without "No Smoking" signs.
27. 150 gallons of Class I liquid stored in a flammable liquid storage cabinet.
28. Forklift operator giving a ride to two personnel on a standard pallet on forks.
29. The dry filter spray booth had an exhaust of less than 50 LFM.
30. Containers used to transfer flammables were not bonded to the dispensing drum.
31. Safety cans containing flammable liquids not in red can nor contents identified.
32. Stairway — 6 risers — no handrail.
33. Hospital 20 miles away, no employee trained in first aid.
34. Open-sided floor — 6-ft. drop; no guardrails.
35. Fixed ladder — 30 ft. high with no cage guard.
36. Wooden extension ladder – ladder safety shoes broken.
37. Stairway more than 44 in. wide does not have stair rails on open sides.
38. Opened-sided work platform (less than 4 ft. high) adjacent to dangerous equipment not guarded with standard railing and toeboard.
39. Elevated area used for storage has no approved floor-loading signs posted in a conspicuous place.
40. Portable dockboard without any securing device to prevent slipping.
41. Stairway with steam pipe 6 ft. above stair tread causing overhead obstruction.
42. Defective portable wooden ladder with split side rail being used in building maintenance operation.
43. Compressed gas cylinders in storage with no valve protection caps.
44. Oxygen and fuel-gas cylinders stored together.
45. Respirators not stored in a clean, sanitary location.
46. Arc welding area — adjacent work area personnel exposed to welding rays.
47. Welding electrode cable lead is damaged and frayed, exposing bare wire.
48. Air receiver not equipped with indicating pressure gauge.
49. There is a loose conduit feeding into a fuse box.
50. Powered industrial truck idling while its operator drinks coffee 200 ft. away.
51. Steel frame of sorter machine not grounded. Machine located 3 ft. from water pipe.
52. Hand-held portable electric grinder with no guard.
53. Hand-held electric circular saw equipped with a lock-on control switch.
54. 157 psi air being used for cleaning purposes in machine shop.
55. Hand-held circular saw being used with no lower blade guard.
56. Portable electric drill owned by employee had defective switch.
57. Radial arm saw has lower portion of blade unguarded.
58. Explosive-actuated fastening tool without a protective shield.
59. Work rest on bench grinder has ½ in. space between wheel and rest.
60. Employee working in a mechanical equipment room daily for eight hours is exposed to 92 dBA.
61. Employer had no energy control (lockout/tagout) procedures.
62. No guarding to protect employees from flying chips of a metal turning lathe.

Hazard Violation Workshop #2

1. Identify what is wrong in each of the following scenarios.
2. Identify what Subpart of the OSHA regulations has been violated.
3. Propose corrective action.

Scenario 1.

Scenario 2.

Scenario 3.

Scenario 4.

Scenario 5.

Scenario 6.

Scenario 7.

Scenario 8.

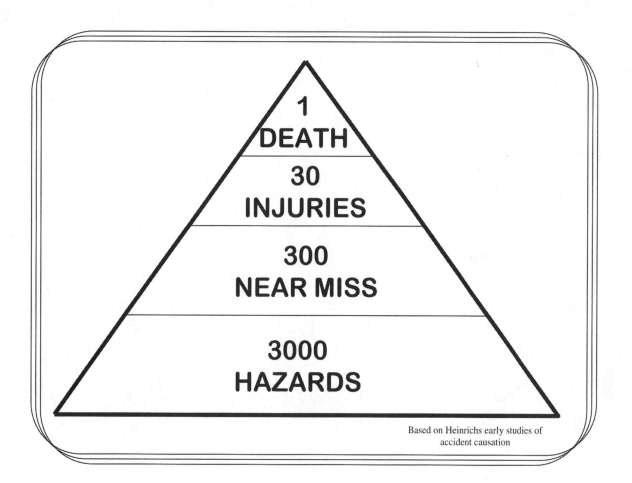

Based on Heinrichs early studies of
accident causation

RECORDING AND REPORTING OCCUPATIONAL INJURIES AND ILLNESSES

The following is an abstract of Section VII, Summary and Explanation of the Final Rule, of 29 CFR 1904, Occupational Injury and Illness Recording and Reporting Requirements (66 Fed. Reg. 5916). Subparts covered include:

A. Purpose
B. Scope
C. Recordkeeping Forms and Recording Criteria
D. Other OSHA Injury and Illness Recordkeeping Requirements
E. Reporting Fatality, Injury and Illness Information to the Government.
F. Transition From the Former Rule
G. Definitions

No attempt has been made to discuss every detail of the regulation. Readers are encouraged to consult the *Federal Register* for the complete text. The corresponding page numbers of major paragraphs as they appear in the *Federal Register* are provided throughout this document to facilitate further reading.

A list of major changes to the recordkeeping rule, released by the Occupational Safety and Health Administration, also is included.

Major Changes To OSHA's Recordkeeping Rule

This document provides a list of the major changes from OSHA's old 1904 recordkeeping rule to the new rule employers began using in 2002. This list summarizes the major differences between the old and new recordkeeping rules to help people who are familiar with the old rule to learn the new rule quickly.

Scope

■ The list of service and retail industries that are partially exempt from the rule has been updated. Some establishments that were covered under the old rule are not required to keep OSHA records under the new rule and some formerly exempted establishments will now have to keep records. (§1904.2)

■ The new rule continues to provide a partial exemption for employers who had 10 or fewer workers at all times in the previous calendar year. (§1904.1)

Forms

- The new OSHA Form 300 (Log of Work-Related Injuries and Illnesses) has been simplified and can be printed on smaller legal-sized paper.
- The new OSHA Form 301 (Injury and Illness Incident Report) includes more data about how the injury or illness occurred.
- The new OSHA Form 300A (Summary of Work-Related Injuries and Illnesses) provides additional data to make it easier for employers to calculate incidence rates.
- Maximum flexibility has been provided so employers can keep all the information on computers, at a central location, or on alternative forms, as long as the information is compatible and the data can be produced when needed. (§1904.29 and §1904.30)

Work-related

- A "significant" degree of aggravation is required before a preexisting injury or illness becomes work-related. (§1904.5(a))
- Additional exceptions have been added to the geographic presumption of work relationship; cases arising from eating and drinking of food and beverages, blood donations, exercise programs, etc., no longer need to be recorded. Common cold and flu cases also no longer need to be recorded. (§1904.5(b)(2))
- Criteria for deciding when mental illnesses are considered work-related have been added. (§1904.5(b)(2))
- Sections have been added clarifying work relationship when employees travel or work out of their home. (§1904.5(b)(6) and §1904.5(b)(7))

Recording criteria

- Different criteria for recording work-related injuries and work-related illnesses are eliminated; one set of criteria is used for both. (The former rule required employers to record all illnesses, regardless of severity). (§1904.4)
- Employers are required to record work-related injuries or illnesses if they result in one of the following: death; days away from work; restricted work or transfer to another job; medical treatment beyond first aid; loss of consciousness; or diagnosis of a significant injury/illness by a physician or other licensed health care professional. (§1904.7(a))
- New definitions are included for medical treatment and first aid. First aid is defined by treatments on a finite list. All treatment not on this list is medical treatment. (§1904.7(b)(5))
- The recording of "light duty" or restricted work cases is clarified. Employers are required to record cases as restricted work cases when the injured or ill employee only works partial days or is restricted from performing their "routine job functions" (defined as work activities the employee regularly performs at least once weekly). (§1904.7(b)(4))
- Employers are required to record all needlestick and sharps injuries involving contamination by another person's blood or other potentially infectious material. (§1904.8)
- Musculoskeletal disorders (MSDs) are treated like all other injuries or illnesses: they must be recorded if they result in days away, restricted work, transfer to another job, or medical treatment beyond first aid.
- Special recording criteria are included for cases involving the work-related transmission of tuberculosis or medical removal under OSHA standards. (§1904.9 and §1904.11)

Day counts

- The term "lost workdays" is eliminated and the rule requires recording of days away, days of restricted work, or transfer to another job. Also, new rules for counting that rely on calendar days instead of workdays are included. (§1904.7(b)(3))
- Employers are no longer required to count days away or days of restriction beyond 180 days. (§1904.7(b)(3))
- The day on which the injury or illness occurs is not counted as a day away from work or a day of restricted work. (§1904.7(b)(3) and §1904.7(b)(4))

Annual Summary

- Employers must review the 300 Log information before it is summarized on the 300A form. (§1904.32(a))
- The new rule includes hours worked data to make it easier for employers to calculate incidence rates. (§1904.32(b)(2))
- A company executive is required to certify the accuracy of the summary. (§1904.32(b)(3))
- The annual summary must be posted for three months instead of one. (§1904.32(b)(6))

Employee involvement

- Employers are required to establish a procedure for employees to report injuries and illnesses and to tell their employees how to report. (§1904.35(a))
- The new rule informs employers that the OSH Act prohibits employers from discriminating against employees who do report. (§1904.36)
- Employees are allowed to access the 301 forms to review records of their own injuries and illnesses. (§1904.35(b)(2))
- Employee representatives are allowed to access those parts of the OSHA 301 form relevant to workplace safety and health. (§1904.35(b)(2))

Protecting privacy

- Employers are required to protect employee's privacy by withholding an individual's name on Form 300 for certain types of sensitive injuries/illnesses (e.g., sexual assaults, HIV infections, mental illnesses, etc.). (§1904.29(b)(6) to §1904.29(b)(8))
- Employers are allowed to withhold descriptive information about sensitive injuries in cases where not doing so would disclose the employee's identity. (§1904.29(b)(9))
- Employee representatives are given access only to the portion of Form 301 that contains information about the injury or illness, while personal information about the employee and his or her health care provider is withheld. (§1904.35(b)(2))
- Employers are required to remove employees' names before providing injury and illness data to persons who do not have access rights under the rule. (§1904.29(b)(10))

Reporting information to the government

- Employers must call in all fatal heart attacks occurring in the work environment. (§1904.39(b)(5))
- Employers do not need to call in public street motor vehicle accidents except those in a construction work zone. (§1904.39(b)(3))
- Employers do not need to call in commercial airplane, train, subway or bus accidents. (§1904.39(b)(4))
- Employers must provide records to an OSHA compliance officer who requests them within 4 hours. (§1904.40(a))

VII. Summary and Explanation [p. 5932]

The following sections discuss the contents of the final 29 CFR Part 1904 and section 1952.4 regulations. OSHA has written these regulations using the plain language guidance set out in a Presidential Memo to the heads of executive departments and agencies on June 1, 1998. The Agency also used guidance from the Plain Language Action Network (PLAN), which is a government-wide group working to improve communications from the Federal government to the public, with the goals of increasing trust in government, reducing government costs, and reducing the burden on the public. For more information on PLAN, see their Internet site at http://www.plainlanguage.gov/. The plain language concepts encourage government agencies to adopt a first person question and answer format, which OSHA used for the Part

1904 rule. The rule contains several types of provisions. Requirements are described using the "you must * * *" construction, prohibitions are described using "you may not * * *", and optional actions that are not requirements or prohibitions are preceded by "you may * * *." OSHA has also included provisions to provide information to the public in the rule.

Subpart A. Purpose [p. 5933]

The Purpose section of the final rule explains why OSHA is promulgating this rule. The Purpose section contains no regulatory requirements and is intended merely to provide information. A Note to this section informs employers and employees that recording a case on the OSHA recordkeeping forms does not indicate either that the employer or the employee was at fault in the incident or that an OSHA rule has been violated. Recording an injury or illness on the Log also does not, in and of itself, indicate that the case qualifies for workers' compensation or other benefits. Although any specific work-related injury or illness may involve some or all of these factors, the record made of that injury or illness on the OSHA recordkeeping forms only shows three things: (1) that an injury or illness has occurred; (2) that the employer has determined that the case is work-related (using OSHA's definition of that term); and (3) that the case is non-minor, i.e., that it meets one or more of the OSHA injury and illness recording criteria. OSHA has added the Note to this first subpart of the rule because employers and employees have frequently requested clarification on these points.

The following paragraphs describe the changes OSHA has made to the Purpose provisions in Subpart A of the final rule, and discusses the Agency's reasons for these changes.

[The final rule's Purpose paragraph states "The purpose of this rule (Part 1904) is to require employers to record and report work-related fatalities, injuries and illnesses." It clearly and succinctly states OSHA's reasons for issuing the final rule.]

Employers have frequently asked OSHA to explain the relationship between workers' compensation reporting systems and the OSHA injury and illness recording and reporting requirements. As NYNEX

(Ex. 15: 199) noted,

[t]he issue of confusion between OSHA recordkeeping and workers' compensation/insurance requirements cannot be totally eliminated as the workers' compensation criteria vary somewhat from state to state. There will always be some differences between OSHA recordability and compensable injuries and illnesses. The potential consequences of these differences can be minimized, however, if all stakeholders in the recordkeeping process (i.e., employers, employees, labor unions, OSHA compliance officials) are well informed that OSHA recordability does not equate to compensation eligibility. This can be facilitated by printed reminders on all of the OSHA recordkeeping documents (e.g., forms, instructions, pamphlets, compliance directives, etc.).

As NYNEX observed, employers must document work-related injuries and illnesses for both OSHA recordkeeping and workers' compensation purposes. Many cases that are recorded in the OSHA system are also compensable under the State workers' compensation system, but many others are not. However, the two systems have different purposes and scopes. The OSHA recordkeeping system is intended to collect, compile and analyze uniform and consistent nationwide data on occupational injuries and illnesses. The workers' compensation system, in contrast, is not designed primarily to generate and collect data but is intended primarily to provide medical coverage and compensation for workers who are killed, injured or made ill at work, and varies in coverage from one State to another.

Although the cases captured by the OSHA system and workers' compensation sometimes overlap, they often do not. For example, many injuries and illnesses covered by workers' compensation are not required to be recorded in the OSHA records. Such a situation would arise, for example, if an employee were injured on the job, sent to a hospital emergency room, and was examined and x-rayed by a physician, but was then told that the injury was minor and required no treatment. In this case, the employee's medical bills would be covered by workers' compensation insurance, but the case would not be recordable under Part 1904.

Conversely, an injury may be recordable for OSHA's purposes but not be covered by workers' compensation. For example, in some states, workers' compensation does not cover certain types of injuries (e.g., certain musculoskeletal disorders) and certain classes of workers (e.g., farm workers, contingent workers). However, if the injury meets OSHA recordability criteria it must be recorded even if the particular injury would not be compensable or the worker not be covered. Similarly, some injuries, although technically compensable under the state compensation system, do not result in the payment of workers' compensation benefits. For example, a worker who is injured on the job, receives treatment from the company physician, and returns to work without loss of wages would generally not receive workers' compensation because the company would usually absorb the costs. However, if the case meets the OSHA recording criteria, the employer would nevertheless be required to record the injury on the OSHA forms.

As a result of these differences between the two systems, recording a case does not mean that the case is compensable, or vice versa. When an injury or illness occurs to an employee, the employer must independently analyze the case in light of both the OSHA recording criteria and the requirements of the State workers' compensation system to determine whether the case is recordable or compensable, or both.

The American Federation of Labor and Congress of Industrial Organizations (AFL-CIO) urged OSHA to emphasize the no-fault philosophy of the Agency's recordkeeping system.

...

OSHA believes that the note to the Purpose paragraph of the final rule will allay any fears employers and employees may have about recording injuries and illnesses, and thus will encourage more accurate reporting. Both the Note to Subpart A of the final rule and the new OSHA Form 300 expressly state that recording a case does not indicate fault, negligence, or compensability.

...

OSHA has rejected the suggestion made by these commenters to limit the admissibility of the forms as evidence in a court proceeding. Such action is beyond the statutory authority of the agency, because OSHA has no authority over the courts, either Federal or State.

...

OSHA notes that many circumstances that lead to a recordable work-related injury or illness are "beyond the employer's control," at least as that phrase is commonly interpreted. Nevertheless, because such an injury or illness was caused, contributed to, or significantly aggravated by an event or exposure at work, it must be recorded on the OSHA form (assuming that it meets one or more of the recording criteria and does not qualify for an exemption to the geographic presumption). This approach is consistent with the no-fault recordkeeping

system OSHA has adopted, which includes work-related injuries and illnesses, regardless of the level of employer control or non-control involved. The issue of whether different types of cases are deemed work-related under the OSHA recordkeeping rule is discussed in the Legal Authority section, above, and in the work-relationship section (section 1904.5) of this preamble.

Subpart B. Scope [p. 5935]

The coverage and partial exemption provisions in Subpart B of the final rule establish which employers must keep OSHA injury and illness records at all times, and which employers are generally exempt but must keep records under specific circumstances. This subpart contains sections 1904.1 through 1904.3 of the final rule.

OSHA's recordkeeping rule covers many employers in OSHA's jurisdiction but continues to exempt many employers from the need to keep occupational injury and illness records routinely. This approach to the scope of the rule is consistent with that taken in the former recordkeeping rule. Whether a particular employer must keep these records routinely depends on the number of employees in the firm and on the Standard Industrial Classification, or SIC code, of each of the employer's establishments. Employers with 10 or fewer employees are not required to keep OSHA records routinely. In addition, employers whose establishments are classified in certain industries are not required to keep OSHA records under most circumstances. OSHA refers to establishments exempted by reason of size or industry classification as "partially exempt," for reasons explained below.

The final rule's size exemption and the industry exemptions listed in non-mandatory Appendix A to Subpart B of the final rule do not relieve employers with 10 or fewer employees or employers in these industries from all of their recordkeeping obligations under 29 CFR Part 1904. Employers qualifying for either the industry exemption or the employment size exemption are not routinely required to record work-related injuries and illnesses occurring to their employees, that is, they are not normally required to keep the OSHA

Log or OSHA Form 301. However, as sections 1904.1(a)(1) and 1904.2 of this final recordkeeping rule make clear, these employers must still comply with three discrete provisions of Part 1904. First, all employers covered by the Act must report work-related fatalities or multiple hospitalizations to OSHA under Sec. 1904.39. Second, under Sec. 1904.41, any employer may be required to provide occupational injury and illness reports to OSHA or OSHA's designee upon written request. Finally, under Sec. 1904.42, any employer may be required to respond to the Survey of Occupational Injuries and Illnesses conducted by the Bureau of Labor Statistics (BLS) if asked to do so. Each of these requirements is discussed in greater detail in the relevant portion of this summary and explanation.

Section 1904.1 Partial Exemption for Employers With 10 or Fewer Employees [p. 5935]

In Sec. 1904.1 of the final rule, OSHA has retained the former rule's size-based exemption, which exempts employers with 10 or fewer employees in all industries covered by OSHA from most recordkeeping requirements. Section 1904.1, "Partial exemption for employers with 10 or fewer employees," states that:

(a) Basic requirement.

 (1) If your company had ten (10) or fewer employees at all times during the last calendar year, you do not need to keep OSHA injury and illness records unless OSHA or the BLS informs you in writing that you must keep records under Sec. 1904.41 or Sec. 1904.42. However, as required by Sec. 1904.39, all employers covered by the OSH Act must report to OSHA any workplace incident that results in a fatality or the hospitalization of three or more employees.

 (2) If your company had more than ten (10) employees at any time during the last calendar year, you must keep OSHA injury and illness records unless your establishment is classified as a partially exempt industry under Sec. 1904.2.

(b) Implementation.

 (1) Is the partial exemption for size based on the size of my entire company or on the size of an individual business establishment?

 The partial exemption for size is based on the number of employees in the entire company.

 (2) How do I determine the size of my company to find out if I qualify for the partial exemption for size?

 To determine if you are exempt because of size, you need to determine your company's peak employment during the last calendar year. If you had no more than 10 employees at any time in the last calendar year, your company qualifies for the partial exemption for size.

The Size-Based Exemption in the Former Rule

The final rule published today maintains the former rule's partial exemption for employers in all covered industries who have 10 or fewer employees. Under the final rule (and the former rule), an employer in any industry who employed no more than 10 employees at any time during the preceding calendar year is not required to maintain OSHA records of occupational illnesses and injuries during the current year unless requested to do so in writing by OSHA (under Sec. 1904.41) or the BLS (under Sec. 1904.42). If an employer employed 11 or more people at a given time during the year, however, that employer is not eligible for the size-based partial exemption.

[Size Exemption Threshold for Construction Companies]

In the final rule, OSHA has decided to continue the Agency's longstanding practice of partially exempting employers with 10 or fewer employees from most recordkeeping requirements, but not to extend the exemption to non-construction businesses with 19 or fewer employees, as was proposed.

Section 1904.2 Partial Exemption for Establishments in Certain Industries [p. 5939]

Section 1904.2 of the final rule partially exempts employers with establishments classified in certain lower-hazard industries. The final rule updates the former rule's listing of partially exempted lower-hazard industries. Lower-hazard industries are those Standard Industrial Classification (SIC) code industries within SICs 52-89 that have an average Days Away, Restricted, or Transferred (DART) rate at or below 75% of the national average DART rate. The former rule also contained such a list based on data from 1978-1980. The final rule's list differs from that of the former rule in two respects: (1) the hazard information supporting the final rule's lower-hazard industry exemptions is based on the most recent three years of BLS statistics (1996, 1997, 1998), and (2) the exception is calculated at the 3-digit rather than 2-digit level.

The changes in the final rule's industry exemptions are designed to require more employers in higher-hazard industries to keep records all of the time and to exempt employers in certain lower-hazard industries from keeping OSHA injury and illness records routinely. For example, compared with the former rule, the final rule requires many employers in the 3-digit industries within retail and service sector industries that have higher rates of occupational injuries and illnesses to keep these records but exempts employers in 3-digit industries within those industries that report a lower rate of occupational injury and illness. Section 1904.2 of the final rule, "Partial exemption for establishments in certain industries," states:

(a) Basic requirement.

(1) If your business establishment is classified in a specific low hazard retail, service, finance, insurance or real estate industry listed in Appendix A to this Subpart B, you do not need to keep OSHA injury and illness records unless the government asks you to keep the records under Sec. 1904.41 or Sec. 1904.42. However, all employers must report to OSHA any workplace incident that results in a fatality or the hospitalization of three or more employees (see Sec. 1904.39).

(2) If one or more of your company's establishments are classified in a non-exempt industry, you must keep OSHA injury and illness records for all of such establishments unless your company is partially exempted because of size under Sec. 1904.1.

(b) Implementation.

(1) Does the partial industry classification exemption apply only to business establishments in the retail, services, finance, insurance or real estate industries (SICs 52-89)?

Yes. Business establishments classified in agriculture; mining; construction; manufacturing; transportation; communication, electric, gas and sanitary services; or wholesale trade are not eligible for the partial industry classification exemption.

(2) Is the partial industry classification exemption based on the industry classification of my entire company or on the classification of individual business establishments operated by my company?

The partial industry classification exemption applies to individual business establishments. If a company has several business establishments engaged in different classes of business activities, some of the company's establishments may be required to keep records, while others may be exempt.

(3) How do I determine the Standard Industrial Classification code for my company or for individual establishments?

You determine your Standard Industrial Classification (SIC) code by using the Standard Industrial Classification Manual, Executive Office of the President, Office of Management and Budget. You may contact your nearest OSHA office or State agency for help in determining your SIC.

Employers with establishments in those industry sectors shown in Appendix A are not required routinely to keep OSHA records for their establishments. They must, however, keep records if requested to do so by the Bureau of Labor Statistics in connection with its Annual Survey (section 1904.42) or by OSHA in connection with its Data Initiative (section 1904.41). In addition, all employers covered by the OSH Act must report a work-related fatality, or an accident that results in the hospitalization of three or more employees, to OSHA within 8 hours (section 1904.39).

...

Evaluating industries at the 3-digit level allows OSHA to identify 3-digit industries with high LWDI rates (DART rates in the terminology of the final rule) that are located within 2-digit industries with relatively low rates. Conversely, use of this approach allows OSHA to identify lower-hazard 3-digit industries within a 2-digit industry that have relatively high LWDI (DART) rates. Use of LWDI (DART) rates at the more detailed level of SIC coding increases the specificity of the targeting of the exemptions and makes the rule more equitable by exempting workplaces in lower-hazard industries and requiring employers in more hazardous industries to keep records.

...

For multi-establishment firms, the industry exemption is based on the SIC code of each establishment, rather than the industrial classification of a firm as a whole. For example, some larger corporations have establishments that engage in different business activities. Where this is the case, each establishment could fall into a different SIC code, based on its business activity. The Standard Industrial Classification manual states that the establishment, rather than the firm, is the appropriate unit for determining the SIC code. Thus, depending on the SIC code of the establishment, one establishment of a firm may be exempt from routine recordkeeping under Part 1904, while another establishment in the same company may not be exempt.

...

For those States with OSHA-approved State plans, the state is generally required to adopt Federal OSHA rules, or a State rule that is at least as effective as the Federal OSHA rule. States with approved plans do not need to exempt employers from recordkeeping, either by employer size or by industry classification, as the final Federal OSHA rule does, although they may choose to do so. For example, States with approved plans may require records from a wider universe of employers than Federal OSHA does. These States cannot exempt more industries or employers than Federal OSHA does, however, because doing so would result in a State rule that is not as effective as the Federal rule. A larger discussion of the effect on the State plans can be found in Section VIII of this preamble, State Plans.

Recordkeeping Under the Requirements of Other Federal Agencies

Section 1904.3 of the final rule provides guidance for employers who are subject to the occupational injury and illness recording and reporting requirements of other Federal agencies. Several other Federal agencies have similar requirements, such as the Mine Safety and Health Administration (MSHA), the Department of Energy (DOE), and the Federal Railroad Administration (FRA). The final rule at section 1904.3 tells the employer that OSHA will accept these records in place of the employer's Part 1904 records under two circumstances: (1) if OSHA has entered into a memorandum of understanding (MOU) with that agency that specifically accepts the other agency's records, the employer may use them in place of the OSHA records, or (2) if the other agency's records include the same information required by Part 1904, OSHA would consider them an acceptable substitute.

...

Subpart C. Recordkeeping Forms and Recording Criteria [p. 5945]

Subpart C of the final rule sets out the requirements of the rule for recording cases in the recordkeeping system. It contains provisions directing employers to keep records of the recordable occupational injuries and illnesses experienced by their employees, describes the forms the employer must use, and establishes the criteria that employers must follow to determine which work-related injury and illness cases must be entered onto the forms. Subpart C contains sections 1904.4 through 1904.29.

Section 1904.4 provides an overview of the requirements in Subpart C and contains a flowchart describing the recording process. How employers are to determine whether a given injury or illness is work-related is set out in section 1904.5. Section 1904.6 provides the requirements employers must follow to determine whether or not a work-related injury or illness is a new case or the continuation of a previously recorded injury or illness. Sections 1904.7 through 1904.12 contain the recording criteria for determining which new work-related injuries and illnesses must be recorded on the

OSHA forms. Section 1904.29 explains which forms must be used and indicates the circumstances under which the employer may use substitute forms.

Section 1904.4 Recording Criteria [p. 5945]

Section 1904.4 of the final rule contains provisions mandating the recording of work-related injuries and illnesses that must be entered on the OSHA 300 (Log) and 301 (Incident Report) forms. It sets out the recording requirements that employers are required to follow in recording cases.

Paragraph 1904.4(a) of the final rule mandates that each employer who is required by OSHA to keep records must record each fatality, injury or illness that is work-related, is a new case and not a continuation of an old case, and meets one or more of the general recording criteria in section 1904.7 or the additional criteria for specific cases found in sections 1904.8 through 1904.12. Paragraph (b) contains provisions implementing this basic requirement.

Paragraph 1904.4(b)(1) contains a table that points employers and their recordkeepers to the various sections of the rule that determine which work-related injuries and illnesses are to be recorded. These sections lay out the requirements for determining whether an injury or illness is work-related, if it is a new case, and if it meets one or more of the general recording criteria. In addition, the table contains a row addressing the application of these and additional criteria to specific kinds of cases (needlestick and sharps injury cases, tuberculosis cases, hearing loss cases, medical removal cases, and musculoskeletal disorder cases). The table in paragraph 1904.4(b)(1) is intended to guide employers through the recording process and to act as a table of contents to the sections of Subpart C.

Paragraph (b)(2) is a decision tree, or flowchart, that shows the steps involved in determining whether or not a particular injury or illness case must be recorded on the OSHA forms. It essentially reflects the same information as is in the table in paragraph 1904.4(b)(1), except that it presents this information graphically.

...

Section 1904.5 Determination of Work-Relatedness [p. 5946]

This section of the final rule sets out the requirements employers must follow in determining whether a given injury or illness is work-related. Paragraph 1904.5(a) states that an injury or illness must be considered work-related if an event or exposure in the work environment caused or contributed to the injury or illness or significantly aggravated a pre-existing injury or illness. It stipulates that, for OSHA recordkeeping purposes, work relationship is presumed for such injuries and illnesses unless an exception listed in paragraph 1904.5(b)(2) specifically applies.

Implementation requirements are set forth in paragraph (b) of the final rule. Paragraph (b)(1) defines "work environment" for recordkeeping purposes and makes clear that the work environment includes the physical locations where employees are working as well as the equipment and materials used by the employee to perform work.

Paragraph (b)(2) lists the exceptions to the presumption of work-relatedness permitted by the final rule; cases meeting the conditions of any of the listed exceptions are not considered work-related and are therefore not recordable in the OSHA recordkeeping system.

This section of the preamble first explains OSHA's reasoning on the issue of work relationship, then discusses the exceptions to the general presumption and the comments received on the exceptions proposed, and then presents OSHA's rationale for including paragraphs (b)(3) through (b)(7) of the final rule, and the record evidence pertaining to each.
...

Final Rule's Exceptions to the Geographic Presumption

Paragraph 1904.5(b)(2) of the final rule contains eight exceptions to the work environment presumption that are intended to exclude from the recordkeeping system those injuries and illnesses that occur or manifest in the work environment, but have been identified by OSHA, based on its years of experience with recordkeeping, as cases that do not provide information useful to the identification of occupational injuries and illnesses and would thus tend to skew national injury and illness statistics. These eight exceptions are the only exceptions to the presumption permitted by the final rule.

(i) Injuries or illnesses will not be considered work-related if, at the time of the injury or illness, the employee was present in the work environment as a member of the general public rather than as an employee. This exception, which is codified at paragraph 1904.5(b)(2)(i), is based on the fact that no employment relationship is in place at the time an injury or illness of this type occurs. A case exemplifying this exception would occur if an employee of a retail store patronized that store as a customer on a non-work day and was injured in a fall. This exception allows the employer not to record cases that occur outside of the employment relationship when his or her establishment is also a public place and a worker happens to be using the facility as a member of the general public. In these situations, the injury or illness has nothing to do with the employee's work or the employee's status as an employee, and it would therefore be inappropriate for the recordkeeping system to capture the case.

...

(ii) Injuries or illnesses will not be considered work-related if they involve symptoms that surface at work but result solely from a non-work-related event or exposure that occurs outside the work environment. OSHA's recordkeeping system is intended only to capture cases that are caused by conditions or exposures arising in the work environment. It is not designed to capture cases that have no relationship with the work environment. For this exception to apply, the work environment cannot have caused, contributed to, or significantly aggravated the injury or illness. This exception is consistent with the position followed by OSHA for many years and reiterated in the final rule: that any job-related contribution to the injury or illness makes the incident work-related, and its corollary—that any injury or illness to which work makes no actual contribution is not work-related. An example of this type of injury would be a diabetic incident that occurs while an employee is working. Because no event or exposure at work contributed in any way to the diabetic incident, the case is not recordable. This exception allows the employer to exclude cases where an employee's non-work activities are the sole cause of the injury or illness.

...

(iii) Injuries and illnesses will not be considered work-related if they result solely from voluntary participation in a wellness program or in a medical, fitness, or recreational activity such as blood donation, physical, flu shot, exercise classes, racquetball, or baseball. This exception allows the employer to exclude certain injury or illness cases that are related to personal medical care, physical fitness activities and voluntary blood donations. The key words here are "solely" and "voluntary." The work environment cannot have contributed to the injury or illness in any way for this exception to apply, and participation in the wellness, fitness or recreational activities must be voluntary and not a condition of employment. This exception allows the employer to exclude cases that are related to personal matters of exercise, recreation, medical examinations or participation in blood donation programs when they are voluntary and are not being undertaken as a condition of work. For example, if a clerical worker was injured while performing aerobics in the company gymnasium during his or her lunch hour, the case would not be work-related. On the other hand, if an employee who was assigned to manage the gymnasium was injured while teaching an aerobics class, the injury would be work-related because the employee was working at the time of the injury and the activity was not voluntary. Similarly, if an employee suffered a severe reaction to a flu shot that was administered as part of a voluntary inoculation program, the case would not be considered work-related; however, if an employee suffered a reaction to medications administered to enable the employee to travel overseas on business, or the employee had an illness reaction to a medication administered to treat a work-related injury, the case would be considered work-related.

...

(iv) Injuries and illnesses will not be considered work-related if they are solely the result of an employee eating, drinking, or preparing food or drink for personal consumption (whether bought on the premises or brought in). This exception responds to a situation that has given rise to many letters of interpretation and caused employer concern over the years. An example of the application of this exception would be a case where the employee injured himself or herself by choking on a sandwich brought from home but eaten in the employer's establishment; such a case would not be considered work-related under this exception. On the other hand, if the employee was injured by a trip or fall hazard present in the employer's lunchroom, the case would be considered work-related. In addition, a note to the exception makes clear that if an employee becomes ill as a result of ingesting food contaminated by workplace contaminants such as lead, or contracts food poisoning from food items provided by the employer, the case would be considered work-related. As a result, if an employee contracts food poisoning from a sandwich brought from home or purchased in the company cafeteria and must take time off to recover, the case is not considered work related. On the other hand, if an employee contracts food poisoning from a meal provided by the employer at a business meeting or company function and takes time off to recover, the case would be considered work related. Food provided or supplied by the employer does not include food purchased by the employee from the company cafeteria, but does include food purchased by the employer from the company cafeteria for business meetings or other company functions. OSHA believes that the number of cases to which this exception applies will be few.

...

(v) Injuries and illnesses will not be considered work-related if they are solely the result of

employees doing personal tasks (unrelated to their employment) at the establishment outside of their assigned working hours. This exception, which responds to inquiries received over the years, allows employers limited flexibility to exclude from the recordkeeping system situations where the employee is using the employer's establishment for purely personal reasons during his or her off-shift time. For example, if an employee were using a meeting room at the employer's establishment outside of his or her assigned working hours to hold a meeting for a civic group to which he or she belonged, and slipped and fell in the hallway, the injury would not be considered work-related. On the other hand, if the employee were at the employer's establishment outside his or her assigned working hours to attend a company business meeting or a company training session, such a slip or fall would be work-related. OSHA also expects the number of cases affected by this exception to be small.

...

(vi) Injuries and illnesses will not be considered work-related if they are solely the result of personal grooming, self-medication for a non-work-related condition, or are intentionally self-inflicted. This exception allows the employer to exclude from the Log cases related to personal hygiene, self-administered medications and intentional self-inflicted injuries, such as attempted suicide. For example, a burn injury from a hair dryer used at work to dry the employee's hair would not be work-related. Similarly, a negative reaction to a medication brought from home to treat a non-work condition would not be considered a work-related illness, even though it first manifested at work. OSHA also expects that few cases will be affected by this exception.

...

(vii) Injuries will not be considered work-related if they are caused by motor vehicle accidents occurring in company parking lots or on company access roads while employees are commuting to or from work. This exception allows the employer to exclude cases where an employee is injured in a motor vehicle accident while commuting from work to home or from home to work or while on a personal errand. For example, if an employee was injured in a car accident while arriving at work or while leaving the company's property at the end of the day, or while driving on his or her lunch hour to run an errand, the case would not be considered work-related. On the other hand, if an employee was injured in a car accident while leaving the property to purchase supplies for the employer, the case would be work-related. This exception represents a change from the position taken under the former rule, which was that no injury or illness occurring in a company parking lot was considered work-related. As explained further below, OSHA has concluded, based on the evidence in the record, that some injuries and illnesses that occur in company parking lots are clearly caused by work conditions or activities—e.g., being struck by a car while painting parking space indicators on the pavement of the lot, slipping on ice permitted to accumulate in the lot by the employer—and by their nature point to conditions that could be corrected to improve workplace safety and health.

(viii) Common colds and flu will not be considered work-related. Paragraph 1904.5(b)(2)(viii) allows the employer to exclude cases of common cold or flu, even if contracted while the employee was at work. However, in the case of other infectious diseases such as tuberculosis, brucellosis, and hepatitis C, employers must evaluate reports of such illnesses for work relationship, just as they would any other type of injury or illness.

(ix) Mental illness will not be considered work-related unless the employee voluntarily provides the employer with an opinion from a physician or other licensed health care professional with appropriate training and experience (psychiatrist, psychologist, psychiatric nurse practitioner, etc.) stating that the employee has a mental illness that is work-related.

...

OSHA agrees that recording work-related mental illnesses involves several unique issues, including the difficulty of detecting, diagnosing and verifying mental illnesses; and the sensitivity and privacy concerns raised by mental illnesses. Therefore, the final rule requires employers to record only those mental illnesses verified by a health care professional with appropriate training and experience in the treatment of mental illness, such as a psychiatrist, psychologist, or psychiatric nurse practitioner. The employer is under no obligation to seek out information on mental illnesses from its employees, and employers are required to consider mental illness cases only when an employee voluntarily presents the employer with an opinion from the health care professional that the employee has a mental illness and that it is work related. In the event that the employer does not believe the reported mental illness is work-related, the employer may refer the case to a physician or other licensed health care professional for a second opinion.

OSHA also emphasizes that work-related mental illnesses, like other illnesses, must be recorded only when they meet the severity criteria outlined in Sec. 1904.7. In addition, for mental illnesses, the employee's identity must be protected by omitting the employee's name from the OSHA 300 Log and instead entering "privacy concern case" as required by Sec. 1904.29.

...

Determining Whether the Precipitating Event or Exposure Occurred in the Work Environment or Elsewhere

Paragraph 1904.5(b)(3) of the final rule provides guidance on applying the geographic presumption when it is not clear whether the event or exposure that precipitated the injury or illness occurred in the work environment or elsewhere. If an employee reports pain and swelling in a joint but cannot say whether the symptoms first arose during work or during recreational activities at home, it may be difficult for the employer to decide whether the case is work-related. The same problem arises when an employee reports symptoms of a contagious disease that affects the public at large, such as a staphylococcus infection ("staph" infection) or Lyme disease, and the workplace is only one possible source of the infection. In these situations, the employer must examine the employee's work duties and environment to determine whether it is more likely than not that one or more events or exposures at work caused or contributed to the condition. If the employer determines that it is unlikely that the precipitating event or exposure occurred in the work environment, the employer would not record the case. In the staph infection example given above, the employer would consider the case work-related, for example, if another employee with whom the newly infected employee had contact at work had been out with a staph infection. In the Lyme disease example, the employer would determine the case to be work-related if, for example, the employee was a groundskeeper with regular exposure to outdoor conditions likely to result in contact with deer ticks.

In applying paragraph 1904.5(b)(3), the question employers must answer is whether the precipitating event or exposure occurred in the work environment. If an event, such as a fall, an awkward motion or lift, an assault, or an instance of horseplay, occurs at work, the geographic presumption applies and the case is work-related unless it otherwise falls within an exception. Thus, if an employee trips while walking across a level factory floor, the resulting injury is considered work-related under the geographic presumption because the precipitating event—the tripping accident—occurred in the workplace.

The case is work-related even if the employer cannot determine why the employee tripped, or whether any particular workplace hazard caused the accident to occur. However, if the employee reports an injury at work but cannot say whether it resulted from an event that occurred at work or at home, as in the example of the swollen joint, the employer might determine that the case is not work-related because the employee's work duties were unlikely to have caused, contributed to, or significantly aggravated such an injury.

Significant Workplace Aggravation of a Pre-existing Condition

In paragraph 1904.5(b)(4), the final rule makes an important change to the former rule's position on the extent of the workplace aggravation of a preexisting injury or illness that must occur before the case is considered work-related. In the past, any amount of aggravation of such an injury or illness was considered sufficient for this purpose. The final rule, however, requires that the amount of aggravation of the injury or illness that work contributes must be "significant," i.e., non-minor, before work-relatedness is established. The preexisting injury or illness must be one caused entirely by non-occupational factors.

...

Paragraph 1904.5(b)(4) of the final rule defines aggravation as significant if the contribution of the aggravation at work is such that it results in tangible consequences that go beyond those that the worker would have experienced as a result of the preexisting injury or illness alone, absent the aggravating effects of the workplace. Under the final rule, a preexisting injury or illness will be considered to have been significantly aggravated, for the purposes of OSHA injury and illness recordkeeping, when an event or exposure in the work environment results in: (i) Death, providing that the preexisting injury or illness would likely not have resulted in death but for the occupational event or exposure; (ii) Loss of consciousness, providing that the preexisting injury or illness would likely not have resulted in loss of consciousness but for the occupational event or exposure; (iii) A day or days away from work or of restricted work, or a job transfer that otherwise would not have occurred but for the occupational event or exposure; or (iv) Medical treatment where no medical treatment was needed for the injury or illness before the workplace event or exposure, or a change in the course of medical treatment that was being provided before the workplace event or exposure. OSHA's decision not to require the recording of cases involving only minor aggravation of preexisting conditions is consistent with the Agency's efforts in this rulemaking to require the recording only of non-minor injuries and illnesses; for example, the final rule also no longer requires employers to record minor illnesses on the Log.

Preexisting Conditions

Paragraph 1904.5(b)(5) stipulates that pre-existing conditions, for recordkeeping purposes, are conditions that resulted solely from a non-work-related event or exposure that occurs outside the employer's work environment. Pre-existing conditions also include any injury or illness that the employee experienced while working for another employer.

Off Premises Determinations

Employees may be injured or become ill as a result of events or exposures away from the employer's establishment. In these cases, OSHA proposed to consider the case work-related only if the employee was engaged in a work activity or was present as a condition of employment (61 FR 4063). In the final rule, (paragraph 1904.5(b)(1)) the same concept is carried forward in the definition of the work environment, which defines the environment as including the establishment and any other location where one or more employees are working or are present as a condition of their employment.

Thus, when employees are working or conducting other tasks in the interest of their employer but at a location away from the employer's establishment, the work-relatedness of an injury or illness that arises is subject to the same decision making process that would occur if the case had occurred at the establishment itself. The case is work-related if one or more events or exposures in the work environment either caused or contributed to the resulting condition or significantly aggravated a pre-existing condition, as stated in paragraph 1904.5(a). In addition, the exceptions for determining work relationship at paragraph 1904.5(b)(2) and the requirements at paragraph 1904.5(b)(3) apply equally to cases that occur at or away from the establishment.

As an example, the work-environment presumption clearly applies to the case of a delivery driver who experiences an injury to his or her back while loading boxes and transporting them into a building. The worker is engaged in a work activity and the injury resulted from an event—loading/unloading—occurring in the work environment. Similarly, if an employee is injured in an automobile accident while running errands for the company or traveling to make a speech on behalf of the company, the employee is present at the scene as a condition of employment, and any resulting injury would be work-related.

Employees on Travel Status

The final rule continues (at Sec. 1904.5(b)(6)) OSHA's longstanding practice of treating injuries and illnesses that occur to an employee on travel status as work-related if, at the time of the injury or illness, the employee was engaged in work activities "in the interest of the employer." Examples of such activities include travel to and from customer contacts, conducting job tasks, and entertaining or being entertained if the activity is conducted at the direction of the employer.

The final rule contains three exceptions for travel-status situations. The rule describes situations in which injuries or illnesses sustained by traveling employees are not considered work-related for OSHA recordkeeping purposes and therefore do not have to be recorded on the OSHA 300 Log. First, when a traveling employee checks into a hotel, motel, or other temporary residence, he or she is considered to have established a "home away from home." At this time, the status of the employee is the same as that of an employee working at an establishment who leaves work and is essentially "at home". Injuries and illnesses that occur at home are generally not considered work related. However, just as an employer may sometimes be required to record an injury or illness occurring to an employee working in his or her home, the employer is required to record an injury or illness occurring to an employee who is working in his or her hotel room (see the discussion of working at home, below).

Second, if an employee has established a "home away from home" and is reporting to a fixed worksite each day, the employer does not consider injuries or illnesses work-related if they occur while the employee is commuting between the temporary residence and the job location. These cases are parallel to those involving employees commuting to and from work when they are at their home location, and do not have to be recorded, just as injuries and illnesses that occur during normal commuting are not required to be recorded.

Third, the employer is not required to consider an injury or illness to be work-related if it occurs while the employee is on a personal detour from the route of business travel. This exception allows the employer to exclude injuries and illnesses that occur when the worker has taken a side trip for personal reasons while on a business trip, such as a vacation or sightseeing excursion, to visit relatives, or for some other personal purpose.

...

Working at Home

The final rule also includes provisions at Sec. 1904.5(b)(7) for determining the work-relatedness of injuries and illnesses that may arise when employees are working at home. When an employee is working on company business in his or her home and reports an injury or illness to his or her employer, and the employee's work activities caused or contributed to the injury or illness, or significantly aggravated a pre-existing injury, the case is considered work-related and must be further evaluated to determine whether it meets the recording criteria. If the injury or illness is related to non-work activities or to the general home environment, the case is not considered work-related.

...

OSHA has recently issued a compliance directive (CPL 2-0.125) containing the Agency's response to many of the questions raised by this commenter. That document clarifies that OSHA will not conduct inspections of home offices and does not hold employers liable for employees' home offices. The compliance directive also notes that employers required by the recordkeeping rule to keep records "will continue to be responsible for keeping such records, regardless of whether the injuries occur in the factory, in a home office, or elsewhere, as long as they are work-related, and meet the recordability criteria of 29 CFR Part 1904."

With more employees working at home under various telecommuting and flexible workplace arrangements, OSHA believes that it is important to record injuries and illnesses attributable to work tasks performed at home. If these cases are not recorded, the Nation's injury and illness statistics could be skewed. For example, placing such an exclusion in the final rule would make it difficult to determine if a decline in the overall number or rate of occupational injuries and illnesses is attributable to a trend toward working at home or to a change in the Nation's actual injury and illness experience. Further, excluding these work-related injuries and illnesses from the recordkeeping system could potentially obscure previously unidentified causal connections between events or exposures in the work environment and these incidents. OSHA is unwilling to adopt an exception that would have these potential effects.

...

Section 1904.6 Determination of New Cases [p. 5962]

Employers may occasionally have difficulty in determining whether new signs or symptoms are due to a new event or exposure in the workplace or whether they are the continuation of an existing work-related injury or illness. Most occupational injury and illness cases are fairly discrete events, i.e., events in which an injury or acute illness occurs, is treated, and then resolves completely. For example, a worker may suffer a cut, bruise, or rash from a clearly recognized event in the workplace, receive treatment, and recover fully within a few weeks. At some future time, the worker may suffer another cut, bruise or rash from another workplace event. In such cases, it is clear that the two injuries or illnesses are unrelated events, and that each represents an injury or illness that must be separately evaluated for its recordability.

However, it is sometimes difficult to determine whether signs or symptoms are due to a new event or exposure, or are a continuance of an injury or illness that has already been recorded. This is an important distinction, because a new injury or illness requires the employer to make a new entry on the OSHA 300 Log, while a continuation of an old recorded case requires, at most, an updating of the original entry.

Section 1904.6 of the final rule being published today explains what employers must do to determine whether or not an injury or illness is a new case for recordkeeping purposes.

The basic requirement at Sec. 1904.6(a) states that the employer must consider an injury or illness a new case to be evaluated for recordability if (1) the employee has not previously experienced a recorded injury or illness of the same type that affects the same part of the body, or (2) the employee previously experienced a recorded injury or illness of the same type that affected the same part of the body but had recovered completely (all signs and symptoms of the previous injury or illness had disappeared) and an event or exposure in the work environment caused the injury or illness, or its signs or symptoms, to reappear.

The implementation question at Sec. 1904.6(b)(1) addresses chronic work-related cases that have already been recorded once and distinguishes between those conditions that will progress even in the absence of workplace exposure and those that are triggered by events in the workplace. There are some conditions that will progress even in the absence of further exposure, such as some occupational cancers, advanced asbestosis, tuberculosis disease, advanced byssinosis, advanced silicosis, etc. These conditions are chronic; once the disease is contracted it may never be cured or completely resolved, and therefore the case is never "closed" under the OSHA recordkeeping system, even though the signs and symptoms of the condition may alternate between remission and active disease.

However, there are other chronic work-related illness conditions, such as occupational asthma, reactive airways dysfunction syndrome (RADs), and sensitization (contact) dermatitis, that recur if the ill individual is exposed to the agent (or agents, in the case of cross-reactivities or RADs) that triggers the illness again. It is typical, but not always the case, for individuals with these conditions to be symptom-free if exposure to the sensitizing or precipitating agent does not occur.

The final rule provides, at paragraph (b)(1), that the employer is not required to record as a new case a previously recorded case of chronic work-related illness where the signs or symptoms have recurred or continued in the absence of exposure in the workplace. This paragraph recognizes that there are occupational illnesses that may be diagnosed at some stage of the disease and may then progress without regard to workplace events or exposures. Such diseases, in other words, will progress without further workplace exposure to the toxic substance(s) that caused the disease. Examples of such chronic work-related diseases are silicosis, tuberculosis, and asbestosis. With these conditions, the ill worker will show signs (such as a positive TB skin test, a positive chest roentgenogram, etc.) at every medical examination, and may experience symptomatic bouts as the disease progresses.

Paragraph 1904.6(b)(2) recognizes that many chronic occupational illnesses, however, such as occupational asthma, RADs, and contact dermatitis, are triggered by exposures in the workplace. The difference between these conditions and those addressed in paragraph 1904.6(b)(1) is that in these cases exposure triggers the recurrence of symptoms and signs, while in the chronic cases covered in the previous paragraph, the symptoms and signs recur even in the absence of exposure in the workplace.

Paragraph 1904.6(b)(3) addresses how to record a case for which the employer requests a physician or other licensed health care professional (HCP) to make a new case/continuation of an old case determination. Paragraph (b)(3) makes clear that employers are to follow the guidance provided by the HCP for OSHA recordkeeping purposes. In cases where two or more HCPs make conflicting or differing recommendations, the employer is required to base his or her decision about recordation based on the most authoritative (best documented, best reasoned, or most persuasive) evidence or recommendation.

...

Section 1904.7 General Recording Criteria [p. 5968]

Section 1904.7 contains the general recording criteria for recording work-related injuries and illnesses. This section describes the recording of cases that meet one or more of the following six criteria: death, days away from work, restricted work or transfer to another job, medical treatment beyond first aid, loss of consciousness, or diagnosis as a significant injury or illness by a physician or other licensed health care professional.

Paragraph 1904.7(a)

Paragraph 1904.7(a) describes the basic requirement for recording an injury or illness in the OSHA recordkeeping system. It states that employers must record any work-related injury or illness that meets one or more of the final rule's general recording criteria. There are six such criteria: death, days away from work, days on restricted work or on job transfer, medical treatment beyond first aid, loss of consciousness, or diagnosis by a physician or other licensed heath care professional as a significant injury or illness. Although most cases are recorded because they meet one of these criteria, some cases may meet more than one criterion as the case continues. For example, an injured worker may initially be sent home to recuperate (making the case recordable as a "days away" case) and then subsequently return to work on a restricted ("light duty") basis (meeting a second criterion, that for restricted work). (see the discussion in Section 1904.29 for information on how to record such cases.)

Paragraph 1904.7(b)

Paragraph 1904.7(b) tells employers how to record cases meeting each of the six general recording criteria and states how each case is to be entered on the OSHA 300 Log. Paragraph 1904.7(b)(1) provides a simple decision table listing the six general recording criteria and the paragraph number of each in the final rule. It is included to aid employers and recordkeepers in recording these cases.

1904.7(b)(2) Death

Paragraph 1904.7(b)(2) requires the employer to record an injury or illness that results in death by entering a check mark on the OSHA 300 Log in the space for fatal cases. This paragraph also directs employers to report work-related fatalities to OSHA within 8 hours and cross references the fatality and catastrophe reporting requirements in Sec. 1904.39 of the final rule, Reporting fatalities and multiple hospitalizations to OSHA. Paragraph 1904.7(b)(2) imple-

ments the OSH Act's requirements to record all cases resulting in work-related deaths.

...

Paragraph 1904.7(b)(3) Days Away From Work

Paragraph 1904.7(b)(3) contains the requirements for recording work-related injuries and illnesses that result in days away from work and for counting the total number of days away associated with a given case. Paragraph 1904.7(b)(3) requires the employer to record an injury or illness that involves one or more days away from work by placing a check mark on the OSHA 300 Log in the space reserved for day(s) away cases and entering the number of calendar days away from work in the column reserved for that purpose. This paragraph also states that, if the employee is away from work for an extended time, the employer must update the day count when the actual number of days away becomes known. This requirement continues the day counting requirements of the former rule and revises the days away requirements in response to comments in the record.

Paragraphs 1904.7(b)(3)(i) through (vi) implement the basic requirements. Paragraph 1904.7(b)(3)(i) states that the employer is not to count the day of the injury or illness as a day away, but is to begin counting days away on the following day. Thus, even though an injury or illness may result in some loss of time on the day of the injurious event or exposure because, for example, the employee seeks treatment or is sent home, the case is not considered a days-away-from-work case unless the employee does not work on at least one subsequent day because of the injury or illness. The employer is to begin counting days away on the day following the injury or onset of illness. This policy is a continuation of OSHA's practice under the former rule, which also excluded the day of injury or onset of illness from the day counts.

Paragraphs 1904.7(b)(3)(ii) and (iii) direct employers how to record days-away cases when a physician or other licensed health care professional (HCP) recommends that the injured or ill worker stay at home or that he or she return to work but the employee chooses not to do so. As these paragraphs make clear, OSHA requires employers to follow the physician's or HCP's recommendation when recording the case.

Further, whether the employee works or not is in the control of the employer, not the employee. That is, if an HCP recommends that the employee remain away from work for one or more days, the employer is required to record the injury or illness as a case involving days away from work and to keep track of the days; the employee's wishes in this case are not relevant, since it is the employer who controls the conditions of work. Similarly, if the HCP tells the employee that he or she can return to work, the employer is required by the rule to stop counting the days away from work, even if the employee chooses not to return to work. These policies are a continuation of OSHA's previous policy of requiring employees to follow the recommendations of health care professionals when recording cases in the OSHA system. OSHA is aware that there may be situations where the employer obtains an opinion from a physician or other health care professional and a subsequent HCP's opinion differs from the first. (The subsequent opinion could be that of an HCP retained by the employer or the employee.) In this case, the employer is the ultimate record-keeping decision-maker and must resolve the differences in opinion; he or she may turn to a third HCP for this purpose, or may make the recordability decision himself or herself.

Paragraph 1904.7(b)(3)(iv) specifies how the employer is to account for weekends, holidays, and other days during which the employee was unable to work because of a work-related injury or illness during a period in which the employee was not scheduled to work. The rule requires the employer to count the number of calendar days the employee was unable to work because of the work-related injury or illness, regardless of whether or not the employee would have been scheduled to work on those calendar days. This provision will ensure that a measure of the length of disability is available, regardless of the employee's work schedule. This requirement is a change from the former policy, which focused on scheduled workdays missed due to injury or illness and excluded from the days away count any normal days off, holidays, and other days the employee would not have worked.

Paragraph 1904.7(b)(3)(v) tells the employer how to count days away for a case where the employee is injured or becomes ill on the last day of work before some scheduled time off, such as on the Friday before the weekend or the day before a scheduled vacation, and returns to work on the next day that he or she was scheduled to work. In this situation, the employer must decide if the worker would have been able to work on the days when he or she was not at work. In other words, the employer is not required to count as days away any of the days on which the employee would have been able to work but did not because the facility was closed, the employee was not scheduled to work, or for other reasons unrelated to the injury or illness. However, if the employer determines that the employee's injury or illness would have kept the employee from being able to work for part or all of time the employee was away, those days must be counted toward the days away total.

Paragraph 1904.7(b)(3)(vi) allows the employer to stop counting the days away from work when the injury or illness has resulted in 180 calendar days away from work. When the injury or illness results in an absence of more than 180 days, the employer may enter 180 (or 180+) on the Log. This is a new provision of the final rule; it is included because OSHA believes that the "180" notation indicates a case of exceptional severity and that counting days away beyond that point would provide little if any additional information.

Paragraph 1904.7(b)(3)(vii) specifies that employers whose employees are away from work because of a work-related injury or illness and who then decide to leave the company's employ or to retire must determine whether the employee is leaving or retiring because of the injury or illness and record the case accordingly. If the employee's decision to leave or retire is a result of the injury or illness, this paragraph requires the employer to estimate and record the number of calendar days away or on restricted work/job transfer the worker would have experienced if he or she had remained on the employer's payroll. This provision also states that, if the employee's decision was unrelated to the injury or illness, the employer is not required to continue to count and record days away or on restricted work/job transfer.

Paragraph 1904.(b)(3)(viii) directs employers how to handle a case that carries over from one year to the next. Some cases occur in one calendar year and then result in days away from work in the next year.

For example, a worker may be injured on December 20th and be away from work until January 10th. The final rule directs the employer only to record this type of case once, in the year that it occurred. If the employee is still away from work when the annual summary is prepared (before February 1), the employer must either count the number of days the employee was away or estimate the total days away that are expected to occur, use this estimate to calculate the total days away during the year for the annual summary, and then update the Log entry later when the actual number of days is known or the case reaches the 180-day cap allowed in Sec. 1904.7(b)(3)(v).

...

Final Rule's Restricted Work and Job Transfer Provisions, and OSHA's Reasons for Adopting Them

Paragraph 1904.7(b)(4) contains the restricted work and job transfer provisions of the final rule. These provisions clarify the definition of restricted work in light of the comments received and continue, with a few exceptions, most of the former rule's requirements with regard to these kinds of cases. OSHA finds, based on a review of the record, that these provisions of the final rule will increase awareness among employers of the importance of recording restricted work activity and job transfer cases and make the recordkeeping system more accurate and the process more efficient.

OSHA believes that it is even more important today than formerly that the definition of restricted work included in the final rule be clear and widely understood, because employers have recently been relying on restricted work (or "light duty") with increasing frequency, largely in an effort to encourage injured or ill employees to return to work as soon as possible. According to BLS data, this category of cases has grown by nearly 70% in the last six

years. In 1992, for example, 9% of all injuries and illnesses (or a total of 622,300 cases) recorded as lost workday cases were classified in this way solely because of restricted work days, while in 1998, nearly 18% of all injury and illness cases (or a total of 1,050,200 cases) were recorded as lost workday cases only because they involved restricted work [BLS Press Release 99-358, 12-16-99]. The return-to-work programs increasingly being relied on by employers (often at the recommendation of their workers' compensation insurers) are designed to prevent exacerbation of, or to allow recuperation from, the injury or illness, rehabilitate employees more effectively, reintegrate injured or ill workers into the workplace more rapidly, limit workers' compensation costs, and retain productive workers. In addition, many employees are eager to accept restricted work when it is available and prefer returning to work to recuperating at home.

The final rule's requirements in paragraph 1904.10(b)(4) of the final rule state:

(4) How do I record a work-related injury or illness that involves restricted work or job transfer? When an injury or illness involves restricted work or job transfer but does not involve death or days away from work, you must record the injury or illness on the OSHA 300 Log by placing a check mark in the space for job transfer or restricted work and entering the number of restricted or transferred days in the restricted work column.

(i) How do I decide if the injury or illness resulted in restricted work? Restricted work occurs when, as the result of a work-related injury or illness:

(A) You keep the employee from performing one or more of the routine functions of his or her job, or from working the full workday that he or she would otherwise have been scheduled to work; or

(B) A physician or other licensed health care professional recommends that the employee not perform one or more of the routine functions of his or her job, or not work the full workday that he or she would otherwise have been scheduled to work.

(ii) What is meant by "routine functions"? For recordkeeping purposes, an employee's routine functions are those work activities the employee regularly performs at least once per week.

(iii) Do I have to record restricted work or job transfer if it applies only to the day on which the injury occurred or the illness began?

No. You do not have to record restricted work or job transfers if you, or the physician or other licensed health care professional, impose the restriction or transfer only for the day on which the injury occurred or the illness began.

(iv) If you or a physician or other licensed health care professional recommends a work restriction, is the injury or illness automatically recordable as a "restricted work" case?

No. A recommended work restriction is recordable only if it affects one or more of the employee's routine job functions. To determine whether this is the case, you must evaluate the restriction in light of the routine functions of the injured or ill employee's job. If the restriction from you or the physician or other licensed health care professional keeps the employee from performing one or more of his or her routine job functions, or from working the full workday the injured or ill employee would otherwise have worked, the employee's work has been restricted and you must record the case.

(v) How do I record a case where the worker works only for a partial work shift because of a work-related injury or illness?

A partial day of work is recorded as a day of job transfer or restriction for recordkeeping purposes, except for the day on which the injury occurred or the illness began.

(vi) If the injured or ill worker produces fewer goods or services than he or she would have produced prior to the injury or illness but otherwise performs all of the activities of his or her work, is the case considered a restricted work case?

No. The case is considered restricted work only if the worker does not perform all of the routine functions of his or her job or does not work the

full shift that he or she would otherwise have worked.

(vii) How do I handle vague restrictions from a physician or other licensed health care professional, such as that the employee engage only in "light duty" or "take it easy for a week"?

If you are not clear about a physician or other licensed health care professional's recommendation, you may ask that person whether the employee can perform all of his or her routine job functions and work all of his or her normally assigned work shift. If the answer to both of these questions is "Yes," then the case does not involve a work restriction and does not have to be recorded as such. If the answer to one or both of these questions is "No," the case involves restricted work and must be recorded as a restricted work case. If you are unable to obtain this additional information from the physician or other licensed health care professional who recommended the restriction, record the injury or illness as a case involving job transfer or restricted work.

(viii) What do I do if a physician or other licensed health care professional recommends a job restriction meeting OSHA's definition but the employee does all of his or her routine job functions anyway?

You must record the injury or illness on the OSHA 300 Log as a restricted work case. If a physician or other licensed health care professional recommends a job restriction, you should ensure that the employee complies with that restriction. If you receive recommendations from two or more physicians or other licensed health care providers, you may make a decision as to which recommendation is the most authoritative, and record the case based upon that recommendation.

...

As the regulatory text for paragraph (b)(4) makes clear, the final rule's requirements for the recording of restricted work cases are similar in many ways to those pertaining to restricted work under the former rule. First, like the former rule, the final rule only requires employers to record as restricted work cases those cases in which restrictions are imposed or recommended as a result of a work-related injury or illness. A work restriction that is made for another reason, such as to meet reduced production demands, is not a recordable restricted work case. For example, an employer might "restrict" employees from entering the area in which a toxic chemical spill has occurred or make an accommodation for an employee who is disabled as a result of a non-work-related injury or illness. These cases would not be recordable as restricted work cases because they are not associated with a work-related injury or illness. However, if an employee has a work-related injury or illness, and that employee's work is restricted by the employer to prevent exacerbation of, or to allow recuperation from, that injury or illness, the case is recordable as a restricted work case because the restriction was necessitated by the work-related injury or illness. In some cases, there may be more than one reason for imposing or recommending a work restriction, e.g., to prevent an injury or illness from becoming worse or to prevent entry into a contaminated area. In such cases, if the employee's work-related illness or injury played any role in the restriction, OSHA considers the case to be a restricted work case.

Second, for the definition of restricted work to apply, the work restriction must be decided on by the employer, based on his or her best judgment or on the recommendation of a physician or other licensed health care professional. If a work restriction is not followed or implemented by the employee, the injury or illness must nevertheless be recorded on the Log as a restricted case. This was also the case under the former rule.

Third, like the former rule, the final rule's definition of restricted work relies on two components: whether the employee is able to perform the duties of his or her pre-injury job, and whether the employee is able to perform those duties for the same period of time as before.

The principal differences between the final and former rules' concept of restricted work cases are these: (1) the final rule permits employers to cap the total number of restricted work days for a particular case at 180 days, while the former rule required all restricted days for a given case to be recorded; (2) the final rule does not require employers to count the restriction of an employee's duties on the day the injury occurred or the illness began as restricted work, providing that the day the incident occurred is the only day on which work is restricted; and (3) the final rule defines work as restricted if the injured or ill employee is restricted from performing any job activity the employee would have regularly performed at least once per week before the injury or illness, while the former rule counted work as restricted if the employee was restricted in performing any activity he or she would have performed at least once per year.

In all other respects, the final rule continues to treat restricted work and job transfer cases in the same manner as they were treated under the former rule, including the counting of restricted days. Paragraph 1904.7(b)(4)(xi) requires the employer to count restricted days using the same rules as those for counting days away from work, using Sec. 1904.7(b)(3)(i) to (viii), with one exception. Like the former rule, the final rule allows the employer to stop counting restricted days if the employee's job has been permanently modified in a manner that eliminates the routine functions the employee has been restricted from performing. Examples of permanent modifications would include reassigning an employee with a respiratory allergy to a job where such allergens are not present, or adding a mechanical assist to a job that formerly required manual lifting. To make it clear that employers may stop counting restricted days when a job has been permanently changed, but not to eliminate the count of restricted work altogether, the rule makes it clear that at least one restricted workday must be counted, even if the restriction is imposed immediately. A discussion of the desirability of counting days of restricted work and job transfer at all is included in the explanation for the OSHA 300 form and the Sec. 1904.29 requirements. The revisions to this category of cases that have been made in the final rule reflect the views of commenters, suggestions made by the Keystone report (Ex. 5), and OSHA's experience in enforcing the former recordkeeping rule.

Paragraph 1904.7(b)(5) Medical Treatment Beyond First Aid

The definitions of first aid and medical treatment have been central to the OSHA recordkeeping scheme since 1971, when the Agency's first recordkeeping rule was issued. Sections 8(c)(2) and 24(a) of the OSH Act specifically require employers to record all injuries and illnesses other than those "requiring only first aid treatment and which do not involve medical treatment, loss of consciousness, restriction of work or motion, or transfer to another job." Many injuries and illnesses sustained at work do not result in death, loss of consciousness, days away from work or restricted work or job transfer. Accordingly, the first aid and medical treatment criteria may be the criteria most frequently evaluated by employers when deciding whether a given work-related injury must be recorded.

In the past, OSHA has not interpreted the distinction made by the Act between minor (i.e., first aid only) injuries and non-minor injuries as applying to occupational illnesses, and employers have therefore been required to record all occupational illnesses, regardless of severity. As a result of this final rule, OSHA will now apply the same recordability criteria to both injuries and illnesses (see the discussion of this issue in the Legal Authority section of this preamble). The Agency believes that doing so will simplify the decision-making process that employers carry out when determining which work-related injuries and illnesses to record and will also result in more complete data on occupational illness, because employers will know that they must record these cases when they result in medical treatment beyond first aid, regardless of whether or not a physician or other licensed health care professional has made a diagnosis.

The former recordkeeping rule defined first aid as "any one-time treatment and any follow-up visit for the purpose of observation, of minor scratches, cuts, burns, splinters, and so forth, which do not ordinarily require medical care." Medical treatment was formerly defined as "treatment administered by a physician or by registered professional personnel under the standing orders of a physician."

To help employers determine the recordability of a given injury, the Recordkeeping Guidelines, issued by the Bureau of Labor Statistics (BLS) in 1986, provided numerous examples of medical treatments and of first aid treatments (Ex. 2). These examples were published as mutually exclusive lists, i.e., a treatment listed as a medical treatment did not also appear on the first-aid list. Thus, for example, a positive x-ray diagnosis (fractures, broken bones, etc.) was included among the treatments generally considered medical treatment, while a negative x-ray diagnosis (showing no fractures) was generally considered first aid. Despite the guidance provided by the Guidelines, OSHA continued to receive requests from employers for interpretations of the recordability of specific cases, and a large number of letters of interpretation addressing the distinction between first aid and medical treatment have been issued.

...

[The final rule] includes a list of first-aid treatments that is inclusive, and defines as medical treatment any treatment not on that list. OSHA recognizes, as several commenters pointed out, that no one can predict how medical care will change in the future. However, using a finite list of first aid treatments—knowing that it may have to be amended later based on new information—helps to limit the need for individual judgment about what constitutes first aid treatment. If OSHA adopted a more open-ended definition or one that relied on the judgment of a health care professional, employers and health care professionals would inevitably interpret different cases differently, which would compromise the consistency of the data. Under the system adopted in the final rule, once the employer has decided that a particular response to a work-related illness or injury is in fact treatment, he or she can simply turn to the first aid list to determine, without elaborate analysis, whether the treatment is first aid and thus not recordable.

OSHA finds that this simple approach, by providing clear, unambiguous guidance, will reduce confusion for employers and improve the accuracy and consistency of the data.

...

Final Rule

The final rule, at Sec. 1904.7(b)(5)(i), defines medical treatment as the management and care of a patient for the purpose of combating disease or disorder. For the purposes of Part 1904, medical treatment does not include:

(A) Visits to a physician or other licensed health care professional solely for observation or counseling;

(B) The conduct of diagnostic procedures, such as x-rays and blood tests, including the administration of prescription medications used solely for diagnostic purposes (e.g., eye drops to dilate pupils); or

(C) "first aid" as defined in paragraph (b)(5)(ii) of this section.

The final rule, at paragraph (b)(5)(ii), defines first aid as follows:

(A) Using a nonprescription medication at nonprescription strength (for medications available in both prescription and non-prescription form, a recommendation by a physician or other licensed health care professional to use a nonprescription medication at prescription strength is considered medical treatment for recordkeeping purposes).

(B) administering tetanus immunizations (other immunizations, such as hepatitis B vaccine or rabies vaccine, are considered medical treatment).

(C) Cleaning, flushing or soaking wounds on the surface of the skin;

(D) Using wound coverings, such as bandages, Band-Aids, gauze pads, etc.; or using butterfly bandages or Steri-Strips (other wound closing devices, such as sutures, staples, etc. are considered medical treatment);

(E) Using hot or cold therapy;

(F) Using any non-rigid means of support, such as elastic bandages, wraps, non-rigid back belts, etc. (devices with rigid stays or other systems designed to immobilize parts of the body are considered medical treatment for recordkeeping purposes);

(G) Using temporary immobilization devices while transporting an accident victim (e.g. splints, slings, neck collars, back boards, etc.)

(H) Drilling of a fingernail or toenail to relieve pressure, or draining fluid from a blister;

(I) Using eye patches;

(J) Removing foreign bodies from the eye using only irrigation or a cotton swab;

(K) Removing splinters or foreign material from areas other than the eye by irrigation, tweezers, cotton swabs, or other simple means;

(L) Using finger guards;

(M) Using massages (physical therapy or chiropractic treatment are considered medical treatment for recordkeeping purposes);

(N) Drinking fluids for relief of heat stress.

This list of first aid treatments is comprehensive, i.e., any treatment not included on this list is not considered first aid for OSHA recordkeeping purposes. OSHA considers the listed treatments to be first aid regardless of the professional qualifications of the person providing the treatment; even when these treatments are provided by a physician, nurse, or other health care professional, they are considered first aid for recordkeeping purposes.

...

The three listed exclusions from the definition—visits to a health care professional solely for observation or counseling; diagnostic procedures, including prescribing or administering of prescription medications used solely for diagnostic purposes; and procedures defined in the final rule as first aid—clarify the applicability of the definition and are designed to help employers in their determinations of recordability.

...

In making its decisions about the items to be included on the list of first aid treatments, OSHA relied on its experience with the former rule, the advice of the Agency's occupational medicine and occupational nursing staff, and a thorough review of the record comments. In general, first aid treatment can be distinguished from medical treatment as follows:

■ First aid is usually administered after the injury or illness occurs and at the location (e.g., workplace) where the injury or illness occurred.

■ First aid generally consists of one-time or short-term treatment.

■ First aid treatments are usually simple and require little or no technology.

■ First aid can be administered by people with little training (beyond first aid training) and even by the injured or ill person.

- First aid is usually administered to keep the condition from worsening, while the injured or ill person is awaiting medical treatment.

The final rule's list of treatments considered first aid is based on the record of the rulemaking, OSHA's experience in implementing the recordkeeping rule since 1986, a review of the BLS Recordkeeping Guidelines, letters of interpretation, and the professional judgment of the Agency's occupational physicians and nurses.

...

In the final rule, OSHA has not included prescription medications, whether given once or over a longer period of time, in the list of first aid treatments. The Agency believes that the use of prescription medications is not first aid because prescription medications are powerful substances that can only be prescribed by a licensed health care professional, and for the majority of medications in the majority of states, by a licensed physician. The availability of these substances is carefully controlled and limited because they must be prescribed and administered by a highly trained and knowledgeable professional, can have detrimental side effects, and should not be self-administered.

...

OSHA has decided to retain its long-standing policy of requiring the recording of cases in which a health care professional issues a prescription, whether that prescription is filled or taken or not. The patient's acceptance or refusal of the treatment does not alter the fact that, in the health care professional's judgment, the case warrants medical treatment. In addition, a rule that relied on whether a prescription is filled or taken, rather than on whether the medicine was prescribed, would create administrative difficulties for employers, because such a rule would mean that the employer would have to investigate whether a given prescription had been filled or the medicine had actually been taken. Finally, many employers and employees might well consider an employer's inquiry about the filling of a prescription an invasion of the employee's privacy. For these reasons, the final rule continues OSHA's longstanding policy of considering the giving of a prescription medical treatment. It

departs from former practice with regard to the administration of a single dose of a prescription medicine, however, because there is no medical reason for differentiating medical treatment from first aid on the basis of the number of doses involved. This is particularly well illustrated by the recent trend toward giving a single large dose of antibiotics instead of the more traditional pattern involving several smaller doses given over several days.

Yet another issue raised by commenters about medications involved the use of non-prescription medications at prescription strength. In recent years, many drugs have been made available both as prescription and "over-the-counter" medications, depending on the strength or dosage of the product. Some examples include various non-steroidal anti-inflammatory drugs (NSAIDs), such as ibuprofen, and cortisone creams.

...

The final rule does not consider the prescribing of non-prescription medications, such as aspirin or over-the-counter skin creams, as medical treatment. However, if the drug is one that is available both in prescription and nonprescription strengths, such as ibuprofen, and is used or recommended for use by a physician or other licensed health care professional at prescription strength, the medical treatment criterion is met and the case must be recorded. There is no reason for one case to be recorded and another not to be recorded simply because one physician issued a prescription and another told the employee to use the same medication at prescription strength but to obtain it over the counter. Both cases received equal treatment and should be recorded equally. This relatively small change in the recordkeeping rule will improve the consistency and accuracy of the data on occupational injuries and illnesses and simplify the system as well.

...

OSHA believes that cleaning, flushing or soaking of wounds on the skin surface is the initial emergency treatment for almost all surface wounds and that these procedures do not rise to the level of medical treatment. This relatively simple type of treatment does not require technology, training, or even a visit to a health care professional. More serious wounds will be captured as recordable cases because they will meet other recording criteria, such as prescription medications, sutures, restricted work, or days away from work. Therefore, OSHA has included cleaning, flushing or soaking of wounds on the skin surface as an item on the first aid list. As stated previously, OSHA does not believe that multiple applications of first aid should constitute medical treatment; it is the nature of the treatment, not how many times it is applied, that determines whether it is first aid or medical treatment.

...

In the final rule, OSHA has included hot and cold treatment as first aid treatment, regardless of the number of times it is applied, where it is applied, or the injury or illness to which it is applied. The Agency has decided that hot or cold therapy must be defined as either first aid or medical treatment regardless of the condition being treated, a decision that departs from the proposal. It is OSHA's judgment that hot and cold treatment is simple to apply, does not require special training, and is rarely used as the only treatment for any significant injury or illness. If the worker has sustained a significant injury or illness, the case almost always involves some other form of medical treatment (such as prescription drugs, physical therapy, or chiropractic treatment); restricted work; or days away from work. Therefore, there is no need to consider hot and cold therapy to be medical treatment, in and of itself. Considering hot and cold therapy to be first aid also clarifies and simplifies the rule, because it means that employers will not need to consider whether to record when an employee uses hot or cold therapy without the direction or guidance of a physician or other licensed health care professional.

...

In the final rule, OSHA has included hot and cold treatment as first aid treatment, regardless of the number of times it is applied, where it is applied, or the injury or illness to which it is applied.

The Agency has decided that hot or cold therapy must be defined as either first aid or medical treatment regardless of the condition being treated, a decision that departs from the

proposal. It is OSHA's judgment that hot and cold treatment is simple to apply, does not require special training, and is rarely used as the only treatment for any significant injury or illness. If the worker has sustained a significant injury or illness, the case almost always involves some other form of medical treatment (such as prescription drugs, physical therapy, or chiropractic treatment); restricted work; or days away from work. Therefore, there is no need to consider hot and cold therapy to be medical treatment, in and of itself. Considering hot and cold therapy to be first aid also clarifies and simplifies the rule, because it means that employers will not need to consider whether to record when an employee uses hot or cold therapy without the direction or guidance of a physician or other licensed health care professional.

...

[OSHA believes] that the use of these devices during an emergency to stabilize an accident victim during transport to a medical facility is not medical treatment. In this specific situation, a splint or other device is used as temporary first aid treatment, may be applied by non-licensed personnel using common materials at hand, and often does not reflect the severity of the injury. OSHA has included this item as G on the first aid list: "[u]sing temporary immobilization devices while transporting an accident victim (e.g. splints, slings, neck collars, etc.)"

...

[Item H on the first aid list is the "drilling of a fingernail or toenail to relieve pressure, or draining fluid from a blister."] These are both one time treatments provided to relieve minor soreness caused by the pressure beneath the nail or in the blister. These are relatively minor procedures that are often performed by licensed personnel but may also be performed by the injured worker. More serious injuries of this type will continue to be captured if they meet one or more of the other recording criteria. OSHA has specifically mentioned finger nails and toenails to provide clarity. These treatments are now included as item H on the first aid list.

...

In the final rule, OSHA has included the use of eye patches as first aid in item I of the first aid list. Eye patches can be purchased without a prescription, and are used for both serious and non-serious injuries and illnesses. OSHA believes that the more serious injuries to the eyes will that NIOSH refers to require medical treatment, such as prescription drugs or removal of foreign material by means other than irrigation or a cotton swab, and will thus be recordable.

...

In the final rule, OSHA has included as item J "Removing foreign bodies from the eye using only irrigation or a cotton swab." OSHA believes that it is often difficult for the health care professional to determine if the object is embedded or adhered to the eye, and has not included this suggested language in the final rule. In all probability, if the object is embedded or adhered, it will not be removed simply with irrigation or a cotton swab, and the case will be recorded because it will require additional treatment.

...

OSHA believes that it is appropriate to exclude those cases from the Log that involve a foreign body in the eye of a worker that can be removed from the eye merely by rinsing it with water (irrigation) or touching it with a cotton swab. These cases represent minor injuries that do not rise to the level requiring recording. More significant eye injuries will be captured by the records because they involve medical treatment, result in work restrictions, or cause days away from work.

...

[OSHA has included as item K "Removal of splinters or foreign material from areas other than the eyes by irrigation, tweezers, cotton swabs or other simple means."] The inclusion of the phrase "other simple means" will provide some flexibility and permit simple means other than those listed to be considered first aid. Cases involving more complicated removal procedures will be captured on the Log because they will require medical treatment such as prescription drugs or stitches or will involve restricted work or days away from work.

...

Paragraph 1904.7(b)(6) Loss of Consciousness

The final rule, like the former rule, requires the employer to record any work-related injury or illness resulting in a loss of consciousness. The recording of occupational injuries and illnesses resulting in loss of consciousness is clearly required by Sections 8(c) and 24 of the OSH Act. The new rule differs from the former rule only in clearly applying the loss of consciousness criterion to illnesses as well as injuries. Since the former rule required the recording of all illnesses, illnesses involving loss of consciousness were recordable, and thus OSHA expects that this clarification will not change recording practices. Thus, any time a worker becomes unconscious as a result of a workplace exposure to chemicals, heat, an oxygen deficient environment, a blow to the head, or some other workplace hazard that causes loss of consciousness, the employer must record the case.

...

Paragraph 1904.7(b)(7) Recording Significant Work-Related Injuries and Illnesses Diagnosed by a Physician or Other Licensed Health Care Professional

Paragraph 1904.7(b)(7) of this final rule requires the recording of any significant work-related injury or illness diagnosed by a physician or other licensed health care professional. Paragraph 1904.7(b)(7) clarifies which significant, diagnosed work-related injuries and illnesses OSHA requires the employer to record in those rare cases where a significant work-related injury or illness has not triggered recording under one or more of the general recording criteria, i.e., has not resulted in death, loss of consciousness, medical treatment beyond first aid, restricted work or job transfer, or days away from work. Based on the Agency's prior recordkeeping experience, OSHA believes that the great majority of significant occupational injuries and illnesses will be captured by one or more of the other general recording criteria in Section 1904.7. However, OSHA has found that there is a limited class of significant work-related injuries and illnesses that may not be captured under the other Sec. 1904.7 criteria. Therefore, the final rule stipulates at paragraph 1904.7(b)(7) that any significant work-related occupational injury or illness that is not captured by any of the general recording criteria but is diagnosed by a physician or other licensed health care professional be recorded in the employer's records.

Under the final rule, an injury or illness case is considered significant if it is a work-related case involving occupational cancer (e.g., mesothelioma), chronic irreversible disease (e.g., chronic beryllium disease), a fractured or cracked bone (e.g., broken arm, cracked rib), or a punctured eardrum. The employer must record such cases within 7 days of receiving a diagnosis from a physician or other licensed health care professional that an injury or illness of this kind has occurred. As explained in the note to paragraph 1904.7(b)(7), OSHA believes that the great majority of significant work-related injuries and illnesses will be recorded because they meet one or more of the other recording criteria listed in Sec. 1904.7(a): death, days away from work, restricted work or job transfer, medical treatment beyond first aid, or loss of consciousness. However, there are some significant injuries, such as a punctured eardrum or a fractured toe or rib, for which neither medical treatment nor work restrictions may be administered or recommended.

There are also a number of significant occupational diseases that progress once the disease process begins or reaches a certain point, such as byssinosis, silicosis, and some types of cancer, for which medical treatment or work restrictions may not be recommended at the time of diagnosis, although medical treatment and loss of work certainly will occur at later stages. This provision of the final rule is designed to capture this small group of significant work-related cases. Although the employer is required to record these illnesses even if they manifest themselves after the employee leaves employment (assuming the illness meets the standards for work-relatedness that apply to all recordable incidents), these cases are less likely to be recorded once the employee has left employment. OSHA believes that work-related cancer, chronic irreversible diseases, fractures of bones or teeth and punctured eardrums are generally recognized as constituting significant diagnoses and, if the condition is work-related, are appropriately recorded at the time of initial diagnosis even if, at that time, medical treatment or work restrictions are not recommended.

As discussed in the Legal Authority section, above, OSHA has modified the Agency's prior position so that, under the final rule, minor occupational illnesses no longer are required to be recorded on the Log. The requirement pertaining to the recording of all significant diagnosed injuries and illnesses in this paragraph of the final rule, on the other hand, will ensure that all significant (non-minor) injuries and illnesses are in fact captured on the Log, as required by the OSH Act. Requiring significant cases involving diagnosis to be recorded will help to achieve several of the goals of this rulemaking. First, adherence to this requirement will produce better data on occupational injury and illness by providing for more complete recording of significant occupational conditions. Second, this requirement will produce more timely records because it provides for the immediate recording of significant disorders on first diagnosis. Many occupational illnesses manifest themselves through gradual onset and worsening of the condition. In some cases, a worker could be diagnosed with a significant illness, such as an irreversible respiratory disorder, not be given medical treatment because no effective treatment was available, not lose time from work because the illness was not debilitating at the time, and not have his or her case recorded on the Log because none of the recording criteria had been met. If such a worker left employment or changed employers before one of the other recording criteria had been met, this serious occupational illness case would never be recorded. The requirements in paragraph 1904.7(b)(7) remedy this deficiency and will thus ensure the capture of more complete and timely data on these injuries and illnesses.

...

Section 1904.8 Additional Recording Criteria for Needlestick and Sharps Injuries [p. 5998]

Section 1904.8 of the final rule being published today deals with the recording of a specific class of occupational injuries involving punctures, cuts and lacerations caused by needles or other sharp objects contaminated or reasonably anticipated to be contaminated with blood or other potentially infectious materials that may lead to bloodborne diseases, such as Acquired Immunodeficiency Syndrome (AIDS), hepatitis B or hepatitis C. The final rule uses the terms "contaminated," "other potentially infectious material," and "occupational exposure" as these terms are defined in OSHA's Bloodborne Pathogens standard (29 CFR 1910.1030). These injuries are of special concern to healthcare workers because they use needles and other sharp devices in the performance of their work duties and are therefore at risk of bloodborne infections caused by exposures involving contaminated needles and other sharps. Although healthcare workers are at particular risk of bloodborne infection from these injuries, other workers may also be at risk of contracting potentially fatal bloodborne disease. For example, a worker in a hospital laundry could be stuck by a contaminated needle left in a patient's bedding, or a worker in a hazardous waste treatment facility could be occupationally exposed to bloodborne pathogens if contaminated waste from a medical facility was not treated before being sent to waste treatment.

Section 1904.8(a) requires employers to record on the OSHA Log all work-related needlestick and sharps injuries involving objects contaminated (or reasonably anticipated to be contaminated) with another person's blood or other potentially infectious material (OPIM). The rule prohibits the employer from entering the name of the affected employee on the Log to protect the individual's privacy; employees are understandably sensitive about others knowing that they may have contracted a bloodborne disease. For these cases, and other types of privacy concern cases, the employer simply enters "privacy concern case" in the space reserved for the employee's name. The employer then keeps a separate, confidential list of privacy concern cases with the case number from the Log and the employee's name; this list is used by the employer to keep track of the injury or illness so that the Log can later be updated, if necessary, and to ensure that the information will be available if a government representative needs information about injured or ill employees during a workplace inspection (see Sec. 1904.40). The regulatory text of Sec. 1904.8 refers recordkeepers

and others to Sec. 1904.29(b)(6) through Sec. 1904.29(b)(10) of the rule for more information about how to record privacy concern cases of all types, including those involving needlesticks and sharps injuries. The implementation section of Sec. 1904.8(b)(1) defines "other potentially infectious material" as it is defined in OSHA's Bloodborne Pathogens Standard (29 CFR Sec. 1910.1030, paragraph (b)). Other potentially infectious materials include (i) human bodily fluids, human tissues and organs, and (ii) other materials infected with the HIV or hepatitis B (HBV) virus such as laboratory cultures or tissues from experimental animals. (For a complete list of OPIM, see paragraph (b) of 29 CFR 1910.1030.)

Although the final rule requires the recording of all workplace cut and puncture injuries resulting from an event involving contaminated sharps, it does not require the recording of all cuts and punctures. For example, a cut made by a knife or other sharp instrument that was not contaminated by blood or OPIM would not generally be recordable, and a laceration made by a dirty tin can or greasy tool would also generally not be recordable, providing that the injury did not result from a contaminated sharp and did not meet one of the general recording criteria of medical treatment, restricted work, etc. Paragraph (b)(2) of Sec. 1904.8 contains provisions indicating which cuts and punctures must be recorded because they involve contaminated sharps and which must be recorded only if they meet the general recording criteria.

Paragraph (b)(3) of Sec. 1904.8 contains requirements for updating the OSHA 300 Log when a worker experiences a wound caused by a contaminated needle or sharp and is later diagnosed as having a bloodborne illness, such as AIDS, hepatitis B or hepatitis C. The final rule requires the employer to update the classification of such a privacy concern case on the OSHA 300 Log if the outcome of the case changes, i.e., if it subsequently results in death, days away from work, restricted work, or job transfer. The employer must also update the case description on the Log to indicate the name of the bloodborne illness and to change the classification of the case from an injury (i.e., the needlestick) to an illness (i.e., the illness that resulted from the needlestick). In no case may the employer enter the employee's name on the Log itself, whether when initially recording the needlestick or sharp injury or when subsequently updating the record.

The privacy concern provisions of the final rule make it possible, for the first time, for the identity of the bloodborne illness caused by the needlestick or sharps injury to be included on the Log. By excluding the name of the injured or ill employee throughout the recordkeeping process, employee privacy is assured. This approach will allow OSHA to gather valuable data about the kinds of bloodborne illnesses healthcare and other workers are contracting as a result of these occupational injuries, and will provide the most accurate and informative data possible, including the seroconversion status of the affected worker, the name of the illness he or she contracted, and, on the OSHA 301 Form for the original case, more detailed information about how the injury occurred, the equipment and materials involved, and so forth. Use of the privacy case concept thus meets the primary objective of this rulemaking, providing the best data possible, while simultaneously ensuring that an important public policy goal—the protection of privacy about medical matters—is met. OSHA recognizes that requiring employers to treat privacy cases differently from other cases adds some complexity to the recordkeeping system and imposes a burden on those employers whose employees experience such injuries and illnesses, but believes that the gain in data quality and employee privacy outweigh these disadvantages considerably.

The last paragraph (paragraph (c)) of Sec. 1904.8 deals with the recording of cases involving workplace contact with blood or other potentially infectious materials that do not involve needlesticks or sharps, such as splashes to the eye, mucous membranes, or non-intact skin. The final recordkeeping rule does not require employers to record these incidents unless they meet the final rule's general recording criteria (i.e., death, medical treatment, loss of consciousness, restricted work or motion, days away from work, diagnosis by an HCP) or the employee subsequently develops an illness caused by bloodborne pathogens. The final

rule thus provides employers, for the first time, with regulatory language delineating how they are to record injuries caused by contaminated needles and other sharps, and how they are to treat other exposure incidents (as defined in the Bloodborne Pathogens standard) involving blood or OPIM. "Contaminated" is defined just as it is in the Bloodborne Pathogens standard: "Contaminated means the presence or the reasonably anticipated presence of blood or other potentially infectious materials on an item or surface."

...

Section 1904.9 Additional Recording Criteria for Cases Involving Medical Removal Under OSHA Standards [p. 6003]

The final rule, in paragraph 1904.9(a), requires an employer to record an injury or illness case on the OSHA 300 Log when the employee is medically removed under the medical surveillance requirements of any OSHA standard. Paragraph 1904.9(b)(1) requires each such case to be recorded as a case involving days away from work (if the employee does not work during the medical removal) or as a case involving restricted work activity (if the employee continues to work but in an area where exposures are not present.) This paragraph also requires any medical removal related to chemical exposure to be recorded as a poisoning illness.

Paragraph 1904.9(b)(2) informs employers that some OSHA standards have medical removal provisions and others do not. For example, the Bloodborne Pathogen Standard (29 CFR 1910.1030) and the Occupational Noise Standard (29 CFR 1910.95) do not require medical removal. Many of the OSHA standards that contain medical removal provisions are related to specific chemical substances, such as lead (29 CFR 1901.1025), cadmium (29 CFR 1910.1027), methylene chloride (29 CFR 1910.1052), formaldehyde (29 CFR 1910.1048), and benzene (29 CFR 1910.1028). Paragraph 1904.9(b)(3) addresses the issue of medical removals that are not required by an OSHA standard. In some cases employers voluntarily rotate employees from one job to another to reduce exposure to hazardous substances; job rotation is an administrative method of reducing exposure that is permitted in some OSHA standards. Removal (job transfer) of an asymptomatic employee for administrative exposure control reasons does not require the case to be recorded on the OSHA 300 Log because no injury or illness—the first step in the recordkeeping process—exists. Paragraph 1904.9(b)(3) only applies to those substances with OSHA mandated medical removal criteria. For injuries or illnesses caused by exposure to other substances or hazards, the employer must look to the general requirements of paragraphs 1910.7(b)(3) and (4) to determine how to record the days away or days of restricted work.

The provisions of Sec. 1904.9 are not the only recording criteria for recording injuries and illnesses from these occupational exposures. These provisions merely clarify the need to record specific cases, which are often established with medical test results, that result in days away from work, restricted work, or job transfer. The Sec. 1904.9 provisions are included to produce more consistent data and provide needed interpretation of the requirements for employers. However, if an injury or illness results in the other criteria of Sec. 1904.7 (death, medical treatment, loss of consciousness, days away from work, restricted work, transfer to another job, or diagnosis as a significant illness or injury by a physician or other licensed health care professional) the case must be recorded whether or not the medical removal provisions of an OSHA standard have been met.

...

OSHA has therefore included section 1904.9 in the final rule to provide a uniform, simple method for recording a variety of serious disorders that have been addressed by OSHA standards. The Sec. 1904.9 provisions of the final rule cover all of the OSHA standards with medical removal provisions, regardless of whether or not those provisions are based on medical tests, physicians' opinions, or a combination of the two. Finally, by relying on the medical removal provisions in any OSHA standard, section 1904.9 of the final rule establishes recording criteria for future standards, and avoids the need to amend the recordkeeping rule whenever OSHA issues a standard containing a medical removal level.

...

Section 1904.10 Recording Criteria for Cases Involving Occupational Hearing Loss [p. 6004]

[The Department of Labor has proposed that the criteria for recording work-related hearing loss not be implemented for one year pending further investigation into the level of hearing loss that should be recorded as a "significant" health condition. Paragraph 1904.10(b)(1) of the final rule had required that a standard threshold shift of an average of 10 decibels (dB) or more at 2000, 3000, or 4000 hertz in one or both ears would be recordable.

Until more information is obtained, a standard threshold shift of 25 decibels, as required by the former regulation, is to be recorded.]

Section 1904.11 Additional Recording Criteria for Work-Related Tuberculosis Cases [p. 6013]

Section 1904.11 of the final rule being published today addresses the recording of tuberculosis (TB) infections that may occur to workers occupationally exposed to TB. TB is a major health concern, and nearly one-third of the world's population may be infected with the TB bacterium at the present time. There are two general stages of TB, tuberculosis infection and active tuberculosis disease. Individuals with tuberculosis infection and no active disease are not infectious; tuberculosis infections are asymptomatic and are only detected by a positive response to a tuberculin skin test. Workers in many settings are at risk of contracting TB infection from their clients or patients, and some workers are at greatly increased risk, such as workers exposed to TB patients in health care settings. Outbreaks have also occurred in a variety of workplaces, including hospitals, prisons, homeless shelters, nursing homes, and manufacturing facilities (62 FR 54159).

The text of Sec. 1904.11 of the final rule states:

(a) **Basic requirement.** If any of your employees has been occupationally exposed to anyone with a known case of active tuberculosis (TB), and that employee subsequently develops a tuberculosis infection, as evidenced by a positive skin test or diagnosis by a physician or other licensed health care professional, you must record the case on the OSHA 300 Log by checking the "respiratory condition" column.

(b) Implementation.

  (1) Do I have to record, on the Log, a positive TB skin test result obtained at a pre-employment physical?

No, because the employee was not occupationally exposed to a known case of active tuberculosis in your workplace.

  (2) May I line-out or erase a recorded TB case if I obtain evidence that the case was not caused by occupational exposure?

Yes. you may line-out or erase the case from the Log under the following circumstances:

  (i) The worker is living in a household with a person who has been diagnosed with active TB;

  (ii) The Public Health Department has identified the worker as a contact of an individual with a case of active TB unrelated to the workplace; or

  (iii) A medical investigation shows that the employee's infection was caused by exposure to TB away from work, or proves that the case was not related to the workplace TB exposure.

Section 1904.12 Recording Criteria for Cases Involving Work-Related Musculoskeletal Disorders [p. 6017]

[This section provides requirements for recording work-related musculoskeletal disorders (MSDs). OSHA has proposed to delay for one year the definition of MSD and the requirement to check the MSD column. However, the same recording criteria applies to musculoskeletal disorders (MSDs) as to all other injuries and illnesses.]

Section 1904.29 Forms [p. 6022]

Section 1904.29, titled "Forms," establishes the requirements for the forms (OSHA 300 Log, OSHA 300A Annual Summary, and OSHA 301 Incident Report) an employer must use to keep OSHA Part 1904 injury and illness records, the time limit for recording an injury or illness case, the use of substitute forms, the use of computer equipment to keep the records, and privacy protections for certain information recorded on the OSHA 300 Log.

Paragraph 1904.29(a) sets out the basic requirements of this section. It directs the employer to use the OSHA 300 (Log), 300A (Summary), and 301 (Incident Report) forms, or equivalent forms, to record all recordable occupational injuries and illnesses. Paragraph 1904.29(b) contains requirements in the form of questions and answers to explain how employers are to implement this basic requirement. Paragraph 1904.29(b)(1) states the requirements for: (1) Completing the establishment information at the top of the OSHA 300 Log, (2) making a one- or two-line entry for each recordable injury and illness case, and (3) summarizing the data at the end of the year. Paragraph 1904.29(b)(2) sets out the requirements for employers to complete the OSHA 301 Incident Report form (or equivalent) for each recordable case entered on the OSHA 300 Log. The requirements for completing the annual summary on the Form 300A are found at Section 1904.32 of the final rule.

Required Forms

In addition to establishing the basic requirements for employers to keep records on the OSHA 300 Log and OSHA 301 Incident Report and providing basic instructions on how to complete these forms, this section of the rule states that employers may use two lines of the OSHA 300 Log to describe an injury or illness, if necessary.

...

OSHA believes that most injury and illness cases can be recorded using only one line of the Log. However, for those cases requiring more space, this addition to the Log makes it clear that two lines may be used to describe the case. The OSHA 300 Log is designed to be a scannable document that employers, employees and government representatives can use to review a fairly large number of cases in a brief time, and OSHA believes that employers will not need more than two lines to describe a given case. Employers should enter more detailed information about each case on the OSHA 301 form, which is designed to accommodate lengthier information.

Deadline for Entering a Case

Paragraph 1904.29(b)(3) establishes the requirement for how quickly each recordable injury or illness must be recorded into the records. It states that the employer must enter each case on the OSHA 300 Log and OSHA 301 Form within 7 calendar days of receiving information that a recordable injury or illness has occurred. In the vast majority of cases, employers know immediately or within a short time that a recordable case has occurred. In a few cases, however, it may be several days before the employer is informed that an employee's injury or illness meets one or more of the recording criteria.

...

Accordingly, paragraphs 1904.29(b)(4) and (b)(5) of the final rule make clear that employers are permitted to record the required information on electronic media or on paper forms that are different from the OSHA 300 Log, provided that the electronic record or paper forms are equivalent to the OSHA 300 Log. A form is deemed to be "equivalent" to the OSHA 300 Log if it can be read and understood as easily as the OSHA form and contains at least as much information as the OSHA 300 Log. In addition, the equivalent form must be completed in accordance with the instructions used to complete the OSHA 300 Log. These provisions are intended to balance OSHA's obligation, as set forth in Section 8(d) of the OSH Act, to reduce information collection burdens on employers as much as possible, on the one hand, with the need, on the other hand, to maintain uniformity of the data recorded and provide employers flexibility in meeting OSHA's recordkeeping requirements. These provisions also help to achieve one of OSHA's goals for this rulemaking: to allow employers to take full advantage of modern technology and computers to meet their OSHA recordkeeping obligations.

...

The final rule does not include a requirement that certain questions on an equivalent form be asked in the same order and be phrased in language identical to that used on the OSHA 301 form. Instead, OSHA has decided, based on a review of the record evidence, that employers may use any substitute form that contains the same information and follows the same recording directions as the OSHA 301 form, and the final rule clearly allows this. Although the consistency of the data on the OSHA 301 form might be improved somewhat if the questions asking for further details were phrased and positioned in an identical way on all employers' forms, OSHA has concluded that the additional burden such a requirement would impose on employers and workers' compensation agencies outweighs this consideration.

...

Handling of Privacy Concern Cases

Paragraphs 1904.29(b)(6) through (b)(10) of the final rule are new and are designed to address privacy concerns raised by many commenters to the record. Paragraph 1904.29(b)(6) requires the employer to withhold the injured or ill employee's name from the OSHA 300 Log for injuries and illnesses defined by the rule as "privacy concern cases" and instead to enter "privacy concern case" in the space where the employee's name would normally be entered if an injury or illness meeting the definition of a privacy concern case occurs. This approach will allow the employer to provide OSHA 300 Log data to employees, former employees and employee representatives, as required by Sec. 1904.35, while at the same time protecting the privacy of workers who have experienced occupational injuries and illnesses that raise privacy concerns. The employer must also keep a separate, confidential list of these privacy concern cases, and the list must include the employee's name and the case number from the OSHA 300 Log. This separate listing is needed to allow a government representative to obtain the employee's name during a workplace inspection in case further investigation is warranted and to assist employers to keep track of such cases in the event that future revisions to the entry become necessary.

Paragraph 1904.29(b)(7) defines "privacy concern cases" as those involving: (i) An injury or illness to an intimate body part or the reproductive system; (ii) an injury or illness resulting from a sexual assault; (iii) a mental illness; (iv) a work-related HIV infection, hepatitis case, or tuberculosis case; (v) needlestick injuries and cuts from sharp objects that are contaminated with another person's blood or other potentially infectious material, or (vi) any other illness, if the employee independently and voluntarily requests that his or her name not be entered on the log. Paragraph 1904.29(b)(8) establishes that these are the only types of occupational injuries and illnesses that the employer may consider privacy concern cases for recordkeeping purposes.

Paragraph 1904.29(b)(9) permits employers discretion in recording case information if the employer believes that doing so could compromise the privacy of the employee's identity, even though the employee's name has not been entered. This clause has been added because OSHA recognizes that, for specific situations, coworkers who are allowed to access the log may be able to deduce the identity of the injured or ill worker and obtain inappropriate knowledge of a privacy-sensitive injury or illness. OSHA believes that these situations are relatively infrequent, but still exist. For example, if knowing the department in which the employee works would inadvertently divulge the person's identity, or recording the gender of the injured employee would identifying that person (because, for example, only one woman works at the plant), the employer has discretion to mask or withhold this information both on the Log and Incident Report.

The rule requires the employer to enter enough information to identify the cause of the incident and the general severity of the injury or illness, but allows the employer to exclude details of an intimate or private nature. The rule includes two examples; a sexual assault case could be described simply as "injury from assault," or an injury to a reproductive organ could be described as "lower abdominal injury." Likewise, a work-related diagnosis of post traumatic stress disorder could be described as "emotional difficulty." Reproductive disorders, certain cancers, contagious diseases and other disorders that are intimate and private in nature may also be described in a general way to avoid privacy concerns. This allows the employer to avoid overly graphic descriptions that may be offensive, without sacrificing the descriptive value of the recorded information.

Paragraph 1904.29(b)(10) protects employee privacy if the employer decides voluntarily to disclose the OSHA 300 and 301 forms to persons other than those who have a mandatory right of access under the final rule. The paragraph requires the employer to remove or hide employees' names or other personally identifying information before disclosing the forms to persons other than government representatives, employees, former employees or authorized representatives, as required by paragraphs 1904.40 and 1904.35, except in three cases. The employer may disclose the forms, complete with personally identifying information, (2) only: (i) to an auditor or consultant hired by the employer to evaluate the safety and health program; (ii) to the extent necessary for processing a claim for workers' compensation or other insurance benefits; or (iii) to a public health authority or law enforcement agency for uses and disclosures for which consent, an authorization, or opportunity to agree or object is not required under section 164.512 of the final rule on Standards for Privacy of Individually Identifiable Health Information, 45 CFR 164.512.

These requirements have been included in Sec. 1904.29 rather than in Sec. 1904.35, which establishes requirements for records access, because waiting until access is requested to remove identifying information from the OSHA 300 Log could unwittingly compromise the injured or ill worker's privacy and result in unnecessary delays. The final rule's overall approach to handling privacy issues is discussed more fully in the preamble discussion of the employee access provisions in Sec. 1904.35.

The Treatment of Occupational Illness and Injury Data on the Forms

The treatment of occupational injury and illness data on the OSHA forms is a key issue in this rulemaking. Although the forms themselves are not printed in the Code of Federal Regulations (CFR), they are the method OSHA's recordkeeping regulation uses to meet the Agency's goal of tracking and reporting occupational injury and illness data. As such, the forms are a central component of the recordkeeping system and mirror the requirements of the Part 1904 regulation. The final Part 1904 rule requires employers to use three forms to track occupational injuries and illnesses: the OSHA 300, 300A, and 301 forms, which replace the OSHA 200 and 101 forms called for under the former recordkeeping rule, as follows:

1. The OSHA Form 300, Log of Work-Related Injuries and Illnesses, replaces the Log portion of the former OSHA Form 200 Log and Summary of Occupational Injuries and Illnesses. The OSHA 300 Log contains space for a description of the establishment name, city and state, followed by a one-line space for the entry for each recordable injury and illness.

2. The OSHA Form 300A, Summary of Work-Related Injuries and Illnesses, replaces the Summary portion of the former OSHA Form 200 Log and Summary of Occupational Injuries and Illnesses. The Form 300A is used to summarize the entries from the Form 300 Log at the end of the year and is then posted from February 1 through April 30 of the following year so that employees can be aware of the occupational injury and illness experience of the establishment in which they work. The form contains space for entries for each of the columns from the Form 300, along with information about the establishment, and the average number of employees who worked there the previous year, and the recordkeeper's and corporate officer's certification of the accuracy of the data recorded on the summary. (These requirements are addressed further in Section 1904.32 of the final rule and its associated preamble.)

3. The OSHA Form 301, Injury and Illness Report, replaces the former OSHA 101 Form. Covered employers are required to fill out a one-page form for each injury and illness recorded on the Form 300. The form contains space for more detailed information about the injured or ill employee, the physician or other health care professional who cared for the employee (if medical treatment was necessary), the treatment (if any) of the employee at an emergency room or hospital, and descriptive information telling what the employee was doing when injured or ill, how the incident occurred, the specific details of the injury or illness, and the object or substance that harmed the employee. (Most employers use a workers' compensation form as a replacement for the OSHA 301 Incident Report.)

...

The OSHA recordkeeping forms required by the final Part 1904 recordkeeping rule are printed on legal size paper (8½" x 14"). The former rule's Log was an 11 by 17-inch form, the equivalent of two standard 8½ by 11-inch pages. The former 200 Log was criticized because it was unwieldy to copy and file and contained 12 columns for recording occupational injury and occupational illness cases.

Accordingly, OSHA has redesigned the OSHA 300 Log to fit on a legal size (8½ x 14 inches) piece of paper and to clarify that employers may use two lines to enter a case if the information does not fit easily on one line. The OSHA forms 300A and 301, and the remainder of the recordkeeping package, have also been designed to fit on the same-size paper as the OSHA 300 Log. For those employers who use computerized systems (where handwriting space is not as important) equivalent computer-generated forms can be printed out on 8½ x 11 sheets of paper if the printed copies are legible and are as readable as the OSHA forms.

...

Defining Lost Workdays

In the final rule, OSHA has eliminated the term "lost workdays" on the forms and in the regulatory text. The use of the term has been confusing for many years because many people equated the terms ``lost workday" with "days away from work" and failed to recognize that the former OSHA term included restricted days. OSHA finds that deleting this term from the final rule and the forms will improve clarity and the consistency of the data.

The 300 Log has four check boxes to be used to classify the case: death, day(s) away from work, days of restricted work or job transfer; and case meeting other recording criteria. The employer must check the single box that reflects the most severe outcome associated with a given injury or illness. Thus, for an injury or illness where the injured worker first stayed home to recuperate and then was assigned to restricted work for several days, the employer is required only to check the box for days away from work (column I). For a case with only job transfer or restriction, the employer must check the box for days of restricted work or job transfer (Column H). However, the final

Log still allows employers to calculate the incidence rate formerly referred to as a "lost workday injury and illness rate" despite the fact that it separates the data formerly captured under this heading into two separate categories. Because the OSHA Form 300 has separate check boxes for days away from work cases and cases where the employee remained at work but was temporarily transferred to another job or assigned to restricted duty, it is easy to add the totals from these two columns together to obtain a single total to use in calculating an injury and illness incidence rate for total days away from work and restricted work cases.

Counting Days of Restricted Work or Job Transfer

Although the final rule does not use the term "lost workday" (which formerly applied both to days away from work and days of restricted or transferred work), the rule continues OSHA's longstanding practice of requiring employers to keep track of the number of days on which an employee is placed on restricted work or is on job transfer because of an injury or illness.

...

In the final rule, OSHA has decided to require employers to record the number of days of restriction or transfer on the OSHA 300 Log. From the comments received, and based on OSHA's own experience, the Agency finds that counts of restricted days are a useful and needed measure of injury and illness severity. OSHA's decision to require the recording of restricted and transferred work cases on the Log was also influenced by the trend toward restricted work and away from days away from work. In a recent article, the BLS noted that occupational injuries and illnesses are more likely to result in days of restricted work than was the case in the past. From 1978 to 1986, the annual rate in private industry for cases involving only restricted work remained constant, at 0.3 cases per 100 full-time workers. Since 1986, the rate has risen steadily to 1.2 cases per 100 workers in 1997, a fourfold increase. At the same time, cases with days away from work declined from 3.3 in 1986 to 2.1 in 1997 (Monthly Labor Review, June 1999, Vol. 122. No. 6, pp. 11-17). It is clear that employers have caused this shift by modifying their return-to-work policies and offering more restricted work opportunities to injured or ill employees. Therefore, in order to get an accurate picture of the extent of occupational injuries and illnesses, it is necessary for the OSHA Log to capture counts of days away from work and days of job transfer or restriction.

The final rule thus carries forward OSHA's longstanding requirement for employers to count and record the number of restricted days on the OSHA Log. On the Log, restricted work counts are separated from days away from work counts, and the term "lost workday" is no longer used. OSHA believes that the burden on employers of counting these days will be reduced somewhat by the simplified definition of restricted work, the counting of calendar days rather than work days, capping of the counts at 180 days, and allowing the employer to stop counting restricted days when the employees job has been permanently modified to eliminate the routine job functions being restricted (see the preamble discussion for 1904.7 General Recording Criteria).

Separate 300 Log Data on Occupational Injury and Occupational Illness

OSHA proposed (61 FR 4036-4037) to eliminate any differences in the way occupational injuries, as opposed to occupational illnesses, were recorded on the forms.

After a thorough review of the comments in the record, however, OSHA has concluded that the proposed approach, which would have eliminated, for recording purposes, the distinction between work-related injuries and illnesses, is not workable in the final rule. The Agency finds that there is a continuing need for separately identifiable information on occupational illnesses and injuries, as well as on certain specific categories of occupational illnesses. The published BLS statistics have included separate estimates of the rate and number of occupational injuries and illnesses for many years, as well as the rate and number of different types of occupational illnesses, and employers, employees, the government, and the public have found this information useful and worthwhile. Separate illness and injury data are particularly useful at the establishment level, where employers and employees can use them to evaluate the establishment's health experience and compare it to the national experience or to the experience of other employers in their industry or their own prior experience. The data are also useful to OSHA personnel performing worksite inspections, who can use this information to identify potential health hazards at the establishment.

Under the final rule, the OSHA 300 form has therefore been modified specifically to collect information on five types of occupational health conditions: musculoskeletal disorders, skin diseases or disorders, respiratory conditions, poisoning, and hearing loss. There is also an "all other illness" column on the Log. To record cases falling into one of these categories, the employer simply enters a check mark in the appropriate column, which will allow these cases to be separately counted to generate establishment-level summary information at the end of the year.

...

In the final rule, two of the illness case columns on the OSHA 300 Log are identical to those on the former OSHA Log: a column to capture cases of skin diseases or disorders and one to capture cases of systemic poisoning. The single column for respiratory conditions on the new OSHA Form 300 will capture data on respiratory conditions that were formerly captured in two separate columns, i.e., the columns for respiratory conditions due to toxic agents (formerly column 7c) and for dust diseases of the lungs (formerly column 7b). Column 7g of the former OSHA Log provided space for data on all other occupational illnesses, and that column has also been continued on the new OSHA 300 Log. On the other hand, column 7e from the former OSHA Log, which captured cases of disorders due to physical agents, is not included on the new OSHA Log form. The cases recorded in former column 7e primarily addressed heat and cold disorders, such as heat stroke and hypothermia; hyperbaric effects, such as caisson disease; and the effects of radiation, including occupational illnesses caused by x-ray exposure, sun exposure and welder's flash. Because space on the form is at a premium, and because column 7e was not used extensively in the past (recorded column 7e cases accounted only for approximately five percent of all occupational illness cases),

OSHA has not continued this column on the new OSHA 300 Log.

...

Column on the Log for Musculoskeletal Disorders
[OSHA has proposed to delay for one year the definition of MSD and the requirement to check the MSD column. However, the same recording criteria applies to musculoskeletal disorders (MSDs) as to all other injuries and illnesses.]

The OSHA 301 Form
Although the final OSHA 300 Log presents information on injuries and illnesses in a condensed format, the final OSHA 301 Incident Record allows space for employers to provide more detailed information about the affected worker, the injury or illness, the workplace factors associated with the accident, and a brief description of how the injury or illness occurred. Many employers use an equivalent workers' compensation form or internal reporting form for the purpose of recording more detailed information on each case, and this practice is allowed under paragraph 1904.29(b)(4) of the final rule.

...

OSHA has also added several items to the OSHA Form 301 that were not on the former OSHA No. 101:
- The date the employee was hired;
- The time the employee began work;
- The time the event occurred;
- Whether the employee was treated at an emergency room; and
- Whether the employee was hospitalized overnight as an in-patient (the form now requires a check box entry rather than the name and address of the hospital).

OSHA concludes that these data fields will provide safety and health professionals and researchers with important information regarding the occurrence of occupational injuries and illnesses. The questions pertaining to what the employee was doing, how the injury or illness occurred, what the injury or illness was, and what object or substance was involved have been reworded somewhat from those contained on the former OSHA No. 101, but do not require employers or employees to provide additional information.

...

The final 301 form contains four questions eliciting case detail information (i.e., what was the employee doing just before the incident occurred?, what happened?, what was the injury or illness?, and what object or substance directly harmed the employee?). The language of these questions on the final 301 form has been modified slightly from that used in the proposed questions to be consistent with the language used on the BLS Survey of Occupational Injuries and Illnesses collection form. The BLS performed extensive testing of the language used in these questions while developing its survey form and has subsequently used these questions to collect data for many years. The BLS has found that the order in which these questions are presented and the wording of the questions on the survey form elicit the most complete answers to the relevant questions. OSHA believes that using the time-tested language and ordering of these four questions will have the same benefits for employers using the OSHA Form 301 as they have had for employers responding to the BLS Annual Survey. Matching the BLS wording and order will also result in benefits for those employers selected to participate in the BLS Annual Survey. To complete the BLS survey forms, employers will only need to copy information from the OSHA Injury and Illness Incident Report to the BLS survey form. This should be easier and less confusing than researching and rewording responses to the questions on two separate forms.

...

Subpart D. Other OSHA injury and illness recordkeeping requirements [p. 6035]

Subpart D of the final rule contains all of the 29 CFR Part 1904 requirements for keeping OSHA injury and illness records that do not actually pertain to entering the injury and illness data on the forms. The nine sections of Subpart D are:

■ Section 1904.30, which contains the requirements for dealing with multiple business establishments;

■ Section 1904.31, which contains the requirements for determining which employees' occupational injuries and illnesses must be recorded by the employer;

■ Section 1904.32, which requires the employer to prepare and post the annual summary;

■ Section 1904.33, which requires the employer to retain and update the injury and illness records;

■ Section 1904.34, which requires the employer to transfer the records if the business changes owners;

■ Section 1904.35, which includes requirements for employee involvement, including employees' rights to access the OSHA injury and illness information;

■ Section 1904.36, which prohibits an employer from discriminating against employees for exercising their rights under the Act;

■ Section 1904.37, which sets out the state recordkeeping regulations in OSHA approved State-Plan states; and

■ Section 1904.38, which explains how an employer may seek a variance from the recordkeeping rule.

Section 1904.30 Multiple Establishments [p. 6035]

Section 1904.30 covers the procedures for recording injuries and illnesses occurring in separate establishments operated by the same business. For many businesses, these provisions are irrelevant because the business has only one establishment. However, many businesses have two or more establishments, and thus need to know how to apply the recordkeeping rule to multiple establishments. In particular, this section applies to businesses where separate work sites create confusion as to where injury and illness records should be kept and when separate records must be kept for separate work locations, or establishments. OSHA recognizes that the recordkeeping system must accommodate operations of this type, and has adopted language in the final rule to provide some flexibility for employers in the construction, transportation, communications, electric and gas utility, and sanitary services industries, as well as other employers with geographically dispersed operations. The final rule provides, in part, that operations are not considered separate establishments unless they continue to be in operation for a year or more. This length-of-site-operation provision increases the chances of discovering patterns of occupational injury and illness, eliminates the burden of creating OSHA 300 Logs for transient work sites, and ensures that useful records are generated for more permanent facilities.

...

The basic requirement of Sec. 1904.30(a) of this final rule states that employers are required to keep separate OSHA 300 Logs for each establishment that is expected to be in business for one year or longer. Paragraph 1904.30(b)(1) states that for short-term establishments, i.e., those that will exist for less than a year, employers are required to keep injury and illness records, but are not required to keep separate OSHA 300 Logs. They may keep one OSHA 300 Log covering all short-term establishments, or may include the short-term establishment records in logs that cover individual company divisions or geographic regions. For example, a construction company with multi-state operations might have separate OSHA 300 Logs for each state to show the injuries and illnesses of its employees engaged in short-term projects, as well as a separate OSHA 300 Log for each construction project expected to last for more than one year. If the same company had only one office location and none of its projects lasted for more than one year, the company would only be required to have one OSHA 300 Log.

Paragraph 1904.30(b)(2) allows the employer to keep records for separate establishments at the business' headquarters or another central location, provided that information can be transmitted from the establishment to headquarters or the central location within 7 days of the occurrence of the injury or illness, and provided that the employer is able to produce and send the OSHA records to each establishment when Sec. 1904.35 or Sec. 1904.40 requires such transmission. The sections of the final rule are consistent with the corresponding provisions of the proposed rule.

Paragraph 1904.30(b)(3) states that each employee must be linked, for recordkeeping purposes, with one of the employer's estab-

lishments. Any injuries or illnesses sustained by the employee must be recorded on his or her home establishment's OSHA 300 Log, or on a general OSHA 300 Log for short-term establishments. This provision ensures that all employees are included in a company's records. If the establishment is in an industry classification partially exempted under Sec. 1904.2 of the final rule, records are not required. Under paragraph 1904.30(b)(4), if an employee is injured or made ill while visiting or working at another of the employer's establishments, then the injury or illness must be recorded on the 300 Log of the establishment at which the injury or illness occurred.

...

Recording Injuries and Illnesses Where They Occur

For the vast majority of cases, the place where the injury or illness occurred is the most useful recording location. The events or exposures that caused the case are most likely to be present at that location, so the data are most useful for analysis of that location's records. If the case is recorded at the employee's home base, the injury or illness data have been disconnected from the place where the case occurred, and where analysis of the data may help reveal a workplace hazard. Therefore, OSHA finds that it is most useful to record the injury or illness at the location where the case occurred. Of course, if the injury or illness occurs at another employer's workplace, or while the employee is in transit, the case would be recorded on the OSHA 300 Log of the employee's home establishment.

For cases of illness, two types of cases must be considered. The first is the case of an illness condition caused by an acute, or short term workplace exposure, such as skin rashes, respiratory ailments, and heat disorders. These illnesses generally manifest themselves quickly and can be linked to the workplace where they occur, which is no different than most injury cases. For illnesses that are caused by long-term exposures or which have long latency periods, the illness will most likely be detected during a visit to a physician or other health care professional, and the employee is most likely to report it to his or her supervisor at the home work location.

Recording these injuries and illnesses could potentially present a problem with incidence rate calculations. In many situations, visiting employees are a minority of the workforce, their hours worked are relatively inconsequential, and rates are thus unaffected to any meaningful extent. However, if an employer relies on visiting labor to perform a larger amount of the work, rates could be affected. In these situations, the hours of these personnel should be added to the establishment's hours of work for rate calculation purposes.

Section 1904.31 Covered employees [p. 6037]

Final Rule Requirements and Legal Background Section 1904.31 requires employers to record the injuries and illnesses of all their employees, whether classified as labor, executive, hourly, salaried, part-time, seasonal, or migrant workers. The section also requires the employer to record the injuries and illnesses of employees they supervise on a day-to-day basis, even if these workers are not carried on the employer's payroll. Implementing these requirements requires an understanding of the Act's definitions of "employer" and "employee." The statute defines "employer," in relevant part, to mean "a person engaged in a business affecting interstate commerce who has employees." 29 U.S.C. 652 (5). The term "person" includes "one or more individuals, partnerships, associations, corporations, business trusts, legal representatives, or any organized group of persons." 29 U.S.C. 652 (4). The term "employee" means "an employee of an employer who is employed in a business of his employer which affects interstate commerce." 29 U.S.C. 652(6). Thus, any individual or entity having an employment relationship with even one worker is an employer for purposes of this final rule, and must fulfill the recording requirements for each employee.

The application of the coverage principles in this section presents few issues for employees who are carried on the employer's payroll, because the employment relationship is usually well established in these cases. However, issues sometimes arise when an individual or entity enters into a temporary relationship with a worker. The first question is whether the worker is an employee of the hiring party. If an employment relationship exists, even if temporary in duration, the employee's injuries and illnesses must be recorded on the OSHA 300 Log and 301 form. The second question, arising in connection with employees provided by a temporary help service or leasing agency, is which employer—the host firm or the temporary help service—is responsible for recordkeeping.

Whether an employment relationship exists under the Act is determined in accordance with established common law principles of agency. At common law, a self-employed "independent contractor" is not an employee; therefore, injuries and illnesses sustained by independent contractors are not recordable under the final Recordkeeping rule. To determine whether a hired party is an employee or an independent contractor under the common law test, the hiring party must consider a number of factors, including the degree of control the hiring party asserts over the manner in which the work is done, and the degree of skill and independent judgment the hired party is expected to apply. Loomis Cabinet Co. v. OSHRC, 20 F.3d 938, 942 (9th Cir. 1994).

Other individuals, besides independent contractors, who are not considered to be employees under the OSH Act are unpaid volunteers, sole proprietors, partners, family members of farm employers, and domestic workers in a residential setting. See 29 CFR Sec. 1975.4(b)(2) and Sec. 1975.6 for a discussion of the latter two categories of workers. As is the case with independent contractors, no employment relationship exists between these individuals and the hiring party, and consequently, no recording obligation arises.

A related coverage question sometimes arises when an employer obtains labor from a temporary help service, employee leasing firm or other personnel supply service. Frequently the temporary workers are on the payroll of the temporary help service or leasing firm, but are under the day-to-day supervision of the host party. In these cases, Section 1904.31 places the recordkeeping obligation upon the host, or utilizing, employer. The final rule's allocation of recordkeeping responsibility to the host employer in these circumstances is consistent with the Act for several reasons.

First, the host employer's exercise of day-to-day supervision of the temporary workers and its control over the work environment demonstrates a high degree of control over the temporary workers consistent with the presence of an employment relationship at common law. See Loomis Cabinet Co., 20 F.3d at 942. Thus, the temporary workers will ordinarily be the employees of the party exercising day-to-day control over them, and the supervising party will be their employer.

Even if daily supervision is not sufficient alone to establish that the host party is the employer of the temporary workers, there are other reasons for the final rule's allocation of recordkeeping responsibility. Under the OSH Act, an employer's duties and responsibilities are not limited only to his own employees. Cf. Universal Constr. Co. v. OSHRC, 182 F.3d 726, 728-731 (10th Cir. 1999). Assuming that the host is an employer under the Act (because it has an employment relationship with someone) it reasonably should record the injuries of all employees, whether or not its own, that it supervises on a daily basis. This follows because the supervising employer is in the best position to obtain the necessary injury and illness information due to its control over the worksite and its familiarity with the work tasks and the work environment.

Section 1904.32 Annual Summary [p. 6042]
At the end of each calendar year, section 1904.32 of the final rule requires each covered employer to review his or her OSHA 300 Log for completeness and accuracy and to prepare an Annual Summary of the OSHA 300 Log using the form OSHA 300-A, Summary of Work-Related Injuries and Illnesses, or an equivalent form. The summary must be certified for accuracy and completeness and be posted in the workplace by February 1 of the year following the year covered by the summary. The summary must remain posted until April 30 of the year in which it was posted. Preparing the Annual Summary requires four steps: reviewing the OSHA 300 Log, computing and entering the summary information on the Form 300-A, certification, and posting. First, the employer must review the Log as extensively as necessary to make sure it is accurate and complete.

Second, the employer must total the columns on the Log; transfer them to the summary form; and enter the calendar year covered, the name of the employer, the name and address of the establishment, the average number of employees on the establishment's payroll for the calendar year, and the total hours worked by the covered employees. If there were no recordable cases at the establishment for the year covered, the summary must nevertheless be completed by entering zeros in the total for each column of the OSHA 300 Log. If a form other than the OSHA 300-A is used, as permitted by paragraph 1904.29(b)(4), the alternate form must contain the same information as the OSHA 300-A form and include identical statements concerning employee access to the Log and Summary and employer penalties for falsifying the document as are found on the OSHA 300-A form.

Third, the employer must certify to the accuracy and completeness of the Log and Summary, using a two-step process. The person or persons who supervise the preparation and maintenance of the Log and Summary (usually the person who keeps the OSHA records) must sign the certification statement on the form, based on their direct knowledge of the data on which it was based. Then, to ensure greater awareness and accountability of the recordkeeping process, a company executive, who may be an owner, a corporate officer, the highest ranking official working at the establishment, or that person's immediate supervisor, must also sign the form to certify to its accuracy and completeness. Certification of the summary attests that the individual making the certification has a reasonable belief, derived from his or her knowledge of the process by which the information in the Log was reported and recorded, that the Log and summary are "true" and "complete."

Fourth, the Summary must be posted no later than February 1 of the year following the year covered in the Summary and remain posted until April 30 of that year in a conspicuous place where notices are customarily posted. The employer must ensure that the Summary is not defaced or altered during the 3 month posting period.

Changes from the former rule. Although the final rule's requirements for preparing the Annual Summary are generally similar to those of the former rule, the final rule incorporates four important changes that OSHA believes will strengthen the recordkeeping process by ensuring greater completeness and accuracy of the Log and Summary, providing employers and employees with better information to understand and evaluate the injury and illness data on the Annual Summary, and facilitating greater employer and employee awareness of the recordkeeping process.

1. **Company Executive Certification of the Annual Summary.** The final rule carries forward the proposed rule's requirement for certification by a higher ranking company official, with minor revision. OSHA concludes that the company executive certification process will ensure greater completeness and accuracy of the Summary by raising accountability for OSHA recordkeeping to a higher managerial level than existed under the former rule. OSHA believes that senior management accountability is essential if the Log and Annual Summary are to be accurate and complete. The integrity of the OSHA recordkeeping system, which is relied on by the BLS for national injury and illness statistics, by OSHA and employers to understand hazards in the workplaces, by employees to assist in the identification and control of the hazards identified, and by safety and health professionals everywhere to analyze trends, identify emerging hazards, and develop solutions, is essential to these objectives. Because OSHA cannot oversee the preparation of the Log and Summary at each establishment and cannot audit more than a small sample of all covered employers' records, this goal is accomplished by requiring employers or company executives to certify the accuracy and completeness of the Log and Summary.

The company executive certification requirement imposes different obligations depending on the structure of the company. If the company is a sole proprietorship or partnership, the certification may be made by the owner. If the company is a corporation, the certification may be made by a corporate officer. For any management structure, the certification may be made by the highest ranking company official working at the establishment covered by the Log (for example, the plant manager or site supervisor), or the latter official's supervisor (for example, a corporate or regional director who works at a different establishment, such as company headquarters).

The company executive certification is intended to ensure that a high ranking company official with responsibility for the recordkeeping activity and the authority to ensure that the recordkeeping function is performed appropriately has examined the records and has a reasonable belief, based on his or her knowledge of that process, that the records are accurate and complete.

The final rule does not specify how employers are to evaluate their recordkeeping systems to ensure their accuracy and completeness or what steps an employer must follow to certify the accuracy and completeness of the Log and Summary with confidence. However, to be able to certify that one has a reasonable belief that the records are complete and accurate would suggest, at a minimum, that the certifier is familiar with OSHA's recordkeeping requirements, and the company's recordkeeping practices and policies, has read the Log and Summary, and has obtained assurance from the staff responsible for maintaining the records (if the certifier does not personally keep the records) that all of OSHA's requirements have been met and all practices and policies followed. In most if not all cases, the certifier will be familiar with the details of some of the injuries and illnesses that have occurred at the establishment and will therefore be able to spot check the OSHA 300 Log to see if those cases have been entered correctly. In many cases, especially in small to medium establishments, the certifier will be aware of all of the injuries and illnesses that have been reported at the establishment and will thus be able to inspect the forms to make sure all of the cases that should have been entered have in fact been recorded.

The certification required by the final rule may be made by signing and dating the certification section of the OSHA 300-A form, which replaces the summary portion of the former OSHA 200 form, or by signing and dating a separate certification statement and appending it to the OSHA Form 300-A. A separate certification statement must contain the identical penalty warnings and employee access information as found on the OSHA Form 300-A. A separate statement may be needed when the certifier works at another location and the certification is mailed or faxed to the location where the Summary is posted.

The certification requirement modifies the certification provision of the former rule (former paragraph 1904.5(c)), which required a certification of the Annual Summary by the employer or an officer or employee who supervised the preparation of the Log and Summary. The former rule required that individual to sign and date the year-end summary on the OSHA Form 200 and to certify that the summary was true and complete. Alternatively, the recordkeeper could, under the former rule, sign a separate certification statement rather than signing the OSHA form.

...

2. **Number of employees and hours worked.** Injury and illness records provide a valuable tool for OSHA, employers, and employees to determine where and why injuries and illnesses occur, and they are crucial in the development of prevention strategies. The final rule requires employers to include in the Annual Summary (the OSHA Form 300-A) the annual average number of employees covered by the Log and the total hours worked by all covered employees.

...

OSHA's view is that the value of the total hours worked and average number of employees information requires its inclusion in the Summary, and the final rule reflects this determination. Having this information will enable employers and employees to calculate injury and illness incidence rates, which are widely regarded as the best statistical measure for the purpose of comparing an establishment's injury and illness experience with national statistics, the records of other establishment, or trends over several years. Having the data available on the Form 300-A will also make it easier for the employer to respond to government requests for the data, which occurs when the BLS and OSHA collect the data by mail, and when an OSHA or State inspector visits the facility. In particular, it will be easier for the employer to provide the OSHA inspector with the hours worked and employment data for past years.

OSHA does not believe that this requirement creates the time and cost burden some commenters to the record suggested, because the information is readily available in payroll or other records required to be kept for other purposes, such as income tax, unemployment, and workers' compensation insurance records. For the approximately 10% of covered employers who participate in the BLS's Annual Survey of Occupational Injuries and Illnesses, there will be no additional burden because this information must already be provided to the BLS. Moreover, the rule does not require employers to use any particular method of calculating the totals, thus providing employers who do not maintain certain records—for example the total hours worked by salaried employees—or employers without sophisticated computer systems, the flexibility to obtain the information in any reasonable manner that meets the objectives of the rule. Employers who do not have the ability to generate precise numbers can use various estimation methods. For example, employers typically must estimate hours worked for workers who are paid on a commission or salary basis. Additionally, the instructions for the OSHA 300-A Summary form include a worksheet to help the employer calculate the total numbers of hours worked and the average number of employees.

3. **Extended posting period.** The final rule's requirement increasing the summary Form 300-A posting period from one month to three months is intended to raise employee awareness of the recordkeeping process (especially that of new employees hired during the posting period) by providing greater access to the previous year's summary without having to request it from management. The additional two months

of posting will triple the time employees have to observe the data without imposing additional burdens on the employer. The importance of employee awareness of and participation in the recordkeeping process is discussed in the preamble to sections 1904.35 and 1904.36.The requirement to post the Summary on February 1 is unchanged from the posting date required by the former rule.

...

After a review of all the comments received and its own extensive experience with the recordkeeping system and its implementation in a variety of workplaces, OSHA has decided to adopt a 3-month posting period. The additional posting period will provide employees with additional opportunity to review the summary information, raise employee awareness of the records and their right to access them, and generally improve employee participation in the recordkeeping system without creating a "wallpaper" posting of untimely data. In addition, OSHA has concluded that any additional burden on employers will be minimal at best and, in most cases, insignificant. All the final rule requires the employer to do is to leave the posting on the bulletin board instead of removing it at the end of the one-month period. In fact, many employers preferred to leave the posting on the bulletin board for longer than the required one-month period in the past, simply to provide workers with the opportunity to view the Annual Summary and increase their awareness of the recordkeeping system in general and the previous year's injury and illness data in particular. OSHA agrees that the 3-month posting period required by the final rule will have these benefits which, in the Agency's view, greatly outweigh any minimal burden that may be associated with such posting. The final rule thus requires that the Summary be posted from February 1 until April 30, a period of three months; OSHA believes that the 30 days in January will be ample, as it has been in the past, for preparing the current year's Summary preparatory to posting.

4. **Review of the records.** The provisions of the final rule requiring the employer to review the Log entries before totaling them for the Annual Summary are intended as an additional quality control measure that will improve the accuracy of the information in the Annual Summary, which is posted to provide information to employees and is also used as a data source by OSHA and the BLS. Depending on the size of the establishment and the number of injuries and illnesses on the OSHA 300 Log, the employer may wish to cross-check with any other relevant records to make sure that all the recordable injuries and illnesses have been included on the Summary. These records may include workers' compensation injury reports, medical records, company accident reports, and/or time and attendance records.

...

Section 1904.33 Retention and Updating [p. 6048]

Section 1904.33 of the final rule deals with the retention and updating of the OSHA Part 1904 records after they have been created and summarized. The final rule requires the employer to save the OSHA 300 Log, the Annual Summary, and the OSHA 301 Incident Report forms for five years following the end of the calendar year covered by the records. The final rule also requires the employer to update the entries on the OSHA 300 Log to include newly discovered cases and show changes that have occurred to previously recorded cases. The provisions in section 1904.33 state that the employer is not required to update the 300A Annual Summary or the 301 Incident Reports, although the employer is permitted to update these forms if he or she wishes to do so.

As this section makes clear, the final rule requires employers to retain their OSHA 300 and 301 records for five years following the end of the year to which the records apply. Additionally, employers must update their OSHA 300 Logs under two circumstances. First, if the employer discovers a recordable injury or illness that has not previously been recorded, the case must be entered on the forms. Second, if a previously recorded injury or illness turns out, based on later information, not to have been recorded properly, the employer must modify the previous entry. For example, if the description or outcome of a case changes (a case requiring medical treatment becomes worse and the employee must take days off work to recuperate), the employer must remove or line out the original entry and enter the new information. The employer also has a duty to enter the date of an employee's return to work or the date of an injured worker's death on the Form 301; OSHA considers the entering of this information an integral part of the recordkeeping for such cases. The Annual Summary and the Form 301 need not be updated, unless the employer wishes to do so. The requirements in this section 1904.33 do not affect or supersede any longer retention periods specified in other OSHA standards and regulations, e.g., in OSHA health standards such as Cadmium, Benzene, or Lead (29 CFR 1910.1027, 1910.1028, and 1910.1025, respectively).

...

Section 1904.34 Change in Business Ownership [p. 6050]

Section 1904.34 of the final rule addresses the situation that arises when a particular employer ceases operations at an establishment during a calendar year, and the establishment is then operated by a new employer for the remainder of the year. The phrase "change of ownership," for the purposes of this section, is relevant only to the transfer of the responsibility to make and retain OSHA-required injury and illness records. In other words, if one employer, as defined by the OSH Act, transfers ownership of an establishment to a different employer, the new entity becomes responsible for retaining the previous employer's past OSHA-required records and for creating all new records required by this rule.

The final rule requires the previous owner to transfer these records to the new owner, and it limits the recording and recordkeeping responsibilities of the previous employer only to the period of the prior owner. Specifically, section 1904.34 provides that if the business changes ownership, each employer is responsible for recording and reporting work-related injuries and illnesses only for that period of the year during which each employer owned the establishment. The selling employer is required

to transfer his or her Part 1904 records to the new owner, and the new owner must save all records of the establishment kept by the prior owner. However, the new owner is not required to update or correct the records of the prior owner, even if new information about old cases becomes available.

...

Sections 1904.35 Employee Involvement, and 1904.36, Prohibition Against Discrimination [p. 6050]

One of the goals of the final rule is to enhance employee involvement in the recordkeeping process. OSHA believes that employee involvement is essential to the success of all aspects of an employer's safety and health program. This is especially true in the area of recordkeeping, because free and frank reporting by employees is the cornerstone of the system. If employees fail to report their injuries and illnesses, the "picture" of the workplace that the employer's OSHA forms 300 and 301 reveal will be inaccurate and misleading. This means, in turn, that employers and employees will not have the information they need to improve safety and health in the workplace. Section 1904.35 of the final rule therefore establishes an affirmative requirement for employers to involve their employees and employee representatives in the recordkeeping process. The employer must inform each employee of how to report an injury or illness, and must provide limited access to the injury and illness records for employees and their representatives. Section 1904.36 of the final rule makes clear that Sec. 11(c) of the Act prohibits employers from discriminating against employees for reporting work-related injuries and illnesses. Section 1904.36 does not create a new obligation on employers. Instead, it clarifies that the OSH Act's anti-discrimination protection applies to employees who seek to participate in the recordkeeping process.

Under the employee involvement provisions of the final rule, employers are required to let employees know how and when to report work-related injuries and illnesses. This means that the employer must establish a procedure for the reporting of work-related injuries and illnesses and train its employees to use that procedure. The rule does not specify how the employer must accomplish these objectives. The size of the workforce, employees' language proficiency and literacy levels, the workplace culture, and other factors will determine what will be effective for any particular workplace.[footnote omitted]

Employee involvement also requires that employees and their representatives have access to the establishment's injury and illness records. Employee involvement is further enhanced by other parts of the final rule, such as the extended posting period provided in section 1904.32 and the access statements on the new 300 and 301 forms.

...

Employee access to OSHA injury and illness records The Part 1904 final rule continues OSHA's long-standing policy of allowing employees and their representatives access to the occupational injury and illness information kept by their employers, with some limitations. However, the final rule includes several changes to improve employees' access to the information, while at the same time implementing several measures to protect the privacy interests of injured and ill employees. Section 1904.35 requires an employer covered by the Part 1904 regulation to provide limited access to the OSHA recordkeeping forms to current and former employees, as well as to two types of employee representatives. The first is a personal representative of an employee or former employee, who is a person that the employee or former employee designates, in writing, as his or her personal representative, or is the legal representative of a deceased or legally incapacitated employee or former employee. The second is an authorized employee representative, which is defined as an authorized collective bargaining agent of one or more employees working at the employer's establishment.

Section 1904.35 accords employees and their representatives three separate access rights. First, it gives any employee, former employee, personal representative, or authorized employee representative the right to a copy of the current OSHA 300 Log, and to any stored OSHA 300 Log(s), for any establishment in which the employee or former employee has worked. The employer must provide one free copy of the OSHA 300 Log(s) by the end of the next business day. The employee, former employee, personal representative or authorized employee representative is not entitled to see, or to obtain a copy of, the confidential list of names and case numbers for privacy cases. Second, any employee, former employee, or personal representative is entitled to one free copy of the OSHA 301 Incident Report describing an injury or illness to that employee by the end of the next business day. Finally, an authorized employee representative is entitled to copies of the right-hand portion of all OSHA 301 forms for the establishment(s) where the agent represents one or more employees under a collective bargaining agreement. The right-hand portion of the 301 form contains the heading "Tell us about the case," and elicits information about how the injury occurred, including the employee's actions just prior to the incident, the materials and tools involved, and how the incident occurred, but does not contain the employee's name. No information other than that on the right-hand portion of the form may be disclosed to an authorized employee representative. The employer must provide the authorized employee representative with one free copy of all the 301 forms for the establishment within 7 calendar days.

Employee privacy is protected in the final rule in paragraphs 1904.29(b)(7) to (10). Paragraph 1904.29(b)(7) requires the employer to enter the words "privacy case" on the OSHA 300 Log, in lieu of the employee's name, for recordable privacy concern cases involving the following types of injuries and illnesses: (i) an injury from a needle or sharp object contaminated by another person's blood or other potentially infectious material; (ii) an injury or illness to an intimate body part or to the reproductive system; (iii) an injury or illness resulting from a sexual assault; (iv) a mental illness; (v) an illness involving HIV, hepatitis, or tuberculosis, or (vi) any other illness, if the employee independently and voluntarily requests that his or her name not be entered on the log. Musculoskeletal disorders (MSDs) are not considered privacy concern cases, and thus employers are required to enter the names of employees experiencing these disorders on the log. The employer must keep a separate, confidential list of the case numbers and employee names for privacy cases. The employer may take additional action in privacy concern cases if warranted. Paragraph 1904.29(b)(9) allows the employer to use discretion in describing the nature of the injury or illness in a privacy concern case, if the employer has a reasonable basis to believe that the injured or ill employee may be identified from the records even though the employee's name has been removed. Only the six types of injuries and illnesses listed in Paragraph 1904.29(b)(7) may be considered privacy concern cases, and thus the additional protection offered by paragraph 1904.29(b)(9) applies only to such cases.

Paragraph 1904.29(b)(10) protects employee privacy if the employer decides voluntarily to disclose the OSHA 300 and 301 forms to persons other than those who have a mandatory right of access under the final rule. The paragraph requires the employer to remove or hide employees' names or other personally identifying information before disclosing the forms to persons other than government representatives, employees, former employees or authorized representatives, as required by paragraphs 1904.40 and 1904.35, except in three cases. The employer may disclose the forms, complete with personally identifying information, (2) only: (i) to an auditor or consultant hired by the employer to evaluate the safety and health program; (ii) to the extent necessary for processing a claim for workers' compensation or other insurance benefits; or (iii) to a public health authority or law enforcement agency for uses and disclosures for which consent, an authorization, or opportunity to agree or object is not required under section 164.512 of the final rule on Standards for Privacy of Individually Identifiable Health Information, 45 CFR 164.512.

Section 1904.37 State Recordkeeping Regulations [p. 6060]

Section 1904.37 addresses the consistency of the recordkeeping and reporting requirements between Federal OSHA and those States where occupational safety and health enforcement is provided by an OSHA-approved State Plan. Currently, in 21 States and 2 territories, the

State government has been granted authority to operate a State OSHA Plan covering both the private and public (State and local government) sectors under section 18 of the OSH Act (see the State Plan section of this preamble for a listing of these States). Two additional States currently operate programs limited in scope to State and local government employees only. State Plans, once approved, operate under authority of State law and provide programs of standards, regulations and enforcement which must be "at least as effective" as the Federal program. (State Plans must extend their coverage to State and local government employees, workers not otherwise covered by Federal OSHA regulations.) Section 1904.37 of the final rule describes what State Plan recordkeeping requirements must be identical to the Federal requirements, which State regulations may be different, and provides cross references to the State Plan regulations codified in Section 1902.3(k), 1952.4, and 1956.10(i). The provisions of Subpart A of 29 CFR part 1952 specify the regulatory discretion of the State Plans in general, and section 1952.4 spells out the regulatory discretion of the State Plans specifically for the recordkeeping regulation.
...

Under Section 18 of the OSH Act, a State Plan must require employers in the State to make reports to the Secretary in the same manner and to the same extent as if the Plan were not in effect. Final section 1904.37 makes clear that States with approved State Plans must promulgate new regulations that are substantially identical to the final Federal rule. State Plans must have recording and reporting regulations that impose identical requirements for the recordability of occupational injuries and illnesses and the manner in which they are entered. These requirements must be the same for employers in all the States, whether under Federal or State Plan jurisdiction, and for State and local government employers covered only through State Plans, to ensure that the occupational injury and illness data for the entire nation are uniform and consistent so that statistics that allow comparisons between the States and between employers located in different States are created.

For all of the other requirements of the Part 1904 regulations, the regulations adopted by the State Plans may be more stringent than or supplemental to the Federal regulations, pursuant to paragraph 1952.4(b). This means that the States' recording and reporting regulations could differ in several ways from their Federal Part 1904 counterparts. For example, a State Plan could require employers to keep records for the State, even though those employers are within an industry exempted by the Federal rule. A State Plan could also require employers to keep additional supplementary injury and illness information, require employers to report fatality and multiple hospitalization incidents within a shorter timeframe than Federal OSHA does, require other types of incidents to be reported as they occur, or impose other requirements. While a State Plan must assure that all employee participation and access rights are assured, the State may provide broader access to records by employees and their representatives. However, because of the unique nature of the national recordkeeping program, States must secure Federal OSHA approval for these enhancements.

...

OSHA understands the advantages to multi-State businesses of following identical OSHA rules in both Federal and State Plan jurisdictions, but also recognizes the value of allowing the States to have different rules to meet the needs of each State, as well as the States' right to impose different rules as long as the State rule is at least as effective as the Federal rule. Accordingly, the Part 1904 rules impose identical requirements where they are needed to create consistent injury and illness statistics for the nation and allows the States to impose supplemental or more stringent requirements where doing so will not interfere with the maintenance of comprehensive and uniform national statistics on workplace fatalities, injuries and illnesses.

Section 1904.38 Variances From the Recordkeeping Rule [p. 6061]

Section 1904.38 of the final rule explains the procedures employers must follow in those rare instances where they request that OSHA grant them a variance or exception to the recordkeeping rules in Part 1904.

The rule contains these procedures to allow an employer who wishes to maintain records in a manner that is different from the approach required by the rules in Part 1904 to petition the Assistant Secretary.

Section 1904.8 allows the employer to apply to the Assistant Secretary for OSHA and request a Part 1904 variance if he or she can show that the alternative recordkeeping system: (1) Collects the same information as this Part requires; (2) Meets the purposes of the Act; and (3) Does not interfere with the administration of the Act.

The variance petition must include several items, namely the employer's name and address; a list of the State(s) where the variance would be used; the addresses of the business establishments involved; a description of why the employer is seeking a variance; a description of the different recordkeeping procedures the employer is proposing to use; a description of how the employer's proposed procedures will collect the same information as would be collected by the Part 1904 requirements and achieve the purpose of the Act; and a statement that the employer has informed its employees of the petition by giving them or their authorized representative a copy of the petition and by posting a statement summarizing the petition in the same way notices are posted under paragraph 1903.2(a).

The final rule describes how the Assistant Secretary will handle the variance petition by taking the following steps:

- The Assistant Secretary will offer employees and their authorized representatives an opportunity to comment on the variance petition. The employees and their authorized representatives will be allowed to submit written data, views, and arguments about the petition.
- The Assistant Secretary may allow the public to comment on the variance petition by publishing the petition in the Federal Register. If the petition is published, the notice will establish a public comment period and may include a schedule for a public meeting on the petition.

- After reviewing the variance petition and any comments from employees and the public, the Assistant Secretary will decide whether or not the proposed recordkeeping procedures will meet the purposes of the Act, will not otherwise interfere with the Act, and will provide the same information as the Part 1904 regulations provide. If the procedures meet these criteria, the Assistant Secretary may grant the variance subject to such conditions as he or she finds appropriate.
- If the Assistant Secretary grants the variance petition, OSHA will publish a notice in the Federal Register to announce the variance. The notice will include the practices the variance allows, any conditions that apply, and the reasons for allowing the variance.

The final rule makes clear that the employer may not use the proposed recordkeeping procedures while the Assistant Secretary is processing the variance petition and must wait until the variance is approved. The rule also provides that, if the Assistant Secretary denies the petition, the employer will receive notice of the denial within a reasonable time and establishes that a variance petition has no effect on the citation and penalty for a citation that has been previously issued by OSHA and that the Assistant Secretary may elect not to review a variance petition if it includes an element which has been cited and the citation is still under review by a court, an Administrative Law Judge (ALJ), or the OSH Review Commission.

The final rule also states that the Assistant Secretary may revoke a variance at a later date if the Assistant Secretary has good cause to do so, and that the procedures for revoking a variance will follow the same process as OSHA uses for reviewing variance petitions. Except in cases of willfulness or where necessary for public safety, the Assistant Secretary will: Notify the employer in writing of the facts or conduct that may warrant revocation of a variance and provide the employer, employees, and authorized employee representatives with an opportunity to participate in the revocation procedures.

...

Like the former variance section of the rule, the final rule does not specifically note that the states operating OSHA-approved state plans are not permitted to grant recordkeeping variances. Paragraph (b) of former section 1952.4, OSHA's rule governing the operation of the State plans, prohibited the states from granting variances, and paragraph (c) of that rule required the State plans to recognize any Federal recordkeeping variances. The same procedures continue to apply to variances under section 1904.37 and section 1952.4 of this final rule. OSHA has not included the provisions from these two sections in the variance sections of this recordkeeping rule, because doing so would be repetitive.

The final rule adds several provisions to those of the former rule. They include (1) the identification of petitioning employers' pending citations in State plan states, (2) the discretion given to OSHA not to consider a petition if a citation on the same subject matter is pending, (3) the clarification that OSHA may provide additional notice via the Federal Register and opportunity for comment, (4) the clarification that variances have only prospective effect, (5) the opportunity of employees and their representatives to participate in revocation procedures, and (6) the voiding of all previous variances and exceptions.

Variance procedures were not discussed in the Recordkeeping Guidelines (Ex. 2), nor have there been any letters of interpretations or OSHRC or court decisions on recordkeeping variances. As noted in the proposal, at 61 FR 4039, only one recordkeeping variance has ever been granted by OSHA. This variance was granted to AT&T and subsequently expanded to its Bell subsidiaries to enable them to centralize records maintenance for workers in the field.

...

Subpart E. Reporting Fatality, Injury and Illness Information to the Government [p. 6062]

Subpart E of this final rule consolidates those sections of the rule that require employers to give recordkeeping information to the government. In the proposed rule, these sections were not grouped together. OSHA believes that grouping these sections into one Subpart improves the overall organization of the rule and will make it easier for employers to find the information when needed. The four sections of this subpart of the final rule are:

(a) Section 1904.39, which requires employers to report fatality and multiple hospitalization incidents to OSHA.

(b) Section 1904.40, which requires an employer to provide his or her occupational illness and injury records to a government inspector during the course of a safety and health inspection.

(c) Section 1904.41, which requires employers to send their occupational illness and injury records to OSHA when the Agency sends a written request asking for specific types of information.

(d) Section 1904.42, which requires employers to send their occupational illness and injury records to the Bureau of Labor Statistics (BLS) when the BLS sends a survey form asking for information from these records.

Each of these sections, and the record evidence pertaining to them, is discussed below.

Section 1904.39 Reporting Fatality or Multiple Hospitalization Incidents to OSHA [p. 6062]

...

Making oral reports of fatalities or multiple hospitalization incidents and the OSHA 800 number.

...

It is essential for OSHA to speak promptly to any employer whose employee(s) have experienced a fatality or multiple hospitalization incident to determine whether the Agency needs to begin an investigation. Therefore, the final rule does not permit employers merely to leave a message on an answering machine, send a fax, or transmit an e-mail message. None of these options allows an Agency representative to interact with the employer to clarify the particulars of the catastrophic incident. Additionally, if the Area Office were closed for the weekend, a holiday, or for some other reason, OSHA might not learn of the incident for several days if electronic or facsimile transmission were permitted. Paragraph 1904.39(b)(1) of the final rule makes this clear.

As noted, OSHA allows the employer to report a fatality or multiple hospitalization incident by speaking to an OSHA representative at the local Area Office either on the phone or in person, or by using the 800 number. This policy gives the employer flexibility to report using whatever mechanism is most convenient. The employer may use whatever method he or she chooses, at any time, as long as he or she is able to speak in person to an OSHA representative or the 800 number operator. Therefore, there is no need to define business hours or otherwise add additional information about when to use the 800 number; it is always an acceptable option for complying with this reporting requirement.

This final rule also includes the 800 number in the text of the regulation. OSHA has decided to include the number in the regulatory text at this time to provide an easy reference for employers. OSHA will also continue to include the 800 number in any interpretive materials, guidelines or outreach materials that it publishes to help employers comply with the reporting requirement.

...

Motor vehicle and public transportation accidents.

...

[OSHA believes] that there is no need for an employer to report a fatality or multiple hospitalization incident when OSHA is clearly not going to make an investigation. When a worker is killed or injured in a motor vehicle accident on a public highway or street, OSHA is only likely to investigate the incident if it occurred in a highway construction zone. Likewise, when a worker is killed or injured in an airplane crash, a train wreck, or a subway accident, OSHA does not investigate, and there is thus no need for the employer to report the incident to OSHA. The text of paragraphs 1904.39(b)(3) and (4) of the final rule clarifies that an employer is not required to report these incidents to OSHA. These incidents are normally investigated by other agencies, including local transit authorities, local or State police, State transportation officials, and the U.S. Department of Transportation.

However, although there is no need to report these incidents to OSHA under the 8-hour reporting requirement, any fatalities and hospitalizations caused by motor vehicle accidents, as well as commercial or public transportation accidents, are recordable if they meet OSHA's recordability criteria. These cases should be captured by the Nation's occupational fatality and injury statistics and be included on the employer's injury and illness forms. The statistics need to be complete, so that OSHA, BLS, and the public can see where and how employees are being made ill, injured and killed. Accordingly, the final rule includes a sentence clarifying that employers are still required to record work-related fatalities and injuries that occur as a result of public transportation accidents and injuries.

Although commenters are correct that OSHA only rarely investigates motor vehicle accidents, the Agency does investigate motor vehicle accidents that occur at street or highway construction sites. Such accidents are of concern to the Agency, and OSHA seeks to learn new ways to prevent these accidents and protect employees who are exposed to them. For example, OSHA is currently participating in a Local Emphasis Program in the State of New Jersey that is designed to protect highway construction workers who are exposed to traffic hazards while performing construction work. Therefore, the final rule provides provisions that require an employer to report a fatality or multiple hospitalization incident that occurs in a construction zone on a public highway or street.

...

Section 1904.40 Providing Records to Government Representatives [p. 6065]

Under the final rule, employers must provide a complete copy of any records required by Part 1904 to an authorized government representative, including the Form 300 (Log), the Form 300A(Summary), the confidential listing of privacy concern cases along with the names of the injured or ill privacy case workers, and the Form 301 (Incident Report), when the representative asks for the records during a workplace safety and health inspection. This requirement is unchanged from the corresponding requirement in OSHA's former recordkeeping rule.

However, the former rule combined the requirements governing both government inspectors' and employers' rights of access to the records into a single section, section 1904.7 "Access to Records." The final rule separates the two. It places the requirements governing access to the records by government inspectors in Subpart E, along with other provisions requiring employers to submit their occupational injury and illness records to the government or to provide government personnel access to them. Provisions for employee access to records are now in section 1904.35, Employee Involvement, in Subpart D of this final rule.

The final regulatory text of paragraph (a) of section 1904.40 requires an employer to provide an authorized government representative with records kept under Part 1904 within four business hours. As stated in paragraph 1904.40(b)(1), the authorized government representatives who have a right to obtain the Part 1904 records are a representative of the Secretary of Labor conducting an inspection or investigation under the Act, a representative of the Secretary of Health and Human Services (including the National Institute for Occupational Safety and Health (NIOSH) conducting an investigation under Section 20(b) of the Act, or a representative of a State agency responsible for administering a State plan approved under section 18 of the Act. The government's right to ask for such records is limited by the jurisdiction of that Agency. For example, a representative of an OSHA approved State plan could only ask for the records when visiting an establishment within that state.

The final rule allows the employer to take into account difficulties that may be encountered if the records are kept at a location in a different time zone from the establishment where the government representative has asked for the records. If the employer maintains the records at a location in a different time zone, OSHA will use the business hours of the establishment at which the records are located when calculating the deadline, as permitted by paragraph 1904.40(b)(2).

...

Government Representatives. Each employer shall provide, upon a request made in person or in writing, copies of the OSHA Forms 300 and 301 or equivalents, and year-end summaries for their own employees, and injury and illness records for "subcontractor employees" as required under this Part to any authorized representative of the Secretary of Labor or Secretary of Health and Human Services or to any authorized representative of a State accorded jurisdiction for occupational safety and health for the purposes of carrying out the Act.

(1) When the request is made in person, the information must be provided in hard copy (paper printout) within 4 hours. If the information is being transmitted to the establishment from some other location, using telefax or other electronic transmission, the employer may provide a copy to the government representative present at the establishment or to the government representative's office.

(2) When the request is made in writing, the information must be provided within 21 days of receipt of the written request, unless the Secretary requests otherwise.

...

Privacy of medical records.

...

This section of the final rule does not give unfettered access to the records by the public, but simply allows a government inspector to use the records during the course of a safety and health inspection. As discussed above in the section covering access to the records for employees, former employees, and employee representatives (Section 1904.35), OSHA does not consider the Forms 300 and 301 to be medical records, for the following reasons. First, they do not have to be completed by a physician or other licensed health care professional. Second, they do not contain the detailed diagnostic and treatment information usually found in medical records. Finally, the injuries and illnesses found in the records are usually widely known among other employees at the workplace where the injured or ill worker works; in fact, these co-workers may even have witnessed the accident that gave rise to the injury or illness.

OSHA does not agree that its inspectors should be required to obtain permission from all injured or ill employees before accessing the full records. Gaining this permission would make it essentially impossible to obtain full access to the records, which is needed to perform a meaningful workplace investigation. For example, an inspector would not be able to obtain the names of employees who were no longer working for the company to perform follow-up interviews about the specifics of their injuries and illnesses. The names of the injured or ill workers are needed to allow the government inspector to interview the injured and ill workers and determine the hazardous circumstances that led to their injury or illness. The government inspector may also need the employee's names to access personnel and medical records if needed (medical records can only be accessed after the inspector obtains a medical access order). Additionally, refusing the inspector access to the names of the injured and ill workers would effectively prohibit any audit of the Part 1904 records by the government, a practice necessary to verify the accuracy of employer recordkeeping in general and to identify problems that employers may be having in keeping records under OSHA's recordkeeping rules. Adopting the inefficient access method suggested by these commenters would also place a substantial administrative burden on the employer, the employees, and the government. Further, since OSHA inspectors do not allow others to see the medical records they have accessed, the privacy of employees is not compromised by CSHO access to the records.

Time for response to requests for records. Paragraphs 1904.40(a) and (b) of the final rule require records to be made available to a government inspector within 4 business hours of an oral request for the records, using the business hours of the establishment at which the records are located.

...

OSHA has concluded that 4 hours is a reasonable and workable length of time for employers to respond to governmental requests for records. The 4-hour time period for providing records from a centralized source strikes a balance between the practical limitations inherent in record maintenance and the government official's need to obtain these records and use the information to conduct a workplace inspection.

...

OSHA believes that it is essential for employers to have systems and procedures that can produce the records within the 4-hour time. However, the Agency realizes that there may be unusual or unique circumstances where the employer cannot comply. For example, if the records are kept by a health care professional and that person is providing emergency care to an injured worker, the employer may need to delay production of the records. In such a situation, the OSHA inspector may allow the employer additional time.

If a government representative requests records of an establishment, but those records are kept at another location, the 4-hour period can be measured in accordance with the normal business hours at the location where the records are being kept.

...

OSHA has designed the final rule to give each employer considerable flexibility in maintaining records. It permits an employer to centralize its records, to use computer and facsimile technologies, and to hire a third party to keep its records. However, an employer who chooses these options must also ensure that they are sufficiently reliable to comply with this rule. In other words, the flexibility provided to employers for recordkeeping must not impede the Agency's ability to obtain and use the records.

Provide copies.

...

OSHA's experience has been that the vast majority of employers willingly provide copies to government representatives during safety and health inspections. Making copies is a routine office function in almost every modern workplace. With the widespread availability of copying technology, most workplaces have copy machines on-site or readily available. The cost of providing copies is minimal, usually less than five cents per copy. In addition, the government representative needs to obtain copes of records promptly, so that he or she can analyze the data and identify workplace hazards. Therefore, in this final rule, OSHA requires the employer to provide copies of the records requested to authorized government representatives.

Section 1904.41 Annual OSHA Injury and Illness Survey of Ten or More Employers [p. 6069]

Section 1904.41 of this final rule replaces section 1904.17, "Annual OSHA Injury and Illness Survey of Ten or More Employers," of the former rule issued on February 11, 1997. The final rule does not change the contents or policies of the corresponding section of the former rule in any way. Instead, the final rule simply rephrases the language of the former rule in the plain language question-and-answer format used in the rest of this rule.

...

Section 1904.42 Requests From the Bureau of Labor Statistics for Data [p. 6069]

...

Section 1904.42 of the final rule derives from the subpart of the former rule titled "Statistical Reporting of Occupational Injuries and Illnesses." The former rule described the Bureau of Labor Statistics annual survey of occupational injuries and illnesses, discussed the duty of employers to answer the survey, and explained the effect of the BLS survey on the States operating their own State plans.

Both OSHA and the BLS collect occupational injury and illness information, each for separate purposes. The BLS collects data from a statistical sample of employers in all industries and across all size classes, using the data to compile the occupational injury and illness statistics for the Nation. The Bureau gives each respondent a pledge of confidentiality (as it does on all BLS surveys), and the establishment-specific injury and illness data are not shared with the public, other government agencies, or OSHA. The BLS's sole purpose is to create statistical data.

OSHA collects data from employers from specific size and industry classes, but collects from each and every employer within those parameters. The establishment-specific data collected by OSHA are used to administer OSHA's various programs and to measure the performance of those programs at individual workplaces.

...

Paragraph 1904.42(a) states the general obligation of employers to report data to the BLS or a BLS designee. Paragraph 1904.42(b)(1) states that some employers will receive a BLS survey form and others will not, and that the employer should not send data unless asked to do so. Paragraph 1904.42(b)(2) directs the employer to follow the instructions on the survey form when completing the information and return it promptly.

Paragraph 1904.42(b)(3) of this final rule notes that the BLS is authorized to collect data from all employers, even those who would otherwise be exempt, under section 1904.1 to section 1904.3, from keeping OSHA injury and illness records. This enables the BLS to produce comprehensive injury and illness statistics for the entire private sector. Paragraph 1904.42(b)(3) combines the requirements of former rule paragraphs 1904.15(b) and 1904.16(b) into this paragraph of the final rule.

In response to the question "Am I required to respond to a BLS survey form if I am normally exempt from keeping OSHA injury and illness records?," the final rule states

"Yes. Even if you are exempt from keeping injury and illness records under Sec. 1904.1 to Sec. 1904.3, the BLS may inform you in writing that it will be collecting injury and illness information from you in the coming year. If you receive such a survey form, you must keep the injury and illness records required by Sec. 1904.4 to Sec. 1904.12 and make survey reports for the year covered by the survey."

Paragraph 1904.42(b)(4) of this final rule replaces section 1904.22 of the former rule. It provides that employers in the State-plan States are also required to fill out and submit survey forms if the BLS requests that they do so. The final rule thus specifies that the BLS has the authority to collect information on occupational fatalities, injuries and illnesses from: (1) employers who are required to keep records at all times; (2) employers who are normally exempt from keeping records; and (3) employers under both Federal and State plan jurisdiction. The information collected in the annual survey enables BLS to generate consistent statistics on occupational death, injury and illness for the entire Nation.

Subpart F. Transition From the Former Rule to the New Rule [p. 6070]

The transition interval from the former rule to the new rule involves several issues, including training and outreach to familiarize employers and employees about the now forms and requirements, and informing employers in newly covered industries that they are now required to keep OSHA Part 1904 records. OSHA intends to make a major outreach effort, including the development of an expert software system, a forms package, and a compliance assistance guide, to assist employers and recordkeepers with the transition to the new rule. An additional transition issue for employers who kept records under the former system and will also keep records under the new system is how to handle the data collected under the former system during the transition year. Subpart F of the final rule addresses some of these transition issues.

Subpart F of the new rule (sections 1904.43 and 1904.44), addresses what employers must do to keep the required OSHA records during the first five years the new system required by this final rule is in effect. This five-year period is called the transition period in this subpart. The majority of the transition requirements apply only to the first year, when the data from the previous year (collected under the former rule) must be summarized and posted during the month of February. For the remainder of the transition period, the employer is simply required to retain the records created under the former rule for five years and provide access to those records for the government, the employer's employees, and employee representatives, as required by the final rule at sections 1904.43 and 44.

...

The transition also raises questions about what should be done in the year 2002 with respect to posting, updating, and retaining the records employers compiled in 2001 and previous years. In the transition from the former rule to the present rule, OSHA intends employers to make a clean break with the former system. The new rule will replace the old rule on the effective date of the new rule, and OSHA will discontinue the use of all previous forms, interpretations and guidance on that date (see, e.g., Exs. 21, 22, 15: 184, 423). Employers will be required to prepare a summary of the OSHA Form 200 for the year 2001 and to certify and post it in the same manner and for the same time (one month) as they have in the past. The following time table shows the sequence of events and postings that will occur:

Date	Activity
2001	Employers keep injury and illness information on the OSHA 200 form
January 1, 2002	Employers begin keeping data on the OSHA 300 form
February 1, 2002	Employers post the 2001 data on the OSHA 200 Form
March 1, 2002	Employers may remove the 2001 posting
February 1, 2003	Employers post the 2002 data on the OSHA 300A form
May 1, 2003	Employers may remove the 2002 posting

The final rule's new requirements for dual certification and a 3-month posting period will not apply to the Year 2000 Log and summary. Employers still must retain the OSHA records from 2001 and previous years for five years from the end of the year to which they refer. The employer must provide copies of the retained records to authorized government representatives, and to his or her employees and employee representatives, as required by the new rule.

However, OSHA will no longer require employers to update the OSHA Log and summary forms for years before the year 2002. The former rule required employers to correct errors to the data on the OSHA 200 Logs during the five-year retention period and to add new information about recorded cases. The former rule also required the employer to adjust the totals on the Logs if changes were made to cases on them (Ex. 2, p. 23). OSHA believes it would be confusing and burdensome for employers to update and adjust previous years' Logs and Summaries under the former system at the same time as they are learning to use the new OSHA occupational injury and illness recordkeeping system.

Subpart G. Definitions [p. 6071]

The Definitions section of the final rule contains definitions for five terms: "the Act," "establishment," "health care professional," "injury and illness," and "you." To reduce the need for readers to move back and forth from the regulatory text to the Definitions section of this preamble, all other definitions used in the final rule are defined in the regulatory text as the term is used. OSHA defines the five terms in this section here because they are used in several places in the regulatory text.

The Act

The Occupational Safety and Health Act of 1970 (the "OSH Act") is defined because the term is used in many places in the regulatory text. The final rule's definition is essentially identical to the definition in the proposal. OSHA received no comments on this definition. The definition of "the Act" follows:

The Act means the Occupational Safety and Health Act of 1970 (84 Stat. 1590 et seq., 29 U.S. 651 et seq.), as amended. The definitions contained in section (3) of the Act and related interpretations shall be applicable to such terms when used in this Part 1904.

Establishment

The final rule defines an establishment as a single physical location where business is conducted or where services or industrial operations are performed. For activities where employees do not work at a single physical location, such as construction; transportation; communications, electric, gas and sanitary services; and similar operations, the establishment is represented by main or branch offices, terminals, stations, etc. that either supervise such activities or are the base from which personnel carry out these activities.

The final rule also addresses whether one business location can include two or more establishments. Normally, one business location has only one establishment. However, under limited conditions, the employer may consider two or more separate businesses that share a single location to be separate establishments for recordkeeping purposes. An employer may divide one location into two or more establishments only when: each of the proposed establishments represents a distinctly separate business; each business is engaged in a different economic activity; no one industry description in the Standard Industrial Classification Manual (1987) applies to the joint activities of the proposed establishments; and separate reports are routinely prepared for each establishment on the number of employees, their wages and salaries, sales or receipts, and other business information. For example, if an employer operates a construction company at the same location as a lumber yard, the employer may consider each business to be a separate establishment.

The final rule also deals with the opposite situation, and explains when an establishment includes more than one physical location. An employer may combine two or more physical locations into a single establishment only when the employer operates the locations as a single business operation under common management; the locations are all located in close proximity to each other; and the employer keeps one set of business records for the locations, such as records on the number of employees, their wages and salaries, sales or receipts, and other kinds of business information. For example, one manufacturing establishment might include the main plant, a warehouse serving the plant a block away, and an administrative services building across the street. The final rule also makes it clear that when an employee telecommutes from home, the employee's home is not a business establishment for recordkeeping purposes, and a separate OSHA 300 Log is not required.

The definition of "establishment" is important in OSHA's recordkeeping system for many reasons. First, the establishment is the basic unit for which records are maintained and summarized. The employer must keep a separate injury and illness Log (the OSHA Form 300), and prepare a single summary (Form 300A), for each establishment. Establishment-specific records are a key component of the recordkeeping system because each separate record represents the injury and illness experience of a given location, and therefore reflects the particular circumstances and hazards that led to the injuries and illnesses at that location. The establishment-specific summary, which totals the establishment's injury and illness experience for the preceding year, is posted for employees at that establishment and may also be collected by the government for statistical or administrative purposes. Second, the definition of establishment is important because injuries and illnesses are presumed to be work-related if they result from events or exposures occurring in the work environment, which includes the employer's establishment. The presumption that injuries and illnesses occurring in the work environment are by definition work-related may be rebutted under certain circumstances, which are listed in the final rule and discussed in the section of this preamble devoted to section 1904.5, Determination of work-relatedness. Third, the establishment is the unit that determines whether the partial exemption from recordkeeping requirements permitted by the final rule for establishments of certain sizes or in certain industry sectors applies (see Subpart B of the final rule). Under the final rule's partial exemption, establishments classified in certain Standard Industrial Classification codes (SIC codes) are not required to keep injury and illness records except when asked by the government to do so. Because a given employer may operate establishments that are classified in different SIC codes, some employers may be required to keep OSHA injury and illness records for some establishments but not for others, e.g. if one or more of the employer's establishments falls under the final rule's partial exemption but others do not.

Fourth, the definition of establishment is used to determine which records an employee, former employee, or authorized employee representative may access. According to the final rule, employees may ask for, and must be given, injury and illness records for the establishment they currently work in, or one they have worked in, during their employment.

...

Subpart G of the final rule defines "establishment" as "a single physical location where business is conducted or where services or industrial operations are performed. For activities such as construction; transportation; communications, electric and gas utility, and sanitary services; and similar operations, the establishment is represented for recordkeeping purposes by main or branch offices, terminals, stations, etc. that either supervise such activities or are the base from which personnel carry out these activities." This part of the definition of "establishment" provides flexibility for employers whose employees (such as repairmen, meter readers, and construction superintendents) do not work at the same workplace but instead move between many different workplaces, often in the course of a single day.

How the definition of "establishment" must be used by employers for recordkeeping purposes is set forth in the answers to the questions posed in this paragraph of Subpart G:

(1) Can one business location include two or more establishments?

(2) Can an establishment include more than one physical location?

(3) If an employee telecommutes from home, is his or her home considered a separate establishment?

The employer may consider two or more economic activities at a single location to be separate establishments (and thus keep separate OSHA Form 300s and Form 301s for each activity) only when: (1) Each such economic activity represents a separate business, (2) no one industry description in the Standard Industrial Classification Manual (1987) applies to the activities carried out at the separate locations; and (3) separate reports are routinely prepared on the number of employees, their wages and salaries, sales or receipts, and other business information. This part of the definition of "establishment" allows for separate establishments when an employer uses a common facility to house two or more separate businesses, but does not allow different departments or divisions of a single business to be considered separate establishments. However, even if the establishment meets the three criteria above, the employer may, if it chooses, consider the physical location to be one establishment.

The definition also permits an employer to combine two or more physical locations into a single establishment for recordkeeping purposes (and thus to keep only one Form 300 and Form 301 for all of the locations) only when (1) the locations are all geographically close to each other, (2) the employer operates the locations as a single business operation under common management, and (3) the employer keeps one set of business records for the locations, such as records on the number of employees, their wages and salaries, sales or receipts, and other business information. However, even for locations meeting these three criteria, the employer may, if it chooses, consider the separate physical locations to be separate establishments. This part of the definition allows an employer to consider a single business operation to be a single establishment even when some of his or her business operations are carried out on separate properties, but does not allow for separate businesses to be joined together. For example, an employer operating a manufacturing business would not be allowed to consider a nearby storage facility to be a separate establishment, while an employer who operates two separate retail outlets would be required to consider each to be a separate establishment.

...

Health Care Professional

The final rule defines health care professional (HCP) as "a physician or other state licensed health care professional whose legally permitted scope of practice (i.e. license, registration or certification) allows the professional independently to provide or be delegated the responsibility to provide some or all of the health care services described by this regulation."

...

OSHA recognizes that injured employees may be treated by a broad range of health care practitioners, especially if the establishment is located in a rural area or if the worker is employed by a small company that does not have the means to provide on-site access to an occupational nurse or a physician. Although the rule does not specify what medical specialty or training is necessary to provide care for injured or ill employees, the rule's use of the term health care professional is intended to ensure that those professionals providing treatment and making determinations about the record-ability of certain complex cases are operating within the scope of their license, as defined by the appropriate state licensing agency.

Injury or Illness

The final rule's definition of injury or illness is based on the definitions of injury and illness used under the former recordkeeping regulation, except that it combines both definitions into a single term "injury or illness." Under the final rule, an injury or illness is an abnormal condition or disorder. Injuries include cases such as, but not limited to, a cut, fracture, sprain, or amputation. Illnesses include both acute and chronic illnesses, such as, but not limited to, a skin disease, respiratory disorder, or systemic poisoning. The definition also includes a note to inform employers that some

injuries and illnesses are recordable and others are not, and that injuries and illnesses are recordable only if they are new, work-related cases that meet one or more of the final rule's recording criteria.

...

"You"

The last definition in the final rule, of the pronoun "you," has been added because the final rule uses the "you" form of the question-and-answer plain-language format recommended in Federal plain-language guidance. "You," as used in this rule, mean the employer, as that term is defined in the Act. This definition makes it clear that employers are responsible for implementing the requirements of this final rule, as mandated by the Occupational Safety and Health Act of 1970 (29 U.S.C. 651 et seq.)

WALKING AND WORKING SURFACES

Slips, trips and falls constitute the majority of general industry accidents. They cause 15 percent of all accidental deaths and are second only to motor vehicles as a cause of fatalities. The OSHA standards for walking and working surfaces apply to all permanent places of employment, except where only domestic, mining or agricultural work is performed.

General Requirements—1910.22

Housekeeping

All places of employment, passageways, storerooms and service rooms shall be kept clean, orderly and in a sanitary condition. The floor of every workroom shall be in a clean and, so far as possible, a dry condition. Where wet processes are used, drainage shall be maintained and gratings, mats or raised platforms shall be provided. Every floor, work area and passageway shall be kept free from protruding nails, splinters, holes or loose boards.

Aisles and Passageways

Aisles and passageways shall be kept clear and in good repair with no obstruction across or in aisles that could create a hazard. Permanent aisles and passageways shall be appropriately marked. Where mechanical handling equipment is used, aisles shall be sufficiently wide. Improper aisle widths coupled with poor housekeeping and vehicle traffic can cause injury to employees, damage the equipment and material, and can limit egress in emergencies.

Covers and Guardrails

Covers and/or guardrails shall be provided to protect personnel from such hazards as open pits, tanks, vats and ditches.

Floor Loading Protection

Load rating limits shall be marked on plates and conspicuously posted. It shall be unlawful to place, cause or permit to be placed on any floor or roof of a building or other structure, a load greater than that for which such floor or roof is approved.

Exhibit 3-1.
A clean, appropriately marked aisle that is wide enough for mechanical handling equipment to travel safely.

Guarding Floor and Wall Openings and Holes—1910.23

Floor openings and holes, wall openings and holes, and the open sides of platforms may create hazards. People may fall through the openings or over the sides to the level below. Objects, such as tools or parts, may fall through the holes and strike people or damage machinery on lower levels.

OSHA standards for guarding openings and holes use the following definitions:

Floor hole. An opening measuring less than 12 in., but more than 1 in., in its least dimension, in any floor, platform, pavement or yard through which materials, but not persons, may fall.

Floor opening. An opening measuring 12 in. or more in its least dimension, in any floor, platform, pavement or yard through which persons may fall.

Platform. A working space for persons, elevated above the surrounding floor or ground.

Wall hole. An opening less than 30 in., but more than 1 in. high, of unrestricted width, in any wall or partition.

Wall opening. An opening at least 30 in. high and 18 in. wide in any wall or partition through which persons may fall.

Protection for Floor Openings

Standard railings shall be provided on all exposed sides of a stairway opening, except at the stairway entrance. For infrequently used stairways, where traffic across the opening prevents the use of a fixed standard railing, the guard shall consist of a hinged floor opening cover of standard strength and construction, along with removable standard railings on all exposed sides, except at the stairway entrance.

A "standard railing" consists of top rail, mid-rail, and posts, and shall have a vertical height of 42 in. nominal from the upper surface of top rail to floor, platform, runway or ramp level. Nominal height of mid-rail is 21 in. (See Exhibit 3-2.).

A "standard toeboard" is 4 in. nominal in vertical height, with not more than 1/4-inch clearance above floor level.

Floor openings may be covered rather than guarded with rails. When the floor opening cover is removed, a temporary guardrail shall be in place or an attendant shall be stationed at the open-

ing to warn personnel.

Either a standard railing with toeboard or a floor hole cover of standard strength or construction shall guard every floor hole into which persons can accidentally

Exhibit 3-2.
A standard railing consists of a top rail, mid-rail and posts.

walk. While the cover is not in place, the floor hole shall be constantly attended by someone or shall be protected by a removable standard railing.

Protection of Open-Sided Floors, Platforms and Runways

One of the most frequently cited violations in Subpart D is the requirement that every open-sided floor or platform 4 ft. or more above adjacent floor or ground level shall be guarded by a standard railing (or the equivalent as specified in paragraph (e)(3) of this section) on all open sides, except where there is an entrance to a ramp, stairway, or fixed ladder. The railing shall be provided with a toeboard wherever, beneath the open sides:

- Persons can pass;
- There is moving machinery; or
- There is equipment with which falling materials could create a hazard.

A standard railing (or the equivalent as specified in paragraph (e)(3) of this section) shall guard every runway on all sides 4 ft. or more above floor or ground level. Wherever tools, machine parts or materials are likely to be used on the runway, a toeboard shall also be provided on each exposed side.

Regardless of height, open-sided floors, walkways, platforms or runways above or adjacent to dangerous equipment, pickling or galvanizing tanks, degreasing units and similar hazards shall be guarded with a standard railing and toeboard.

Stairway Railings and Guards

Every flight of stairs with four or more risers shall have standard stair railings or standard handrails as specified below. Stair width is measured clear of all obstructions except handrails.

- On stairways less than 44 in. wide having both sides enclosed, at least one handrail shall be affixed, preferably on the right side descending.
- On stairways less than 44 in. wide with one open side, at least one stair rail shall be affixed on the open side.
- On stairways less than 44 in. wide having both sides open, two stair rails shall be provided, one for each side.
- On stairways more than 44 in. wide, but less than 88 in., one handrail shall be provided on each enclosed side and one stair rail on each open side.
- On stairways 88 in. or more in width, one handrail shall be provided on each enclosed side, one stair rail on each open side, and one intermediate stair rail placed approximately in the middle of the stairs.

A "standard stair railing" (stair rail) shall be of construction similar to a standard railing, but the vertical height shall be not more than 34 in. nor less than 30 in. from the upper surface of the top rail to the surface of the tread in line with the face of the riser at the forward edge of the tread.

A "standard handrail" consists of a lengthwise member mounted directly on a wall or partition by means of brackets attached to the lower side of the handrail in order to keep a smooth, unobstructed surface along the top and both sides of the handrail. The brackets shall hold the rail 3 in. from the wall and be no more than 8 ft. apart

The height of handrails shall be no more than 34 in. nor less than 30 in. from the upper surface of the handrail to the surface of the tread in line with the face of the riser or to the surface of the ramp.

Winding stairs shall have a handrail that is offset to prevent people from walking on any portion of the treads where the width is less than 6 in.

Fixed Industrial Stairs—1910.24

This section contains specifications for the safe design and construction of fixed general industrial stairs. This includes interior and exterior stairs around machinery, tanks and other equipment as well as stairs leading to or from floors, platforms or pits. This section does not apply to stairs used for fire exit purposes, to construction operations, to private residences, or to articulated stairs, such as may be installed on floating roof tanks, the angle of which changes with the rise and fall of the base support. Intermediate landings and platforms on stairways shall be no less than the stair width and a minimum of 30 in. in length measured in the direction of travel.

Fixed industrial stairs shall be provided for access to and from places of work where operations necessitate regular travel between levels. OSHA requirements include:

- Fixed industrial stairs shall be strong enough to carry five times the normal anticipated live load.
- At the very minimum, any fixed stairway shall be able to safely carry a moving concentrated load of 1,000 lbs.
- All fixed stairways shall have a minimum width of 22 in.
- Fixed stairs shall be installed at angles to the horizontal of between 30° and 50°.
- Vertical clearance above any stair tread to an overhead obstruction shall be at least 7 ft., measured from the leading edge of the tread.

When inspecting the condition of stairways, items to look for include:
- Handrails and stair rails:
  - Lack of handrails;
  - Placement of handrails;
  - Smoothness of surface;
  - Strength; and
  - Clearance between rail and wall or other object.
- Treads:
  - Strength;
  - Slip resistance;
  - Dimensions;
  - Evenness of surface; and
  - Visibility of leading edge.

- General inspection points:
  - Improper or inadequate design, construction or location of staircases;
  - Wet, slippery or damaged walking or grasping surfaces;
  - Improper illumination (Note: There is no horizontal OSHA standard for illumination levels; the Illuminating Engineering Society publications should be consulted for recommendations.);
  - Poor housekeeping; and
  - Length of a staircase—long flights of steps without landings should be avoided whenever possible.

Portable Ladders—1910.25, 1910.26

The chief hazard when using a ladder is falling. A poorly designed, maintained or improperly used ladder may collapse under the load placed upon it and cause the employee to fall. A ladder is an appliance consisting of two side rails joined at regular intervals by crosspieces on which a person may step to ascend or descend. Types of portable ladders include:

Stepladder. A self-supporting portable ladder, non-adjustable in length, having flat steps and hinged back.

Single ladder. A non-self-supporting portable ladder, nonadjustable in length, consisting of one section. Its size is designed by the overall length of the side rail.

Extension ladder. A non-self-supporting portable ladder adjustable in length.

OSHA's requirements for portable ladders include:

- Portable stepladders longer than 20 ft. shall not be used.
- Stepladders shall be equipped with a metal spreader or locking device of sufficient size and strength to securely hold the front and back sections in an open position.
- Single ladders longer than 30 ft. shall not be used.
- Extension ladders longer than 60 ft. shall not be used.
- Ladders shall be maintained in good condition at all times.

Ladders shall be inspected frequently and those that have developed defects shall be withdrawn from service for repair or destruction and tagged or marked as "Dangerous, Do Not Use." Portable ladders should extend 3 ft. past the level to which the employee is climbing. The 1-in-4 rule should also be used: For every 4 ft. in height, the base of the ladder should come out 1 ft. from the building (See Exhibit 3-3.). Ladders shall be placed with a secure footing or they shall be lashed, or held in position.

Exhibit 3-3.
The base and top the ladder must extend a certain distance from the climbing surface.

The foot of a ladder shall, where possible, be used at such a pitch that the horizontal distance from the top support to the foot of the ladder is one-quarter of the working length of the ladder (the length along the ladder between the foot and the support). OSHA standards also require that:

- The worker shall always face the ladder when climbing up or down;
- Short ladders shall not be spliced together to make long ladders;
- Ladders shall never be used in the horizontal position as scaffolds or work platforms;
- The top of a regular stepladder shall not be used as a step;
- Use both hands when climbing and descending ladders; and
- Metal ladders shall never be used near electrical equipment.

Fixed Ladders—1910.27

A fixed ladder is a ladder permanently attached to a structure, building or equipment. A point to remember is that fixed ladders, with a length of more than 20 ft. to a maximum unbroken length of 30 ft. shall be equipped with cages or a ladder safety device.

A "cage" is a guard that is fastened to the side rails of the fixed ladder or to the structure to encircle the climbing space of the ladder for the safety of the person who must climb the ladder. Cages shall extend a minimum of 42 in. above the top of a landing, unless other acceptable protection is provided. Cages shall extend down the ladder to a point not less than 7 ft. nor more than 8 ft. above the base of the ladder.

A ladder safety device is any device, other than a cage or well, designed to eliminate or reduce the possibility of accidental falls and may incorporate such features as life belts, friction brakes and sliding attachments. Another feature of fixed ladders is the landing platform that provides a means of interrupting a free fall and serves as a resting-place during long climbs.

When fixed ladders are used to ascend to heights exceeding 20 ft., except on landing, platforms shall be provided. Where no cage, well or ladder safety device is provided, a landing platform shall be provided for each 20 ft. of height or fraction thereof.

Ladder safety devices may be used on tower, water tank and chimney ladders more than 20 ft. in unbroken length in lieu of cage protection. No landing platform is required in these cases.

Exhibit 3-4.
Fixed ladders must be installed within a certain pitch range. The substandard range shown above may sometimes be permitted.

The preferred pitch of fixed ladders shall be considered to come in the range of 75° and 90° with the horizontal. Fixed ladders shall be considered to be substandard if they are installed within the pitch range of 60° and 75° with the horizontal. Substandard fixed ladders are permitted only when it is found necessary to meet conditions of installation. This substandard pitch range shall be considered a critical range to be avoided, if possible. Ladders having a pitch in excess of 90° with the horizontal are prohibited.

As with all ladders, fixed ladders shall be maintained in a safe condition and inspected regularly.

Safety Requirements for Scaffolding— 1910.28

This section establishes safety requirements for the construction, operation, maintenance and use of scaffolds used in the maintenance of buildings and structures. It is important to note some of the general requirements of 1910.28(a), which apply to all scaffolds:

The footing or anchorage for scaffolds shall be sound, rigid and capable of carrying the maximum intended load without settling or displacement. Unstable objects, such as barrels, boxes, loose brick, or concrete blocks shall not be used to support scaffolds or planks.

Scaffolds and their components shall be capable of supporting at least four times the maximum intended load. Scaffolds shall be maintained in a safe condition and shall not be altered or moved horizontally while they are in use or occupied. Damaged or weakened scaffolds shall be immediately repaired and shall not be used until repairs have been completed. A safe means must be provided to gain access to the working platform level through the use of a ladder, ramp or other such item. Overhead protection must be provided for personnel on a scaffold exposed to overhead hazards.

Guardrails, mid-rails and toeboards must be installed on any open sides and ends of platforms more than 10 ft. above the ground or floor. Wire mesh must be installed between the toeboard and the guardrail along the entire opening, except where persons are required to work or pass under the scaffolds.

Employees shall not work on scaffolds during storms or high winds or if the scaffolds are covered with ice or snow.

Manually Propelled Mobile Ladder Stands and Scaffolds (Towers)—1910.29

This section contains requirements for the design, construction and use of mobile work platforms (including ladder stands excluding aerial ladders) and rolling (mobile) scaffolds (towers). As in the previous section, there are a variety of materials and design possibilities involved, and no attempt will be made to discuss detailed design criteria.

General requirements include:

- All exposed surfaces of mobile ladder stands and scaffolds shall be free from sharp edges, burrs or other safety hazards.
- The maximum work height shall not exceed four times the minimum base dimensions unless outriggers, guys or braces are added to provide stability.
- Mobile scaffolds are mounted on casters with fixed working levels. The working height is limited to four times the minimum base dimensions to achieve a stable work platform.
- Access is required to be provided by ladder and minimum platform width is 18 in.

This standard requires guardrails and toeboards for work levels 10 ft. or more above the ground or floor.

Other Working Surfaces—1910.30

Portable dock boards (bridge plates) shall be secured in position, either by being anchored or equipped with devices that will prevent their slipping. Movement of the dock boards during material handling operations has resulted in forklifts overturning or falling off the dock, often with serious injury or death to the driver and damage to equipment and material.

Many accidents occur during material handling. Handholds shall be provided on portable dock boards to permit safe handling when the dock board must be repositioned or relocated.

OSHA Instruction OCT 30, 1978 STD 1-1.4
OSHA PROGRAM DIRECTIVE #100-60
TO: REGIONAL ADMINISTRATORS/OSHA
SUBJECT: **29 CFR 1910.22(b)(2), Markings For Aisles and Passageways**

1. **Purpose.** To provide an interpretation of "appropriately marked" as applies to permanent aisles and passageways where there are dirt floors or floors having continuous concentrations of sand or fine dusts.
2. **Documentation Affected.** None.
3. **Background.**
   a. In some instances, 29 CFR.1910.22(b)(2) has been narrowly interpreted to mean that aisles and passageways must be marked by painted floor lines.
   b. The intent of "appropriately marked" is not to restrict the markings to one method only. It would be impractical to paint lines on dirt floors or floors that have continuous concentrations of sand or other dusts. These conditions may exist in such industries as foundries, scrap salvage operations or motor winding facilities.
4. **Action.** Painted lines remain the most feasible method of marking, where practical, since they may last several years without maintenance or repainting. Other appropriate methods such as marking pillars, powder stripping, flags, traffic cones or barrels are acceptable, when the training programs for vehicle operators and employees include the recognition of such markings.
5. **Effective Date.** This directive is effective immediately upon receipt and will remain in effect until canceled or superseded.

Richard P. Wilson Deputy Director, Federal Compliance and State Programs

OSHA Instruction STD 1-1.12 JUN 20, 1983 Office of Compliance Programming
SUBJECT: **Application of 29 CFR 1910.27,**
 Fixed Ladders, to Fixed Ladders Used in Emergency Situations

A. **Purpose.** This instruction clarifies the meaning of 29 CFR 1910.27 as it applies to the protection of employees exposed to falling from fixed ladders used only as a means of escape from fire and other emergency situations.

B. **Scope.** This instruction applies OSHA-wide.

C. **Reference.** OSHA Instruction STD 1-1.3, October 30, 1978, dated January 18, 1977.

D. **Action.** Regional Administrators and Area Directors shall ensure that the interpretative guidelines given in this instruction are addressed when inspecting sites with fixed ladders used only during fire and other emergency situations.

E. **Federal Program Change.** This instruction describes a Federal program change which affects State programs. Each Regional Administrator shall:

1. Ensure that this change is forwarded to each State designee.
2. Explain the technical content of the change to the State designee as requested.
3. Ensure that State designees are asked to acknowledge receipt of this Federal program change in writing, within 30 days of notification, to the Regional Administrator. This acknowledgment should include a description either of the State's plan to implement the change or of the reasons why the change should not apply to that State.
4. Review policies, instructions and guidelines issued by the State to determine that this change has been communicated to State program personnel. Routine monitoring activities (accompanied inspections and case file reviews) shall also be used to determine if this change has been implemented in actual performance.

F. **Background.** OSHA has historically established that the requirements of 29 CFR 1910.27 for cages, platforms, or similar fall prevention protection devices are not appropriate for fixed ladders on structures where the fixed ladders are used only as a means of access by fire fighters, other emergency personnel, or escape for employees in fire and other emergency situations. Sometimes these ladders are not provided with employee protection as presently required in 29 CFR 1910.27, when they are intended to be used only in an emergency. In these circumstances, it is sometimes more hazardous to install a cage, well, landing platform or ladder safety device pursuant to the standard than it is not to comply. A cage or well, etc., may interfere with fire fighting or other rescue equipment, or employee escape from fire or other emergency situations.

G. **Guidelines.** This instruction provides performance criteria for fixed ladders used only as a means of access for fire fighters and other emergency personnel, or escape for employees in fire and other emergency situations.

1. Employers must establish and implement adequate administrative controls such as barricades and signs to prevent nonemergency use of fixed ladders which are meant for fire fighter use and emergency escape only.
2. In the event the employer does not provide adequate administrative controls such as barricades or signs and employees use an emergency ladder for other than its intended purpose, the employer may be appropriately cited under 29 CFR 1910.27.
3. Fixed ladders not equipped with cages, landing platforms, ladder safety devices, or other forms of employee protection, in some situations may be allowed as a means of access for fire fighters and other emergency personnel, or escape for employees in fire and other emergency situations. These guidelines are provided because it may be more hazardous to comply with 29 CFR 1910.27 than not to comply.

Thomas G Auchter, Assistant Secretary

Walking and Working Surfaces

DEC 27, 1984
Memorandum FOR: R.A. Clark, REGIONAL Administration
From JOHN B. MILES, Jr., Director of Field Operations
SUBJECT: **Interpretation of 1910.22(b)(l) , Aisles and passageways**

   This is in response to your memorandum of November 2, 1984. The requested interpretations follow:
   1. 1910.22(b)(1) applies to mobile material handling equipment such as carts, wagons, loaders and industrial trucks. Indeed the Review Commission has repeatedly held that the standard is designed to protect only the operators of such equipment rather than pedestrians. Floor operated overhead hoists and cranes are regulated by 1910.179 or by Section 5(a)(1) of the Act, with reference to an applicable ANSI standard.
   2. 1910.22(b)(1) does not apply when the aisles and passageways are not used by material handling equipment. Therefore where hazards are created by objects other than material handling equipment citations of 1910.22(a)(1) and 1910.37 should be considered.

May 21, 1984
MEMORANDUM FOR MR. BYRON R. CHADWICK, REGIONAL ADMINISTRATOR
FROM JOHN B. Miles Director DIRECTORATE OF FIELD OPERATIONS
SUBJECT: **Interpretation: 1910.178(m)(12)**

   This is in response to your memorandum dated May 7, 1984, requesting an interpretation of 1910.178(m)(12).
   29 CFR 1910.178(m)(12) is exclusively applicable to lift trucks equipped with elevatable controls. The standard does not require or mandate that such controls must be installed on trucks not so equipped. The current industry consensus standard ANSI B56.1-1975 helps to clear up the confusion because it addresses the use of Personnel safety platforms on trucks without elevatable controls as well as those with such controls. Sections 427 and 513A of the 1975 ANSI standard (copy attached) specify the safety requirements for fabrication and use of elevatable personnel platforms for use with powered industrial trucks. Since the OSHA standard does not require elevatable controls on such platforms employers who comply with these sections of the 1975 ANSI standard would be compliance with the OSHA Act and are not subject to citation unless an unusually' hazardous situation exists.
   In this instance, it appears that the employer's position is correct. Under the circumstances described in the Area Director's memo to you, the employer is not required to have an elevatable power shut-off when there are no elevatable controls on the platform. However, he is required to have a vehicle operator remain at the controls whenever employees are elevated.

OSHA Standards Interpretation and Compliance Letters
02/09/1983 - Perimeter protection at setback roof levels.
Subject: **Perimeter protection at setback roof levels.**

February 9, 1983
Lawrence R. Stafford, P.E.
Consulting Engineer, 8 Gracemore St., Albany, New York 12203

Dear Mr. Stafford:

  This is in response to your letter of January 28, 1983, concerning perimeter protection at setback roof levels. A parapet height of 29 inches, where employees are exposed to falls from a roof, does not comply with the height requirement in 29 CFR 1910.23(e)(1) and cannot be considered acceptable by OSHA. The employer may install a temporary portable section of guardrail which will comply with 29 CFR 1910.23(e)(3)(v) and provide a minimum height of 36 inches at the exposure locations. Employers may also use a safety belt and rope tie-off system in this type of exposure. If I may be of further assistance, please feel free to contact me.

Sincerely,
John K. Barto
Chief, Division of Occupational
Safety Programming

OSHA Standards Interpretation and Compliance Letters
04/05/1978 - Clarification of 1910.23(c)(1).
Subject: **Clarification of 1910.23(c)(1)**.

April 5, 1978
Mr. John R. Reilly
Corporate Director   Fisher Scientific Company
711 Forbes Avenue   Pittsburgh, Pennsylvania 15219

Dear Mr. Reilly:

  This is in response to your letter dated February 20, 1978, requesting a clarification of 29 CFR 1910.23(c)(1) and confirms your telephone conversation with Mr. William Simms of my staff.

  The aforementioned General Industry Safety Standard requires that every open-sided floor or platform more than four feet above the adjacent level shall be provided with a standard railing. This requirement is applied to areas where employees are required to work or walk as part of fulfilling conditions of their employment. If the roof platform on top of a walk-in refrigerator is visited even a few days each year to store materials, employees required to work adjacent to or near the edge shall be provided with some means of protection.

  Such protection could be a life belt and lanyard tied off of a structural member so as to prevent the employee from walking off or falling from the exposed edges of the refrigerator roof top used as a storage platform.

  If I may be of any further assistance, please feel free to contact me.

Sincerely,
Janet H. Sprickman,
Acting Chief
Division of Occupational Safety Programming

02/16/1984 - Guarding requirements for skylights.
Record Type: Interpretation Standard Number: 1910.23(a)(4); 1910.23(e)(8)
Subject: **Guarding requirements for skylights.**

February 16, 1984
Mr. Joseph P. Stanton
Iovine & Woods, P.C., Suite 200, 7908 Frankford Ave., Philadelphia, PA 19136

Dear Mr. Stanton:

This is in response to your letter of December 21, 1983, regarding skylights as regulated by the Occupational Safety and Health Administration (OSHA). This response provides an interpretation and clarification of the General Industry Standard 29 CFR 1910.23(a)(4) and (e)(8).

These regulations are included in 29 CFR 1910, Subpart D--Waling-Working Surfaces. 29 CFR 1910.21(a)(1) of the same Subpart defines floor opening as: An opening measuring 12 inches or more in its least dimension, in any floor, platform, pavement, or yard through which persons may fall, such as a hatchway, stair or ladder opening, pit, or large manhole.

Moreover, a definition given in Webster's New Collegiate Dictionary 1977 edition) for "hatch" is "an opening in the...floor or roof of a building;" the same entry gives "hatchway" as a synonym.

Using these definitions, therefore, OSHA concludes that a skylight should be regarded as a hatchway, i.e., an opening in the roof of a building through which persons may fall. 29 CFR 1910.23(a)(4) therefore requires that skylights in the roof of buildings through which persons may fall while walking or working shall be guarded by a standard skylight screen or a fixed standard railing on all exposed sides.

When a skylight screen is selected for safeguarding the opening, and in the event the skylight is constructed of plastic material subject to fracture (as glass would be), then the skylight must at a minimum be provided with a skylight screen capable of withstanding a load of at least 200 pounds applied perpendicularly at any one area on the screen. On the other hand, a plastic skylight which can provide the necessary structural integrity to support the 200-pound load would not be required to be further safeguarded, since it would meet the intended function of a screen as well.

As expressed in 29 CFR 1910.23(e)(8), the primary function of the screen is to support at least a 200-pound load such as a person may place upon it. This provision further relates that the screen shall provide a minimum deflection so as not to break the glass; but that portion of the requirement may be inapplicable when no glass is present. (The concern for breaking the glass results from the possible fragment exposure to persons beneath the skylight.)

We hope this information is helpful to you. If we may be of further assistance, please contact us.

Sincerely,
John B. Miles, Jr., Director
Directorate of Field Operations

[OSHA Instruction STD 1-1.13 April 16, 1984 Office of General Industry Compliance Assistance
Subject: **Protection in General Industry: 29 CFR 1910.23(c)(1), (c)(3), and 29 CFR 1910.132(a)**

A. **Purpose.** This instruction clarifies the applicability of 29 CFR 1910.23(c)(1), (c)(3) and 1910.132(a) where employees are exposed to falling hazards while performing various tasks including maintenance from elevated surfaces.

B. **Scope.** This instruction applies OSHA-wide.

C. **Action.** Regional Administrators and Area Directors shall ensure that the interpretations in F. and the guidelines in G. of this instruction are adhered to when inspecting general industry facilities where employees are exposed to the hazard of falling from elevated surfaces.

D. **Federal Program Change.** This instruction describes a Federal program change which affects State programs. Each Regional Administrator shall:

  1. Ensure that this change is forwarded to each State designee.
  2. Explain the technical content of the change to the State designee as requested.
  3. Ensure that State designees are asked to acknowledge receipt of this Federal program change in writing, within 30 days of notification, to the Regional Administrator. This acknowledgment should include a description either of the State's plan to implement the change or of the reasons why the change should not apply to that State.
  4. Review policies, instructions and guidelines issued by the State to determine that this change has been communicated to State program personnel. Routine monitoring shall also be used to determine if this change has been implemented in actual performance.

E. **Background.** Adjudicated decisions concerning employee exposures to falls from elevated surfaces have been inconsistent. As a result, OSHA has cited employers for violations of 29 CFR 1910.23(c)(1) or of Section 5(a)(1) of the OSH Act when employees have been engaged in various tasks which include inspections, service, repairs and maintenance on elevated surfaces such as, but not limited to, conveyers, tops of machinery and other structures not normally considered "walking and working" surfaces.

  1. Although 29 CFR 1910.23(c)(1) requires the safeguarding of "platforms" used by employees, there has been disagreement as to when an "elevated surface" constitutes a platform within the meaning of the standard.
  2. In at least one instance (General Electric Company v. OSHRC, 583 F. 2d 61 (2d Cir. 1978) the court noted the need for increased clarity of definition by OSHA regarding its intended meaning of the term "platform". Therefore, this instruction clarifies and defines the conditions and circumstances under which a "platform" is deemed to exist, and where the requirements of 29 CFR 1910.23(c) apply.

F. **Interpretation.** The following interpretations are established for uniform enforcement and application of G. of this instruction.

  1. Platforms are interpreted to be any elevated surface designed or used primarily as a walking or working surface, and any other elevated surfaces upon which employees are required or allowed to walk or work while performing assigned tasks on a predictable and regular basis (See 29 CFR 1910.21(a)(4) for definition of "platform".)
  2. Predictable and regular basis means employee functions such as, but not limited to, inspections, service, repair and maintenance which are performed:
      a. At least once every 2 weeks, or
      b. For a total of 4 man-hours or more during any sequential 4-week period (e.g., 2 employees once every 4 weeks for 2 hours = 4 man-hours per 4-week period).

G. Guidelines. The following guidelines are established for the uniform enforcement of 29 CFR 1910.23(c)(1), 1910.23(c)(3) and 1910.132(a) regarding employee exposures to falls from elevated surfaces.

  1. Employee exposures to falls from platforms (interpreted in F.1.) are regulated by the following OSHA standards:

a. 29 CFR 1910.23(c)(1), or

b. 29 CFR 1910.23(c)(3).

2. In situations where the safeguarding requirements of G.1. are not applicable because employees are exposed to falls from an elevated surface other than a predictable and regular basis, personal protective equipment as required by 29 CFR 1910.132(a) or other effective fall protection shall be provided.

Thorne G. Auchter Assistant Secretary

OCCUPATIONAL HEALTH AND INDUSTRIAL HYGIENE

Some significant events in occupational safety in the United States include:

In 1812, the Embargo of the War of 1812 spurred the development of the New England textile industry and the founding of factory mutual companies. These early insurance companies inspected properties for hazards and suggested loss control and prevention methods in order to secure low rates for their policyholders.

In 1864 the Pennsylvania Mine Safety Act (PMSA) was passed into law.

In 1864 North America's first accident insurance policy was issued.

In 1867 the state of Massachusetts instituted the first government-sponsored factory inspection program.

In 1877 the state of Massachusetts passed a law requiring guarding for dangerous machinery, and took authority for enforcement of factory inspection programs.

In 1878 the first recorded call by a labor organization for a federal occupational safety and health law is heard.

In 1896 an association to prevent fires and write codes and standards, the National Fire Protection Association (NFPA), was founded.

In 1902 the state of Maryland passed the first workers' compensation law.

In 1904 the first attempt by a state government to force employers to compensate their employees for on-the-job injuries was overturned when the U.S. Supreme Court declared Maryland's workers' compensation law to be unconstitutional.

In 1911 a professional, technical organization responsible for developing safety codes for boilers and elevators, the American Society of Mechanical Engineers (ASME), was founded.

From 1911 to 1915 30 states passed workers' compensation laws.

In 1911 the American Society of Safety Engineers (ASSE) was founded. The ASSE was dedicated to the development of accident prevention techniques and the advancement of safety engineering as a profession.

In 1912 a group of engineers representing insurance companies, industry and government met in Milwaukee to exchange data on accident prevention. The organization formed at this meeting was to become the National Safety Council (NSC). (Today, the NSC carries on major safety campaigns for the general public, as well as assists industry in the development of safety promotion programs.)

In 1916 the U.S. Supreme Court upheld the constitutionality of state workers' compensation laws.

In 1918 the American Standards Association was founded. Responsible for the development of many voluntary safety standards, some of which are referenced into laws it is now called the American National Standards Institute (ANSI).

In 1936 Frances Perkins, Secretary of Labor, called for a federal occupational safety and health law. This action came a full 58 years after organized labor's first recorded request for a law of this nature.

In 1936 the Walsh-Healey (Public Contracts) Act passed. This law required that all federal contracts be fulfilled in a healthful and safe working environment.

In 1948 all 48 states had workers' compensation laws.

In 1952 Coal Mine Safety Act (CMSA) was passed into law.

In 1960 specific safety standards were promulgated for the Walsh-Healey Act.

In 1966 the Metal and Nonmetallic Mines Safety Act (MNMSA) was passed.

In 1966 the U.S. Department of Transportation (DOT) and its sections, the National Highway Traffic Safety Administration (NHTSA) and the National Transportation Safety Board (NTSB), were established.

In 1968 President Lyndon Johnson called for a federal occupational safety and health law.

In 1969 the Construction Safety Act (CSA) was passed.

In 1969 the Board of Certified Safety Professionals (BCSP) was established. This organization certifies practitioners in the safety profession.

In 1970 President Richard Nixon signed into law the Occupational Safety and Health Act thus creating the Occupational Safety and Health Administration (OSHA) and the National Institute for Occupational Safety and Health (NIOSH).

Industrial Hygiene

Industrial hygiene has been defined as

> that science and art devoted to the anticipation, recognition, evaluation, and control of those environmental factors or stresses arising in or from the workplace, which may cause sickness, impaired health and well-being, or significant discomfort among workers or among the citizens of the community.

Industrial hygienists use environmental monitoring and analytical methods to detect the extent of worker exposure and employ engineering, work practice controls and other methods to control potential health hazards.

There has been an awareness of industrial hygiene since antiquity. The environment and its relation to worker health was recognized as early as the fourth century B.C. when Hippocrates noted lead toxicity in the mining industry. In the first century A.D., Pliny the Elder, a Roman scholar, perceived health risks to those working with zinc and sulfur. He devised a face mask made from an animal bladder to protect workers from exposure to dust and lead fumes. In the second century A.D., the Greek physician Galen accurately described the pathology of lead poisoning and also recognized the hazardous exposures of copper miners to acid mists.

In the Middle Ages, guilds worked at assisting sick workers and their families.

In 1556, the German scholar Agricola advanced the science of industrial hygiene even further when in his book De Re Metallica, he described the diseases of miners and prescribed preventive measures. The book included suggestions for mine ventilation and worker protection, discussed mining accidents and described diseases associated with mining occupations such as silicosis.

Industrial hygiene gained further respectability in 1700 when in Italy, Bernardo Ramazzini, known as the "father of industrial medicine," published the first comprehensive book on industrial medicine, De Morbis Artificum Diatriba (The Diseases of Workmen). The book contained accurate descriptions of the occupational diseases of most of the workers of his time. Ramazzini greatly affected the future of industrial hygiene because he asserted that occupational diseases should be studied in the work environment rather than in hospital wards.

Industrial hygiene received another major boost in 1743 when Ulrich Ellenborg published a pamphlet on occupational diseases and injuries among gold miners. Ellenborg also wrote about the toxicity of carbon monoxide, mercury, lead, and nitric acid.

In England in the 18th century, Percival Pott, as a result of his findings on the insidious effects of soot on chimney sweepers, was a major force in getting the British

Parliament to pass the *Chimney-Sweepers Act of 1788*. The passage of the English Factory Acts beginning in 1833 marked the first effective legislative acts in the field of industrial safety. The acts, however, were intended to provide compensation for accidents rather than to control their causes. Later, several other European nations developed workers' compensation acts, which stimulated the adoption of increased factory safety precautions and the establishment of medical services within industrial plants.

In the early 20th century in the United States, Dr. Alice Hamilton led efforts to improve industrial hygiene. She observed industrial conditions first hand and startled mine owners, factory managers and state officials with evidence that there was a correlation between worker illness and exposure to toxins. She also presented definitive proposals for eliminating unhealthful working conditions.

At about the same time, U.S. federal and state agencies began investigating health conditions in industry. In 1908 public awareness of occupationally related diseases stimulated the passage of compensation acts for certain civil employees. States passed the first workers' compensation laws in 1911. In 1913 the New York Department of Labor and the Ohio Department of Health established the first state industrial hygiene programs. All states enacted such legislation by 1948. In most states, there is some compensation coverage for workers who contract occupational diseases.

The U.S. Congress has passed three landmark pieces of legislation related to safeguarding workers' health:
- The Metal and Nonmetallic Mines Safety Act of 1966;
- The Federal Coal Mine Safety and Health Act of 1969; and
- The Occupational Safety and Health Act of 1970.

Today nearly every employer is required to implement the elements of an industrial hygiene and safety, occupational health, or hazard communication program and to be responsive to the Occupational Safety and Health Administration (OSHA) and its regulations.

OSHA and Industrial Hygiene

Under the OSH Act, OSHA develops and sets mandatory occupational safety and health requirements applicable to the more than 6 million workplaces in the United States. OSHA relies on, among many others, industrial hygienists to evaluate jobs for potential health hazards. Developing and setting mandatory occupational safety and health standards involves determining the extent of employee exposure to hazards and deciding what is needed to control these hazards to protect workers. Industrial hygienists are trained to anticipate, recognize, evaluate and recommend controls for environmental and physical hazards that can affect the health and well-being of workers.

More than 40 percent of the OSHA compliance officers who inspect U.S. workplaces are industrial hygienists. Industrial hygienists also play a major role in developing and issuing OSHA standards to protect workers from health hazards associated with toxic chemicals, biological hazards and harmful physical agents. They also provide technical assistance and support to the agency's national and regional offices. OSHA also employs industrial hygienists who assist in setting up field enforcement procedures and issue technical interpretations of OSHA regulations and standards.

Industrial hygienists analyze, identify and measure workplace hazards or stresses that can cause sickness, impaired health or significant discomfort in workers through chemical, physical, ergonomic or biological exposures. The two main roles of the OSHA industrial hygienist are to spot those conditions and help eliminate or control them through appropriate measures.

Worksite Analysis

A worksite analysis is an essential first step that helps an industrial hygienist determine the jobs and workstations where problems could arise. During the worksite analysis, the industrial hygienist measures and identifies exposures, problem tasks and risks. The most-effective worksite analyses include all jobs, operations and work activities. The industrial hygienist inspects, researches or analyzes how the particular chemicals or physical hazards at that worksite affect worker health. If a situation hazardous to health is discovered, the industrial hygienist recommends the appropriate corrective actions.

Recognizing and Controlling Hazards

Industrial hygienists recognize that engineering, work practice and administrative controls are the primary means of reducing employee exposure to occupational hazards. Engineering controls minimize employee exposure by either reducing or removing the hazard at the source or isolating the worker from the hazard. Engineering controls include eliminating toxic chemicals and substituting nontoxic chemicals, enclosing work processes or confining work operations, and installing general and local ventilation systems.

Work practice controls alter the manner in which a task is performed. Some fundamental and easily implemented work practice controls include:

- changing existing work practices to follow proper procedures that minimize exposures when operating production and control equipment;
- inspecting and maintaining process and control equipment on a regular basis;
- implementing good housekeeping procedures;
- providing good supervision; and
- mandating that eating, drinking, smoking, chewing tobacco or gum and applying cosmetics in regulated areas is prohibited.

Administrative controls include controlling employees' exposure by scheduling production and tasks, or both, in ways that minimize exposure levels. For example, the employer might schedule operations with the highest exposure potential during periods when the fewest employees are present.

When effective work practices or engineering controls are not feasible or while such controls are being instituted, appropriate personal protective equipment must be used. Examples of personal protective equipment are gloves, safety goggles, helmets, safety shoes, protective clothing and respirators. To be effective, personal protective equipment must be:

- individually selected;
- properly fitted and periodically refitted;
- conscientiously and properly worn;
- regularly maintained; and
- replaced, as necessary.

Examples of Job Hazards

To be effective in recognizing and evaluating on-the-job hazards and recommending controls, industrial hygienists must be familiar with the hazards' characteristics. Potential hazards can include air contaminants and chemical, biological, physical and ergonomic hazards.

Air Contaminants

Air contaminants are commonly classified as either particulate or gas and vapor contaminants. The most common particulate contaminants include dusts, fumes, mists, aerosols and fibers. Dusts are solid particles generated by handling, crushing, grinding, colliding, exploding and heating organic or inorganic materials such as rock, ore, metal, coal, wood and grain. Any process that produces dust fine enough to remain in the air long enough to be inhaled or ingested should be regarded as hazardous until proven otherwise.

Fumes are formed when material from a volatilized solid condenses in cool air. In most cases, the solid particles resulting from the condensation react with air to form an oxide.

The term mist is applied to liquid suspended in the atmosphere. Mists are generated by liquids condensing from a vapor back to a liquid or by a liquid being dispersed by splashing or atomizing. Aerosols are also a form of a mist characterized by highly respirable, minute liquid particles.

Fibers are solid particles whose length is several times greater than their diameter, such as asbestos.

Gases are formless fluids that expand to occupy the space or enclosure in which they are confined. They are atomic, diatomic or molecular in nature as opposed to droplets or particles that are made up of millions of atoms or molecules.

Through evaporation, liquids change into vapors and mix with the surrounding atmosphere. Vapors are the volatile form of substances that are normally in a solid or liquid state at room temperature and pressure. Vapors are gases in that true vapors are atomic or molecular in nature.

Chemical Hazards

Harmful chemical compounds in the form of solids, liquids, gases, mists, dusts, fumes and vapors exert toxic effects by inhalation (breathing), absorption (through direct contact with the skin) or ingestion (eating or drinking). Airborne chemical hazards exist as concentrations of mists, vapors, gases, fumes or solids. Some are toxic through inhalation and some of them irritate the skin on contact; some can be toxic by absorption through the skin or through ingestion; and some are corrosive to living tissue.

The degree of worker risk from exposure to any given substance depends on the nature and potency of the toxic effects and the magnitude and duration of exposure.

Information on the risk to workers from chemical hazards can be obtained from the material safety data sheet (MSDS) that OSHA's Hazard Communication Standard requires be supplied by the manufacturer or importer to the purchaser of all hazardous materials (29 CFR 1910.1200). The MSDS is a summary of the important health, safety, and toxicological information on the chemical or the mixture's ingredients. Other provisions of the Hazard Communication Standard require that all containers of hazardous substances in the workplace have appropriate warning and identification labels.

Biological Hazards

These include bacteria, viruses, fungi and other living organisms that can cause acute and chronic infections by entering the body either directly or through breaks in the skin. Occupations that deal with plants, animals or their products, or with food and food processing may expose workers to biological hazards. Laboratory and medical personnel also can be exposed to biological hazards. Any occupations that result in contact with bodily fluids pose a risk to workers from biological hazards.

In occupations where animals are involved, biological hazards are dealt with by preventing and controlling diseases in the animal population as well as properly caring for and handling infected animals. Also, effective personal hygiene, particularly proper attention to minor cuts and scratches, especially on the hands and forearms, helps keep worker risks to a minimum.

In occupations where there is potential exposure to biological hazards, workers should practice proper personal hygiene, particularly hand washing. Hospitals should provide proper ventilation, proper personal protective equipment such as gloves and respirators, adequate infectious waste disposal systems, and appropriate controls, including isolation in instances of particularly contagious diseases such as tuberculosis.

Physical Hazards

These include excessive levels of ionizing and nonionizing electromagnetic radiation, noise, vibration, illumination and temperature.

In occupations where there is exposure to ionizing radiation, time, distance and shielding are important tools in ensuring worker safety. Danger from radiation increases with the amount of time one is exposed to it; hence, the shorter the time of exposure, the smaller the radiation danger.

Distance also is a valuable tool in controlling exposure to both ionizing and nonionizing radiation. Radiation levels from some sources can be estimated by comparing the squares of the distances between the worker and the source. For example, at a reference point of 10 ft. from a source, the radiation is 1/100 of the intensity at 1 ft. from the source.

Shielding also is a way to protect against radiation. The greater the protective mass between a radioactive source and the worker, the lower the radiation exposure.

Similarly, shielding workers from nonionizing radiation can also be an effective control method. For example, workers exposed to radiant heat can be protected by installing reflective shields and providing them with protective clothing. In some instances, however, limiting exposure to or increasing distance from certain forms of nonionizing radiation, such as lasers, is not effective. For example, an exposure to laser radiation that is faster than the blinking of an eye can be hazardous and would require workers to be miles from the laser source before being adequately protected.

Noise, another significant physical hazard, can be controlled by various measures. Noise can be reduced by:

■ Installing equipment and systems that have been engineered, designed, and built to operate quietly;

Occupational Health and Industrial Hygiene

- Enclosing or shielding noisy equipment;
- Making certain that equipment is in good repair and properly maintained with all worn or unbalanced parts replaced;
- Mounting noisy equipment on special mounts to reduce vibration; and
- Installing silencers, mufflers or baffles.

Substituting quiet work methods for noisy ones is another significant way to reduce noise (e.g., welding parts rather than riveting them). Also, treating floors, ceilings and walls with acoustical material can reduce reflected or reverberant noise. In addition, erecting sound barriers at adjacent workstations around noisy operations will reduce those workers' exposure to noise.

It is also possible to reduce noise exposure by:
- Increasing the distance between the source and the receiver;
- Isolating workers in acoustical booths;
- Limiting workers' exposure time to noise; and
- Providing hearing protection.

OSHA also requires that workers in noisy surroundings be periodically tested as a precaution against hearing loss.

Ergonomic Hazards

The science of ergonomics is the study and evaluation of a range of tasks including, but not limited to, lifting, holding, pushing, walking and reaching. Many ergonomic problems result from technological changes, such as increased assembly line speeds, added specialized tasks and increased repetition. However, some problems arise from poorly designed job tasks. Any of those conditions can cause ergonomic hazards such as excessive vibration and noise, eye strain, repetitive motion and heavy lifting problems. Improperly designed tools or work areas also can be ergonomic hazards. Repetitive motions or repeated shocks over prolonged periods of time as in jobs involving sorting, assembling and data entry can often cause irritation and inflammation of the tendon sheath of the hands and arms, a condition known as carpal tunnel syndrome.

Ergonomic hazards are avoided primarily by the effective design of a job or job site and by better designed tools or equipment that meet workers' needs in terms of physical environment and job tasks. Through thorough worksite analyses, employers can set up procedures to correct or control ergonomic hazards by:

- Using the appropriate engineering controls (e.g., designing or redesigning workstations, lighting, tools, equipment);
- Teaching correct work practices (e.g., proper lifting methods);
- Employing proper administrative controls (e.g., shifting workers among several different tasks, reducing production demand and increasing rest breaks); and
- Providing and mandating personal protective equipment, if necessary.

Evaluating working conditions from an ergonomics standpoint involves looking at the total physiological and psychological demands of the job on the worker. Overall, the benefits of a well-designed, ergonomic work environment can include increased efficiency, fewer accidents, lower operating costs and more effective use of personnel.

Routes of Entry

For a harmful agent to exert its toxic effect, it must come into contact with a body cell and must enter the body through inhalation, skin absorption or ingestion. Chemical compounds in the form of liquids, gases, mists, dusts, fumes and vapors can cause problems by inhalation, absorption or ingestion.

Inhalation

Inhalation involves those airborne contaminants that can be inhaled directly into the lungs and can be physically classified as gases, vapors and particulate matter that includes dusts, fumes, smokes and mists.

Inhalation, as a route of entry, is particularly important because of the rapidity with which a toxic material can be absorbed in the lungs, pass into the bloodstream and reach the brain. Inhalation is the major route of entry for hazardous chemicals in the work environment.

Absorption

Penetration through the skin can occur quite rapidly if the skin is cut or abraded. Intact skin, however, offers a reasonably good barrier to chemicals. Unfortunately, there are many compounds that can be absorbed through intact skin.

Some substances are absorbed via hair follicle openings and others dissolve in the fats and oils of the skin, such as organic lead compounds, many nitro compounds and organic phosphate pesticides. Compounds that are good solvents for fats (e.g., toluene, xylene) also can cause problems by being absorbed through the skin.

Many organic compounds, such as cyanides and most aromatic aniines, amides and phenols, can produce systemic poisoning by direct contact with the skin. Absorption of toxic chemicals through the skin and eyes is the second most important route of entry.

Ingestion

In the workplace, people can unknowingly eat or drink harmful chemicals if they store drinking containers in the workplace or do not wash before eating. Toxic compounds are capable of being absorbed from the gastrointestinal tract into the blood stream. Lead oxide can cause serious problems if people working with this material are allowed to eat or smoke in work areas. In this situation, careful and thorough washing is required both before eating and at the end of every shift.

Inhaled toxic dusts can also be ingested in amounts that may cause trouble. If the toxic dust swallowed with food or saliva is not soluble in digestive fluids, it is eliminated directly through the intestinal tract. Toxic materials that are readily soluble in digestive fluids can be absorbed into the blood from the digestive system.

In addition to studying all routes of entry when evaluating the work environment (e.g., snack foods or lunches in the work area, solvents being used to clean work clothing and hands), specific types of air contaminants must be identified.

Types of Air Contaminants

There are precise meanings of certain words commonly used in industrial hygiene. These must be used correctly in order to:

- Understand the requirements of OSHA's regulations;

- Effectively communicate with other workers in the field of industrial hygiene; and
- Intelligently prepare purchase orders to procure health services and personal protective equipment.

For example, a fume respirator is worthless as protection against gases or vapors. Too frequently, terms (e.g., gases, vapors, fumes, mists) are used interchangeably. Each term has a definite meaning and describes a certain state of matter. Air contaminants are commonly classified as either particulate contaminants or gas and vapor contaminants.

Particulate Contaminants

The most common particulate contaminants include dusts, fumes, mists and fibers.

Dusts

Dusts are solid particles generated by handling crushing grinding, rapid impact, detonation and decrepitation (breaking apart by heating) of organic or inorganic materials, such as rock, ore, metal, coal, wood and grain.

Dust is a term used in industry to describe airborne solid particles that range in size from 0.1 to 25 micrometers. One micrometer is a unit of length equal to one millionth of a meter. A micrometer is also referred to as a "micron" and is equal to 1/25,400 of an inch. Dust can enter the air from various sources, such as the handling of dusty materials, or during processes such as grinding, crushing, blasting and shaking.

Most industrial dusts consist of particles that vary widely in size, with the small particles greatly outnumbering the large ones. Consequently (with few exceptions), when dust is noticeable in the air near a dusty operation, more invisible dust particles than visible ones are probably present. A process that produces dust fine enough to remain in the air long enough to be inhaled should be regarded as hazardous until proven otherwise.

An airborne dust of a potentially toxic material will not cause pulmonary illness if its particle size is too large to gain access to the lungs. Particles 10 ppm in diameter and larger are known as nonrespirable These particles will be deposited in the respiratory system long before they reach the alveolar sacs – the most important area in the lungs.

Particles less than 10 ppm in diameter are known as respirable. Because the particles are likely to reach the alveoli in great quantities, they are potentially more harmful than larger particles.

By using a size-selective device (e.g., a cyclone) ahead of a filter at a specific airflow-sampling rate, it is possible to collect respirable-sized particles on the filter. This allows one to determine the dust concentration of respirable particles.

Fumes

Fumes are formed when the material from a volatilized solid condenses in cool air. The solid particles that are formed make up a fume that is extremely fine – usually less than 1.0 micron in diameter. In most cases, the hot vapor reacts with the air to form an oxide. Gases and vapors are not fumes, although the terms are often mistakenly used interchangeably.

Welding, metalizing and other operations involving vapors from molten metals may produce fumes; these may be harmful under certain conditions. Arc welding volatilizes metal vapor that condenses as the metal or its oxide in the air around the arc. In addition, the rod coating is partially volatilized. Because these fumes are extremely small, they are readily inhaled.

Other toxic fumes, such as those formed when welding structures that have been painted with lead-based paints or when welding galvanized metal, can produce severe symptoms of toxicity rather rapidly in the absence of good ventilation or proper respiratory protection.

Mists

Mists are suspended liquid droplets generated by condensation of liquids from the vapor back to the liquid state or by breaking up a liquid into a dispersed state, such as by splashing or atomizing. The term mist is applied to a finely divided liquid suspended in the atmosphere. Examples include oil mist produced during cutting and grinding operations, acid mists from electroplating acid or alkali mists from pickling operations, and spray mist from spray-finishing operations.

Fibers

Fibers are solid particles that have a slender, elongated structure with length several times as great as their diameter. Examples include asbestos, fibrous talc, and fiberglass. Airborne fibers may be found in construction activities, mining friction product manufacturing and fabrication, and demolition operations.

Gas and Vapor Contaminants

Gases

Gases are formless fluids that expand to occupy the space or enclosure in which they are confined. Gases are a state of matter in which the molecules are unrestricted by cohesive forces. Examples are arc-welding gases, internal combustion engine exhaust gases and air.

Vapors

Vapors are the volatile form of substances that are normally in the solid or liquid state at room temperature and pressure. Evaporation is the process by which a liquid is changed into the vapor state and mixed with the surrounding atmosphere. Some of the most common exposures to vapors in industry occur from organic solvents. Solvents with low boiling points readily form vapors at room temperature. Solvent vapors enter the body mainly by inhalation, although some skin absorption can occur.

Units of Concentration

In addition to the definitions concerning states of matter that find daily usage in the vocabulary of the industrial hygienist, other terms used to describe degree of exposure include the following:

ppm. Parts per million. Parts of contaminated air on a volumetric basis. It is used for expressing the concentration of a gas or vapor.

mg/m3. Milligrams of a substance per cubic meter of air. The term is most commonly used for expressing concentrations of dusts, metal fumes or other particles in the air.

mppcf. Millions of particles of a particulate per cubic foot of air.

f/cc. The number of fibers per cubic centimeter of air. This term is used for expressing the concentration of airborne asbestos fibers.

The concentration of a gas or vapor in air is usually expressed in parts per million (ppm), but may be converted to mg/m3 at a temperature of 25°C and a pressure of 760 mm Hg:

$$mg/m3 = ppm \times (Molecular\ Weight/24.45)$$

Example: A 50-ppm concentration of carbon monoxide (molecular weight = 28) is equivalent to a concentration of 57.26 mg/m3 at 25°C and 760 mm Hg. Note also that:

$$Concentration\ (ppm) = Concentration\ (\%) \times 10,000$$

Example: A concentration of a gas or vapor equal to 0.01 percent is equivalent to a concentration of 100 ppm. The health and safety professional recognizes that air contaminants exist as a gas, dust, fumes, mist or vapor in the workroom air. In evaluating the degree of exposure, the measured concentration of the air is compared to limits or exposure guidelines.

Threshold Limit Values

Threshold limit values (TLVs) have been established for airborne concentrations of many chemical compounds. It is important to understand something about TLVs and the terminology in which their concentrations are expressed.

The American Conference of Governmental Industrial Hygienists (ACGIH) publishes annually the list of "Threshold Limit Values and Biological Exposure Indices." The ACGIH is not an official government agency. Membership is limited to professional personnel in government agencies or educational institutions engaged in occupational safety and health programs.

The data for establishing TLVs comes from animal studies, human studies and industrial experience. The limit may be selected for several reasons; it may be based on the fact that a substance is very irritating to the majority of people exposed, or, other substances may be asphyxiants. Other reasons for establishing a TLV include the fact that certain chemical compounds are anesthetic, or fibrogenic, or can cause allergic reactions or malignancies. Some additional TLVs have been established because exposure above a certain airborne concentration is a nuisance.

The basic idea of TLVs is fairly simple. They refer to airborne concentrations of substances and represent conditions under which it is believed that nearly all workers may be repeatedly exposed, day after day, without adverse effect.

Because individual susceptibility varies widely, an occasional exposure of an individual at (or even below) the threshold limit may not prevent discomfort, aggravation of a preexisting condition or occupational illness. In addition to the TLVs set for chemical compounds, there are limits for physical agents, such as noise, microwaves, and heat stress.

Several important points should be noted concerning TLVs. First, "TLV" is a copyrighted trademark of the ACGIH. It should not be used to refer to the values published in OSHA or other standards. OSHA's limits are known as permissible exposure limits and will be discussed later. The ACGIH TLVs are not mandatory federal or state employee exposure standards. These limits are not fine lines between safe and dangerous concentrations nor are they a relative index of toxicity. Three categories of TLVs are specified.

Time-weighted average (TLV-TWA) is the time-weighted average concentration for a normal eight-hour workday or 40-hour workweek to which nearly all workers may be repeatedly exposed, day after day, without adverse effect. Time-weighted averages permit excursions above the limit, provided they are compensated by equivalent excursions below the limit during the workday.

Short-term exposure limit (TLV-STEL) is the maximal concentration to which workers can be exposed continuously for a short period of time without suffering from any of the following:
- Irritation;
- Chronic or irreversible tissue change; or
- Narcosis of sufficient degree to increase accident proneness, impair self-rescue or materially reduce work efficiency.

The STEL is a 15-minute TWA exposure that should not be exceeded at any time during a workday, even if the eight-hour time weighted average, is within the TLV-TWA. Exposures above the TLV-TWA up to the STEL should not be longer than 15 minutes and should not occur more than four times per day. There should be at least 60 minutes between successive exposures in this range.

The STEL is not a separate independent exposure limit; rather it supplements the time-weighted average limit where there are recognized acute effects from a substance whose toxic effects are primarily of a chronic nature. STELs are recommended only where toxic effects have been reported from high short-term exposures in humans or animals.

Ceiling (TLV-C) is the concentration that should not be exceeded even instantaneously. Although the time-weighted average concentration provides the most satisfactory, practical way of monitoring airborne agents for compliance with the limits, there are certain substances for which it is inappropriate. In the latter group are substances that are predominantly fast acting and whose threshold limit is more appropriately based on this particular response. A ceiling limit that should not be exceeded best controls substances with this type of response.

For some substances (e.g., irritant gases), only one category, the TLV-C, may be relevant. For other substances, either two or three categories may be relevant, depending upon their physiologic action. It is important to observe that if any one of these three TLVs is exceeded, a potential hazard from that substance is presumed to exist.

Skin Notation

Nearly one-fourth of the substances in the TLV list are followed by the designation "Skin." This refers to the potential significant contribution to the overall exposure by the cutaneous route, including mucous membranes and the eyes, usually by direct contact with the substance. This designation is intended to suggest appropriate measures for the prevention of cutaneous absorption.

Federal Occupational Safety And Health Standards

The first compilation of health and safety standards promulgated by the Department of Labor's OSHA in 1970 was derived from the then-existing federal standards and national consensus standards. Thus, many of the 1968 TLVs established by the ACGIH became federal standards or permissible exposure limits (PEL).

Also, certain workplace quality standards known as maximal acceptable concentrations of the American National Standards Institute (ANSI) were incorporated as federal health standards in 29 CFR 1910.1000 as national consensus standards. These PEL values for general industry were subsequently updated in 1989. Unlike the TLVs, OSHA's PELs are enforceable by law. Employers must keep employee exposure levels below the PELs of regulated substances. As with TLVs, there are three types of PELs.

Time-Weighted Average

In adopting the TLVs of the ACGIH, OSHA also adopted the concept of the time-weighted average concentration for a workday. The eight-hour time-weighted average (TWA) is the average concentration of a chemical in air over an eight-hour exposure period. In general:

$$TWA = \frac{C_aT_a + C_bT_b + C_cT_c....C_rT_r}{8}$$

Where:
- T_a is the time of the first exposure period.
- C_a is the concentration of contaminant in period "a."
- T_b is another time period during the shift.
- C_b is the concentration during period "b."
- C_r is the concentration during the "no" time period.
- T_r is the "nth" time period.

To illustrate the formula prescribed above, assume that a substance has an eight-hour TWA PEL of 100 ppm. Assume that an employee is subject to the following exposure:
- Two hours exposure at 150 ppm;
- Two hours exposure at 75 ppm; and
- Four hours exposure at 50 ppm.

Substituting this information in the formula, we have:

$$TWA = \frac{(150)(2) + (75)(2) + (50)(4)}{8} = 81.25 \text{ ppm}$$

Since 81.25 ppm is less than 100 ppm, the eight-hour TWA limit, the exposure is acceptable.

Amendments
to OSHA's Air Contaminant Standard

On January 19, 1989, OSHA amended its Air Contaminant standard, 1910.1000 (54 Fed. Reg. 2332). New limits were established for many substances and many new PELs were set for substances previously not regulated by OSHA.

The Eleventh Circuit Court of Appeals issued a decision vacating the "Final Rules" of the Air Contaminants Standard (29 CFR 1910.1000) on July 7, 1992. The court's decision struck down the entire standard. However, PELs specified in 29 CFR 1910.1001 through the end of Subpart Z of Part 1910 are unaffected by the court's decision.

Effective March 22, 1993, OSHA is enforcing only the following Permissible Exposure Limits (PELs) in 29 CFR 1910.1000:

- Those limits specified in the "Transitional Limits" column of Table Z-1-A;
- All limits in Table Z-2; and
- All limits in Table Z-3.

Expanded Health—Work Practice Standards

OSHA also has promulgated expanded health standards at 1910.1001 through 1910.1101 for substances including asbestos, vinyl chloride, arsenic, lead, benzene, coke oven emissions, cotton dust, dibromoc1oropropane, acrylonitrile, ethylene oxide and formaldehyde. Additionally, 13 identified carcinogens are regulated.

These standards contain work practice requirements such as exposure monitoring protective equipment, housekeeping hygiene facilities, medical surveillance, and employee training in addition to permissible limits. Additional information regarding industrial hygiene, including sampling instrumentation and methods, can be found in OSHA Technical Manual, CPL 2-2.20B.

Early in its history, OSHA recognized industrial hygiene as an integral part of a healthful work setting. OSHA places a high priority on using industrial hygiene concepts in its health standards and as a tool for effective enforcement of job safety and health regulations. By recognizing and applying the principles of industrial hygiene to the work environment, U.S. workplaces will become more healthful and safer.

The National Institute for Occupational Safety and Health publishes a Pocket Guide to Chemical Hazards. It may be obtained at no charge by calling 1-800-35NIOSH (1-800-356-4674) or by logging on to www.cdc.gov/niosh/homepage.html.

Bloodborne Pathogens

Bloodborne pathogens are pathogenic microorganisms that are present in human blood and can infect and cause disease in humans. These pathogens include, but are not limited to, Hepatitis B Virus (HBV), which causes Hepatitis B, a serious liver disease and Human Immune Deficiency Virus (HIV), which causes Acquired Immunodeficiency Syndrome (AIDS).

OSHA has determined that certain employees (particularly healthcare employees) face a significant health risk as a result of occupational exposure to blood and other potentially infectious materials (OPIM) because they may contain bloodborne pathogens.

To minimize or eliminate the risk of occupational exposure to bloodborne pathogens, OSHA issued the Occupational Exposure to Bloodborne Pathogens Standard (29 CFR 1910.1030). This standard prescribes actions that employers must take to reduce the risk of exposure to bloodborne pathogens in the workplace. These actions include the use of:

- Engineering and work practice controls;
- Personal protective equipment;
- Training;
- Medical surveillance;
- Hepatitis B vaccinations; and
- Signs and labels.

Scope and Application

The standard applies to all employees with occupational exposure to blood and OPIM. Occupational exposure means "a reasonably anticipated skin, eye, mucous membrane or parenteral contact with blood or OPIM that may result from the performance of the employees duties." Blood is defined as "human blood, human blood components, and products made from human blood."

OPIM includes the following human body fluids:

- Semen;
- Vaginal secretions;
- Cerebrospinal fluid;
- Synovial fluid;
- Pleural fluid;

- Perinicardial fluid;
- Peritoneal fluid;
- Amniotic fluid;
- Saliva in dental procedures;
- Any body fluid visibly contaminated with blood; and
- All body fluids in situations where it is difficult or impossible to differentiate between body fluids.

OPIM also includes:
- Unfixed tissue or organs from a human;
- FHV-containing cells or tissue cultures;
- Organ cultures and HIV- or HBV-containing culture medium or other solutions; and
- Blood, organs or other tissue from experimental animals infected with HIV or HBV.

The Bloodborne Pathogens Standard covers many types of employees including those in healthcare, non-healthcare, and permanent and temporary worksites. Examples of employees in healthcare facilities include physicians and surgeons, nurses, dentists and dental workers, and laboratory personnel. Non-healthcare facilities employees include those who service and repair medical and dental equipment, infectious waste disposal employees and employees in law enforcement and correctional institutions.

Exposure Control Plan

The Exposure Control Plan (ECP) is the key provision of the standard. It requires the employer to identify employees who will receive training, protective equipment, vaccination and other provisions of the standard.

The ECP requires employers to identify, in writing, tasks and procedures as well as job classifications where occupational exposure to blood occurs without regard to personal protective equipment. The plan must also set forth the schedule for implementing other provisions of the standard and specify the procedure for evaluating circumstances surrounding exposure incidents. It must be accessible to employees and available to OSHA and National Institute for Occupational Safety and Health (NIOSH) representatives. Employers must review and update the plan annually or more often if changes in exposure occur.

Methods of Compliance

The standard describes various methods of compliance that the employer must take to protect their employees from exposure to bloodborne pathogens. These methods include universal precautions, engineering and work practice controls, personal protective equipment and housekeeping.

Universal precautions is an approach to infection control in which all human blood and certain body fluids are treated as if known to be infectious for HIV, HBV, and other bloodborne pathogens. Universal precautions are OSHA's required method of control to protect employees from exposure to all human blood and OPIM.

Engineering controls are controls that isolate or remove the bloodborne pathogens hazard from the workplace. Examples of engineering controls include puncture-resistant sharps containers; mechanical needle recapping devices; and biosafety cabinets. To ensure effectiveness, engineering controls must be examined and maintained or replaced on a regularly scheduled basis.

Work practice controls reduce the likelihood of exposure by altering the manner in which a task is performed. Some examples of work practice requirements in the standard include not bending or breaking contaminated sharps and hand washing when gloves are removed and as soon as possible after contact with body fluids.

**Exhibit 4-1.
Puncture-resistant
sharps containers
are an effective
engineering control.**

Personal protective equipment must be used if occupational exposure remains after instituting engineering and work practice controls or if these controls are not feasible. Personal protective equipment is specialized clothing or equipment that is worn by an employee for protection against a hazard. Employers must provide, at no cost, and require employees to use appropriate personal protective equipment such as gloves, gowns, masks, mouthpieces, and resuscitation devices. The employer must clean, repair and replace these safety items when necessary.

In addition to other compliance methods, the standard requires that the employer maintain the work site in a clean and sanitary condition. Employees must follow certain procedures for cleaning and decontaminating the environment, equipment and work surfaces and for handling contaminated laundry and regulated waste.

Contaminated work surfaces must be decontaminated with a disinfectant upon completion of procedures or when contaminated by splashes, spills or contact with blood or OPIM. The employer must develop a written schedule for cleaning and decontaminating the work site based on the location within the facility, type of surface to be cleaned, amount of soil and the task being performed. Reusable trash containers must also be cleaned on a regular basis and after contamination.

Contaminated laundry is any laundry that may contain blood or OPIM or may contain sharps. The standard requires that contaminated laundry be handled as little as possible with a minimum of agitation. It must be bagged or containerized at the location where it was used and not be sorted or rinsed where it was used. Contaminated laundry must also be placed and transported in bags or containers and properly labeled. When a facility uses universal precautions in handling soiled laundry, alternative labeling or color-coding is sufficient if it permits all employees to recognize the containers as requiring compliance with universal precautions.

Regulated waste is defined in the standard as:
- Liquid or semi-liquid blood or OPIM;
- Contaminated items that would release blood or OPIM in a liquid or semi-liquid state if compressed;
- Items that are caked with dried blood or OPIM and are capable of releasing these materials during handling;
- Contaminated sharps; and
- Pathological and microbiological waste containing blood or OPIM.

Regulated waste must be placed in closeable, leak-proof containers designed to contain all contents during handling, storing, transporting, or shipping and labeled appropriately.

HIV and HBV Research Laboratories and Production Facilities

The standard describe various requirements for HIV and HBV research laboratories and production facilities. A research laboratory produces or uses research laboratory-scale amounts of HIV or HBV. Research laboratories may produce high concentrations of HIV or HBV, but not in the volume found in production facilities that produce high volumes and high concentrations of HIV and HBV.

Some requirements in the standard specific to these facilities include that regulated waste must be incinerated, autoclaved or decontaminated before disposal and that laboratory doors must be closed when work involves HIV and HBV hazards.

In addition, warning signs must be placed on access doors and biological safety cabinets must be used when working with potentially infectious material. Employees in these facilities also require additional training.

Hepatitis B Vaccination and Post-Exposure Evaluation and Follow-up

The employer is required to make available the Hepatitis B vaccine and vaccination series to all employees who may be exposed in the workplace and post-exposure evaluation and follow-up to all employees who have had an exposure incident. All medical evaluations and procedures must be provided:
- At no cost to the employee;
- At a reasonable time and place;
- Under the supervision of a licensed physician or health care professional; and
- According to current recommendations of the U.S. Public Health Service.

The Hepatitis B vaccine and vaccination series must be offered within 10 working days of initial assignment to employees who have occupational exposure to blood or OPIM. Exceptions to this requirement are:
- When employees have previously completed the Hepatitis B vaccination series;
- Immunity is confirmed through anti-body testing; or
- The vaccine is contraindicated for medical reasons.

Employees must sign a declination form if they choose not to be the vaccinated; however, they may request and obtain the vaccination at a later date at no cost.

A confidential medical evaluation and follow-up must be made available to an employee involved in an exposure incident. An exposure incident is a specific eye, mouth, other mucous membrane, nonintact skin or parenteral contact with blood or OPIM that results from the performance of an employee's duties.

The evaluation and follow-up procedures must include

- Documenting the circumstances of exposure;
- Identifying and testing the source individual, if feasible;
- Testing the exposed employee's blood if he or she consents; and
- Conducting post-exposure prophylaxis, counseling and evaluation of reported illnesses.

Following the post-exposure evaluation, the healthcare professional must provide a written opinion to the employer. This opinion is limited to a statement that the employee has been informed of the need, if any, for further evaluation or treatment. All other findings are confidential. The employer must provide a copy of the written opinion to the employee within 15 days of the evaluation.

Communication of Hazards to Employees

The hazards of bloodborne pathogens must be communicated to employees through signs, labels and training. The standard requires that warning labels be attached to containers of regulated waste, refrigerators or freezers containing blood or OPIM, and other containers used to store, transport, or ship blood or OPIM.

The warning label must include the universal biohazard symbol followed by the term "BIOHAZARD" in a fluorescent orange or orange-red color with lettering or symbols in a contrasting color.

The labels are not required when:

- Red bags or red containers are used for regulated waste;
- Regulated waste has been decontaminated;
- Individual containers of blood or OPIM are placed in a labeled container during storage, transport, shipment or disposal; and

- Containers of blood or blood products are labeled as to their content and have been released for transfusion or other clinical use.

Contaminated equipment must also be marked with a label that states which portion of the equipment remains contaminated.

The biohazard label must also be posted at the entrance to HIV and HBV research laboratories and production facilities work areas. The employer must ensure that all employees with occupational exposure participate in an effective training program. Training must be provided within 90 days after the effective date of the standard and annually thereafter.

An individual who is knowledgeable in the subject matter must provide training at no cost to employees during a time that is regularly accessible to employees. The training program must include an:

- Accessible copy of the regulatory text and explanation of its contents;
- Explanation of the modes of transmitting and epidemiology of HBV and HIV;
- Explanation of the written exposure control plan and how to obtain a copy;
- Explanation of use and limitations of engineering controls, work practices and personal protective equipment.

The training materials must be appropriate in content, language and vocabulary to the educational, literacy, and language background of the employees.

Recordkeeping

Employers must establish and maintain accurate records for each employee with occupational exposure. The standard requires employers to maintain two types of employee-related records: medical and training. The medical records must include:

- Employee's name and social security number,
- Employee's Hepatitis B vaccination status;
- Post-exposure evaluation and follow-up procedures results, as necessary;
- The healthcare professional's written opinion, as necessary; and
- Other specific information that has been provided to the healthcare professional.

The medical record must be kept confidential and retained for the duration of employment plus 30 years in accordance with OSHA's Access to Employee Exposure and Medical Records Standard. These records must be made available upon request to employees, anyone with the written consent of the employee and OSHA and NIOSH representatives.

Training records must include:

- Training dates;
- Contents or summary of the training session;
- Names and qualifications of the trainers; and

- Names of job titles of trainees.

All training records must be kept for three years from the date of the training. If the employer ceases to do business, medical and training records must be transferred to the successor employer. If there is no successor employer, the employer must notify the Director of NIOSH for instructions regarding the disposal of records. This must be done at least three months prior to the disposing of the records.

Work Activities Involving Potential Exposure to Bloodborne Pathogens

Below are listed the tasks and procedures in our facility where human blood and other potentially infectious materials are handled that may result in exposure to bloodborne pathogens:

Procedure/Task	Job Classification	Location/Department

Vaccination Declination Form

DATE:

Employee Name:

Employee ID #:

I understand that due to my occupational exposure to blood or other potential infectious materials I may be at risk of acquiring Hepatitis B virus (HBV) infection. I have been given the opportunity to be vaccinated with Hepatitis B vaccine at no charge to myself.

However, I decline the Hepatitis B vaccination at this time. I understand that by declining this vaccine, I continue to be at risk of acquiring Hepatitis B, a serious disease. If, in the future, I continue to have occupational exposure to blood or other potentially infectious materials and I want to be vaccinated with Hepatitis B vaccine, I can receive the vaccination series at no charge to me.

Employee Signature   Date

Facility Representative Signature   Date

Asbestos and Lead Awareness

OSHA regulations apply for industrial applications and construction uses of asbestos and lead. OSHA enforces safety rules through their regional offices . OSHA can issue citations to federal agencies, but cannot issue fines.

Asbestos Exposure

Asbestos is a naturally occurring mineral that is used in vehicle brakes and building materials. It is highly resistant to heat and corrosion and has been used extensively in the past. Auto workers may be exposed to asbestos during brake and clutch repairs.

Inhaling asbestos fibers can cause serious lung disease that may not appear for years. Asbestos can cause a buildup of scar-like tissue in the lungs, resulting in a loss of lung functions and often disability and death.

Simply being exposed to asbestos does not mean a person will become ill or die. In an eight-hour work shift, employees can be exposed to 0.1 fiber per cubit centimeter of air. This small amount of asbestos is normally filtered by the body's system of defense, such as mucous membranes and nose hairs.

Lead Exposure

Like asbestos, lead is very resistant to corrosion and has a low melting temperature. For these reasons it is used extensively in manufacturing, construction work, welding, cutting, brazing and some painting. Lead also can be found in radiator repair shops, motor gaskets and firing ranges.

Once lead gets into the blood, it settles in the blood and soft tissues, such as the kidney, bone marrow, liver and brain. It also settles in the bones and teeth of workers. Overexposure to lead is a leading cause of workplace illnesses. Lead has a permissible exposure level based on an eight-hour day of less than 50 micrograms per cubic meter of air.

Worker Protection

Both asbestos and lead must enter the body to cause damage. The primary route of entry is inhalation. In some small cases, they may enter via ingestion when a worker eats or smokes in an area where airborne lead or asbestos is found.

The best way to protect workers is to keep the material from getting into the air, typically by using a wet method or process. If the asbestos or lead is wet, it cannot float in the air and thus cannot enter workers' lungs. For example, if materials contain lead or asbestos, the worker may wet the material using a spray bottle or mister to reduce or eliminate the possibility of inhalation.

Employees should never use compressed air to clean asbestos or lead particles because the resulting blast of air throws the contaminant into the air where it will float for a long time, often until someone inhales it.

Personal protective equipment, gloves and respirators with a HEPA filter provide protection as well. If there is a possibility of eye irritation, employees must wear the goggles and face shields (See Exhibit 4-2).

**Exhibit 4-2.
Respirators and goggles
can provide protection
from asbestos.**

After working with asbestos or lead, the employee should immediately wash his or her hands when finished with the procedure. Naturally, smoking should not be allowed in any area where these contaminants are used.

Medical Considerations

Before any work with asbestos began, the facility should have been monitored to determine if the level of asbestos exceeded the permissible exposure limit of 0.1 fibers per cubic centimeter. If a process has changed and more asbestos is possibly being released into the air through a particular process, contact the safety office to arrange for another evaluation.

If the company's work requires that workers be exposed beyond the PEL, they should alert their personal physicians so that the physicians can monitor them for possible asbestos-related problems.

If exposed to lead or asbestos on a routine basis beyond the PEL, workers also should contact the local safety office and enroll in a medical surveillance program.

Significant Changes in the Asbestos Standard

for General Industry, 29 CFR 1910.1001 (through June 29, 1995)

Topic	Change
PEL	The PEL has been reduced to 0.1 fibers/cc from 0.2 fibers/cc as a TWA. The Excursion Limit remains 1.0 fibers/cc averaged over 30 minutes.
PACM	Installed thermal system insulation and sprayed-on and troweled-on surfacing materials found in buildings constructed no later than 1980 are presumed to be asbestos-containing materials (greater than 1% asbestos). Asphalt and vinyl flooring material installed no later than 1980 also must be treated as asbestos-containing. These presumptions may be rebutted by specified inspection and testing.
Asbestos-containing flooring material	Sanding of asbestos-containing flooring material is prohibited. Specific procedures for floor care are mandated.
Brake/clutch repair	Employers must use specific controls and methods specified in Appendix F, unless another method is demonstrated to achieve equivalent results.
Duties of building owners (identification, recordkeeping, notification, signs and labels)	Building and facility owners must determine the presence, location, and quantity of ACM/PACM and keep records of asbestos-containing material and presumed asbestos-containing material. They must inform other employers, and their own employees who will perform housekeeping activities, of the presence and location of such materials. They must post signs at entrances to mechanical rooms/areas that contain ACM/PACM and that employees may enter. Previously installed ACM/PACM must be identified by labels or signs.
Asbestos awareness training	Employers must provide an asbestos awareness training course to employees who will perform housekeeping activities in an area containing ACM or PACM.
Medical surveillance	A pre-employment exam may not be used as a "recent exam" to fulfill any of the standard's medical surveillance requirements, unless the employer paid for the pre-employment exam.

Occupational Noise Exposure

It is estimated by OSHA that there are 2.9 million workers in U.S. production industries who experience eight-hour noise exposures in excess of 90 dBA (46 Fed. Reg. 4078). An additional 2.3 million experience exposure levels in excess of 85 dBA. The Hearing Conservation Amendment (HCA) applies to all 5.2 million employees except for those in oil and gas well drilling and service industries, which are specifically exempted. Additionally, the amendment does not apply to those engaged in construction and agriculture, although a construction industry noise standard exists (29 CFR 1926.52, 1926.101). This standard is identical to paragraphs (a) and (b) of the general industry noise standard (29 CFR 1910.95).

Prior to promulgation of the HCA, the existing noise standard (29 CFR 1910.95(a), (b)) established a permissible noise exposure level of 90 dBA for eight hours and required the employer to reduce exposure to that level by use of feasible engineering and administrative controls. In all cases in which sound levels exceeded the permissible exposure, regardless of the use of hearing-protective devices, "a continuing, effective hearing conservation program" was required. However, the details of such a program were never mandated. Paragraphs (c) through (p) of the HCA replaced paragraph (b)(3) of 29 CFR 1910.95 and supplemented OSHA's definition of an "effective hearing conservation program."

All employees whose noise exposures equal or exceed an eight-hour TWA of 85 dBA must be included in a hearing conservation program composed of five basic components:

- Exposure monitoring;
- Audiometric testing;
- Hearing protection;
- Employee training; and
- Recordkeeping.

Note that although the eight-hour TWA permissible exposure remains 90 dBA, a hearing conservation program becomes mandatory at an eight-hour TWA exposure of 85 dBA.

Monitoring

The HCA requires employers to monitor noise exposure levels in a manner that will accurately identify employees who are subjected to an eight-hour TWA exposure of 85 dBA or more. The exposure measurement must include all noise within an 80 to 130 dBA range. The requirement is performance oriented and allows employers to choose the monitoring method that best suits each situation.

Employees are entitled to observe monitoring procedures and they must be notified of the results of exposure monitoring. However, the method used to notify employees is left to the discretion of the employer.

Employers must re-monitor workers' exposures whenever changes in exposures are sufficient to require new hearing protectors or whenever employees not previously included in the program because they were not exposed to an eight-hour TWA of 85 dBA are included in the program.

Instruments used for monitoring employee exposures must be calibrated to ensure the measurements are accurate. Since calibration procedures are unique to specific instruments, employers should follow the manufacturer's instructions to determine when and how extensively to calibrate.

Audiometric Testing Program

Audiometric testing not only monitors employee hearing acuity over time but also provides an opportunity for employers to educate employees about their hearing and the need to protect it. The audiometric testing program includes obtaining baseline audiograms and annual audiograms and initiating training and follow-up procedures. The audiometric testing program should indicate whether hearing loss is being prevented by the employer's hearing conservation program. Audiometric testing must be made available to all employees who have an average exposure level of 85 dBA. The program shall be provided at no cost to employees

A professional (e.g., audiologist, otolaryngologist, physician) must be responsible for the program, but he or she does not have to be present when a qualified technician is actually conducting the testing. Professional responsibilities include overseeing the program and the work of the technicians, reviewing problem audiograms and determining whether referral is necessary. Either a professional or a trained technician may conduct audiometric testing.

In addition to administering audiometric tests, the tester (or the supervising professional) is also responsible for:

- Ensuring the tests are conducted in an appropriate test environment;
- Seeing that the audiometer works properly;
- Reviewing audiograms for standard threshold shifts (as defined in the HCA); and
- Identifying audiograms that require further evaluation by a professional.

Baseline and Annual Audiograms

There are two types of audiograms required in the hearing conservation program: baseline and annual audiograms. The baseline audiogram is the reference audiogram against which future audiograms are compared. Baseline audiograms must be provided within six months of an employee's first exposure at or above a TWA of 85 dBA.

Testing to establish a baseline audiogram shall be preceded by at least 14 hours without exposure to workplace noise. Hearing protectors may be used as a substitute for this requirement.

Employees shall be notified regarding the need to avoid high levels of nonoccupational noise exposure during the 14-hour period immediately preceding the audiometric examination.

Table 4-1. How Loud Is It?

Typical A-Weighted Sound Levels
(dB, re: 20 micropascals)

150	Loud rock concert
140	Fire arms and air raid sirens
130	Jack hammer
120	Jet plane take-off, car stereo, bands
110	Discotheque
106	Timpani and bass drum rolls
100	Snowmobiles, chain saws, pneumatics
90	Lawnmower, subway noise
70	Vacuum cleaner at 3 meters
60	Conversation at 1 meter
50	Urban Residence
30	North Rim of Grand Canyon
0	Threshold of Hearing (1000 Hz)

When employers obtain audiograms in mobile test vans, baseline audiograms must be completed within one year after an employee's first exposure to workplace noise at or above an average of 85 dBA. Additionally, when mobile vans are used and employers are allowed to delay baseline testing for up to one year, those employees exposed to levels of 85 dBA or more must be issued and fitted with hearing protectors six months after initial exposure. The hearing protectors are to be worn until the baseline audiogram is obtained. Baseline audiograms taken before the effective date of the amendment are acceptable as baselines in the program if the professional supervisor determines that the audiogram is valid. The annual audiogram must be conducted within one year of the baseline. It is important to test hearing on an annual basis to identify changes in hearing acuity so that protective follow-up measures can be initiated before hearing loss progresses.

Evaluation of Audiograms

Annual audiograms must be routinely compared to baseline audiograms to determine whether the audiogram is accurate and whether the employee has lost hearing ability (i.e., to determine whether a standard threshold shift (STS) has occurred). An effective program depends on a uniform definition of an STS. An STS is defined in the amendment as an average shift (or loss) in either ear of 10 dB or more at the 2,000, 3,000, and 4,000 Hertz (Hz) frequencies. A method of determining an STS by computing an average was chosen because it diminishes the number of persons identified as having an STS who are later shown not to have had a significant change in hearing ability.

If an STS is identified, the employee must be fitted or refitted with adequate hearing protectors, instructed in how to use them and required to wear them. In addition, employees must be notified in writing within 21 days from the time the determination is made that their audiometric test results indicate an STS. Some employees with an STS may need to be referred for further testing if the professional determines that their test results are questionable or if they have an ear problem of a medical nature caused or aggravated by wearing hearing protectors. If the suspected medical problem is not thought to be related to wearing protectors, employees must merely be informed that they should see a physician. If subsequent audiometric tests show that the STS identified on a previous audiogram is not persistent, employees exposed to an average level of 90 dBA may discontinue wearing hearing protectors.

A subsequent audiogram may be substituted for the original baseline audiogram if the professional supervising the program determines that the employee has experienced a persistent STS. The substituted audiogram becomes known as the revised baseline audiogram. This substitution will ensure that the same shift is not repeatedly identified. The professional may also need the baseline audiogram after an improvement in hearing has occurred, which will ensure that the baseline reflects actual thresholds as much as possible. When a baseline audiogram is revised, the employer must also retain the original audiogram.

Audiometric Test Requirements

Audiometric tests shall be pure tones, air conduction and hearing threshold examinations, with test frequencies including, at a minimum, 500, 1000, 2000, 3000, 4000, and 6000 Hz. Tests at each frequency shall be taken separately for each ear.

To obtain valid audiograms, audiometers must be used, maintained and calibrated according to the specifications detailed in appendices C and E of the standard.

Hearing Protectors

Hearing protectors must be made available to all workers exposed to an eight-hour TWA of 85 dBA or more at no cost to the employees. This requirement will ensure that employees have access to protectors before they experience a loss in hearing. When baseline audiograms are delayed because it is inconvenient for mobile test vans to visit the workplace more than once a year, protectors must be worn by employees for any period exceeding six months from the time they are first exposed to eight-hour average noise levels of 85 dBA or more until their baseline audiograms are obtained. The use of hearing protectors is also mandatory for em-

Exhibit 4-3.
Employees must be able to select from a variety of hearing protectors. Here, a popular choice is shown.

ployees who have experienced STSs, since these workers are particularly susceptible to noise.

With the help of a person who is trained in fitting hearing protectors, employees shall be given the opportunity to select their hearing protectors from a suitable variety provided by the employer. The protector selected should be comfortable to wear and offer sufficient attenuation to prevent hearing loss. Employees must be shown how to use and care for their protectors; they also must be supervised on the job to ensure that they continue to wear them correctly. Hearing protectors shall be replaced as necessary.

Hearing protectors must provide adequate attenuation in each employee's work environment. The employer must reevaluate the suitability of the employee's present protector whenever there is a change in working conditions that may render the hearing protector inadequate. If workplace noise levels increase, employees must be given more effective protectors. The protector must reduce the level of exposure to at least 90 dBA or 85 dBA when an STS has occurred. A variety of hearing protection is available, ranging from earplugs to ear bands to earmuffs. Some even have radios attached so

Exhibit 4-4.
Headphones with a radio attached to allow worker communication as well as hearing protection.

that workers can communicate in loud environments (See Exhibit 4-4.).

Training

Employee training is important because when workers understand the hearing conservation programs requirements and why it is necessary to protect their hearing, they will be better motivated to actively participate in the program. Employees will be more willing to cooperate by wearing their protectors and by undergoing audiometric tests. Employees exposed to

TWAs of 85 dBA or more must undergo at least annual training in the following:

- Effects of noise;
- Purpose, advantages, disadvantages and attenuation characteristics of various types of hearing protectors;
- Selection, fitting and care of protectors; and
- Purposes and procedures of audiometric testing.

Training does not have to be accomplished in one session. The program may be structured in any format and different parts may be conducted by different individuals as long as the required topics are covered. For example, audiometric procedures could be discussed immediately prior to audiometric testing. The training requirements are such that employees must be reminded on an annual basis that noise is hazardous to hearing and that they can prevent damage by wearing hearing protectors, when appropriate, and by participating in audiometric testing.

Recordkeeping

Noise exposure measurement records must be kept for two years. Records of audiometric test results must be maintained for the duration of the affected employee's employment. Audiometric test records must include the name and job classification of the employee, the date the test was performed, the examiner's name, the date of acoustic or exhaustive calibration, measurements of the background sound pressure levels in audiometric test rooms and the employee's most recent noise exposure measurement. All records required by this section shall be provided upon request to employees, former employees, representatives designated by the individual employee and OSHA.

The effectiveness of a hearing conservation program depends on the cooperation of employers, supervisors, employees and others concerned. Management's responsibility in this type of program includes:

- Taking noise measurements;
- Initiating noise-control measures;
- Undertaking the audiometric testing of employees;
- Providing hearing-protective equipment where it is required;

- Enforcing the use of such protective equipment with sound policies and by example;
- Informing employees of the benefits to be derived from a hearing conservation program; and
- Providing annual training.

OSHA also requires employers to make available to affected employees or their representatives copies of the OSHA noise standard and post a copy in the workplace.

It is the employee's responsibility to make proper use of the protective equipment provided by management. It is also the employee's responsibility to observe any rules or regulations in the use of equipment designed to minimize noise exposure.

Detailed references to noise, its management, effects, and control can be found in a great many books and periodicals. For those employers needing assistance in establishing hearing conservation programs, consultation services are available in a number of professional areas through private consultation, insurance, and governmental groups.

Hearing Conservation Glossary

Acoustic trauma. A hearing injury produced by exposure to sudden intense acoustic energy, such as from blasts and explosions, or from direct trauma to the head or ear. It should be thought of as one single incident relating to the onset of hearing loss.

Air conduction. The process by which sound is conducted to the inner ear through the air in the outer ear canal using the tympanic membrane (eardrum) and the ossicles as part of the pathway.

Airborne gap. The difference in decibels between the hearing levels for sound at a particular frequency as determined by air conduction and bone conduction threshold measurements.

Airborne sound. Sound transmitted through air as a medium.

Audible. Capable of being heard.

Audible range. The frequency range over which normal ears hear (approximately 20 Hz through 20,000 Hz).

Audiogram. A chart or table relating hearing level (for pure tones) to frequency. Referred to in OSHA standards as a "pure tone, air conduction, hearing threshold examination."

Audiologist. A person trained in the specialized problems of hearing and deafness.

Audiometer, pure tone. An electro-acoustical generator that provides pure tones of selected frequencies and of calibrated output for the purpose of determining an individual's threshold of audibility. OSHA's standard requires testing at frequencies including as a minimum 500, 1000, 2000, 3000, 4000 and 6000 Hz.

Audiometric reference level. That sound pressure level (ASA, ISO, or ANSI) to which the audiometer is calibrated. A declared value, at a particular frequency, of the threshold of hearing for normal persons within a given age range, normally 18 to 25 years.

Bone conduction. The process by which sound is conducted to the inner ear through the cranial bones.

Cycle per second (cps). A unit of frequency. The preferred terminology is hertz, abbreviated Hz.

Decibel (dB). A nondimensional unit used to express sound levels. It is a logarithmic expression of the ratio of a measured quantity to a reference quantity. In audiometry, a level of zero decibels roughly represents the weakest sound that can be heard by a person with good hearing.

Where a weighted network filter is employed in making sound pressure measurements, this is indicated by a suffix added to the unit symbol. For example, a sound-level reading in decibels made on the A-weighted network of a sound level meter is designated as "dBA."

Dosimeter. A device worn on the person for determining the accumulated sound exposure with regard to level and time.

Eustachian tube. A tube approximately 2½ in. long leading from the back of the throat to the middle ear. It equalizes the pressure of air in the middle ear with that outside the eardrum.

Hearing conservation. The prevention or minimization of noise-induced hearing loss through the use of hearing protection devices and the control of noise through engineering methods or administrative procedures.

Hearing loss. An increase in the threshold of audibility, at specific frequencies, as the result of normal aging, disease or injury to the hearing organs.

Hearing threshold level (HTL). Amount (in decibels) by which the threshold of audibility for that ear exceeds a standard audiometric threshold.

Hertz (Hz). Synonymous term for cycles per second. It is the preferred unit of frequency.

Kilohertz (kHz). 1000 Hz

Meniere's Disease. The combination of deafness, tinnitus, nausea and vertigo.

Noise-induced hearing loss. Usually restricted to mean the slowly progressive inner ear hearing loss that results from exposure to noise over a long period of time as contrasted to acoustic trauma or physical injury to the ear.

Ossicles. Any one of the small bones (i.e., malleus, incus, stapes) that forms a chain for the transmission of sound from the tympanic membrane to the oval window.

Otolaryngologist. A physician or surgeon specializing in the practice of otology (ear disease), rhinology (nose disease) and laryngology (throat and larynx diseases).

Otologist. A physician or surgeon who specializes in the diagnosis and treatment of the disorders and diseases of the ear.

Presbycusis. Decline in hearing acuity that normally occurs as part of the aging process.

Standard threshold shift (STS). Defined in OSHA's hearing conservation regulation as an average shift (or loss) in either ear of 10 dB or more at the 2,000, 3,000, and 4,000 Hertz (Hz) frequencies.

Temporary threshold shift (TTS). The component of threshold shift which shows progressive reduction with the passage of time when the apparent cause has been removed.

Threshold of hearing of a continuous sound. The value of the sound pressure that excites the sensation of hearing.

Threshold of pain for a specified signal. The minimum effective sound pressure level of that signal, which in a specified fraction of the trials, will stimulate the ear to a point at which there is a sensation of pain that is distinct from a feeling of discomfort (usually above 120 dBA).

Tinnitus. A subjective sense of noises in the head or ringing in the ears for which there is no observable external cause.

2008 Subpart G 1910.94-98
Occupational Health

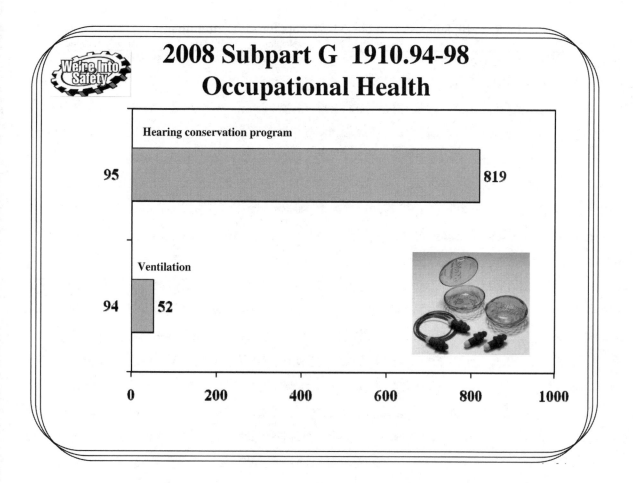

Hearing conservation program

95 ┤ 819

Ventilation

94 ┤ 52

0   200   400   600   800   1000

29 C.F.R. 1910, Subpart Z, Table Z-1—Limits for Air Contaminants

Substance	CAS No. (c)	ppm (a)[1]	mg/m³ (b)[1]	Skin designation
Acetaldehyde	75-07-0	200	360	
Acetic acid	64-19-7	10	25	
Acetic anhydride	108-24-7	5	20	
Acetone	67-64-1	1000	2400	
Acetonitrile	75-05-8	40	70	
2-Acetylaminofluorine; see 1910.1014.	53-96-3			
Acetylene dichloride; see 1,2-Dichloroethylene.				
Acetylene tetrabromide	79-27-6	1	14	
Acrolein	107-02-8	0.1	0.25	
Acrylamide	79-06-1	....	0.3	X
Acrylonitrile; see 1910.1045.	107-13-1			
Aldrin	309-00-2	....	0.25	X
Allyl alcohol	107-18-6	2	5	X
Allyl chloride	107-05-1	1	3	
Allyl glycidyl ether (AGE)	106-92-3	(C)10	(C)45	
Allyl propyl disulfide	2179-59-1	2	12	
Alpha-Alumina	1344-28-1			
Total dust		....	15	
Respirable fraction			5	
Aluminum, metal (as Al)	7429-90-5			
Total dust			15	
Respirable fraction		....	5	
4-Aminodiphenyl; see 1910.1011	92-67-1			
2-Aminoethanol; see Ethanolamine.				
2-Aminopyridine	504-29-0	0.5	2	
Ammonia	7664-41-7	50	35	
Ammonium sulfamate	7773-06-0			
Total dust		....	15	
Respirable fraction		....	5	
n-Amyl acetate	628-63-7	100	525	
sec-Amyl acetate	626-38-0	125	650	
Aniline and homologs	62-53-3	5	19	X
Anisidine (o-, p-isomers)	29191-52-4	....	0.5	X
Antimony and compounds (as Sb)	7440-36-0		0.5	
ANTU (alpha Naphthylthiourea)	86-88-4		0.3	
Arsenic, inorganic compounds (as As); see 1910.1018.	7440-38-2			
Arsenic, organic compounds (as As)	7440-38-2		0.5	
Arsine	7784-42-1	0.05	0.2	
Asbestos; see 1910.1001.	(4)			
Azinphos-methyl	86-50-0	....	0.2	X
Barium, soluble compounds (as Ba)	7440-39-3		0.5	
Barium sulfate	7727-43-7			
Total dust		....	15	
Respirable fraction			5	
Benomyl	17804-35-2			
Total dust		....	15	
Respirable fraction		....	5	
Benzene; see 1910.1028.	71-43-2			
See Table Z-2 for the limits applicable in the operations or sectors excluded in 1910.1028d				
Benzidine; see 1910.1010.	92-87-5			
p-Benzoquinone; see Quinone.				
Benzo(a)pyrene; see Coal tar pitch volatiles.				
Benzoyl peroxide	94-36-0	....	5	
Benzyl chloride	100-44-7	1	5	
Beryllium and beryllium compounds (as Be)	7440-41-7		(2)	
Biphenyl; see Diphenyl.				
Bismuth telluride, Undoped	1304-82-1			
Total dust		....	15	
Respirable fraction		....	5	
Boron oxide	1303-86-2			
Total dust		....	15	
Boron trifluoride	7637-07-2	(C)1	(C)3	
Bromine	7726-95-6	0.1	0.7	
Bromoform	75-25-2	0.5	5	X
			1 ppm/5	
Butadiene (1,3-Butadiene);See 29 CFR 1910.1051; 29 CFR 1910.19(l).	106-99-0	ppm STEL		
Butanethiol; see Butyl mercaptan.				
2-Butanone (Methyl ethyl ketone)	78-93-3	200	590	
2-Butoxyethanol	111-76-2	50	240	X

29 C.F.R. 1910, Subpart Z, Table Z-1—Limits for Air Contaminants (Continued)

Substance	CAS No. (c)	ppm (a)[1]	mg/m³ (b)[1]	Skin designation
n-Butyl-acetate	123-86-4	150	710	
sec-Butyl acetate	105-46-4	200	950	
tert-Butyl acetate	540-88-5	200	950	
n-Butyl alcohol	71-36-3	100	300	
sec-Butyl alcohol	78-92-2	150	450	
tert-Butyl alcohol	75-65-0	100	300	
Butylamine	109-73-9	(C)5	(C)15	X
tert-Butyl chromate (as CrO₃); see 1910.1026[6]	1189-85-1	....		
n-Butyl glycidyl ether (BGE)	2426-08-6	50	270	
Butyl mercaptan	109-79-5	10	35	
p-tert-Butyltoluene	98-51-1	10	60	
Cadmium (as Cd); see 1910.1027	7440-43-9			
Calcium carbonate	1317-65-3			
Total dust		....	15	
Respirable fraction		....	5	
Calcium hydroxide	1305-62-0			
Total dust		....	15	
Respirable fraction		....	5	
Calcium oxide	1305-78-8		5	
Calcium silicate	1344-95-2			
Total dust		....	15	
Respirable fraction		....	5	
Calcium sulfate	7778-18-9			
Total dust		....	15	
Respirable fraction		....	5	
Camphor, synthetic	76-22-2		2	
Carbaryl (Sevin)	63-25-2		5	
Carbon black	1333-86-4		3.5	
Carbon dioxide	124-38-9	5000	9000	
Carbon disulfide	75-15-0		(2)	
Carbon monoxide	630-08-0	50	55	
Carbon tetrachloride	56-23-5		(2)	
Cellulose	9004-34-6			
Total dust		....	15	
Respirable fraction		....	5	
Chlordane	57-74-9		0.5	X
Chlorinated camphene	8001-35-2		0.5	X
Chlorinated diphenyl oxide	55720-99-5		0.5	
Chlorine	7782-50-5	(C)1	(C)3	
Chlorine dioxide	10049-04-4	0.1	0.3	
Chlorine trifluoride	7790-91-2	(C)0.1	(C)0.4	
Chloroacetaldehyde	107-20-0	(C)1	(C)3	
a-Chloroacetophenone (Phenacyl chloride)	532-27-4	0.05	0.3	
Chlorobenzene	108-90-7	75	350	
o-Chlorobenzylidene malononitrile	2698-41-1	0.05	0.4	
Chlorobromomethane	74-97-5	200	1050	
2-Chloro-1,3-butadiene; see beta-Chloroprane				
Chlorodiphenyl (42% Chlorine) (PCB)	53469-21-9	....	1	X
Chlorodiphenyl (54% Chlorine) (PCB)	11097-69-1	....	0.5	X
1-Chloro-2,3-epoxypropane; see Epichlorohydrin				
2-Chloroethanol; see Ethylene chlorohydrin				
Chloroethylene; see Vinyl chloride				
Chloroform (Trichloromethane)	67-66-3	(C)50	(C)240	
bis(Chloromethyl) ether; see 1910.1008	542-88-1			
Chloromethyl methyl ether; see 1910.1006	107-30-2			
1-Chloro-1-nitropropane	600-25-9	20	100	
Chloropicrin	76-06-2	0.1	0.7	
beta-Chloroprene	126-99-8	25	90	X
2-Chloro-6-(trichloromethyl) pyridine	1929-82-4			
Total dust		....	15	
Respirable fraction		....	5	
Chromium (II) compounds. (as Cr)	7440-47-3	....	0.5	
Chromium (III) compounds. (as Cr)	7440-47-3	....	0.5	
Chromium (VI) compounds; see 1910.1026[5]		....		
Chromium metal and insol. salts (as Cr)	7440-47-3	....	1	
Chrysene; see Coal tar pitch volatiles				
Clopidol	2971-90-6			
Total dust		....	15	
Respirable fraction		....	5	

29 C.F.R. 1910, Subpart Z, Table Z-1—Limits for Air Contaminants (Continued)

Substance	CAS No. (c)	ppm (a)[1]	mg/m³ (b)[1]	Skin designation
Coal dust (less than 5% SiO₂), respirable fraction			(3)	
Coal dust (greater than or equal to 5% SiO₂), respirable fraction			(3)	
Coal tar pitch volatiles (benzene soluble fraction), anthracene, BaP, phenanthrene, acridine, chrysene, pyrene	65966-93-2	....	0.2	
Cobalt metal, dust, and fume (as Co)	7440-48-4		0.1	
Coke oven emissions; see 1910.1029.				
Copper	7440-50-8			
Fume (as Cu)		....	0.1	
Dusts and mists (as Cu)		....	1	
Cotton dustᵉ; see 1910.1043.		....	1	
Crag herbicide (Sesone)	136-78-7			
Total dust		....	15	
Respirable fraction		....	5	
Cresol, all isomers	1319-77-3	5	22	X
Crotonaldehyde	123-73-9; 4170-30-3	2	6	
Cumene	98-82-8	50	245	X
Cyanides (as CN)	(4)	....	5	X
Cyclohexane	110-82-7	300	1050	
Cyclohexanol	108-93-0	50	200	
Cyclohexanone	108-94-1	50	200	
Cyclohexene	110-83-8	300	1015	
Cyclopentadiene	542-92-7	75	200	
2,4-D (Dichlorophenoxyacelic acid)	94-75-7	....	10	
Decaborane	17702-41-9	0.05	0.3	X
Demeton (Systox)	8065-48-3	....	0.1	X
Diacetone alcohol (4-Hydroxy-4 methyl-2-pentanone)	123-42-2	50	240	
1,2-Diaminoethane; see Ethylenediamine.				
Diazomethane	334-88-3	0.2	0.4	
Diborane	19287-45-7	0.1	0.1	
1,2-Dibromo-3-chloropropane (DBCP); see 1910.1044.	96-12-8			
1,2-Dibromoethane; see Ethylene dibromide.				
Dibutyl phosphate	107-66-4	1	5	
Dibutyl phthalate	84-74-2	....	5	
o-Dichlorobenzene	95-50-1	(C)50	(C)300	
p-Dichlorobenzene	106-46-7	75	450	
3,-Dichlorobenzidine; see 1910.1007.	91-94-1			
Dichlorodifluoromethane	75-71-8	1000	4950	
1,3-Dichloro-5,5-dimethyl hydantoin	118-52-5	....	0.2	
Dichlorodiphenyltrichloroethane (DDT)	50-29-3	....	1	X
1,1 Dichloroethane	75-34-3	100	400	
1,2-Dichloroethane; see Ethylene dichloride.				
1,2-Dichloroethylene	540-59-0	200	790	
Dichloroethyl ether	111-44-4	(C)15	(C)90	X
Dichloromethane; see Methylene chloride.				
Dichloromonofluoromethane	75-43-4	1000	4200	
1,1-Dichloro-1-nitroethane	594-72-9	(C)10	(C)60	
1,2-Dichloropropane; see Propylene dichloride.				
Dichlorotetrafluoroethane	76-14-2	1000	7000	
Dichlorvos (DDVP)	62-73-7	....	1	X
Dicyclopentadienyl iron	102-54-5			
Total dust		....	15	
Respirable fraction		....	5	
Dieldrin	60-57-1	....	0.25	X
Diethylamine	109-89-7	25	75	
2-Diethylaminoethanol	100-37-8	10	50	
Diethyl ether; see Ethyl ether.				
Difluorodibromomethane	75-61-6	100	860	
Diglycidyl ether (DGE)	2238-07-5	(C)0.5	(C)2.8	
Dihydroxybenzene; see Hydroquinone.				
Diisobutyl ketone	108-83-8	50	290	
Diisopropylamine	108-18-9	5	20	X
4-Dimethylaminoazobenzene; see 1910.1015.	60-11-7			
Dimethoxymethane; see Methylal.				
Dimethyl acetamide	127-19-5	10	35	X
Dimethylamine	124-40-3	10	18	
Dimethylaminobenzene; see Xylidine.				
Dimethylaniline (N,N-Dimethylaniline)	121-69-7	5	25	X
Dimethylbenzene; see Xylene.				

29 C.F.R. 1910, Subpart Z, Table Z-1—Limits for Air Contaminants (Continued)

Substance	CAS No. (c)	ppm (a)[1]	mg/m³ (b)[1]	Skin designation
Dimethyl-1,2-dibromo-2,2-dichloroethyl phosphate	300-76-5	....	3	
Dimethylformamide	68-12-2	10	30	X
2,6-Dimethyl-4-heptanone; see Diisobutyl ketone.				
1,1-Dimethylhydrazine	57-14-7	0.5	1	X
Dimethylphthalate	131-11-3	....	5	
Dimethyl sulfate	77-78-1	1	5	X
Dinitrobenzene (all isomers)			1	X
(ortho)	528-29-0			
(meta)	99-65-0			
(para)	100-25-4			
Dinitro-o-cresol	534-52-1	....	0.2	X
Dinitrotoluene	25321-14-6	....	1.5	X
Dioxane (Diethylene dioxide)	123-91-1	100	360	X
Diphenyl (Biphenyl)	92-52-4	0.2	1	
Diphenylmethane diisocyanate; see Methylene bisphenyl isocyanate.				
Dipropylene glycol methyl ether	34590-94-8	100	600	X
Di-sec octyl phthalate (Di-(2-ethylhexyl) phthalate)	117-81-7	....	5	
Emery	12415-34-8			
Total dust		....	15	
Respirable fraction			5	
Endrin	72-20-8	....	0.1	X
Epichlorohydrin	106-89-8	5	19	X
EPN	2104-64-5	....	0.5	X
1,2-Epoxypropane; see Propylene oxide.				
2,3-Epoxy-1-propanol; see Glycidol.				
Ethanethiol; see Ethyl mercaptan.				
Ethanolamine	141-43-5	3	6	
2-Ethoxyethanol (Cellosolve)	110-80-5	200	740	X
2-Ethoxyethyl acetate (Cellosolve acetate)	111-15-9	100	540	X
Ethyl acetate	141-78-6	400	1400	
Ethyl acrylate	140-88-5	25	100	X
Ethyl alcohol (Ethanol)	64-17-5	1000	1900	
Ethylamine	75-04-7	10	18	
Ethyl amyl ketone (5-Methyl-3-heptanone)	541-85-5	25	130	
Ethyl benzene	100-41-4	100	435	
Ethyl bromide	74-96-4	200	890	
Ethyl butyl ketone (3-Heptanone)	106-35-4	50	230	
Ethyl chloride	75-00-3	1000	2600	
Ethyl ether	60-29-7	400	1200	
Ethyl formate	109-94-4	100	300	
Ethyl mercaptan	75-08-1	(C)10	(C)25	
Ethyl silicate	78-10-4	100	850	
Ethylene chlorohydrin	107-07-3	5	16	X
Ethylenediamine	107-15-3	10	25	
Ethylene dibromide	106-93-4		(2)	
Ethylene dichloride (1,2-Dichloroethane)	107-06-2		(2)	
Ethylene glycol dinitrate	628-96-6	(C)0.2	(C)1	X
Ethylene glycol methyl acetate; see Methyl cellosolve acetate.				
Ethyleneimine; see 1910.1012	151-56-4			
Ethylene oxide; see 1910.1047.	75-21-8			
Ethylidene chloride; see 1,1-Dichloroethane.				
N-Ethylmorpholine	100-74-3	20	94	X
Ferbam	14484-64-1			
Total dust		....	15	
Ferrovanadium dust	12604-58-9	....	1	
Fluorides (as F)	(4)	....	2.5	
Fluorine	7782-41-4	0.1	0.2	
Fluorotrichloromethane (Trichlorofluoromethane)	75-69-4	1000	5600	
Formaldehyde; see 1910.1048	50-00-0			
Formic acid	64-18-6	5	9	
Furfural	98-01-1	5	20	X
Furfuryl alcohol	98-00-0	50	200	
Grain dust (oat, wheat, barley)		....	10	
Glycerin (mist)	56-81-5			
Total dust		....	15	
Respirable fraction		....	5	
Glycidol	556-52-5	50	150	
Glycol monoethyl ether; see 2-Ethoxyethanol.				
Graphite, natural, respirable dust	7782-42-5		(3)	

29 C.F.R. 1910, Subpart Z, Table Z-1—Limits for Air Contaminants (Continued)

Substance	CAS No. (c)	ppm (a)[1]	mg/m³ (b)[1]	Skin designation
Graphite, synthetic				
Total dust		....	15	
Respirable fraction		....	5	
Guthion; see Azinphos methyl.				
Gypsum	13397-24-5			
Total dust		....	15	
Respirable fraction		....	5	
Hafnium	7440-58-6	....	0.5	
Heptachlor	76-44-8	....	0.5	X
Heptane (n-Heptane)	142-82-5	500	2000	
Hexachloroethane	67-72-1	1	10	X
Hexachloronaphthalene	1335-87-1	....	0.2	X
n-Hexane	110-54-3	500	1800	
2-Hexanone (Methyl n-butyl ketone)	591-78-6	100	410	
Hexone (Methyl isobutyl ketone)	108-10-1	100	410	
sec-Hexyl acetate	108-84-9	50	300	
Hydrazine	302-01-2	1	1.3	X
Hydrogen bromide	10035-10-6	3	10	
Hydrogen chloride	7647-01-0	(C)5	(C)7	
Hydrogen cyanide	74-90-8	10	11	X
Hydrogen fluoride (as F)	7664-39-3		(2)	
Hydrogen peroxide	7722-84-1	1	1.4	
Hydrogen selenide (as Se)	7783-07-5	0.05	0.2	
Hydrogen sulfide	7783-06-4		(2)	
Hydroquinone	123-31-9	....	2	
Iodine	7553-56-2	(C)0.1	(C)1	
Iron oxide fume	1309-37-1	....	10	
Isoamyl acetate	123-92-2	100	525	
Isoamyl alcohol (primary and secondary)	123-51-3	100	360	
Isobutyl acetate	110-19-0	150	700	
Isobutyl alcohol	78-83-1	100	300	
Isophorone	78-59-1	25	140	
Isopropyl acetate	108-21-4	250	950	
Isopropyl alcohol	67-63-0	400	980	
Isopropylamine	75-31-0	5	12	
Isopropyl ether	108-20-3	500	2100	
Isopropyl glycidyl ether (IGE)	4016-14-2	50	240	
Kaolin	1332-58-7			
Total dust		....	15	
Respirable fraction		....	5	
Ketene	463-51-4	0.5	0.9	
Lead, inorganic (as Pb); see 1910.1025.	7439-92-1			
Limestone	1317-65-3			
Total dust		....	15	
Respirable fraction		....	5	
Lindane	58-89-9	....	0.5	X
Lithium hydride	7580-67-8	....	0.025	
L.P.G. (Liquefied petroleum gas)	68476-85-7	1000	1800	
Magnesite	546-93-0			
Total dust		....	15	
Respirable fraction		....	5	
Magnesium oxide fume	1309-48-4			
Total particulate		....	15	
Malathion	121-75-5			
Total dust		....	15	X
Maleic anhydride	108-31-6	0.25	1	
Manganese compounds (as Mn)	7439-96-5	....	(C)5	
Manganese fume (as Mn)	7439-96-5	....	(C)5	
Marble	1317-65-3			
Total dust		....	15	
Respirable fraction		....	5	
Mercury (aryl and inorganic) (as Hg)	7439-97-6		(2)	
Mercury (organo) alkyl compounds (as Hg)	7439-97-6		(2)	
Mercury (vapor) (as Hg)	7439-97-6		(2)	
Mesityl oxide	141-79-7	25	100	
Methanethiol; see Methyl mercaptan.				
Methoxychlor	72-43-5			
Total dust		....	15	
2-Methoxyethanol (Methyl cellosolve)	109-86-4	25	80	X

29 C.F.R. 1910, Subpart Z, Table Z-1—Limits for Air Contaminants (Continued)

Substance	CAS No. (c)	ppm (a)[1]	mg/m³ (b)[1]	Skin designation
2-Methoxyethyl acetate (Methyl cellosolve acetate)	110-49-6	25	120	X
Methyl acetate	79-20-9	200	610	
Methyl acetylene (Propyne)	74-99-7	1000	1650	
Methyl acetylene-propadiene mixture (MAPP)		1000	1800	
Methyl acrylate	96-33-3	10	35	X
Methylal (Dimethoxy-methane)	109-87-5	1000	3100	
Methyl alcohol	67-56-1	200	260	
Methylamine	74-89-5	10	12	
Methyl amyl alcohol; see Methyl isobutyl carbinol.				
Methyl n-amyl ketone	110-43-0	100	465	
Methyl bromide	74-83-9	(C)20	(C)80	X
Methyl butyl ketone; see 2-Hexanone.				
Methyl cellosolve; see 2-Methoxyethanol.				
Methyl cellosolve acetate; see 2-Methoxyethyl acetate.				
Methyl chloride	74-87-3		(2)	
Methyl chloroform (1,1,1-Trichloroethane)	71-55-6	350	1900	
Methylcyclohexane	108-87-2	500	2000	
Methylcyclohexanol	25639-42-3	100	470	
o-Methylcyclohexanone	583-60-8	100	460	X
Methylene chloride	75-09-2		(2)	
Methyl ethyl ketone (MEK); see 2-Butanone.				
Methyl formate	107-31-3	100	250	
Methyl hydrazine (Monomethyl hydrazine)	60-34-4	(C)0.2	(C)0.35	X
Methyl iodide	74-88-4	5	28	X
Methyl isoamyl ketone	110-12-3	100	475	
Methyl isobutyl carbinol	108-11-2	25	100	X
Methyl isobutyl ketone; see Hexone.				
Methyl isocyanate	624-83-9	0.02	0.05	X
Methyl mercaptan	74-93-1	(C)10	(C)20	
Methyl methacrylate	80-62-6	100	410	
Methyl propyl ketone; see 2-Pentanone.				
alpha-Methyl styrene	98-83-9	(C)100	(C)480	
Methylene blsphenyl isocyanate (MDI)	101-68-8	(C)0.02	(C)0.2	
Mica; see Silicates.				
Molybdenum (as Mo)	7439-98-7			
Soluble compounds			5	
Insoluble compounds.				
Total dust			15	
Monomethyl aniline	100-61-8	2	9	X
Monomethyl hydrazine; see Methyl hydrazine.				
Morpholine	110-91-8	20	70	X
Naphtha (Coal tar)	8030-30-6	100	400	
Naphthalene	91-20-3	10	50	
alpha-Naphthylamine; see 1910.1004.	134-32-7			
beta-Naphthylamine; see 1910.1009.	91-59-8			
Nickel carbonyl (as Ni)	13463-39-3	0.001	0.007	
Nickel, metal and insoluble compounds (as Ni)	7440-02-0		1	
Nickel, soluble compounds (as Ni)	7440-02-0		1	
Nicotine	54-11-5		0.5	X
Nitric acid	7697-37-2	2	5	
Nitric oxide	10102-43-9	25	30	
p-Nitroaniline	100-01-6	1	6	X
Nitrobenzene	98-95-3	1	5	X
p-Nitrochlorobenzene	100-00-5		1	X
4-Nitrodiphenyl; see 1910.1003.	92-93-3			
Nitroethane	79-24-3	100	310	
Nitrogen dioxide	10102-44-0	(C)5	(C)9	
Nitrogen trifluoride	7783-54-2	10	29	
Nitroglycerin	55-63-0	(C)0.2	(C)2	X
Nitromethane	75-52-5	100	250	
1-Nitropropane	108-03-2	25	90	
2-Nitropropane	79-46-9	25	90	
N-Nitrosodimethylamine; see 1910.1016.				
Nitrotoluene (all isomers)		5	30	X
o-isomer	88-72-2			
m-isomer	99-08-1			
p-isomer	99-99-0			
Nitrotrichloromethane; see Chloropicrin.				
Oclachloronaphthalene	2234-13-1		0.1	X

29 C.F.R. 1910, Subpart Z, Table Z-1—Limits for Air Contaminants (Continued)

Substance	CAS No. (c)	ppm (a)[1]	mg/m³ (b)[1]	Skin designation
Octane	111-65-9	500	2350	
Oil mist, mineral	8012-95-1	....	5	
Osmium tetroxide (as Os)	20816-12-0	....	0.002	
Oxalic acid	144-62-7	....	1	
Oxygen difluoride	7783-41-7	0.05	0.1	
Ozone	10028-15-6	0.1	0.2	
Paraquat, respirable dust	4685-14-7;	....	0.5	X
	1910-42-5;			
	2074-50-2			
Parathion	56-38-2	....	0.1	X
Particulates not otherwise regulated (PNOR)[f].				
Total dust		....	15	
Respirable fraction		....	5	
PCB; see Chlorodiphenyl (42% and 54% chlorine).				
Pentaborane	19624-22-7	0.005	0.01	
Pentachloronaphthalene	1321-64-8		0.5	X
Pentachlorophenol	87-86-5		0.5	X
Pentaerythritol	115-77-5			
Total dust		....	15	
Respirable fraction		....	5	
Pentane	109-66-0	1000	2950	
2-Pentanone (Methyl propyl ketone)	107-87-9	200	700	
Perchloroethylene (Tetrachloroethylene)	127-18-4		(2)	
Perchloromethyl mercaptan	594-42-3	0.1	0.8	
Perchloryl fluoride	7616-94-6	3	13.5	
Petroleum distillates (Naphtha) (Rubber Solvent)		500	2000	
Phenol	108-95-2	5	19	X
p-Phenylene diamine	106-50-3		0.1	X
Phenyl ether, vapor	101-84-8	1	7	
Phenyl ether-biphenyl mixture, vapor		1	7	
Phenylethylene; see Styrene.				
Phenyl glycidyl ether (PGE)	122-60-1	10	60	
Phenythydrazine	100-63-0	5	22	X
Phosdrin (Mevinphos)	7786-34-7	....	0.1	X
Phosgene (Carbonyl chloride)	75-44-5	0.1	0.4	
Phosphine	7803-51-2	0.3	0.4	
Phosphoric acid	7664-38-2	....	1	
Phosphorus (yellow)	7723-14-0	....	0.1	
Phosphorus pentachloride	10026-13-8	....	1	
Phosphorus pentasulfide	1314-80-3	....	1	
Phosphorus trichloride	7719-12-2	0.5	3	
Phthalic anhydride	85-44-9	2	12	
Picloram	1918-02-1			
Total dust		....	15	
Respirable fraction			5	
Picric acid	88-89-1	....	0.1	X
Pindone (2-Pivalyl-1,3-indandione)	83-26-1	....	0.1	
Plaster of Paris	26499-65-0			
Total dust		....	15	
Respirable fraction		....	5	
Platinum (as Pt)	7440-06-4			
Metal		....	....	
Soluble salts		....	0.002	
Portland cement	65997-15-1			
Total dust		....	15	
Respirable fraction		....	5	
Propane	74-98-6	1000	1800	
beta-Propriolactone; see 1910.1013.	57-57-8			
n-Propyl acetate	109-60-4	200	840	
n-Propyl alcohol	71-23-8	200	500	
n-Propyl nitrate	627-13-4	25	110	
Propylene dichloride	78-87-5	75	350	
Propylene imine	75-55-8	2	5	X
Propylene oxide	75-56-9	100	240	
Propyne; see Methyl acetylene.				
Pyrethrum	8003-34-7	....	5	
Pyridine	110-86-1	5	15	
Quinone	106-51-4	0.1	0.4	
RDX; see Cyclonite.				

29 C.F.R. 1910, Subpart Z, Table Z-1—Limits for Air Contaminants (Continued)

Substance	CAS No. (c)	ppm (a)[1]	mg/m³ (b)[1]	Skin designation
Rhodium (as Rh), metal fume and insoluble compounds	7440-16-6	....	0.1	
Rhodium (as Rh), soluble compounds	7440-16-6	....	0.001	
Ronnel	299-84-3		15	
Rotenone	83-79-4	....	5	
Rouge				
Total dust		....	15	
Respirable fraction			5	
Selenium compounds (as Se)	7782-49-2	....	0.2	
Selenium hexafluoride (as Se)	7783-79-1	0.05	0.4	
Silica, amorphous, precipitated and gel	112926-00-8		(3)	
Silica, amorphous, diatomaceous earth, containing less than 1% crystalline silica	61790-53-2		(3)	
Silica, crystalline cristobalite, respirable dust	14464-46-1		(3)	
Silica, crystalline quartz, respirable dust	14808-60-7		(3)	
Silica, crystalline tripoli (as quartz), respirable dust	1317-95-9		(3)	
Silica, crystalline tridymite, respirable dust	15468-32-3		(3)	
Silica, fused, respirable dust	60676-86-0		(3)	
Silicates (less than 1% crystalline silica)				
Mica (respirable dust)	12001-26-2		(3)	
Soapstone, total dust			(3)	
Soapstone, respirable dust	....		(3)	
Talc (containing asbestos); use asbestos limit; see 29 CFR 1910.1001	....		(3)	
Talc (containing no asbestos), respirable dust	14807-96-6		(3)	
Tremolite, asbestiform; see 1910.1001.				
Silicon	7440-21-3			
Total dust		....	15	
Respirable fraction		....	5	
Silicon carbide	409-21-2			
Total dust		....	15	
Respirable fraction		....	5	
Silver, metal and soluble compounds (as Ag)	7440-22-4	....	0.01	
Soapstone; see Silicates.				
Sodium fluoroacetate	62-74-8	....	0.05	X
Sodium hydroxide	1310-73-2	....	2	
Starch	9005-25-8			
Total dust		....	15	
Respirable fraction		....	5	
Stibine	7803-52-3	0.1	0.5	
Stoddard solvent	8052-41-3	500	2900	
Strychnine	57-24-9	....	0.15	
Styrene	100-42-5		(2)	
Sucrose	57-50-1			
Total dust		....	15	
Respirable fraction		....	5	
Sulfur dioxide	7446-09-5	5	13	
Sulfur hexafluoride	2551-62-4	1000	6000	
Sulfuric acid	7664-93-9	....	1	
Sulfur monochloride	10025-67-9	1	6	
Sulfur pentafluoride	5714-22-7	0.025	0.25	
Sulfuryl fluoride	2699-79-8	5	20	
Systox; see Demeton.				
2,4,5-T (2,4,5-trichlorophenoxyacetic acid)	93-76-5		10	
Tato; see Silicates.				
Tantalum, metal and oxide dust	7440-25-7	....	5	
TEDP (Sulfotep)	3689-24-5	....	0.2	X
Tellurium and compounds (as Te)	13494-80-9	....	0.1	
Tellurium hexafluoride (as Te)	7783-80-4	0.02	0.2	
Temephos	3383-96-8			
Total dust		....	15	
Respirable fraction		....	5	
TEPP (Tetraethyl pyrophosphate)	107-49-3	....	0.05	X
Terphenyls	26140-60-3	(C)1	(C)9	
1,1,1,2-Tetrachloro-2,2-difluoroethane	76-11-9	500	4170	
1,1,2,2-Tetrachloro-1,2-difluoroethane	76-12-0	500	4170	
1,1,2,2-Tetrachloroethane	79-34-5	5	35	X
Tetrachloroethylene; see Perchloroethylene.				
Tetrachloromethane; see Carbon tetrachloride.				
Tetrachloronaphthalene	1335-88-2	....	2	X
Tetraethyl lead (as Pb)	78-00-2	....	0.075	X
Tetrahydrofuran	109-99-9	200	590	

29 C.F.R. 1910, Subpart Z, Table Z-1—Limits for Air Contaminants (Continued)

Substance	CAS No. (c)	ppm (a)[1]	mg/m³ (b)[1]	Skin designation
Tetramethyl lead (as Pb)	75-74-1	....	0.075	X
Tetramethyl succinonitrile	3333-52-6	0.5	3	X
Tetranitromethane	509-14-8	1	8	
Tetryl (2,4,6-Trinitrophenylmethylnitramine)	479-45-8	....	1.5	X
Thallium, soluble compounds (as Tl)	7440-28-0	....	0.1	X
4,4'-Thiobis (6-tert, Butyl-m-cresol)	96-69-5			
Total dust		....	15	
Respirable fraction		....	5	
Thiram	137-26-8	....	5	
Tin, inorganic compounds (except oxides) (as Sn)	7440-31-5	....	2	
Tin, organic compounds (as Sn)	7440-31-5		0.1	
Titanium dioxide	13463-67-7			
Total dust		....	15	
Toluene	108-88-3		([2])	
Toluene-2,4-diisocyanate (TDI)	584-84-9	(C)0.02	(C)0.14	
o-Toluidine	95-53-4	5	22	X
Toxaphene; see Chlorinated camphene.				
Tremolite; see Silicates.				
Tributyl phosphate	126-73-8	....	5	
1,1,1-Trichloroethane; see Methyl chloroform				
1,1,2-Trichloroethane	79-00-5	10	45	X
Trichloroethylene	79-01-6		([2])	
Trichloromethane; see Chloroform.				
Trichloronaphthalene	1321-65-9	....	5	X
1,2,3-Trichloropropane	96-18-4	50	300	
1,1,2-Trichloro-1,2,2-trifluoroethane	76-13-1	1000	7600	
Triethylamine	121-44-8	25	100	
Trifluorobromomethane	75-63-8	1000	6100	
2,4,6-Trinitrophenol; see Picric acid.				
2,4,6-Trinitrophenylmethylnitramine; see Tetryl.				
2,4,6-Trinitrotoluene (TNT)	118-96-7	....	1.5	X
Triorthocresyl phosphate	78-30-8	....	0.1	
Triphenyl phosphate	115-86-6	....	3	
Turpentine	8006-64-2	100	560	
Uranium (as U)	7440-61-1			
Soluble compounds		....	0.05	
Insoluble compounds		....	0.25	
Vanadium	1314-62-1			
Respirable dust (as V_2O_5)		....	(C)0.5	
Fume (as V_2O_5)		....	(C)0.1	
Vegetable oil mist				
Total dust		....	15	
Respirable fraction		....	5	
Vinyl benzene; see Styrene.				
Vinyl chloride; see 1910.1017	75-01-4			
Vinyl cyanide; see Acrylonitrile.				
Vinyl toluene	25013-15-4	100	480	
Warfarin	81-81-2	....	0.1	
Xylenes (o-, m-, p-isomers)	1330-20-7	100	435	
Xylidine	1300-73-8	5	25	X
Yttrium	7440-65-5	....	1	
Zinc chloride fume	7646-85-7	....	1	
Zinc oxide fume	1314-13-2	....	5	
Zinc oxide	1314-13-2			
Total dust		....	15	
Respirable fraction		....	5	
Zinc stearate	557-05-1			
Total dust		....	15	
Respirable fraction		....	5	
Zirconium compounds (as Zr)	7440-67-7	....	5	

29 C.F.R. 1910, Subpart Z, Table Z-1—Limits for Air Contaminants (Continued)

Endnotes

[1] The PELs are 8-hour TWAs unless otherwise noted; a (C) designation denotes a ceiling limit. They are to be determined from breathing-zone air samples.

[a] Parts of vapor or gas per million parts of contaminated air by volume at 25 °C and 760 torr.

[b] Milligrams of substance per cubic meter of air. When entry is in this column only, the value is exact; when listed with a ppm entry, it is approximate.

[c] The CAS number is for information only. Enforcement is based on the substance name. For an entry covering more than one metal compound, measured as the metal, the CAS number for the metal is given—not CAS numbers for the individual compounds.

[d] The final benzene standard in 1910.1028 applies to all occupational exposures to benzene except in some circumstances the distribution and sale of fuels, sealed containers and pipelines, coke production, oil and gas drilling and production, natural gas processing, and the percentage exclusion for liquid mixtures; for the excepted subsegments, the benzene limits in Table Z-2 apply. See 1910.1028 for specific circumstances.

[e] This 8-hour TWA applies to respirable dust as measured by a vertical elutriator cotton dust sampler or equivalent instrument. The time-weighted average applies to the cottom waste processing operations of waste recycling (sorting, blending, cleaning and willowing) and garnetting. See also 1910.1043 for cotton dust limits applicable to other sectors.

[f] All inert or nuisance dusts, whether mineral, inorganic, or organic, not listed specifically by substance name are covered by the Particulates Not Otherwise Regulated (PNOR) limit which is the same as the inert or nuisance dust limit of Table Z-3.

[2] **See Table Z-2.**

[3] **See Table Z-3.**

[4] **Varies with compound.**

[5] **See Table Z-2 for the exposure limits for any operations or sections where the exposure limits in §1910.1026 are stayed or are otherwise not in effect.**

[6] **If the exposure limit in §1910.1026 is stayed or is otherwise not in effect, the exposure limit is a ceiling of 0.1 mg/m³**

Occupational Health and Industrial Hygiene

HAZARD COMMUNICATION

Nearly 32 million workers are potentially exposed to one or more chemical hazards. There are an estimated 575,000 existing chemical products, and hundreds of new ones being introduced annually. This poses a serious problem for exposed workers and their employers.

Chemical exposure may cause or contribute to many serious health effects such as heart ailments, kidney and lung damage, sterility, cancer, burns and rashes. Some chemicals may also be safety hazards and have the potential to cause fires and explosions and other serious accidents.

Because of the seriousness of these safety and health problems, and because many employers and employees know little or nothing about them, the Occupational Safety and Health Administration (OSHA) has issued a rule called "Hazard Communication." The basic goal of the standard is to be sure employers and employees know about work hazards and how to protect themselves — which should help to reduce the incidence of chemical source illness and injuries.

The Hazard Communication Standard establishes uniform requirements to make sure that the hazards of all chemicals imported into, produced or used in U.S. workplaces are evaluated, and the subsequent hazard information is transmitted to affected employers and exposed employees.

Chemical manufacturers and importers must convey the hazard information they learn from their evaluations to downstream employers by means of labels on containers and material safety data sheets (MSDSs). In addition, all covered employers must have a hazard communication program to get this information to their employees through labels on containers, MSDSs and training.

This program ensures that all employers receive the information they need to inform and train their employees properly and to design and put in place employee protection programs. It also provides necessary hazard information to employees, so they can participate in, and support, the protective measures in place at their workplaces.

The Hazard Communication Standard is different from other OSHA health rules as it covers all hazardous chemicals. The rule also incorporates a "downstream flow of information," which means that producers of chemicals have the primary responsibility of generating and disseminating information, while users of chemicals must obtain the information and transmit it to their own employees.

In general, it works like this:

- Chemical Manufacturers/Importers determine the hazards of each product.
- Chemical Manufacturers/ Importers/Distributors communicate the hazard information and associated measures downstream to customers through labels and MSDSs.

- Employers
  - Identify and list hazardous chemicals in their workplaces.
  - Obtain MSDSs and labels for each hazardous chemical.
  - Develop and implement a written hazard communication program, including labels, MSDSs, and employee training based on the list of chemicals, and the MSDS and label information.
  - Communicate hazard information to their employees through labels, MSDSs and formal training programs.

Hazard Evaluation

The quality of the hazard communication program depends on the adequacy and accuracy of the hazard assessment Chemical manufacturers and importers are required to review available scientific evidence concerning the hazards of chemicals they produce or import, and to report the information they find their employees and to employers who distribute or use their products Downstream employers can rely on the evaluations performed by the chemical manufactures or importers to establish the hazards of the chemicals they use.

Each chemical must be evaluated for its potential to cause adverse health effects and to pose physical hazards such as flammability. (Definitions of hazards covered are included in the standard.) Chemicals that are listed in one of the following sources are to be considered hazardous in all cases:

- 29 CFR 1910, Subpart Z, and Hazardous Substances, Occupational Safety and Health Administration, (OSHA); and
- Threshold Limit Values for Chemical Substances and Physical Agents in the Work Environment, American Conference of Governmental Industrial Hygienists (ACGIH).

OSHA considers chemical to be hazardous if it is:

- A carcinogen;
- Corrosive;
- Highly toxic;
- Toxic;
- An irritant;
- A sensitizer; or
- Targets organ effects.

Written Program

Employers must develop, implement and maintain at the workplace a written, comprehensive hazard communication program that includes provisions for container labeling, collection and availability of material safety data sheets and an employee-training program. It also must contain a list of the hazardous chemicals in each work area, the means the employer will use to inform employees of the hazards of non-routine tasks (for example, the cleaning of reactor vessels) and the hazards associated with chemicals in unlabeled pipes. If the workplace has multiple employers onsite (e.g., a construction site), the rule requires these employers to ensure that information regarding hazards and protective measures be made available to the other employers' onsite, where appropriate.

The written program does not have to be lengthy or complicated, and some employers may be able to rely on existing hazard communication programs to comply with the above requirements. The written program must be available to employees, their designated representatives, the Assistant Secretary of Labor for Occupational Safety and Health and the Director of the National Institute for Occupational Safety and Health (NIOSH).

Labels and Other Forms of Warnings

Chemical manufacturers, importers and distributors must be sure that containers of hazardous chemicals leaving the workplace are labeled, tagged or marked with the identity of the chemicals, appropriate hazard warnings and the name and address of the manufacturer or other responsible party.

Each container must be labeled, tagged or marked with the identity of hazardous chemicals contained therein, and must show hazard warnings appropriate for employee protection. The hazard warning can be any type of message, words, pictures or symbols that convey the hazards of the chemicals in the container (See Exhibit 5-1.). Labels must be legible, in English (plus other languages, if desired) and prominently displayed.

Table 5-1. Information found on MSDSs.

Section	Contents
I	Product Identity
II	Hazardous Ingredients
III	Physical/Chemical Characteristics/Fire Hazards
IV	Health Hazards
V	Routes of Entry
VI	Exposure Limits/IH information
VII	Precautions for Safe Handling and Use
VIII	Control Measures/Protection Information
IX	First Aid
X	Date of preparation and manufacturer

Exhibit 5-1.
Labels on containers must show the hazards associated with the chemicals therein.

Exemptions to the requirement for in-plant individual container labels are as follows:

- Employers can post signs or placards that convey the hazard information if there are a number of stationary containers within a work area that have similar contents and hazards.

- Employers can substitute various types of standard operating procedures, process sheets, batch tickets, blend tickets and similar written materials for container labels on stationary process equipment if they contain the same information and are readily available to employees in the work area.

- Employers are not required to label portable containers when the hazardous chemicals are being transferred from labeled containers and the portable container is only for the immediate use of the employee who is making the transfer. Employers are not required to label pipes or piping systems.

Material Safety Data Sheets

Chemical manufacturers and importers must develop an MSDS for each hazardous chemical they produce or import, and must automatically provide the MSDS with the initial shipment of a hazardous chemical to a downstream distributor or user. Distributors must also ensure that downstream employers are provided an MSDS. Each MSDS must be in English and include information regarding the specific chemical identity of the hazardous chemicals involved as well as their common names. In addition, information must be provided on:

- the physical and chemical characteristics of the hazardous chemical;
- known acute and chronic health effects and related health information;
- exposure limits;
- whether the chemical is considered to be a carcinogen by the NTP, IARC, or OSHA;
- precautionary measures;
- emergency and first-aid procedures; and
- the identification of the organization responsible for preparing the sheet.

Copies of the MSDS for hazardous chemicals in a given work site are to be readily accessible to employees in that area.

Hazard Communication

List of Hazardous Chemicals

Employers must prepare a list of all hazardous chemicals in the workplace. When the list is complete, it should be checked against the collected MSDSs that the employer has been sent. If there are hazardous chemicals used for which no MSDS has been received, the employer must write to the supplier, manufacturer or importer to obtain the missing MSDS. If employers do not receive the MSDS within a reasonable period of time, they should contact the nearest OSHA office.

Employee Training and Information

Employers must establish a training and information program for employees who are exposed to hazardous chemicals in their work area at the time of initial assignment and whenever a new hazard is introduced into their work area.

At a minimum, the discussion topics must include:

- The existence and requirements of the hazard communication standard;
- The components of the hazard communication program in the employees' workplaces;
- Operations in work areas where hazardous chemicals are present; and
- Where the employer will keep the written hazard evaluation procedures, communications program, lists of hazardous chemicals and required MSDS forms.

The employee-training plan must include:

- How the hazard communication program is implemented in that workplace, how to read and interpret information on labels and MSDSs and how employees can obtain and use the available hazard information;
- The hazards of the chemicals in the work area. Some hazards may be discussed by individual chemical or by hazard categories such as flammability;
- Measures employees can take to protect themselves from the hazards;
- Specific procedures put into effect by the employer to provide protection such as engineering controls, work practices and the use of personal protective equipment; and
- Methods and observations, such as visual appearance or smell, workers can use to detect the presence of a hazardous chemical to which they may be exposed.

Trade Secrets

A "trade secret" is something that gives an employer an opportunity to obtain an advantage over competitors who do not know about the trade secret or who do not use it. For example, a trade secret may be a confidential device, pattern, information or chemical make-up. Chemical industry trade secrets are generally formulas, process data, or a "specific chemical identity." The latter is the type of trade secret information referred to in the hazard communication standard. The term includes the chemical name, the Chemical Abstracts Services (CAS) registry number, or any other specific information that reveals the precise designation. It does not include common names.

The standard strikes a balance between the need to protect exposed employees and the employer's need to maintain the confidentiality of a bona fide trade secret. This is achieved by providing for limited disclosure to health professionals who are furnishing medical or other occupational health services to exposed employees, employees and their designated representatives, under specified conditions of need and confidentiality.

Medical Emergency

The chemical manufacturer, importer or employer must immediately disclose the specific chemical identity of a hazardous chemical to a treating physician or nurse when the information is needed for proper emergency or first aid treatment. As soon as circumstances permit, the chemical manufacturer, importer or employer may obtain a written statement of need and a confidentiality agreement.

Under the contingency described here, the treating physician or nurse has the ultimate responsibility for determining that a medical emergency exists. At the time of the emergency, the professional judgment of the physician or nurse regarding the situation must form the basis for triggering the immediate disclosure requirement. Because the chemical manufacturer, importer or employer can demand a written statement of need and a confidentiality agreement to be completed after the emergency is abated, further disclosure of the trade secret can be effectively controlled.

Nonemergency Situation

In nonemergency situations, chemical manufacturers, importers or employers must disclose the withheld specific chemical identity to health professionals providing medical or other occupational health services to exposed employees and to employees and their designated representatives, if certain conditions are met. In this context, "health professionals" include physicians, occupational health nurses, industrial hygienists, toxicologists and epidemiologists.

The request for information must be in writing and must describe with reasonable detail the medical or occupational health need for the information. The request will be considered if the information will be used to:

- Assess the hazards of the chemicals to which employees will be exposed;
- Conduct or assess sampling of the workplace atmosphere to determine employee exposure levels;
- Conduct pre-assignment or periodic medical surveillance of exposed employees;
- Provide medical treatment to exposed employees;
- Select or assess appropriate personal protective equipment for exposed employees;
- Design or assess engineering controls or other protective measures for exposed employees; or
- Conduct studies to determine the health effects of exposure.

The health professional, employee or designated representative must also specify why alternative information is insufficient. The request for information must explain in detail why disclosure of the specific chemical identity is essential, and include the procedures that will be used to protect the confidentiality of the information. The request must include an agreement not to use the information for any purpose other than the health need stated or to release the information under any circumstances, except to OSHA.

The standard details the steps to be followed in the event that an employer decides not to disclose the specific chemical identity requested by the health professional, employee or designated representative.

Guidelines for Compliance

The Hazard Communication Standard (HCS) is based on a simple concept — that employees have both a need and a right to know the hazards and identities of the chemicals they are exposed to when working. They also need to know what protective measures are available to prevent adverse effects from occurring. Knowledge acquired under the HCS will help employers provide safer workplaces for their employees. When employers have information about the chemicals being used, they can take steps to reduce exposures, substitute less hazardous materials and establish proper work practices. These efforts will help prevent the occurrence of work-related illnesses and injuries caused by chemicals.

The HCS addresses the issues of evaluating and communicating hazards to workers. The evaluation of chemical hazards involves a number of technical concepts, and is a process that requires the professional judgment of experienced experts. Therefore, the HCS is designed so that employers who simply use chemicals, rather than produce or import them, are not required to evaluate the hazards of those chemicals. Hazard determination is the responsibility of the producers and importers of the materials, who are then required to provide the hazard information to employers who purchase their products.

Employers who do not produce or import chemicals need only focus on those parts of the rule that deal with establishing a workplace program and communicating information to their workers. This lesson provides a general guide for such employers to help determine what is required under the rule. It does not supplant or substitute for the regulatory provisions, but rather provides a simplified outline of the steps an average employer would follow to meet those requirements.

Become Familiar with the Rule

The standard is long, and some parts of it are technical, but the basic concepts are simple. In fact, the requirements reflect what many employers have been doing for years. An employer may find that it is already largely in compliance with many of the provisions and will simply have to modify existing programs somewhat. The rule requires information to be prepared and transmitted regarding all hazardous chemicals. The regulation covers both physical hazards (e.g., flammability) and health hazards (e.g., irritation, lung damage, cancer). Most chemicals used in the workplace have some hazard potential, and thus will be covered by the rule.

One difference between this rule and many others adopted by OSHA is that this one is performance oriented. That means that the employer has the flexibility to adapt the rule to the needs of the workplace, rather than having to follow specific, rigid requirements. It also means that the employer has to exercise more judgment to implement an appropriate and effective program.

The standard's design is simple. Chemical manufacturers and importers must evaluate the hazards of the chemicals they produce or import. Using that information, they must then prepare labels for containers and MSDSs.

Chemical manufacturers, importers and distributors of hazardous chemicals are required to provide the appropriate labels and MSDSs to the employers to whom they ship the chemicals. Every container of hazardous chemicals the company receives must be labeled, tagged or marked with the required information. Suppliers must also send the company a properly completed MSDS at the time of the first shipment of the chemical, and with the next shipment after the MSDS is updated with new and significant information about the hazards. Employers can rely on the information received from suppliers. They have no independent duty to analyze the chemical or evaluate the hazards of it.

Employers that use hazardous chemicals must have a program to ensure the information is provided to exposed employees. "Use" means to package, handle, react or transfer. This is an intentionally broad scope, and includes any situation where a chemical is present in such a way that employees may be exposed under normal conditions of use or in a foreseeable emergency.

The requirements of the rule that deal specifically with the hazard communication program are found in the standard in paragraphs (e) Written Hazard Communication Programs; (f) Labels and Other Forms of Warning; (g) Ma-

terial Safety Data Sheets; and (h) Employee Information and Training. The requirements of these paragraphs should be the focus of your attention. Concentrate on becoming familiar with them using paragraphs (b), Scope and Application, and (c), Definitions, as references when needed to help explain the provisions.

There are two types of work operations where the coverage of the rule is limited. These are laboratories and operations where chemicals are only handled in sealed containers (e.g., a warehouse). The limited provisions for these workplaces can be found in paragraph (b), Scope and Application. Basically, employers having these types of work operations need only keep labels on containers as they are received; maintain material safety data sheets that are received and give employees access to them; and provide information and training for employees. Employers do not have to have written hazard communication programs and lists of chemicals for these types of operations.

The limited coverage of laboratories and sealed container operations addresses the obligation of an employer to the workers in the operations involved, and does not affect the employer's duties as a distributor of chemicals. For example, a distributor may have warehouse operations where employees would be protected under the limited sealed container provisions. In this situation, requirements for obtaining and maintaining MSDSs are limited to providing access to those received with containers while the substance is in the workplace, and requesting MSDSs when employees request access for those not received with the containers. However, as a distributor of hazardous chemicals, that employer will still have responsibilities for providing MSDSs to downstream customers at the time of the first shipment and when the MSDS is updated. Therefore, although they may not be required for the employees in the work operation, the distributor may, nevertheless, have to have MSDSs to satisfy other requirements of the rule.

Identify Responsible Staff

Hazard communication is going to be a continuing program in your facility. Compliance with the HCS is not a "one shot deal." In order to have a successful program, it will be necessary to assign responsibility for both the initial and ongoing activities that have to be undertaken to comply with the rule. In some cases, these activities may already be part of current job assignments. For example, site supervisors are frequently responsible for on-the-job training sessions. Early identification of the responsible employees, and involvement of them in the development of the plan of action, will result in a more effective program design. Evaluation of the effectiveness of the program will also be affected by the involvement of affected employees.

Identify Hazardous Chemicals in the Workplace

The standard requires a list of hazardous chemicals in the workplace as part of the written hazard communication program. The list will eventually serve as an inventory of everything for which an MSDS must be maintained. At this point, however, preparing the list will help complete the rest of the program since it will give some idea of the scope of the program required for compliance in a facility.

The best way to prepare a comprehensive list is to survey the workplace. Purchasing records may also help, and certainly employers should establish procedures to ensure that in the future purchasing procedures result in MSDSs being received before a material is used in the workplace.

The broadest possible perspective should be taken when doing the survey. Sometimes people think of "chemicals" as being only liquids in containers. The HCS covers chemicals in all physical forms — liquids, solids, gases, vapors, fumes and mists — whether they are "contained" or not. The hazardous nature of the chemical and the potential for exposure are the factors that determine whether a chemical is covered. If it is not hazardous, it is not covered. If there is no potential for exposure (e.g., the chemical is inextricably bound and cannot be released), the rule does not cover the chemical.

Look around. Identify chemicals in containers, including pipes, but also think about chemicals generated in the work operations. For example, welding fumes, dusts and exhaust fumes are all sources of chemical exposures. Read labels provided by the suppliers for haz-

ard information. Make a list of all chemicals in the workplace that are potentially hazardous. For your own information and planning, the employer may also want to note on the list the locations of the products within the workplace and an indication of the hazards as found on the label. This will help as the employer prepares the rest of the program.

Paragraph (b), Scope and Application, includes exemptions for various chemicals and workplace situations. After compiling the complete list of chemicals, you should review paragraph (b) to determine if any of the items can be eliminated from the list because they are exempt materials. For example, food, drugs and cosmetics brought into the workplace for employee consumption are exempt; rubbing alcohol in the first-aid kit also is not covered.

Once an employer has compiled as complete a list as possible of the potentially hazardous chemicals in the workplace, the next step is to determine if you have received MSDSs for all of them. Check files against the inventory just compiled. If any are missing, contact your supplier and request one. It is a good idea to document these requests, either by copy of a letter or a note regarding telephone conversations. If you have MSDSs for chemicals that are not in your list, figure out why. Maybe you don't use the chemical anymore. Or maybe you missed it in your survey. Some suppliers do provide MSDSs for products that are not hazardous. These do not have to be maintained by you.

Do not allow employees to use any chemicals for which you have not received an MSDS. The MSDS provides information you need to ensure proper protective measures are implemented prior to exposure.

Preparing and Implementing a Hazard Communication Program

All workplaces where employees are exposed to hazardous chemicals must have a written plan that describes how the standard will be implemented in that facility. Preparation of a plan is not just a paper exercise — all of the elements must be implemented in the workplace in order to be in compliance with the rule. See paragraph (e) of the standard for the specific

Hazard Communication

requirements regarding written hazard communication programs. The only work operations that do not have to comply with the written plan requirements are laboratories and work operations where employees only handle chemicals in sealed containers. See paragraph (b), Scope and Application, for the specific requirements for these two types of workplaces.

The plan does not have to be lengthy or complicated. It is intended to be a blueprint for implementation of your program — an assurance that all aspects of the requirements have been addressed. Many trade associations and other professional groups have provided sample programs and other assistance materials to affected employers. These have been very helpful to many employers since they tend to be tailored to the particular industry involved. Although such general guidance may be helpful, keep in mind that the written program must be specific to your workplace.

Therefore, if you use a generic program it must be adapted to address the facility it covers. For example, the written plan must list the chemicals present at the site, indicate who is to be responsible for the various aspects of the program in your facility and indicate where written material will be made available to employees.

If OSHA inspects your workplace for compliance with the HCS, the OSHA compliance officer will ask to see the written plan at the outset of the inspection. In general, the following items will be considered in evaluating your program.

The written program must describe how the requirements for labels and other forms of warnings material safety data sheets, and employee information and training, are going to be met in your facility. The following discussion provides the type of information compliance officers will be looking for to decide whether these elements of the hazard communication program have been properly addressed.

Labels and Other Forms of Warning

In-plant containers of hazardous chemicals must be labeled, tagged or marked with the identity of the material and appropriate hazard warnings. Chemical manufacturers, importers and distributors are required to ensure that every container of hazardous chemicals

they ship is appropriately labeled with such information and with the name and address of the producer or other responsible party. Employers purchasing chemicals can rely on the labels provided by their suppliers. If the employer subsequently transfers the material from a labeled container to another container, the employer will have to label that container unless it is subject to the portable container exemption.

The information needed on a label is the identity for the material and appropriate hazard warnings. The identity is any term that appears on the label, MSDS and list of chemicals, thus linking these three sources of information. The identity used by the supplier may be a common or trade name (e.g., Black Magic Formula) or a chemical name (e.g., trichloroethane). The hazard warning is a brief statement of the hazardous effects of the chemical (e.g., flammable, causes lung damage). Labels frequently contain other information, such as precautionary measures (e.g., do not use near open flame); however, this information is provided voluntarily and is not required by the rule. Labels must be legible and prominently displayed. There are no specific requirements for size, color or text.

With these requirements in mind, the OSHA compliance officer will be looking for the following types of information to ensure that labeling will be properly implemented in your facility:

- Designation of person(s) responsible for ensuring labeling of in-plant containers;
- Designation of person(s) responsible for ensuring labeling of any shipped containers;
- Description of labeling system(s) used;
- Description of written alternatives to labeling of in-plant containers (if used); and
- Procedures to review and update label information when necessary.

Employers that are purchasing and using hazardous chemicals — rather than producing or distributing them — will primarily be concerned with ensuring that every purchased container is labeled. If materials are transferred into other containers, the employer must ensure that these are labeled as well, unless they fall under the portable container exemption (paragraph (f)(7)). In terms of labeling systems, an employer can simply choose to use the labels provided by suppliers on the containers. These will generally be verbal text labels and do not usually include numerical rating systems or symbols that require special training. The most important thing to remember is that this is a continuing duty — all in-plant containers of hazardous chemicals must always be labeled. Therefore, it is important to designate someone to be responsible for ensuring that the labels are maintained as required on the containers in your facility and that newly purchased materials are checked for labels prior to use.

Material Safety Data Sheets

Chemical manufacturers and importers are required to obtain or develop a material safety data sheet for each hazardous chemical they produce or import. Distributors are responsible for ensuring that their customers are provided a copy of these MSDSs. Employers must have an MSDS for each hazardous chemical that they use. Employers may rely on the information received from their suppliers.

There is no specified format for the MSDS under the rule, although there are specific information requirements. OSHA has developed a non-mandatory format, OSHA Form 174, that may be used by chemical manufacturers and importers to comply with the rule. The MSDS must be in English. An employer is entitled to receive from its supplier a data sheet that includes all of the information required under the rule. If you do not receive one automatically, you should request one. If you receive one that is obviously inadequate, with, for example, blank spaces that are not completed, you should request an appropriately completed one.

The role of MSDSs under the rule is to provide detailed information on each hazardous chemical, including its potential hazardous effects; its physical and chemical characteristics; and recommendations for appropriate protective measures. This information should be useful to you as the employer responsible for designing protective programs, as well as to the workers. If you are not familiar with material safety data sheets or chemical terminology, you may need to learn to use them yourself. A glossary of MSDS terms may be helpful in this regard. Generally speaking most employers using hazardous chemicals will primarily be concerned with MSDS information regarding hazardous effects and recommended protective measures. Focus on the sections of the MSDS that are applicable to your situation.

MSDSs must be readily accessible to employees when they are in their work areas during their work shifts. This may be accomplished in several ways. You must decide what is appropriate for your particular workplace. Some employers keep the MSDSs in a binder in a central location (e.g., in the pick-up truck on a construction site). Others, particularly in workplaces with large numbers of chemicals, computerize the information and provide access through terminals. As long as employees can get the information when they need it, any approach may be used. The employees must have access to the MSDSs themselves — simply having a system where the information can be read to employees over the phone is only permitted under the mobile worksite provision, paragraph (g)(9), when employees must travel between workplaces during the shift. In this situation, employees have access to the MSDSs at the primary worksite so the telephone system is simply an emergency arrangement.

To ensure that you have a current MSDS for each chemical in the facility and employee access is provided, the OSHA compliance officer will be looking for the following types of information in your written program:

- Designation of person(s) responsible for obtaining and maintaining the MSDSs;
- How such sheets are to be maintained in the workplace (e.g., in notebooks in the work area(s) or in a computer with terminal access) and how employees can obtain access to them when they are in their work areas during the work shifts;
- Procedures to follow when the MSDS is not received at the time of the first shipment;
- For producers, procedures to update the MSDS when new and significant health information is found; and
- Description of alternatives to actual MSDSs in the workplace, if necessary.

For employers using hazardous chemicals, the most important aspect of the written program in terms of MSDSs is to ensure that someone is responsible for obtaining and maintaining the MSDSs for every hazardous chemical in the workplace. The list of hazardous chemicals required to be maintained as part of the written program will serve as an inventory. As new chemicals are purchased, the list should be updated. Many companies have found it convenient to include on their purchase orders the name and address of the person designated in their company to receive MSDSs.

Employee Information and Training

Each employee who may be exposed to hazardous chemicals when working must be provided information and be trained prior to initial assignment to work with a hazardous chemical and whenever the hazard changes. "Exposure" or "exposed" under the rule means "an employee is subjected to a hazardous chemical in the course of employment through any route of entry (inhalation, ingestion, skin contact or absorption, etc.) and includes potential (e.g., accidental or possible) exposure." Information and training may be done either by individual chemical or by categories of hazards (e.g., flammability, carcinogenicity). If there are only a few chemicals in the workplace, then you may want to discuss each one individually. Where there are large numbers of chemicals or the chemicals change frequently, you will probably want to train generally based on the hazard categories (e.g., flammable liquids, corrosive materials, and carcinogens). Employees must have access to the substance-specific information on the labels and MSDSs.

Information regarding hazards and protective measures is provided to workers through written labels and MSDSs. However, through effective information and training, workers will learn to read and understand such information, determine how it can be obtained and used in their own work areas, and understand the risks of exposure to the chemicals in their work areas as well as the ways to protect themselves. Properly conducted training programs will ensure comprehension and understanding. It is not sufficient to either read material to the workers or hand them material to read. Create a climate where workers feel free to ask questions. This will help to ensure that the information is understood. Remember that the underlying purpose of the HCS is to reduce the incidence of chemical source illnesses and injuries. If your employees' comprehension is increased, proper work practices will be implemented and used, resulting in fewer injuries. The procedures you establish regarding, for example, purchasing, storage and handling of these chemicals will improve and thereby reduce the risks posed to employees exposed to the chemical hazards involved.

In reviewing your written program with regard to information and training consider the following:

- Designation of person(s) responsible for conducting training;
- Format of the program to be used (e.g., audiovisuals, classroom instruction);
- Elements of the training program (should be consistent with the elements in paragraph (h) of the HCS); and
- Procedures to train new employees at the time of their initial assignment to work with a hazardous chemical and to train employees when a new hazard is introduced into the workplace.

The written program should provide enough details about the employer's plans in this area to assess whether or not a good-faith effort is being made to train employees. OSHA does not expect that every worker will be able to recite all of the information about each chemical in the workplace. In general, the most important aspects of training under the HCS are to ensure that employees are aware that they are being exposed to hazardous chemicals, that they know how to read and use labels and MSDSs and that as a consequence of learning this information, they are following the appropriate protective measures established by the employer. OSHA compliance officers will speak to employees to determine whether they have received training and understand those aspects discussed previously.

The rule does not require employers to maintain records of employee training, but many employers choose to do so. This may help you monitor your own program to ensure that all employees are appropriately trained. If you already have a training program, you may simply have to supplement it with whatever additional information is required under the HCS. For example, construction employers that are already in compliance with the construction standard (29 CFR 1926.21) will have little extra training to do.

An employer can provide employees with information and training through whatever means it deems appropriate. Although there should always be some on-site training (e.g., informing employees of the location and availability of the written program and MSDSs), employee training may be satisfied in part by general training regarding the requirements of the HCS and chemical hazards on the job. This general training could be provided by, for example, trade associations, unions, colleges and professional schools. Similarly, the previous training, education and experience of a worker may relieve the employer of some of the burdens of training that worker. Regardless of the method relied upon; however, the employer is ultimately responsible for ensuring that employees are adequately trained. If the OSHA compliance officer finds the training is deficient, the employer will be cited for the deficiency regardless of who actually provided the training.

Other Requirements

In addition to these specific items, OSHA compliance officers will also ask the following questions when assessing the adequacy of the program:

- Does a list of the hazardous chemicals exist in each work area or at a central location?
- Are methods the employer will use to inform employees of the hazards of non-routine tasks outlined?
- Are employees informed of the hazards associated with chemicals contained in unlabeled pipes in their work areas?
- On multi-employer worksites, has the employer provided other employers with information about labeling systems and precautionary measures where the other employers have employees exposed to the initial employer's chemicals?
- Is the written program made available to employees and their designated representatives?

If your program adequately addresses the means of communicating information to employees in your workplace and provides answers to the basic questions outlined above, it will be found to be in compliance with the rule.

Table 5-2.
Chemical Hazard Communication Checklist
- Obtain a copy of the rule.
- Read and understand the requirements.
- Assign responsibility for tasks by name or job title.
- Prepare an annual inventory of chemicals.
- Ensure all containers of hazardous chemicals are labeled.
- Obtain MSDS for each chemical.
- Prepare written program
- Make MSDSs available to affected workers.
- Conduct initial training of workers.
- Retrain workers when new chemicals are introduced.
- Establish procedures to maintain current program.

Establish procedures to evaluate effectiveness. The hazard evaluation procedures required by the standard are performance-oriented. Basically, OSHA's concern is that the information on labels and data sheets, and in the training program, is adequate and accurate. Although specific procedures to follow and number of sources to be consulted cannot be established, general guidance can be provided. The hazard evaluation process can be characterized as a "tiered" approach--the extent to which a chemical must be evaluated depends to a large degree upon the common knowledge regarding the chemical, whether its health effects are under review, and how prevalent it is in the workplace.

The first step for a compliance officer's evaluating chemicals is to determine whether the chemical is part of the "floor" of chemicals to be considered hazardous in all situations.

The floor of chemicals consists of three sources. They are:

- Any substance for which OSHA has a permissible exposure limit (PEL) in 1910.1000, or a comprehensive substance-specific standard in Subpart Z. This includes any compound of such substances where OSHA would sample to determine compliance with the PEL.
- Any substance for which the American Conference of Governmental Industrial Hygienists (ACGIH) has a Threshold Limit Value (TLV) in the latest edition of their annual list is to be included in the Hazard Communication Program. Any mixture or combination of these substances would also be included.

- Any substance, which the National Toxicology Program (NTP) or the International Agency for Research on Cancer (IARC) has found to be a suspect, or confirmed carcinogen, or that OSHA regulates as a carcinogen is to be included in the Hazard Communication Program.

Sources to generally establish hazards of the chemicals that are part of the floor of hazardous chemicals covered by the standard include:
- The OSHA Chemical Information Manual, OSHA Instruction CPL 2-2.43, October 1987.
- NIOSH/OSHA Occupational Health Guidelines.
- Documentation for the Threshold Limit Values.
- NTP Summary of the Annual Report on carcinogens.
- IARC Monographs

Check the NIOSH *Registry of Toxic Effects of Chemical Substances* (RTECS) to see if any hazards are indicated which do not appear in these sources. If there are, further study should be done to evaluate the hazards. RTECS should never be considered a definitive source for establishing a hazard since it consists of data that has not been evaluated. It is, however, a useful screening resource.

The second step is to consult other generally available sources to see what has been published regarding the chemical. Patty's *Industrial Hygiene and Toxicology* would be one such source. OCIS contains a number of other chemical information sources. Material Safety Data Sheets available through information services would also be useful.

The third step, for those chemicals where information is not readily available or where such available information is not complete, is to perform searches of bibliographic, databases. In general, the National Library of Medicine (NLM) services should be used. These include the Toxicology Data Bank (TDB), TOXLINE, and MEDLARS. The information generated by these data bases should be evaluated using the criteria in Appendix B of the HCS; i.e., to qualify as an acceptable study, it must be conducted according to scientific principles (e.g., in animal

studies, number of subjects is adequate to do statistical analyses of the results; control group is used, and the study must show statistically significant results indicating an adverse health effect). This evaluation obviously requires a subjective, professional assessment. Any questions should be referred to the Directorate of Compliance Programs, office of Health Compliance Assistance (through the Regional Office) for assistance. In general, uncorroborated cases reports and in vitro studies, such as Ames tests, are useful pieces of information, but not definitive findings of hazards. Animal studies involving species other than those indicated in the acute hazard definitions must be evaluated as well.

The acute hazard definitions are not included in the standard to "categorize" chemicals but rather to establish that chemicals meeting those definitions fall under the coverage of the standard.

In some cases, the only information available on a substance may be employer-generated data. If the employer indicates that such information is the basis for the hazard evaluation, the Compliance Safety and Health Officer (CSHO) shall ask to see it to complete the OSHA evaluation.

In cases where the employer denies the CSHO access to its own hazard data and no published data on the chemical can be found to review the sufficiency of the hazard determination, the Regional Office shall be contacted for assistance in obtaining an administrative subpoena. The Directorate of Compliance Programs shall be contacted if assistance is required in order to obtain unpublished chemical hazard information available from other Federal agencies such as Environmental Protection Agency.

If an employer has found any chemical to be non-hazardous, and the CSHO has reason to believe it is hazardous, further investigation is required. The definitions of hazard in the standard are very broad, and it is not expected that many chemicals can be considered non-hazardous under this approach. Those most likely to be exempted would be chemicals that pose no physical hazards, and which have lethal dose findings above the limits found in the acute hazard definitions.

In some cases, the employer may not have addressed in the Hazard Communication Program a specific chemical that the CSHO knows to be present through knowledge of the process or through sampling or other investigation of the workplace. This situation should also be further investigated. If the CSHO has information to indicate that there is a hazard, the employer must be able to defend the finding of no hazard.

Eye and Body Flushing

OSHA Regulation 29 CFR 1910.151(c) states "Where the eyes or body of any person may be exposed to injurious corrosive materials, suitable facilities for quick drenching or flushing of the eyes and body shall be provided within the work area for immediate emergency use."

The ANSI standard Z358.1-1998 specifies requirements for eyewash and shower units:

- Sole purpose must be an emergency eyewash or shower unit
- If shower is needed, eyewash must be available (combination unit is ok)
- Valves must be quick opening- equal or less than one second
- Unit must operate with both hands free
- Water temperature- tepid or lukewarm (60-95 degrees F)
- Travel time to unit less than eleven seconds
- Unit on same level as the hazardous substance
- Immediate access means unobstructed route to unit
- Compliance with ANSI Z358 must be verified annually

Requirements for eyewashes only:

- Nozzles are 33-45 inches from floor
- Minimum of 1.5 liters per minute (.4 gallons) potable water or commercial flush for 15 minutes
- Weekly checks to flush lines for three minutes
- Nozzles protected from contamination by covers
- Squeeze bottles do not replace a fixed or portable eyewash

Requirements for showers only:

- Overhead mounting of head height of 82-96 inches from floor or platform
- Minimum flow of 75.7 liters (20 gallons) per minute
- Weekly checks to flush lines
- Valve actuator 69 inches above floor or platform

Requirements for training:

- Employees must be trained on the location and proper use
- Training shall address holding eyelids open and rolling eyeballs to flush entire eye
- If squeeze bottles are provided, employees must be trained on proper use in conjunction with eyewash stations

Exhibit 5-3.
Example of an eyewash station.

Hazard Communication Glossary

ACGIH. American Conference of Governmental Industrial Hygienists, which develops and publishes recommended occupational exposure limits for hundreds of chemical substances and physical agents. See also Threshold limit value (TLV).

Acid. Any chemical with a low pH that in water solution can burn the skin or eyes. Acids turn litmus paper red and have pH values of 0 to 6.

Action level. Term used by OSHA and NIOSH to express the level of toxicant that requires medical surveillance, usually one half of the permissible exposure limit.

Activated charcoal. Charcoal is an amorphous form of carbon formed by burning wood, nutshells, animal bones and other carbonaceous materials. Heating it with steam to between 800°C and 900°C activates charcoal. During this treatment, a porous, submicroscopic internal structure is formed that gives it an extensive internal surface area. Activated charcoal is commonly used as a gas or vapor adsorbent in air-purifying respirators and as a solid sorbent in air sampling.

Acute effect. Adverse effect on a human or animal that has severe symptoms developing rapidly and coming quickly to a crisis. See also Chronic effect.

Adsorption. The condensation of gases, liquids or dissolved substances on the surfaces of solids.

AIHA. American Industrial Hygiene Association.

Air. The mixture of gases that surround the earth; its major components are as follows: 78.08% nitrogen, 20.95 percent oxygen, 0.03 percent carbon dioxide and 0.93 percent argon. Water vapor (humidity) varies.

Airline respirator. A respirator that is connected to a compressed breathing air source by a hose of small inside diameter. The air is delivered continuously or intermittently in a sufficient volume to meet the wearer's breathing requirements.

Air-purifying respirator. A respirator that uses chemicals to remove specific gases and vapors from the air or uses a mechanical filter to remove particulate matter. An air- purifying respirator must only be used when there is sufficient oxygen to sustain life and the air contaminant level is below the concentration limits of the device.

Alkali. Any chemical with a high pH that in water solution is irritating or caustic to the skin. Strong alkalis in solution are corrosive to the skin and mucous membranes. Example: Sodium hydroxide, referred to as caustic soda or lye. Alkalis turn litmus paper blue and have pH values from 8 to 14. Another term for alkali is base.

Allergy. An abnormal response of a hypersensitive person to chemical and physical stimuli. Allergic manifestations of major importance occur in about 10 percent of the population.

ANSI. The American National Standards Institute is a voluntary membership organization (run with private funding) that develops consensus standards nationally for a variety of devices and procedures.

Asphyxiant. A vapor or gas that can cause unconsciousness or death by suffocation (lack of oxygen). Asphyxiation is one of the principal potential hazards of working in confined spaces.

ASTM. American Society for Testing and Materials.

Atmosphere-supplying respirator. A respirator that provides breathing air from a source independent of the surrounding atmosphere. There are two types: airline and self-contained breathing apparatus.

Atmospheric pressure. The pressure exerted in all directions by the atmosphere. At sea level, mean atmospheric pressure is 29.92 in. Hg, 14.7 psi, or 407 in. Hg.

Base. A compound that reacts with an acid to form a salt. It is another term for alkali.

Benign. Not malignant. A benign tumor is one that does not metastasize or invade tissue. Benign tumors may still be lethal, due to pressure on vital organs.

Biohazard. A combination of the words *biological* and *hazard*. Organisms or products of organisms that present a risk to humans.

Boiling point. The temperature at which the vapor pressure of a liquid equals atmospheric pressure.

Carbon monoxide. A colorless, odorless toxic gas produced by any process that involves the incomplete combustion of carbon-containing substances. It is emitted through the exhaust of gasoline-powered vehicles.

Carcinogen. A substance or agent capable of causing or producing cancer in mammals, including humans. A chemical is considered to be a carcinogen if: (a) it has been evaluated by the International Agency for Research on Cancer (IARC) and found to be a carcinogen or potential carcinogen; (b) it is listed as a carcinogen or potential carcinogen in the Annual Report on Carcinogens published by the National Toxicology Program (NTP) (latest edition) or (c) it is regulated by OSHA as a carcinogen.

CAS. Chemical Abstracts Service is an organization under the American Chemical Society. CAS abstracts and indexes chemical literature from all over the world in Chemical Abstracts. CAS Numbers are used to identify specific chemicals or mixtures.

Ceiling limit (C). An airborne concentration of a toxic substance in the work environment, which should never be exceeded.

CERCLA. Comprehensive Environmental Response, Compensation and Liability Act of 1980. Commonly known as Superfund (U.S. EPA).

Chemical cartridge respirator. A respirator that uses various chemical substances to purify inhaled air of certain gases and vapors. This type of respirator is effective for concentrations no more than 10 times the TLV of the contaminant if the contaminant has warning properties (odor or irritation below the TLV).

CHEMTREC. Chemical Transportation Emergency Center. Public service of the Chemical Manufacturers Association that provides immediate advice for those at the scene of hazardous materials emergencies. CHEMTREC has a 24-hour toll-free telephone number (1-800-424-9300) to help respond to chemical transportation emergencies.

Chronic effect. An adverse effect on a human or animal body, with symptoms that develop slowly over a long period of time or recur frequently. See also Acute effect.

Combustible liquid. Those liquids having a flash point at or above 37.8°C.

Concentration. The amount of a given substance in a stated unit of measure. Common methods of stating concentration include percent by weight or by volume, weight per unit volume and normality.

Corrosive. A substance that causes visible destruction or permanent changes in human skin tissue at the site of contact.

CFR. Code of Federal Regulations. A collection of the regulations that have been promulgated under United States Law.

Cutaneous. Pertaining to or affecting the skin.

Degrees Celsius (Centigrade). The temperature on a scale in which the freezing point of water is 0°C and the boiling point is 100°C. To convert to Degrees Fahrenheit, use the following formula: $°F = (C \times 1.8) + 32$.

Degrees Fahrenheit. The temperature on a scale in which the boiling point of water is 212°F and the freezing point is 32°F.

Density. The mass per unit volume of a substance. For example, lead is much denser than aluminum.

Dermatitis. Inflammation of the skin from any cause.

Dermatosis. A broader term than dermatitis; it includes any cutaneous abnormality, thus encompassing follicullitis, pigmentary changes, and nodules and tumors.

Dose-response relationship Correlation between the amount of exposure to an agent or toxic chemical and the resulting effect on the body.

DOL. U.S. Department of Labor. OSHA and MSHA are part of the DOL.

DOT. U.S. Department of Transportation.

Dusts. Solid particles generated by handling, crushing, grinding, rapid impact, detonation, and decrepitation of organic or inorganic materials, such as rock, ore, metal, coal, wood and grain. Dusts do not tend to flocculate, except under electrostatic forces; they do not diffuse in air, but settle under the influence of gravity.

Dyspnea. Shortness of breath, difficult or labored breathing.

Evaporation. The process by which a liquid is changed into the vapor state.

Evaporation rate. The ratio of the time required to evaporate a measured volume of a liquid to the time required to evaporate the same volume of a reference liquid (e.g., butyl acetate, ethyl ether) under ideal test conditions. The higher the ratio, the slower the evaporation rates. The evaporation rate can be useful in evaluating the health and fire hazards of a material.

Federal Register. Publication of U.S. government documents officially promulgated under the law documents whose validity depends upon such publication. It is published on each day following a government working day. It is, in effect, the daffy supplement to the Code of Federal Regulations.

Fire point. The lowest temperature at which a material can evolve vapors fast enough to support continuous combustion.

First aid. Emergency measures to be taken when a person is suffering from overexposure to a hazardous material, before regular medical help can be obtained.

Flammable limits. Flammables have a minimum concentration below which propagation of flame does not occur on contact with a source of ignition. This is known as the lower flammable explosive limit (LEL). There is also a maximum concentration of vapor or gas in air above which propagation of flame does not occur. This is known as the upper flammable explosive limit (UEL). These units are expressed in percent of gas or vapor in air by volume.

Flammable liquid. Any liquid having a flash point below 37.8°C (100°F), except any mixture having components with flashpoints of 100°F or higher, the total of which make up 99 percent or more of the total volume of the mixture.

Flammable range. The difference between the lower and upper flammable limits, expressed in terms of percentage of vapor or gas in air by volume. Also referred to as explosive range.

Flash point. The minimum temperature at which a liquid gives off vapor within a test vessel in sufficient concentration to form an ignitable mixture with air near the surface of the liquid. Two tests are used: open cup and closed cup.

Fume. Airborne particulate formed by the evaporation of solid materials (e.g. metal fume emitted during welding). Usually less than 1 micron in diameter.

Gage pressure. Pressure measured with respect to atmospheric pressure.

Gas. A state of matter in which the material has very low density and viscosity; can expand and contract greatly in response to changes in temperature and pressure; easily diffuses into other gases; and readily and uniformly distributes itself throughout any container. A gas can be changed to the liquid or solid state only by the combined effect of increased pressure and decreased temperature. Examples include sulfur dioxide, ozone and carbon monoxide.

Gram (g). A metric unit of weight. One ounce equals 28.4 grams.

HEPA filter. High-efficiency particulate air filter. A disposable, extended medium, dry type filter with a particle removal efficiency of no less than 99.97 percent for 0.3pm particles.

IARC. International Agency for Research on Cancer.

IDLH. Immediately dangerous to life and health. An atmospheric concentration of any toxic, corrosive or asphyxiant substance that poses an immediate threat to life, would cause irreversible or delayed adverse health effects or would interfere with an individual's ability to escape from a dangerous atmosphere. Also known as "I Don't Leave Here."

Ignition source. Anything that provides heat, sparks or flame sufficient to cause combustion or explosion.

Ignition temperature. The minimum temperature to initiate or cause self-sustained combustion in the absence of any source of ignition.

Impervious. A material that does not allow another substance to pass through or penetrate it. Frequently used to describe gloves.

Inches of mercury column. A unit used in measuring pressures. One inch of mercury column equals a pressure of 1.66 kPa (0.491 psi).

Inches of water column. A unit used in measuring pressures. One inch of water column equals a pressure of 0.25 kPa (0.036 psi).

Incompatible. Materials that could cause dangerous reactions from direct contact with one another.

Ingestion. Taking in by the mouth.

Inhalation. Breathing of a substance in the form of a gas, vapor, fume, mist or dust.

Insoluble. Incapable of being dissolved in a liquid.

Irritant. A chemical, which is not corrosive, but which causes a reversible inflammatory effect on living tissue by chemical action at the site of contact.

Latent period. The time that elapses between exposure and the first manifestation of damage.

LC. Lethal concentration that will kill 50 percent of the test animals within a specified time. See LD50.

LD50. The dose required to produce the death in 50 percent of the exposed species within a specified time.

Liter (L). A measure of capacity. One quart equals O.9L.

Lower explosive limit (LEL). The lower limits of flammability of a gas or vapor at ordinary ambient temperatures expressed in percent of the gas or vapor in air by volume. This limit is assumed constant for temperatures up to 120°C (250°F). Above this, it should be decreased by a factor of 0.7 because explosability increases with higher temperatures.

Malignant. As applied to a tumor. Cancerous and capable of undergoing metastasis or invasion of surrounding tissue.

Metastasis. Transfer of the causal agent (cell or microorganism) of a disease from a primary focus to a distant one through the blood or lymphatic vessels. Also, spread of malignancy from site of primary cancer to secondary sites.

Meter. A metric unit of length, equal to about 39 inches.

Micron Micrometer (pW). A unit of length equal to one millionth of a meter, approximately 1/25 of an inch.

Milligram (mg). A unit of weight in the metric system. One thousand equals 1 gram.

Milligrams per cubic meter (mg/m). Unit used to measure air concentrations of dusts, gases, mists and fumes.

Milliliter (mL). A metric unit used to measure volume. One milliliter equals one cubic centimeter.

Millimeter of mercury (mmHg). The unit of pressure equal to the pressure exerted by a column of liquid mercury 1mm high at a standard temperature.

Mists. Suspended liquid droplets generated by condensation from the gaseous to the liquid state or by breaking up a liquid into a dispersed state, such as by splashing, foaming or atomizing. Mist is formed when a finely divided liquid is suspended in air.

MSDS. Material safety data sheet.

MSHA. Mine Safety and Health Administration, U.S. Department of Labor.

Mucous membranes. Lining of the hollow organs of the body, notably the nose, mouth, stomach, intestines, bronchial tubes and urinary tract.

NFPA. The National Fire Protection Association is a voluntary membership organization whose aim is to promote and improve fire protection and prevention. The NFPA publishes 16 volumes of codes known as the National Fire Codes.

NIOSH. The National Institute for Occupational Safety and Health is a federal agency. It conducts research on health and safety concerns, tests and certifies respirators, and trains occupational health and safety professionals.

NTP. National Toxicology Program. The NTP publishes an annual report on carcinogens.

Nuisance dust. Dust having a long history of little adverse effect on the lungs and does not produce significant organic disease or

toxic effect when exposures are kept under reasonable control.

OSHA. U.S. Occupational Safety and Health Administration, U.S. Department of Labor.

Oxidizer. A substance that gives up oxygen readily. Presence of an oxidizer increases the risk of fire.

Oxygen deficiency. That concentration of oxygen by volume below which atmosphere supplying respiratory protection must be provided. It exists in atmospheres where the percentage of oxygen by volume is less than 19.5 percent oxygen.

Oxygen-enriched atmosphere. An atmosphere containing more than 23.5 percent oxygen by volume.

Particulate matter. A suspension of fine solid or liquid particles in air, such as dust, fog, fume, dust, smoke or sprays. Particulate matter suspended in air is commonly known as an aerosol.

Permissible exposure limit (PEL). An exposure limit that is published and enforced by OSHA as a legal standard.

Personal protective equipment (PPE). Devices worn by the worker to protect against hazards in the environment. Respirators, gloves and hearing protectors are examples.

pH. Means used to express the degree of acidity or alkalinity of a solution with neutrality indicated as seven.

Polymerization. A chemical reaction in which two or more small molecules (monomers) combine to form larger molecules (polymers) that contain repeating structural units of the original molecules. A hazardous polymerization is the above reaction, with an uncontrolled release of energy.

ppm. Parts per million parts of air by volume of vapor or gas or other contaminant. Used to measure air concentrations of vapors and gases.

psi. Pounds per square inch (for MSDS purposes) is the pressure a material exerts on the walls of a confining vessel or enclosure. For technical accuracy, pressure must be expressed as psig (pounds per square inch gauge) or psia (pounds per square absolute; that is, gauge pressure plus sea level atmospheric pressure or psig plus approximately 14.7 lbs. per square inch).

RCRA. Resource Conservation and Recovery Act of 1976 (U.S. EPA).

Reactivity (chemical). A substance's susceptibility to undergo a chemical reaction or change that may result in dangerous side effects, such as an explosion, burns and corrosive or toxic emission.

Respirable size particulates. Particulates in the size range that permits them to penetrate deep into the lungs upon inhalation.

Respirator (approved). A device designed to protect the wearer from harmful atmospheres, meets the requirements of 30 CFR Part 11 and has been approved by the National Institute for Occupational Safety and Health and the Mine Safety and Health Administration.

Respiratory system. Consists of (in descending order) the nose, mouth, nasal passages, nasal pharynx, pharynx, larynx, trachea, bronchi, bronchioles, air sacs (alveoli) of the lungs and muscles of respiration.

Route of entry. The path by which chemicals can enter the body. There are three main routes of Entry: inhalation, ingestion and skin absorption.

SARA. Superfund Amendments and Reauthorization Act of 1986 (U.S. EPA).

SCBA. Self-contained breathing apparatus.

Sensitizer. A substance that on first exposure causes little or no reaction but which on repeated exposure may cause a marked response not necessarily limited to the contact site. Skin sensitization is the most common form of sensitization in the industrial setting.

Short-term exposure limit (STEL). ACGIH-recommended exposure limit. Maximum concentration to which workers can be exposed for a short period of time (15 minutes) for only four times throughout the day with at least one hour between exposures.

"Skin." A notation (sometimes used with PEL or TLV exposure data) that indicates the stated substance may be absorbed by the skin, mucous membranes, and eyes — either airborne or by direct contact — and that this additional exposure must be considered part of the total exposure to avoid exceeding the PEL or TLV for that substance.

Solubility in water. A term expressing the percentage of a material (by weight) that will dissolve in water at ambient temperature. Solubility information can be useful in determining

spill-cleanup methods and re-extinguishing agents and methods for a material

Solvent. A substance, usually a liquid, in which other substances are dissolved. The most common solvent is water.

Sorbent. (1) A material that removes toxic gases and vapors from air inhaled through a canister or cartridge. (2) Material used to collect gases and vapors during air sampling.

Specific gravity. The ratio of the mass of a unit volume of a substance to the mass of the same volume of a standard substance at a standard temperature. Water at 4°C (39.2°F) is the standard usually referred to for liquids; for gases, dry air (at the same temperature and pressure as the gas) is often taken as the standard substance. See also Density.

Stability. An expression of the ability of a material to remain unchanged. A material is stable if it remains in the same form under expected and reasonable conditions of storage or use. Conditions that may cause instability (dangerous change) are stated. Examples are temperatures above 150°F, shock from dropping.

Synergistic. Cooperative action of substances whose total effect is greater than the sum of their separate effects.

Systemic. Spread throughout the body. Affecting all body systems and organs, not localized in one spot or area.

Threshold. The lowest dose or exposure to a chemical at which a specific effect is observed.

Threshold limit value (TLV). A time-weighted average concentration under which most people can work consistently for eight hours a day, day after day, with no harmful effects. A table of these values and accompanying precautions is published annually by the American Conference of Governmental Industrial Hygienists.

Time-weighted average concentration (TWA). Refers to concentrations of airborne toxic materials that have been weighted for certain time duration, usually eight hours.

Toxicity. A relative property of a chemical agent. Refers to a harmful effect on some biologic mechanism and the conditions under which this effect occurs.

Upper explosive limit (UEL). The highest concentration (expressed in percent vapor or gas in the air by volume) of a substance that will burn or explode when an ignition source is present.

Vapor pressure. Pressure (measured in pounds per square inch absolute (psia) exerted by a vapor. If a vapor is kept in confinement over its liquid so that the vapor can accumulate above the liquid (the temperature being held constant), the vapor pressure approaches a fixed limit called the maximum (or saturated) vapor pressure, dependent only on the temperature and the liquid.

Vapors. The gaseous form of substances that are normally in the solid or liquid state (at room temperature and pressure). The vapor can be changed back to the solid or liquid state either by increasing the pressure or decreasing the temperature alone. Vapors also diffuse. Evaporation is the process by which a liquid is changed into the vapor state and mixed with the surrounding air. Solvents with low boiling points will volatilize readily. Examples include benzene, methyl alcohol, mercury and toluene.

Viscosity. The property of a fluid that resists internal flow by releasing counteracting forces.

Volatility. The tendency or ability of a liquid to vaporize. Such liquids as alcohol and gasoline, because of their well-known tendency to evaporate rapidly, are called volatile liquids.

Water column. A unit used in measuring pressure. See also Inches of water column.

Guide for Reviewing MSDS Completeness

While reviewing the MSDS, the compliance officer may ask the following questions:

1. Do chemical manufacturers and importers have an MSDS for each hazardous chemical produced or imported into the United States?
2. Do employers have an MSDS for each hazardous chemical used?
3. Is each MSDS in at least English?
4. Does each MSDS contain at least the:
   (a) Identity used on the label?
   (b) Chemical and common name(s) for single substance hazardous chemicals?
   (c) For mixtures tested as a whole:
      (1) Chemical and common name(s) of the ingredients that contribute to the known hazards?
      (2) Common name(s) of the mixture itself?
   (d) For mixtures not tested as a whole:
      (1) Chemical and common name(s) of all ingredients that are health hazards (1 percent concentration or greater), including carcinogens (0.1 percent concentration or greater)?
      (2) Chemical and common name(s) of all ingredients that are health hazards and present a risk to employees, even though they are present in the mixture in concentrations of less than 1 percent or 0.1 percent for carcinogens?
   (e) Chemical and common name(s) of all ingredients that have been determined to present a physical hazard when present in the mixture?
   (f) Physical and chemical characteristics of the hazardous chemical (e.g., vapor pressure, flash point)?
   (g) Physical hazards of the hazardous chemical, including the potential for fire, explosion and reactivity?
   (h) Health hazards of the hazardous chemical, including signs, symptoms and medical conditions aggravated?
   (i) Primary routes of entry? OSHA permissible exposure limit? The American Conference of Governmental Industrial Hygienists threshold limit value? Other exposure limit(s), including ceiling and other short-term limits?
   (k) Information on carcinogen listings (reference OSHA-regulated carcinogens, those indicated in the National Toxicology Program Annual Report on Carcinogens and/or those listed by the International Agency for Research on Carcinogens)?
   (l) Generally applicable procedures and precautions for safe handling and use of the chemical (e.g., hygienic practices, maintenance and spill procedures)?
   (m)Generally applicable control measures (e.g., engineering controls, work practices, personal protective equipment)?
   (n) Pertinent emergency and first-aid procedures?
   (o) Date that the MSDS was prepared or the date of the last change?
   (p) Name, address and telephone number of the responsible party?
5. Are all sections of the MSDS completed?

Sample MSDS

OATEY ALL PURPOSE CEMENT 4 & 8 oz   Latest Revision Date   06/21/93

SECTION 1	IDENTITY OF MATERIAL
TRADE NAME	CEMENT 001 – OATEY ALL PURPOSE CEMENT
PRODUCT NUMBERS	30818 4 oz., 30821 8 oz.
FORMULA	PVC Resin in Solvent Solution
CHEMICAL FAMILY	PVC Organisol
SYNONYMS	PVC Plastic Pipe Cement

SECTION 2 — HAZARDOUS INGREDIENTS

INGREDIENTS	%	CAS NUMBER	C 313
CPVC Resin (non-hazardous)	12-17%	686-48-B2-8	No
Tetrahydrofuran	40-55%	109-99-9	No
Acetone	<0.25%	67-W-1	Yes
Methyl Ethyl Ketone	25-35%	7S-93-3	Yes
Cyclohexanone	11-16%	108-94-1	No
Fumed Silica (non-hazardous)	1-2%	7631-86-9	No

SECTION 3 — KNOWN HAZARDS UNDER 29 CFR 1910.1200

HAZARDS	YES	NO	HAZARDS	YES	NO
Combustible liquid	X		Skin hazard	X	
Flammable liquid	X		Eye hazard	X	
Pyrophoric material	X		Toxic agent	X	
Explosive material	X		Highly toxic agent	X	
Unstable material	X		Sensitizer	X	
Water reactive material	X		Kidney toxin		X
Oxidizer		X	Reproductive toxin		X
Organic peroxide	X		Blood toxin	X	
Corrosive material	X		Nervous system toxin	X	
Compressed gas	X		Lung toxin	X	
Irritant	X		Liver toxin	X	

SECTION 4 — REGULATIONS

	TLV (TEA)	PEL (Transitional Limit) STEL	Hazard Action Level
Tetrahydrofuran	200ppm,590mg/cm	200ppm,590mg/cm	250ppm,35mg/cm
Acetone	750ppm,1800mg/cm	1000ppm,2400mg/cm	1000ppm,2400mg/cm
Cyclohexanone	25ppm,100mg/cm (skin)	50ppm,200mg/cm	N/A
Methyl ethyl ketone	200ppm,5909mg/cm	200ppm,5990mg/cm	300ppm,885mg/cm

SECTION 5 — REGULATED IDENTIFICATION

DOT PROPER SHIPPING NAME	CEMENT
DOT HAZARD CLASS	Flammable Liquid
SHIPPING ID NUMBER	NA 1133 (Gallons Only)
EPA HAZARDOUS WASTE ID NUMBER	D-001
EPA HAZARD WASTE CLASS	Ignitable Waste/Toxic Waste

SECTION 6 — EFFECTS OF EXPOSURE

ENTRY ROUTE	INHALE–YES INGES–YES SKIN–YES EYE–YES
INHALATION	May cause irritation of mucous membranes, nose and throat, headache, dizziness, nausea, numbness of the extremities and narcosis in high concentrations. Has caused CNS depression and liver damage in animals, high concentrations have caused retardation of fetal development in rats.
SKIN	Chronic contact may lead to irritation and dermatitis. Chronic exposure to vapors of high concentration may cause dermatitis. May be absorbed through the skin.
EYE	Vapors or direct contact may cause irritation.
INGESTION	May be aspirated into the lungs/cause effects described under inhalation.
TARGET ORGANS	Eye, Skin, Kidney, Lung, Liver, Central Nervous System

SECTION 7 — EMERGENCY AND FIRST-AID PROCEDURES—303/623-5716

SKIN	If irritation arises, wash thoroughly with soap and water. Seek medical attention if irritation persists.
EYES	If fumes cause irritation, move to fresh air and irrigate eyes with water for 15 minutes. If irritation persists, seek medical attention. If eye is struck with wire, seek medical attention.
INHALATION	Move to fresh air. It breathing is difficult, give oxygen. If not breathing, give artificial respiration. Keep victim quiet and warm. Call a poison control center or physician immediately.
INGESTION	Drink water and call a poison control center or physician immediately. Avoid alcoholic beverages. Never give anything by mouth to an unconscious person.

SECTION 8 — PHYSICAL AND CHEMICAL PROPERTIES

NFPA HAZARD SIGNAL	HEALTH STABILITY FLAMMABILITY
BOILING POINT	15° F/66° C
MELTING POINT	N/A
VAPOR PRESSURE	145 nmHg 2 20° psi
VAPOR DENSITY (AIR = 1)	2.5
VOLATILE COMPONENTS	84-88X
SOLUBILITY IN WATER	Negligible
PH	N/A
SPECIFIC GRAVITY	0.90 +/- 0.02
EVAPORATION RATE	(8UAC = 1) = 5.5 - 8.0
APPEARANCE	Milky liquid
COLOR	Ether-like
WILL DISSOLVE IN	Tetrahydrofuran
MATERIAL IS	Liquid

SECTION 9	FIRE AND EXPLOSION HAZARD DATA
FLAMMABILITY	LEL =1.8 X Volume LIEL= 11.8 X Volt
FLASHPOINT AND METHOD USED	0-5°F/ PMCC
STABILITY	Stable
CONDITIONS TO AVOID:	Heat, sparks and open flame
HAZARDOUS DECOMPOSITION POTENTIAL:	Carbon monoxide/ carbon dioxide/hydrogen chloride/smoke.
HAZARDOU S POLYMERIZATION	Will Not Occur.
CONDITIONS TO AVOID:	None
INCOMPATIBILITY/MATERIAL TO AVOID	Acids, oxidizing materials, alkalis, chlorinated inorganics (potassium, calcium and sodium hypochlorite), copper or copper alloys.
SPECIAL FIRE FIGHTING PROCEDURE	FOR SMALL FIRES: Use dry chemical, CO_2, water or foam extinguisher.
	FOR LARGE FIRES: Evacuate area and call fire department immediately.

SECTION 10	SPILL AND DISPOSAL INFORMATION
SPILL OR LEAK PROCEDURES	Ventilate area. Stop leak if it can be done without risk. Take up with sand, earth, or other non-combustible absorbing material.
WASTE DISPOSAL	Dispose of according to local, state, and federal regulations.

SECTION 11	SAFE USAGE DATA

PROTECTIVE EQUIPMENT TYPES

EYES:	Safety glasses with side shields.
RESPIRATORY:	NIOSH-approved canister respirator in absence of adequate ventilation.
GLOVES:	Rubber gloves
OTHER:	Eyewash and safety shower should be available.

VENTILATION...

GENERAL MECHANICAL:	Exhaust ventilation capable of maintaining emissions at the point of use below PEL.
LOCAL EXHAUST:	Open doors and windows. If used in enclosed area, use exhaust fans.

PRECAUTIONS

HANDLING and STORAGE:	Keep away from heat, sparks, and flames. Store in cool, dry place.
OTHER:	Containers, even empties, still retain residue and vapors.

SECTION 12	MANUFACTURER, OR SUPPLIER DATA
FIRM NAME AND MAILING ADDRESS	OATEY COMPANY, P.O. BOX 35906, 4700 West 160th Street, Cleveland, Ohio 44135
OATEY PHONE NUMBER	(216) 267-7100
EMERGENCY PHONE NUMBER	For emergency first aid (303) 623-5716 (COLLECT)

SECTION 13	DISCLAIMER

The information herein has been compiled from sources believed to be reliable, up-to-date, and is accurate to the best of our knowledge. However, Oatey cannot give any guarantees regarding information from other sources and expressly does not make warranties nor assumes any liability for its use.

Sample Letter Requesting an MSDS

Blitz Manufacturing Company
1923 Oak Grove Lane
Springfield, Massachusetts 02110

Dear Sir:

The Occupational Safety and Health Administration (OSHA) Hazard Communication Standard (29 CFR 1910.1200) requires employers be provided Material Safety Data Sheets (MSDSs) for hazardous substances used in their facility, and to make these MSDSs available to employees potentially exposed to these hazardous substances.

We, therefore, request a copy of the MSDS for your product listed as Stock Number _____. We did not receive an MSDS with the initial shipment of the Blitz Solvent 90 we received from you on October 1st. We also request any additional information, supplemental MSDSs, or any other relevant data that your company or supplier has concerning the safety and health aspects of this product.

Please consider this letter as a standing request to your company for any information concerning the safety and health aspects of using this product that may become known in the future.

The MSDS and any other relevant information should be sent to us within 10, 20, 30 days (select appropriate time). Delays in receiving the MSDS information may prevent use of your product. Please send the requested information to Mr. Robert Smith, Safety and Health Manager, XYZ Company, Boston, Massachusetts 02109.

Please be advised that if we do not receive the MSDS on the above chemical by (date), we may have to notify OSHA of our inability to obtain this information. It is our intent to comply with all provisions of the Hazard Communication Standard (1910.1200) and the MSDSs are integral to this effort.

Your cooperation is greatly appreciated. Thank you for your timely response to this request. If you have any questions concerning this matter, please contact Mr. Smith at (555) 123-4567.

Sincerely,
George Rogers, President
XYZ Company

Material Safety Data Sheet Checklist

Ensure that each MSDS contains the following information:

1. Product or chemical identity used on the label.
2. Manufacturer's name and address.
3. Chemical and common names of each hazardous ingredient.
4. Name, address, and phone number for hazard and emergency information.
5. Preparation or revision date.
6. The hazardous chemical's physical and chemical characteristics, such as vapor pressure and flashpoint, physical hazards the chemical presents, including the potential for fire, explosion, and reactivity.
7. Known health hazards.
8. OSHA permissible exposure limit (PEL), ACGIH threshold limit value (TLV) or other exposure limits.
9. Emergency and first-aid procedures.
10. Whether OSHA, NTP or IARC lists the ingredient as a carcinogen.
11. Precautions for safe handling and use.
12. Control measures such as engineering controls, work practices, hygienic practices, or personal protective equipment required.
13. Primary routes of entry.
14. Procedures for spills, leaks, and clean-up.

CHAPTER
6

PERSONAL PROTECTIVE EQUIPMENT

Hard hats, goggles, face shields, steel-toed shoes, respirators, aprons, gloves and full body suits. These are all various forms of personal protective equipment (PPE).

Personal protective equipment should not be used as a substitute for engineering, work practice or administrative controls. To provide for employee safety and health in the workplace, personal protective equipment should be used in conjunction with these controls. Personal protective equipment includes all clothing and other work accessories designed to create a barrier against workplace hazards. The basic element of any management program for PPE should be an in-depth evaluation of the equipment needed to protect against the hazards at the workplace. Management dedicated to the safety and health of employees should use that evaluation to set a standard operating procedure for employees, and then train employees on the protective limitations of PPE, as well as the proper use and maintenance of PPE.

Using personal protective equipment requires hazard awareness and training on the part of the user. Employees must be aware that the equipment does not eliminate the hazard. If the equipment fails, exposure will occur. To reduce the possibility of failure, equipment must be properly fitted and maintained in a clean and serviceable condition.

Selection of the proper personal protective equipment for a job is important. Employers and employees must understand the equipment's purpose and its limitations. The equipment must not be altered or removed even though an employee may find it uncomfortable. In fact, sometimes equipment may be uncomfortable simply because it does not fit properly. Where possible, employees should test or try on equipment before using it during a shift to ensure proper fit.

General Requirements—1910.132

This regulation requires employers to ensure that personal protective equipment be "provided, used, and maintained in a sanitary and reliable condition wherever it is necessary" to prevent injury. This includes protection of any part of the body from hazards through absorption, inhalation or physical contact.

For example, many hazards can threaten the torso: heat, splashes from hot metals and liquids, impacts, cuts, acids and radiation. A variety of protective clothing is available: vests, jackets, aprons, coveralls, and full body suits.

Wool and specially treated cotton are two natural fibers that are fire resistant, comfortable and adaptable to a variety of workplace temperatures.

Duck, a closely woven cotton fabric, is good for light-duty protective clothing. It can protect against cuts and bruises on jobs where employees handle heavy, sharp or rough material.

Heat-resistant material, such as leather, is often used in protective clothing to guard against dry heat and flame. Rubber and rubberized fabrics, neoprene and plastics give protection against some acids and chemicals. It is important to refer to manufacturer's selection guides for the effectiveness of specific materials against specific chemicals.

Disposable suits of plastic-like or other similar synthetic material are particularly important for protection from dusty materials or materials that can splash. If the substance is extremely toxic, a completely enclosed chemical suit may be necessary. The clothing should be inspected to ensure proper fit and function for continued protection.

Employee-Owned Equipment

When employees provide their own equipment, the employer shall ensure the adequacy, including the proper maintenance and sanitation, of such equipment.

Design

All personal protective equipment must be of safe design and construction for the work to be performed.

Hazard Assessment and Equipment Selection

Employers are required to assess the workplace to determine if hazards that require the use of personal protective equipment are present or are likely to be present. If hazards or the likelihood of hazards are found, employers must select and have affected employees use properly fitted PPE suitable for protection from existing hazards.

Employers must certify in writing that a workplace hazard assessment has been performed. Defective and damaged equipment and defective or damaged personal protective equipment shall not be used.

Training

Before doing work requiring the use of personal protective equipment, employees must be trained to know when personal protective equipment is necessary, what type is necessary, how it is to be worn, what its limitations are and its proper care, maintenance, useful life, and disposal.

Employers are required to certify in writing that training has been carried out and that employees understand it. Each written certification shall contain the name of each employee trained, the date(s) of training and identify the subject in which the employee is certified.

Eye and Face Protection—1910.133

OSHA requires eye and face protective equipment where there is a reasonable probability of preventing injury when such equipment is used. Employers must provide a type of protector suitable for work to be performed and employees must use the protectors. These stipulations also apply to supervisors and management personnel and should apply to visitors while they are in hazardous areas.

Suitable eye protectors must be provided where there is a potential for injury to the eyes or face from flying particles, molten metal, liquid chemicals, acids or caustic liquids, chemical gases or vapors, potentially injurious light radiation or a combination of these. Protectors must meet the following minimum requirements:

- Provide adequate protection against the particular hazard;
- Be reasonably comfortable when worn under the designated conditions;
- Fit snugly without interfering with the movements or vision of the wearer;
- Be durable;
- Be capable of being disinfected;
- Be easily cleanable and kept clean and in good repair; and
- Every protector shall be distinctly marked to facilitate identification of the manufacturer.

Each affected employee shall use equipment with filter lenses that have a shade number appropriate for the work being performed for protection from injurious light radiation. Start with a shade that is too dark to see the weld zone. Then go to a lighter shade that gives sufficient view of the weld zone without going below the minimum. In oxyfuel gas welding or cutting where the torch produces a high yellow light, it is desirable to use a filter lens that absorbs the yellow or sodium line in the visible light of the (spectrum) operation.

Selection

Each eye, face or face-and-eye protector is designed for a particular hazard. In selecting a protector, consideration should be given to the kind and degree of hazard. Where a choice of protectors is given and the degree of protection required is not an important issue, worker comfort may be a deciding factor. When the manufacturer indicates limitations or precautions, they should be transmitted to the user and strictly observed.

Persons using corrective spectacles and those who are required by OSHA to wear eye protection must wear face shields, goggles or spectacles of one of the following types:

- Spectacles with protective lenses providing optical correction;
- Goggles worn over corrective spectacles that do not disturb the adjustment of the spectacles; or
- Goggles that incorporate corrective lenses mounted behind the protective lenses.

Goggles come in a number of different styles: eyecups, flexible or cushioned goggles, plastic eye shield goggles and foundrymen's goggles. Goggles are manufactured in several styles for specific uses such as protecting against dusts and splashes, in chippers, and for welders and cutters.

Safety spectacles require special frames. Combinations of normal streetwear frames with safety lenses are not in compliance. Many hard hats and nonrigid helmets are designed with face and eye protective equipment.

Design, construction, tests, and use of eye and face protection purchased prior to July 3, 1994, must be in accordance with ANSI Z87.1-1968 LISA Standard Practice for Occupational and Educational Eye and Face Protection. Protective eye and face devices purchased after July 5, 1994, must comply with ANSI Z87.1 1989, American National Standard Practice for Occupational and Educational Eye and Face Protection.

Fit

Someone skilled in the procedure should perform the fitting of goggles and safety spectacles. Only qualified optical personnel should fit prescription safety spectacles.

Inspection and Maintenance

It is essential that the lenses of eye protectors be kept clean. Continuous vision through dirty lenses can cause eyestrain—often an excuse for not wearing the eye protectors. Daily inspection and cleaning of the eye protector with soap and hot water or with a cleaning solution and tissue is recommended. Pitted lenses, like dirty lenses, can be a source of reduced vision. They should be replaced. Deeply scratched or excessively pitted lenses are apt to break more readily.

Slack, worn out, sweat-soaked, or twisted headbands do not hold the eye protector in proper position. Visual inspection can determine when the headband elasticity is reduced to a point beyond proper function.

Goggles should be kept in a case when not in use. Spectacles, in particular, should be given the same care as one's own glasses because the frame, nose pads and temples can be damaged by rough use.

Personal protective equipment that has been previously used should be disinfected before being issued to another employee. Also, when each employee is assigned protective equipment for extended periods, it is recommended that such equipment be cleaned and disinfected regularly.

Several methods for disinfecting eye-protective equipment are acceptable. The most effective method is to disassemble the goggles or spectacles and thoroughly clean all parts with soap and warm water. Equipment should be carefully rinsed to eliminate all traces of soap and defective parts should be replaced with new ones. All parts should be swabbed thoroughly and immersed for 10 minutes in a solution of germicidal deodorant fungicide. Once removed from the solution, equipment should be suspended in a clean place for air-drying at room temperature or with heated air (See Exhibit 6-1.). Equipment should not be rinsed after being removed from the solution because this will remove the germicidal residue that retains its effectiveness after drying.

Exhibit 6.1.
Personal protective equipment should be cleaned and disinfected regularly.

The dry parts or items should be placed in a clean, dust-proof container, such as a box, bag, or plastic envelope to protect them until reissue.

Respiratory Protection—1910.134

OSHA standards require employers to establish and maintain a respiratory protective program whenever respirators are necessary to protect the health of employees. Respiratory protective devices fall into three classes:

- Air purifying;
- Atmosphere or air supplying; and
- Combination air-purifying and air-supplying devices.

Class 1: Air-Purifying Devices

The air-purifying device cleanses the contaminated atmosphere. Chemicals can be used to remove specific gases and vapors and mechanical filters can remove particulate matter. This type of respirator is limited in its use to those environments where the air contaminant level is within the specified concentration limitation of the device. These devices do not protect against oxygen deficiency.

"Oxygen deficiency" occurs in an atmosphere with an oxygen content below 19.5 percent by volume.

Types of air-purifying devices include:

- Mechanical-filter cartridge;
- Chemical-cartridge;
- Combination mechanical-filter/chemical-cartridge;

- Gas masks; and
- Powered air-purifying respirators.

Mechanical-filter respirators offer respiratory protection against airborne particulate matter, including dusts, mists, metal fumes and smoke, but do not provide protection against gases or vapors.

Chemical-cartridge respirators afford protection against low concentrations of certain gases and vapors by using various chemical filters to purify the inhaled air. They differ from mechanical-filter respirators in that they use cartridges containing chemicals to remove harmful gases and vapors.

Combination mechanical-filter/chemical-cartridge respirators use dust, mist or fume filters with a chemical cartridge for dual or multiple exposures.

Gas masks provide respiratory protection against certain gases, vapors and particulate matter. Gas masks are designed solely to remove specific contaminants from the air; therefore, it is essential that their use be restricted to atmospheres that contain sufficient oxygen to support life. Gas masks may be used for *escape only* from atmospheres that are immediately dangerous to life or health, and never for entry into such environments.

Immediately dangerous to life or health (IDLH) means an atmospheric concentration of any toxic, corrosive or asphyxiant substance that poses an immediate threat to life or would cause irreversible or delayed adverse health effects or would interfere with an individual's ability to escape from a dangerous atmosphere.

Canisters for gas masks are color-coded according to the contaminant against which they provide protection. This information is included in the standard.

Powered air-purifying respirators protect against particulates, gases and vapors, or both. The air-purifying element may be a filter, chemical cartridge, combination filter and chemical cartridge, or canister. The powered air-purifying respirator uses a power source (usually a battery pack) to operate a blower that passes air across the air-cleaning element to supply purified air to the respirator. The great advantage of the powered air-purifying respirator is that it usually supplies air at positive pressure (relative to atmospheric) so that any leakage is outward from the face piece. However, it is possible at high work rates to create a negative pressure in the face piece, thereby increasing face-piece leakage.

Class 2: Atmosphere- or Air-Supplying Devices

Atmosphere- or air-supplying devices are the class of respirators that provide a respirable atmosphere to the wearer, independent of the ambient air. Atmosphere-supplying respirators fall into three groups: supplied-air respirators, self-contained breathing apparatus (SCBA), and combination-SCBA and supplied-air respirators.

Supplied-air respirators deliver breathing air through a supply hose connected to the wearer's face piece or enclosure. The air delivered must be free of contaminants and must be from a source located in clean air. The OSHA requirements for compressed air used for breathing, including monitoring for carbon monoxide, are listed in 1910.134(d). Supplied-air respirators should only be used in non-IDLH atmospheres.

There are three types of supplied-air respirators, which are classified by type. Type A supplied-air respirators are also known as hose masks with blower. A motor-driven or hand-operated blower through a strong, large diameter hose supplies air. Type B supplied-air respirators are hose masks as in Type A, but without a blower. The wearer draws air through the hose by breathing. Type C supplied-air respirators are commonly referred to as airline respirators. An airline respirator must be supplied with respirable air conforming to Grade D Compressed Gas Association's Standard CGA G-7.1-73, Commodity Specification for Air, 1973. This standard requires air to have the oxygen content normally present in the atmosphere, no more than 5 mg/NV of condensed hydrocarbon contamination, no more than 20-ppm carbon monoxide, no pronounced odor and a maximum of 1,000 ppm of carbon dioxide.

There are three basic classes of airline respirators.

- **Continuous flow.** A continuous-flow unit has a regulated amount of air fed to the face piece and is normally used where there is

an ample air supply such as that provided by an air compressor.
- **Demand flow.** These airline respirators deliver airflow only during inhalation. Such respirators are normally used when the air supply is restricted to high-pressure compressed air cylinders. A suitable pressure regulator is required to make sure that the air is reduced to the proper pressure for breathing.
- **Pressure-demand flow.** For those conditions where the possible inward leakage (caused by the negative pressure during inhalation that is always present in demand systems) is unacceptable and there cannot be the relatively high air consumption of the continuous-flow units, a pressure-demand airline respirator may be the best choice. It provides a positive pressure during both inhalation and exhalation.

Types A, B, and C that are approved for abrasive blasting are designated AE, BE and CE, respectively. These respirators are equipped with additional devices designed to protect the wearer's head and neck against impact and abrasion from rebounding abrasive material and with shielding to protect the windows of face pieces, hoods and helmets.

Self-contained breathing apparatus (SCBA) provide complete respiratory protection against toxic gases and oxygen deficiency. The wearer is independent of the surrounding atmosphere because he or she is breathing with a system that is portable and admits no outside air. The oxygen or air supply of the apparatus itself takes care of respiratory requirements.

There are two basic types of self-contained breathing apparatus: closed circuit and open-circuit. In a closed-circuit apparatus, the exhalation is rebreathed by the wearer after the carbon dioxide has been effectively removed and a suitable oxygen concentration restored from sources composed of compressed oxygen, chemical oxygen or liquid oxygen. In an open-circuit apparatus, exhalation is vented to the atmosphere and is not rebreathed. There are two types of open-circuit SCBAs: demand and pressure-demand.

Combination SCBA and supplied-air respirators are airline respirators with auxiliary self-contained air supplies. An auxiliary SCBA is an independent air supply that allows a person to evacuate an area or enter such an area for a very short period of time where a connection to an outside air supply can be made.

These devices are approved for use in IDLH atmospheres. The auxiliary air supply can be switched to in the event the primary air supply fails to operate. This allows the wearer to escape from the IDLH atmosphere. Combination airline respirators with auxiliary SCBA are designed to operate in three modes: continuous-flow, demand flow, and pressure-demand flow.

Class 3: Combination Air-Purifying and Atmosphere-Supplying Devices

These respirators are available in either continuous-flow or pressure-demand flow and are most often used with a high-efficiency filter as the air purifying element. Use in the filtering mode is allowed for escape only. Because of the positive pressure and escape provisions, these respirators have been recommended for asbestos work.

Exhibit 6-2. Classifications of Respiratory Protective Devices.

I. Air-Purifying Devices
   A. Mechanical-filter cartridge
   B. Chemical-cartridge
   C. Combination mechanical-filter/chemical cartridge
   D. Gas masks
   E. Powered air purifying
II. Atmosphere- or Air-Supplying Devices
   A. Supplied-air
      1. Types A and AE
      2. Types B and BE
      3. Types C and CE (airline)
         a. Continuous-flow
         b. Demand-flow
         c. Pressure-demand flow
   B. Self-contained breathing apparatus (SCBA)
      1. Closed-circuit
      2. Open-circuit
         a. Demand
         b. Pressure-demand
   C. Combination SCBA and supplied-air
      1. Continuous-flow
      2. Demand-flow
      3. Pressure-demand flow

III. Combination Air-Purifying and Atmosphere Supplying Devices
   A. Continuous-flow
   B. Pressure-demand flow

Requirements for a minimal acceptable respirator program are specified in 1910.134(b)(1) through 1910.134(b)(11). Other sections of the standard also refer to these requirements as listed in Exhibit 6-3.

Exhibit 6-3. Minimal Acceptable Respirator Program Requirements.

Requirement	Standard
Written Operating Procedures	1910.134(b)(1), (e)(1) and (e)(3)
Proper Selection	1910.134(b)(2), (c) and (e)(2)
Training and Fitting	1910.134(b)(3), (e)(5) and (e)(5)(i-iii)
Cleaning and Disinfecting	1910.134(b)(5) and (f)(3)
Storage	1910.134(b)(6), and (f)(5)(i-iii)
Inspection and Maintenance	1910.134(b)(7), (e)(4), (f)(2)(i-iv) and (f)(4)
Work Area Surveillance	1910.134(b)(8) only
Inspection/Evaluation of Program	1910.134(b)(9) only
Medical Examinations	1910.134(b)(10) only
Approved Respirators	1910.134(b)(11) only

Written Operating Procedures

OSHA standards state that the employer is responsible not only for providing appropriate respirators, but also for developing written standard operating procedures for their selection, use and care. The procedures must include a discussion or explanation of all items specified in 29 CFR 1910.134(b).

Program Selection

Respirators shall be selected on the basis of hazards to which the worker is exposed. A qualified individual supervising the respiratory protective program usually specifies the respirator type in the work procedures. The individual issuing them shall be adequately instructed to ensure that the correct respirator is issued.

In selecting the correct respirator for a given circumstance, many factors must be taken into consideration (e.g., the nature of the hazard, location of the hazardous area, employee's health, work activity, and respirator characteristics, capabilities and limitations).

In order to make subsequent decisions, the nature of the hazard must be identified to ensure that an overexposure does not occur. One important factor to consider is oxygen deficiency.

NIOSH/MSHA approval for supplied-air and air-purifying respirators is valid only for atmospheres containing greater than 19.5 percent oxygen. If oxygen deficiency is not an issue, then the contaminant(s) and their concentrations must be determined. Exhibit 6-4 presents an outline for the selection process based on these criteria.

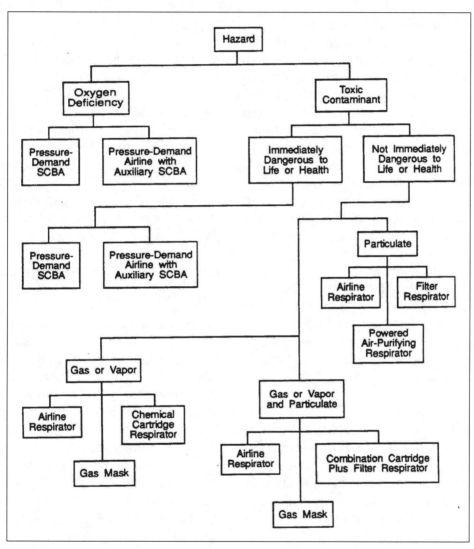

Exhibit 6-4.
Respirator Selection Criteria. The type of respirator used should be based on the contaminants to which the worker will be exposed as well as their concentrations.

ticipate and control. Where these conditions exist, head protection must be provided to eliminate injury.

Head injuries are caused by falling or flying objects, or by bumping the head against a fixed object. Head protection, in the form of protective hats, must do two things: (1) resist penetration and (2) absorb the shock of a blow. This is accomplished by making the shell of the hat of a material hard enough to resist the blow, and by utilizing a shock-absorbing lining composed of headband and crown straps to keep the shell away from the wearers skull. Protective hats also are used to protect against electrical shock.

Criteria for Head Protection

The standards recognized by OSHA for head protection purchased prior to July 5, 1994, are contained in ANSI Requirements for Industrial Head Protection, Z89.1-1969, and ANSI Requirements for Industrial Protective Helmets for Electrical Workers, Z89.2-1971. These standards should be consulted for further details. The standards for protective helmets purchased after July 5, 1994, are contained in ANSI Personnel Protection-Protective Headwear for Industrial Workers-Requirements, Z89.1-1986. Later editions of these standards are available and acceptable for use.

Selection

Each type and class of head protectors is intended to provide protection against specific hazardous conditions. An understanding of these conditions will help in selecting the right protection for the particular situation. Head protection is made in the following types and classes:

- Type 1: Helmets with full brim, not less than 1¼ in. wide; and
- Type 2: Brimless helmets with a peak extending forward from the crown.

For industrial purposes, three classes are recognized:

- Class A: General service, limited voltage protection;
- Class B: Utility service, high-voltage helmets; and
- Class C: Special service, no voltage protection.

For firefighters, head protection must consist of a protective head device with ear flaps and a chin strap that meet the performance, construction and testing requirements stated in 29 CFR 1910.156(e)(5).

Helmets under Class A are intended for protection against impact hazards. They are used in mining, construction, shipbuilding, tunneling, lumbering and manufacturing.

Class B, utility service helmets protect the wearer's head from impact and penetration by falling or flying objects and from high-voltage shock and burn. Electrical workers use them extensively.

The safety helmets in Class C are designed specifically for lightweight comfort and impact protection. This class is usually manufactured from aluminum and offers no dielectric protection. Class C helmets are used in certain construction and manufacturing occupations, oil fields, refineries and chemical plants where there is not danger from electrical hazards or corrosion. They also are used on occasions where there is a possibility of bumping the head against a fixed object.

Materials used in helmets should be water resistant and slow burning. Each helmet consists essentially of a shell and suspension. Ventilation is provided by a space between the headband and the shell. Each helmet should be accompanied by instructions explaining the proper method of adjusting and replacing the suspension and headband.

The wearer should be able to identify the type of helmet by looking inside the shell for the manufacturer, ANSI designation and class. For example:

- Manufacturer's name;
- ANSI Z89.1-1969 (or later year);
- Class (A, B or C).

Fit

Headbands are adjustable in 1/8-size increments. When the headband is adjusted to the right size, it provides sufficient clearance between the shell and the headband. The removable or replaceable-type sweatband should cover at least the forehead portion of the headband. The shell should be of one-piece seamless construction and designed to resist the impact of a blow from falling material. The internal cradle of the headband and sweatband forms the suspension. Any part that comes into contact with the wearer's head must not be irritating to normal skin. Hard hats must be worn correctly for the headband to do its job. When workers wear baseball caps beneath their hard hats it defeats the purpose of the headband and does not provide adequate protection.

Inspection and Maintenance

Manufacturers should be consulted with regard to paint or cleaning materials for their helmets because some paints and thinners may damage the shell and reduce protection by physically weakening it or negating electrical resistance.

A common method of cleaning shells is to dip them in hot water containing a good detergent for at least one minute. Shells should then be scrubbed and rinsed in clear hot water. After rinsing, the shell should be carefully inspected for any signs of damage.

All components, shells, suspensions, headbands, sweatbands and any accessories should be visually inspected daily for signs of dents, cracks, penetration or any other damage that might reduce the degree of safety originally provided.

Users are cautioned that if unusual conditions occur (e.g., higher or lower extreme temperatures than described in the standards) or if there are signs of abuse or mutilation of the helmet or any component, the margin of safety may be reduced. If damage is suspected, helmets should be replaced or representative samples tested in accordance with procedures contained in ANSI Z89.1-1986. This discussion references national consensus standards, for example, ANSI standards that were adopted into OSHA regulations. Employers are encouraged to use up-to-date national consensus standards that provide employee protection equal to or greater than that provided by OSHA standards.

Helmets should not be stored or carried on the rear-window shelf of an automobile because sunlight and extreme heat may adversely affect the degree of protection.

Occupational Foot Protection— 1910.136

According to a survey by the Bureau of Labor Statistics, most of the workers in selected occupations who suffered foot injuries were not wearing protective footwear. Furthermore, most of their employers did not require them to wear safety shoes. These injuries occurred while workers were performing normal job activities at their worksites.

For protection of feet and legs from falling or rolling objects, sharp objects, molten metal, hot surfaces and wet slippery surfaces, workers should use appropriate foot guards, safety shoes, or boots and leggings. Leggings protect the lower leg and feet from molten metal or welding sparks. Safety snaps permit their rapid removal.

Aluminum alloy, fiberglass or galvanized steel foot guards can be worn over usual work shoes, although they may present the possibility of catching on something and causing workers to trip. Heat-resistant soled shoes protect against hot surfaces like those found in the roofing, paving and hot metal industries.

Safety shoes should be sturdy and have an impact-resistant toe. In some shoes, metal insoles protect against puncture wounds. Additional protection, such as metatarsal guards, may be found in some types of footwear. Safety shoes come in a variety of styles and materials, such as leather and rubber boots and oxfords.

Safety footwear is classified according to its ability to meet minimum requirements for both compression and impact tests. These requirements and testing procedures may be found in American National Standards Institute standards. Protective footwear purchased prior to July 5, 1994, must comply with ANSI Z41.1-1967, USA Standard for Men's Safety-Toe Footwear. Protective footwear purchased after July 5, 1994, must comply with ANSI Z41-1991, American National Standard for Personal Protection-Protective Footwear.

Electrical Protective Devices—1910.137

Insulating blankets, matting, covers, line hose, gloves and sleeves made of rubber shall meet specified requirements for manufacture, marking, electrical properties, workmanship and finish.

In-Service Care and Use

Electrical protective equipment shall be maintained in a safe, reliable condition. Specific requirements for in-service care and use are given for insulating blankets, covers, line hose, gloves and sleeves made of rubber.

Hand Protection—1910.138

Employers shall select and require employees to use appropriate hand protection when employees' hands are exposed to hazards such as those from skin absorption of harmful substances; severe cuts or lacerations; severe abrasions; punctures; chemical burns; thermal burns; and harmful temperature extremes.

Selection

There is a wide assortment of gloves, hand pads, sleeves and wristlets for protection against various hazardous situations. Employers need to determine what hand protection their employees need. The work activities of the employees should be studied to determine the degree of dexterity required, the duration, frequency, and degree of exposure to hazards and the physical stresses that will be applied.

Also, it is important to know the performance characteristics of gloves relative to the specific hazard anticipated (e.g., exposure to chemicals, heat or flames). Standard test procedures should assess gloves' performance characteristics.

Before purchasing gloves, the employer should request documentation from the manufacturer that the gloves meet the appropriate test standard(s) for the hazard(s) anticipated. For example, for protection against chemical hazards, the toxic properties of the chemicals must be determined, particularly the ability of the chemical(s) to pass through the skin and cause systemic effects.

The protective device should be selected to fit the job. For example, some gloves are designed to protect against specific chemical hazards. Employees may need to use gloves, such as wire mesh, leather and canvas, that have been tested and provide insulation from burns and cuts. The employee should become acquainted with the limitations of the clothing used.

Hearing Protection—1910.95

Exposure to high noise levels can cause hearing loss or impairment. It can create physical and psychological stress. There is no cure for noise-induced hearing loss, so the prevention of excessive noise exposure is the only way to avoid hearing damage. Specially designed protection is required, depending on the type of noise encountered.

A professional should individually fit preformed or molded earplugs. Waxed cotton, foam and fiberglass wool earplugs are self-forming. When properly inserted, they work as well as most molded earplugs.

Some earplugs are disposable—to be used one time and then thrown away. The non-disposable type should be cleaned after each use for proper protection. Plain cotton is ineffective as protection against hazardous noise.

Earmuffs need to make a perfect seal around the ear to be effective. Glasses, long sideburns, long hair and facial movements, such as chewing, can reduce protection. Special equipment is available for employees with glasses or beards.

For extremely noisy situations, earplugs should be worn in addition to earmuffs. When used together, earplugs and earmuffs change the nature of sounds; all sounds are reduced including one's own voice, but other voices or warning devices are easier to hear.

29 CFR Part 1910, Subpart I Personal Protective Equipment

GENERAL REQUIREMENTS: The employer must assess the workplace to determine if hazards are present, or are likely to be present, which necessitate the use of personal protective equipment (PPE). If such hazards are present, or are likely to be present, the employer shall select, and have each affected employee use, the types of PPE that will protect against the identified hazards. PPE must properly fit each affected employee and the employer shall verify the hazard assessment in writing.

Damaged or defective equipment shall not be used.

The employer must provide training to each employee required to use PPE.

Training will include when PPE is necessary, what PPE is necessary, how to wear PPE, and the proper care, maintenance, useful life, and disposal of the PPE. The employer has to certify in writing that the employee has received and understands the training.

EYE AND FACE PROTECTION: Employees must use appropriate eye or face protection when exposed to eye or face hazards from flying particles, molten metal, liquid chemicals, acids or caustic liquids, chemical gases or vapors, or potentially injurious light radiation. Requirements for side protection, prescription lenses, filter lenses, and identification of the manufacturer are spelled out. Protective eye and face devices purchased after July 5, 1994 must comply with ANSI Z87.1-1989 or be demonstrated to be equally effective. Devices purchased before that date must comply with ANSI Z87.1-1968 or are equally effective. The ANSI standard was updated in 2003.

HEAD PROTECTION: Employees must wear protective helmets when working in areas where there is a potential for injury to the head from falling objects. Each such affected employee when near exposed electrical conductors which could contact the head shall wear protective helmets designed to reduce electrical shock hazards. Protective helmets purchased after July 5, 1994 shall comply with ANSI Z89.1-1994 or be equally effective. Helmets purchased before that date shall comply with ANSI Z89-1-1969 or are equally effective.

FOOT PROTECTION: Employees must wear protective footwear when working in areas where there is a danger of foot injuries due to falling or rolling objects, or objects piercing the sole, and where employees' feet are exposed to electrical hazards. Protective footwear purchased after July 5, 1994 must comply with ANSI Z41-1991 or is equally effective. Protective footwear purchased before that date must comply with ANSI Z41.1-1967 or is equally effective.

HAND PROTECTION: Employers must select and require employees to use appropriate hand protection when employees' hands are exposed to hazards such as those from skin absorption of harmful substances; severe cuts or lacerations; severe abrasions; punctures; chemical burns; thermal burns and harmful temperature extremes. Employers shall base the selection of the appropriate hand protection on evaluation of the performance characteristics of the hand protection relative to the tasks to be performed, conditions present, duration of use and the hazards and potential hazards identified.

Questions and Answers Concerning the PPE Standards

Question: Does all PPE have to be replaced with PPE that meets the new revised standards?

Answer: No. The final standards "grandfather" existing PPE. That is, PPE that was purchased before the effective date of the standard can continue in use if it meets the pertinent ANSI standard in effect at the time of purchase, or if it can be demonstrated to be equally effective.

Q: Must all eye protective devices be equipped with side protectors?

A: No, not in all situations. However, side protectors, such as side shields, are required when it is determined (through the hazard assessment) that there is a hazard from flying objects.

Q: May side protectors be detachable?

A: Yes. Detachable side protectors (i.e., clip-on or slide-on side shields) are permitted if they meet the pertinent requirements of 1910.133.

Q: Is it permissible to wear contact lenses with eye protection?

A: Yes. OSHA believes that contact lenses do not pose additional hazards to the wearer. However, it is important to note that contact lenses are not eye protective devices. If eye hazards are present, appropriate eye protection must be worn instead of, or in conjunction with, contact lenses.

Q: Do PPE manufacturers have to obtain third-party certification that their equipment has been tested in accordance with, and meets the requirements of, the OSHA PPE standards?

A: No. However, many PPE manufacturers already voluntarily obtain third-party certification of their equipment.

Q: Since PPE manufacturers are not required to obtain third-party certification, what should employers do when purchasing PPE?

A: Employers can request the manufacturer to document that the PPE has been tested to meet specified criteria and employers can determine if the PPE is marked as meeting the pertinent ANSI standard. For instance, head protective devices should be marked as meeting ANSI Z41.1. In addition, as stated previously, many PPE manufacturers already obtain third-party certification. Therefore, when purchasing PPE, employers should determine whether or not the PPE has such certification.

Q: Is an employer required to have a written hazard assessment?

A: No, although a written hazard assessment is certainly recommended. Employers are, however, required to verify that the hazard assessment has been performed through a written certification that identifies the workplace evaluated, the person certifying that the evaluation has been performed, the date(s) of the hazard assessment and identifies the document as a certification of hazard assessment.

Q: Is PPE required for certain SIC codes or certain job titles? For example, is foot protection required for employees who work in a warehouse?

A: The PPE standard contains performance-oriented requirements and does not specify SIC codes or job titles to mandate the use of certain types of PPE. Instead, the employer is required to perform a hazard assessment of the workplace to determine what hazards, if any, are present. The employer must then make

a selection of the appropriate PPE that will protect employees from the hazards identified by the hazard assessment.

Q: Many female employees have complained that they have to wear PPE that does not fit properly because the PPE has been sized to fit only male employees. Is this situation going to continue?

A: No. One of the new requirements of the PPE standard is that employers are now required to select PPE that properly fits employees (29 CFR 1910.132(d)(1)(iii)). PPE is now available in many different sizes or can be adjusted to many sizes (such as head protective devices). Even protective footwear is now available in sizes that will properly fit female employees.

Q: How often must employees be trained?

A: Employees must be trained before being allowed to perform work requiring the use of PPE. Employees must also be retrained: when there are changes in the workplace that impact the use of PPE; there are changes in the types of PPE to be used or when inadequacies in an employee's knowledge or use of assigned PPE indicate that the employee has not retained understanding or skill.

Q: The final standards reference specific editions of the ANSI standards that different types of PPE must meet. For example, protective eye and face devices must meet the 1989 edition of ANSI Z87.1. In the future, what happens if an employer wants to purchase PPE that meets a later edition of the same ANSI standard?

A: OSHA will accept PPE as complying with the standard if the PPE is demonstrated to be as effective as the PPE meeting the specific ANSI standard referenced by the final standard. For example, eye and face protective devices meeting a subsequent edition of the same ANSI standard would be acceptable to OSHA if it could be demonstrated that they were as effective as those meeting the 1989 edition. Employers would need to establish either that there was no substantive difference between a subsequent edition of Z87.1 and the 1989 edition, or that PPE that satisfied subsequently modified test criteria provided protection equivalent to that provided by PPE that satisfied the 1989 edition.

Q: What constitutes an adequate hazard assessment?

A: The final standard is performance oriented to allow the flexibility needed for employers to perform a hazard assessment that best reflects their particular workplace. An adequate hazard assessment will result as long as the employer meets the requirements of §1910.132(d)(1). Additionally, Appendix B contains an example of procedures that satisfy the hazard assessment requirement.

Fact Sheet—Personal Protective Equipment (PPE) Standards

- The previous standards for head, face, eye and foot protection were adopted from the 1971 ANSI standards. These standards are outdated and do not reflect current technology and improvements in PPE.
- The final rule is a revision that updates the standards to be more consistent with the latest editions of the ANSI standards.
- The final rule provides guidance for the selection and use of PPE, as well as performance-oriented requirements, where appropriate.
- The standards also contain some new requirements. Employers will now have to perform a hazard assessment of the workplace to determine if any hazards are present that would necessitate the need for PPE. Based on this assessment, the employer would then select the appropriate PPE for the hazards that were found.
- Employers will also have to provide PPE training to employees.
- The new rule contains a section addressing hand protection. This fills a gap in employee protection since the prior standards had no requirement for hand protection.
- The proposal was published in August 1989. Hearings were held in Washington, D.C. on April 3 and 4, 1990. The rulemaking record contains 173 comments, 577 pages of testimony and 53 exhibits.
- The final rule was published in the *Federal Register* on April 6, 1994. It became effective on July 5, 1994.
- The new standards will cover 1.1 million work establishments and 11.7 million employees.
- It is estimated that compliance with the new provisions of the final rule will cost $52.4 million annually and will prevent four fatalities and 712,000 lost workdays annually.

HAZARD ASSESSMENT FORM

Instructions: This is a two-part form printed back to back. The first part is on the front page; the second part is on the back page. Fill in the heading to identify the area being assessed, and then conduct a walk-through survey of the work area. Fill in the front page to identify the hazards during a normal operation in the area. This form is an assessment of workplace hazards as required by OSHA.

AREA: _____

OPERATION: _____

YOUR NAME: _____

DATE OF ASSESSMENT: _____

Head Hazards – Working beneath material or other workers that could fall and strike the head; working on electrical equipment, chemicals or other hazards that could affect the head of the worker.
- ☐ Impact
- ☐ Electrical shock
- ☐ Chemical splash

Describe hazard here: _____
_____
_____

Eye and Face Hazards – Working with chemicals, acids, grinding, sanding, welding, woodworking operations or anytime there is the possibility of something flying through the air and striking the worker in the face or eyes.
- ☐ Impact
- ☐ Dust
- ☐ Chemical splash
- ☐ Light/radiation

Describe hazard here: _____
_____
_____

Hand Hazards – Cutting stock material, working with hot or cold items or chemicals.
- ☐ Cuts
- ☐ Puncture
- ☐ Chemical splash
- ☐ Hot/cold temperature

Describe hazard here: _____
_____
_____

Foot Hazards – Look for the potential for tools or stock to be dropped on the foot of workers or chemical spills or spike-like items that may puncture the bottom of the foot.
- ☐ Impact
- ☐ Puncture
- ☐ Compression
- ☐ Chemical splash

Describe hazard here: _____
_____
_____

Based on the hazard assessment conducted on the previous page, the following personal protective equipment is required for the job classification of_____.

Head Hazards

Job	Identified Hazard	PPE to be Worn

Eye and Face Hazards

Job	Identified Hazard	PPE to be Worn

Hand Hazards

Job	Identified Hazard	PPE to be Worn

Foot Hazards

Job	Identified Hazard	PPE to be Worn

Ensure that workers are issued the correct PPE and are fitted and trained on how to use and maintain the equipment. Workers also must be trained on the limitations of the equipment as well as the proper disposal and replacement of the equipment.

EMPLOYEE SAFETY AND HEALTH RECORD

Name: _____ Permanent___
Job Title: _____ Temporary___
Department: _____ Date Hired: _____

List Hazards Associated with Present Duties:

_____

Occupational Health Medical Examination Required:
Asbestos: _____ Hearing: _____
Lead: _____ Other (specify): _____

MANDATORY TRAINING TOPICS (To be briefed to all personnel; initial when conducted)

_____ Location of required and appropriate safety bulletin boards, OSHA Poster
_____ OSHA and Company Safety Rules that apply to the job and workplace
_____ Hazards of the work area to include physical, physiological and chemical.
_____ Reason for specific medical evaluation
_____ Hazards of the assigned job or tasks and safety procedures to be followed
_____ Personal protective equipment (PPE), required, how, when and where to use it
_____ Emergency procedures for evacuation, fire reporting, emergency equipment
_____ Location of alarms and extinguishers
_____ Emergency telephone numbers
_____ Location of medical facilities or first aid kits
_____ Need to report of unsafe/unhealthful equipment, conditions or procedures
_____ How to report unsafe/unhealthful equipment, conditions or procedures
_____ Requirements for documentation and notification of on-the-job injury or illness
_____ Hazard communications program
_____ Company safety program

INITIAL INDIVIDUAL TRAINING TOPICS (As needed; initial when conducted)

_____ Respirator protection program   _____ Lockout/tagout
_____ Permit-required confined space program _____ Back injury prevention
_____ Hearing conservation   _____ Bloodborne pathogens
_____ Jewelry safety   _____ PPE use and care
_____ Fall protection   _____ Others (list and initial)

PERSONAL PROTECTION ISSUED (Initial when issued)

_____ Head protection   _____ Eye protection   _____ Face protection
_____ Arm/hand protection _____ Foot protection   _____ Hearing protection
_____ Respiratory protection _____ Other (specify) _____ Other (specify)

Personal Protective Equipment

PERSONAL PROTECTION PROVIDED IN THE WORK AREA

_____ Head protection	_____ Eye protection	_____ Face protection
_____ Arm/hand protection	_____ Foot protection	_____ Hearing protection
_____ Respiratory protection	_____ Other (specify)	_____ Other (specify)

RECORD OF CONTINUOUS JOB SAFETY TRAINING

DATE	INITIAL	ANNUAL	SUPERVISOR SIGNATURE	EMPLOYEE SIGNATURE

RECORD OF JOB SAFETY NON-COMPLIANCE

Verbal Warning for _____ Date: _____ Supervisor: _____

Written Warning for _____ Date: _____ Supervisor: _____

Written Warning for _____ Date: _____ Supervisor: _____

Written Warning for _____ Date: _____ Supervisor: _____

Written Warning for _____ Date: _____ Supervisor: _____

Notice of intent to Terminate: _____ Date: _____ Human Resources

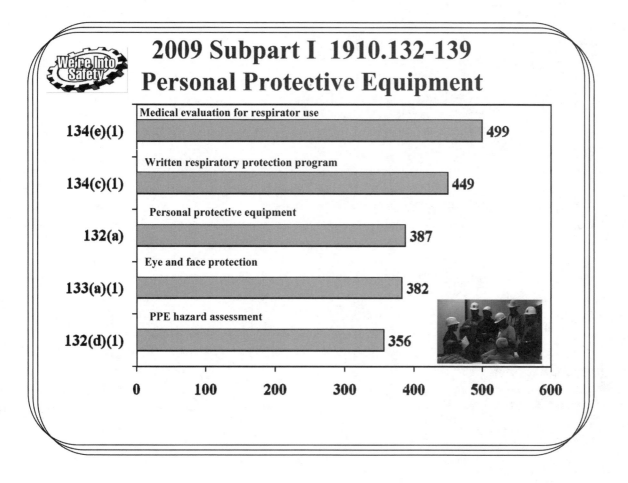

2009 Subpart I 1910.132-139
Personal Protective Equipment

- **134(e)(1)** Medical evaluation for respirator use — 499
- **134(c)(1)** Written respiratory protection program — 449
- **132(a)** Personal protective equipment — 387
- **133(a)(1)** Eye and face protection — 382
- **132(d)(1)** PPE hazard assessment — 356

HAZARDOUS WASTE OPERATIONS AND PROCESS SAFETY MANAGEMENT

Hazardous Waste Operations and Emergency Response
This standard, set forth at 29 CFR 1910.120, regulates hazardous waste clean up, treatment, and emergency response for general industry. This standard applies to employees involved in:

■ **Clean-up operations**
 1. Clean-up operations required by a governmental body, whether federal, state, local, or other, involving hazardous substances that are conducted at uncontrolled hazardous waste sites.
 2. Corrective actions involving clean-up operations at sites covered by the Resource Conservation and Recovery Act (RCRA).
 3. Voluntary clean-up operations at sites recognized by federal, state, local, or other governmental bodies as uncontrolled hazardous waste sites.

■ **Treatment, storage, and disposal of hazardous wastes**
 1. Operations involving hazardous wastes that are conducted at treatment, storage, and disposal facilities licensed under the RCRA.

■ **Emergency response operations**
 1. Emergency response operations for the release of, or substantial threats of the release of, hazardous substances. This is the type of operation with which the majority of employers will be concerned. Exceptions are permitted if the employer can demonstrate that the operation does not involve employee exposure or a reasonable possibility of such exposure to hazards.

General Requirements
■ Development by each hazardous waste site employer of a safety and health program designed to identify, evaluate, and control safety and health hazards and to provide for emergency response.
■ A preliminary evaluation of the site's characteristics prior to entry by a trained person to identify potential site hazards and to aid in the selection of appropriate employee protection methods. Included would be all suspected conditions immediately dangerous to life or health or that may cause serious harm.
■ Implementation of a site control program to protect employees from hazardous contamination. At a minimum, it must have a site map, site work zones, site communications, safe work practices, and identification of the nearest medical assistance. The "buddy system" also is required as a protective measure in particularly hazardous situations so that employees can keep watch on one another to provide quick aid if needed.

- Training of employees before they are allowed to engage in hazardous waste or emergency response operations that could expose them to safety and health hazards. However, experienced workers will be allowed to continue operations and then be given refresher courses when appropriate. Specific training requirements are listed for clean-up personnel, equipment operators, general laborers and supervisory employees and for various levels of emergency response personnel. Persons completing specified training for hazardous waste operations shall be certified. Those neither certified nor with proper experience shall be prohibited from engaging in those operations specified by the standard.

Training requirements vary with the type of operation involved. The various operations and their dependent training requirements are:
- Uncontrolled hazardous waste operations mandated by the government.
  - These workers must have 40 hours of initial training before they may enter the site and at least three days of actual field experience under a trained, experienced supervisor.
  - Employees visiting the site occasionally need only 24 hours of training and one day of supervised field experience before they may enter.
  - Managers and supervisors directly responsible for clean-up operations must have an additional eight hours of specialized training in waste management.
- Annual refresher training of eight hours is required for site workers and managers.
- Sites licensed under the RCRA. Employees must have 24 hours of training plus eight hours of annual refresher training.

Medical surveillance is required at least annually and at the end of employment for all employees exposed to any particular hazardous substance at or above established exposure levels and/or those who wear approved respirators for 30 days or more on site. Surveillance also will be conducted if a worker is exposed by unexpected or emergency releases as well.

Engineering controls, work practices, and personal protective equipment, or a combination of these methods, must be implemented to reduce exposure below established exposure levels for the hazardous substance involved. Air monitoring must be initiated periodically to identify and quantify levels of hazardous substances to ensure that proper protective equipment is being used.

An informational program that includes the names of key personnel and their alternates who are responsible for site safety and health, and the requirements of the standard must be provided to employees.

Before any employee or equipment may leave an area where there is a potential for hazardous exposure, a decontamination procedure must be implemented. Standard operating procedures to minimize exposure through contact with exposed equipment, employees, or used clothing must be established and showers and change rooms must be provided where needed. The employer must establish an emergency response plan to handle possible onsite emergencies before any hazardous waste operations may begin. The emergency response plan must address:
- Personnel roles;
- Lines of authority;
- Training and communications;
- Emergency recognition and prevention;
- Safe places of refuge;
- Site security;
- Evacuation routes and procedures;
- Emergency medical treatment; and
- Methods of sounding the emergency alert.

Employers also must have an off-site emergency plan to better coordinate emergency action by local emergency services and to implement appropriate control actions.

Emergency Response to Hazardous Substance Releases

In the event of a release of hazardous material or in response to an emergency or potential emergency, employees must comply with 1910.120(q). This section concerns more employers than any other part of the standard.

The regulation defines "emergency response" or "responding to emergencies" as:

[A] response effort by employees from outside the immediate release area or by other designated responders (i.e., mutual-aid groups, local fire departments, etc.) to an occurrence which results, or is likely to result, in an uncontrolled release of a hazardous substance."

Incidental releases of hazardous substances where the substance can be absorbed, neutralized, or otherwise controlled at the time of release by employees in the immediate release area or by maintenance personnel are not considered to be emergency releases within the scope of this standard. Responses to releases of hazardous substances where there is no potential safety or health hazard (i.e., fire, explosion, chemical exposure) are not considered to be emergency responses.

If there is a potential safety or health hazard, there may be an emergency and hence an emergency response that requires compliance with 1910.120(q). This applies whether the release is responded to by employees from outside the work area, outside groups such as the fire department, or employees from the immediate work areas who have been designated by the employer to respond to emergencies.

On the other hand, if there is no potential safety or health hazard, there is no emergency. This applies whether the release is cleaned up by personnel within the immediate work area or from outside the work area. Generally, employees will be trained under the hazard communication standard to deal with such incidental releases as 1910.120(q) does not apply.

Situations generally resulting in emergency responses include:

- The response comes from outside the immediate release area;
- The release requires evacuation of employees in the area;
- The release poses, or has the potential to pose, conditions that are immediately dangerous to life and health (IDLH);
- The release poses a serious threat of fire or explosion;

- The release requires immediate attention because of imminent danger;
- The release may cause high levels of exposure to toxic substances;
- There is uncertainty that the employees in the work area can handle the severity of the hazard with the personal protective equipment and other equipment that has been provided and the exposure limit could easily be exceeded; and
- The situation is unclear or data is lacking key factors.

The companies and employers whose employees will be engaged in emergency responses must develop and implement an emergency response plan. Employers may be exempt from developing and implementing a plan in the following circumstances:

- When an emergency occurs, they evacuate all of their employees from the danger area and do not permit any of their employees to assist in handling the emergency. This action should be outlined in the company emergency action plan.
- Those organizations that have developed programs for handling releases of hazardous substances in accordance with the Superfund Amendments and the Reauthorization Act of 1986 (Emergency Planning and Community Right-to-Know Act of 1986) may use those programs to meet the requirements of 1910.120 as long as they are equivalent. These firms may use the local emergency response or state emergency response plans as part of their plans to avoid duplication.

The emergency response plan must be in writing and contain the following elements:

- Pre-emergency planning and coordination with outside parties;
- Personnel roles, lines of authority, and communication;
- Emergency recognition and prevention;
- Safe distances and places of refuge;
- Site security and control;
- Evacuation routes and procedures;
- Decontamination procedures that are not covered by the site safety and health plan;
- Emergency medical treatment and first aid;
- Emergency alerting and response procedures;

- Critique of response and follow up (after-action review procedures); and
- Personnel protective equipment and emergency equipment needed.

Procedures for Handling Emergency Response

The senior emergency response official responding to an emergency shall become the individual in charge of a site-specific Incident Command System (ICS). All emergency responders and their communications must be coordinated and controlled through the individual in charge of the ICS who is assisted by the senior official present for each employer. The Incident Commander is normally the responding fire department chief who establishes a Command Post with which the employer should be familiar. All operations in the hazardous area must be performed using the buddy system where workers are organized to work in groups of two or more so they can observe each other for contamination. Back-up personnel must stand by with equipment ready to provide assistance or rescue. Advanced first-aid support personnel, as a minimum, also must stand by with medical equipment and transportation capability.

Training

Different levels of initial training are required depending on the duties and functions of the employee-responder. Demonstrated competence or annual refresher training is required to maintain that competence.

First Responders at the Awareness Level

These individuals are likely to witness or discover the hazardous substance release and initiate the emergency response. They must demonstrate competency in such areas as recognizing the presence of hazardous materials in an emergency, the risks involved, and the role they are expected to perform in such situations.

First Responders at the Operations Level

These employees respond to protect people, property and the nearby environment while not actually trying to stop the release. They must have eight hours of training as well as the training required of first responders at the awareness level, or a demonstrated competence in their roles.

Hazardous Materials Technicians

These workers respond to stop the release. They must have 24 hours of training equal to the operations level and demonstrate their competence in several specific areas.

Hazardous Materials Specialists

These workers support the technicians, but require a more specific knowledge of the substances being contained. They must have 24 hours of training equal to the technical level and demonstrate competence in certain areas.

On-Scene Incident Commander

This individual assumes control of the incident scene beyond the awareness level. This person must have 24 hours of training equal to the operations level and must demonstrate competence in specific areas.

Other Personnel

Skilled support personnel such as heavy earth-moving equipment operators who are needed on a temporary basis are not required to meet the training required for an employer's regular employees. They must be given an initial briefing at the site prior to their participation in an emergency response. This briefing must include instruction in the wearing of appropriate personal protective equipment, what chemical hazards are involved, and what duties are to be performed.

Specialist employees who work regularly with and are trained in hazards of specific hazardous substances and will provide technical advice or assistance at a hazardous substance release incident must receive training or demonstrate their competency on an annual basis.

Medical Surveillance and Consultation

Members of designated hazardous materials (HAZMAT) teams and HAZMAT specialists must have a baseline physical examination and be provided with medical surveillance as required for employees at uncontrolled hazardous waste sites. Any emergency response employees who exhibit signs or symptoms that may have resulted from exposure during the course of an emergency incident must be provided with medical consultation.

Post-Emergency Response Operations

After the emergency response is over, clean up of released hazardous substances, health hazards, or contaminated materials may be necessary. In this case, the employer may either comply with all of the requirements for uncontrolled hazardous waste sites or clean up the plant property using plant or workplace employees. If the employer elects to clean up its material using its own employees and equipment, the employer must ensure its employees have completed the training requirements of the following sections:

- Emergency action plan training, 1910.38;
- Respirator training, 1910.134;
- Hazard communication training, 1910.1200; and
- Any other appropriate safety training such as personal protective equipment or decontamination procedures.

Process Safety Management of Highly Hazardous Chemicals

Unexpected releases of toxic, reactive, or flammable liquids and gases in processes involving highly hazardous chemicals have been reported for many years. Incidents continue to occur in various industries that use highly hazardous chemicals that may be toxic, reactive, flammable, explosive, or may exhibit a combination of these properties. Regardless of the industry that uses these highly hazardous chemicals, there is a potential for an accidental release any time 'they are not properly controlled. This, in turn, creates the possibility of disaster.

Recent major disasters include the 1984 Bhopal, India, incident resulting in more than 2,000 deaths; the October 1989 Phillips Petroleum Company, Pasadena, Texas, incident resulting in 23 deaths and 132 injuries; the July 1990 BASF, Cincinnati, Ohio, incident resulting in two deaths, and the May 1991 IMC, Sterlington, Louisiana, incident resulting in 8 deaths and 128 injuries.

Although these major disasters involving highly hazardous chemicals drew national attention to the potential for major catastrophes, the public record is replete with information concerning many other less notable releases of highly hazardous chemicals. Hazardous chemical releases continue to pose a significant threat to employees and provide impetus, internationally and nationally, for authorities to develop or consider developing legislation and regulations to eliminate or minimize the potential for such events. OSHA's standard emphasized the management of hazards associated with highly hazardous chemicals and established a comprehensive management program that integrated technologies, procedures, and management practices.

Approximately four months after the publication of OSHA's proposed standard for process safety management of highly hazardous chemicals, the Clean Air Act Amendments (CAAA) were enacted into law (November 15, 1990). Section 304 of the CAAA requires that the Secretary of Labor, in coordination with the Administrator of the Environmental Protection Agency (EPA), promulgate, pursuant to the Occupational Safety and Heath Act of 1970, a chemical process safety standard to prevent the accidental release of chemicals that could pose a threat to employees.

The CAAA requires that the standard include a list of highly hazardous chemicals that includes toxic, flammable, highly reactive, and explosive substances. The CAAA also specified minimum elements that the OSHA standard must require of employers:

- Develop and maintain written safety information identifying workplace chemical and process hazards, equipment used in the processes, and technology used in the processes;
- Perform a workplace hazard assessment, including, as appropriate, identification of potential sources of accidental releases, identification of any previous release within the facility that had a potential for catastrophic consequences in the workplace, estimation of workplace effects of a range of releases, and estimation of the health and safety effects of such a range on employees;
- Consult with employees and their representatives on the development and conduct of hazard assessments and the development of chemical accident prevention plans and

provide access to these and other records required under the standard;

- Establish a system to respond to the workplace hazard assessment findings, which shall address prevention, mitigation, and emergency responses;
- Review periodically the workplace hazard assessment and response system;
- Develop and implement written operating procedures for the chemical processes, including procedures for each operating phase, operating limitations, and safety and health considerations;
- Provide written safety and operating information for employees and employee training in operating procedures by emphasizing hazards and safe practices that must be developed and made available;
- Ensure contractors and contract employees are provided with appropriate information and training;
- Train and educate employees and contractors in emergency response procedures in a manner as comprehensive and effective as that required by the regulation promulgated pursuant to section 126(d) of the Superfund Amendments and Reauthorization Act;
- Establish a quality assurance program to ensure that initial process-related equipment, maintenance materials, and spare parts are fabricated and installed consistent with design specifications;
- Establish maintenance systems for critical process-related equipment, including written procedures, employee training, appropriate inspections, and testing of such equipment to ensure ongoing mechanical integrity;
- Conduct pre-startup safety reviews of all newly installed or modified equipment;
- Establish and implement written procedures managing changes to process chemicals, technology, equipment and facilities; and
- Investigate incidents that result in or could have resulted in a major accident in the workplace, with any findings and modifications made to be reviewed by operating personnel.

How the Standard Works

The OSHA final process safety management (PSM) standard applies mainly to manufacturing industries, particularly those pertaining to chemicals, transportation equipment, and fabricated metal products. Other affected sectors include natural gas liquids; farm product warehousing; electric, gas, and sanitary services; and wholesale trade. It also applies to pyrotechnics and explosives manufacturers covered under other OSHA rules and has special provisions for contractors working in covered facilities.

In each industry, the PSM standard applies to those companies that deal with any of more than 130 specific toxic and reactive chemicals in listed quantities; it also includes flammable liquids and gases in quantities of 10,000 lbs. (4,535.9 kg) or more.

Subject to the rules and procedures set forth in OSHA's hazard communication standard (29 CFR 1910.1200), employees and their designated representatives must be given access to trade secret information contained within the process hazard analysis and other documents required to be developed by the PSM standard.

The key provision of the PSM standard is process hazard analysis—a careful review of what could go wrong and what safeguards must be implemented to prevent the release of hazardous chemicals. Covered employers must identify those processes that pose the greatest risks and begin evaluating those first. The PSM standard clarifies the responsibilities of employers and contractors involved in work that affects or takes place near covered processes to ensure the safety of both plant and contractor employees is considered. The standard also mandates written operating procedures; employee training; pre-startup safety reviews; the evaluation of mechanical integrity of critical equipment; and written procedures for managing change. The PSM standard specifies a permit system for hot work; the investigation of incidents involving releases or near misses of covered chemicals; emergency action plans; compliance audits at least every three years; and trade secret protection.

Process means any activity involving a highly hazardous chemical, including using, storing, manufacturing, handling, or moving such chemicals at the site, or any combination of these activities. For purposes of this definition, any group of vessels that are interconnected and separate vessels located in a way that could involve a highly hazardous chemical in a potential release are considered a single process.

Process Safety Information

Employers must complete a compilation of written process safety information before conducting any process hazard analysis required by the standard. The compilation of written process safety information will help the employer and the employees involved in operating the process to identify and understand the hazards that the processes pose.

Process safety information must include information on the hazards of the highly hazardous chemicals used or produced by the process, information on the technology of the process, and information on the equipment in the process.

Information on the hazards of the highly hazardous chemicals in the process shall consist of at least the following:
- Toxicity;
- Permissible exposure limits;
- Physical data;
- Reactivity data;
- Corrosivity data;
- Thermal and chemical stability data; and
- The hazardous effects of inadvertently mixing different materials.

Information on the technology of the process must include at least the following:
- A block flow diagram or simplified process flow diagram;
- Process chemistry;
- Maximum intended inventory; and
- Safe upper and lower limits for such items as temperatures, pressures, and flows.

NOTE: Material safety data sheets (MSDSs) meeting the requirements of the hazard communication standard (29 CFR 1910.1200) may be used to comply with this requirement to the extent they contain the required information.

Where the original technical information no longer exists, such information may be developed in conjunction with the process hazard analysis in sufficient detail to support the analysis.

Information on the equipment in the process must include the following:

- Materials of construction;
- Piping and instrument diagrams;
- Electrical classification;
- Relief system design and design basis;
- Ventilation system design;
- Design codes and standards employed;
- Material and energy balances for processes built after May 26, 1992; and
- Safety systems (e.g., interlocks, detection, suppression systems).

The employer shall document that equipment complies with recognized and generally accepted good engineering practices. For existing equipment designed and constructed in accordance with codes, standards, or practices that are no longer in general use, the employer shall determine and document that the equipment is designed, maintained, inspected, tested, and operated in a safe manner.

Process Hazard Analysis

The process hazard analysis is a thorough, orderly, systematic approach for identifying, evaluating, and controlling the hazards of processes involving highly hazardous chemicals. The employer must perform an initial process hazard analysis (hazard evaluation) on all processes covered by this standard. The process hazard analysis methodology selected must be appropriate to the complexity of the process and must identify, evaluate, and control the hazards involved in the process.

First, employers must determine and document the priority order for conducting process hazard analyses based on a rationale that includes such considerations as the extent of the process hazards, the number of potentially affected employees, the age of the process, and the operating history of the process. All initial process hazard analyses should be conducted as soon as possible.

Process hazard analyses completed after May 26, 1987, that meet the requirements of the PSM standard are acceptable as initial process hazard analyses. All process hazard analyses must be updated and revalidated, based on their completion date, at least every five years.

The employer must use one or more of the following methods, as appropriate, to determine and evaluate the hazards of the process being analyzed:

- What-if;
- Checklist;
- What-If /checklist;
- Hazard and operability study (HAZOP);
- Failure mode and effects analysis (FMEA);
- Fault tree analysis; or
- An appropriate equivalent methodology.

Whichever method(s) are used, the process hazard analysis must address the following:
- The hazards of the process;
- The identification of any previous incident that had a potential for catastrophic consequences in the workplace;
- Engineering and administrative controls applicable to the hazards and their inter-relationships, such as the appropriate application of detection methodologies to provide early warning of releases. Acceptable detection methods might include process monitoring and control instrumentation with alarms and detection hardware such as hydrocarbon sensors;
- Consequences of failure of engineering and administrative controls;
- Facility site;
- Human factors; and
- Qualitative evaluation of a range of the possible safety and health effects on employees if there is a failure of controls.

For best results, the process hazard analysis should be conducted by a team that includes employees with expertise in engineering and process operations, at least one employee who has experience with and knowledge of the process being evaluated, and at least one employee who has knowledge of the specific analysis methods being used.

The employer must:
- Establish a system to address promptly the team's findings and recommendations;
- Ensure the recommendations are resolved in a timely manner and the resolutions are documented;
- Document what actions are to be taken;
- Develop a written schedule of when these actions are to be completed;
- Complete actions as soon as possible; and
- Communicate the actions to operating, maintenance, and other employees whose work assignments are in the process and who may be affected by the recommendations or actions.

At least every five years after the completion of the initial process hazard analysis, the process hazard analysis must be updated and revalidated by a team meeting the standard's requirements to ensure the hazard analysis is consistent with the current process.

Employers must keep on file and make available to OSHA, on request, process hazard analyses and updates or revalidation for each process covered by the PSM standard, as well as the documented resolution of recommendations, for the life of the process.

Operating Procedures

The employer must develop and implement written operating procedures, consistent with the process safety information, that provide clear instructions for safely conducting activities involved in each covered process. The tasks and procedures related to the covered process must be appropriate, clear, consistent, and most importantly, well communicated to employees. The procedures must address at least the following elements:
- Steps for each operating phase:
  - Initial startup;
  - Normal operations;
  - Temporary operations;
  - Emergency shutdown, including the conditions under which emergency shutdown is required and the assignment of shutdown responsibility to qualified operators to ensure emergency shutdown is executed in a safe and timely manner;
  - Emergency operations;
  - Normal shutdown; and
  - Startup following a turnaround or emergency shutdown; and
- Operating limits:
  - Consequences of deviation; and
  - Steps required to correct or avoid deviation; and
- Safety and health considerations:
  - Properties of and hazards presented by the chemicals used in the process;
  - Precautions necessary to prevent exposure, including engineering controls,

administrative controls, and personal protective equipment;

- Control measures to be taken if physical contact or airborne exposure occurs;
- Quality control for raw materials and control of hazardous chemical inventory levels;
- Any special or unique hazards; and
- Safety systems (e.g., interlocks, detection, suppression systems) and their functions.

To ensure that a ready and up-to-date reference is available and to form a foundation for needed employee training, operating procedures must be readily accessible to employees who work in or maintain a process. The operating procedures must be reviewed as often as necessary to ensure they reflect current operating practices, including changes in process chemicals, technology and equipment, and facilities. To guard against outdated or inaccurate operating procedures, the employer must certify annually that its operating procedures are current and accurate.

The employer must develop and implement safe work practices to provide for the control of hazards during work activities such as lockout/tagout; confined space entry; opening process equipment or piping; and control over entrance into a facility by maintenance, contractor, laboratory, or other support personnel. These safe work practices must apply to both employees and to contractor-employees.

Employee Participation

Employers must develop a written plan of action to implement the employee participation required by the PSM standard. Employers must consult with employees and their representatives on the conduct and development of process hazard analyses and on the development of the other elements of process management. They also must provide access to process hazard analyses and to all other information required to be developed by the standard to employees and their representatives.

Training

Initial Training

The implementation of an effective training program is one of the most important steps that an employer can take to enhance employee safety. Accordingly, the PSM standard requires that each employee presently involved in operating a process or a newly assigned process must be trained in an overview of the process and its operating procedures. The training must include emphasis on the specific safety and health hazards of the process, emergency operations, including shutdown, and other safe work practices that apply to the employee's job tasks.

Refresher Training

Refresher training must be provided at least every three years to each employee involved in operating a process to ensure he or she understands and adheres to the current operating procedures of the process. The employer, in consultation with the employees involved in operating the process, must determine the appropriate frequency of refresher training.

Training Documentation

The employer must determine whether each employee operating a process has received and understands the training required by the PSM standard. A record must be kept containing the identity of the employee, the date of training, and how the employer verified that the employee understood the training.

Contractors

Application

Many categories of contract labor may be present at a job site; such workers may actually operate the facility or perform only certain tasks because they have specialized knowledge or skill. Others work only for short periods when there is need for increased staff quickly, such as in turnaround operations. The PSM standard includes special provisions for contractors and their employees so they do nothing to endanger those working nearby.

The PSM standard therefore applies to contractors performing maintenance or repair, turnaround, major renovation, or specialty work on or adjacent to a covered process. It does not apply, however, to contractors providing incidental services that do not influence process safety, such as janitorial, food and drink, laundry, delivery, or other supply services.

Employer Responsibilities

When selecting a contractor, the employer must obtain and evaluate information regarding the contract employer's safety performance and programs. The employer must:

- Inform contract employers of the known potential fire, explosion, or toxic release hazards related to the contractor's work and the process;
- Explain to contract employers the applicable provisions of the emergency action plan;
- Develop and implement safe work practices to control the presence, entrance, and exit of contract employers and employees in covered process areas;
- Evaluate periodically the performance of contract employers in fulfilling their obligations; and
- Maintain an employee injury and illness log related to the contractor's work in the process areas.

Contract Employer Responsibilities

The contract employer must:

- Ensure contract employees are trained in the work practices necessary to perform their jobs safely;
- Ensure contract employees are instructed in the known potential for fire, explosion, or toxic release hazards related to their jobs and the processes, and in the applicable provisions of the emergency action plan;
- Document that each contract employee has received and understands the training required by the standard by preparing a record that contains the identity of the contract employee, the date of his or her training, and the means used to verify that he or she understood the training;
- Ensure each contract employee follows the safety rules of the facility, including the required safe work practices required in the operating procedures section of the standard; and
- Advise the employer of any unique hazards presented by the contract employer's work.

Pre-Startup Safety Review

It is important that the employer conduct a safety review before any highly hazardous chemical is introduced into a process. The PSM standard therefore requires the employer to perform a pre-startup safety review for new facilities and modified facilities when the modification is significant enough to require a change in the process safety information. Before a highly hazardous chemical is introduced to a process, the pre-startup safety review must confirm the following:

- Construction and equipment are in accordance with design specifications;
- Safety, operating, maintenance, and emergency procedures are in place and adequate;
- A process hazard analysis has been performed for new facilities and recommendations have been resolved or implemented before startup, and modified facilities meet the management of change requirements; and
- Each employee involved in operating a process has been trained.

Mechanical Integrity

It is important to maintain the mechanical integrity of critical process equipment to ensure it is designed and installed correctly and operates properly. The PSM mechanical integrity requirements apply to the following equipment:

- Pressure vessels and storage tanks;
- Piping systems, including piping components such as valves;
- Relief and vent systems and devices;
- Emergency shutdown systems;
- Controls, including monitoring devices and sensors, alarms, and interlocks; and
- Pumps.

The employer must establish and implement written procedures to maintain the ongoing integrity of process equipment. Employees involved in maintaining the ongoing integrity of process equipment must be trained in an overview of that process and its hazards as well as the procedures applicable to his or her specific job tasks. Inspection and testing must be performed on process equipment, using procedures that follow recognized and generally accepted good engineering practices. The frequency of inspections and tests of process equipment must conform to the manufacturer's recommendations and good engineering practices, or more frequently if determined to be necessary by previous operating experience. Each inspection and test on process equipment must be documented, identifying:

- The date of the inspection or test;
- The name of the person who performed the inspection or test;
- The serial number or other identifier of the equipment on which the inspection or test was performed;
- A description of the inspection or test performed; and
- The results of the inspection or test.

Equipment deficiencies outside the acceptable limits defined by the process safety information must be corrected before further use. When other necessary steps are taken to ensure safe operation, it may not be necessary to correct deficiencies before further use, as long as the deficiencies are corrected in a safe and timely manner.

When constructing new plants and equipment, the employer must ensure that equipment as it is fabricated is suitable for the process application for which it will be used. Appropriate checks and inspections must be performed to ensure the equipment is installed properly and is consistent with design specifications and the manufacturer's instructions. The employer also must ensure that maintenance materials, spare parts, and equipment are suitable for the process application for which they will be used.

Hot Work Permit

A permit must be issued for hot work operations conducted on or near a covered process. The permit must document that the OSHA fire prevention and protection regulations (29 CFR 1910.252(a)) were implemented before the hot work operations commenced; indicate the date(s) authorized for hot work; and identify the object on which hot work is to be performed. The permit must be kept on file until the hot work is completed.

Management of Change

Before changes to a process are implemented, they must be thoroughly evaluated to fully assess their impact on employee safety and health and to determine whether other changes to the operating procedures are necessary. To this end, the PSM standard contains a section on procedures for managing changes to processes. Written procedures to manage changes (except for "replacements in kind") to process chemicals, technology, equipment, and procedures and changes to facilities that affect a covered process must be established and implemented. These written procedures must ensure the following considerations are addressed prior to any change:

- The technical basis for the proposed change;
- The impact of the change on employee safety and health;
- Modifications to operating procedures;
- Necessary time period for the change; and
- Authorization requirements for the proposed change.

Employees who operate a process and maintenance and contract employees whose job tasks will be affected by a change in the process must be informed of and trained in the change before startup of the process or startup of the affected part of the process. If a change covered by these procedures results in a change in the required process safety information, such information also must be updated accordingly. If a change covered by these procedures changes the required operating procedures or practices, they also must be updated.

Incident Investigation

A crucial part of the process safety management program is a thorough investigation of incidents to identify the chain of events and causes so that corrective measures can be developed and implemented. Accordingly, the PSM standard requires the investigation of each incident that resulted in, or could have reasonably resulted in, a catastrophic release of a highly hazardous chemical in the workplace. Such an investigation must be initiated as promptly as possible, but no later than 48 hours following the incident.

The investigation must be conducted by a team consisting of at least one person knowledgeable in the process involved, including a contract employee if the incident involved the work of a contractor, and other persons with appropriate knowledge and experience to investigate and analyze the incident thoroughly.

The team must submit a written investigation report to the employer that includes, at a minimum:

- The date of the incident;
- The date the investigation began;
- A description of the incident;
- Factors that contributed to the incident; and
- Recommendations resulting from the investigation.

A system must be established to promptly address and resolve the incident report's findings and recommendations. Resolutions and corrective actions must be documented and the report reviewed by all affected personnel whose job tasks are relevant to the incident findings (including contract employees when applicable).

The employer must keep an investigation report for five years after the incident's occurrence.

Emergency Planning and Response

If despite the best planning an incident occurs, it is essential that emergency pre-planning and training make employees aware of, and able to execute, proper actions. For this reason, an emergency action plan for the entire site must be developed and implemented in accordance with the provisions of 29 CFR 1910.38. In addition, the emergency action plan must include procedures for handling small releases of hazardous chemicals. Employers covered under the PSM standard also may be subject to the hazardous waste and emergency response standards set forth at 29 CFR 1910.120(a), (p), and (q).

Compliance Audits

To be certain process safety management is effective, employers must certify that they have evaluated their compliance with the PSM standard at least every three years. This audit will verify that the procedures and practices developed under the standard are adequate and are being followed. The compliance audit must be conducted by at least one person knowledgeable in the process. The employer must determine and document an appropriate response to each of the findings of the compliance audit and document whether (and how) deficiencies have been corrected. The two most recent compliance audit reports must be kept on file.

Trade Secrets

Employers must make available all information necessary to comply with the PSM standard to those persons responsible for compiling the process safety information; developing the process hazard analysis; developing the operating procedures; and performing incident investigations, emergency planning and response, and compliance audits, without regard to the possible trade secret status of such information. Nothing in the PSM standard however precludes the employer from requiring those persons to enter into confidentiality agreements not to disclose any proprietary information.

PERMIT-REQUIRED CONFINED SPACES

The regulation covers general industry workers including 1.6 million who enter confined spaces annually and an additional 10.6 million employed at the 240,000 worksites covered by the standard (29 CFR 1910.146). This standard is expected to prevent nearly 85 percent of deaths and injuries (i.e., 54 deaths and 10,949 injuries) each year.

A confined space is defined as an area that:
- Has adequate size and configuration for employee entry;
- Has limited means of access or egress; and
- Is not designed for continuous employee occupancy.

A permit-required confined space is a confined space that presents or has the potential for hazards related to atmospheric conditions (e.g., toxic, flammable, asphyxiating), engulfment, configuration or any other recognized serious hazard.

A prohibited condition is defined as any condition not allowed by permit during entry operations.

The standard requires employers initially to evaluate their workplaces and determine if there are any permit-required confined spaces, inform employees through signs or other equally effective means and prevent unauthorized entry.

The permit-required confined space program:
- Mandates a written program to:
  - prevent unauthorized entry;
  - identify and evaluate hazards; and
  - establish procedures and practices for safe entry, including testing and monitoring conditions;
- Calls for:
  - an attendant be stationed outside permit spaces during entry;
  - procedures to summon rescuers and prevent unauthorized personnel from attempting rescue; and
  - a system for preparing, issuing, using and canceling entry permits; and
- Requires:
  - coordinated entry for more than one employer;
  - procedures for concluding entry operations and canceling entry permits; and
  - review of permit program at least annually and additionally as necessary.

A permit system must be established that requires an entry supervisor to authorize entry, prepare and sign written permits, order corrective measures if necessary and cancel permits when work is completed. Permits must be available to all employees and extend only for duration of the task. Permits must be retained for one year to facilitate review of the confined space program. Permits must include:

- Identification of space;
- Purpose of entry;
- Date and duration of permit;
- List of authorized entrants;
- Names of current attendants and entry supervisor;
- List of hazards in the permit space;
- List of measurements to isolate permit space and eliminate or control hazards;
- The acceptable entry conditions;
- Results of tests initialed by the person(s) performing tests;
- Rescue emergency services and means to summon;
- Communication procedures for attendants or entrants;
- Required equipment (e.g., respirators, communications, alarm);
- Any additional permits (e.g., for hot work).

Training mandates initial and refresher training (when duties change, hazards in spaces change or whenever evaluation determines inadequacies in employees' knowledge) to provide employees understanding, skills and knowledge to do jobs safely. Employer certification of training must include employee's name, signature or initials of trainer and date of training.

Authorized entrants must know the hazards they may face, be able to recognize signs or symptoms of exposure and understand the consequences of exposure to hazards. Entrants must know how to use any needed equipment, communicate with attendants as necessary, alert attendants when a warning symptom or other hazardous condition exists and exit as quickly as possible whenever ordered or alerted (by alarm, warning sign or prohibited condition) to do so.

Attendants must know the hazards of confined spaces, be aware of behavioral effects of potential exposures, maintain continuous count and identification of authorized attendants, remain outside space until relieved, communicate with entrants as necessary to monitor entrant status. Attendants also must monitor activities inside and outside the permit space and order exit if required, summon rescuers if necessary, prevent unauthorized entry into confined space, and perform non-entry rescues if required. They may not perform other duties that interfere with their primary duties to monitor and protect the safety of authorized entrants.

Entry supervisors must know hazards of confined spaces, verify that all tests have been conducted and all procedures and equipment are in place before endorsing permit, terminate entry and cancel permits and verify that rescue services are available and the means for summoning them are operable. Supervisors are to remove unauthorized individuals who enter confined space. They also must determine at least when shifts and entry supervisors change—that acceptable conditions as specified in the permit continue.

Rescue services may be on-site or off-site. Rescue teams are to use employee retrieval systems whenever possible. On-site rescue teams must be properly equipped and receive the same training as authorized entrants plus training to use personal protective and rescue equipment and first aid, including CPR. They must practice simulated rescues at least once every 12 months. Outside rescue services must be made aware of hazards, receive access to comparable permit spaces to develop rescue plans and practice rescues. Employers must provide hospitals or treatment facilities with any material safety data sheets (MSDSs) or other information on a permit-required space hazard exposure situation that may aid in the treatment of rescued employees.

Contractors call for host employers to provide information to contractors on permit-required confined spaces, the permit space program, and procedures and likely hazards that the contractor might encounter. Joint entries must be coordinated and the contractor debriefed at the conclusion of entry operations.

Alternative Protection Procedures

For permit spaces where the only hazard is atmospheric and ventilation alone can control the hazard, employers may use alternative procedures for entry.

To qualify for alternative procedures employers must:

- Ensure it is safe to remove the entrance cover;
- Determine that ventilation alone is sufficient to maintain the permit space safe for entry and work to be performed within the permit-required space must introduce no additional hazards;
- Gather monitoring and inspection data to support the above two items;
- If entry is necessary to conduct initial data gathering, perform such entry under the full permit program; and
- Document the determinations and supporting data and make them available to employees.

Entry can take place after:

- It has been determined safe to remove the entrance cover;
- Any openings have been guarded to protect against falling and falling objects;
- Internal atmospheric testing has been performed;
- Air remains without hazard whenever any employee is inside the space;
- Continuous forced air ventilation has eliminated any hazardous atmosphere; and
- The space is tested periodically.

Employees must exit immediately if a hazardous atmosphere is detected during entry Afterward. the space must be evaluated to determine how the hazardous atmosphere developed.

Permit-Required Confined Spaces— 1910.146

Many workplaces contain spaces that are considered to be "confined" because their configurations hinder the activities of any employees who must enter into, work in and exit from them. In many instances, employees who work in confined spaces also face increased risk of exposure to serious physical injury from hazards such as entrapment, engulfment and hazardous atmospheric conditions. Confinement itself may pose entrapment hazards, and work in confined spaces may keep employees closer to hazards, such as an asphyxiating atmosphere, than they would be otherwise. For example, confinement, limited access and restricted airflow can result in hazardous conditions that would not arise in an open workplace.

The term "permit-required confined space" refers to those spaces that meet the definition of a "confined space" and pose health or safety hazards, thereby requiring a permit for entry.

A confined space may include, but are not limited to, underground vaults, tanks, storage bins, pits and diked areas, vessels, and silos that have the following characteristics:

- Limited or restricted means of entry or exit;
- Is large enough for an employee to enter and perform assigned work; and
- Is not designed for continuous occupancy by the employee.

A permit-required confined space is one that meets the definition of a confined space and has one or more of the following characteristics:

- Contains or has the potential to contain a hazardous atmosphere;
- Contains a material that has the potential for engulfing an entrant;
- Has an internal configuration that might cause an entrant to be trapped or asphyxiated by inwardly converging walls or by a floor that slopes downward and tapers to a smaller cross-section; or
- Contains any other recognized serious safety or health hazards.

In general, employers must evaluate the workplace to determine if spaces are permit-required confined spaces. If there are permit spaces in the workplace, the employer must inform exposed employees of the existence, location and danger posed by the spaces. This can be accomplished by posting danger signs or by another equally effective means (See Exhibit 8-1.). The following language would satisfy the requirements for such a sign:

DANGER
PERMIT-REQUIRED CONFINED SPACE

AUTHORIZED ENTRANTS ONLY

If employees are not to enter and work in permit spaces, employers must take effective measures to prevent their employees from entering the permit spaces.

Exhibit 8-1.
Permit-required confined spaces should be clearly marked as dangerous.

If employees are to enter permit spaces, the employer must develop a written permit space program that shall be made available to employees or their representatives. Under certain conditions, the employer may use alternate procedures for worker entry into a permit space. For example, if employers can demonstrate with monitoring and inspection data that the only hazard is an actual or potential hazardous atmosphere that can be made safe for entry by the use of continuous forced-air ventilation, they may be exempted from some requirements, such as permits and attendants. Even in such circumstances, however, the internal atmosphere of the space must be tested first for oxygen content, second for flammable gases and vapors, and third for potential toxic air contaminants before any employee enters.

Written Program

The employer who allows employee entry must develop and implement a written program for permit-required confined spaces.

The OSHA standard requires the employer's program to:

- Identify and evaluate permit space hazards before allowing employee entry;

- Test conditions in the permit space before entry operations and monitor the space during entry;
- Perform appropriate testing for atmospheric hazards in the following order:
  - Oxygen;
  - Combustible gases or vapors; and
  - Toxic gases or vapors; and
- Implement necessary measures to prevent unauthorized entry;
- Establish and implement the means, procedures and practices, such as specifying acceptable entry conditions, isolating the permit space, providing barriers, verifying acceptable entry conditions, purging, making inert, flushing, or ventilation of the permit space to eliminate or control hazards necessary for safe permit-space entry operations;
- Identify employee job duties;
- Provide, maintain and require, at no cost to the employee, the use of personal protective equipment and any other equipment necessary for safe entry (e.g., testing, monitoring, ventilating, communications, and lighting equipment; barriers; shields and ladders);
- Ensure that at least one attendant is stationed outside the permit space for the duration of entry operations;
- Coordinate entry operations when employees of more than one employer are to be working in the permit space;
- Implement appropriate procedures for summoning rescue and emergency services;
- Establish, in writing, and implement a system for the preparation, issuance, use and cancellation of entry permits;
- Review established entry operations and annually revise the permit-space entry program; and
- When an attendant is required to monitor multiple spaces, implement the procedures to be followed during an emergency in one or more of the permit spaces being monitored.

If hazardous conditions are detected during entry, employees must immediately leave the space and the employer must evaluate the space to determine the cause of the hazardous atmospheres.

When entry to permit spaces is prohibited, the employer must take effective measures to prevent unauthorized entry. Non-permit confined spaces must be reevaluated when there are changes in their use or configuration and, where appropriate, must be reclassified.

If testing and inspection data prove that a permit-required confined space no longer poses hazards, that space may be reclassified as a non-permit confined space. If entry is required to eliminate hazards and to obtain the data, the employer must follow procedures as set forth under sections (d) through (k) of the standard. A certificate documenting the data must be made available to employees entering the space. The certificate must include the date, location of the space and the signature of the person making the certification.

Contractors must be informed of permit spaces and permit-space entry requirements, any identified hazards, the employer's experience with the space (i.e., the knowledge of hazardous conditions), and precautions or procedures to be followed when in or near permit spaces.

When employees of more than one employer are conducting entry operations, the affected employers must coordinate entry operations to ensure that affected employees are appropriately protected from permit space hazards. Contractors also must be given any other pertinent information regarding hazards and operations in permit spaces and be debriefed at the conclusion of entry operations.

Permit System

A permit must be posted at entrances or otherwise made available to entrants before they enter a permit space. The permit must be signed by the entry supervisor, attest that pre-entry preparations have been completed and that the space is safe to enter.

The duration of entry permits must not exceed the time required to complete an assignment. Also, the entry supervisor must terminate entry and cancel permits when an assignment has been completed or when new conditions exist. New conditions must be noted on the canceled permit and used in revising the permit space program. The standard also requires the employer to keep all canceled entry permits for at least one year.

Entry Permits

Entry permits must include the following information:

- Test results;
- Tester's initials or signature;
- Name and signature of the supervisor who authorizes entry;
- Name of permit space to be entered, authorized entrant(s), eligible attendants and individual(s) authorized to be entry supervisor(s);
- Purpose of entry and known space hazards;
- Measures to be taken to isolate permit spaces and to eliminate or control space hazards (i.e., locking out or tagging of equipment and procedures for purging, making inert, ventilating and flushing permit spaces);
- Name and telephone numbers of rescue and emergency services;
- Date and authorized duration of entry;
- Acceptable entry conditions;
- Communication procedures and equipment to maintain contact during entry;
- Additional permit(s), such as for hot work, that have been issued to authorize work in the permit space;
- Special equipment and procedures, including personal protective equipment and alarm systems; and
- Any other information needed to ensure employee safety.

Training and Education

Before an initial work assignment begins, the employer must provide proper training for all workers who are required to work in permit spaces. Upon completing this training, employers must ensure that employees have acquired the understanding, knowledge and skills necessary for the safe performance of their duties. Additional training is required when:

- The job duties change;
- There is a change in the permit-space program or the permit-space operation presents a new hazard; or
- When an employee's job performance shows deficiencies.

Training also is required for rescue team members, including cardiopulmonary resuscitation (CPR) and first aid (see Emergencies).

Employers must certify this training has been accomplished.

Upon completion of training, employees must receive a certificate of training that includes the employee's name, signature or initials of trainer(s), and dates of training. The certification must be made available for inspection by employees and their authorized representatives. In addition, the employer also must ensure that employees are trained in their assigned duties.

Authorized Entrant's Duties

- Know space hazards, including information on the mode of exposure (e.g., inhalation or dermal absorption), signs or symptoms and consequences of the exposure;
- Use appropriate personal protective equipment properly (e.g., face and eye protection and other forms of barrier protection such as gloves, aprons and coveralls);
- As necessary, maintain communication (i.e., telephone, radio, visual observation) with attendants to enable the attendant to monitor the entrant's status as well as to alert the entrant to evacuate;
- Exit from permit space as soon as possible when ordered by an authorized person, the entrant recognizes the warning signs or symptoms of exposure exist, a prohibited condition exists, or an automatic alarm is activated; and
- Alert the attendant when a prohibited condition exists or warning signs or symptoms of exposure exist.

Attendant's Duties

- Remain outside permit space during entry operations unless relieved by another authorized attendant;
- Perform no-entry rescues when specified by employer's rescue procedure;
- Know existing and potential hazards, including information on the mode of exposure, signs or symptoms, consequences of the exposure and their physiological effects;
- Maintain communication with and keep an accurate account of those workers entering the permit-required space;
- Order evacuation of the permit space when a prohibited condition exists, a worker shows signs of physiological effects of

hazardous exposure, an emergency outside the confined space exists, or the attendant cannot effectively and safely perform required duties;
- Summon rescue and other services during an emergency;
- Ensure that unauthorized persons stay away from permit spaces or exit immediately if they have entered the permit space;
- Inform authorized entrants and entry supervisor of entry by unauthorized persons; and;
- Perform no other duties that interfere with the attendant's primary duties.

Entry Supervisor's Duties

- Know space hazards, including information on the mode of exposure, signs or symptoms and consequences of exposure;
- Verify emergency plans and specified entry conditions such as permits, tests, procedures and equipment before allowing entry;
- Terminate entry and cancel permits when entry operations are completed or if a new condition exists;
- Take appropriate measures to remove unauthorized entrants; and
- Ensure that entry operations remain consistent with the entry permit and that acceptable entry conditions are maintained.

Emergencies

The standard requires the employer to ensure that rescue service personnel are provided with and trained in the proper use of personal protective and rescue equipment, including respirators; trained to perform assigned rescue duties; and have had authorized entrant's training. The standard also requires that rescuers be trained in first aid and CPR and, at a minimum, one rescue team member be currently certified in first aid and in CPR. The employer also must ensure that practice rescue exercises are performed annually, and that rescue services are provided access to permit spaces so they can practice rescue operations. Rescuers also must be informed of the hazards of the permit space.

Also, when appropriate, authorized entrants who enter a permit space must wear a chest or full body harness with a retrieval line attached to the center of their backs near shoulder level or above their heads. Wristlets may be used if the employer can demonstrate that the use of a chest or full body harness is infeasible or creates a greater hazard. Also, the employer must ensure that the other end of the retrieval line is attached to a mechanical device or to a fixed point outside the permit space. A mechanical device must be available to retrieve personnel from vertical type permit spaces more than 5 ft. deep.

In addition, if an injured entrant is exposed to a substance for which an MSDS or other similar written information is required to be kept at the worksite, that MSDS or other written information must be made available to the medical facility treating the exposed entrant.

ELECTRICAL

Electricity has become an essential of modern life, both at home and on the job. Some employees work with electricity directly, as is the case with engineers, electricians or people who do wiring, such as overhead lines, cable harnesses or circuit assemblies. Others, such as office workers and salespeople, work with it indirectly. As a source of power, electricity is accepted without much thought to the hazards encountered. Perhaps because it has become such a familiar part of our surroundings, it often is not treated with the respect it deserves.

The Bureau of Labor Statistics reported that work-related death occurred in private-sector workplaces employing 11 workers or more have been reduced since 1992 when 334 electrocutions were reported. Still, more than 200 workers are electrocuted each year.

Exhibit 9-1.
Annual workplace electrocutions as reported by the Bureau of Labor Statistics.

Year	Annual
1992	334
1993	325
1994	348
1995	348
1996	281
1997	298
1998	334
1999	280
2000	256 (p)
(p): preliminary	

OSHA's electrical standards address the government's concern that electricity has long been recognized as a serious workplace hazard, exposing employees to such dangers as electric shock, electrocution, fires and explosions. The objective of the standards is to minimize such potential hazards by specifying design characteristics of safety in use of electrical equipment and systems.

OSHA's electrical standards were carefully developed to cover only those parts of any electrical system that an employee would normally use or contact. The exposed and/or operating elements of an electrical installation (e.g., lighting equipment, motors, machines, appliances, switches, controls, enclosures) must be so constructed and installed as to minimize electrical dangers to people in any workplace.

The OSHA electrical standards were based on the National Fire Protection Association's standard NFPA 70E, Electrical Safety Requirements for Employee Workplaces, and the NFPA 70 Committee derived Part I of their document from the 1978 edition of the National Electrical Code (NEC). The standards extracted from the NEC were those considered to most directly apply to employee safety and least likely to change with each new edition of the NEC. OSHA's electrical standards are performance oriented; therefore, they contain few direct references to the NEC. However, the NEC contains specific information as to how the required performance can be obtained.

General Requirements—1910.303

The conductors and equipment required or permitted by this subpart shall be acceptable only if approved.

Examination, Installation and Use of Equipment

Examination

Electrical equipment shall be free from recognized hazards that are likely to cause death or serious physical harm to employees. Safety of equipment shall be determined using the following considerations:

- Suitability for installation and use in conformity with the provisions of this subpart;
- Suitability of equipment for an identified purpose may be evidenced by listing or labeling for that identified purpose;
- Mechanical strength and durability, including, for parts designed to enclose and protect other equipment, the adequacy of the protection thus provided;
- Electrical insulation;
- Heating effects under conditions of use;
- Arcing effects;
- Classification by type, size, voltage, current capacity, and specific use; and
- Other factors that contribute to the practical safeguarding of employees using or likely to come in contact with the equipment.

Installation and Use

Listed or labeled equipment shall be used or installed in accordance with any instructions included in the listing or labeling.

Splices

Conductors shall be spliced or joined with splicing devices suitable for such use or by brazing, welding or soldering with a fusible metal or alloy. Soldered splices shall be so spliced or joined as to be mechanically and electrically secure without solder and then soldered. All splices and joints and the free ends of conductors shall be covered with insulation equivalent to that of the conductors or with an insulating device suitable for the purpose.

Arcing Parts

Parts of electric equipment that in ordinary operation produce arcs, sparks, flames or molten metal shall be enclosed or separated and isolated from all combustible material.

Marking

Electrical equipment may not be used unless the manufacturer's name, trademark or other descriptive marking that may identify the organization responsible for the product is placed on the equipment. Other markings shall be provided giving voltage, current, wattage or other ratings as necessary. The markings shall be of sufficient durability to withstand the environment involved.

Sometimes this section is confused with the section "Identification of Disconnecting Means." The difference is that *identification* (as used in OSHA standards) means marked to indicate the purpose of a disconnecting means, rather than its rating.

Marking is very important. If an item of equipment is connected to a voltage higher than its rating, the chances are that a violent failure will result. If it is connected to a voltage below its rating, it may attempt to perform its intended function, but may overheat badly and eventually fail. If AC equipment is energized with the wrong frequency, or with direct current, it will probably fail violently. These occurrences can cause burns to employees and may cause fires. If equipment is connected to a circuit not adequate for the load, conductors may overheat and deteriorate. Overcurrent protective devices should prevent serious damage in such a case, but sometimes these devices have been tampered with and do not protect properly.

If the manufacturer's name is not marked on the nameplate, there will be difficulty in tracing the reasons for faulty performance and in preventing future failures. Sometimes it is necessary to know the manufacturer in order to determine if equipment is approved for a particular purpose. The manufacturer's name is also necessary in many cases so that the user can obtain information or replacement parts.

The marking described above is almost always provided on the nameplate of the equipment of reputable manufacturers. Violations usually appear when the nameplate is covered by some part of the installation, is removed or is obliterated by painting or other abuse.

Identification of Disconnecting Means and Circuits

Each disconnecting means required by this subpart for motors and appliances shall be legibly marked to indicate its purpose, unless located and arranged so the purpose is evident. Each service, feeder and branch circuit, at its disconnecting means or overcurrent device, shall be legibly marked to indicate its purpose, unless located and arranged so the purpose is evident. These markings shall be of sufficient durability to withstand the environment involved.

A disconnecting means is a switch that is used to disconnect the conductors of a circuit from the source of electric current. Having the ability to stop electricity provides better protection for workers and equipment.

Each disconnect switch or overcurrent device required for a service, feeder, or branch circuit must be clearly labeled to indicate the circuit's function, and the label or marking should be located at the point where the circuit originates.

For example, on a panel that controls several motors or on a motor control center, each disconnect must be clearly marked to indicate the motor to which each circuit is connected. In Exhibit 9-2, the Number 2 circuit breaker in the panel box supplies current only to disconnect Number 2, which in turn controls the current to motor Number 2. The current to motor Number 2 can be shut off by the Number 2 circuit breaker or the Number 2 disconnect.

If the purpose of the circuit is obvious, no identification of the disconnect is required.

All labels and markings must be durable enough to withstand weather, chemicals, heat, corrosion, or any other environment to which they may be exposed.

600 Volts, Nominal, or Less

Working Space About Electric Equipment
Note that this particular section is concerned with the safety of a person qualified to work on the equipment (presumably an electrician). Obviously, the hazard must be treated in a different way if the person will remove guards and enclosures and actually work on the live parts. Sufficient access and working space shall be provided and maintained about all electric equipment to permit ready and safe operation and maintenance of such equipment.

Working Clearances
Except as required or permitted elsewhere in this subpart, the dimension of the working space in the direction of access to live parts operating at 600 volts or less and likely to require examination, adjustment, servicing or maintenance while alive may not be less

Panel Schedule

1. Motor No. 1
2. Motor No. 2
3. Motor No. 3
4. Motor No. 4

Motor No. 1 is Controlled by Disconnect No. 1 and Circuit Breaker No. 1

NOTE: As shown in diagram, the purposes of these disconnecting switches are clearly evident. In such cases identification may be omitted. In the actual installation however, the motors may not be within sight of the disconnects or arranged in such a way that the purpose is not evident and identification would be required.

Exhibit 9-2.
Each disconnect and circuit requires identification.

than indicated in Table S-1 of 1910.303(g)(1)(i). In addition, workspace may not be less than 30 inches wide in front of the electrical equipment. Distances shall be measured from the live parts if they are exposed or from the enclosure front or opening if the live parts are enclosed. Concrete, brick or tile walls are considered to be grounded. Working space is not required in back of assemblies such as dead-front switchboards or motor control centers where there are no renewable or adjustable parts, such as fuses or switches, on the back and where all connections are accessible from locations other than the back.

The remaining paragraphs of this section require that the working spaces shall not be used for storage, that access to the working space be maintained, and that reasonable illumination and headroom be maintained.

Guarding of Live Parts

It should be noted that the purpose of this requirement is to protect *any person* who may be in the vicinity of electrical equipment against accidental contact. These people are presumably not electricians working on the equipment and are not qualified or trained to be in close proximity to live parts.

Except as required or permitted elsewhere in this subpart, live parts of electric equipment operating at 50 volts or more shall be guarded against accidental contact by approved cabinets, other forms of approved enclosures or by any of the following means:

- By location in a room, vault or similar enclosure that is accessible only to qualified persons.
- By suitable permanent substantial partitions or screens so arranged that only qualified persons would have access to the space within reach of the live parts. Any openings in such partitions or screens shall be so sized and located that persons are not likely to come into accidental contact with the live parts or to bring conducting objects into contact with them.
- By location on a suitable balcony, gallery or platform.
- By elevation of 8 ft. or more above the floor or other working surface.

- In locations where electric equipment would be exposed to physical damage, enclosures or guards shall be so arranged and of such strength as to prevent such damage.

Over 600 Volts, Nominal

Enclosure for Electrical Installations

Electrical installations in a vault, room, closet or in an area surrounded by a wall, screen, or fence, access to which is controlled by lock and key or other approved means, are considered accessible to qualified persons only. A wall, screen or fence less than 8 ft. in height is not considered to prevent access unless it has other features that provide a degree of isolation equivalent to an 8-ft. fence. The entrances to all buildings, rooms or enclosures containing exposed live parts or exposed conductors operating at over 600 volts, nominal, shall be kept locked or under the observation of a qualified person at all times.

Workspace About Equipment

Electrical installations having exposed live parts shall be accessible to qualified persons only. Sufficient space shall be provided and maintained about electric equipment to permit ready and safe operation and maintenance of such equipment. Where energized parts are exposed, the minimum clear workspace may not be less than 6 ft. 6 in. high (measured vertically from the floor or platform) or less than 3 ft. wide (measured parallel to the equipment). The minimum depth of clear working space in front of electric equipment is given in Table S-2 of 1910.303(h)(3)(i).

Illumination

Adequate illumination shall be provided for all working spaces about electric equipment. The lighting outlets shall be so arranged that live parts or other equipment will not endanger persons changing lamps or making repairs on the lighting system. The points of control shall be so located that persons are not likely to come in contact with any live part or moving part of the equipment while turning on the lights.

Elevation of Unguarded Live Parts
Unguarded live parts above working space shall be maintained at elevations not less than specified in Table S-3 of 1910.303(h)(3)(iii).

Entrance and Access to Workspace
At least one entrance not less than 24 in. wide and 6 ft. 6 in. high shall be provided to give access to the workspace about electric equipment. On switchboard and control panels exceeding 48 in. in width, there shall be one entrance at each end of such board where practicable. Where bare energized parts at any voltage or insulated energized parts above 600 volts are located adjacent to such entrance, they shall be suitably guarded.

Permanent ladders or stairways shall be provided to give safe access to the working space around electric equipment installed on platforms, balconies, mezzanine floors, or in attic or roof rooms or spaces.

Wiring Design and Protection—1910.304

Use and Identification of Grounded and Grounding Conductors

Identification of Conductors
A conductor used as a grounded conductor shall be identifiable and distinguishable from all other conductors. A conductor used as an equipment-grounding conductor shall be identifiable and distinguishable from all other conductors.

The grounded conductor is an energized circuit conductor that is connected to earth through the system ground. It is commonly referred to as the neutral. The equipment-grounding conductor is not an energized conductor under normal conditions. The equipment-grounding conductor acts as a safeguard against insulation failure or faults in the other circuit conductors. The equip-ment-grounding conductor is energized only if there is a leak or fault in the normal current path and it directs this current back to the source. Directing the fault current back to the source enables protective devices, such as circuit breakers or fuses, to operate thus preventing fires and reducing the hazard of electrical shocks.

The grounded and equipment-grounding conductors of an electrical circuit must be marked or color-coded in a way that allows employees to identify them and tell them apart from each other and from the other conductors in the circuit (See Exhibit 9-3).

Acceptable color-coding includes the method required by the National Electrical Code, Section 210-5. The Code states:

[t]he grounded conductor of a branch circuit shall be identified by a continuous white or natural gray color.... The equipment ground-ing conductor of a branch circuit shall be identified by a continuous green color or a continuous green color with one or more yellow stripes unless it is bare.

Polarity of Connections
No grounded conductor may be attached to any terminal or lead so as to reverse designated polarity.

Exhibit 9-3.
Color-coding is an effective way to identify and distinguish conducter types.

Use of Grounding Terminals and Devices

A grounding terminal or grounding-type device on a receptacle, cord connector or attachment plug may not be used for purposes other than grounding.

Reversed Polarity

The above two subparagraphs dealing with polarity of connections and use of grounding terminals and devices address one potentially dangerous aspect of alternating current: Many pieces of equipment will operate properly even though the supply wires are not connected in the order designated by design or the manufacturer. Improper connection of these conductors is most prevalent on the smaller branch circuit typically associated with standard 120 volt receptacle outlets, lighting fixtures and cord- and plug-connected equipment. When plugs, receptacles and connectors are used in an electrical branch circuit, correct polarity between the ungrounded (hot) conductor, the grounded (neutral) conductor and the grounding conductor must be maintained.

Reversed polarity is a condition when the identified circuit conductor (the grounded conductor or neutral) is incorrectly connected to the ungrounded or "hot" terminal of a plug, receptacle or other type of connector. Exhibit 9-4 shows the correct wiring for the common 120-volt outlet with a portable hand tool attached.

Suppose now that the black (ungrounded) and white (grounded) conductors are reversed as shown in Exhibit 9-5. This is the traditional reversed

TYPICAL 120 VOLT BRANCH CIRCUIT WITH CORRECT WIRING

Exhibit 9-4.
Typical 120-volt branch circuit with correct wiring.

120 VOLT BRANCH CIRCUIT WITH BLACK AND WHITE WIRES REVERSED

Exhibit 9-5.
A 120-volt branch circuit with black and white wires reversed.

120 VOLT BRANCH CIRCUIT WITH BLACK AND WHITE WIRES REVERSED INTERNAL FAULT IN EQUIPMENT WIRING

Exhibit 9-6.
A 120-volt branch circuit with an internal fault.

WHITE AND GREEN WIRES REVERSED

Exhibit 9-7.
A 120-volt branch circuit with white and green wires reversed.

Exhibit 9-8.
A 120-volt branch circuit with black and green wires reversed.

polarity. Although a shock hazard may not exist, there are other mechanical hazards that can occur.

For example, if an internal fault should occur in the wiring as shown in Exhibit 9-6, the equipment would not stop when the switch is released or would start as soon as a person plugged the supply cord into the improperly wired outlet. This could result in serious injury.

Exhibit 9-7 shows the white (grounded) and green (grounding) conductors reversed. Although it is not accurate, considering OSHA or code terminology, to call this reversed polarity, a hazard can still exist. In this case, due to the wiring error, the white wire is being used to provide equipment grounding. Under certain conditions, this could be dangerous.

Exhibit 9-8 shows an extremely dangerous situation. In this example, the black (ungrounded) and green (grounding) conductors have been reversed. The metal case of the equipment is at 120 volts with reference to the surroundings. As soon as a person picks up the equipment and touches a conductive surface in his or her surroundings, he or she will receive a serious, perhaps deadly, shock.

Although the equipment will not work with this wiring error, it would not be unusual for a person to pick up the equipment before realizing this. The person may even attempt to troubleshoot the problem before unplugging the power cord.

Correct polarity is achieved when the grounded conductor is connected to the corresponding grounded terminal and the ungrounded conductor is connected to the corresponding ungrounded terminal. The reverse of the designated polarity is prohibited. Exhibit 9-9 illustrates a duplex receptacle correctly wired. Terminals are designated and identified to avoid confusion. An easy way to remember the correct polarity is:

- White to light: The white (grounded) wire should be connected to the light or nickel-colored terminal;
- Black to brass: The black or multi-colored (ungrounded) wire should be connected to the brass terminal; and
- Green to green: The green or bare (grounding) wire should be connected to the green hexagonal head terminal screw.

Services

Disconnecting Means

Means shall be provided to disconnect all conductors in a building or other structure from the service-entrance conductors. The disconnecting means shall plainly indicate whether it is in the open or closed position and shall be installed at a readily accessible location nearest the point of entrance of the service-entrance conductors.

A readily accessible means of disconnecting conductors is required to be located at a point near the service entrance. The service entrance is the location where the serving conductors enter a building. The disconnecting means can be a switch or circuit breaker and must be capable of interrupting the circuit from the source of supply.

Exhibit 9-9.
A correctly wired duplex receptacle.

This will disconnect the electrical equipment within the building from its source of supply in the event of an emergency or during normal servicing operations.

Services Over 600 Volts, Nominal

The following additional requirements apply to services over 600 volts, nominal:

- Guarding. Service-entrance conductors installed as open wires shall be guarded to make them accessible only to qualified persons.
- Warning signs. Signs warning of high voltage shall be posted where other than qualified employees might come in contact with live parts.

Overcurrent Protection

600 Volts, Nominal, or Less

The following requirements apply to overcurrent protection of circuits rated 600 volts, nominal, or less.

Protection of Conductors and Equipment

Conductors and equipment shall be protected from overcurrent in accordance with their ability to safely conduct current.

Electric current is the flow of electrons through a conductor. The size of the wire is the main determining factor as to how much current can safely flow through a conductor. The larger the wire, the more current can flow safely. If too much current flows through a conductor excess heat is produced. If the circuit is not protected, the heat may continue to build and reach a temperature high enough to destroy the insulation and cause a fire.

Fuses and circuit breakers are protective devices designed to disconnect a circuit from its source of supply when a maximum allowable heat level is reached. The basic idea of a protective device is to make a weak link in the circuit. In the case of a fuse, the fuse is destroyed before another part of the system is destroyed. In the case of a circuit breaker, a set of contacts opens the circuit. Unlike a fuse, a circuit breaker can be reused by reclosing the contacts. Fuses and circuit breakers are designed to protect equipment and facilities, and in so doing, they provide considerable protection against shock in most

situations. It is important to ensure that overcurrent devices have adequate interrupting ratings in order to protect employees from shock.

The National Electrical Code specifies the allowable current flow permitted in certain-sized conductors. Ampacity is the term used to describe the current-carrying capacity of a conductor. The size of the fuse or circuit breaker required to provide protection is determined by the ampacity of the conductor in the circuit to be protected and the type of load that is on the circuit.

Grounded Conductors

Except for motor-running overload protection, overcurrent devices may not interrupt the continuity of the grounded conductor unless all conductors of the circuit are opened simultaneously. Unless excepted, overcurrent devices are always placed in the "hot" side of a circuit (usually a black wire) and in series with the load so that all the current in the circuit must flow through them.

Disconnection of Fuses and Thermal Cutouts

Except for service fuses, all cartridge fuses that are accessible to other than qualified persons and all fuses and thermal cutouts on circuits over 150 volts to ground shall be provided with disconnecting means. This disconnecting means shall be installed so that the fuse or thermal cutout can be disconnected from its supply without disrupting service to equipment and circuits unrelated to those protected by the overcurrent device.

Location in or on Premises

Overcurrent devices shall be readily accessible to each employee or authorized building management personnel. These overcurrent devices may not be located where they will be exposed to physical damage or in the vicinity of easily ignitable material.

The functions that overcurrent devices perform require proper operation and maintenance because of the tremendous amounts of energy likely to be handled during a fault. Also, when trouble occurs, it may be necessary to reach these devices quickly.

Physical damage often results when overcurrent devices are located where they can be struck by lift trucks or other vehicles, by crane hooks, by materials being handled, etc.

Easily ignitable material should not be stored in the vicinity of overcurrent devices. Most fuses and circuit breakers operate at elevated temperatures, at least some of the time, and they may on occasion emit flashes or sparks.

Arcing or Suddenly Moving Parts
Fuses and circuit breakers shall be so located or shielded that employees will not be burned or otherwise injured by their operation.

Circuit Breakers
Circuit breakers shall clearly indicate whether they are in the open (off) or closed (on) position.

Where circuit breaker handles on switchboards are operated vertically rather than horizontally or rotationally, the up position of the handle shall be the closed (on) position. If used as switches in 120-volt, fluorescent lighting circuits, circuit breakers shall be approved for the purpose and marked "SWD."

Over 600 Volts, Nominal
Feeders and branch circuits over 600 volts, nominal, shall have short-circuit protection.

Grounding
This section contains grounding requirements for systems, circuits and equipment. Grounding electrical circuits and electrical equipment is required to protect employees from electrical shock and fire and electrical equipment from damage. There are two kinds of grounding: (1) electrical circuit or system grounding and (2) electrical equipment grounding (See Exhibit 9-10.).

Electrical system grounding is accomplished when one conductor of the circuit is intentionally connected to earth. This is done to protect the circuit should lightning strike or other high voltage contact occur. Grounding a system also stabilizes the voltage in the system so "expected voltage levels" are not exceeded under normal conditions.

Electrical equipment grounding is accomplished when all metal frames of equipment

Exhibit 9-10.
There are two types of grounding: system grounding and equipment grounding.

and enclosures containing electrical equipment or conductors are grounded by means of a permanent and continuous connection or bond. The equipment grounding conductor provides a path for dangerous fault current to return to the system ground at the supply source of the circuit should an insulation failure take place. If installed properly, the equipment-grounding conductor is the current path that enables protective devices, such as circuit breakers and fuses, to operate when a fault occurs.

Grounding Path

The path to ground from circuits, equipment and enclosures shall be permanent and continuous.

This requirement was extracted from NEC 250-51, Effective Grounding Path, which is more complete and fundamental to the understanding of electrical safety. It states that the path to ground:

- "Shall be permanent and continuous." (If the path is installed in such a way that damage, corrosion, loosening, etc. may impair the continuity during the life of the installation, shock and burn hazards will develop.)
- "Shall have capacity to conduct safely any fault current likely to be imposed on it." (Fault currents may be many times normal currents, and such high currents may melt or burn metal at points of poor conductivity. These high temperatures may be a hazard in themselves and may destroy the continuity of the ground-fault path.)
- "Shall have sufficiently low impedance to limit the voltage to ground and to facilitate the operation of the circuit protective devices in the circuit." (If the ground-fault path has a high impedance, there will be hazardous voltages whenever fault currents attempt to flow. If the impedance is high, the fault current will be limited to some value so low that the fuse or circuit breaker will not operate promptly, if at all.)

It is important to remember the following regarding safe grounding paths:
- The fault current in AC circuits will be limited by the sum of resistance and reactance; the only low-reactance path is that which closely follows the circuit conductors.

- If a metallic raceway system is used, the metallic system must be continuous and permanent.
- In cases where a metallic raceway system is not used, a green or bare equipment-grounding conductor must be close to the supply conductors to ensure all enclosures are bonded together and to the source.

Supports, Enclosures and Equipment to be Grounded

Supports and Enclosures for Conductors

Metal cable trays, metal raceways and metal enclosures for conductors shall be grounded, except:
- Metal enclosures, such as sleeves, that are used to protect cable assemblies from physical damage need not be grounded; and
- Metal enclosures for conductors added to existing installations of open wire, knob-and-tube wiring and nonmetallic-sheathed cable need not be grounded if all of the following conditions are met:
  - Runs are less than 25 ft.;
  - Enclosures are free from probable contact with ground, grounded metal, or other conductive materials; and
  - Enclosures are guarded against employee contact.

Service Equipment Enclosures

Metal enclosures for service equipment shall be grounded.

Frames of Ranges and Clothes

Frames of electric ranges, wall-mounted ovens, counter-mounted cooking units, clothes dryers and metal outlet or junction boxes that are part of the circuit for these appliances shall be grounded.

Fixed Equipment

Exposed noncurrent-carrying metal parts of fixed equipment that may become energized shall be grounded if:
- Within 8 ft. vertically or 5 ft. horizontally of ground or grounded metal objects and subject to employee contact;
- Located in a wet or damp location and not isolated;

- In electrical contact with metal;
- In a hazardous (classified) location; or
- Supplied by a metal-clad, metal-sheathed or grounded metal raceway wiring method.
- Equipment operates with any terminal at over 150 volts to ground; however, the following need not be grounded:
  - Enclosures for switches or circuit breakers used for other than service equipment and accessible to qualified persons only;
  - Metal frames of electrically heated appliances that are permanently and effectively insulated from ground; and
  - The cases of distribution apparatus such as transformers and capacitors mounted on wooden poles at a height exceeding 8 ft. above ground or grade level.

Equipment Connected by Cord and Plug

Under any of the conditions described below, exposed noncurrent-carrying metal parts of cord- and plug-connected equipment that may become energized shall be grounded if:

- In a hazardous (classified) location;
- Operated at over 150 volts to ground, except for guarded motors and metal frames of electrically heated appliances if the appliance frames are permanently and effectively insulated from ground; or
- The equipment is of the following type:

- Refrigerators, freezers and air conditioners;
- Clothes-washing, clothes-drying and dishwashing machines, sump pumps and electrical aquarium equipment;
- Hand-held motor-operated tools;
- Motor-operated appliances of the following types: hedge clippers, lawn mowers, snow blowers and wet scrubbers;
- Cord- and plug-connected appliances used in damp or wet locations or by employees standing on the ground or metal floors or working inside of metal tanks or boilers;
- Portable and mobile X-ray and associated equipment;
- Tools likely to be used in wet and conductive locations; and
- Portable hand lamps.

Under the conditions described above, exposed noncurrent-carrying metal parts of cord- and plug-connected equipment must be grounded. Grounding metal parts is not required where the equipment is supplied through an isolating transformer with an ungrounded secondary of not over 50 volts or if portable tools are protected by an approved system of double insulation. To ground cord- and plug-connected equipment, a third wire is commonly provided in the cord set and a third prong in the plug. The

Exhibit 9-11.
If no grounding conductor is present, some portion of the fault current will return to ground through the worker.

third wire serves as an equipment-grounding conductor that is connected to the metal housing of a portable tool and a metal grounding bus inside the service entrance equipment. The service entrance equipment is located at the entrance point of the electric supply for a building or plant and contains, or serves other panel boards that contain, branch circuit protective devices such as fuses and circuit breakers. The third wire provides a path for fault current should an insulation failure occur. In this manner, dangerous fault current will be directed back to the source, the service entrance, and will enable circuit breakers or fuses to operate thus opening the circuit and stopping the current flow.

Exhibit 9-11 illustrates the potential shock hazard that exists when no third wire, grounding conductor, is used. If a fault occurs, most of the current will follow the path of least resistance. If the worker provides a path to ground as shown, some portion of the current will flow away from the grounded white conductor (neutral) and return to ground through the worker. The severity of the shock received will depend on the amount of current that flows through the worker.

To keep this from occurring it is important to ensure that the electrical system is properly grounded. Exhibit 9-12 illustrates the advantage of a properly connected grounded conductor.

It should be noted that properly bonded conduit and associated metal enclosures can also serve as a grounding conductor.

Tools likely to be used in wet and conductive locations need not be grounded if supplied through an isolating transformer with an ungrounded secondary of not over 50 volts. Listed or labeled portable tools and appliances protected by an approved system of double insulation, or its equivalent, need not be grounded. If such a system is employed, the equipment shall be distinctively marked to indicate that the tool or appliance uses an approved system of double insulation.

Nonelectrical Equipment

The metal parts of the following nonelectrical equipment shall be grounded: frames and tracks of electrically operated cranes; frames of nonelectrically driven elevator cars to which electric conductors are attached; hand-operated, metal-shifting ropes or cables of electric elevators, and metal partitions, grill work, and similar metal enclosures around equipment of over 750 volts between conductors.

Methods of Grounding Fixed Equipment

Noncurrent-carrying metal parts of fixed equipment, if required to be grounded by this subpart (Electrical), shall be grounded by an

Exhibit 9-12.
Cord- and plug-connected equipment with a grounding connector will protect the worker.

Figure 1

Figure 2

Exhibit 9-13.
The equipment-grounding conductor must be run with the circuit conductors powering fixed equipment (Fig. 1) or the metal conduit that encloses the power conductors servicing fixed equipment may serve as the equipment-grounding conductor for that equipment (Fig. 2).

equipment-grounding conductor that is contained within the same raceway, cable, or cord, or runs with or encloses the circuit conductors. For DC circuits only, the equipment-grounding conductor may be run separately from the circuit conductors (See Exhibit 9-13.).

Grounding of Systems and Circuits of 1000 Volts and Over (High Voltage)

If high voltage systems are grounded, they shall comply with all applicable provisions previously discussed in this subpart (Electrical) as well as additional requirements and modifications contained in this section.

Wiring Methods—Components and Equipment for General Use— 1910.305
Wiring Methods
The provisions of this section do not apply to the conductors that are an integral part of factory-assembled equipment.

General Requirements for Electrical Continuity of Metal Raceways and Enclosures
Metal raceways, cable armor and other metal enclosures for conductors shall be metallically joined together into a continuous electric conductor and shall be so connected to all boxes, fittings and cabinets as to provide effective electrical continuity.

Wiring in Ducts
No wiring systems of any type shall be installed in ducts used to transport dust, loose stock or flammable vapors. No wiring system of any type may be installed in any duct used for vapor removal or for ventilation of commercial-type cooking equipment or in any shaft containing only such ducts.

Temporary Wiring
Temporary electrical power and lighting wiring methods may be of a class less than would be required for a permanent installation. Except as specifically modified in this paragraph, all other requirements of this subpart (Electrical) for permanent wiring shall apply to temporary wiring installations.

Uses Permitted, 600 Volts, Nominal, or Less
Temporary electrical power and lighting installations 600 volts, nominal, or less may be used only:
- During and for remodeling, maintenance, repair, or demolition of buildings, structures, or equipment, and similar activities;
- For experimental or development work; and
- For a period not to exceed 90 days for Christmas decorative lighting, carnivals and similar purposes.

Uses Permitted, Over 600 Volts, Nominal
Temporary wiring over 600 volts, nominal may be used only during periods of tests, experiments or emergencies.

General Requirements for Temporary Wiring
- Feeders shall originate in an approved distribution center. The conductors shall be run as multi-conductor cord or cable assemblies or, where not subject to physical damage, they may be run as open conductors or insulators not more than 10 ft. apart.
- Branch circuits shall originate in an approved power outlet or panel board. Conductors shall be multi-conductor cord or cable assemblies or open conductors. If run

as open conductors, they shall be fastened at ceiling height every 10 ft. No branch-circuit conductor may be laid on the floor. Each branch circuit that supplies receptacles or fixed equipment shall contain a separate equipment-grounding conductor if run as open conductors.

- Receptacles used in temporary wiring circuits must provide a connection for an equipment-grounding conductor (See Exhibit 9-14.). Unless the receptacle is supplied by a metallic raceway that provides a continuous grounding path back to the source, a separate equipment-grounding conductor must be placed in the branch circuit. There must be good electrical connection between the receptacle grounding terminal and the equipment-grounding conductor.

- No bare conductors nor earth returns may be used for the wiring of any temporary circuit. Bare conductors are conductors that do not have any coverings whatsoever.

- Earth returns use the earth itself to provide a current path back to the supply source. Implanting a grounding electrode at the equipment being served and connecting the equipment to the ungrounded conductor and to the grounding electrode do this. Because one side of the supply source is also connected to ground through a grounding electrode, a return path exists. However, its effectiveness is dependent on varying soil conditions. Earth returns must not be used for wiring temporary circuits because they are not always effective and may present a serious hazard on temporary work sites. Exhibit 9-15 shows an earth return, which is not allowed, in contrast to a proper return system.

- In addition, a separate equipment-grounding conductor must be used to provide a low-impedance path to the source. This path will allow sufficient current to flow to operate the circuit breaker when a fault occurs.

- Suitable disconnecting switches or plug connectors shall be installed to permit the disconnection of all ungrounded conductors of each temporary circuit.

- Lamps for general illumination shall be protected from accidental contact or breakage. Protection shall be provided by elevation of at least 7 ft. from normal working surface or by a suitable fixture or lamp holder with a guard.

Exhibit 9-14.
Temporary branch circuit with connections for equipment-grounding conductors.

Exhibit 9-15.
Examples of an earth return and a proper return system.

- Flexible cords and cables shall be protected from accidental damage. Sharp corners and projections shall be avoided. Where passing through doorways or other pinch points, flexible cords and cables shall be provided with protection to avoid damage.

Cabinets, Boxes and Fittings

Conductors Entering Boxes, Cabinets or Fittings

Because conductors can be damaged if they rub against the sharp edges of cabinets, boxes or fittings, they must be protected from damage where they enter. To protect the conductors, some type of clamp or rubber grommet must be used. The device used must close the hole through which the conductor passes as well as provide protection from abrasion. If the conductor is in a conduit and the conduit fits tightly in the opening, additional sealing is not required.

The knockouts in cabinets, boxes and fittings should be removed only if conductors are to be run through them. However, if a knockout is missing or if there is another hole in the box, the hole or opening must be closed.

Covers and Canopies

All pull boxes, junction boxes and fittings shall be provided with covers approved for the purpose. If metal covers are used, they shall be grounded. In completed installations, each outlet box shall have a cover, faceplate or fixture canopy. Covers of outlet boxes having holes through which flexible cord pendants pass shall be provided with bushings designed for the purpose or shall have smooth, well-rounded surfaces on which the cords may bear.

Pull and Junction Boxes for Systems over 600 Volts, Nominal

Boxes shall provide a complete enclosure for the contained conductors or cables. Suitable covers securely fastened in place shall close boxes. Underground box covers that weigh more than 100 lbs. meet this requirement. Covers for boxes shall be permanently marked "HIGH VOLTAGE." The marking shall be on the outside of the box cover and shall be readily visible and legible.

Switches

Knife Switches

Single-throw knife switches have one energized (closed or "ON") position and one open (dead or "OFF") position. The switch must be designed so that when it is in the open position, the blades are not energized (i.e., the blades must be connected to the load side, not the supply side of the circuit). The switches must also be installed so that if the switch falls downward, it will not fall into its energized position. However, some single-throw knife switches

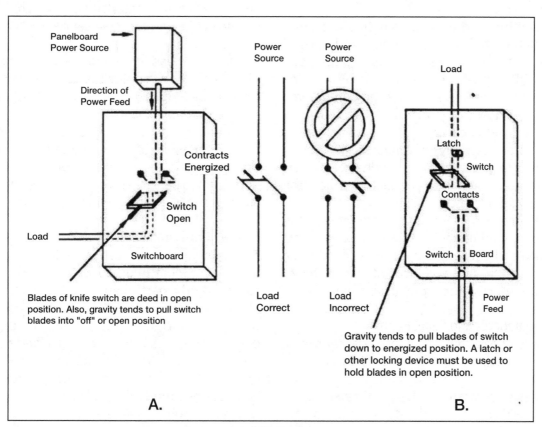

Exhibit 9-16.
Examples of single-throw knife switches.

ELECTRICAL

DOUBLE-THROW KNIFE SWITCHES WITH LOCKING DEVICE

Exhibit 9-17.
A double-throw knife switch with locking device.

are designed to be installed so that they open upward. To be approved for this type of installation, they must have a latch or other locking device (e.g., a spring-loaded device) used to secure the switch in the open position. In Exhibit 9-16, Illustration A shows a single-throw knife switch connected so that the blades are dead when the switch is open. Illustration B shows a latch arrangement that holds the blade in the open position and will prevent gravity from pulling the switch closed.

Double-throw knife switches are knife switches that have two energized (closed or "ON") positions and one open (dead or "OFF") position. These switches can be mounted vertically so that they are moved up and down or horizontally so that they are moved back and forth. If switches are mounted vertically, they must have a locking device (e.g., a spring-loaded device) that will hold the switchblades in the open position (See Exhibit 9-17.).

Flush snap switches that are mounted in ungrounded metal boxes and located within reach of conducting floors or other conducting surfaces shall be provided with faceplates of nonconducting, noncombustible material.

Switchboards and Panel Boards

A switchboard that has exposed live parts must be located in an area that is not subject to wetness or dampness. One purpose of this regulation is to lessen the chance of severe shock if a worker accidentally comes into contact with the five parts. Additionally, only qualified persons may have access to switchboards with

exposed live parts. To limit access, the switchboard should be located in a locked room or within a locked cage or fenced area. Keys to the locks should be controlled to ensure that only properly trained personnel are allowed to enter the area.

Enclosures for Damp or Wet Locations

Cabinets, cutout boxes, fittings, boxes and panel board enclosures in damp or wet locations shall be installed so as to prevent moisture or water from entering and accumulating within the enclosures. In wet locations, the enclosures shall be weatherproof. Switches, circuit breakers and switchboards installed in wet locations shall be enclosed in weatherproof enclosures.

Conductors for General Wiring

To provide adequate protection against shock and fire hazards, conductors must be insulated with approved materials. Insulating material should be the appropriate composition and thickness for the voltage and current the conductor will carry, for the temperature extremes and other environmental factors to which it will be subjected, and for the location in which it will be placed.

Insulated conductors must also be easily identifiable; color-coding is used most often. Neutral, or grounded, conductors should be white or natural gray.

Grounding conductors such as equipment-grounding conductors should be green or green with yellow stripes. Grounding conductors are permitted to be bare wires. Other types of circuit wires may be any colors except these.

Flexible Cords and Cables

This standard for safe use of flexible cords is one of the most frequently violated electrical standards, particularly in smaller plants. There is a definite need and place for cords, but there is also a temptation to misuse them because they seem to offer a quick and easy way to carry electricity to where it is needed. The basic problem is that flexible cords in general are more vulnerable than the fixed wiring of the building. Therefore, cords should not be used if one of the recognized wiring methods could be used instead.

Use of Flexible Cords and Cables

Flexible cords and cables shall be approved and suitable for conditions of use and location. The standard lists specific situations in which flexible cords may be used. Flexible cords and cables shall be used only for:

- Pendants (a lamp holder or cord-connector body suspended by a length of cord properly secured and terminated directly above the suspended device);
- Wiring of fixtures;
- Connection of portable lamps or appliances;
- Elevator cables;
- Wiring of cranes and hoists (where flexibility is necessary);
- Connection of stationary equipment to facilitate their frequent interchange (equipment that is not normally moved from place to place, but might be on occasion);
- Prevention of the transmission of noise or vibration (in some cases, vibration might fatigue fixed wiring and result in a situation more hazardous than flexible cord);
- Appliances where the fastening means and mechanical connections are designed to permit removal for maintenance and repair (e.g., water coolers, exhaust fans); and
- Data processing cables approved as a part of the data processing system.

Note that all of the above situations involve conditions where flexibility is necessary. Unless specifically permitted by one of these situations, flexible cords and cables may not be used:

- As a substitute for the fixed wiring of the structure;
- Where run through holes in walls, ceilings, or floors;
- Where run through doorways, windows or similar openings;
- Where attached to building surfaces; or
- Where concealed behind building walls, ceilings or floors.

There is usually not much question about the use of the short length of cord that is furnished as part of an approved appliance or tool; the use of an extension cord to permit the temporary use of an appliance or tool in its intended manner at some distance from a fixed outlet, but there are questions when the use obviously is not temporary and the cord is extended to some distant outlet to avoid providing a fixed outlet where needed.

Flexible cord used in violation of this standard is likely to be damaged by activities in the area, door or window edges, staples or fastenings, abrasion from adjacent materials, or simply by aging. If the conductors become partially exposed over a period of time, there will be an increased chance of shocks, burns or fire.

Identification, Splices and Termination

Flexible cords shall be used only in continuous lengths without splice or tap. Hard service flexible cords, No. 14 or larger, may be repaired if spliced so that the splice retains the insulation, outer sheath properties and usage characteristics of the cord being spliced. Flexible cords shall be connected to devices and fittings so that strain relief is provided that will prevent pull from being directly transmitted to joints or terminal screws.

Portable Cables Over 600 Volts, Nominal

Multi-conductor portable cable for use in supplying power to portable or mobile equipment at over 600 volts, nominal, shall consist of No. 8 or larger conductors employing flexible stranding. Cables operated at over 2000 volts shall be shielded for the purpose of confining the voltage stresses to the insulation. Grounding conductors shall be provided. Connectors for these cables shall be of a locking type, with provisions to prevent their opening or closing while energized. Strain relief shall be provided at connections and terminations. Portable cables may not be operated with splices unless the splices are of the permanent molded, vulcanized or other approved type. Termination enclosures shall be suitably marked with a high voltage hazard warning, and terminations shall be accessible only to authorized and qualified personnel.

Equipment for General Use

Lighting Fixtures, Lamp Holders, Lamps and Receptacles

Fixtures, lamp holders, lamps, rosettes, and receptacles may have no live parts normally exposed to employee contact. However, rosettes and cleat-type lamp holders and receptacles located at least 8 ft. above the floor may have exposed parts.

Portable-type hand lamps supplied through flexible cords shall be equipped with a handle of molded composition or other material approved for the purpose. A substantial guard also shall be attached to the lamp holder or the handle.

Screw-shell-type lamp holders shall be installed for use as lamp holders only and must not be used with screw-base socket adapters. These adapters screw into the existing lamp socket and convert lamp holders into receptacles. These adapters are not permitted because equipment-grounding connections cannot be made through the two-blade adapters and because the fixture has been designed only for lighting. Only weatherproof lamp holders may be installed in wet or damp areas. Unprotected lamp holders might allow moisture to enter the lamp holder socket, creating an electrical shock hazard.

Receptacles, Cord Connectors and Attachment Plugs

Cord connectors are devices that join two sections of electrical cord together. Attachment plugs are devices that are fastened onto the end of a cord so that electrical contact can be made between the conductors in the cord and the conductors in a receptacle. Connectors, plugs and receptacles are uniquely designed for different voltages and currents so that only matching plugs will fit into the correct receptacle or cord connector. In this way, a piece of equipment rated for one voltage combination cannot be plugged into a power system that is of a different voltage or current capacity.

The only exceptions to this are 125-volt and 250-volt, 20-ampere, T-slot receptacles

RECEPTACLES AND PLUGS WITH NEMA CONFIGURATIONS

Exhibit 9-18.
Receptacles and plugs with NEMA configurations.

(See Exhibit 9-18.). A 125-volt and 250-volt, 15-ampere plug will fit into a 20-ampere T-slot receptacle or connector of the same voltage rating as well as in a 120-volt, 15-ampere grounding type receptacle or connector of the same voltage rating. An electrical appliance that is rated for 15 amperes will not overload a 20-ampere circuit, and the 20-ampere breaker will still provide overcurrent protection for 15-ampere equipment. Note that the opposite is not necessarily true and that a 20-ampere plug will not fit into a 15-ampere receptacle or cord connector.

The National Electrical Manufacturer's Association (NEMA) has standard plug and receptacle connector blade configurations. Each has been developed to standardize the use of plugs and receptacles for different voltages, amperages, and phases from 115 volts through 600, from 15 amperes through 60, and for single- and three-phase systems.

A receptacle installed in a wet or damp location shall be suitable for the location.

Appliances

Electrical appliances such as portable air conditioning units, coffee makers and fans must not have any exposed live wires or electrical parts that might create an electrical shock hazard.

Exceptions to this are appliances such as heaters or toasters that must have exposed current-carrying parts that operate at high temperatures to transfer heat (e.g., a space heater). The heat generated by these parts minimizes the possibility of direct contact and resultant electric shock.

A disconnecting means is a switch or plug that can open any electric circuit under load and safely stop the flow of current. All appliances must have a disconnecting means. Each appliance shall be marked with its rating in volts and amperes or volts and watts.

Motors

Disconnecting Means
- A disconnecting means shall be located in sight from the controller (i.e., visible from and located within 50 ft. of the controller). However, a single disconnecting means may be located adjacent to a group of coordinated controllers mounted adjacent to one another on a multi-motor continuous process machine. The controller disconnecting means for motor branch circuits over 600 volts, nominal, may be out of sight of the controller if the controller is marked with a warning label giving the location and identification of the disconnecting means that is to be locked in the open position.
- The disconnecting means shall disconnect the motor and the controller from all ungrounded supply conductors and shall be so designed that no pole can be operated independently.
- If a motor and the driven machinery are not in sight from the controller location, the installation shall comply with one of the following conditions:
  - The controller disconnecting means shall be capable of being locked in the open position.
  - A manually operable switch that will disconnect the motor from its source of supply shall be placed in sight from the motor location.
- The disconnecting means shall plainly indicate whether it is in the open (off) or closed (on) position.

- The disconnecting means shall be readily accessible. If more than one disconnect is provided for the same equipment, only one need be readily accessible.
- An individual disconnecting means shall be provided for each motor, but a single disconnecting means may be used for a group of motors if:
  - A number of motors drive special parts of a single machine or piece of apparatus, such as a metal or woodworking machine, crane or hoist;
  - A group of motors is under the protection of one set of branch-circuit protective devices; or
  - A group of motors is in a single room in sight from the location of the disconnecting means.

Motor Overload, Short-Circuit and Ground Fault Protection

Motors, motor-control apparatus and motor branch-circuit conductors shall be protected against overheating due to motor overloads or failure to start and against short-circuit or ground faults. These provisions shall not require overload protection that will stop a motor where a shutdown is likely to introduce additional or increased hazards, as in the case of fire pumps, or where continued operation of a motor is necessary for a safe shutdown of equipment or process and motor overload-sensing devices are connected to a supervised alarm.

Protection of Live Parts—All Voltages
Stationary motors having commutators, collectors and brush rigging located inside of motor end brackets and not conductively connected to supply circuits operating at more than 150 volts to ground need not have such parts guarded.

Exposed live parts of motors and controllers operating at 50 volts or more between terminals shall be guarded against accidental contact by:
- Installation in a room or enclosure that is accessible only to qualified persons;
- Installation on a suitable balcony, gallery or platform so elevated and arranged as to exclude unqualified persons; or
- Elevation 8 ft. or more above the floor.

Where live parts of motors or controllers operating at over 150 volts to ground are guarded against accidental contact only by location and adjustment or other attendance may be necessary during the operation of the apparatus, suitable insulating mats or platforms shall be provided so the attendant cannot readily touch live parts unless standing on the mats or platforms.

Transformers

These requirements apply to most transformers, with some exceptions noted in the standard.

- Warning signs or visible markings on the equipment or structure shall indicate the operating voltage of exposed live parts of transformer installations.
- Dry-type, high fire point liquid-insulated and asbestos-insulated transformers installed indoors and rated over 35kV shall be in a vault.
- If they present a fire hazard to employees, oil-insulated transformers installed indoors shall be in a vault.
- Combustible material, combustible buildings and parts of buildings, fire escapes, and door and window openings shall be safeguarded from fires that may originate in oil-insulated transformers attached to or adjacent to a building or combustible material.
- Transformer vaults shall be constructed so as to contain fire and combustible liquids within the vault and to prevent unauthorized access. Locks and latches shall be so arranged that a vault door can be readily opened from the inside.
- Any pipe or duct system foreign to the vault installation may not enter or pass through a transformer vault.
- Materials may not be stored in transformer vaults.

Capacitors

Capacitors store electrical charges and can be a source of severe shock unless that charge is drained when the capacitors are disconnected from the power source. Unless some type of automatic discharge is designed into a system, devices such as resistors must be permanently attached across the terminals of the capacitors to drain the charge when the circuit is open (deenergized). Most capacitors are manufactured with this type of discharge resistor already built in. Surge capacitors, which act like lightning rods, do not require an automatic means for draining the charge.

Storage Batteries

Storage batteries, which are usually lead-acid or alkali, produce explosive gases, including hydrogen, if they are overcharged. These explosive gases must not accumulate in quantities that may form an explosive mixture with air. A spark or open flame could ignite the mixture and cause an explosion. Good ventilation must be provided to prevent this accumulation.

Hazardous (Classified) Locations— 1910.307

Hazardous (classified) locations are those areas where a potential for explosion and fire exists because of flammable gases, vapors or finely pulverized dusts in the atmosphere or because of the presence of easily ignitable fibers or flyings. Hazardous locations may result from the normal processing of certain volatile chemicals, gases, grains, etc., or it may result from accidental failure of storage systems for these materials. It also is possible that a hazardous location may be created when volatile solvents or fluids, used in a normal maintenance routine, vaporize to form an explosive atmosphere.

Hazardous (classified) locations may be found in occupancies such as aircraft hangars, gasoline dispensing and service stations, bulk storage plants for gasoline or other volatile flammable liquids, paint-finishing process plants, health care facilities, agricultural or other facilities where excessive combustible dusts may be present, marinas, boat yards, and petroleum and chemical processing plants. Each room, section or area shall be considered individually in determining its classification.

Regardless of the cause of a hazardous location, it is necessary that every precaution be taken to guard against ignition of the atmosphere. Certainly no open flames would be permitted in these locations, but there are other potential sources of ignition, including electrical equipment. The normal operation of switches, circuit breakers, motor starters, contactors and plugs and receptacles release this energy in the form of arcs and sparks as contacts open and close, making and breaking circuits.

Electrical equipment such as lighting fixtures and motors are classified as "heat producing" and they will become a source of ignition if they reach a surface temperature that exceeds the ignition temperature of the particular gas, vapor or dust in the atmosphere.

It is also possible that an abnormality or failure in an electrical system could provide a source of ignition. The failure of insulation from cuts, nicks or aging can also act as an ignition source again from sparking, arcing and heat.

There are several OSHA standards that require the installation of electrical wiring and equipment in hazardous (classified) locations according to the requirements of Subpart S, Electrical. Most of these standards are contained in Subpart H, Hazardous Materials. Some examples include Acetylene, Flammable and Combustible Liquids, Spray Finishing Using Flammable and Combustible Liquids, and Dip Tanks Containing Flammable or Combustible Materials. The basis for OSHA Standard 1910.307 is the National Electrical Code (NEC), NFPA 70. A general overview of the guidelines contained in the NEC for installation of electrical wiring and equipment in hazardous (classified) locations can be found in this document under the section "Hazardous Materials."

Electrical Safety-Related Work Practices

OSHA's Safety-Related Work Practice standards for general industry, 1910.331 to 1910.399 are performance-oriented regulations that complement the existing electrical installation standards. These work-practice standards include requirements for work performed on or near exposed energized and deenergized parts of electric equipment; the use of electrical protective equipment and the safe use of electric equipment.

These rules are intended to protect employees from the electrical hazards that they may be exposed to even though equipment may be in compliance with the installation requirements in Subpart S, Electrical. When

employees are working with electric equipment, they must use safe work practices. Such safety-related work practices include keeping a prescribed distance from exposed energized lines, avoiding the use of electric equipment when the employee or the equipment is wet, and locking out and tagging equipment that is deenergized for maintenance.

Another important safety practice involves the use of electrical protective devices, such as rubber gloves and rubber mats, for the purpose of insulation against live parts. Another practice is to have hand tools for purposes of both insulation and manipulation of energized parts from a distance. However, to ensure the protection of the employee, this equipment must be properly manufactured and maintained.

It is important to understand the distinction between these standards and OSHA Standard 1910.147, Control of Hazardous Energy (Lockout/Tagout). The lockout/tagout standard helps safeguard employees from hazardous energy while they are servicing or performing maintenance on machines and equipment. The standard covers electrical energy sources, but it specifically excludes "exposure to electrical hazards from work on, near, or with conductors or equipment in electrical utilization installations," which is covered by Subpart S (Electrical). Thus, the lockout/tagout standard does not cover electrical hazards associated with conductors and equipment, but only covers electrical equipment that relates to machinery and equipment that is covered by the lockout standard.

Covered Work by Both Qualified and Unqualified Persons—1910.331

The provisions of these standards cover electrical safety-related work practices for both qualified persons (those who have training in avoiding the electrical hazards of working on or near exposed energized parts) and unqualified persons (those with little or no such training) working on, near or with the following installations:

- Premises wiring. Installations of electric conductors and equipment within or on buildings or other structures on other premises, such as yards, carnival, parking, and other lots, and industrial substations.

- Wiring for connections to supply. Installations of conductors that connect to the supply of electricity.
- Other wiring. Installations of other outside conductors on the premises.
- Optical fiber cable. Installations of optical fiber cable where such installations are made along with electric conductors.

Other Covered Work by Unqualified Persons

The provisions of these standards also cover work performed by unqualified persons on, near or with the following installations:

- Generation, transmission and distribution installations. Installations for the generation, control, transformation, transmission, and distribution of electric energy (including communication and metering) located in buildings used for such purposes or located outdoors.
- Communications installations. Installations of communications equipment to the extent that the work is covered under 1910.268.
- Installations in vehicles. Installations in ships, watercraft, railway rolling stock, aircraft, or automotive vehicles other than mobile homes and recreational vehicles.
- Railway installations. Installations of railways for generation, transformation, transmission or distribution of power used exclusively for the operation of rolling stock or installation of railways used exclusively for signaling and communication purposes.

Excluded Work by Qualified Persons

The provisions of these standards do not apply to work performed by qualified persons on or directly associated with the four types of installations described above.

Training—1910.332

The training requirements contained in this section apply to employees who face a risk of electric shock that is not reduced to a safe level by the electrical installation requirements of 1910.303 to 1910.308. Employees in occupations listed below face such a risk and are required to be trained:

- Blue-collar supervisors;
- Electrical and electronic engineers;
- Electrical and electronic equipment engineers;
- Electrical and electronic technicians;

- Electricians;
- Industrial machine operators;
- Material handling equipment operators;
- Mechanics and repairers;
- Painters;
- Riggers and roustabouts;
- Stationary engineers; and
- Welders.

With the exception of electricians and welders, workers in the above groups do not need to be trained if their work or the work of those they supervise does not bring them or the employees they supervise close enough to exposed parts of electric circuits operating at 50 volts or more to ground for a hazard to exist. Other employees who also may reasonably be expected to face a comparable risk of injury due to electric shock or other electrical hazards must also be trained.

Content of Training

Employees shall be trained in and be familiar with the safety-related work practices required by 1910.331 to 1910.355 that pertain to their respective job assignments.

Employees who are covered by the scope of this standard but who are not qualified persons shall also be trained in and be familiar with any electrically related safety practices not specifically addressed by 1910.331 to 1910.335 but which are necessary for their safety.

Qualified persons (i.e., those permitted to work on or near exposed energized parts) shall, at a minimum, be trained in and be familiar with the following:

- The skills and techniques necessary to distinguish exposed live parts from other parts of electric equipment;
- The skills and techniques necessary to determine the nominal voltage of exposed live parts; and
- The clearance distances specified in this standard and the corresponding voltages to which the qualified person will be exposed.

Type of Training

The training required by this section shall be of the classroom or on-the-job type. The degree of training provided shall be determined by the risk to the employee.

Selection and Use of Work Practices—1910.333

Safety-related work practices shall be employed to prevent electric shock or other injuries resulting from either direct or indirect electrical contacts when work is performed near or on equipment or circuits that are or may be energized. The specific safety-related work practices shall be consistent with the nature and extent of the associated electrical hazards.

Deenergized Parts

Live parts to which an employee may be exposed shall be deenergized before the employee works on or near them, unless the employer can demonstrate that deenergizing would introduce additional or increased hazards or is not feasible due to equipment design or operational limitations. Live parts that operate at less than 50 volts to ground need not be deenergized if there will not be increased exposure to electrical burns or explosion due to electric arcs.

Energized Parts

If the exposed live parts are not deenergized, (i.e., for reasons of increased or additional hazards or unfeasibility), other safety-related work practices shall be used to protect employees who may be exposed to the electrical hazards involved. Such work practices shall protect employees from making contact with energized circuit parts—either directly with any part of their body or indirectly through some other conductive object.

Working On or Near Exposed Deenergized Parts

Application

This paragraph applies to work on exposed deenergized parts or near enough to them to expose the employee to any electrical hazard they present.

Conductors and parts of electric equipment that have been deenergized but have not been locked out or tagged shall be treated as *energized* parts.

Lockout and Tagout

While any employee is exposed to contact with parts of fixed electric equipment or circuits that have been deenergized, the circuits energizing the parts shall be locked out, tagged or both in accordance with the requirements of this paragraph in the following order:

1. Procedures shall be in place before equipment may be deenergized.
2. Circuits and equipment to be worked on shall be disconnected from all electrical energy sources.
3. Stored electrical energy that poses a hazard to workers shall be released.
4. Stored nonelectrical energy in devices that could reenergize electric circuit parts shall be blocked or relieved to the extent that the circuit parts could not be accidentally energized by the device.
5. A lock and a tag shall be placed on each disconnecting means used to deenergize circuits and equipment on which work is to be performed, except as provided below.
6. Each tag shall contain a statement prohibiting unauthorized operation of the disconnecting means and removal of the tag.
7. If a lock cannot be applied or if the employer can demonstrate that tagging procedures will provide a level of safety equivalent to that obtained by the use of a lock, a tag may be used without a lock.
8. A tag used without a lock, as permitted above, shall be supplemented by at least one additional safety measure that provides a level of safety equivalent to that obtained by the use of a lock (e.g., the removal of an isolating circuit element, blocking of a controlling switch, opening of an extra disconnecting device).
9. A lock may be placed without a tag only under the following conditions:
   a. Only one circuit or piece of equipment is deenergized;
   b. The lockout period does not extend beyond the work shift; and
   c. Employees exposed to the hazards associated with reenergizing the circuit or equipment are familiar with this procedure.
10. Before any circuits or equipment can be considered and worked as deenergized:

a. A qualified person shall operate the equipment operating controls or otherwise verify that the equipment cannot be restarted.

b. A qualified person shall use test equipment to test the circuit elements and electrical parts of equipment to which employees will be exposed and shall verify that the circuit elements and equipment parts are deenergized.

11. Before circuits and equipment are reenergized, even temporarily, the following requirements shall be met, in the order given:

a. A qualified person shall conduct tests and visual inspections, as necessary, to verify that all tools, electrical jumpers, shorts, grounds and other such devices have been removed so that the circuits and equipment can be safely energized.

b. Employees exposed to the hazards associated with reenergizing the circuit or equipment shall be warned to stay clear of such circuits and equipment.

c. Each lock and tag shall be removed by the employee who applied it or under his or her direct supervision. However, if this employee is absent from the workplace, the lock or tag may be removed by a qualified person designated to perform this task, provided that the employer ensures that the employee who applied the lock or tag is not available at the workplace and is aware that the lock or tag has been removed before he or she resumes work at that workplace.

d. There shall be a visual determination that all employees are clear of the circuits and equipment.

Lockout/Tagout Injury

The photos in Exhibit 9-19 are the result of an accident that occurred while an apprentice electrician was changing the ballast on a fluorescent light fixture that was not deenergized.

No pre-job briefing or lockout/tagout was performed.

The apprentice electrician stripped the wrong wire and got severely shocked, badly burning his right hand. He was holding a wire nut in his mouth at the time of the accident. He has now undergone three surgeries. The first surgery was to remove the wire nut that he swallowed when he was shocked. The wire nut went all the way to the bottom of his lung. The other surgeries included amputations necessary to try to regain some use of his right hand.

Exhibit 9-19.
The effects of electrical shock
as a result of no lockout/tagout.

Working On or Near Exposed Energized Parts

Application
This paragraph applies to work performed on exposed live parts (involving either direct contact or contact by means of tools or materials) or near enough to them for employees to be exposed to any hazard they present.

Work on Energized Equipment
Only qualified persons may work on electric circuit parts or equipment that have not been deenergized under the procedures of these standards. Such persons shall be capable of working safely on energized circuits and shall be familiar with the proper use of special precautionary techniques, personal protective equipment, insulating and shielding materials, and insulated tools.

Overhead Lines
If work is to be performed near overhead lines, the lines shall be deenergized and grounded, or other protective measures shall be provided before work is started. If the lines are to be deenergized, arrangements shall be made with the operator or controller of the appropriate electric circuits to have them deenergized or grounded. If protective measures such as guarding, isolating or insulating are provided, these precautions shall prevent employees from contacting such lines directly with any part of their body or indirectly through conductive materials, tools or equipment.

Unqualified Persons
When an unqualified person is working in an elevated position near overhead lines, the location shall be such that the person and the longest conductive object he or she may contact cannot come closer to any unguarded, energized overhead line than the following distances:

- For voltages to ground 50 kV or below, 10 ft.; and
- For voltages to ground over 50 kV, 10 ft. plus 4 in. for every 10 kV over 50 kV.

When an unqualified person is working on the ground in the vicinity of overhead lines, that person may not bring any conductive object closer to unguarded, energized overhead lines than the distances given above.

Qualified Persons
When a qualified person is working in the vicinity of overhead lines, whether in an elevated position or on the ground, the person may not approach or take any conductive object without an approved insulating handle closer to exposed energized parts than shown in Table S-5 of 1910.333(c)(3)(ii), unless certain insulation requirements are met.

Vehicular and Mechanical Equipment
Any vehicle or mechanical equipment capable of having parts of its structure elevated near energized overhead lines shall be operated so that a clearance of 10 ft. is maintained. If the voltage is higher than 50 kV, the clearance shall be increased 4 in. for every 10 kV over that voltage. The standard outlines several conditions under which this clearance may be reduced.

Illumination
Employees may not enter spaces containing exposed energized parts, unless illumination is provided that enables the employees to perform the work safely. Where lack of illumination or an obstruction precludes observation of the work to be performed, employees may not perform tasks near exposed energized parts. Employees may not reach blindly into areas that may contain energized parts.

Confined or Enclosed Work Sites
When an employee works in a confined or enclosed space (e.g., a manhole or vault) that contains exposed energized parts, the employer shall provide, and the employee shall use, protective shields, protective barriers or insulating materials as necessary to avoid inadvertent contact with these parts. Doors, hinged panels and the like shall be secured to prevent their swinging into an employee and causing the employee to contact exposed energized parts.

Conductive Materials and Equipment
Conductive materials and equipment that are in contact with any part of an employee's body shall be handled in a manner that will prevent them from contacting exposed energized conductors

or circuit parts. If an employee must handle long, dimensional conductive objects (e.g., ducts, pipes) in areas with exposed live parts, the employer shall institute work practices (e.g., the use of insulation, guarding, material handling techniques) that will minimize the hazard.

Portable Ladders

Portable ladders shall have nonconductive side rails if they are used where the employee or the ladder could contact exposed energized parts.

Conductive Apparel

Conductive articles of jewelry and clothing may not be worn if they might contact exposed energized parts, unless they are rendered nonconductive by covering, wrapping or other insulating means.

Housekeeping Duties

Where live parts present an electrical contact hazard, employees may not perform housekeeping duties at such close distances to the parts that there is a possibility of contact, unless adequate safeguards (e.g., insulating equipment, barriers) are provided. Electrically conductive cleaning materials may not be used in proximity to energized parts unless procedures are followed that will prevent electrical contact.

Interlocks

Only a qualified person following the requirements of this section may defeat an electrical safety interlock. If the interlock is defeated, it may only be while he or she is working on the equipment; the interlock system must be returned to its operable condition when the work is completed.

Use of Equipment—1910.334

Portable Electric Equipment

This paragraph applies to the use of cord- and plug-connected equipment, including flexible cord sets (extension cords).

Handling

Portable equipment shall be handled in a manner that will not cause damage. Flexible electric cords connected to equipment may not be used for raising or lowering the equipment. Flexible cords may not be fastened with staples or otherwise hung in such a fashion as could damage the outer jacket or insulation.

Visual Inspection

Portable cord- and plug-connected equipment and flexible cord sets (extension cords) shall be visually inspected before use on any shift for external defects and for evidence of possible internal damage. Cord- and plug-connected equipment and extension cords that remain connected once they are put in place and are not exposed to damage need not be visually inspected until they are relocated. Defective or damaged items shall be removed from service until repaired.

Grounding-Type Equipment

A flexible cord used with grounding-type equipment shall contain an equipment-grounding conductor.

Attachment plugs and receptacles may not be connected or altered in a manner that would prevent proper continuity of the equipment-grounding conductor at the point where plugs are attached to receptacles. In addition, these devices may not be altered to allow the grounding pole of a plug to be inserted into slots intended for connection to the current-carrying conductors. Adapters, which interrupt the continuity of the equipment grounding connection, may not be used.

Conductive Work Locations

Portable electric equipment and flexible cords used in highly conductive work locations (e.g., those inundated with water or other conductive liquids) or in job locations where employees are likely to contact water or conductive liquids shall be approved for those locations.

Connecting Attachment Plug

Employee's hands may not be wet when plugging and unplugging flexible cords and cord- and plug-connected equipment if energized equipment is involved.

Energized plug and receptacle connections may be handled only with insulating protective equipment if the condition of the connection could provide a conducting path to the employee's hand. Locking-type connectors shall be properly secured after connection.

Electric Power and Lighting Circuits

Routine Opening and Closing of Circuits
Load-rated switches, circuit breakers or other devices specifically designed as disconnecting means shall be used for the opening, reversing or closing of circuits under load conditions. Cable connectors not of the load-break type, fuses, terminal lugs and cable splice connections may not be used for such purposes, except in an emergency.

Reclosing Circuits after Protective Device Operation
After a circuit is deenergized by a circuit protective device, the circuit may not be manually reenergized until it has been determined that the equipment and circuit can be safely energized. The repetitive manual reclosing of circuit breakers or reenergizing of circuits through replaced fuses is prohibited.

Overcurrent Protection Modification
Overcurrent protection of circuits and conductors may not be modified, even on a temporary basis, beyond that allowed in 1910.304(e), the installation safety requirements for overcurrent protection.

Test Instruments and Equipment
Only qualified persons may perform testing work on electric circuits or equipment.

Visual Inspection
Test instruments and equipment and all associated test leads, cables, power cords, probes and connectors shall be visually inspected for external defects and damage before the equipment is used. If there is a defect or evidence of damage that might expose an employee to injury, the defective or damaged item shall be removed from service and no employee may use it until necessary repairs and tests to render the equipment safe have been made.

Rating of Equipment
Test instruments and equipment and their accessories shall be rated for the circuits and equipment to which they will be connected and shall be designed for the environment in which they will be used.

Occasional Use of Flammable or Ignitable Materials

Where flammable materials are present only occasionally, electric equipment capable of igniting them shall not be used, unless measures are taken to prevent hazardous conditions from developing.

Safeguards for Personnel Protection— 1910.335
Use of Protective Equipment

Personal Protective Equipment
Employees working in areas where there are potential electrical hazards shall be provided with, and shall use, electrical protective equipment that is appropriate for the specific parts of the body to be protected and for the work to be performed.

Protective equipment shall be maintained in a safe, reliable condition and shall be periodically inspected or tested, as required by 1910.137. If the insulating capability of protective equipment may be subject to damage during use, the insulating material shall be protected. For example, an outer covering of leather is sometimes used for the protection of rubber insulating material.

Employees shall wear nonconductive head protection wherever there is a danger of head injury from electric shock or burns due to contact with exposed energized parts. Employees shall wear protective equipment for the eyes or face wherever there is danger of injury to the eyes or face from electric arcs or flashes or from flying objects resulting from electrical explosion.

General Protective Equipment and Tools
When working near exposed energized conductors or circuit parts, each employee shall use insulated tools or handling equipment if the tools or handling equipment might make contact with such conductors or parts. If the insulating capability of insulated tools or handling equipment is subject to damage, the insulating material shall be protected.

Fuse-handling equipment, insulated for the circuit voltage, shall be used to remove or install fuses when the fuse terminals are energized. Ropes and hand lines used near exposed energized parts shall be nonconductive.

Protective shields, protective barriers or insulating materials shall be used to protect each employee from shock, burns, or other electrical-related injuries while that employee is working near exposed energized parts that might be accidentally contacted or where dangerous electric heating or arcing might occur. When normally enclosed live parts are exposed for maintenance or repair, they shall be guarded to protect unqualified persons from contact with the live parts.

Alerting Techniques

The following alerting techniques shall be used to warn and protect employees from hazards that could cause injury due to electric shock, burns or failure of electric equipment parts:

- **Safety signs and tags.** Safety signs, safety symbols or accident prevention tags shall be used where necessary to warn employees about electrical hazards that may endanger them, as required by 1910.145.
- **Barricades.** Barricades shall be used in conjunction with safety signs where it is necessary to prevent or limit employee access to work areas that will expose employees to uninsulated energized conductors or circuit parts. Conductive barricades may not be used where they might cause an electrical contact hazard.
- **Attendants.** If signs and barricades do not provide sufficient warning and protection from electrical hazards, an attendant shall be stationed to warn and protect employees.

Hazards of Electricity

Shock. Electric shock occurs when the human body becomes part of a path through which electrons can flow. The resulting effect on the body can be either direct or indirect.

- **Direct.** Injury or death can occur whenever electric current flows through the human body. Currents of less than 30 mA can result in death.
- **Indirect.** Although the electric current through the human body may be well below

the values required to cause noticeable injury, human reaction can result in falls from ladders or scaffolds, or movement into operating machinery. Such reaction can result in serious injury or death.

Burns. Burns can result when a person touches electrical wiring or equipment that is improperly used or maintained. Typically, such burn injuries occur on the hands.

Arc-blast. Arc-blasts occur from high-amperage currents arcing through air. This abnormal current flow (arc-blast) is initiated by contact between two energized points. This contact can be caused by persons who have an accident while working on energized components or by equipment failure due to fatigue or abuse. Temperatures as high as 35,000° have been recorded in arc-blast research. The three primary hazards associated with an arc-blast are:

Thermal radiation. In most cases, the radiated thermal energy is only part of the total energy available from the arc. Numerous factors, including skin color, area of skin exposed and type of clothing have an effect on the degree of injury. Proper clothing, work distances and overcurrent protection can improve the chances of curable burns.

Pressure wave. A high-energy arcing fault can produce a considerable pressure wave. Research has shown that a person 2 ft. away from a 25 kA arc would experience a force of approximately 480 lbs. on the front of his or her body. In addition, such a pressure wave can cause serious ear damage and memory loss due to mild concussions.

In some instances, the pressure wave may propel the victim away from the arc-blast, reducing the exposure to the thermal energy. However, such rapid movement could also cause serious physical injury.

Projectiles. The pressure wave can propel relatively large objects over a considerable distance. In some cases, the pressure wave has sufficient force to snap the heads of 3/8 in. steel bolts and knock over ordinary construction walls.

The high-energy arc also causes many of the copper and aluminum components in the electrical equipment to become molten. These "droplets" of molten metal can be propelled great distances by the pressure wave. Although these droplets cool rapidly, they can still be above temperatures capable of causing serious burns or igniting ordinary clothing at distances of 10 ft. or more. In many cases, the burning effect is much worse than the injury from shrapnel effects of the droplets.

Explosions. Explosions occur when electricity provides a source of ignition for an explosive mixture in the atmosphere. Ignition can be due to overheated conductors or equipment or normal arcing (sparking) at switch contacts. OSHA standards, the National Electrical Code and related safety standards have precise requirements for electrical systems and equipment when applied in such areas.

Fires. Electricity is one of the most common causes of fire both in the home and workplace. Defective or misused electrical equipment is a major cause, with high resistance connections being one of the primary sources of ignition. High resistance connections occur where wires are improperly spliced or connected to other components such as receptacle outlets and switches. This was the primary cause of fires associated with the use of aluminum wire in buildings during the 1960s and 1970s.

Heat is developed in an electrical conductor by the flow of current at the rate I^2R. The heat thus released elevates the temperature of the conductor material. A typical use of this formula illustrates a common electrical hazard. If there is a bad connection at a receptacle, resulting in a resistance of 2 ohms, and a current of 10 amperes flows through that resistance, the rate of heat produced W would be:

$$W = I^2R = 10^2 \times 2 = 200 \text{ watts}$$

If you have ever touched an energized 200 watt light bulb, you will realize that this is a lot of heat to be concentrated in the confined space of a receptacle. Situations similar to this can contribute to electrical fires.

Effects of Electricity on the Human Body

The effects of electric shock on the human body depend on several factors. The muscular structure of the body is also a factor in

that people having less muscle and more fat typically show similar effects at lesser current values. Major factors are:
- Current and voltage;
- Resistance;
- Path through body; and
- Duration of shock.

Current and Voltage
Although high voltage often produces massive destruction of tissue at contact locations, it is generally believed that the detrimental effects of electric shock are due to the current actually flowing through the body. Any electrical device used on a house wiring circuit can, under certain conditions, transmit a fatal current. Although currents greater than 10 mA are capable of producing painful to severe shock, currents between 100 and 200 mA can be lethal.

With increasing alternating current, the sensations of tingling give way to contractions of the muscles. The muscular contractions and accompanying sensations of heat increase as the current is increased. Sensations of pain develop, and voluntary control of the muscles that lie in the current pathway becomes increasingly difficult. As current approaches 15 mA, the victim cannot let go of the conductive surface being grasped. At this point, the individual is said to "freeze" to the circuit. This is frequently referred to as the "let-go" threshold.

As current approaches 100 mA, ventricular fibrillation of the heart occurs. Ventricular fibrillation is defined as "very rapid uncoordinated contractions of the ventricles of the heart resulting in loss of synchronization between heartbeat and pulse beat." Once ventricular fibrillation occurs, it will continue and death will ensue within a few minutes. Use of a defibrillator is required to save the victim.

Heavy current flow can result in severe burns and heart paralysis. If shock is of short duration, the heart stops during current passage and usually restarts normally on current *interruption*, improving the victim's chances for survival.

Resistance
Studies have shown that the electrical resistance of the human body varies with the amount of moisture on the skin, the pressure

applied to the contact point, and the contact area. The outer layer of skin, the epidermis, has very high resistance when dry. Wet conditions, a cut or other break in the skin will drastically reduce resistance.

Shock severity increases with an increase in pressure of contact. Also, the larger the contact area, the lower the resistance. Whatever protection is offered by skin resistance decreases rapidly with increase in voltage. Higher voltages have the capability of "breaking down" the outer layers of the skin, thereby reducing the resistance.

Path Through Body

The path the current takes through the body affects the degree of injury. A small current that passes from one extremity through the heart to the other extremity is capable of causing severe injury or electrocution. There have been many cases where an arm or leg was almost burned off when the extremity came in contact with electrical current and the current only flowed through a portion of the limb before it went out into the other conductor. Had the current gone through the trunk of the body, the person almost surely would have been electrocuted. A large number of serious electrical accidents in industry involve current flow from hands to feet. Because such a path involves both the heart and the lungs, the effects are often fatal.

Current flow through the chest, neck, head, or major nerve centers controlling respiration may result in a failure of the respiratory system. This is usually caused by a disruption of the nerve impulses between the respiratory control center and the respiratory muscles. Such a condition is dangerous since it is possible for the respiratory failure to continue even after the current flow has stopped.

The most dangerous condition can occur when fairly small amounts of current flow through the heart area. Such current flow can cause ventricular fibrillation. This asynchronous movement of the heart causes the heart's usual rhythmic pumping action to cease. Death occurs within minutes.

When relatively large currents flow through the heart area, heart action may be stopped entirely. If the shock duration is short and no physical damage to the heart has occurred, the heart may begin rhythmic pumping automatically when the current ceases. Extensive tissue damage, including internal organ damage due to high temperatures, occurs when very large currents flow through major portions of the body.

Duration of Shock

Current flow greater than the "let-go" threshold of an individual may cause a person to collapse, become unconscious, and even result in death. In most cases, the current flow would have to continue for more than five seconds. Although it may not be possible to determine the exact cause of death with certainty, asphyxiation or heart failure are the prime suspects.

The duration of the shock has a great bearing on the final outcome. If the shock is of short duration, it may only be a painful experience for the person. If the level of current flow reaches the approximate ventricular fibrillation threshold of 100 mA, shock duration of a few seconds could be fatal. This is not much current considering that a small light-duty portable electric drill draws about 30 times as much. At relatively high currents, death is inevitable if the shock is of appreciable duration; however, if the shock is of short duration, and if the heart has not been damaged, interruption of the current may be followed by a spontaneous resumption of its normal rhythmic contractions.

Delayed Effects

There are recorded cases of delayed death after a person has been revived following an electrical shock. This may occur within minutes, hours, or even days after the event has occurred. Several assumptions for such delayed effects are:
- Internal or unseen hemorrhaging;
- Emotional or psychological effects of the shock; and
- Aggravation of a pre-existing condition.

In many accidents, there is a combination of the above effects as well as conditions that develop after the initial accident.

Electrical Protective Devices

As a power source, electricity can create conditions almost certain to result in bodily harm, property damage, or both. It is important for workers to understand the hazards involved when they are working around electrical power tools, maintaining electrical equipment, or installing equipment for electrical operation.

Electrical protective devices, including fuses, circuit breakers, and ground-fault circuit interrupters, are therefore critically important to electrical safety. Overcurrent devices should be installed where required. They should be of the size and type to interrupt current flow when it exceeds the capacity of the conductor. Proper selection takes into account not only the capacity of the conductor, but also the rating of the power supply and potential short circuits.

Types of Overcurrent

There are two types of overcurrent:

- **Overload** - When you ask a 10 hp motor to do the work of a 12 hp motor, an overload condition exists. The overcurrent may be 150 percent of normal current.
- **Fault** - When insulation fails in a circuit, a fault current can result that may be from 5 times to 50 times that of normal current.

When a circuit is overloaded, the plasticizers in the insulation are vaporized over a long period of time, and the insulation becomes brittle. The brittle insulation has slightly better electrical insulating properties. However, movement of the conductors due to magnetic or other forces can crack the insulation, and a fault can result. Conductors should be protected from overload and the eventual damage that results.

Faults occur in two ways. Most of the time a fault will occur between a conductor and an enclosure. This is called a ground fault. Infrequently, a fault will occur between two conductors. This is called a short circuit.

To predict what will happen in a normal circuit and a ground-fault circuit, it is important to understand the terminology of an electrical system. As illustrated in Exhibit 9-20, the dashed lines represent the enclosures surrounding the electrical system. These enclo-

Exhibit 9-20.
The terminology and layout of an electrical system.

sures include the service panel, conduit, and boxes enclosing such parts as switches, controllers, and equipment terminals. The conduit bonds all of the enclosures together so there is no electrical potential between them. It also provides an emergency path for ground-fault current to return to the voltage source that, in this case, is shown as secondary windings of a transformer.

Notice that there must be a wire between the grounded conductor and the enclosure to allow the fault current to return to its source. This wire is called the main bonding jumper. If there is no wire, then the electrical system is isolated and requires extra safety features.

The basic idea of an overcurrent protective device is to make a weak link in the circuit. In the case of a fuse, the fuse is destroyed before another part of the system is destroyed. In the case of a circuit breaker, a set of contacts opens the circuit. Unlike a fuse, a circuit breaker can be reused by reclosing the contacts. Fuses and circuit breakers are designed to protect equipment and facilities, and in so doing, they also provide considerable protection against shock in most situations. However, the only electrical protective device whose sole purpose is to protect people is the ground-fault circuit-interrupter.

Fuses

A fuse is an electrical device that opens a circuit when the current flowing through it exceeds the rating of the fuse. The "heart" of a fuse is a special metal strip (or wire) designed to melt and blow out when its rated amperage is exceeded. Overcurrent devices (e.g., fuses, circuit breakers) are always placed in the "hot" side of a circuit (usually a black wire) and in series with the load, so that all the current in the circuit must flow through them.

If the current flowing in the circuit exceeds the rating of the fuse, the metal strip will melt and open the circuit so that no current can flow. A fuse cannot be reused and must be replaced after eliminating the cause of the overcurrent. Fuses are designed to protect equipment and conductors from excessive current. It is important to always replace fuses with the proper type and current rating. Too low a rating will result in unnecessary blowouts, while too high a rating may allow dangerously high currents to pass.

Circuit Breaker

Circuit breakers provide protection for equipment and conductors from excessive current without the inconvenience of changing fuses. Circuit breakers trip (open the circuit) when the current flow is excessive.

There are two primary types of circuit breakers based on the current-sensing mechanism. In a magnetic circuit breaker, a coil that forms an electromagnet senses the current. When the current is excessive, the electromagnet actuates a small armature that pulls the trip mechanism thus opening the circuit breaker. In a thermal-type circuit breaker, the current heats a bi-metallic strip that, when heated sufficiently, bends enough to allow the trip mechanism to operate.

Ground-Fault Circuit Interrupter

A ground-fault circuit interrupter (GFCI) is not an overcurrent device. A GFCI is used to open a circuit if the current flowing to the load does not return by the prescribed route. In a simple 120-volt circuit, the current usually flows through the black (ungrounded) wire to the load and returns to the source through the white (grounded) wire. If it does not return through the grounded wire, then it must go somewhere else, usually to ground. The GFCI is designed to limit electric shock to a current and time-duration level that will not produce serious injury.

The National Electric Code and the NFPA 70E

In 1881 Thomas Edison replied to a newspaper article in which the underwriters asked for information about the danger of fire from electric wires. Edison responded with "I beg to say that the system of lighting of the Edison Electric Light company is absolutely free from any possible danger from fire, even in connection with the most inflammable material."

Since electrical systems were a new development, no codes had been developed for safe installation. Installers had to make decisions based on their limited experience of this new technology. It is no wonder why electrical fires became prevalent throughout the United States. Eight years after Edison wrote his safety note about fires there were five different electrical installation codes in use in the United States. Each code was sufficiently different from the others that confusion reigned and the need for a uniform electrical code was recognized.

In 1896 a committee was formed by the American Society of Mechanical Engineers. This committee was given the task of selecting the most suitable rules from the five outstanding codes and developing a consensus through a review of their findings. The code was recognized by the National Board of Fire Underwriters and published as the "National Electrical Code of 1897."

In 1911 the work of periodically revising the National Electric Codes (NEC) was transferred to the Electrical Committee of the National Fire Protection Association (NFPA). This organization had been formed in 1896 to reduce fire and safety hazards. It has published over two hundred articles (codes and standards). These codes cover a variety of topics from NFPA 10 "Standard for Portable Fire Extinguishers" to Article 70 which is the National Electric Code.

When the Williams-Steiger Occupational Safety and Health Act of 1970 created OSHA, the need for industrial regulation of electricity became apparent. OSHA adopted the most widely accepted electrical standard in the world, the National Fire Protection Association's Standard, NFPA 70. However, when the

NEC was updated periodically, OSHA would have to go through an extensive legal process to adopt the new NEC edition and resolve conflicts between the adopted version and the updated version. The NEC only referred to electrical installation and OSHA needed a regulation that addressed operation, maintenance and repair as well.

How did OSHA solve this problem? Employers have a specific duty to follow the rules enacted by OSHA, and a general duty to provide a safe and healthy workplace. This "general duty" requires that each employer furnish to their workers a place that is free from recognized hazards. Generally, if there is a serious hazard that could result in death or serious injury, the hazard must be abated, regardless of whether or not OSHA has specifically addressed the hazard. An important example of recognized hazards that may not be covered by a specific standard drafted by OSHA is the national consensus standard. This type of standard is developed by the same persons it affects, is adopted by a nationally recognized organization and carries the same weight and is as enforceable as the OSHA regulations. NFPA 70E is a national consensus standard.

The most recent edition of the NFPA 70E was adopted in 2004. It reorganizes the article into the NEC format. There are four chapters and thirteen annexes to the article.

- Chapter 1 covers safety related work practices, qualified versus unqualified persons and training. This chapter calls for an electrical safety program that includes electrical hazard analysis for shock and flash, energized electrical work permits and lockout/tagout procedures. Personal protective equipment, protective clothing and approach boundaries are also discussed.
- The second chapter outlines safety related maintenance requirements necessary to ensure that electrical wiring, components and equipment are maintained in a safe condition.
- Chapter 3 discusses special equipment such as batteries, lasers, arc welding equipment, and other select equipment.
- Chapter 4 describes installation safety requirements and is a truncated version of the National Electrical Code.

While parts of the NFPA 70E have been around since 1981, only recently has OSHA begun to refer to the article in their documents and citations. This consensus standard covers electrical safety related work practices and procedures for employees who work on or near exposed energized electrical conductors or circuit parts. Relevant requirements include:

Power must be proven to be off before performing work. This includes

- The safe interruption of the load & opening of the disconnect
- Visual verification/voltage testing to ensure deenergization

The potential electrical hazard must be identified and documented

- Flash hazard analysis must be performed
- Flash protection boundaries must be determined

Appropriate steps must be taken to protect persons working near live parts or within the flash protection boundary.

- Personal Protective Equipment must be provided based on the relevant incident energy exposure levels (cal/cm2)
- Only properly qualified persons shall be allowed to perform work.

NFPA 70 (NEC) differs from NFPA 70E

The National Electrical Code is generally considered an electrical_installation document and protects employees under normal circumstances. NFPA 70E is intended to provide guidance with respect to electrical *safe work practices*.

NFPA not incorporated by reference

OSHA does not enforce NFPA 70E since it is not incorporated by reference.

However, OSHA has several comparable requirements that are enforceable:

- **29 CFR 1910.132 (d)(1):** Requires employers perform a personal protective equipment (PPE) hazard assessment to determine necessary PPE;
- **29 CFR 1910.269 (l)(6)(iii):** Requires employers ensure each employee working at electric power generation, transmission, and distribution facilities who is exposed to the

hazards of flames or electric arcs does not wear clothing that could increase the extent of injury when exposed to such a hazard;

- **29 CFR 1910.335 (a)(1)(i):** Employees working in areas where there are potential electrical hazards shall use electrical protective equipment appropriate for the specific parts of the body for the work being performed;
- **29 CFR 1910.335 (a)(1)(iv):** Requires employees wear nonconductive head protection whenever exposed to electric shock or burns due to contact with exposed energized parts;
- **29 CFR 1910.335 (a)(1)(v):** Employees shall wear protective equipment for the eyes or face wherever there is danger of injury to the eyes or face from electric arcs or flashes or from flying objects resulting from an electrical explosion;
- **29 CFR 1910.335 (a)(2):** Employees shall use insulated tools or handling equipment when working near exposed energized conductors or circuit parts;
- **29 CFR 1926.28 (a):** Employer shall require employees wear appropriate personal protective equipment (PPE) during construction work.

Boundaries for flash protection

NFPA 70E specifies boundaries within which flash protection is required as a means to reduce the extent of injuries. Protective equipment is also specified including flash resistant clothing and face shielding. Boundary distances vary depending on both the qualifications of the person being exposed and the voltage involved. Unqualified personnel must be accompanied by qualified personnel. All personnel within the defined boundaries must wear specified protective equipment.

The following boundary distances for flash protection have been established in NFPA 70E. For workers within the following approach distances, flash protection is required:

Voltage Flash Protection Boundary

up to 750V	3 feet
750V to 2kV	4 feet
2kV to 15kV	16 feet
15kV to 36kV	19 feet
over 36kV	Must be Calculated

Flash resistant personal protection equipment does not protect you from shock, but it will give substantial protection from the effects of flash, especially burns and eye damage. Flash protective clothing is specified by ASTM F1506 while eye protection must comply with ANSI Z87.1. Clothing coverage must be 100%, i.e., coveralls or shirt and trousers.

NFPA 70E: 130.1 requires employers perform a flash hazard analysis to identify work tasks performed on energized electrical conductors. Appropriate flame retardant clothing (FRC), as well as voltage rated tools, may then be selected.

It is possible to protect an employee exposed to an electric arc incident from experiencing a burn that will cause irreversible tissue damage – a curable burn. This is a 2° burn where the skin temperature does not exceed 175° with a duration no longer than 0.1 second.

Although not specifically required by NFPA 70E, it is recommended that covered employees be provided FRC daily wear with an ATPV (Arc Thermal Performance Value) of at least 8. This satisfies the garment requirements for a Hazard Risk Classification 2 task.

The term "clearing time" is discussed under NFPA 70E: 130.3 (A). This refers to the time necessary for an electrical circuit breaker or disconnect to switch from an energized state to a deenergized state. A faster clearing time reduces the potential for an electric arc incident.

The Hazard Risk Category (HRC) classifications (0 – 4) listed in Table 130.7 (C)(9)(a) do not have a have a direct correlation to voltage. The hazard risk category (HRC) classifications are based upon estimated incident energy. Consider two work tasks with different voltages:

Task #1: Examination of insulated cable in open area ≥ 1,000 volts: **HRC 2 task**.

Task #2: Insertion or removal of 600 volt class individual starter buckets: **HRC 3 task.**

Although task #2 involves less voltage than task #1, it has a higher HRC.

Seventh edition changes

The National Fire Protection Association (NFPA) published the seventh edition of the 70E Standard for Electrical Safety Requirements for Employee Workplaces in February 2004. This edition contains many significant changes from the sixth edition: The edition stresses safe work practices.

The issue of multi-employer relationships (110.4) is addressed. The addition of multi-employer relationships now makes the employer liable whenever outside contractors are engaged in activities covered by the scope and application of this standard. The employer and contractor must inform each other of existing hazards, personal protective equipment/clothing requirements, safe work practices, and emergency evacuation procedures applicable to the work to be performed. This coordination must include a meeting and documentation.

NFPA 70E covers the full range of electrical safety issues, including safety related work practices, maintenance, special equipment requirements, and installation. It focuses on protecting people and identifies requirements that are considered necessary to provide a workplace that is free of electrical hazards. OSHA bases its electrical safety mandates, found in Subpart S part 1910 and Subpart K part 1926, on the comprehensive information found in NFPA 70E. NFPA 70E is recognized as the tool that illustrates how an employer might comply with these OSHA standards. The relationship between the OSHA regulations and NFPA 70E can be described as OSHA is the "shall" and NFPA 70E the "how."

OSHA mandates that all services to electrical equipment be done in a de-energized state. Working live can only be under special circumstances. If it is necessary to work live (>50 volts to ground), the regulations outlined in NFPA 70E, Article 130 should be used as a tool to comply with OSHA mandates Subpart S part 1910.333(a)(1).

- **Shock hazard analysis (paragraph 130.2):** Determines the voltage to which personnel will be exposed, boundary requirements, and PPE necessary. Table 130.2(C) is used to determine boundary distances.
- **Flash hazard analysis (paragraph 130.3):** Determines the flash protection boundary and PPE needed within that boundary. The flash protection boundary is determined by methods found in 130.3(A) or Annex D of the standard. Protective clothing is determined by using tables 130.7(C)(9)(a), 130.7(C)(10), and 130.7(C)(11). See question and answer number 1 for more details.

Remember, OSHA only allows work on live electrical parts under two special circumstances: (1) when continuity of service is required, and (2) when de-energizing equipment would create additional hazards. In all other cases, lockout/tagout is the law.

Employers are also responsible for complying with the 2002 NEC 110.6 labeling requirements. This requires all switchboards, panel boards, industrial control panels, and motor control centers to be field marked. Any equipment installed after 2002 needs to be labeled. For equipment installed before 2002, labeling must be applied if ANY modifications or upgrades take place. Some of the labels listed below require boundary distances calculated in Article 130 of the standard. Examples of labels that meet this requirement are:

Each FR garment is assigned an ATPV rating by the manufacturer. The ATPV value represents the amount of incident energy that would cause the onset of second-degree burns. It also signifies the amount of protection the clothing affords when an electrical arc comes in contact with the fabric. Most of the industry falls into either Category 1 or 2 protection. Most uniforms already meet Category 1 or 2 requirements, but people who fall into this category typically are not covered by this standard. The employees addressed by this standard fall into Category 3 and 4. The garments must also be designed to withstand a cleaning process to remove soils and then be returned to service without damage to the protective characteristic of the fabric. The label on the garment must contain the following information: tracking ID number, meet ASTM spec F1506, name of manufacturer, size and care instructions, ATPV rating, and must meet ASTM spec f1506.

Summary of the New 2007 Electrical Standard

Changes to the electrical subpart of OSHA's 29CFR1910 standard were published in the **Federal Register** on February 14, 2007. To give firms time to comply with the changes, the effective date of the regulation is August 13, 2007.

The change clarifies some of the information that was in the electrical section and draws heavily on the 2002 National Electric Code. The section was originally drafted in the 1970's and stood the test of time. This updated version creates a more easily read and understood regulation while providing for changes in technology that make the workplace safer.

The following changes are effective in August 2007:

- **1910.303(a):** A reference to the Sec. 1910.399 definition of "approved" is added for clarification.
- **1910.303(b)(1)(111):** Adds wire-bending and connection space to the explicit list of things to consider when judging equipment.
- **1910.303(b)(3):** Adds a requirement for completed wiring to be free from short circuits and grounds other than those required in the standard.
- **1910.303(b)(4):** Adds requirements for equipment intended to interrupt current to have adequate interrupting ratings.
- **1910.303(b)(5):** Adds requirements for the coordination of over current protection for circuits and equipment.
- **1910.303(b)(6):** Adds a requirement for conductors and equipment to be identified for the purpose when installed in an environment containing deteriorating agents.
- **1910.303(b)(7):** Adds requirements for installing electric equipment in a neat and workmanlike manner.
- **1910.303(b)(8):** Adds requirements for equipment to be mounted securely and to allow for proper cooling.
- **1910.303(c)(1):** Adds requirements to ensure that electrical connections are secure and electrically safe.
- **1910.303(c)(2):** Adds requirements for connections at terminals and for the identification of terminals intended for connection to more than one conductor or to aluminum.
- **1910.303(c)(3)(ii):** Adds a requirement that wire connectors or splicing means installed on directly buried conductors be listed for such use.
- **1910.303(f)(4):** Adds a requirement for disconnecting means required by Subpart S to be capable of accepting a lock. This provision is added to make the Subpart S requirements on disconnecting means consistent with Sec. 1910.147(c)(2)(iii), which requires energy isolating devices (a generic term, which includes electrical disconnecting means) to be designed to accept a lockout device.
- **1910.303(f)(5):** Adds marking requirements for series combination ratings of circuit breakers or fuses.
- **1910.303(g)(1)(i):** Table S-1, Note 3: The final rule revises the language to clarify how wide and high the clear space must be. (See detailed explanation later in the preamble.)
- **1910.303(g)(1)(iv):** Adds a requirement for a second entrance on equipment rated 1200 amperes under certain conditions.
- **1910.303(g)(1)(iv):** Reduces the minimum width of the clear space to 762 mm.
- **1910.303(g)(1)(v):** Adds a prohibition against controlling illumination for working spaces by automatic means only.

- **1910.303(g)(1)(vi):** Increased the minimum height of the working space from 1.91m to 1.98m for new installations.
- **1910.303(g)(1)(vii):** Adds requirements for switchboards, panel boards, and distribution boards installed for the control of light and power circuits, and motor control centers to be installed in dedicated space and to be protected against damage.
- **1910.303(h)(2)(i) and (h)(2)(ii):** The minimum height of fences restricting access to electrical installations over 600 V is reduced from 2.44 m to 2.13 m.
- **1910.303(h)(2)(iii), (h)(2)(iv),(h)(2)(v), and (h)(5)(iii):** 1. The final rule organizes these requirements based on whether the installations are indoors or outdoors. (The existing standard organized them based on whether or not the installations were accessible to unqualified employees). 2. Adds requirements intended to prevent tampering by the general public. 3. Removes requirement to lock underground box covers weighing more than 45.4 kg.
- **1910.303(h)(5)(i), Table S-2, Note 3.:** The distances in Table S-2 for the Table S-2, Note 3 depth of working space in front of electrical equipment is increased for new installations to match the distances in NFPA 70E-2000.
- **1910.303(h)(5)(v):** The distances in Table S-3 for the elevations of unguarded live parts are increased for new installations to match the distances in NFPA 70E-2000.
- **1910.303(h)(4)(i):** The existing standard requires a second entrance to give access to the working space about switchboards and control panels over 600 V if the equipment exceeds 1.22 m in width if it is practical to install a second entrance. The final rule requires an entrance on each end of switchboards and panel boards exceeding 1.83 m unless the working space permits a continuous and unobstructed way of travel or the working space is doubled. In addition, the final rule requires the lone entrance permitted under either of these exceptions to be at least the distance specified in Table S-2 from exposed live parts.
- **1910.303(h)(5)(ii):** Adds requirements for equipment operating at 600 V or less in-

stalled in rooms or enclosures containing exposed live parts or exposed wiring operating at more than 600 V.
- **1910.303(h)(5)(vi):** Adds requirements limiting the installation of pipes or ducts that are foreign to electrical installation operating at more than 600 V.
- **1910.304(b)(1):** Adds requirements for the identification of multiwire branch circuits.
- **1910.304(b)(2)(i):** Adds requirements that receptacles installed on 15- and 20-ampere circuits be of the grounding type and that grounding-type receptacles be installed in circuits within their rating.
- **1910.304(b)(2)(ii):** Adds a requirement for grounding contacts on receptacles to be effectively grounded.
- **1910.304(b)(2)(iii):** Adds requirements on the methods used to ground receptacles and cord connectors.
- **1910.304(b)(2)(iv):** Adds requirements on the replacement of receptacles.
- **1910.304(b)(2)(v):** Adds a requirement that receptacles installed on branch circuits having different voltages, frequencies, or types of current be noninterchangeable.
- **1910.304(b)(3):** Adds requirements for ground fault circuit interrupter protection. (These requirements are discussed in this section of the preamble to the final rule).
- **1910.304(b)(4)(i):** Adds requirements for ratings of lampholders.
- **1910.304(b)(4)(ii):** Adds requirements for ratings of receptacles.
- **1910.304(b)(5):** Adds requirements for receptacles to be installed wherever cords with attachment plugs are used.
- **1910.304(c)(1):** Adds a requirement for the separation of conductors on poles.
- **1910.304(c)(2):** Increases the minimum clearances for new installations of open conductors and service drops to match those in NFPA 70E-2000.
- **1910.304(c)(3)(ii):** Adds restrictions for installing overhead service conductors near building openings through which materials may be moved.
- **1910.304(c)(4):** Adds an exception to the minimum clearance requirement for conductors attached to the side of a building. (The final rule also clarifies that paragraph (c)(2)

applies to roof surfaces that are subject to pedestrian or vehicular traffic).

- **1910.304(e)(1)(iii):** Adds a requirement for service disconnecting means to be suitable for the prevailing conditions.
- **1910.304(f)(1)(iii):** The types of circuits that are allowed to have a single switch disconnect for multiple fuses are now specified in the standard.
- **1910.304(f)(1)(v):** Adds a requirement to clarify that handles of circuit breakers and similar moving parts also need to be guarded so that they do not injure employees.
- **1910.304(f)(1)(viii):** Adds circuit breakers used on 277-volt fluorescent lighting circuits to the types of breakers required to be marked "SWD."
- **1910.304(f)(1)(ix):** Adds a requirement to clarify ratings of circuit breakers.
- **1910.304(f)(2):** Adds specific requirements on how to protect feeders and branch circuits energized at more than 600 volts.
- **1910.304(g)(1)(v):** Adds an exception to the requirement to ground systems for high-impedance grounded systems of 480 V to 1000 V under certain conditions.
- **1910.304(g)(3):** Changes requirements for grounding portable and vehicle mounted generators so that the requirements are equivalent to those in OSHA's Construction Standards (Sec. 1926.404 (f) (3)). The sentence in the construction standard reading: "No other [nonneutral] conductor need be bonded to the generator frame" has been dropped from the general industry version.
- **1910.304(g) (4):** No longer allows employers to use a cold water pipe as a source of ground for installations made or modified after the effective date.
- **1910.304(g)(5):** Adds a requirement that the path to ground be effective.
- **1910.304(g)(6)(iv) and (g)(6)(v):** The exceptions for grounding fixed equipment operating at more than 150 V are extended to all fixed electric equipment regardless of voltage. Also, the final rule includes a new exception for double-insulated equipment.
- **1910.304(g)(6)(vi) and (g)(6)(vii):** Adds the following equipment to the list of cord- and plug-connected equipment required to be grounded: stationary and fixed motor-oper-

ated tools and light industrial motor-operated tools.

- **1910.304(g)(7):** Adds frames and tracks of electrically operated hoists to the list of Nonelectrical equipment required to be grounded.
- **1910.305(a)(1)(i):** Adds a requirement that equipment be bonded so as to provide adequate fault-current- carrying capability. Also, clarifies that nonconductive coatings need to be removed unless the fittings make this unnecessary.
- **1910.305(a)(1)(ii):** Adds an exception to the bonding requirement for the reduction of electrical noise.
- **1910.305(a)(2)(i)(A):** Removes demolition from the list of activities for which temporary wiring is permitted. Demolition is a form of construction work, which is not covered by the Subpart S installation requirements.
- **1910.305(a)(2)(i)(C):** Adds emergencies to the list of activities for which temporary wiring is permitted.
- **1910.305(a)(2)(iii):** Adds "construction-like activities" to the list of permitted uses for temporary electrical installations over 600 volts.
- **1910.305(a)(2)(iv):** Feeders may now only be run as single insulated conductors when accessible to qualified employees only and used for experiments, development work, or emergencies. (Individual requirements are placed in separate paragraphs).
- **1910.305(a)(2)(viii):** Adds a requirement that disconnecting means for a multiwire circuit simultaneously disconnect all ungrounded conductors of the circuit.
- **1910.305(a)(2)(ix):** This provision no longer allows installing fixtures or lampholders more than 2.1 meters above the working surface as a means of guarding. Also, the final rule adds a requirement for grounding metal-case sockets.
- **1910.305(a)(2)(xi):** Adds requirements for cable assemblies and flexible cords and cables to be adequately supported.
- **1910.305(a)(3)(ii):** Adds several types of cables and single insulated conductors to the list of types permitted in industrial establishments.
- **1910.305(a)(3)(iii):** Adds a requirement limiting the use of metallic cable trays as an equipment grounding conductor.

- **1910.305(a)(4)(ii):** Adds specific support requirements and limits the application of these requirements to conductors smaller than No. 8.
- **1910.305(b)(1)(iii):** Adds requirements for supporting cables entering cabinets, cutout boxes, and meter sockets.
- **1910.305(b)(2)(ii):** Adds a requirement for any exposed edge of a combustible ceiling finish at a fixture canopy or pan to be covered with noncombustible material.
- **1910.305(c)(3)(ii):** Adds a requirement for load terminals on switches to be deenergized when the switches are open except under limited circumstances.
- **1910.305(c)(4):** Adds a specific requirement for flush-mounted switches to have faceplates that completely cover the opening and that seat against the finished surface.
- **1910.305(c)(5):** Adds a requirement to ground faceplates for snap switches.
- **1910.305(e)(1):** Adds a requirement for metallic cabinets, cutout boxes, fittings, boxes, and panel board enclosures installed in damp or wet locations to have an air space between the enclosure and the mounting surface.
- **1910.305(g)(1)(i) and (g)(1)(ii):** Adds the following to the types of connections permitted for flexible cords and cables: Portable and mobile signs and connection of moving parts. The final rule also clarifies that flexible cords and cables may be used for temporary wiring as permitted in final Sec. 1910.305 (a) (2).
- **1910.305(g)(1)(v):** Permits additional cord types to be used in show windows and show cases.
- **1910.305(g)(2)(i):** Adds new types of cords to the list of those that must be marked with their type designation.
- **1910.305(g) (2) (ii):** Changes the minimum size of hard service and junior hard service cords that may be spliced from No. 12 to 14.
- **1910.305(h), introductory text, (h)(1) , (h)(2), (h)(3), (h)(6), (h)(7), and (h)(8):** Permits the minimum introductory size of the insulated ground-check conductor of Type G-GC cables to be No. 10 rather than No. 8. (Individual requirements are placed in separate paragraphs).
- **1910.305(h)(4):** Adds a requirement for shields to be grounded.
- **1910.305(h)(5):** Adds minimum bending radii requirements for portable cables.
- **1910.305(i) (3):** Also permits fixture wire to be used in fire alarm circuits.
- **1910.305(j)(1)(iii):** Adds a requirement that the grounded circuit conductor, where present, be connected to the screw shell.
- **1910.305(j)(2)(i):** Adds requirements to ensure that attachment plugs and connectors have no exposed live parts.
- **1910.305(j)(2)(iii):** Clarifies that nongrounding-type receptacles may not be used with grounding-type attachment plugs.
- **1910.305(j)(2)(v), (j)(2)(vi), and (j)(2)(vii):** Adds requirements for receptacles outdoors to be installed in weatherproof enclosures appropriate for the use of the receptacle and for the location.
- **1910.305(j)(3)(ii):** Adds a requirement to group and identify disconnecting means for appliances supplied by more than one source.
- **1910.305(j)(3)(iii):** Adds requirements for marking frequency and required external overload protection for appliances.
- **1910.305(j)(3)(iv):** Clarifies that markings must be visible or easily accessible after installation.
- **1910.305(j)(6)(ii)(A) and (j)(6)(ii)(B):** Adds requirements to provide disconnecting means of adequate capacity for capacitors operating at more than 600 V.
- **1910.306(a)(1)(i), (a)(2)(i), and (a)(2)(ii):** Reorganized and clarified the requirements for disconnecting means for signs. The final rule does not apply these requirements to exit signs.
- **1910.306(a) (1) (ii):** Adds a requirement for the disconnects for signs located within fountains to be at least 1.52 m from the fountain wall.
- **1910.306(b) (1):** Adds specific requirements for the type and location of disconnecting means for runway conductors.
- **1910.306(c):** This paragraph now covers wheelchair lifts, and stairway chair lifts.
- **1910.306(c)(3)** Adds requirements for the type of disconnecting means.
- **1910.306(c)(4):** Adds requirements for the operation of disconnecting means.
- **1910.306(c)(5):** Adds requirements for the location of disconnecting means.

- **1910.306(c)(6):** Adds requirements for the identification of disconnecting means.
- **1910.306(c)(7):** Adds requirements for disconnecting means for single car and multicar installations supplied by more than one source.
- **1910.306(c)(9):** Adds requirements for warning signs for interconnected multicar controllers.
- **1910.306(c)(10):** Adds exceptions related to the location of motor controllers.
- **1910.306(d)(1):** Adds requirements for the type and rating of the disconnecting means.
- **1910.306(d)(2):** Clarifies that a supply circuit switch may be used as a disconnecting means if the circuit supplies only one welder.
- **1910.306(e):** Adds a requirement to group the disconnecting means for the HVAC systems serving information technology rooms with the disconnecting means for the information technology equipment. The final rule exempts integrated electrical systems covered by Sec. 1910.308(g). (The existing standard refers to this equipment as data processing equipment).
- **1910.306(f), introductory text:** Adds coverage of X-rays for dental or medical use.
- **1910.306(g)(1)(iii):** Adds a requirement for the installation of doors or detachable panels to provide access to internal parts. Adds a requirement that detachable panels not be readily removable.
- **1910.306(g)(1)(vi):** Adds a requirement to ensure adequate rating of disconnecting means. The final rule also clarifies when the supply circuit disconnecting means may be used as the disconnecting means for induction and dielectric heating equipment.
- **1910.306(h)(4)(i):** Adds requirements limiting primary and secondary voltage on isolating transformers supplying receptacles for ungrounded cord- and plug-connected equipment. Also, adds requirement for overcurrent protection for circuits supplied by these transformers.
- **1910.306(i)(2):** Allows the disconnecting means for a center pivot irrigation machine to be located not more than 15.2 m (50 ft) from the machine if the disconnecting means is visible from the machine.

- **1910.306(j), introductory text:** Clarifies that hydro-massage bathtubs are covered by this paragraph.
- **1910.306(j)(1)(ii):** Extends the boundary within which receptacles require ground-fault circuit interrupter protection from 4.57 m (15 ft) to 6.08 m (20 ft) for new installations.
- **1910.306(j)(1)(iii):** Adds requirements for the installation of at least one receptacle near permanently installed pools at dwelling units.
- **1910.306(j)(2)(i):** Clarifies that ceiling suspended (paddle) fans are covered by this requirement.
- **1910.306(j)(4)(iii):** Adds a requirement to guard lighting fixtures facing upward.
- **1910.306(k):** Adds requirements for carnivals, circuses, fairs, and similar events. Sec. 1910.307 Hazardous (classified) locations.
- **1910.307(a):** Adds the Zone classification system for Class I locations. (See detailed discussion later in this section of the preamble).
- **1910.307(b):** Adds documentation requirements for hazardous locations classified using either the division or zone classification system.
- **1910.307(c)(2)(ii)(B):** Also permits fixtures approved for Class II, Division 2 locations to omit the group marking.
- **1910.307(c)(2)(ii)(E):** Adds a requirement that electric equipment suitable for an ambient temperature exceeding 40 [deg] C (104 [deg] F) be marked with the maximum ambient temperature.
- **1910.307(b)(3), Note:** The last sentence of the note is removed to make it clear that the OSHA standard does not incorporate the National Electrical Code by reference. The NEC continues to be a guideline that employers may reference in determining the type and design of equipment and installations that will meet the OSHA standard.
- **1910.307(f):** The final rule adds a list of specific protective techniques for electrical installations in hazardous locations classified under the division classification system.
- **1910.307(g):** Adds the zone classification system as an alternative method of installing electric equipment in hazardous locations. This paragraph sets the protective tech-

niques and other requirements necessary for safe installation of electric equipment in hazardous locations classified under the zone classification system.

- **1910.308(a)(1)(i) and (a)(3)(ii):** Adds the following wiring methods to those acceptable for installations operating at more than 600 V: Electrical metallic tubing, rigid nonmetallic conduit, busways, and cable bus. The proposal also removes the specific requirement to support cables having a bare lead sheath or a braided outer covering in a manner to prevent damage to the braid or sheath. This hazard is covered by Sec. 1910.303(b) (1) and (b) (8) (i) and new Sec. 1910.308(a) (4).

- **1910.308(a)(2) and (a)(3)(i):** Adds requirements to ensure that high- voltage cables can adequately handle the voltage stresses placed upon them and to ensure that any coverings are flame retardant.

- **1910.308(a)(4):** Adds requirements for the protection of high-voltage cables against moisture and physical damage where the cable conductors emerge from a metal sheath.

- **1910.308(a)(5)(ii):** Adds requirements for fuses to protect each ungrounded conductor, for adequate ratings of fuses installed in parallel, and for the protection of employees from power fuses of the vented type.

- **1910.308(a)(5)(iii):** Clarifies that distribution cutouts are not suitable for installation in buildings or transformer vaults.

- **1910.308(a)(5)(iv):** Adds requirements for fused cutouts to either be capable of interrupting load current or be supplemented by a means of interrupting load current. In addition, a warning sign would be required for fused cutouts that cannot interrupt load current.

- **1910.308(a)(5)(v):** Adds a requirement for guarding nonshielded cables and energized parts of oil-filled cutouts.

- **1910.308(a)(5)(vi):** Adds requirements to ensure that load interrupting switches will be protected against interrupting fault current and to provide for warning signs for back fed switches.

- **1910.308(a)(7)(ii):** Clarifies that multiconductor portable cable may supply mobile equipment.

- **1910.308(a)(7)(vi):** Limits the conditions under which switch or contactor enclosures may be used as junction boxes or raceways.

- **1910.308(b)(2):** Clarifies that emergency illumination includes all required means of egress lighting, illuminated exit signs, and all other lights necessary to provide required illumination.

- **1910.308(b)(3):** Adds requirements to provide signs indicating the presence and location of on-site emergency power sources under certain conditions.

- **1910.308(c)(1)(i), (c)(1)(ii), and (c)(1)(iii):** Clarifies the power limitations of Class 1, 2, and 3 remote control, signaling, and power-limited circuits based on equipment listing.

- **1910.308(c)(3):** Adds requirements for the separation of cables and conductors of Class 2 and Class 3 circuits from cables and conductors of other types of circuits.

- **1910.308(d)(2)(ii):** Adds a requirement for power-limited fire alarm circuit power sources to be listed and marked as such.

- **1910.308(d)(3)(ii), (d)(3)(iii), and (d)(3)(iv):** Clarifies the requirements for installing power-limited fire- protective signaling circuits with other types of circuits. (Individual requirements are placed in separate paragraphs).

- **1910.308(e)(1):** Clarifies the requirement for listed primary protectors to make it clear that circuits confined within a block do not need protectors.

- **1910.308(f):** Adds requirements to separate conductors of solar photovoltaic systems from conductors of other systems and to provide a disconnecting means for solar photovoltaic systems.

- **1910.308(g):** Adds an exception to the provisions on the location of over current protective devices for integrated electrical systems.

Sources for More Information

NFPA 70E Standard for Electrical Safety Requirements for Employee Workplaces, National Fire Protection Association, 1-617-770-3000.

Hazard Risk Category Table as defined by NFPA 70E

Task Being Performed (240 Volts and below)	Hazard Category
Opening hinged cover to access circuit breakers	0
Flipping Circuit breaker with covers on	0
Voltage testing or work on energized parts	1
Removing or installing circuit breakers	1
Removing bolted covers to expose bare energized parts	1
Task Being Performed (241 Volts and above)	**Hazard Category**
Opening hinged cover to access circuit breakers	0
Flipping Circuit breaker with covers on	0
Voltage testing or work on energized parts	2

Protective Clothing Characteristics

Hazard/Risk Category	Clothing Description Number of Layers ( )	APTV Rating Cal/cm2
0	Untreated Cotton, Wool, Rayon, Silk, or Blend. Fabric weight >4.5oz/Yd2 (1)	N/A
1	FR Shirt and FR Pants or FR Coverall (1)	4
2	Cotton underwear plus FR shirt and FR pants (1 or 2)	8
3	Cotton underwear plus FR shirt and FR pants plus FR coverall, cotton underwear plus two FR Coveralls (2 or 3)	25
4	Cotton underwear plus FR shirt and FR pants plus multilayer flash suit (3 or more)	40

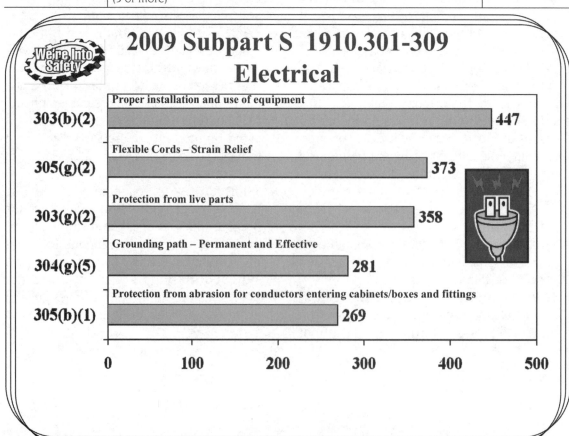

2009 Subpart S 1910.301-309
Electrical

We're Into Safety

303(b)(2) Proper installation and use of equipment — 447

305(g)(2) Flexible Cords – Strain Relief — 373

303(g)(2) Protection from live parts — 358

304(g)(5) Grounding path – Permanent and Effective — 281

305(b)(1) Protection from abrasion for conductors entering cabinets/boxes and fittings — 269

0   100   200   300   400   500

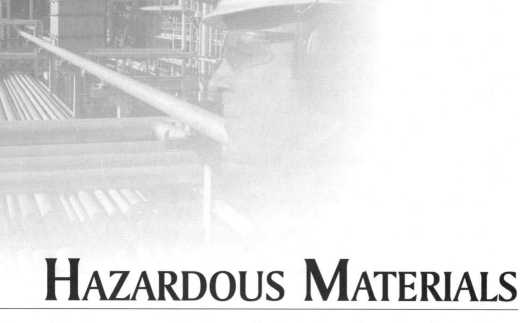

HAZARDOUS MATERIALS

Flammable and Combustible Liquids—1910.106

The primary basis of this standard is the National Fire Protection Association's publication NFPA 30, *Flammable and Combustible Liquids Code*. This standard applies to the handling, storage and use of flammable and combustible liquids with a flash point below 200°F. There are two primary hazards associated with flammable and combustible liquids: explosion and fire. In order to prevent these hazards, this standard addresses the primary concerns of design and construction, ventilation, ignition sources and storage.

Definitions

These definitions were derived from consensus standards and were not uniquely developed for OSHA regulations. Some of the more important definitions are discussed below.

Aerosol shall mean a material that is dispensed from its container as a mist, spray or foam by a propellant under pressure.

Approved shall mean approved or listed by a nationally recognized testing laboratory.

Boiling point shall mean the boiling point of a liquid at a pressure of 14.7 pounds per square inch absolute (psia). This pressure is equivalent to 760 millimeters of mercury (760 mm Hg). At temperatures above the boiling point, the pressure of the atmosphere can no longer hold the liquid in the liquid state and bubbles begin to form. The lower the boiling point, the greater the vapor pressure at normal ambient temperatures and, consequently, the greater the fire risk.

Container shall mean any can, barrel or drum.

Closed container shall mean a container so sealed by means of a lid or other device from which neither liquid nor vapor will escape at ordinary temperatures.

Fire area shall mean an area of a building separated from the remainder of the building by construction, having a fire resistance of at least one hour and having all communicating openings properly protected by an assembly having a fire resistance rating of at least one hour.

Flash point means the minimum temperature at which a liquid gives off vapor within a test vessel in sufficient concentration to form an ignitable mixture with air near the surface of the liquid. The flash point is normally an indication of susceptibility to ignition.

The flash point is determined by heating the liquid in test equipment and measuring the temperature at which a flash will be obtained when a small flame is introduced in the vapor zone above the surface of the liquid.

A standard closed container is used to determine the closed-cup flash point and a standard open-surface dish for the open-cup flash point temperature, as specified by the American Society for Testing and Materials (ASTM). These methods are referenced in OSHA's 1910.106 standard.

Combustible liquid means any liquid having a flash point at or above 100°F (37.8°C). Combustible liquids shall be divided into two classes as follows:

- **Class II liquids** shall include those with flash points at or above 100°F (37.8°C) and below 140°F (60°C), except any mixture having components with flash points of 200°F (93.3°C) or higher, the volume of which makes up 99 percent or more of the total volume of the mixture (See Exhibit 10-1.).
- **Class III liquids** shall include those with flash points at or above 140°F (60°C) (See Exhibit 10-2.). Class II liquids are subdivided into two subclasses:
- **Class IIIA liquids** shall include those with flash points at or above 140°F (60°C) and below 200°F (93.3°C), except any mixture having components with flash points of 200°F (93.3°C), or higher, the total volume of which makes up 99 percent or more of the total volume of the mixture.
- **Class IIIB liquids** shall include those with flash points at or above 200°F (93.3°C). This section does not regulate Class IIIB liquids. Where the term "Class III liquids" is used in this section, it shall mean only Class 111A liquids. When a combustible liquid is heated to within 30°F (16.7°C) of its flash point, it shall be handled in accordance with the requirements for the next lower class of liquids.

Flammable liquid means any liquid having a flash point below 100°F (37.8°C) or higher, the total of which makes up 99 percent or more of the total volume of the mixture. Flammable liquids shall be known as Class I liquids. Class I liquids are divided into three classes as follows:

- Class IA shall include liquids having flash points below 73°F (22.8°C) and having boiling points below 100°F (37.8°C) (See Exhibit 10-3.).
- Class IB shall include liquids having flash points below 73°F (22.8°C) and having boiling points at or above 100°F (37.8°C) (See Exhibit 10-4.).
- Class IC shall include liquids having flash points at or above 73°F (22.8°C) and below 100°F (37.8°C) (See Exhibit 10-5.).

It should be mentioned that flash point was selected as the basis for classification of flammable and combustible liquids because it is directly related to a liquid's ability to generate vapor (i.e., its volatility). Since it is the vapor of the liquid not the liquid itself that burns, vapor generation becomes the primary factor in determining the fire hazard. The expression "low flash-high hazard" applies. Liquids having flash points below ambient storage temperatures generally display a rapid rate of flame spread over the surface of the liquid because it is not necessary for the heat of the fire to expend its energy in heating the liquid to generate more vapor (See Exhibit 10-7).

Exhibit 10-1 further illustrates these classifications.

Exhibit 10-1.
Examples of Class II material.

Liquid		Flash Point (°F)	Boiling Point (°F)	Flammable Limits		Vapor Density Air =1	PEL (ppm)
Common Name	Other Names			LEL	UEL		
Isoamyl Alcohol		109	268	1.2	-	3.0	100
Cellosolve Acetate	2-Ethooxyethyl Acetate	117	313	1.7	-	4.7	100
Cyclohexanone		111	313	-	-	3.4	50
Fuel Oil #1 & #2		100+	-	-	-	-	-
Fuel Oil #4		110+	-	-	-	-	-
Fuel Oil #5		130+	-	-	-	-	-
Kerosene		110-150	180-300	0.7	5.0	4.5	-
Naphtha (coal tar)	100-110	300-400	-	-	4.3	100	
Naphtha (High Flash)	100° Naphtha Safety Solvent, Stoddard Solvent	100-110	300-400	0.8	6.0	>4.2	500
Methyl Cellosolve	2-Methoxyethanol	115	255	2.5	14.0	-	25

Exhibit 10-2.
Examples of Class III material.

Liquid		Flash Point (°F)	Boiling Point (°F)	Flammable Limits		Vapor Density Air = 1	PEL (ppm)
Common Name	Other Names			LEL	UEL		
Aniline		158	363	1.3	-	3.2	5
Butyl Cellosolve	2-Butoxyethanol	160	340	1.1	10.6	4.1	50
Cellosolve Solvent	2-Ethoxyethanol Cellosolve Solvent	202	275	1.8	14.0	3.1	200
Cyclohexanol		162	322	-	-	2.5	50
Ethylene Glycol	Glycol	232	387	3.2	-	-	-
Furfural		140	324	2.1	19.3	3.3	5
Glycerine	Glycerol	320	554	-	-	3.2	-
Isophorone		184	419	0.8	3.8	-	25
Nitrobenzene		190	412	-	-	4.3	1

Exhibit 10-3.
Examples of Class IA material.

Liquid		Flash Point (°F)	Boiling Point (°F)	Flammable Limits		Vapor Density Air = 1	PEL (ppm)
Common Name	Other Names			LEL	UEL		
1-1 Dichloroethylene	Vinylidene chloride	0	x99	7.3	10.0	3.4	-
Ethulamine		<0	63	3.5	14.0	1.6	10
Ethyl Chloride	Chloroethane	-58	54	3.8	15.4	2.2	1000
Ethyl Ether	Ether	-49	95	1.9	36.0	2.6	400
Isopentane		<-60	82	1.4	7.6	2.5	-
Isopropyl Chloride	2-Chloropropane	-26	97	2.8	10.7	2.7	-
Methyl Formate		-2	90	5.0	23.0	2.1	100
Pentane		<-40	97	1.5	7.8	2.5	1000
Propylene Oxide		-35	93	2.8	37.0	2.0	100

Exhibit 10-4.
Examples of Class IB material.

Liquid		Flash Point (°F)	Boiling Point (°F)	Flammable Limits		Vapor Density Air = 1	PEL (ppm)
Common Name	Other Names			LEL	UEL		
Acetone		0	134	2.6	12.8	2.0	1000
Benzene	Benzol	12	176	1.3	7.1	2.8	1
Carbon Disulfide	Carbon bisulfide	-22	115	1.3	50.0	2.6	20
1.2-Dichloroethylene	Acetylene dichloride	43	140	9.7	12.8	3.4	200
Ethyl Acetate		24	171	2.2	11.0	3.0	400
Ethyl Alcohol	Ethanol, Grain alcohol	55	173	3.3	19	1.6	1000
Ethyl Benzene		59	277	1.0	6.7	3.7	100
Gasoline	x	-45	100-399	1.4	7.6	3-4	-
Hexane	x	-7	156	1.1	7.5	3.0	500
Methyl Acetate		14	135	3.1	16	2.6	200
Methyl Alcohol	Wood alcohol, Methanol	52	147	6.7	36	1.1	200
Methyl Ethyl Ketone	MEK, 2-Butanone	21	176	1.8	10	2.5	200
Methyl Propyl Ketone	2-Pentanone	45	216	1.5	8.2	2.9	200
VM&P Naphtha	76° Naphtha	20-45	212-320	0.9	6.0	4.2	-
Octane		56	257	1.0	6.5	3.9	500
Propyl Acetate		58	215	2.0	8.0	3.5	200
Isopropyl Acetate		58	215	2.0	8.0	3.5	200
Isopropyl Alcohol	IPA, 2-Propanol	53	180	2.0	12	2.1	400
Toulene	Toluol	40	232	1.2	7.1	3.1	200
Butyl Acetate		72	260	1.7	7.6	4.0	150

Exhibit 10-5.
Examples of Class IC material.

Liquid		Flash Point (°F)	Boiling Point (°F)	Flammable Limits		Vapor Density Air = 1	PEL (ppm)
Common Name	Other Names			LEL	UEL		
Isoamyl Acetate	Banana Oil	77	288	1.0	7.5	4.5	100
Amyl Alcohol	Pentanol	91	281	1.2	10	3.0	-
Butyl Alcohol	Butanol	84	243	1.4	11.2	2.6	100
Methyl Isobutyl Ketone	MIBK, Hexone	73	246	1.4	7.5	3.5	100
Naphtha (Petroleum)	Mineral Spirits, Petroleum Ether	85-110	302-399	0.8	6.0	4.2	-
Propyl Alcohol	Propanol	77	208	2.1	13.5	2.1	200
Styrene (Monomer)	Vinyl Benzene	90	295	1.1	6.1	3.6	100
Turpentine		95	307-347	0.8	-	-	100
Xylene	Xylol	81-115	281-291	1.1	7.0	3.7	100

Exhibit 10-6.
Examples of nonflammable material.

Liquid		Boiling Point (°F)	PEL (ppm)
Common Name	Other Names		
Carbon Tetrachloride		171	10
Chloroform	Trichloromethane	142	50
Ethylene Dibromide	1,2-Dibromoethane	270	20
Methyl Chloroform	1,1,1-Trichloroethane	165	350
Methylene Chloride	Dichloromethane	104	500
Perchloroethylene	Tetrachloroethylene	248	100
Trichloroethylene	TCE, Trichlor	190	100

* Non-Flammable under normal conditions. Unstablizied trichloroethylene can decompose violently in presence of fine aluminum powder.

Exhibit 10-7.
Classifications and flashpoints for flammable and combustible liquids.

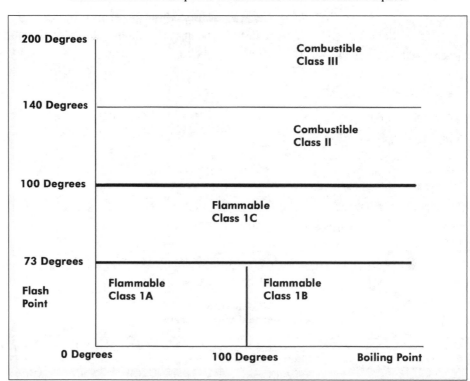

Portable tank shall mean a closed container having a liquid capacity of more than 60 U.S. gallons and not intended for fixed installation.

Safety can shall mean an approved container of not more than 5-gallon capacity, having a spring-closing lid and spout cover and so designed that it will safely relieve internal pressure when subjected to fire exposure.

Vapor pressure shall mean the pressure, measured in pounds per square inch (absolute), exerted by a volatile liquid as determined by the American Society for Testing and Materials' Standard Method of Test for Vapor Pressure of Petroleum Products (Reid Method), ASTM D323-68.

Vapor pressure is a measure of a liquid's propensity to evaporate. The higher the vapor pressure, the more volatile the liquid and thus the more readily the liquid gives off vapors.

Ventilation as specified in this section is for the prevention of fire and explosion. It is considered adequate if it is sufficient to prevent accumulation of significant quantities of vapor-air mixtures in concentration over one-fourth of the lower flammable limit.

Flammable (Explosive) Limits

When vapors of a flammable or combustible liquid are mixed with air in the proper proportions in the presence of a source of ignition, rapid combustion or an explosion can occur. The proper proportion is called the *flammable range* and is also often referred to as the *explosive range*. The flammable range includes all concentrations of flammable vapor or gas in air, in which a flash will occur or a flame will travel if the mixture is ignited. There is a minimum concentration of vapor or gas in air below which propagation of flame does not occur on contact with a source of ignition. There is also a maximum proportion of vapor in air above which propagation of flame does not occur. These boundary-line mixtures of vapor with air are known as the *lower* and *upper flammable* or *explosive limits* (LEL or UEL) respectively, and they are usually expressed in terms of percentage by volume of vapor in air (See Exhibit 10-8.).

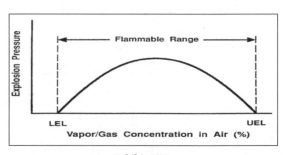

Exhibit 10-8.
When mixed with air, vapors and gases have minimum and maximum concentrations at which propagation of flame will not occur.

In popular jargon, a vapor-air mixture below the flammable limit is too "lean" to burn or explode, and a mixture above the upper flammable limit is too "rich" to burn or explode. No attempt is made to differentiate between the terms *flammable* and *explosive* as applied to the lower and upper limits of flammability.

Container and Portable Tank Storage

This section applies only to the storage of flammable or combustible liquids in drums or other containers (including flammable aerosols) not exceeding 60-gallon individual capacity and portable tanks of less than 660-gallon individual capacity. A portable tank is a closed container that has a liquid capacity of more than 60 gallons and is not intended for fixed installations.

This section does not apply to the following:
- Storage of containers in bulk plants, service stations, refineries, chemical plants and distilleries;
- Class I or Class II liquids in the fuel tanks of a motor vehicle, aircraft, boat, or portable or stationary engine;
- Flammable or combustible paints, oils, varnishes and similar mixtures used for painting or maintenance when not kept for a period in excess of 30 days; and
- Beverages when packed in individual containers not exceeding 1 gallon in size.

Design, Construction and Capacity of Containers

Only approved containers and portable tanks may be used to store flammable and combustible liquids. Metal containers and portable tanks meeting the requirements of the Department of Transportation (DOT) (49 CFR 178) are deemed acceptable when containing products authorized by the DOT (49 CFR 173).

The latest version of NFPA 30, Flammable and Combustible Liquids Code, indicates that certain petroleum products may be safely stored within plastic containers if the terms and conditions of the following specifications are met:
- Plastic Containers (Jerry Cans) for Petroleum Products, ANSI/ASTM D 3435-80;
- Standard for Portable Gasoline Containers for Consumer Use, ASTM F852-86;

- Standard for Portable Kerosene Containers for Consumer Use, ASTM F 976-86; and
- Nonmetallic Safety Cans for Petroleum Products, ANSI/UL 1313-83.

This standard also requires portable tanks to have provision for emergency venting. Top-mounted emergency vents must be capable of limiting internal pressure under fire exposure conditions to 10 psig or 30 percent of the bursting pressure of the tank, whichever is greater. Portable tanks are also required to have at least one pressure-activated vent with a minimum capacity of 6,000 cu. ft. of free air at 14.7 psia and 60°F. These vents must be set to open at not less than 5 psig. If fusible vents are used, they shall be actuated by elements that operate at a temperature not exceeding 300°F.

Maximum allowable sizes of various types of containers and portable tanks are specified based on the class of flammable and combustible liquid they contain.

Design, Construction and Capacity of Storage Cabinets

Flammable and combustible materials should be kept in fire safety storage cabinets. The amount that can be stored in each cabinet varies with the type of material as indicated here.
- Class I and/or Class II liquids
  Not more than 60 gallons
- Class III liquids
  Not more than 120 gallons

This standard permits both metal and wooden storage cabinets. Storage cabinets shall be designed and constructed to limit the internal temperature to not more than 325°F when subjected to a standardized 10-minute fire test. All joints and seams shall remain tight and the door shall remain securely closed during the fire test. Storage cabinets shall be conspicuously labeled "Flammable—Keep Fire Away."

The bottom, top, door and sides of metal cabinets shall be at least No. 18 gage sheet metal and double walled with ½-in, air space. The door shall be provided with a three-point lock, and the doorsill shall be raised at least 2 in. above the bottom of the cabinet.

Exhibit 10-9.
Table H-12 - Maximum Allowable Size of Containers
and Portable Tanks

Container type	Flammable liquids			Combustible liquids	
	Class IA	Class IB	Class IC	Class II	Class III
Glass or approved plastic	1 pt	1 qt	1 gal	1 gal	1 gal.
Metal (other than DOT drums)	1 gal	5 gal	5 gal	5 gal	5 gal.
Safety cans	2 gal	5 gal	5 gal	5 gal	5 gal.
Metal drums (DOT specifications)	60 gal	60 gal	60 gal	60 gal	60 gal.
Approved portable tanks	660 gal	660 gal	660 gal	660 gal	660 gal.

NOTE: Container exemptions: [a] Medicines, beverages, foodstuffs, cosmetics, and other common consumer items, when packaged according to commonly accepted practices, shall be exempt from the requirements of 1910.106(d)(2)(i) and (ii).

Design and Construction of Inside Storage Rooms

Construction is to comply with the test specifications included in Standard Methods of Fire Tests of Building Construction and Materials, NFPA 2511969.

Openings to other rooms or buildings shall be provided with non-combustible liquid-tight raised sills or ramps at least 4 inches in height, or the floor in the storage area shall be at least 4 in. below the surrounding floor. Openings shall be provided with approved self-closing fire doors. The room shall be liquid-tight where the walls join the floor. A permissible alternate to the sill or ramp is an open-grated trench inside of the room that drains to a safe location. This method may be preferred if there is an extensive need to transfer flammable liquids into and out of the room by means of hand trucks.

Rating and capacity. Storage in inside storage rooms shall comply with Table H-13 (See Exhibit 10-10.):

Exhibit 10-10.
Table H-13. Storage in Inside Rooms

Fire protection provided	Fire resistance	Maximum size	Total allowable quantities (gals./sq. ft./floor area)
Yes	2 hours	500 sq. ft.	10
No	2 hours	500 sq. ft.	5
Yes	1 hour	150 sq. ft.	4
No	1 hour	150 sq. ft.	2

Wiring. Electrical wiring and equipment located in inside storage rooms used for Class I liquids shall be approved under Subpart S, Electrical, for Class I, Division 2 Hazardous Locations; for Class III and Class III liquids, shall be approved for general use.

Ventilation. Every inside storage room shall be provided with either a gravity or a mechanical exhaust ventilation system designed to provide for a complete change of air within the room at least six times per hour. Ventilation is vital to the prevention of flammable liquid fires and explosions. It is important to ensure that airflow through the system is constant and prevents the accumulation of any flammable vapors.

Storage. In every inside storage room, there shall be maintained an aisle at least 3 ft. wide. Easy movement within the room is necessary in order to reduce the potential for spilling or damaging the containers and to provide both access for fire fighting and a ready escape path for occupants of the room should a fire occur.

Containers with more than a 30-gallon capacity shall not be stacked one upon the other. Such containers are built to DOT specifications and are not required to withstand a drop test greater than 3 ft. when full. Dispensing shall be only by approved pump or self-closing faucet.

Storage Inside Building

Egress. Flammable or combustible liquids, including stock for sale, shall not be stored so as to limit use of exits, stairways or areas normally used for the safe egress of people.

Office occupancies. Storage shall be prohibited except that which is required for maintenance and operation of equipment. Such storage shall be kept in closed metal containers stored in a storage cabinet or in safety cans or in an inside storage room not having a door that opens into that portion of the building used by the public.

General purpose public warehouses. There are tables in the standard summarizing the storage requirements applicable to "General Purpose Public Warehouses." These tables refer to indoor storage of flammable and combustible liquids that are confined in containers and portable tanks. Storage of incompatible materials that create a fire exposure (e.g., oxidizers, water-reactive chemicals, certain acids) is not permitted.

Warehouses or storage buildings. The last type of inside storage covered by this paragraph addresses storage in "warehouses or storage buildings." These structures are sometimes referred to as outside storage rooms. Any quantity of flammable and combustible liquid can be stored in these buildings, provided that they are stored in a configuration consistent with the tables in this paragraph.

Pallets or dunnage shall separate containers in piles, where necessary, to provide stability and to prevent excessive stress on container walls.

Stored material shall not be piled within 3 ft. of beams or girders and shall be at least 3 ft. below sprinkler deflectors, discharge orifices of water spray or other fire protection equipment.

Aisles of at least 3 ft. in width shall be maintained to access doors, windows or standpipe connections.

Storage Outside Building

Requirements covering "storage outside buildings" are summarized in tables in this paragraph. Associated requirements are given for storage adjacent to buildings. Also included are requirements involving controls for diversion of spills away from buildings and security measures for protection against trespassing and tampering. Certain housekeeping requirements are given that relate to control of weeds, debris and accumulation of unnecessary combustibles.

Fire control

Suitable fire control devices, such as small hose or portable fire extinguishers, shall be available at locations where flammable or combustible liquids are stored. At least one portable fire extinguisher having a rating of not less than 12-B units shall be located:

- Outside of, but not more than 10 ft. from, the door opening into any room used for storage; and
- Not less than 10 ft., nor more than 25 ft., from any Class I or Class II liquid storage area located outside of a storage room, but inside a building.

The reason for requiring that portable fire extinguishers be located a distance away from the storage room is that fires involving Class I and Class II flammable liquids are likely to escalate rapidly. If the fire is too close to the storage area, it may be impossible to get to it once the fire has started. Open flames and smoking shall not be permitted in flammable or combustible liquid storage areas.

Materials that react with water shall not be stored in the same room with flammable or combustible liquids. Automatic sprinkler or water spray systems and hose lines protect many flammable and combustible liquid storage areas. Consequently, any storage of water-reactive material in the storage area creates an unreasonable risk.

Industrial Plants

This paragraph shall not apply to chemical plants, refineries or distilleries.

This paragraph applies to those industrial plants where:

- The use of flammable or combustible liquids is incidental to the principal business; or
- Where flammable or combustible liquids are handled or used only in unit physical operations such as mixing, drying, evaporating, filtering, distillation and similar operations that do not involve chemical reaction.

Incidental Storage or Use of Flammable or Combustible Liquids

This subparagraph is applicable to those portions of an industrial plant where the use and handling of flammable or combustible liquids is only incidental to the principal business, such as paint thinner storage in an automobile assembly plant, solvents used in the construction of electronic equipment and flammable finishing materials used in furniture manufacturing.

Containers. Flammable or combustible liquids shall be stored in tanks or closed containers.

The quantity of liquid that may be located outside of an inside storage room or storage cabinet in a building or in any one fire area of a building shall not exceed:

- 25 gallons of Class IA liquids in containers;
- 120 gallons of Class IB, IC, II, or III liquids in containers; or
- 660 gallons of Class IB, IC, II, or III liquids in a single portable tank.

Handling liquids at point of final use. Flammable liquids shall be kept in covered containers when not actually in use. Where flammable or combustible liquids are used or handled, except in closed containers, means shall be provided to dispose promptly and safely of leakage or spills. Flammable or combustible liquids shall be drawn from or transferred into vessels, containers or portable tanks within a building only in the following manner:

- Through a closed piping system;
- From safety cans;
- By means of a device drawing through the top; or
- From containers or portable tanks by gravity through an approved self-closing valve.

Transfer operations must be provided with adequate ventilation. Sources of ignition are not permitted in areas where flammable vapors may travel. Transferring liquids by means of air pressure on the container or portable tanks is prohibited. This may result in an overpressure that could exceed what the container or tank could withstand. In addition, a flammable atmosphere could be created within the container or tank. This atmosphere would be particularly sensitive to ignition because of the increased pressure.

Unit Physical Operations

This subparagraph applies to those portions of industrial plants where flammable or combustible liquids are handled or used in unit physical operations such as mixing, drying, evaporating, filtering, distillation and similar operations that do not involve chemical change. Examples are plants compounding cosmetics, pharmaceuticals, solvents, cleaning fluids, insecticides and similar activities.

Location. Industrial plants shall be located so that each building or unit of equipment is accessible from at least one side for firefighting and fire control purposes.

Drainage. Emergency drainage systems shall be provided to direct flammable or combustible liquid leakage and fire protection water to a safe location.

Ventilation. The standard requires that adequate ventilation be provided in operating areas. Appropriate measures must be taken to trap and remove hazardous vapors.

Tank Vehicle and Tank Car Loading and Unloading

Tank vehicle and tank car loading or unloading facilities shall be separated from above-ground tanks, warehouses and similar facilities by a distance of 25 ft. for Class I liquids and 15 ft. for Class II and Class III liquids measured from the nearest position of any fill stem.

Fire Control

These requirements basically state that hazards shall be evaluated and appropriate fire protection provided. Such an evaluation must consider the hazards of the operation, the various materials used, the design of the plant and equipment, materials handling and transfer requirements, any unusual conditions and the available fire protection sprinkler systems and other types of protective systems that may be necessary to protect employees.

Sources of Ignition

Adequate precautions shall be taken to prevent the ignition of flammable vapors. Sources of ignition include, but are not limited to:

- Open flames;
- Lightning;
- Smoking; cutting and welding;
- Hot surfaces;
- Frictional heat;
- Static, electrical and mechanical sparks;
- Spontaneous ignition, including heat-producing chemical reactions; and
- Radiant heat.

These are some examples of common ignition sources, although the list is neither all-inclusive nor applicable in all cases. Again, it is emphasized that control of ignition sources is the second line of defense; minimizing the possibility of a spill or leak is the primary objective of this regulation.

Bonding. Class I liquids shall not be dispensed into containers unless the nozzle and container are electrically interconnected.

Electrical

All electrical wiring and equipment shall be installed according to the requirements of Subpart S, Electrical.

Locations where flammable vapor-air mixtures may exist under normal operations shall be classified Class I, Division 1, according to the requirements of Subpart S. For those pieces of equipment installed in accordance with the above paragraphs on unit physical operations, the Division 1 area shall extend 5 ft. in all directions from all points of vapor liberation. Unventilated pits within any Class I area are classified as Division 1 locations.

Locations where flammable vapor-air mixtures may exist under abnormal conditions and for a distance beyond Division 1 locations shall be classified Division 2 according to the requirements of Subpart S, Electrical. These locations include an area within 20 ft. horizontally, 3 ft. vertically beyond a Division 1 area, and up to 3 ft. above floor or grade level within 25 ft., if indoors, or 10 ft. if outdoors, from any pump, bleeder, withdrawal fitting, meter or similar device handling Class I liquids. Adequately ventilated pits are Class I, Division 2 locations.

Repairs to Equipment
Hot work, such as welding or cutting operations, use of spark-producing power tools and chipping operations shall be permitted only under supervision of an individual in responsible charge.

Housekeeping
Maintenance and operating practices shall follow established procedures that control leakage and prevent accidental escape of flammable or combustible liquids. Spills shall be cleaned up promptly. Combustible waste material and residues in a building or unit operating area shall be kept to a minimum, stored in covered metal receptacles and disposed of daily.

Bulk Plants
Storage
Class I liquids shall be stored in closed containers, in storage tanks above ground outside of buildings or underground in accordance with the requirements of this section.

Class II and III liquids shall be stored in containers, in tanks within buildings, above ground outside of buildings or underground in accordance with the requirements of this section.

Building
Rooms in which flammable or combustible liquids are stored or handled by pumps shall have exit facilities arranged to prevent occupants from being trapped in the event of fire.

Rooms in which Class I liquids are stored or handled shall be heated only by means not constituting a source of ignition, such as steam or hot water. Adequate ventilation shall be provided for all rooms, buildings or enclosures in which Class I liquids are pumped or dispensed.

Loading and Unloading Facilities
Tank vehicle and tank car loading or unloading facilities shall be separated from above-ground tanks, warehouses and similar facilities a distance of 25 ft. for Class I liquids and 15 ft. for Class II and Class III liquids measured from the nearest position of any fill spout. (Buildings for pumps or shelters for personnel may be considered a part of the loading and unloading facilities).

Equipment such as piping, pumps and meters used for the transfer of Class I liquids between storage tanks and the fill stem of the loading rack shall not be used for the transfer of Class II or Class III liquids.

Static Protection. Bonding facilities for protection against static sparks during the loading of tank vehicles through open domes shall be provided:
- Where Class I liquids are loaded; or
- Where Class II or Class III liquids are loaded into vehicles that may contain vapors from previous cargoes of Class I liquids.

The standard requires appropriate bonding equipment and procedures. Facilities for materials that do not have a static electricity hazard are not required to be bonded.

Container Filling Facilities. Class I liquids shall not be dispensed into containers unless the nozzle and container are electrically interconnected.

Electrical Equipment
This subparagraph applies to areas where Class I liquids are stored or handled. For areas where only Class II or Class III liquids are stored or handled, the electrical equipment may be installed in accordance with requirements for ordinary (i.e., nonhazardous) locations.

Sources of Ignition
Class I liquids shall not be handled, drawn or dispensed where flammable vapors may

reach a source of ignition. Smoking shall be prohibited except in designated locations. "No Smoking" signs shall be conspicuously posted where a hazard from flammable liquid vapors is normally present.

Drainage and Waste Disposal

Provision shall be made to prevent flammable or combustible liquids that may be spilled at loading or unloading points from entering public sewers, drainage systems or natural waterways. Connection to such sewers, drains or waterways by which flammable or combustible liquids might enter shall be provided with separator boxes or other approved means whereby such entry is precluded. Crankcase drainings and flammable or combustible liquids shall not be dumped into sewers, but shall be stored in tanks or tight drums outside of any building until removed from the premises.

Fire Control

Suitable fire-control devices, such as a small hose or portable fire extinguishers, shall be available in locations where fires are likely to occur.

Service Stations

Liquids shall be stored in approved closed containers not exceeding 60 gallons in capacity, in underground tanks or in tanks in special enclosures or above ground as provided for in this section.

No Class I liquids may be dispensed into portable containers unless the metal container has a tight closure with screwed or spring cover and is fitted with a spout or so designed that the contents can be poured without spilling.

A clearly identified and easily accessible switch(es) or circuit breaker(s) shall be provided at a location remote from dispensing devices, including remote pumping systems, to shut off the power to all dispensing devices in the event of an emergency.

Processing Plants

This paragraph applies to those plants or buildings that house chemical operations such as oxidation, reduction, halogenation, hydrogenation, alkylation, polymerization and other chemical processes, but does not apply to chemical plants, refineries or distilleries.

Processing Building

This section requires that appropriate facilities be provided for flammable and combustible liquid processing within buildings. Buildings must be safely constructed with appropriate drainage, ventilation and explosion relief. Emergency drainage systems shall be provided to direct flammable or combustible liquid leakage and fire protection water to a safe location. If connected to public sewers or discharged into public waterways, these systems shall be equipped with traps or separators.

Liquid Handling

The storage of flammable or combustible liquids in tanks shall be in accordance with the provisions of this section. Piping must be identified and meet safety requirements.

The transfer of large quantities of flammable or combustible liquids shall be through piping by means of pumps or water displacement. Except as required in process equipment, gravity flow shall not be used. The use of compressed air as a transferring medium is prohibited. Equipment must be designed to ensure containment. Where the vapor space is usually within the flammable range or other operational hazards indicate a need, equipment must be protected against explosion by construction or other appropriate measures.

Fire Control

Fire control provisions, including portable extinguishers, water supply, fixed extinguishing systems and alarm systems shall be provided. An analysis similar to that required for plants having unit physical operations must be performed. Appropriate fire control facilities must be provided as indicated by the special hazards of the plant.

Sources of Ignition

As in other paragraphs of this section, sources of ignition shall be prevented from igniting flammable vapors.

Waste and Residues

Combustible waste material and residues in a building or operating area shall be kept to a minimum, stored in closed metal waste cans and disposed of daily.

Refineries, Chemical Plants and Distilleries

Plants must be protected from catastrophic fire, explosion and/or release of toxic materials. Refer to 29 CFR 1910.119, *Process Safety Management of Highly Hazardous Chemicals*, which requires programmatic controls regarding these hazards. Recognized safe-practice documents from the affected industries identify necessary controls.

Storage Tanks

Flammable and combustible liquids shall be stored in tanks, containers or portable tanks in accordance with the requirements of this section.

Wharves

Wharves handling flammable or combustible liquids shall be in accordance with the requirements of this section.

Location of Process Units

Process units shall be located so that they are accessible from at least one side for the purpose of fire control.

Fire Control

Fire control provisions, including portable fire extinguishers, water supply and fixed extinguishing systems, shall be provided.

Spray Finishing Using Flammable and Combustible Materials—1910.107

This regulation is based on the National Fire Protection Association's standard NFPA 33, Spray Finishing Using Flammable and Combustible Materials, 1969 edition. Many technological changes have occurred in the field of spray finishing since this edition was published. The current edition of NFPA 33 is called Spray Application Using Flammable and Combustible Materials to recognize the hazards inherent to operations such as spray-up molding (e.g., fiberglass).

This section applies to flammable and combustible finishing materials when applied as a spray by compressed air, "airless" or "hydraulic atomization," steam, electrostatic methods or by any other means in continuous or intermittent processes. This section also covers the application of combustible powders by powder spray guns, electrostatic powder spray guns, fluidized beds or electrostatic fluidized beds. This section does not apply to outdoor spray application of buildings, tanks or other similar structures, nor to small portable spraying apparatus not used repeatedly in the same location. In these situations, there would be lesser chance of combustible residue buildup and greater chance of atmospheric dilution of flammable vapors.

Authority having jurisdiction. As defined in NFPA 33, the organization, office or individual responsible for "approving" equipment, an installation or a procedure. Where public safety is primary, the "authority having jurisdiction" may be a federal, state, local or other regional department or individual such as a fire chief, fire marshal, chief of a fire prevention bureau, labor department, health department, building official, electrical inspector or others having statutory authority.

Dry spray booth. A spray booth not equipped with a water-washing system. A dry spray booth may be equipped with (1) distribution or baffle plates to promote an even flow of air through the booth or cause deposit of over spray before it enters exhaust ducts; or (2) over spray dry filters to minimize dust or residue entering exhaust ducts; or (3) overspray dry filter rolls designed to minimize dust or residue entering exhaust ducts; or (4) where dry powders are being sprayed, with powder collection systems so arranged in the exhaust to capture oversprayed material (See Exhibit 10-11.).

Exhibit 10-11.
Types of filters for dry spray booths.

Spray Area. Any area in which dangerous quantities of flammable vapors or mists or combustible residues, dusts or deposits are present due to the operation of spraying processes. The current edition of NFPA 33 offers greater insight into the meaning of the spray area.

According to OSHA, a spray area shall include:

- The interior of spray booths or rooms;
- The interior of ducts exhausting from spraying processes; and
- Any area in the direct path of spraying operations.

The "authority having jurisdiction" may define the limits of the spray area in any specific case. When spraying operations are strictly confined to predetermined spaces that are provided with adequate and reliable ventilation, such as a properly constructed spray booth, the "spray area" will ordinarily not extend beyond the booth enclosure. When the spray operations are not confined to adequately ventilated spaces, the spray area may extend to the entire room that contains spraying operations.

The implications of the above definition are as follows. A spray area is, by definition, a Class I, Division 1 hazardous location. As discussed later in this section, electrical devices and wiring within the spray area must comply with Subpart S, Electrical. The authority having jurisdiction may define the entire room to be a spray area if operations are not confined. Installation of expensive electrical devices and wiring would then be required throughout the entire room.

It is therefore in the employer's interest to conduct spray operations in a spray booth or room in order to confine the vapors, mist and residue and limit the area requiring the use of Class I, Division 1 electrical equipment. Confining spray operations to a spray booth or room also increases the safety of the operation, facilitates maintenance and clean up and provides a healthier working environment. The employer also may then be eligible fir preferred insurance rates.

Spray Room. A power-ventilated fully enclosed room used exclusively for the open spraying of flammable or combustible materials. The entire spray room is a spray area. A spray booth is not a spray room.

Spray Booths

Construction
Spray booths shall be substantially constructed of securely and rigidly supported steel, concrete or masonry; however, aluminum or other substantial non-combustible material may be used for intermittent or low-volume spraying. Spray booths shall be designed to sweep air currents toward the exhaust outlet.

Interiors
The interior surfaces of spray booths shall be smooth and continuous, without edges and otherwise designed to prevent the pocketing of residue and facilitate cleaning and washing without injury (See Exhibit 10-12.).

Exhibit 10-12.
Anatomy of a spray booth.

FRONTAL AREA
Each spray booth having a frontal area larger than 9 square feet shall have a metal deflector or curtain not less than 2 1/2 inches deep installed at the outer edge of the booth over the opening.

CONVEYORS
Where conveyors are arranged to carry work into and out of spray booths, the conveyor openings shall be as small as practical.

EXHAUST

Arrestor Bank

AIR FLOW

Space within the spray booth on the downstream and upstream sides of filters shall be protected with an automatic sprinkler, dry chemical, or carbon dioxide extinguishing system.

Visible gauges or audible alarm or pressure-activated devices shall be installed to indicate or insure that the required air velocity is maintained.

ACCESS DOORS
When necessary to facilitate cleaning, exhaust ducts shall be provided with an ample number of access doors.

ARRESTOR BANK
All discarded filter pads and filter rolls shall be immediately removed to a safe, well-detached location or placed in a water-filled metal container or disposed of at the close of the day's operation unless maintained completely in water.

The average air velocity over the open face of the booth (or booth cross section during spraying operations) shall be not less than 100 fpm; for electrostatic spraying, the minimum velocity is 60 fpm.

MINIMUM SEPARATION
There shall be no open flame or spark producing equipment in any spraying area nor within 20 feet thereof, unless separated by a partition.

CONSTRUCTION
Spray booths shall be substantially constructed of steel, securely and rigidly supported, or of concrete or masonry except that aluminum or other substantial noncombustible material may be used for intermittent or low volume spraying.

INTERIORS
The interior surfaces of spray booths shall be smooth and continuous without edges and otherwise designed to prevent pocketing of residues and facilitate cleaning and washing without injury.

DISCHARGE CLEARANCE
Unless the spray booth exhaust duct terminal is from a water-wash spray booth, the terminal discharge point shall be not less than 6 feet from any combustible exterior wall or roof nor discharge in the direction of any combustible construction or unprotected opening in any noncombustible exterior wall within 25 feet.

Floors

The floor surface of a spray booth and operator's working area, if combustible, shall be covered with non-combustible material of such character as to facilitate the safe cleaning and removal of residue.

Distribution or Baffle Plates

Distribution or baffle plates, if installed to promote an even flow of air through the booth or cause the deposit of overspray before it enters the exhaust duct, shall be of non-combustible material and readily removable or accessible on both sides for cleaning. Such plates shall not be located in exhaust ducts.

Dry-Type Overspray Collectors

In conventional dry-type spray booths, overspray dry filters or filter rolls, if installed, shall conform to the following:

■ The spraying operations except electrostatic spraying operations shall be so designed, installed and maintained that the average air velocity over the open face of the booth (or booth cross section during spraying operations) shall be not less than 100 linear feet per minute (fpm). Electrostatic spraying operations may be conducted with an air velocity over the open face of the booth of not less than 60 fpm.

NOTE: These requirements were taken from NFPA 33-1969. They pertain to those hazards associated with fire protection or the removal of flammable vapor accumulation. These requirements apply to maintaining the concentration of flammable vapors below the lower explosive limit in a spray booth but do not apply to maintaining operator exposure to within the permissible exposure limits. Where a health hazard has been established, controls and modifications may be required and could include increasing the air velocity beyond that stated here.

- Visible gauges or audible alarms or pressure-activated devices shall be installed to indicate or ensure that the required air velocity is maintained. Filter rolls shall be inspected to insure proper replacement of filter media.
- All discarded filter pads and filter rolls shall be immediately removed to a safe, well-detached location or placed in a water-filled metal container and disposed of at the close of the day's operation, unless maintained completely in water.
- Space within the spray booth on the downstream and upstream sides of filters shall be protected with an automatic sprinkler, dry chemical or carbon dioxide extinguishing system.
- Filters or filter rolls shall not be used when applying a spray material known to be highly susceptible to spontaneous heating and ignition.
- Clean filters or filter rolls shall be non-combustible or a type having a combustibility not in excess of class 2 filters as listed by Underwriter's Laboratories, Inc.
- Filters and filter rolls shall not be alternately used for different types of coating materials, where the combination of materials may be conducive to spontaneous ignition.

Frontal Area
Each spray booth having a frontal area larger than 9 sq. ft. shall have a metal deflector or curtain not less than 2½ in. deep installed at the upper outer edge of the booth over the opening.

Conveyors
Where conveyors are arranged to carry work into and out of spray booths, the conveyor openings shall be as small as practical.

Separation of Operations
Each spray booth shall be separated from other operations by not less than 3 ft., or by a greater distance, or by such partition or wall as to reduce the danger from juxtaposition of hazardous operations (See Exhibit 10-13.).

Exhibit 10-13.
Spray booths must be separated from other operations by at least 3 ft. on all sides.

Cleaning
Spray booths shall be so installed that all portions are readily accessible for cleaning. A clear space of not less than 3 ft. on all sides shall be kept free from storage or combustible construction.

Illumination
When spraying areas are illuminated through glass panels or other transparent materials, only fixed lighting units shall be used as a source of illumination. Panels shall effectively isolate the spraying area from the area in which the lighting unit is located and shall be of a noncombustible material of such a nature or so protected that breakage will be unlikely. Panels shall be so arranged that normal accumulation of residue on the exposed surface of the panel will not be raised to a dangerous temperature by radiation or conduction from the source of illumination.

Electrical and Other Sources of Ignition

Minimum Separation
There shall be no open flame or spark-producing equipment in any spraying area nor within 20 ft. thereof, unless separated by a partition.

Hot Surfaces
Space-heating appliances, steam pipes or hot surfaces shall not be located in a spraying area

where deposits of combustible residues may readily accumulate.

Wiring Conformance
Electrical wiring and equipment shall conform to the provisions of this section and shall otherwise be in accordance with Subpart S, Electrical.

Combustible Residue, Areas
Unless specifically approved for locations containing both deposits of readily ignitable residue and explosive vapors, there shall be no electrical equipment in any spraying area, whereon deposits of combustible residue may readily accumulate, except wiring in rigid conduit or in boxes or fittings containing no taps, splices or terminal connections.

Wiring Type Approved
Electrical wiring and equipment not subject to deposits of combustible residue but located in a spraying area as herein defined shall be of explosion-proof type approved for Class I, Group D locations and shall otherwise conform to the provisions of Subpart S, Electrical, for Class I, Division 1 hazardous locations. Electrical wiring, motors and other equipment outside of but within 20 ft. of any spraying area, and not separated there from by partitions, shall not produce sparks under normal operating conditions and shall otherwise conform to the provisions of Subpart S, Electrical, for Class I, Division 2 hazardous locations.

The current edition of the NEC is more specific in defining the extent of Class I or Class II, Division 1 and Division 2 locations for spraying operations using flammable and combustible materials. The current definitions are briefly summarized below.

Class I or Class II, Division 1 Locations
- The interiors of spray booths or rooms.
- The interior of exhaust ducts.
- Any area in the direct path of spray operations.

Class I or Class II, Division 2 Locations
The following spaces shall be considered Class I or Class II, Division 2, as applicable:
- For open spraying, all space outside of but within 20 ft. horizontally and 10 ft. vertically of the Class I, Division 1 location and not separated from it by partitions (See Exhibit 10-14.).

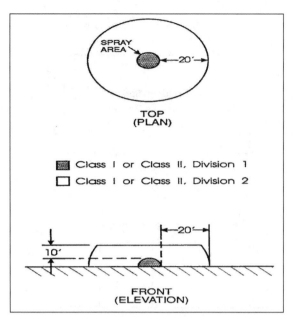

Exhibit 10-14.
Open spraying parameters in a Class, Division 2 location.

- For spraying operations conducted within a closed top, open face or front spray booth, the space within 3 ft. in all directions from openings other than the open face or front.

The Class II, Division 2 location shown in Exhibit 10-15 shall extend from the open face or front of the spray booth in accordance with the following:
- If the ventilation system is interlocked with the spraying equipment so as to make the spraying equipment inoperable when the ventilation system is not in operation, the space shall extend 5 ft. from the open face or front of the spray booth, and as otherwise shown in Figure "A" of Exhibit 10-15.
- If the ventilation system is not interlocked with the spraying equipment so as to make the spraying equipment inoperable when the ventilation system is not in operation, the space shall extend 10 ft. from the open face or front of the spray booth, and as otherwise shown in Figure "B" of Exhibit 10-15.

Exhibit 10-15.
Class I or Class II, Division 2 locations adjacent to a closed top, open faced or open front spray booth.

■ For spraying operations confined to an enclosed spray booth or room, the space within 3 ft. in all directions from any openings shall be considered Class I or Class II, Division 2 locations, as shown in Exhibit 10-16.

Exhibit 10-16.
In an enclosed spray area, the space within 3 ft. on all sides is a Class I or Class II, Division 2 location.

Lamps

Electric lamps outside of, but within 20 ft. of any spraying area, and not separated therefrom by a partition, shall be totally enclosed to prevent the falling of hot particles and shall be protected from mechanical injury by suitable guards or by location.

Portable Lamps

Portable electric lamps shall not be used in any spraying area during spraying operations. Portable electric lamps, if used during cleaning or repairing operations, shall be of the type approved for hazardous Class I locations.

Grounding

All metal parts of spray booths, exhaust ducts and piping systems conveying flammable or combustible liquids or aerated solids shall be properly electrically grounded in an effective and permanent manner.

Ventilation

All spraying areas shall be provided with mechanical ventilation adequate to remove flammable vapors, mists or powders to a safe location and to confine and control combustible residue so that life is not endangered. Mechanical ventilation shall be kept in operation at all times while spraying operations are being conducted and for a sufficient time thereafter to allow vapors from drying coated articles and finishing material residue to be exhausted.

Independent Exhaust

Each spray booth shall have an independent exhaust duct system discharging to the exterior of the building. However, multiple cabinet spray booths in which identical spray finishing material is used that have a combined frontal area of not more than 18 sq. ft. may have a common exhaust. If more than one fan serves one booth, all fans shall be so interconnected that one fan cannot operate without all fans being operated.

Fan-Rotating Element

The fan-rotating element shall be non-ferrous or non-sparking or the casing shall consist of or be lined with such material. Electric motors driving exhaust fans shall not be placed inside booths or ducts.

Belts

Belts shall not enter the duct or booth unless the belt and pulley within the duct or booth are thoroughly enclosed.

Exhaust Ducts

Exhaust ducts shall be constructed of steel and shall be substantially supported. Exhaust ducts without dampers are preferred; however, if dampers are installed, they shall be maintained so that they will be in a full-open position at all times the ventilating system is in operation.

Discharge Clearance

Unless the spray booth exhaust duct terminal is from a water-wash spray booth, the terminal discharge point shall be not less than 6 ft. from any combustible exterior wall or roof nor discharge in the direction of any combustible construction or unprotected opening in any non-combustible exterior wall within 25 ft.

Air Exhaust

Air exhaust from spray operations shall not be directed so that it will contaminate makeup air being introduced into the spraying area or other ventilating intakes. Air exhausted from spray operations shall not be recirculated.

Access Doors

When necessary to facilitate cleaning, exhaust ducts shall be provided with an ample number of access doors.

Drying Spaces

Freshly sprayed articles shall be dried only in spaces provided with adequate ventilation to prevent the formation of explosive vapors. In the event adequate and reliable ventilation is not provided, such drying spaces shall be considered a spraying area.

Flammable and Combustible Liquids— Storage and Handling

Conformance

The storage of flammable or combustible liquids in connection with spraying operations shall conform to the requirements of 1910.106, where applicable.

Quantity

The quantity of flammable or combustible liquids kept in the vicinity of spraying operations shall be the minimum required for operations and should ordinarily not exceed a supply for one day or one shift.

Containers

Original closed containers, approved portable tanks, approved safety cans or a properly arranged system of piping shall be used to bring flammable or combustible liquids into spray finishing rooms. Open or glass containers shall not be used.

Transferring Liquids

Except as discussed in the paragraph, "Spraying Containers," the withdrawal of flammable and combustible liquids from containers having a capacity of greater than 60 gallons shall be by approved pumps. The withdrawal of flammable or combustible liquids from containers and the filling of containers, including portable mixing tanks, shall be done only in a suitable mixing room or in a spraying area when the ventilating system is in operation. Adequate precautions shall be taken to protect against liquid spillage and from sources of ignition.

Spraying Containers

Containers supplying spray nozzles shall be of closed type or provided with metal covers that are kept closed. Containers supplying spray nozzles by gravity flow shall not exceed 10 gallons in capacity.

Original shipping containers shall not be subject to air pressure for supplying air nozzles. Containers under air pressure supplying spray nozzles shall be of limited capacity, not exceeding that necessary for one day's operation; shall be designed and approved for such use; shall be provided with a visible pressure gauge; and shall be provided with a relief valve; all in conformance with the ASME Code for Unfired Pressure Vessels.

Containers under pressure supplying spray nozzles, air storage tanks and coolers shall conform to the standards of the ASME Code for Unfired Pressure Vessels for construction, tests and maintenance.

Pipes and Hoses

All containers or piping to which a hose or flexible connection is attached shall be provided with a shut-off valve at the connection. Such valves shall be kept shut when spraying operations are not being conducted. When a pump is used to deliver products, automatic means shall be provided to prevent pressure in excess of the design working pressure of accessories, piping and hose.

All pressure hoses and couplings shall be inspected at regular intervals appropriate to this service. The hoses and couplings shall be tested with the hose extended and using the "in-service maximum operating pressures." Any hose showing material deterioration, signs of leakage or weakness in its carcass or at the couplings shall be withdrawn from service and repaired or discarded.

Piping systems conveying flammable or combustible liquids shall be of steel or other material having comparable properties of resistance to heat and physical damage. Piping systems shall be properly bonded and grounded.

Spray Liquid Heaters

Electrical-powered spray liquid heaters shall be approved and fisted for the specific location in which they are used. Heaters shall not be located in spray booths or other locations subject to the accumulation of deposits or combustible residue.

Pump Relief

If flammable or combustible liquids are supplied to spray nozzles by positive displacement pumps, means shall be provided to prevent the discharge pressure from exceeding the safe operating pressure of the system. Any discharge shall be to a safe location.

Grounding

Whenever flammable or combustible liquids are transferred from one container to another, both containers shall be effectively bonded and grounded to prevent discharge sparks of static electricity.

Protection

Conformance

In sprinklered buildings, the automatic sprinkler system in rooms containing spray-finishing operations shall conform to the requirements of 1910.159. In unsprinklered buildings where sprinklers are installed only to protect spraying areas, the installation shall conform to such standards insofar as they are applicable. Sprinkler heads shall be located so as to provide water distribution throughout the entire booth.

Valve Access

Automatic sprinklers protecting each spray booth (together with its connecting exhaust) shall be under an accessibly located separate outside stem and yoke sub-control valve.

Cleaning of Heads

Sprinklers protecting spraying areas shall be kept as free from deposits as practical by cleaning, daily if necessary.

Portable Extinguishers

An adequate supply of suitable portable fire extinguishers shall be installed near all spraying areas.

Operations and Maintenance

Spraying

Spraying shall not be conducted outside of predetermined spraying areas.

Cleaning

All spraying areas shall be kept as free from the accumulation of deposits of combustible residue as practical, with cleaning conducted daily if necessary. Scrapers, spuds, or other such tools used for cleaning shall be constructed of nonsparking material.

Residue Disposal

Residue scrapings and debris contaminated with residue shall be immediately removed from the premises and properly disposed of. Approved metal waste cans shall be provided wherever rags or waste are impregnated with finishing material, and all such rags or waste deposited therein immediately after use. The contents of waste cans shall be properly disposed of at least once daily or at the end of each shift.

Clothing Storage
Spray-finishing employees' clothing shall not be left on the premises overnight unless kept in metal lockers.

Cleaning Solvents
The use of solvents for cleaning operations shall be restricted to those having flash points not less than 100°F; however, for cleaning spray nozzles and auxiliary equipment, solvents having flash points not less than those normally used in spray operations may be used. Such cleaning shall be conducted inside spray booths and ventilating equipment operated during cleaning.

Hazardous Materials Combinations
Spray booths shall not be alternately used for different types of coating materials, where the combination of the materials may be conducive to spontaneous ignition, unless all deposits of the first used material are removed from the booth and exhaust ducts prior to spraying with the second used material. Examples of dangerous combinations are:
- Deposits of lacquers containing nitrocellulose combined with finishes containing drying oils, such as varnishes, oil-based stains, air-drying enamels and primers.
- Bleaching compounds based on hydrogen peroxide, hypochlorites, perchlorates, or other oxidizing compounds combined with any organic finishing materials.

"No Smoking" Signs
"No Smoking" signs in large letters on contrasting color background shall be conspicuously posted at all spraying areas and paint storage rooms.

Fixed Electrostatic Apparatus

Location
Transformers, power packs, control apparatus, and all other electrical portions of the equipment, with the exception of high-voltage grids, electrodes and electrostatic atomizing heads and their connections, shall be located outside of the spraying area or shall otherwise conform to the requirements for electrical contained earlier in this section.

Insulators, Grounding
High-voltage leads to electrodes shall be properly insulated and protected from mechanical injury or exposure to destructive chemicals. Electrostatic atomizing heads shall be effectively and permanently supported on suitable insulators and shall be effectively guarded against accidental contact or grounding. An automatic means shall be provided for grounding the electrode system when it is electrically de-energized for any reason. All insulators shall be kept clean and dry.

Safe Distance
A safe distance shall be maintained between goods being painted and electrodes or electrostatic atomizing heads or conductors of at least twice the sparking distance. A suitable sign indicating this safe distance shall be conspicuously posted near the assembly.

Conveyors Required
Goods being painted using this process are to be supported on conveyors. The conveyors shall be so arranged as to maintain safe distances between the goods and the electrodes or electrostatic atomizing heads at all times.

Fail-Safe Controls
Electrostatic apparatus shall be equipped with automatic controls that will operate without time delay to disconnect the power supply to the high voltage transformer and to signal the operator under any of the following conditions:
- Stoppage of ventilating fans or failure of ventilating equipment from any cause;
- Stoppage of the conveyor carrying goods through the high voltage field;
- Occurrence of a ground or of an imminent ground at any point on the high voltage system; and
- Reduction of clearance below that specified in "Safe Distance" above.

Guarding
Adequate booths, fencing, railings or guards shall be so placed about the equipment that they, either by their location, character or both, ensure that a safe isolation of the process is maintained from plant storage or personnel. Such railings, fencing and guards shall be of conducting material, adequately grounded.

Ventilation
Where electrostatic atomization is used, the spraying area shall be so ventilated as to ensure safe conditions from a fire and health standpoint.

Fire Protection
Automatic sprinklers shall protect all areas used for spraying, including the interior of the booth, where this protection is available. Where this protection is not available, other approved automatic extinguishing equipment shall be provided.

Electrostatic Hand-Spraying Equipment

Application
This paragraph shall apply to any equipment using electrostatically charged elements for the atomization and/or precipitation of materials for coatings on articles or for other similar purposes in which the atomizing device is hand held and manipulated during the spraying operation.

Spray Gun Ground
The handle of the spraying gun shall be electrically connected to ground by a metallic connection and to be so constructed that the operator in normal operating position is in intimate electrical contact with the grounded handle.

Grounding—General
All electrically conductive objects in the spraying area shall be adequately grounded. This requirement shall apply to paint containers, wash cans and any other objects or devices in the area. The equipment shall carry a prominent, permanently installed warning regarding the necessity for this grounding feature.

Maintenance of Grounds
Objects being painted or coated shall be maintained in metallic contact with the conveyor or other grounded support. Hooks shall be regularly cleaned to ensure this contact and areas of contact shall be sharp points or knife-edges where possible. Points of support of the object shall be concealed from random spray where feasible and where the objects being sprayed are supported from a conveyor; the point of attachment to the conveyor shall be so located as to not collect spray material during normal operation.

Interlocks
The electrical equipment shall be so interlocked with the ventilation of the spraying area that the equipment cannot be operated unless the ventilation fans are in operation.

Ventilation
The spraying operation shall take place within a spray area that is adequately ventilated to remove solvent vapors released from the operation.

Drying, Curing or Fusion Apparatus

Conformance
This standard adopts the provisions of the Standard for Ovens and Furnaces, NFPA 86A-1969, which is incorporated by reference, where process ovens and similar items are used in connection with spray finishing. To prevent oven explosions, the workspace must be preventilated before starting the oven. A safe atmosphere must be maintained at any source of ignition. In addition, the heating system must shut down in the event of a failure of the ventilation system.

Alternate Use Prohibited
Spray booths, rooms or other enclosures used for spraying operations shall not alternately be used for the purpose of drying by any arrangement that will cause a material increase in the surface temperature of the spray booth, room or enclosure.

Alternate Use Permitted

Automobile refinishing spray booths or enclosures, otherwise installed and maintained in full conformity with this section, may alternately be used for drying with portable electrical infrared drying apparatus when conforming with the following:

- Interior (especially floors) of spray enclosures shall be kept free of overspray deposits.
- During spray operations, the drying apparatus and electrical connections and wiring thereto shall not be located within spray enclosures nor in any other location where spray residue may be deposited thereon.
- The spraying apparatus, the drying apparatus and the ventilating system of the spray enclosure shall be equipped with suitable interlocks so arranged that:
  - The spraying apparatus cannot be operated while the drying apparatus is inside the spray enclosure.
  - The spray enclosure will be purged of spray vapors for a period of not less than three minutes before the drying apparatus can be energized.
  - The ventilating system will maintain a safe atmosphere within the enclosure during the drying process and the drying apparatus will automatically shut off in the event of failure of the ventilating system.
- All electrical wiring and equipment of the drying apparatus shall conform with the applicable sections of Subpart S, Electrical.
- The drying apparatus shall contain a prominently located, permanently attached warning sign indicating that ventilation should be maintained during the drying period and that spraying should not be conducted in the vicinity that spray will deposit on apparatus.

Powder Coating

This finishing process is increasing in industrial importance. It generally invokes application of plastic particles to pre-warmed parts. The coating is then fused in place by heating the part in an oven. Electrostatic forces are frequently used to apply the coating.

Electrical and Other Sources of Ignition

Powder-coating operations must conform to the general spray-finishing requirements that provide protection against open flames, spark-producing equipment and hot surfaces. Wiring must conform to OSHA electrical requirements for Class II hazardous locations regarding combustible dusts. Powder-coating equipment and booths must be grounded. Portable lamps may not be used during spraying operations. Only approved portable lamps may be used during cleaning and repair.

Ventilation

This standard requires appropriate exhaust ventilation. Powders must be safely removed to recovery equipment and must not be released to the outside atmosphere.

Drying, Curing, or Fusion Equipment

NFPA 86A-1969 is adopted by reference to safeguard fusion ovens. See description above regarding such ovens.

Operation and Maintenance

Accumulation of combustible dust must be prevented on ledges and similar surfaces. Good housekeeping must be practiced and hazardous dust clouds must not be created during cleaning operations.

Electrostatics

The use of electrostatic energy to apply powder must not create an ignition hazard. The controls for electrostatic application of liquid droplets also apply to powders. In addition, the standard requires that equipment be maintained at less than 150°F. (Note that warmed parts are often coated). There are specific requirements to prevent spark ignition of powder and to provide appropriate bonding and grounding.

Organic Peroxides and Dual Component Coatings

Organic peroxides are a group of chemicals in the high hazard class that have become increasingly useful as chain reaction initiators or catalysts in the manufacture of plastics and other materials. These chemicals, which were formerly consumed by chemical process industries in limited quantities, are now being stored in greater volume and processed in more dangerous concentrations in a wider variety of industries. A number of fires and explosions have been attributed to these chemicals. The reinforced plastics manufacturing industry is one of the larger consumers of organic peroxides. The plastic is frequently applied to the reinforcing material by spraying automatically proportioned mixtures of a resin monomer and an organic peroxide catalyst.

Organic peroxides are marketed in a large number of commercial peroxide preparations and in the form of solids, liquids and pastes. Some of the materials are diluted in order to decrease their hazard potential. The most widely used peroxides are benzyl peroxide and methyl ethyl ketone (MEK) peroxide. These per-oxygen materials contain a large amount of active oxygen; this is an important factor in determining hazard characteristics as it supports combustion even though air is excluded. Organic peroxides burn much more rapidly than ordinary flammable liquids or combustible solids.

Conformance. All spraying operations involving the use of organic peroxides and other dual-component coatings shall be conducted in approved sprinklered spray booths meeting the requirements of this section.

Smoking. Smoking shall be prohibited and "No Smoking" signs shall be prominently displayed and only non-sparking tools shall be used in any area where organic peroxides are stored, mixed or applied.

NOTE: The use of organic peroxides and monomers in spray finishing involves possible hazardous chemical reactions. Reference should be made to various industry-recognized documents that address control methods relating to these processes and materials. The following are examples of relevant standards and guidance documents in this area:

- NFPA 43A, Liquid, Solid Oxidizing Materials;
- NFPA 43B, Organic Peroxide Formulations; and
- NFPA 49, Hazardous Chemicals Data.

Hazardous (Classified) Locations

The National Electrical Code (NEC) defines hazardous locations as those areas "where fire or explosion hazards may exist due to flammable gases or vapors, flammable liquids, combustible dust, or ignitable fibers or flyings."

A substantial part of the NEC is devoted to the discussion of hazardous locations. That's because electrical equipment can become a source of ignition in these volatile areas. The writers of the NEC developed a shorthand method of describing areas classified as hazardous locations. One of the purposes of this discussion is to explain this classification system. Hazardous locations are classified in three ways by the National Electrical Code: Type, Condition and Nature.

Hazardous Location Types

Class I Locations
According to the NEC, there are three types of hazardous locations. The first type of hazard is one that is created by the presence of flammable gases or vapors in the air, such as natural gas or gasoline vapor. When these materials are found in the atmosphere, a potential for explosion exists, which could be ignited if an electrical or other source of ignition is present. The Code writers have referred to this first type of hazard as Class I. So, a *Class I hazardous location* is one in which *flammable gases or vapors* may be present in the air in sufficient quantities to be explosive or ignitable. Some typical Class I locations are:
- Petroleum refineries and gasoline storage and dispensing areas;
- Dry cleaning plants where vapors from cleaning fluids can be present;
- Spray finishing areas;
- Aircraft hangars and fuel servicing areas; and
- Utility gas plants and operations involving storage and handling of liquefied petroleum gas or natural gas.

The above Class I hazardous locations require special Class I hazardous location equipment.

Class II Locations
The second types of hazard listed by the National Electrical Code are those areas made hazardous by the presence of combustible dust.

These are referred to in the Code as "Class II Locations." Finely pulverized material, suspended in the atmosphere, can cause as powerful an explosion as one occurring at a petroleum refinery. Some typical Class II locations are:

- Grain elevators;
- Flour and feed mills;
- Plants that manufacture, use or store magnesium or aluminum powders;
- Producers of plastics, medicines and fireworks;
- Producers of starch or candies;
- Spice-grinding plants, sugar plants and cocoa plants; and
- Coal preparation plants and other carbon-handling or processing areas.

Class III Locations

Class III hazardous locations, according to the NEC, are areas where there are easily ignitable fibers or flyings present, due to the types of materials being handled, stored or processed. The fibers and flyings are not likely to be suspended in the air, but can collect around machinery, on lighting fixtures and where heat, a spark or hot metal can ignite them. Some typical Class III locations are:

- Textile mills and cotton gins;
- Cotton seed mills and flax processing plants; and
- Plants that shape, pulverize or cut wood and create sawdust or flyings.

Hazardous Location Conditions

In addition to the types of hazardous locations, the National Electrical Code also concerns itself with the kinds of conditions under which these hazards are present. The code specifies that hazardous material may exist in several different kinds of conditions that, for simplicity, can be described as, first, normal conditions and, second, abnormal conditions.

In normal conditions, the hazard would be expected to be present in everyday production operations or during frequent repair and maintenance activity. When the hazardous material is expected to be confined within closed containers or closed systems and will be present only through accidents rupture, breakage or unusual faulty operation, the situation would be considered abnormal.

The code writers have designated these two kinds of conditions very simply as Division 1—normal and Division 2—abnormal. Class I, Class II and Class III hazardous locations can be either Division 1 or Division 2. Good examples of Class I, Division 1 locations would be the areas near open-dome loading facilities or adjacent to relief valves in a petroleum refinery because the hazardous material would be present during normal plan operations.

Closed storage drums containing flammable liquids in an inside storage room would not normally allow the hazardous vapors to escape into the atmosphere. However, if one of the containers is leaking, it would be considered a Class I, Division 2 (abnormal) hazardous location.

In summary, there are three types of hazardous locations:

- Class I—gas or vapor;
- Class II—dust; and
- Class III—fibers and flyings; and

Two types of conditions:

- Division 1—normal conditions, and
- Division 2—abnormal conditions.

Each of the above categories can be broken down further.

Nature of Hazardous Substances

The gases and vapors of Class I locations are broken into four groups by the code: A, B, C and D. These materials are grouped according to the ignition temperature of the substance, its explosion pressure and other flammable characteristics.

The only substance in Group A is acetylene. Acetylene makes up only a very small percentage of hazardous locations. Consequently, little equipment is available for this type of location. Acetylene is a gas with extremely high explosion pressures.

Group B is another relatively small segment of classified areas. This group includes hydrogen and other materials with similar characteristics. If certain specific restrictions in the code are followed, some of these Group B locations, other than hydrogen, can actually be satisfied with Group C and Group D equipment.

Group C and Group D are by far the most usual Class I groups. They comprise the greatest percentage of all Class I hazardous locations. Found in Group D are many of the most common flammable substances, including butane, gasoline, natural gas and propane.

Class II, dust locations, includes the hazardous materials in Groups E, F and G. These groups are classified according to the ignition temperature and the conductivity of the hazardous substance. Conductivity is an important consideration in Class II locations, especially with metal dusts.

Metal dusts are categorized in the code as Group E. Included here are aluminum and magnesium dusts and other metal dusts of similar nature. Group F atmospheres contain such materials as carbon black, charcoal dust, coal and coke dust. Group G includes grain dusts, flour, starch, cocoa and similar types of materials.

The National Electric Code classifies hazardous locations the same way.

2009 Subpart H 1910.101-126
Hazardous Materials

101(b)	Compressed gases- handling, storage and use — 126
106(e)(6)(ii)	Dispensing Class I liquids — 87
107(g)(2)	Spray areas – Cleaning — 71
107(c)(6)	Spray Areas – Approved wiring/equipment — 58
107(b)(5)(i)	Spray booth – Air velocity — 54

0   20   40   60   80   100   120   140

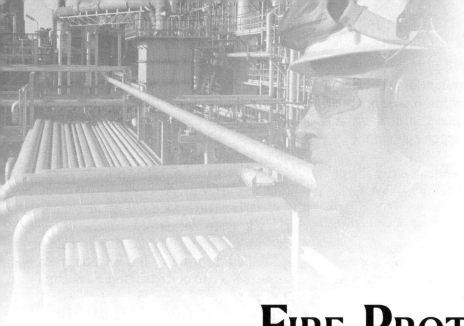

FIRE PROTECTION

Scope, Application and Definitions—1910.155

This subpart contains requirements for fire brigades and all portable and fixed fire suppression equipment, fire detection systems, and fire and employee alarm systems installed to meet the fire protection requirements of 29 CFR 1910. It applies to employment other than maritime, construction and agriculture.

Definitions

Class A fire. A fire involving ordinary combustible materials such as paper, wood, cloth, and some rubber and plastic materials.

Class B fire. A fire involving flammable or combustible liquids; flammable gases, greases and similar materials; and some rubber and plastic materials.

Class C fire. A fire involving energized electrical equipment where safety to the employee requires the use of electrically nonconductive extinguishing media.

Class D fire. A fire involving combustible metals such as magnesium, titanium, zirconium, sodium, lithium or potassium.

Dry chemical. An extinguishing agent primarily composed of very small particles of chemicals (e.g., sodium bicarbonate, potassium bicarbonate, monoammonium phosphate).

Dry powder. A compound used to extinguish or control Class D fires.

Extinguisher rating. The numerical rating given to an extinguisher, which indicates the extinguishing potential of the unit, based on standardized tests developed by Underwriters' Laboratories Inc.

Fire brigade. An organized group of employees, who are knowledgeable, trained and skilled in at least basic firefighting operations.

Halon 1211. A colorless, faintly sweet-smelling, electrically nonconductive liquefied gas (CBrC1F2) that is a medium for extinguishing fires by inhibiting the chemical chain reaction of fuel and oxygen. It is also known as bromochlorodifluoromethane.

Halon 1301. A colorless, odorless, electrically nonconductive gas (CBRF) that is a medium for extinguishing fires by inhibiting the chemical chain reaction of fuel and oxygen. It is also known as bromotrifluoromethane.

Incipient stage fire. A fire that is in the initial or beginning stage and that can be controlled or extinguished by portable fire extinguishers, Class II standpipe or small hose systems without the need for protective clothing or breathing apparatus.

Interior structural firefighting. The physical activity of fire suppression, rescue or both, inside of buildings or enclosed structures that are involved in a fire situation beyond the incipient stage.

Multi-purpose dry chemical. A dry chemical that is approved for use on Class A, Class B and Class C fires.

Standpipe Systems

- **Class I** system means a 2½ in. hose connection for use by fire departments and those trained in handling heavy fire streams.
- **Class II** system means a 1½ in. hose system that provides a means for the control or extinguishment of incipient stage fires.
- **Class III** system means a combined system of hose that is for the use of employees trained in hose operations and is capable of furnishing effective water discharge during the more advanced stages of fire (beyond the incipient stage) in the interior of workplaces. Hose outlets are available for both 1½ in. and 2½ in. hose.
- Small hose system means a system of hose (5/8 in. to 1½ in. diameter) that is for the use of employees for the control or extinguishment of incipient stage fires.

Fire Brigades—1910.156

This section contains requirements for the organization, training and personal protective equipment of fire brigades whenever they are established by an employer. It should be noted that this regulation does not require an employer to establish fire brigades. If they are established, however, the requirements of this section must be met. The requirements of this section apply to fire brigades, industrial fire departments and private or contractual fire departments. This section does not apply to airport crash rescue or forest firefighting operations.

Organization

The employer must ensure that employees who are expected to do interior structural firefighting are physically capable of performing duties that may be assigned to them during emergencies. The employer shall prepare and maintain a written policy statement that:

- Establishes the fire brigade and its organi-

zational structure;
- Defines the functions to be performed; and
- States training program requirements.

Training and Education

- Training shall be conducted prior to assignment to the fire brigade
- Training shall take place at least annually for all fire brigade members.
- Quarterly training or education sessions are required for those fire brigade members expected to perform interior structural firefighting.
- Training must be provided by qualified training instructors who are available from:
  - Local municipal fire department;
  - State Fire Marshal's office;
  - State University extension service;
  - International Society of Fire Service Instructors; or
  - Community College Fire Science programs.

Firefighting Equipment

The employer shall maintain and inspect firefighting equipment to ensure safe operational condition of the equipment. This inspection shall take place at least annually. Portable fire extinguishers and respirators must be inspected at least monthly.

Protective Clothing

These requirements apply to those employees who perform interior structural firefighting. The requirements do not apply to employees who use fire extinguishers or standpipe systems to control or extinguish fires only in the incipient stage. These requirements are for members of the fire brigade:

- Foot and leg protection;
- Body protection;
- Hand protection;
- Head, eye and face protection; and
- Respiratory protection:
  - Must meet requirements of 1910.134; and
  - Must be certified under 30 CFR Part 11.

Portable Fire Extinguishers—1910.157

Exemptions

The standard does not require the employees to use extinguishers. Where the employer has a total evacuation policy, an emergency action plan and a fire prevention plan that meet the requirements of 1910.38, and extinguishers are not available in the workplace, the employer is exempt from all requirements of this section unless a specific standard in Part 1910 requires that a portable extinguisher be provided. Where the employer has an emergency action plan meeting the requirements of 1910.38, which establishes fire brigades and requires all other employees to evacuate, the employer is exempt from the distribution requirements of this section.

General Requirements

General requirements regarding portable fire extinguishers include:

- The employer shall provide portable fire extinguishers and shall mount, locate and identify them so they are readily accessible to employees but do not subject them to possible injury.
- Only approved portable fire extinguishers shall be used.
- The employer shall not provide or make available in the workplace portable fire extinguishers that use carbon tetrachloride or chlorobromomethane extinguishing agents.
- The employer shall ensure portable fire extinguishers are maintained in a fully charged and operable condition and kept in their designated places at all times, except during use.
- The employer shall remove from service all soldered or riveted shell inverting type of extinguishers.

Selection and Distribution

Extinguishers shall be provided for employee use and selected and distributed based on the classes of anticipated workplace fires and on the size and degree of hazard that would affect their use. Extinguishers shall be distributed so that the following maximum travel distances apply:

- Class A   75 ft.
- Class B   50 ft.
- Class C   Based on appropriate pattern for existing Class A or B hazards.
- Class D   75 ft.

Inspection, Maintenance and Testing

Extinguishers shall be visually inspected monthly, maintained annually and hydrostatically tested periodically as per Table L-1 of this standard (See Exhibit 11-1.).

Exhibit 11-1. Fire extinguishers must be tested at the intervals listed in the table below.
Table L-1

Type of extinguishers	Time interval (years)
Soda acid (soldered brass shells) (until 1/1/82)	(\1\)
Soda acid (stainless steel shell)	5
Cartridge operated water and/or antifreeze	5
Stored pressure water and/or antifreeze	5
Wetting agent	5
Foam (soldered brass shells) (until 1/1/82)	(\1\)
Foam (stainless steel shell)	5
Aqueous Film Forming foam (AFFF)	5
Loaded stream	5
Dry chemical with stainless steel	5
Carbon dioxide	5
Dry chemical, stored pressure, with mild steel, brazed brass or aluminum shells	12
Dry chemical, cartridge or cylinder operated, with mild steel shells	12
Halon 1211	12
Halon 1301	12
Dry powder, cartridge or cylinder operated with mild steel shells	12

\1\ Extinguishers having shells constructed of copper or brass joined by soft solder or rivets shall not be hydrostatically tested and shall be removed from service by January 1, 1982. (Not permitted)

Training and Education

Employees shall be educated in the use of extinguishers and associated hazards upon initial employment and at least annually thereafter. In addition, The employees who have been designated to use firefighting equipment as part of an emergency action plan shall be trained in the use of the appropriate equipment.

Standpipe and Hose Systems—1910.158

This section applies to all small hose, Class II and Class III standpipe systems required by other OSHA standards. It does not apply to Class I standpipe systems.

Protection of Standpipes

Standpipes shall be located or otherwise protected against mechanical damage. Damaged standpipes shall be repaired promptly.

Equipment

Hose Reels and Cabinets

Where reels or cabinets are provided to contain fire hoses, the employer shall ensure they are designed to facilitate prompt use at the time of an emergency.

Hose Outlets and Connections

Hose outlets and connections must be located high enough above the floor to avoid being obstructed and to be accessible to employees.

Hose

Each required hose outlet shall be equipped with a hose that is connected and ready for use.

Where the hose may be damaged by extreme cold, it may be kept in a protected location as long as it is readily available to be connected for use.

Nozzles

The employer shall ensure the standpipe hose is equipped with shut-off type nozzles. There are two basic nozzle types: straight stream and fog (also referred to as variable stream, spray or combination). While fog is generally preferred, straight stream is acceptable.

Water Supply

The minimum water supply for standpipe and hose systems, which are provided for the use of employees, shall be sufficient to provide 100 gallons per minute for at least 30 minutes.

Tests and Maintenance

Acceptance Tests

Piping and hose of Class II and Class III systems shall be hydrostatically tested before being placed in service.

Maintenance

The following maintenance items are required for standpipe and hose systems:
- Water supply tanks are to be kept filled, except during repairs.
- Valves in the main piping connections to the automatic sources of water supply must always be kept fully open except during repairs.
- Hose systems must be inspected at least annually and after each use.
- Any unserviceable portion of the system must be removed immediately and replaced with equivalent protection during repair.
- Hemp or linen hoses shall be unpacked, inspected for deterioration and repacked using a different fold pattern at least annually. Defective hoses shall be replaced.
- Trained persons shall be designated to conduct all these required inspections.

Automatic Sprinkler Systems—1910.159

This section applies to all automatic sprinkler systems installed to meet a particular OSHA standard. Systems installed solely for property protection are not covered.

All automatic sprinkler designs must provide the necessary discharge patterns, densities, and water flow characteristics for complete coverage. Only approved equipment and devices shall be used.

Maintenance

Systems shall be properly maintained. A main drain flow test must be performed on each system annually. The inspector's test valve shall be opened at least every two years to ensure proper operation of the system.

Acceptance Tests

New systems shall have proper acceptance tests conducted, including:
- Flushing of underground connections;
- Hydrostatic tests of system piping;
- Air tests in dry-pipe systems; and
- Test of drainage facilities.

Water Supplies

Every automatic sprinkler system must be provided with at least one automatic water supply capable of providing design water flow for at least 30 minutes.

Sprinkler Spacing

In order to provide a maximum protection area per sprinkler and a minimum of interference to the discharge pattern, the vertical clearance between sprinklers and material below shall be at least 18 in.

Fixed Extinguishing Systems, General— 1910.160

This section applies to all fixed extinguishing systems installed to meet a particular OSHA standard except for automatic sprinkler systems covered by 1910.159. Certain paragraphs of this section also apply to fixed systems not installed to meet a particular OSHA standard, but which, by their operation, may expose employees to possible injury, death or adverse health consequences caused by the extinguishing agent. Specific fixed extinguishing systems using dry chemical, gaseous agents, and water spray and foam are covered in later sections.

Fixed extinguishing system components and agents must be designed and approved for use on the specific fire hazards they are expected to control. If the system becomes inoperable, the employer shall notify employees and take the necessary temporary precautions to ensure their safety until the system is restored to operating order.

Except where discharge is immediately recognizable, a distinctive alarm or signaling system that complies with 1910.165 and is capable of being perceived above ambient noise or light levels shall be provided on all extinguishing systems in those areas covered by the system.

Effective safeguards shall be provided to warn employees against entry into discharge areas where the atmosphere remains hazardous to employee safety or health. Hazard warning or caution signs shall be posted at the entrance to, and inside of, areas protected by systems that use agents in hazardous concen-trations. A person knowledgeable in the design and function of the system shall inspect fixed systems annually. The weight and pressure of refillable containers and the weight of non-refillable containers shall be checked at least semi-annually.

Total Flooding Systems with Potential Health and Safety Hazards to Employees

The employer shall provide an emergency action plan per 1910.38 for each area protected by a total flooding system that provides agent concentrations exceeding the maximum safe levels specified in 1910.162(b)(5) and (b)(6).

All systems must have a pre-discharge alarm that complies with 1910.165 and is capable of being perceived above ambient light or noise levels, which will give the employees time to safely exit from the discharge area prior to discharge. An approved fire detection device interconnected with the pre-discharge employee alarm system shall provide automatic actuation of the system.

Fixed Extinguishing Systems, Dry Chemical—1910.161

This section applies to all fixed systems using dry chemical as the extinguishing agent, installed to meet a particular OSHA standard. These systems must also comply with 1910.160.

Dry chemical agents must be compatible with any foams or wetting agents with which they are used. When dry chemical discharge may obscure vision, a pre-discharge employee alarm is required which complies with 1910.165 and which will give employees time to safely exit from the discharge area prior to system discharge.

The rate of application of dry chemicals must be such that the designed concentration of the system will be reached within 30 seconds of initial discharge.

Fixed Extinguishing Systems, Gaseous Agent—1910.162

This section applies to all fixed extinguishing systems, using a gas as the extinguishing agent, installed to meet a particular OSHA standard. These systems shall also comply with 1910.160. For total flooding systems, the designed extinguishing concentration must be reached within 30 seconds of initial discharge except for Halon systems that must achieve design concentration within 10 seconds.

For total flooding systems, a pre-discharge alarm is required on Halon 1211 and carbon dioxide systems with a design concentration of 4 percent or greater and for Halon 1301 systems with a design concentration of 10 percent or greater. The alarm must provide employees time to safely exit the discharge area prior to system discharge.

For total flooding systems using Halon 1301:

- Agent concentrations of more than 7 percent shall not be used where egress from an area takes more than one minute.
- Agent concentrations are limited to 10 percent where egress takes longer than 30 seconds, but less than one minute.
- Agent concentrations greater than 10 percent are only permitted in areas not normally occupied, provided that any employee in the area can escape within 30 seconds. The employer shall assure that no unprotected employees enter the area during agent discharge.

Fixed Extinguishing Systems, Water Spray and Foam—1910.163

This section applies to all fixed extinguishing systems using water or foam solution as the extinguishing agent, installed to meet a particular OSHA standard. These systems must also comply with 1910.160. This section does not apply to automatic sprinkler systems, which are covered under 1910.159.

The foam and water spray systems must be designed to be effective in at least controlling fire in the protected area or on protected equipment. Drainage of water spray systems must be directed away from areas where employees are working and no emergency egress is permitted through the drainage path.

Fire Detection Systems—1910.164

Installation and Restoration

Only approved devices and equipment may be used. All fire detection systems and components

shall be restored to normal operating condition as soon as possible after each test or alarm.

Maintenance and Testing

All systems must be maintained in an operable condition, except during repairs or maintenance. Fire detectors and fire detection systems (unless factory calibrated) must be tested and adjusted as often as needed to maintain proper reliability and operating condition. Servicing, maintenance and testing of fire detection systems must be performed by a trained person knowledgeable in the operations and functions of the system.

Protection of Fire Detectors

Fire detection equipment installed outdoors or in the presence of corrosive atmospheres shall be protected from corrosion. Detection equipment must be located and/or protected from mechanical or physical impact.

Response Time

Fire detection systems installed for the purpose of actuating fire extinguishment or suppression systems shall be designed to operate in time to control or extinguish a fire. Detection systems installed for the purpose of employee alarm and evacuation must be designed and installed to provide a warning for emergency action and safe escape of employees.

Number, Location and Spacing of Detecting Devices

The number, location and spacing of fire detectors must be based upon design data obtained from field experience, tests, engineering surveys, manufacturer's recommendations or a recognized testing laboratory listing.

Employee Alarm Systems—1910.165

This section applies to all emergency employee alarms installed to meet a particular OSHA standard.

The employee alarm system shall provide warning for necessary emergency action as called for in the emergency action plan or for the reaction time for safe escape of employees. The employee alarm shall be capable of being perceived above ambient noise or light levels by all employees in the affected portions of the workplace. The alarm must be distinctive and recognizable as a signal to evacuate the work area or to perform actions designated under the emergency action plan. The employer shall explain to each employee the preferred means of reporting emergencies, such as manual pull-box alarms, public address systems, radio or telephones.

Installation and Restoration

All devices, components and systems installed to comply with this standard must be approved. All employee alarm systems must be restored to normal operating condition as promptly as possible after each test or alarm.

Maintenance and Testing

All employee alarm systems shall be maintained in operating condition, except when undergoing repairs or maintenance. A test of the reliability and adequacy of non-supervised employee alarm systems must be made every two months. A different actuation device shall be used in each test of a multi-actuation device system so that no individual device is used for two consecutive tests.

All supervised employee alarm systems must be tested at least annually for reliability and adequacy. Servicing, maintenance and testing of systems must be done by persons trained in the designed operation and functions necessary for reliable and safe operation of the system.

Manual Operation

Manually operated actuation devices for use in conjunction with employee alarms shall be unobstructed, conspicuous and readily accessible.

Classification of Portable Fire Extinguishers

Portable fire extinguishers are classified to indicate their ability to handle specific classes and sizes of fires. Labels on extinguishers indicate the class and relative size of fire that they can be expected to handle.

Class A extinguishers are used on fires involving ordinary combustibles, such as wood, cloth and paper.

Class B extinguishers are used on fires involving liquids, greases and gases.

Class C extinguishers are used on fires involving energized electrical equipment.

Class D extinguishers are used on fires involving metals, such as magnesium, titanium, zirconium, sodium and potassium.

The recommended marking system to indicate the extinguisher suitability according to class of fire is a pictorial concept that combines the uses and non-uses of extinguishers on a single label (See Exhibit 11-2.)

Exhibit 11-2.
Portable fire extinguishers should be labeled to indicate the class and size of fire for which they are appropriate.

The first row of symbols illustrated in Exhibit 11-2 is a label for uses on a Class A extinguisher. The symbol at the left, which depicts a Class A fire, is blue. Since the extinguisher is not recommended for use on Class B or C fires, the remaining two symbols, which depict Class B and Class C fires, are black, with a diagonal red line through them.

The second row of symbols is a label for use on a Class A/B extinguisher. The two left symbols are blue. Since the extinguisher is not recommended for use on Class C fires, the symbol on the far right, which depicts a Class C fire, is black, with a diagonal red line through it.

The third set of symbols is a label for use on Class B/C extinguishers. The two right symbols are blue. Since the extinguisher is not recommended for use on Class A fires, this symbol is black, with a diagonal red line through it. The fourth set of symbols is for use on Class A/B/C extinguishers. All symbols on this label are blue.

ORDINARY
A
COMBUSTIBLES

FLAMMABLE
B
LIQUIDS

ELECTRICAL
C
EQUIPMENT

COMBUSTIBLE
D
METALS

Exhibit 11-3.
Labels with
letter-shaped
symbols also
may be used
to identify the
class of fire
for which the
extinguisher is
suitable.

Letter-shaped symbol markings are also used to indicate extinguisher suitability according to class of fire (See Exhibit 11-3.). Extinguishers suitable for Class A fires should be identified by a triangle containing the letter "A." If colored, the triangle should be green.

Extinguishers suitable for Class B fires should be identified by a square containing the letter "B." If colored, the square shall be red.

A circle containing the letter "C" should identify extinguishers suitable for Class C fires. If colored, the circle should be blue.

A five-pointed star containing the letter "D" should identify extinguishers suitable for fires involving metals. If colored, the star should be yellow.

Extinguishers suitable for more than one class of fire should be identified by multiple symbols placed in a horizontal sequence.

Class A and Class B extinguishers carry a numerical rating to indicate how large a fire an experienced person can put out with the extinguisher. The ratings are based on reproducible physical tests conducted by Underwriters' Laboratories, Inc. Class C extinguishers have only a letter rating because there is no readily measurable quantity for Class C fires, which are essentially Class A or B fires involving energized electrical equipment. Class D extinguishers likewise do not have a numerical rating. Their effectiveness is described on the faceplate.

Class A Rating

An extinguisher for Class A fires could have any one of the following ratings: 1-A, 2-A, 3-A, 4-A, 6-A, 10-A, 20-A, 30-A, and 40-A. A 4-A extinguisher, for example, should extinguish about twice as much fire as a 2-A extinguisher.

Class B Rating

An extinguisher for Class B fires could have any one of the following ratings: 1-B, 2-B, 5-B, 10-B, 20-B, 30-B, 40-B, and up to 640-B.

Class C Ratings

Extinguishers rated for Class C fires are tested only for electrical conductivity. However, no extinguisher gets a Class C rating without a Class A and/or Class B rating.

Class D Ratings

Class D extinguishers are tested on metal fires. The agent used depends on the metal for which the extinguisher was designed. Check the extinguisher faceplate for the unit's effectiveness on specific metals.

Common Fire Extinguishing Agents

Water
- Removes heat
- Effective on Class A fires
- Inexpensive
- Plentiful
- Non-toxic
- Disadvantages:
  - Conducts electricity
  - May spread Class B fires
  - Freezes in cold climates
  - May carry pollutants as run-off water

Carbon Dioxide (CO_2)
- Reduces oxygen to less than 15 percent
- Effective on Class B and C fires
- No residue
- Relatively inert
- Disadvantages:
  - Generally greater than 35 percent concentration by volume required for total flooding systems
  - Toxic to humans at greater than 4 percent by volume
  - Not the best agent for smoldering deep-seated fires (maintain concentration for more than 20 minutes)
  - Dissipates rapidly; allows reflash
  - Has a cooling/chilling effect on some electronic components
  - Vapor density = 1.5 (collects in pits and low areas)

Dry Chemical
- Interrupts chemical reactions
- Sodium bicarbonate (baking soda)
- Very effective on Class B and C fires
- Not considered toxic

- Disadvantages:
  - Leaves a residue
  - Obscures vision
  - Not good on deep-seated Class A fires
  - Absorbs moisture and may "cake" within container
  - May be irritating
  - Nozzle pressure may cause burning liquids to splash

Multipurpose Dry Chemical
- Interrupts chemical reactions
- Ammonium phosphate
- Effective on Class A, B, and C fires
- Nonconductive
- Disadvantages:
  - Obscures vision
  - More irritating than ordinary dry chemical
  - Nozzle pressure may cause burning liquids to splash

Halon
- Halon 104: Carbon tetrachloride (CC_4)
- Halon 1211: Bromochlorodifluoromethane ($CBrC1F_2$)
- Halon 1301: Bromotrifluoromethane ($CBrF_3$)

Halon 1211
- Interrupts chemical reactions
- Bromochlorodifluoromethane
- Effective on Class A, B and C fires
- No residue
- May be sprayed (Boiling Point = 25°F)
- Used in portable fire extinguishers
- Disadvantages:
  - Acutely toxic at greater than 4 percent by volume (dizziness, impaired coordination and cardiac effects)
  - Must be used at greater than 5 percent by volume
  - Toxic decomposition products are generated by fire
  - Vapor density = 5.7 (collects in pits and low areas)
  - Production restricted per Montreal Protocol due to depletion of ozone layer
- Halon 1211 decomposition products:
  - Hydrogen bromide (HBr)
  - Hydrogen chloride (HCl)
  - Hydrogen fluoride (HF)
  - Bromine (Br_2)
  - Chlorine (C_2)

- Fluorine (F_2)
- Carbonyl bromide ($COBr_2$)
- Carbonyl chloride (COC'_2)
- Carbonyl fluoride (COF_2)

Halon 1301
- Interrupts chemical reactions
- Bromotrifluoromethane
- Effective on Class A, B, and C fires
- Not acutely toxic at less than 10 percent by volume
- Generally used at less than 7 percent by volume
- No residue
- No chilling effect on electronic parts and components
- Disadvantages:
  - Acutely toxic at greater than 10 percent by volume (anesthetic and cardiac effects)
  - Delayed effects and effects of chronic exposure not well known
  - Toxic decomposition products are generated by fire
  - Vapor density = 5 (collects in pits and low areas)
  - Production restricted per Montreal Protocol due to depletion of ozone layer
- Halon 1301 decomposition products:
  - Hydrogen fluoride (HF)
  - Hydrogen bromide (HBr)
  - Bromine (Br_2)
  - Carbonyl Fluoride (COF_2)
  - Carbonyl Bromide ($COBr_2$)

Fire Protection
- Fire brigades
- Portable and fixed fire suppression equipment
- Fire alarm and detection systems

Fire Brigades
- Organization:
  - Written policy statement establishing duties, organization and program requirements (physically capable of duties)
- Training:
  - Initial and annually
  - Quarterly for interior structural firefighting
- Equipment:
  - Firefighting and protective clothing
  - Respiratory devices

Portable Fire Extinguishers

General requirements
- Mount, locate and identify extinguishers for ready access
- Approved equipment that is maintained fully charged and operable at all times

Selection and distribution
- Class A – Paper, wood, cloth
- Class B – Flammable/combustible liquids, grease or gases
- Class C – Electrical equipment
- Class D – Combustible metals

Maximum travel distances
- Class A – 75 ft.
- Class B – 50 ft.
- Class C – Based on appropriate pattern for existing Class A or B
- Class D – 75 ft.

Inspection, maintenance and testing
- Visual monthly inspection
- Maintained annually
- Periodic hydrostatic testing

Training and education
- Employees educated in use on initial employment and at least annually
- Employees designated to use firefighting equipment shall be trained

Fixed fire-suppression equipment
- Standpipes and hoses
- Automatic sprinkler systems
- Fixed extinguishing systems

General, dry chemical, gaseous, water, foam
- Other fire protection systems
- Fire detection systems
- Employee alarm systems

Fixed Fire-Suppression Equipment
- Protection of standpipes from damage
- Equipment requirements
  - Hose reels, cabinet, connections nozzles—fog, stream
  - Water supply—100 gpm/30min
  - Test and maintenance
  - Filled water supplies, valves open, hose inspected annually

Automatic sprinkler systems
Necessary discharge patterns, densities, and water flow for complete coverage, 18 inch clearance between sprinklers and materials
- Dry chemical—compatible and warning time to exit prior to discharge
- Gaseous agents—total flood time 30 seconds, but specific exit times given
- Foam/water —effective and drain away from exits

Fire Alarm and Detection System
- Installation and restoration
- Maintenance and testing
- Protection of fire detectors
- Corrosive atmospheres
- Mechanical/physical impact
- Response time; time to control fires
- Number, location and spacing of devices

Employee Alarm Systems
- Provide warning and perceived above ambient noise or light levels, distinctive and recognizable and explained to employees
- Installation and restoration
- Maintenance and testing
- Manual operation—unobstructed, conspicuous

2009 Subpart L 1910.155-165
Fire Protection

Portable extinguishers provided and accessible
157(c)(1) — 174

Extinguisher training program
157(g)(1) — 161

Extinguishers- initial and annual training
157(g)(2) — 151

Annual checks on extinguishers
157(e)(3) — 102

Extinguishers – Monthly visual inspection
157(e)(2) — 78

0   50   100   150   200

Fire Protection

EXIT ROUTES, EMERGENCY ACTION PLANS, AND FIRE PREVENTION PLANS

This subpart deals with a subject that has been familiar to all of us since our early childhood days. Many of us remember the fire drills at school, with the primary classes trying for an orderliness award and the older students welcoming a break in the routine. In school, or elsewhere, the exit sign represents a sight so familiar that we hardly take note of it. We see them in stores, factories, theaters, office buildings, hotels, apartment buildings, practically everywhere. Yet we rarely notice them until we look for them.

Egress, as defined by Webster means "a place or means of going out."

Subpart E was rewritten and finalized on December 9, 2002. OSHA kept the intent of the original regulation so that companies already in compliance with the old rule will automatically be in compliance with the revised rule. The goal of the revision was to rewrite the existing requirements in clearer language and make them performance-oriented to the extent possible. The name of the subpart was changed from "Means of Egress" to "Exit Routes, Emergency Action Plans and Fire Prevention Plans" to describe the contents more accurately.

During the review of the regulation, OSHA discovered that some provisions were outdated and not consistent with contemporary life safety options in the NPFA 101, Life Safety Code, 1994 Edition (the current edition at the time of the review). In an effort to expand the employer compliance options without lessening employee safety, the revision included some of the options from NFPA 101. For example, the Life Safety Code allows for the exit to lead to a place of refuge rather than to an outside public way and allows the use of self-luminous and electroluminescent exit signs.

The revised regulation contains definitions of terms related to the topic and was reorganized around the three aspects of exit routes:

1. Design and construction requirements;
2. Maintenance, safety guards and operational requirements; and
3. Requirements for warning employees of the need to escape.

Because this regulation is referenced in other subparts, OSHA referred to those affected subparts in the regulation to ensure that there was continuity throughout the workplace with regard to emergency exits, emergency action plans and fire prevention plans. For example, the latter part of the rule refers to subpart H, L, R and Z where those rules require an Emergency Action Plan or Fire Prevention Plan.

While this discussion is devoted to the subject of emergency exit and subsequent planning, the emphasis may appear to be on escaping from fires. While this is certainly a primary reason for emergency egress from a building, there are a multitude of events that may result in exercising this sort of plan.

Hazards that must be considered include:

- Terrorist activity
- Workplace violence
- Explosion
- Earthquake
- Smoke (without fire)
- Toxic vapors
- Bomb threat
- Storms (e.g., tornado, hurricane)
- Flash floods
- Nuclear radiation exposure and
- Actions or threatened actions of mentally ill persons or political radicals

Each of these hazards to the occupants of a building can occur individually or in combination with others. Depending on the hazard, the people involved, the characteristics of the building and the quality of the means of egress provided, each hazard can be compounded by:

- Panic and confusion
- Poor visibility and
- Lack of information or misinformation.

These compounding factors frequently cause more injuries and fatalities than the hazard itself. Providing the proper means of egress can enable persons to successfully escape from the primary hazard.

Coverage and Definitions—1910.34

This section applies to workplaces in general industry and every employer is covered. This section does not cover mobile workplaces such as vehicles or vessels. OSHA set forth the minimum requirements for exit routes that employers must provide in order to evacuate the workers safely during an emergency as well as cover the minimum requirements for emergency action plans and fire prevention plans.

Definitions

Electroluminescent means a light-emitting capacitor. Alternating current excites phosphor atoms when placed between the electrically conductive surfaces to produce light. This light source is typically contained inside the device.

Exit means that portion of an exit route that is generally separated from other areas to provide a protected way of travel to the exit discharge. An example of an exit is a two-hour fire resistance-rated enclosed stairway that leads from the fifth floor of an office building to the outside of the building.

Exit access means that portion of an exit route that leads to an exit. An example of an exit access is a corridor on the fifth floor of an office building that leads to a two-hour fire resistance-rated enclosed stairway (the exit).

Exit discharge means the part of the exit route that leads directly outside or to a street, walkway, refuge area, public way or open space with access to the outside. An example of an exit discharge is a door at the bottom of a two-hour fire resistance-rated enclosed stairway that discharges to a place of safety outside the building.

Exit route means a continuous and unobstructed path of exit travel from any point within a workplace to a place of safety (including refuge areas). An exit route consists of three parts: the exit access, the exit and the exit discharge. (An exit route includes all vertical and horizontal areas along the route.)

High hazard area means an area inside a workplace in which operations include high hazard materials, processes or contents.

Occupant load means the total number of persons that may occupy a workplace or portion of a workplace at any one time. The occupant load of a workplace is calculated by dividing the gross floor area of the workplace or portion of a workplace by the occupant load factor for that particular type of workplace occupancy. Information regarding "occupant load" is located in NFPA 101-2000, Life Safety Code.

Refuge area means (1) A space along an exit route that is protected from the effects of fire by separation from other spaces within the building by a barrier with at least a one-hour fire resistance-rating; or (2) A floor with at least two spaces, separated from each other by smoke-resistant partitions, in a building protected throughout by an automatic sprinkler system that complies with §1910.159 of this part.

Self-luminous means a light source that is illuminated by a self-contained power source (e.g., tritium) and that operates independently from external power sources. Batteries are not acceptable self-contained power sources. The light source is typically contained inside the device.

Compliance with NFPA 101-2000, Life Safety Code—1910.35

In order to enhance the opportunity for employers to comply with the intent of the regulation, OSHA has provided owners a choice of complying with the OSHA regulation or the most recent NFPA standard on Life Safety. The regulation was revised using the 1996 NFPA standard, which has been replaced with a 2000 standard.

Subpart E is promulgated from NFPA 101, Life Safety Code. This document is prepared, maintained and published by the National Fire Protection Association. Copies of the NFPA standard can be obtained for a small fee from them by writing to them at 11 Tracy Drive, Avon, MA 02322.

Because this code is used as the basis for most local fire codes, it is written for general applicability. Keep in mind that your concern is its application primarily for the protection of employees, not the preservation of facilities.

The Life Safety Code, formerly the Building Exits Code, originated from work performed by the Committee on Safety to Life, The National Fire Protection Association, in 1913. At first, the committee devoted its attention to a study of the notable fires involving loss of life. That led to the preparation of standards for the construction of stairways and fire escapes, for fire drills in various occupancies and for the construction and arrangement of exit facilities for factories, schools, etc. These form the basis of the present code.

In 1921, the committee was enlarged to provide a comprehensive guide to exits and related features of life safety from fire in all classes of occupancy. This guide was to be known as the Building Exits Code.

During the Coconut Grove nightclub disaster in Boston in 1942, 492 lives were lost, focusing national attention upon the importance of adequate exits and related fire safety features. Public attention to exit matters was further stimulated by a series of hotel fires in 1946. The Building Exits Code thereafter was used to an increasing extent for legal regulatory purposes. The code, however, was not in suitable form for adoption into law and the entire code was edited to limit the body of the text to requirements suitable for mandatory application. This involved adding provisions to the code of many features that had not been previously covered in order to produce a complete document.

In 1966, the code title was changed from "Building Exits Code" to "The Code for Safety to Life from Fire in Buildings and Structures," known as the "Life Safety Code."

The regulation reflects that an employer who demonstrates compliance with the exit route provisions of NFPA 101-2000, the Life Safety Code, will be deemed to be in compliance with the corresponding requirements in 1910.34, 1910.36 and 1910.37.

Design and Construction Requirements for Exit Routes—1910.36

This subpart contains general fundamental requirements essential to providing a safe means of egress from fire and other emergencies. The requirements in Subpart E are minimum requirements. The standards do not prohibit better construction, more exits or safer conditions that these minimums set forth.

These requirements are not intended to apply to exits from vehicles, vessels or other mobile structures.

Fundamental Requirements for Exit Routes

This subparagraph contains requirements that apply to all buildings, new or old, that are intended for human occupancy. They may be summarized as follows:

- Each exit route must be a permanent part of the workplace.
- Exits must be separated from other parts of the workplace by fire resistant materials.
  - One-hour rating for less than four story buildings.
  - Two-hour rating for four story buildings or higher.
- Openings to exits must be limited to those needed to allow exit discharge or access to the exit from occupied areas of the workplace. Openings into an exit must be protected by an approved self-closing fire door.
- Number of exit routes must be adequate.
  - Two exit routes located as far away as practical from each other.

- Single exit route is allowed if the size of the building, its occupancy or the workplace is arranged so that all employees would be able to evacuate safely through one exit.
  - NFPA 101-2000, Life Safety Code, provides assistance in determining the required number of exits.
- Exit discharge must lead directly outside to a street, public way, walkway, open space or a refuge area that is large enough to hold all the building occupants.
- Exit stairs that lead beyond the exit discharge must have doors and partitions to clearly indicate the direction to lead to the actual exit.
- Exit doors must be unlocked.
  - Employees must be able to open the exit route door without keys, tools or special knowledge.
  - Panic bars are permitted on exit discharge doors.
  - Exit route doors may be locked from the inside only in mental, penal or correctional facilities only if supervisory personnel are continuously on duty and the employer has a written plan to remove those occupants during an emergency.
- Side-hinged exit doors must be used.
  - If the room is designed to hold more than 50 people or is a high hazard area, the door must swing out in the direction of exit travel.
- Exit routes must support the maximum permitted occupant load of each floor.
- The capacity of an exit route may not get smaller in the direction of exit route travel.
- The ceiling of an exit route must be at least 7 ft. 6 in. high and items reaching down from the ceiling must be at least 6 ft. 8 in. from the floor.
- Exit access must be at least 28 in. wide, but must accommodate the maximum permitted occupant load of each floor served by that route. No object may stick out into the path of the exit route in such a way as to reduce the minimum width requirement.

Exterior Routes of Exit Access

Under certain conditions it is permissible to plan an exterior route as a way of exit access

from one interior part of a building to another or to an exterior exit. Such routes may include flat rooftops, enclosed courtyards and balconies.

Normally, when thinking of an exit, people visualize a door or doorway through which one can pass from the inside to the outside. As used in this subpart, an exit can be such a doorway and it can also be an interior stairwell or anteroom. It also can be an exterior fire escape.

Requirements for exit routes that are outside include:

- The ceiling of an exit route must be at least 7 ft. 6 in. high and items reaching down from the ceiling must be at least 6 ft. 8 in. from the floor.
- Exit access must be at least 28 in. wide, but must accommodate the maximum permitted occupant load of each floor served by that route. No object may stick out into the path of the exit route in such a way as to reduce the minimum width requirement.
- If a fall hazard exists, the route must have guardrails.
- If there is the likelihood of snow or ice accumulation, the route must be covered unless the employer can demonstrate that snow and ice is removed before it becomes a slipping hazard.
- The outdoor route must be reasonably straight with smooth, solid and substantially level walkways.
- No route more than 20 ft. long may lead to a dead end.

Width and Capacity of Means of Egress

The capacity in number of persons per unit of exit width for approved components of means of egress shall be as follows:

- Level Egress Components (including Class A ramps): 100 persons/unit
  - A Class A ramp is one that has a slope no greater than 1 3/16 in. in a 12-in. length, a width at least 44 in., and no limit on the maximum height between landings.
- Inclined Egress Components (including Class B ramps): 60 persons/unit
  - A Class B ramp is one that has a slope of 1 3/16 to 2 in. in a 12-in. length, a width of 30 to 44 in., and a maximum height between landings of 12 ft.

Maintenance, Safeguards and Operational Features for Exit Routes—1910.37

Minimizing the danger to employees

This section is established to minimize the danger to employees. During the Coconut Grove fire disaster in Boston, flames ignited wall decorations and wall coverings, which emitted toxic smoke as they burned. Fire exits were locked, forcing patrons to exit through dangerous areas. As a result of the lessons learned at that disaster, this section requires that all exit routes be kept free of any explosive or flammable furnishings or decorations and that the routes to exits must be set up so that employees do not have to travel towards any high hazard area. If the exit requires the employees to move towards this type of hazard, the exit path must be shielded by partitions or barriers that effectively protect the employee.

Nothing may be placed in the path of the exit route and these routes must not be locked. They must not be blocked by materials, even temporarily. Exit access cannot go through a room that may be locked, such as a bathroom, because if that room was locked it would be eliminated as an exit route. If there is a change of elevation along the exit route, stairs or a ramp must be provided.

Any fire-retardant material applied to the surfaces must be renewed as often as necessary. This material is not permanent and may only last for five years. Follow the manufacturers' recommendations for retaining the fire-retardant properties of the materials used in the structure.

Exit Marking and Lighting

Exit markings fall into two categories:
- Signs or markings that clearly identify an exit or the way to an exit.
- Signs or markings that clearly identify doors or areas that are not means of egress.

All exits must have enough light so that the employees can see along the exit route. The exits must be clearly visible and marked by a sign that says "Exit" in legible letters not less than 6 in. high and ¾ in. wide.

Exit signs must be illuminated to a surface value of at least five foot candles and be a distinctive color so that it stands out in an emer-

gency. Glow in the dark signs (Self-luminous or electroluminescent) are permitted as long as they have a minimum luminance surface value of 0.06 footlamberts or more.

Decorations or signs that make it difficult to see or understand the exit route doors are prohibited. Any doorway or passage that is not an exit, but may be mistaken for an exit, must be marked so workers do not attempt to escape through that route. Placing a sign on the door that says "Not an Exit" or a sign that indicates the actual use of the room such as "Store Room" or "Linen Closet" meets the requirements of the standard.

Any time the employee cannot see the exit or the way to the exit is not immediately apparent, signs must be installed indicating the direction of travel to the nearest exit. A line of sight to an exit or an exit sign must be visible to workers at all time.

All workers are not the same height. It is important to realize that shorter workers may be a workstation previously occupied by a tall employee. The shorter worker may not be able to see the exit signs due to his or her height. To ensure compliance and employee safety, the employer must relocate the signs so that all employees can maintain a line of sight to an exit or exit sign.

Construction, Repairs or Alterations

Facilities are constantly being built, upgraded, altered and repaired. When construction crews are working on new buildings, they are focused on the construction job; facility managers are usually focused on occupying the building as soon as possible. However, the facility manager must ensure that workers do not occupy the workplace of a new building until all of the exit routes are completed and ready for use.

During the construction process itself, employees must not be exposed to any hazardous equipment or flammable substances used by the construction workers that would impede their exit from the work area during an emergency. Employees may not work in or occupy the workplace unless the exit routes are available or fire protection is provided that gives an equivalent level of safety.

Employee Alarm System

An alarm system must be provided that has a distinctive signal to warn employees of fire dangers or other emergencies. Some firms have one sound or signal for a fire and another for the accidental release of chemicals. For example, one long blast on the horn could signal a fire, while two short blasts on the horn could signal a chemical release. Another long, uninterrupted blast may indicate that the facility must be immediately evacuated for unspecified reasons. The alarm system must meet the requirements of 1910.165 and be maintained in an operable manner.

In some small shops, the work area is so small that workers could immediately see the danger and exit the facility. If the employees can see or small the hazard in a sufficient amount of time to provide adequate warning, no alarm system is required.

Emergency Action Plans—1910.38

This section applies to all emergency action and fire prevention plans required by a particular OSHA standard.

For companies with more than 10 employees, the emergency action plan must be in writing. The plan must be kept at the workplace and be available for employees to review. If the company has less than 10 employees, the plan may be communicated to the workers orally.

The emergency action plan should address all potential emergencies that can be expected in the workplace. It may be helpful to perform a hazard audit to determine potentially toxic materials and unsafe conditions. For information on chemicals, the manufacturer or supplier can be contacted to obtain material safety data sheets. These sheets describe the hazards that a chemical may present; list precautions to take when handling, storing, or using the substance; and outline emergency and first aid procedures.

The employer should list in detail the procedures to be taken by those employees who must remain behind for essential plant operations until their evacuation becomes absolutely necessary. This may include monitoring plant power supplies, water supplies, and other essential services that cannot be shut down for every emergency alarm.

For emergency evacuation, floor plans or workplace maps that clearly show emergency escape routes and safe, or refuge, areas should be included in the plan. All employees must be told what actions they are to take in an emergency situation.

Alarm System

Employers shall establish an employee alarm system that complies with 1910.165. Alarms should be audible or able to be seen by all people in the plant and should have an auxiliary power supply in the event electricity is affected. The alarm should be distinctive and recognizable as a signal to evacuate the work area or perform actions designated under the emergency action plan.

Evacuation

The employer shall establish in the emergency action plan the types of evacuation to be used in emergency circumstances. At the time of an emergency, employees should know what type of evacuation is necessary and what their role is in carrying out the plan. In instances where the emergency is very grave, total and immediate evacuation of all employees is necessary. In other emergencies, a partial evacuation of nonessential employees (with a delayed evacuation of others) may be necessary for continued plant operation.

In some cases, only those employees in the immediate area of the fire may be expected to evacuate or move to a safe area, such as when a local application fire suppression system discharge employee alarm is sounded. Employees must be sure that they know what is expected of them in all such foreseeable emergency possibilities to provide assurance of their safety from fire or other emergency.

The designation of refuge or safe areas for evacuation should be identified in the plan. In a building divided into fire zones by firewalls, the refuge area may still be within the same building, but in a different zone from where the emergency occurs.

Exterior refuge or safe areas may include parking lots, open fields or streets that are located away from the site of the emergency and provide sufficient space to accommodate the employees. Employees should be instructed to move away from the exit discharge doors of the building and to avoid congregating close to the building where they may hamper emergency operations.

The emergency action plan must include, at a minimum, the following elements:

- Procedures for reporting fires or emergencies;
- Procedures for emergency evacuation, including:
  - Exit route assignments; and
  - Type of evacuation (partial or full evacuation);
- Procedures to be followed by employees who remain in place to operate critical plant operations before they evacuate;
- Procedures to account for all employees after evacuation;
- Procedures to be followed by employees performing rescue, medical or assistance duties; and
- The name or job title of every employee who may be contacted to learn more about the plan.

Training

Training is important to the effectiveness of an emergency plan. Before implementing an emergency action plan, a sufficient number of persons must be trained to assist in the safe and orderly evacuation of employees. Training for each type of disaster response is necessary so those employees know what actions are required. The employer shall review with each employee upon initial assignment those parts of the plan that the employee must know to protect himself or herself in the event of an emergency. In addition, the employer shall review the plan with each employee covered by the plan:

- Initially when the plan is developed;
- Whenever the employee's responsibilities or designated actions change; or
- Whenever the plan is changed.

The employer should ensure that an adequate number of employees are available at all times during working hours to act as evacuation wardens so that employees can be swiftly moved from the dangerous location to a safe area. Generally, one warden for each 20 employees in the workplace should be able to provide adequate guidance and instruction at the time of a fire emergency.

The employees selected or who volunteer to serve as wardens should be trained in the complete workplace layout and the various alternative escape routes from the workplace. All wardens and fellow employees should be made aware of handicapped employees who may need extra assistance, such as using the buddy system and of hazardous areas to be avoided during emergencies. Before leaving, wardens should check rooms and other enclosed spaces in the workplace for employees who may be trapped or otherwise unable to evacuate the area. After the desired degree of evacuation is completed, the wardens should be able to account for or otherwise verify that all employees are in the safe area.

Medical Assistance

In a major emergency, time is a critical factor in minimizing injuries. Most small businesses do not have a formal medical program, but they are required to have the following medical and first aid services:

- In the absence of an infirmary, clinic or hospital in close proximity to the workplace that can be used for the treatment of all injured employees, the employer must ensure that a person or persons are adequately trained to administer first aid.
- Where the eyes or body of any employee may be exposed to injurious corrosive materials, eye washes or suitable equipment for quick drenching and flushing must be provided in the work area for immediate emergency use. Employees must be trained to use the equipment.
- The employer must ensure the ready availability of medical personnel for advice and consultation on matters of employee health. This does not mean that health care must be provided, but rather that if health problems develop in the workplace, medical help will be available to resolve them.

Fire Prevention Plan—1910.39

Although Subpart E is devoted to the provisions for ensuring that personnel can exit from a building under emergency conditions, it also contains several provisions for preventing or reducing the risk of such an emergency. Detailed requirements for fire protection are in Subpart L.

Subpart E requires that where protection (e.g., automatic sprinklers, fire-retardant paints) are required and/or installed, they shall be regularly inspected or tested, maintained, and replenished or renewed as necessary to keep them in good operating condition.

Employers must inform employees of the fire hazards of the materials and processes to which they are exposed. Upon initial assignment, the employer shall review those parts of the fire prevention plan that each employee must know to protect him or herself in the event of an emergency. The written plan shall be kept in the workplace and available to the employee. The plan may be communicated orally in establishments with 10 or fewer employees.

The following elements, at a minimum, shall be included in a fire prevention plan:

- A list of all major workplace hazards and their proper handling and storage procedures, potential ignition sources and the type of fire equipment or systems used to control a fire involving them;
- Procedures to control the accumulation of flammable and combustible waste materials and residue;
- Procedures for the regular maintenance of safeguards installed on heat-producing equipment to prevent accidental ignition;
- Names or job titles of people responsible for the maintenance of equipment used to prevent or control sources of ignition or fires; and
- Names or job titles of people responsible for the control of fuel source hazards.

The employer shall control accumulations of flammable and combustible waste materials and residues so they do not contribute to a fire emergency. These procedures shall be included in the fire prevention plan.

Upon initial assignment, the employer shall review those parts of the fire prevention plan that each employee must know to protect him or herself in the event of an emergency.

The written plan shall be kept in the workplace and available to all employees. The plan may be communicated orally in establishments with 10 or fewer employees. Equipment and systems installed on heat-producing equipment shall be maintained in order to prevent accidental ignition of combustible materials.

It can be expected that egress will:
- Exist
- Provide convenient escape
- Have redundancy in design of exits and safeguards
- Not complicate escape by the building structure and design
- Not be locked or cluttered
- Require people to be trained for emergencies

Fundamental Requirements
- Shall have exists sufficient for prompt escape
- Designed with redundancy
- Building structures will not cause danger
- No locks to prevent escape
- Clearly visible and appropriately marked
- Illuminated
- Alarm to warn of emergencies
- Side-hinged doors

Exit Components
- Protective enclosure of exit (one-hour rating for three stories, two-hour rating for four or more stories)
- Width (22 in. units) and capacity
- Capacity and occupant load

- Sufficient for occupant load
- Occupant load is the maximum number of persons that may be in the room
- Exit capacity must not constrict or get smaller in direction of travel

Arrangement of and Access to Exits
- Separated from other exits to minimize chance of more than one being blocked
- Readily accessible at all times
- Doors swing with exit travel in rooms designed to hold 50 or more persons
- Clearly recognizable
- Safe discharge

Exit Marking
- Signs or markings that clearly identify exits
- Signs or markings that clearly identify doors and areas as not exits

Fire Prevention and Emergency Action Plans
- Housekeeping—Control accumulations
- Training—Written plan kept in workplace
- Maintenance—Heat producing equipment is maintained to prevent fires

Exhibit 12-1. Mean of Egress Expectations.

These procedures shall be included in the written fire prevention plan.

Emergency Escape Route and Procedures

Employees should be taught not to stop for clothing, food or other possessions when ordered to evacuate and to proceed directly to the evacuation point or exit. Designate emergency escape routes and post them in conspicuous places around the plant. Conduct evacuation drills a number of times each year to ensure that the workers remember where they are supposed to go. Depending on the facility, indicate a secondary escape route in case the primary route is blocked.

Emergency action plan. Emergency action plan shall cover those designated actions employers and employees must take to ensure employee safety from fire and other emergencies.

Fire prevention plan. Fire prevention plan must include a list of the major workplace fire hazards and their proper handling and storage procedures, potential ignition sources and their control procedures, and the type of fire-protection equipment or systems that can control a fire involving them.

Alarm system. The employer shall establish an employee alarm system.

Evacuation. The employer shall establish in the emergency action plan the types of evacuation to be used in emergency circumstances.

Training. Before implementing the emergency action plan, the employer shall designate and train sufficient number of persons to assist in the safe and orderly emergency evacuation of employees.

Housekeeping. The employer shall control the accumulations of flammable or combustible waste materials and residues so that they do not contribute to a fire emergency.

Maintenance. The employer shall regularly and properly maintain equipment and systems installed to prevent accidental ignition of combustible materials.

Fact Sheet No. OSHA 92-19

Responding to Workplace Emergencies

Employers should establish effective safety and health programs and prepare their workers to handle emergencies before they arise.

Planning

Where required by the Occupational Safety and Health Administration (OSHA), firms with more than 10 employees must have a written emergency action plan; smaller companies may communicate their plans orally. [See 29 Code of Federal Regulation (CFR) Part 1910.38(a) for further information.] Essential to an effective emergency action plan are top management support and commitment and the involvement of all employees. Management should review plans with employees initially and whenever the plan itself, or employees responsibilities under it, change. Plans should be re-evaluated and updated periodically. Emergency procedures, including the handling of any toxic chemicals, should include:

- Escape procedures and escape route assignments.
- Special procedures for employees who perform or shut down critical plant operations.
- A system to account for all employees after evacuation.
- Rescue and medical duties for employees who perform them.
- Means for reporting fires and other emergencies.
- Contacts for information about the plan.

Chain of Command

An emergency response coordinator and a back-up coordinator must be designated. The coordinator may be responsible for plant-wide operations, public information and ensuring that outside aid is called in. A back-up coordinator ensures that a trained person is always available. Duties of the coordinator include:

- Determining what emergencies may occur and seeing that emergency procedures are developed to address them.
- Directing all emergency activities including evacuation of personnel.
- Ensuring that outside emergency services such as medical aid and local fire departments are called when necessary.
- Directing the shutdown of plant operations when necessary.

Emergency Response Teams

Members of emergency response teams should be thoroughly trained for potential emergencies and physically capable of carrying out their duties; know about toxic hazards in the workplace and be able to judge when to evacuate personnel or depend on outside help (e.g. when a fire is too large for them to handle). One or more teams must be trained in:

- Use of various types of fire extinguishers.
- First aid, including cardiopulmonary resuscitation (CPR).
- The requirements of the OSHA bloodborne pathogens standard.
- Shutdown procedures.
- Chemical spill control procedures.
- Use of self-contained breathing apparatus (SCBA).
- Search and emergency rescue procedures.
- Hazardous materials emergency response in accordance with 29 CFR 1910.120.

Response Activities

Effective emergency communication is vital. An alternate area for a communications center other than management offices should be established in the plans and the emergency response coordinator should operate from this center. Management should provide emergency alarms and ensure that employees know how to report emergencies. An updated list of key personnel and off-duty telephone numbers should be maintained. A system should be established for accounting for personnel once workers have been evacuated with a person in the control center responsible for notifying police or emergency response team members of persons believed missing.

Effective security procedures, such as cordoned off areas, can prevent unauthorized access and protect vital records and equipment. Duplicate records can be kept in off-site locations for essential accounting files, legal documents and lists of employees relatives to be notified in case of emergency.

Training

Every employee needs to know details of the emergency action plan, including evacuation plans, alarm systems, reporting procedures for personnel, shutdown procedures, and types of potential emergencies. Drills should be held at random intervals, at least annually, and include, if possible, outside police and fire authorities.

Training must be conducted initially, when new employees are hired, and at least annually. Additional training is needed when new equipment, materials, or processes are introduced, introduced, when procedures have been updated or revised, or when exercises show that employee performance is inadequate.

Personal Protection

Employees exposed to accidental chemical splashes, falling objects, flying particles, unknown atmospheres with inadequate oxygen or toxic gases, fires, live electrical wiring, or similar emergencies need personal protective equipment, including:

- Safety glasses, goggles, or face shields for eye protection.
- Hard hats and safety shoes.
- Properly selected and fitted respirators.
- Whole body coverings, gloves, hoods, and boots.
- Body protection for abnormal environmental conditions such as extreme temperatures.

Medical Assistance

Employers not near an infirmary, clinic, or hospital should have someone on-site trained in first aid, have medical personnel readily available for advice and consultation, and develop written emergency medical procedures.

It is essential that first aid supplies are available to the trained medical personnel, that emergency phone numbers are placed in conspicuous places near or on telephones, and prearranged ambulance services for any emergency are available.

Emergency Preparedness and Response

The following is an excerpt from an Instructional Guide developed for the OSHA's Small Business Outreach Training Program.

Introduction

The importance of an effective workplace safety and health program cannot be overemphasized.

There are many benefits from such a program including increased productivity, improved employee morale, reduced absenteeism and illness, and reduced workers' compensation rates; however, incidents still occur in spite of efforts to prevent them. Therefore, proper planning for emergencies is necessary to minimize employee injury and property damage.

Purpose

This discussion details the basic steps to handle emergencies in the workplace. These emergencies include accidental releases of toxic gases, chemical spills, fires, explosions, and bodily harm and trauma caused by workplace violence. This discussion is intended to assist small businesses that do not have safety and health professionals. It is not intended as an all inclusive safety program but rather to provide guidelines for planning for emergencies.

Planning

The effectiveness of response during emergencies depends on the amount of planning and training performed. Management must show its support of plant safety programs and the importance of emergency planning. If management is not interested in employee protection and minimizing property loss, little can be done to promote a safe workplace. It is therefore management's responsibility to see that a program is instituted and that it is frequently reviewed and updated. The input and support of all employees must be obtained to ensure an effective program. The emergency response plan should be developed locally and be comprehensive enough to deal with all types of emergencies. When emergency action plans are required by a particular OSHA standard, the plan must be in writing. Although for firms with 10 or fewer employees, the plan may be communicated orally to employees. The plan must include the following elements:

- Emergency escape procedures and emergency escape route assignments;
- Procedures to be followed by employees who remain to perform (or shut down) critical plant operations before they evacuate;
- Procedures to account for all employees after emergency evacuation has been completed;
- Rescue and medical duties for those employees who are to perform them;

- The preferred means for reporting fires and other emergencies; and
- Names or regular job titles of persons or departments to be contacted for further information or explanation of duties under the plan.

The emergency action plan should address all potential emergencies that can be expected in the workplace. Therefore, it will be necessary to perform a hazard audit to determine potentially toxic materials and unsafe conditions. For information on chemicals, the manufacturer or supplier can be contacted to obtain material safety data sheets. These sheets describe the hazards that a chemical may present; list precautions to take when handling, storing, or using the substances and outline emergency and first-aid procedures.

The employer should list in detail the procedures to be taken by those employees who must remain behind to care for essential plant operations until their evacuation becomes absolutely necessary. This may include monitoring plant power supplies, water supplies, and other essential services that cannot be shut down for every emergency alarm.

For emergency evacuation, floor plans or workplace maps that clearly show the emergency escape routes and safe or refuge areas should be included in the plan. All employees must be told what actions they are to take in the emergency situations that may occur in the workplace.

This plan should be reviewed with employees initially when the plan is developed, whenever the employees' responsibilities under the plan change and whenever the plan is changed. A copy should be kept where employees can refer to it at convenient times. In fact, to go a step further, the employer could provide the employees with a copy of the plan, particularly all new employees.

Chain of Command

A chain of command should be established to minimize confusion so those employees will have no doubt about who has authority for making decisions. Responsible individuals should be selected to coordinate the work of the emergency response team. In larger organizations, there may be a plant coordinator in charge of plant-wide operations, public relations and ensuring that outside aid is called. Because of the importance of these functions, adequate backup must be arranged so that trained personnel are always available. The duties of the Emergency Response Team Coordinator should include the following:

- Assessing the situation and determining whether an emergency exists that requires activating the emergency procedures;
- Directing all efforts in the area including evacuating personnel and minimizing property loss;
- Ensuring outside emergency services such as medical aid and local fire departments are called when necessary; and
- Directing the shutdown of plant operations when necessary.

Communications

During a major emergency involving a fire or explosion, it may be necessary to evacuate offices in addition to manufacturing areas. Also, normal services, such as electricity, water and telephones may be nonexistent. Under these conditions, it may be necessary to have an alternate area to which employees can report or that can act as a focal point for incoming and outgoing calls. Because time is an essential element for adequate response, the person designated as being in charge should make this the alternate headquarters so that he or she can be easily reached.

Emergency communications equipment, such as amateur radio systems, public address systems or portable radio units, should be present to notify employees of the emergency and contact local authorities, such as law enforcement officials, the fire department and Red Cross.

A method of communication also is needed to alert employees to evacuate or to take other action as required in the plan. Alarms should be audible or seen by all people in the plant and should have an auxiliary power supply in the event electricity is affected. The alarm should be distinctive and recognizable as a signal to evacuate the work area or perform actions designated under the emergency action plan. The employer should explain to each employee the means for reporting emergencies, such as manual pull-box alarms, public address systems or telephones. Emergency

phone numbers should be posted on or near telephones, on employees' notice boards or in other conspicuous locations. The warning plan should be in writing and management must be sure each employee knows what it means and what action is to be taken.

It may be necessary to notify other key personnel such as the plant manager or physician during off-duty hours. An updated written list should be kept of key personnel listed in order of priority.

Accounting for Personnel

Management will need to know when all personnel have been accounted for. This can be difficult during shift changes or if contractors are on site. A responsible person in the control center should be appointed to account for personnel and to inform police or Emergency Response Team members of those persons believed missing.

Emergency Response Teams

Emergency Response Teams are the first line of defense in emergencies. Before assigning personnel to these teams, the employer must ensure that employees are physically capable of performing the duties that may be assigned to them. Depending on the size of the plant, there may be one or several teams trained in the following areas:

- Use of various types of fire extinguishers;
- First aid, including cardiopulmonary resuscitation (CPR);
- Shutdown procedures;
- Evacuation procedures;
- Chemical spill control procedures;
- Use of self-contained breathing apparatus (SCBA);
- Search and emergency rescue procedures; and
- Incipient and advanced stage firefighting.

The type and extent of the emergency will depend on the plant operations and the response will vary according to the type of process, the material handled, the number of employees and the availability of outside resources. Emergency Response Teams should be trained in the types of possible emergencies and the emergency actions to be performed. They should be informed of special hazards

WHAT EVERY SUPERVISOR MUST KNOW ABOUT OSHA-GENERAL

to which they may be exposed during fire and other emergencies, such as storage and use of flammable materials, toxic chemicals, radioactive sources and water-reactive substances. It is important to determine when not to intervene. For example, team members must be able to determine if the fire is too large for them to handle or whether search and emergency rescue procedures should be performed. If there is a possibility of members of the Emergency Response Team receiving fatal or incapacitating injuries, they should wait for professional firefighters or emergency response groups.

Training

Training is important to the effectiveness of an emergency plan. Before implementing an emergency action plan, a sufficient number of persons must be trained to assist in the safe and orderly evacuation of employees. Training for each type of disaster response is necessary so those employees know what actions are required.

In addition to the specialized training for Emergency Response Team members, all employees should be trained on the firms' evacuation plans, alarm systems, shutdown procedures, types of potential emergency and reporting procedures for all personnel.

These training programs should be provided for all employees as follows:
- Initially when the plan is developed;
- When new equipment, materials or processes are introduced;
- When procedures have been updated or revised;
- When exercises show that employee performance must be improved; and
- At least annually.

The emergency control procedures should be written in concise terms and made available to all personnel. A drill should be held for all personnel at random intervals at least annually, and an evaluation of performance made immediately by management and employees. When possible, drills should include groups supplying outside services such as fire and police departments. In buildings with several employers, the emergency plans should be coordinated with other companies and employees in the building. Finally, the emergency plan should be reviewed periodically and updated to maintain adequate response personnel and program efficiency.

Personal Protection

Personal protection is essential for any person exposed to potentially hazardous substances. In emergency situations, employees may be exposed to a variety of hazardous circumstances, including:
- Chemical splashes or contact with toxic materials;
- Falling objects and flying particles;
- Unknown atmospheres that may contain toxic gases vapors or mists, or inadequate oxygen to sustain life; and
- Fires and electrical hazards.

It is extremely important for employees to be adequately protected in these situations. Some of the safety equipment that may be used includes:
- Safety glasses, goggles or face shields for eye protection;
- Hard hats and safety shoes for head and foot protection;
- Proper respirators for breathing protection;
- Whole-body coverings, gloves, hoods and boots for body protection from chemicals; and
- Body protection for abnormal environmental conditions (e.g., extreme temperatures).

The equipment selected must meet the criteria contained in the OSHA standards. The choice of proper equipment is not a simple matter; consultation should be made with health and safety professionals before making any purchases. Manufacturers and distributors of health and safety products may be able to answer questions if they have enough information about the potential hazards involved. Professional consultation will most likely be needed when providing adequate respiratory protection.

Respiratory protection is necessary for toxic atmospheres of dust, mists, gases, or vapors and for oxygen-deficient atmospheres. There are four basic categories of respirators:
- Air-purifying devices (e.g., filters, gas masks, chemical cartridges), which remove contaminants from the air but cannot be used in oxygen-deficient atmospheres;

- Air-supplied respirators (e.g., hose masks, air line respirators), which should not be used in atmospheres that are immediately dangerous to life or health;
- Self-contained breathing apparatus, which are required for unknown atmospheres, oxygen-deficient atmospheres or atmospheres immediately dangerous to life or health (positive-pressure type only); and
- Escape masks.

Before assigning or using respiratory equipment the following conditions must be met:
- A medical evaluation should be made to determine if the employees are physically able to use the respirator.
- Written procedures must be prepared covering safe use and proper care of the equipment and employees must be trained in these procedures and the use and maintenance of respirators.
- A fit test must be made to determine a proper match between the face piece of the respirator and the face of the wearer. This testing must be repeated periodically. Training must provide the employee an opportunity to handle the respirator have it fitted properly, test its face-to-face seal, wear it in normal air for a familiarity period and wear it in a test atmosphere.
- A regular maintenance program must be instituted, including cleaning, inspecting and testing of all respiratory equipment. Respirators used for the emergency response must be inspected after each use and at least monthly to ensure that they are in satisfactory working condition. A written record of inspection must be maintained.
- Distribution areas for equipment used in emergencies must be readily accessible to employees.

Self-contained breathing apparatus (SCBA) offers the best protection to employees involved in controlling emergency situations. It should have a minimum service life rating of 30 minutes. Conditions that require a SCBA include the following:
- Leaking cylinders or containers, smoke from chemical fires or chemical spills that indicate high potential for exposure to toxic substances.

- Atmospheres with unknown contaminants or unknown contaminant concentrations in confined spaces that may contain toxic substances or oxygen-deficient atmospheres.

Emergency situations may involve entering confined spaces to rescue employees who are overcome by toxic compounds or who lack oxygen. These confined spaces include tanks, vaults, pits, sewers, pipelines and vessels. Entry into confined spaces can expose the employee to a variety of hazards, including toxic gases, explosive atmospheres, oxygen deficiency, electrical hazards and hazards created by mixers and impellers that have not been deactivated and locked out. Personnel should never enter a confined space under normal circumstances unless the atmosphere has been tested for adequate oxygen, combustibility and toxic substances. Conditions in a confined space must be considered immediately dangerous to life and health unless shown otherwise.

If a confined space must be entered in an emergency, the following precautions must be taken:
- All lines containing inert, toxic, flammable or corrosive materials must be disconnected or blocked off before entry.
- All impellers, agitators or other moving equipment inside the vessel must be locked out.
- Employees must wear appropriate personal protective equipment before entering the vessel. Mandatory use of safety belts and harnesses should be stressed.
- Rescue procedures must be specifically designed for each entry. A trained stand-by person must be present. This person should be assigned a fully charged, positive-pressure self-contained breathing apparatus with a full face. The stand-by person must maintain unobstructed lifelines and communications to all workers within the confined space and be prepared to summon rescue personnel if necessary. The stand-by person should not enter the confined space until adequate assistance is present. While awaiting rescue personnel, the stand-by person may make a rescue attempt using lifelines from outside the confined space.

Medical Assistance

In a major emergency, time is a critical factor in minimizing injuries. Most small businesses do not have a formal medical program, but they are required to have the following medical and first-aid services:

- In the absence of an infirmary, clinic or hospital in close proximity to the workplace that can be used for treatment of all injured employees, the employer must ensure that a person or persons are adequately trained to administer first aid.
- Where the eyes or body of any employee may be exposed to injurious corrosive materials, eye washes or suitable equipment for quick drenching or flushing must be provided in the work area for immediate emergency use. Employees must be trained to use the equipment.
- The employer must ensure the ready availability of medical personnel for advice and consultation on matters of employees' health. This does not mean that health care must be provided. Rather, if health problems develop in the workplace, medical help will be available to resolve them.

To fulfill the above requirements, the following actions should be considered:

- Survey the medical facilities near the place of business and make arrangements to handle routine and emergency cases. A written emergency medical procedure should then be prepared for handling accidents with minimum confusion.

- If the business is located far from medical facilities, at least one and preferably more employees on each shift must be adequately trained to render first aid. The American Red Cross, some insurance carriers, local safety councils, fire departments and others may be contacted for this training.
- First-aid supplies should be provided for emergency use. This equipment should be ordered through consultation with a physician.
- Emergency phone numbers should be posted in conspicuous places near or on telephones.
- Sufficient ambulance service should be available to handle any emergency. This requires advance contact with ambulance services to ensure they become familiar with the plant location, access routes and hospital locations.

Security

During an emergency, it is often necessary to secure the area to prevent unauthorized access and to protect vital records and equipment. An off-limits area must be established by cordoning off the area with ropes and signs. It may be necessary to notify local law enforcement personnel or to employ private security personnel to secure the area and prevent the entry of unauthorized personnel.

Certain records also may need to be protected, such as essential accounting files, legal documents and lists of employees' relatives to be notified in case of emergency. These records may be stored in duplicate outside the plant or in protected secure locations within the plant.

Final Rule 29 CFR Part 1910 Subpart E Exit Routes, Emergency Action Plans, and Fire Prevention Plans (67 Fed. Reg. 67949)

SUMMARY: The Occupational Safety and Health Administration (OSHA) is revising its standards for means of egress. The purpose of this revision is to rewrite the existing requirements in clearer language so they will be easier to understand by employers, employees, and others who use them.

The revisions reorganize the text, remove inconsistencies among sections, and eliminate duplicative requirements. The rules are performance-oriented to the extent possible, and more concise than the original, with fewer subparagraphs, and fewer cross-references to other OSHA standards. Additionally, a table of contents has been added that is intended to make the standards easier to use.

Also, OSHA is changing the name of the subpart from "Means of Egress" to **"Exit Routes, Emergency Action Plans, and Fire Prevention Plans"** to better describe the contents.

Finally, OSHA has evaluated the National Fire Protection Association's Standard 101, Life Safety Code, 2000 Edition (NFPA 101-2000), and has concluded that the standard provides comparable safety to the **Exit Routes** Standard. Therefore, employers who wish to comply with the NFPA 101-2000 instead of the OSHA standards for **Exit Routes** may do so.

DATES: The final rule becomes effective December 9, 2002.

ADDRESSES: In accordance with 28 U.S.C. 2112(a), the Agency designates the Associate Solicitor of Labor for Occupational Safety and Health, Office of the Solicitor of Labor, Room S-4004, U.S. Department of Labor, 200 Constitution Avenue, NW., Washington, DC 20210 to receive petitions for review of the final rule.

FOR FURTHER INFORMATION CONTACT: OSHA, Ms. Bonnie Friedman, Director, Office of Public Affairs, N-3647, Occupational Safety and Health Administration, U.S. Department of Labor, 200 Constitution Avenue, NW., Washington, DC 20210; telephone: (202) 693-1999. For additional copies of this Federal Register document, contact: OSHA, Office of Publications, U.S. Department of Labor, Room N-3103, 200 Constitution Avenue, NW., Washington, DC 20210; telephone: (202) 693-1888.

For electronic copies of this Federal Register document, as well as news releases, fact sheets, and other relevant documents, visit OSHA's homepage at http://www.osha.gov.

SUPPLEMENTARY INFORMATION: References to comments and testimony in the rulemaking record (Docket S-052) are found throughout the text of the preamble. In the preamble comments are identified by an assigned exhibit number as follows: "Ex. 5-1" means Exhibit 5-1 in Docket S-052. For quoted material in the preamble, the page number where the quote can be located is included if other than page one. The transcript of the public hearing is cited by the page number as follows: Tr. 37. A list of the exhibits, copies of the exhibits, and transcripts are available in the OSHA Docket Office.

I. Background

In 1971 and 1972, OSHA adopted hundreds of national consensus and established Federal standards under section 6(a) of the Occupational Safety and Health Act of 1970. Section 6(a) allowed the Agency to adopt these standards for a limited period of time without going through traditional rulemaking. Many of these "start-up standards" have been criticized for being overly wordy, difficult to understand, repetitive and internally inconsistent.

On September 10, 1996, OSHA published a proposed rule in the Federal Register (61 FR 47712) proposing to revise subpart E of part 1910. OSHA proposed to rewrite the existing requirements of subpart E in plain language so that the requirements would be easier to understand by employers, employees, and others who use them. The proposal did not intend to change the regulatory obligations of employers or the safety and health protection provided to employees by the original standard.

OSHA proposed two versions of the revision of subpart E. The first version was organized in the traditional regulatory format characteristic of most OSHA standards. The second version was in a question and answer format. OSHA invited interested parties to comment on the content and effectiveness of the proposed changes and to indicate which version they preferred. Both versions left unchanged the regulatory obligations placed on employers and the safety and health protection provided to employees. Based on the majority of comments (e.g., Exs. 5-13, 17, 24-26, 45-47, 58-60) OSHA has decided to use its traditional regulatory text format for this final rule. OSHA believes that the revised subpart E is more performance-oriented and more compliance options will be available to employers.

In the proposal, OSHA stated what it expected to achieve by revising subpart E: (1) To maintain the safety and health protection provided to employees without increasing the regulatory burden on employers; (2) to create a regulation that is easily understood and; (3) to state employers' obligations in performance-oriented language to the extent possible.

The proposal attempted to simplify, rather than to substantively revise, OSHA's means of egress standards. In finalizing this proposal, the Agency has been careful to ensure that the protections afforded employees were not weakened. Employers who are in compliance with the original subpart E will continue to be in compliance with the revised subpart E that is being promulgated in this rule.

In developing the proposal, OSHA reviewed relevant OSHA decisions of the Federal courts, the Occupational Safety and Health Review Commission, and Agency letters of interpretation (Ex. 2) to determine how each provision of subpart E has been interpreted. Also, OSHA reviewed comparable State regulations, training materials and current consensus standards including the National Fire Protection Association's Life Safety Code, NFPA 101 (at that time the 1994 Edition). This review enabled OSHA to reorganize subpart E, eliminate duplicative provisions, and have confidence that the revisions did not diminish the safety and health protection afforded by existing rules.

OSHA discovered during the review process that some provisions of subpart E were outdated and not consistent with contemporary fire safety options in then current NFPA 101,

Life Safety Code, 1994 Edition. Where it was possible to expand permissible employer compliance options without lessening employee safety, the proposal included these expanded options. For example, OSHA incorporated NFPA 101, 1994 Edition, the Life Safety Code's option to exit to a refuge area rather than to the outside (proposed paragraph 1910.36(f)(3)). The proposal also permitted the use of self-luminous and electroluminescent exit signs (proposed paragraph 1910.37(c)(6)). (E.g., Exs. 5-18, 40, 45, 54.) The proposal enabled employers to avail themselves of these newer options or continue with current compliance methods. In this way OSHA increased compliance flexibility without reducing safety.

OSHA did not substitute performance-oriented language for current language where doing so would either eliminate a requirement that protects employee safety and health, or expand an employer's compliance obligation. For example, the proposal continued the existing requirement that a means of egress must be at least 28 inches wide (proposed paragraph 1910.37(j)). The Agency chose not to substitute performance-oriented criteria for this provision (such as "means of egress be of adequate width to support building occupants") because this change would eliminate the existing minimum width specification and might not provide adequate protection to employees leaving the workplace in an **emergency**. For this reason, OSHA decided not to revise the minimum clearance requirement.

OSHA noted in the proposal that for some employers, reliance on performance-oriented standards might create confusion as to the specific precautions necessary in a variety of situations. In the past, OSHA has used NFPA 101 as an aid in interpreting subpart E. OSHA intends to continue to rely on NFPA 101 as guidance in implementing performance-oriented provisions of revised subpart E.

In addition to organizing the requirements of the revised subpart E in a logical and understandable manner, OSHA has organized the requirements around three aspects of **exit routes:**

(1) Design and construction requirements;
(2) maintenance, safeguards, and operational requirements; and

(3) requirements for warning employees of the need to escape. Reorganizing subpart E in this manner has enabled OSHA to eliminate many duplicative provisions.

For example, in existing subpart E, both paragraph 1910.36(b)(8) and paragraph 1910.37(e) contain the design requirements that where workplaces are required to have two means of egress, these means of egress must be located as far away as practical (remote) from one another.

Other significant revisions to subpart E include: Removal of obligations that are not related to employee protection but pertain to the protection of the general public, and the deletion of any recommended as opposed to required actions (i.e., provisions that use "should" or "may").

II. Regulatory Format

As noted above, OSHA proposed two versions of subpart E; a traditional regulatory text version and a question and answer version. The traditional regulatory text version was preceded by a descriptive section heading that told the reader what information could be found in that section. The question and answer version was written in a form by which an employer might ask a question about the rule, and this question was then followed by an answer that told the employer about the requirement.

Other efforts to make subpart E more user-friendly included: removal of unused terms and ordinary terms from the definitions; elimination of cross-references to other standards; removal of overly technical terms in favor of more common words; use of the active voice; and, the use of positive as opposed to negative sentences.

The Agency invited public comment and requests for a hearing on the proposed revision to subpart E. An informal public hearing was requested by the National Fire Protection Association (Ex. 5-18) and Hallmark Cards (Ex. 5-51).

On March 3, 1997, OSHA published a notice in the Federal Register (62 FR 9402) announcing an informal public hearing and a reopening of the written comment period. Written comments on the proposed standard were to be postmarked by April 19, 1997. The hearing was held in Washington, DC on April 29-30, 1997.

In the hearing notice, OSHA invited comment on ten issues that will be discussed below in more detail. In summary, OSHA asked: (1) How OSHA should use the Life Safety Code in the final rule; (2) how or if OSHA should use model building codes; (3) whether the use of performance language creates new enforcement problems;
(4) how OSHA should address the issues of exit capacity and the number of required exits;
(5) whether or not the exit sign provisions were too general;
(6) whether or not the revised requirements for exit illumination were too general;
(7) whether or not there were still provisions or terms in the proposed revision that were too technical or difficult to understand;
(8) whether OSHA achieved in the proposed revision its goal of not changing employers obligations;
(9) whether any of the proposed provisions provided greater protection than in the original subpart E; and
(10) whether any of the requirements presented technological feasibility problems for affected employers.

The subpart E rulemaking record contains 23 exhibits, 69 comments, 170 pages of testimony and four post-hearing comments.

III. Summary and Explanation of the Final Rule

This section contains an analysis of the record evidence and policy decisions pertaining to the various provisions of revised subpart E.

As stated previously, OSHA's goals in revising subpart E were to maintain the safety and health protection provided to employees in subpart E without increasing the regulatory burden on employers, create a regulation that is easily understood, and, to the extent possible, express employers' obligations in performance-oriented language.

The majority of commenters supported OSHA's use of plain language. Owens Manufacturing, Inc. (Ex. 5-1) stated they were "in favor of this change as it allows the production people in our manufacturing area to understand the scope and meaning of this regulation much easier."

United Refining Company (Ex. 5-2) remarked "For those individuals who occasionally reference a standard the Plain English version will be beneficial." The commenter from Medical Environment, Inc. (Ex. 5-7) stated "I commend your actions in correcting the highly technical language into wording that is understandable to the average person. I have read your proposed changes, and find them to be significantly improved." The Institute for Interconnecting and Packaging Electronic Circuits (IPC) (Ex. 5-25) observed that:

* * * Because IPC members are predominantly small companies, they have limited resources to track down, read, understand, and comply with the substantial volume of federal, state, and local regulations. In many firms, the company president, plant manager, or production supervisor is responsible for facility-wide health and safety compliance in addition to running production and perhaps running the company.

Given IPC members' commitment to advancing employee health and safety, IPC applauds OSHA's proposed Means of Egress rule. The proposed changes are designed to make the standard more understandable and, therefore promote industry compliance. "Translating" OSHA's current regulations into "plain English" is an outstanding activity that should be aggressively applied to ALL federal regulations—not just OSHA regulations, and IPC supports OSHA's actions to effect such change.

The International Brotherhood of Teamsters (Ex. 5-31) commended OSHA for undertaking the revision effort and stated that the International:

[I]s pleased to see the Occupational Safety and Health Administration attempt to develop plain English standards. This International Union feels that this approach to safety and health standards will enable our members and other workers across the country to better understand their OSHA rights and their employer's obligations.

The National Institute for Occupational Safety and Health (NIOSH, Ex. 5-42) also supported the effort observing that "By revising the Means of Egress rule in easy to understand terms as part of a shorter, performance-oriented standard, the standard will be easier to use and provide more compliance options for employers."

Schirmer Engineering Corporation (Ex. 5-57) stated:

Review of the revisions introduced in the proposed rule indicates an effort to provide language which is more condensed and clear, with the removal of verbose wording. The sections that were deleted from the original version did not greatly affect the overall life safety concept as it pertains to egress from a building. In addition, the reorganization helps to clarify some of the requirements of the code which, in turn, facilitates overall compliance.

(See also Exs. 5-5, 12, 13, 15-17, 20-24, 26, 27, 29, 30, 34, 35, 37, 39, 43, 45, 47, 51, 52, 54-56, 58, 59, 60, 61, 70.)

On the other hand, some commenters did object to the revision of subpart E on the grounds either that it was not productive for OSHA to re-write these standards, or that the revised language actually changed the requirements. For example, James R. Hutton, a fire protection engineer (Ex. 5-9), believed the "proposed revisions will complicate and cause more difficulties, not less, for smaller businesses who do not have the resources to undergo the time or expense required to develop "custom solutions" to "plain English" requirements." OSHA disagrees. The revised subpart E only makes compliance requirements clearer and it refers employers and employees to NFPA 101 for added details, when necessary.

It was also suggested by some commenters that instead of finalizing the proposed revision, OSHA should adopt NFPA 101, the Life Safety Code, or that OSHA should rely on building codes, instead of revising subpart E. (See e.g., Exs. 5-10, 15, 18, 19, 26, 41, 46, 48, 61, 68; Tr. 14, 23; Ex. 10.)

The National Fire Protection Association (NFPA, Ex. 5-18) remarked:

NFPA agrees with several of the goals as contained in the OSHA/NPRM but find serious flaws in the methodology being proposed to attain these goals. Specifically, NFPA applauds OSHA's goal "to maintain the safety and health protection provided to employees by subpart E * * *" and "to create a regulation that is easily understood." We also applaud OSHA's desire "to allow employers the flexibility of relying on more contemporary compliance approaches."

However, we do not believe these goals can be achieved by either "plain English" alternative taken together or separately as being proposed by OSHA in the NPRM. Specifically, NFPA recommends OSHA abandon its attempt to rewrite a 25-year old standard as represented in the first alternative of the NPRM * * *.

Further, NFPA asserted that OSHA's rewrite would make enforcement more difficult especially when performance-oriented language is substituted for specifications; that the proposal drops all references to the NFPA Life Safety Code even though the proposal indicated OSHA would continue to rely on that Code; and, that the proposed rewrite did not specifically allow for contemporary compliance options as contemplated by OSHA and as set forth in the current edition of NFPA 101 (1994). NFPA recommended that:

[T]he first alternative be abandoned [traditional regulatory text] and that OSHA instead adopt by reference the 1994 edition of NFPA 101 * * * Further, NFPA believes the adoption of the 1994 edition of NFPA 101, together with a supplemental Q&A (question and answer) format as proposed in the second NPRM alternative, would be the best approach to achieve the desired goals as stated by OSHA in the NPRM.

At the time of the proposal, the latest version of NFPA 101 was the 1994 Edition. NFPA subsequently issued a 1997 edition and then a 2000 edition. OSHA has reviewed the NFPA 101-2000 edition carefully and found that compliance with its provisions would protect employees as well as the parallel provisions of subpart E. Adopting NFPA 101 as an OSHA standard would require OSHA to conduct a full rulemaking under section 6(b) of the OSH Act, scrutinizing each provision, accounting for each cost impact on employers, justifying why the new standard is reasonably necessary and appropriate, and showing that the adoption would reduce significant risk to employees. This would be inconsistent with the goal of this project which was to clarify employer obligations without increasing compliance burdens. However, OSHA has been convinced by commenters that consideration should be given to compliance with NFPA 101.

The 2000 Life Safety Code goes far beyond the requirements of OSHA's standard, both in details of compliance and flexibility for unique workplace conditions. If an employer complies with NFPA 101-2000, OSHA will deem such compliance to be compliance with the OSHA standard. OSHA believes that allowing employers to comply with NFPA 101 as an alternative to the revised Exit Routes standard will provide greater flexibility to employers who want to go beyond OSHA's basic provisions. Additionally, the National Technology Transfer and Advancement Act of 1995 (15 U.S.C. 3701 (1996)) directs Federal agencies to use voluntary consensus standards to the extent practicable. Under section 6(b)(8) of the OSH Act, the Agency must consider using national consensus standards as the basis for its safety and health standards wherever possible. By allowing employers to comply with the exit route provisions of NFPA 101-2000, OSHA has struck a balance that is consistent with its goals for this rulemaking as well as the spirit of the National Technology Transfer and Advancement Act.

OSHA has evaluated NFPA 101-2000 and has concluded that an employer who complies with the provisions of that code for means of egress will provide employees with safety that is comparable with compliance with OSHA's revised Exit Routes standard. OSHA is adding a new Sec. 1910.35 to the final rule to recognize NFPA 101-2000 in this regard.

The South Carolina Department of Labor, Licensing & Regulation (Ex. 5-49, p.2) remarked that "It is a shame to spend this amount of time to adjust the wording when the whole standard is in need of repair."

Others criticized the proposal, feeling that it did not achieve its stated goal. For example, the American Health Care Association (Ex. 53) indicated that by "Developing new terminology for traditional means of egress requirements, we firmly believe, is a step backward and counter to OSHA's stated goal of creating a regulation that is easily understood." The United Steelworkers of America (Ex. 5-69) objected "to the very general performance language of this proposal. The language gives little, if any direction to employers and employees on how to comply with this proposed standard * * * Further, the proposed standard is somewhat confusing." (See also Exs. 5-33, 38, 40, 62, 66-68, 71).

OSHA does not agree with commenters who have concluded that OSHA has failed to meet its goals of (1) maintaining the safety and health protection provided to employees by subpart E without increasing the regulatory burden; (2) creating a regulation that is easily understood; and, (3) stating employers' obligations in performance-oriented language to the extent possible. Many commenters suggested improvements and language changes. Unfortunately in some cases the recommendations would have made substantive changes in the requirements of subpart E (e.g., Exs. 5-4, 11, 18, 21, 24, 40, 47, 49, 63). OSHA has considered and incorporated many comments that improve the clarity of the text, without making substantive changes in the obligations and protections offered by existing subpart E. The final rule as revised and reorganized, incorporates many commenter suggestions. OSHA strongly believes the final rule fulfills its goal of providing employers and employees with much clearer standards in subpart E. In addition, as already discussed, employers may take advantage of a more recent version of NFPA 101 under Sec. 1910.35 which recognizes compliance with the 2000 Edition of the Life Safety Code.

In response to comments, OSHA has changed the name of subpart E to better reflect the contents of the final rule. OSHA proposed to call the subpart "Exit Routes," but several commenters (Exs. 5-24, 40, 45) noted that the subpart contains provisions not only for exit routes but also for emergency action plans, and fire prevention plans. OSHA agrees with these commenters and has therefore changed

the name of subpart E to reflect its coverage of Exit Routes, Emergency Action Plans, and Fire Prevention Plans.

In the preamble to the proposal OSHA stated that it included a table of contents to make it easier to access the provisions. The table was inadvertently left out of the proposed regulatory language in the Federal Register notice. OSHA believes that a table of contents will be helpful to employers and employees in locating provisions in the subpart and therefore, is including a table of contents in Sec. 1910.33.

As indicated in the Regulatory Format section above, the proposed rule offered two versions of a revised subpart E. The first version was written in the traditional format of OSHA standards. The second version was written in a question and answer format.

Commenters who addressed this issue indicated a preference for the traditional regulatory format as opposed to the question and answer format. For example, Medical Environment, Inc. (Ex. 5-7) supported the traditional "regulatory format, because this is what everyone is used to seeing. The question/answer format seemed too "loose" to find an answer to a specific question." Similarly, the International Dairy Foods Association (IDFA) (Ex. 5-22) believed "that the "traditional" plain English version is the preferred version. In contrast, we find that the question and answer format quickly becomes condescending, and to a degree, annoying."

The American Petroleum Institute (API) (Ex. 5-29, p.2) supported the traditional format because of perceived pitfalls in the question and answer format.

While the Q/A version has some appeal in terms of better first-impression, API believes that the traditional format makes it easier to understand the rule in total, and to locate specific requirements.

Another API concern is that of confusion. The Q/A format could be associated with OSHA's Field Directives, in which questions and answers are sometimes used to explain requirements. The questions and answers in Field Directives, however, do not hold the same weight as regulatory language. As a result, confusion could be caused by the use of questions and answers in both the OSHA standards and in Field Directives.

EXIT ROUTES, EMERGENCY ACTION PLANS, AND FIRE PREVENTION PLANS

API is also concerned that the potential for inadvertent change of requirements is greater during a Q/A conversion. This is because more structural revision and reorganization is required to accommodate the Q/A approach, as demonstrated by comparison of the two approaches in this pilot conversion. It follows that the Q/A approach would face even greater conversion problems for other, more complicated safety and health regulations.

In addition, the International Brotherhood of Teamsters recommended that OSHA not adopt the question and answer format because the union believed that the format is neither well organized nor easy to read. (See also Exs. 5-2, 3, 12, 13, 14, 15, 16, 17, 20, 21, 24, 25, 26, 27, 30, 31, 34, 36, 37, 40, 41, 43, 45, 46, 47, 49.)

Several commenters stated that either version would be acceptable (Exs. 5-12, 17, 25). Other commenters supported the question and answer version (Exs. 5-16, 23, 32, 42, 48). Some suggested that the question and answer version be included in an appendix or some other OSHA publication (Exs. 5-20, 24, 26, 45, 54, 59). The Agency, after considering the comments, has decided to use the traditional format in the final rule. The Agency believes that including the question and answer version in an appendix might result in confusion. OSHA does use the question and answer format for other, non-regulatory documents, and will consider that format for future guidance in this area.

Additional comments ranged from remarks that OSHA should do nothing, revise subpart E and reference NFPA 101, or adopt NFPA 101 entirely (Exs. 5-10, 18, 28, 38, 41, 47, 53, 62, 66, 68, 71). The subject of how to address NFPA 101 in the plain language revision was also issue 1 in the hearing notice (at 62 FR 9403). Liberty Mutual Insurance Group (Ex. 5-19) recommended that OSHA "include a provision that compliance with a national consensus standard such as NFPA 101, Life Safety Code * * *would be recognized as compliance with the OSHA standard." The Building Owners and Managers Association (BOMA) stated that it believed that "it is essential for OSHA to add appendix language stating that compliance with the Life Safety Codes NFPA 101, constitutes compliance with subpart E. Current OSHA practices essentially recognize this now (Tr. 23)."

OSHA's intention in the proposed rule was to simplify subpart E, not to replace it. First, OSHA could not simply adopt "NFPA 101" as an OSHA standard, because it can only consider versions of that standard that are currently in existence. To do otherwise (i.e., attempting to approve a future edition) would result in an illegal delegation of agency authority. Second, adoption of NFPA 101-2000 as the OSHA standard goes beyond the limited purpose of this rulemaking. Such action would involve substantive rulemaking, including detailed analysis of the differences between OSHA current rules and NFPA 101-2000, including costs to employers and benefits to employees.

As discussed earlier, OSHA has reviewed NFPA 101-2000 and has determined that compliance with that standard will provide comparable protection to subpart E. Although the Agency is not adopting NFPA 101-2000, an employer who demonstrates compliance with that standard will be deemed to be in compliance with Sec. Sec. 1910.34, 1910.36, and 1910.37 of subpart E. Many commenters (e.g., Exs. 5-10, 18, 19, 41, 46, 48, 61) supported language that would allow employers to comply with the NFPA 101 standard as an alternative to the OSHA standard for Exit Routes. OSHA has incorporated such language into Sec. 1910.35 of the final rule.

Some commenters also asserted that OSHA should base its standard on the model building codes or allow compliance with the various national building codes (Exs. 5-19, 27, 47, 67; Tr. 23, 26, 32, 43). At the time of the rulemaking, there were three different national building codes in the United States: The Building Officials and Code Administrators' (BOCA) National Building Code, the International Conference of Building Officials' (ICBO) Uniform Building Code, and the Southern Building Code Congress International's (SBCCI) Standard Building Code.

OSHA emphasizes again that it did not propose to substantively revise subpart E, nor did it propose to allow the use of building codes to comply with subpart E. OSHA is not familiar enough with the detailed requirements of the various building codes to determine unequivocally whether compliance with any or all of them could be considered to fulfill employer obligations imposed by subpart E. Moreover the contents of these building codes were not analyzed, evaluated or considered as part of this rulemaking. The BOCA, ICBO, and SBCCI Codes vary considerably in their requirements and coverage relating to areas covered by subpart E. This rulemaking was not designed to address these differences, nor was it intended to expand the coverage of subpart E. Accordingly, OSHA declines to extend recognition to building codes as a means of determining compliance with subpart E. This decision only involves the narrow issue of whether compliance with a given building code demonstrates compliance with subpart E. OSHA recognizes and acknowledges the importance and the value of building codes in assuring that buildings are constructed safely.

Final Rule

Section 1910.34, Coverage and Definitions

In the proposal, Sec. 1910.35 was entitled "Coverage." It noted that all general industry employers were covered by subpart E, and that "exits" and "exit routes" were covered. The section went on to define these unique terms in the proposal. OSHA has retitled this section as "coverage and definitions," and has moved it to Sec. 1910.34 of the final rule. The "coverage" paragraph, Sec. 1910.34(a), specifies that the standard covers all workplaces in general industry except mobile workplaces. Paragraph (b) sets forth the "coverage" of the subpart: The minimum requirements for exit routes, emergency action plans, and fire prevention plans. Paragraph (c) of Sec. 1910.34 includes the definitions pertinent to the subpart.

In the proposal, OSHA included definitions for "Exit" and "Exit Route," eliminating all other definitions, believing they were unnecessary. However, commenters thought that OSHA went too far by not defining other terms or inappropriately failed to define other important terms (e.g., Exs. 5-18, 21, 24, 28, 41, 45, 47, 49.) After due consideration, OSHA agrees with these commenters and in the final rule (now paragraph 1910.34(c)) has added and clarified definitions for words used in the proposal that commenters found unclear. OSHA has clarified the terms "exit" and "exit route" and has added definitions

for electroluminescent, exit access, exit discharge, high hazard area, occupant load, refuge area, and self-luminous.

Section 1910.35, Compliance With NFPA 101-2000, Life Safety Code

As discussed previously in this preamble, this section provides that an employer who complies with corresponding provisions of NFPA 101-2000 is deemed to be in compliance with subpart E, sections 1910.34-1910.37.

Section 1910.36, Design and Construction Requirements for Exit Routes

Section 1910.36 contains requirements for the design and construction of exit routes. It includes a requirement that exit routes be permanent, addresses fire resistance-ratings of construction materials used in exit stairways (exits), describes openings into exits, defines the minimum number of exit routes in workplaces, addresses exit discharges, and discusses locked exit route doors, and exit route doors. It also addresses the capacity, height and width of exit routes, and finally, it sets forth requirements for exit routes that are outside a building.

Many of these requirements are identical or nearly the same as those proposed, but have been rearranged in a more logical order or reworded so that the requirements are clearer and easier to understand and follow.

Paragraph (a)(1) of 1910.36 (proposed paragraph 1910.36(a)), requires that exit routes be a permanent part of the workplace. This provision remains as proposed. OSHA believes that exit routes must be a permanent part of a structure and that employees must know the route to safety. Otherwise, during an emergency, employees may become confused and take the wrong path to safety.

Paragraph (a)(2) of 1910.36 (proposed paragraph 1901.36(d)), specifies the fire resistance-rating of construction materials used to separate exits from other parts of the workplace (e.g., stairways). For example, where an exit stairway connects three or fewer stories, it must be constructed of materials having a 1-hour fire resistance-rating. If the exit stairway connects four or more stories, it must be constructed of materials having a 2-hour fire resistance-rating.

One commenter, IMC Global, Inc. (Ex. 5-54), suggested that OSHA include information in the standard or the appendix that would specify what construction materials or combination of materials would meet the fire resistance-ratings required by the standard. They explained that the information would be used by in-house personnel who make alterations or repairs to the building. OSHA believes that the reference to NFPA 101 in Sec. 1910.35 will assist employers and employees in answering these questions.

IMC Global, Inc. also recommended that OSHA define the term "story," suggesting that OSHA use the definition used in the NFPA 101, Life Safety Code, but did not provide any rationale or support to demonstrate that the failure to include a definition would have a negative impact on worker safety or health. OSHA notes that the NPFA 101-2000, defines the term "story" to mean "That portion of a building between the upper surface of a floor and the upper surface of the floor or roof next above." OSHA believes this definition to be generally understood and has determined not to include a definition of "story" in the regulatory text of the final rule.

Another commenter, the American Trucking Association (Ex. 5-52), suggested that OSHA reword proposed paragraph 1910.36(d), to make it similar to the wording in the existing subpart E concerning fire resistant-materials (paragraphs 1910.37(b)(1) and (b)(2)). That wording requires that for exits protected by separation from other parts of the building, the separation shall meet certain construction requirements. The commenter noted that the proposed wording appears to require all exits to be separated by fire resistant-materials. OSHA agrees that the provision was not clearly worded and has revised the language of the final rule to specify the required fire resistance-rating of materials used to construct separations, i.e., enclosed stairways. The revised language reflects the concerns raised by the commenter.

Paragraph (a)(3) of 1910.36 (proposed paragraph 1910.36(c)), restricts the number of openings into exits to those openings necessary to allow access to the exit from occupied areas of the workplace, or from the exit to the exit discharge. It also specifies that openings must be protected by a self-closing fire door that remains closed unless the fire door automatically closes in an emergency when the fire alarm or employee alarm system is sounded.

The final rule differs from the proposal in that it permits fire doors to remain open as long as they close automatically during an emergency. This change was made in response to comments from H. M. Bucci and the NFPA (Exs. 5-10, 18). Both pointed out that NFPA 101, Life Safety Code, permits the exception. OSHA notes that the additional flexibility provided from this provision is in keeping with the Agency's intent in rewriting subpart E, i.e., to add flexibility if it does not detract from employee safety or health and does not impose additional costs or compliance obligations.

A commenter, Dennis Kirson (Ex. 5-4), noted that the proposed provision did not provide guidance on the fire rating for fire doors opening into an exit. Such ratings are based on the purpose of the door. To be listed or approved as a fire door, the door would have to meet the fire rating set by a nationally recognized testing laboratory (see next paragraph).

Paragraph 1910.36(a)(3) (proposed paragraph 1910.36(c)), requires that each fire door, including its frame and hardware, be listed or approved by a nationally recognized testing laboratory. The International Dairy Foods Association (Ex. 5-22), suggested that OSHA include the definition of the terms "listed," "approved," and "nationally recognized testing laboratory" in the regulatory language of the final rule instead of giving a cross-reference to another section of the standards. Section 1910.7 contains what employers need to know about "listed," "approved," and "nationally recognized testing laboratory." OSHA does not agree that adding additional definitions, which are duplicated elsewhere in part 1910, to the standard would be particularly helpful. Therefore, OSHA has retained in the final rule the cross-reference to the standard containing the terms.

Two commenters (Exs. 5-10, 11) commented on OSHA's failure to address other openings in exits made for electrical and mechanical systems. One commenter (Ex. 5-11) suggested that OSHA delete the provision because it precludes the use of protected openings when such openings are necessary for certain mechanical or electrical penetrations. The other commenter (Ex. 5-10) asked OSHA to address such openings by requiring that they be sealed with an approved fire barrier sealant or fire stop. The existing rule does not contain requirements addressing such openings and, as discussed above, the purpose of the revision is not to add new requirements that would impose new obligations on employers. If an employer has these openings, OSHA notes that such openings into exits are addressed in NFPA 101. The employer may use NFPA 101-2000 for guidance even though the final rule does not address this issue.

Paragraph 1910.36(b) of the final rule, the proposal, and issue 4 in the hearing notice (at 62 FR 9403), all address the general requirement that all workplaces have at least two exit routes, as far away as practical from each other, to ensure that all employees and other building occupants can promptly and safely evacuate the workplace during an emergency. Where two are insufficient, the employer must have additional exit routes (see NFPA 101-2000 for guidance). The number of exit routes can be reduced to one where the number of employees, the size of the building, its occupancy, or the arrangement of the workplace is such that all employees would be able to evacuate safely during an emergency.

Although OSHA does not have direct authority to regulate non-employee occupants of a building, in assuring the safe evacuation of employees, the impact of other occupants in a building must be taken into consideration to assure a safe evacuation of all employees. Thus, OSHA refers to "other building occupants" generally as it does in the existing subpart E.

"As far away as practical" ("remote" in the proposal) means that exit routes must be located far enough apart so that if one exit route is blocked by fire or smoke, employees can evacuate using the second exit route. The paragraph also provides a note that employers must consider the number of employees, the size of the building, its occupancy, and the arrangement of the workplace to determine the correct number of exit routes, recommending

that employers consult the NFPA 101-2000 for the number of exit routes appropriate to their particular workplace.

The provision in the final rule differs from the proposed rule in that it has been reworded to state specifically that an employer must have at least two exits (final paragraph 1910.36(b)(1)), or a sufficient number of exit routes (final paragraph 1910.36(b)(2)) to ensure that all occupants can safely and promptly leave the workplace during an emergency. An exception to the two-exit route rule is provided in those circumstances where an employer can demonstrate that the number of employees, size of the building or arrangement of the workplace is such that one exit route alone is sufficient (final paragraph 1910.36(b)(3)).

There were a number of comments on the required number of exit routes provision in the proposal (e.g., Exs. 5-4, 5, 8, 11, 18, 24, 26, 40, 41, 43, 45, 47, 49, 54, 63) with many commenters suggesting that the provision be rewritten to state clearly that two exit routes are required. Commenters also suggested that OSHA more fully explain how to determine when one exit route would be permitted or suggested that this exception be eliminated (Exs. 5-4, 5, 8, 26, 40, 41, 43, 45, 49, 54, 63).

OSHA agrees with some of the commenters in part, and has made it clear that employers must have at least two exit routes, except where one exit route would be sufficient to allow all employees to evacuate the workplace safely and promptly. OSHA has added a note to provision stating that employers may consult NFPA 101-2000 for guidance on how to determine the appropriate number of exit routes.

Other commenters suggested that the expression in proposed paragraph 1910.36(b)(2), "other means of escape * * * should be available," invited confusion, made the provision vague, and was unenforceable, and that OSHA should remove it in the final rule (Exs. 5-4, 11, 24, 40). OSHA agrees with the commenters and has eliminated the advisory wording in the final provision.

Paragraph 1910.36(c)(1) of the final rule (proposed paragraph 1910.36(f)) requires that each exit discharge lead directly outside or to a street, walkway, refuge area, public way, or open space with access to the outside. Paragraph 1910.36(c)(2) requires that the street, walkway, refuge area, public way, or open space to which an exit discharge leads must be large enough to accommodate the building occupants likely to use the exit.

Lastly, paragraph 1910.36(c)(3) (proposed paragraph 1910.36(f)(4)) requires that exit stairs that continue beyond the level on which the exit discharge is located must be interrupted at that level by doors, partitions, or other effective means to make clear the direction to go to the exit discharge. This paragraph differs from the proposed provision. It has been reworded to make it clear that where exit stairs continue beyond the level of the exit discharge, there must be some effective way to direct occupants to the exit discharge. This rewording responds to comments questioning the clarity of the provision as proposed (Exs. 5-22, 41).

A number of commenters indicated their support for allowing exit discharges to lead to a refuge area as proposed in paragraph 1910.36(f)(3) (Exs. 5-24, 29, 40, 45); they also suggested that the paragraph heading and the definition of exit route needed to be reworded to reflect the acceptability of refuge areas. The American Petroleum Institute remarked:

Section 1910.35(b)(2) should be revised to clarify that an exit route does not necessarily lead to the outside but could lead to a refuge area * * *.

As currently written, section 1910.35(b)(2) incorrectly defines an `exit route' as a means of travel to safety `outside' and further states that one part of an `exit route' is the way from the exit to the `outside.' is incorrectly misleads users into thinking that the only endpoint for an exit route is outside.

Similarly, the heading of section 1910.36(f) incorrectly states that an exit must lead to the outside. This heading should be amended to include the endpoint of a refuge area. Organization Resources Counselors, Inc. (5-45, p. 3) stated that it "agrees that the concept of refuge areas is one that should be adopted by OSHA."

In response to the comments, OSHA has revised the definition of exit route (paragraph 1910.34(c) of the final rule) to reflect the acceptability of refuge areas. Also, the heading to paragraph 1910.36(f) of the proposal, "An Exit Must Lead Outside," has been changed to "Exit Discharge" in final rule paragraph 1910.36(c).

Paragraphs 1910.36(d)(1), (2), and (3) of the final rule (proposed as paragraph 1910.36(g)), address locking exit route doors. Paragraph 1910.36(d)(1) specifies that employees must be able to open an exit route door from the inside at all times without keys, tools, or special knowledge. Devices that only lock from the outside at the exit discharge door, such as panic bars, are permitted. Paragraph 1910.36(d)(2) specifies that exit route doors must be free of any device or alarm that could restrict emergency use of the exit route if the device or alarm fails. Finally, paragraph 1910.36(d)(3) of the final rule states that in mental, penal or correctional facilities, an exit route door may be locked from the inside if supervisory personnel are continuously on duty and the employer has a plan to remove occupants from the facility during an emergency.

The final rule requirements on locking exit doors are essentially those in the proposal, except that the provisions are now located in paragraph 1910.36(d) in the final rule (instead of paragraph 1910.36(g) in the proposal). There were three comments on the proposal addressing locking exit doors. Commenter Dennis Kirson (Ex. 5-4) suggested that OSHA delete the sentence "A device that locks from the outside such as a panic bar is permitted because," he said, "it deals with ingress (to be locked out) rather than egress (to be locked in), it serves no purpose." Mr. Kirson further noted that this sentence did not modify the first sentence. OSHA has not made the suggested change because to avoid any misunderstandings it believes that the rule should include specific language to indicate what is acceptable. The Agency believes it is necessary in this context to state what is permitted along with what is not permitted, because of the widespread use of panic bars. The commenter also suggested OSHA delete the reference to mental, penal, or correctional institutions because they did not appear to fit the definition of general industry worksites. OSHA has not made the suggested change because such institutions are indeed "general industry" establishments and employees in these establishments are afforded the same protections as employees in other general industry workplaces. In recognition of the unique problems these institutions have with regard to the need to ensure occupants remain inside the facilities, OSHA is providing specific language to indicate clearly the performance to be achieved at these worksites.

Another commenter, the Department of Energy (Ex. 5-11), suggested that this last provision should also reflect national security at Federal locations and that OSHA should add "or other facility requiring security from unauthorized access." While OSHA does not disagree with the commenter, it has not made the suggested change because the inclusion of this additional language is beyond the stated scope of this proceeding. However the Agency will consider adding the suggested language in the future when substantive revisions are made to this subpart.

Paragraph 1910.36(e) (proposed paragraph 1910.36(h)), sets out requirements for doors leading to an exit route. The paragraph requires that a side-hinged door must be used to connect any room to an exit route and that the door that connects any room to an exit route must swing out in the direction of exit travel if the room is designed to be occupied by more than 50 people or if the room is used as a high hazard area (i.e., contains contents that are likely to burn with extreme rapidity or explode).

The final rule provision in paragraph 1910.36(e) is essentially the same as the proposed provision (paragraph 1910.36(h) in the proposal) with minor reorganizing to emphasize the requirements of the provisions. OSHA has divided the paragraph into two concise paragraphs in the final rule, paragraphs 1910.36(e)(1) and (2). Two commenters recommended changing the language of the proposed provision that required exit doors "swing out." Mr. Dennis Kirson (Ex. 5-4) suggested adding an exception to the provision that doors swing out, to allow for containment of hazardous materials, because of the greater hazard (to the public) of loss of containment of such materials. Such a change is beyond the scope of this project but the Agency may consider such a change as part of a future rulemaking. Tenneco (Ex. 5-41) suggested the phrase be changed to "swing with the exit travel" for further clarity. OSHA has revised the provision to incorporate the recommended change.

Eastman Kodak Company (Ex. 5-21) asked if security pass-through gates/turnstiles that free wheel when an alarm goes off would be considered an exit. Another commenter (Ex. 5-18) suggested that sliding doors be acceptable to OSHA if their operation is maintained to NFPA 101 specifications. The commenter noted that the current code (at that time NFPA 101-1994) allows vertical and sliding doors. OSHA has not modified the provision to address sliding doors or turnstiles because it would be a substantive change to the Exit Routes standard. However, these configurations are addressed in NFPA 101-2000. Employers who comply with that standard for the requirements concerning gates, turnstiles, and vertical or sliding doors, will be deemed to comply with this provision of subpart E.

Final rule paragraph 1910.36(f) (proposed paragraph 1910.36(i)) and issue 4 in the hearing notice (at 62 FR 9403)), address the required capacity for exit routes. The paragraph requires that exit routes be able to support the maximum permitted occupant load for each floor served by the exit routes, and that the capacity of exit routes may not decrease in the direction of exit route travel to the exit discharge.

OSHA has divided this proposed provision into two provisions in the final rule. The Agency has also made an editorial change in response to a concern raised by the Tennessee Valley Authority (TVA) (Ex. 5-47). TVA pointed out that in the existing standard, each exit route does not have to support the maximum permitted occupant load; rather, the existing standard requires that the combined capacity of the exits must support the maximum permitted occupant load for that floor. OSHA agrees with the commenter and has revised final paragraph 1910.36(f) accordingly.

Several commenters (Exs. 5-14, 36) expressed concerns about how to determine adequate capacity or the expected occupancy load for each floor. Argonne National Laboratory (Ex. 5-14) suggested that OSHA adopt the latest NFPA 101 to determine "whether or not adequate exiting capacity is provided from an area." Another commenter, Mr. Donald R. Delano (Ex. 5-36), suggested that OSHA define "maximum permitted occupant load" and "expected occupant load." IMC Global, Inc. (Ex. 5-54) asked that OSHA define "occupant load." In response to these comments OSHA has added a definition for the term "occupant load" and explained generally how to calculate the occupant load in the definition. The calculation can be done in accordance with NFPA 101-2000, since there are a wide variety of general industry occupancies which may be subject to different considerations.

Final rule paragraph 1910.36(g) (proposed paragraph 1910.36(j)) addresses the height and width requirements for exit routes and specifies that the ceiling of an exit route must be at least seven feet six inches (2.3 m) high. The paragraph specifies that any projection from the ceiling cannot decrease the space between the projection and the floor to less than six feet eight inches (2.0 m). Paragraph 1910.36(g) also specifies that the width of an exit access must be at least 28 inches (71.1 cm) wide at all points and that where a single way of exit access leads to an exit, its width must be at least equal to the width of the exit to which it leads.

Final paragraph 1910.36(g) also specifies that the width of an exit route must be sufficient to accommodate the maximum permitted occupant load of each floor served by the exit route. Lastly, the paragraph specifies that any objects that project into the exit route must not reduce the width of the exit route to less than the minimum width requirements for exit routes.

Paragraphs 1910.36(h)(1) through (4) (proposed paragraphs 1910.36(k)(1)(i) through (iv)), set out special requirements for exit routes that are outside of a building. The paragraphs require that each outdoor exit route must meet the minimum height and width requirements for indoor exit routes and must also meet certain other requirements. Specifically, (1) an outdoor exit route must have guardrails to protect unenclosed sides if a fall hazard exists; (2) an outdoor exit route must be covered if snow or ice is likely to accumulate along the route, unless the employer can demonstrate that any snow or ice accumulation will be removed before it presents a slipping hazard; (3) an outdoor exit route must be reasonably straight and have smooth, solid, substantially level walkways; and (4) an outdoor exit route must not have a dead-end that is longer than 20 feet (6.2 m).

Several commenters addressed this paragraph. Two commenters (Exs. 5-29, 40) suggested adding the wording "if a fall hazard exists" to the requirement for guardrails. OSHA agrees that guardrails only need to protect unenclosed sides if a fall hazard exists. One commenter (Ex. 5-10) suggested that the Agency use a 50 foot dead-end rather than a 20 foot dead-end. This would be a significant change and appears to be a decrease in safety to employees during emergencies and therefore OSHA has not changed the length of a dead-end. Other changes to these provisions are editorial only.

Section 1910.37, Maintenance, Safeguards, and Operational Features for Exit Routes

OSHA proposed in Sec. 1910.37 to include provisions covering the operation and maintenance of exit routes. OSHA has expanded the name from the proposal's "Operation and Maintenance Requirements for Exit Routes" to better reflect its contents. In the final rule, Sec. 1910.37 is entitled "Maintenance, safeguards, and operational features for exit routes." Provisions of this section include the safe use of exit routes during an emergency, lighting and marking exit routes, fire retardant paints, exit routes during construction, repairs, or alterations, and employee alarm systems.

OSHA has made several changes to paragraph 1910.37(a) of the proposed rule, by combining related provisions. In the final rule, paragraph 1910.37(a) remains titled "The Danger To Employees Must Be Minimized" and addresses furnishings and decorations (proposed paragraph 1910.37(a)(2)), travel toward a high hazard area (proposed paragraph 1910.37(a)(3)), unobstructed access to exit routes (proposed paragraph 1910.36(e)), and properly operating safeguards designed to protect employees (proposed paragraphs 1910.37(a) and 1910.37(e)).

Minor editorial changes have been made to these paragraphs, with the exception that final paragraph 1910.37(a)(2) has been modified because commenters found the requirement confusing (Exs. 5-5, 18, 26, 63). This confusion resulted from OSHA's use of the terminology "An exit route must not require employees to travel toward materials that burn very quickly, emit poisonous fumes, or are explosive." OSHA has modified the language to more closely reflect the current subpart E language: "Exit routes must be arranged so that employees will not have to travel toward a high hazard area, unless the path of travel is effectively shielded from the high hazard area by suitable partitions or other physical barriers." In addition, OSHA added a definition for "high hazard area" to the final rule's definition section, 1910.34. The new definition is from NFPA-101 with slight editorial changes.

In the proposal, paragraph 1910.37(b) required that exit route lighting be adequate, and paragraph 1910.37(c) required that exits be marked appropriately. OSHA has combined these paragraphs into paragraph 1910.37(b) in the final rule, in part because the provisions are closely related and the Agency believes that the standard will be easier to understand and use if all the requirements covering lighting and marking of exit routes are arranged together. The content of these paragraphs remains virtually the same in the final rule except for editorial clarifications (e.g., "lighted" instead of "illuminated") and the addition of specifications (issue 5 in the hearing notice at 62 FR 9403) for exit signs in response to comments (e.g., Exs. 5-4, 14, 18, 21, 43, 54). OSHA believes that these changes will enable employers and employees to have better and clearer information concerning the requirements for exit routes.

Issue 6 in the hearing notice (62 FR at 9403) asked whether the proposed requirements for exit lighting were too general. Some commenters objected to OSHA's use of the word "adequate" to describe the required amount of lighting in exit routes (Exs. 5-4, 18, 19, 22, 54, 57, 63, 64). (Issue 6 in the hearing notice at 62 FR 9403.) OSHA's current subpart E uses the term "adequate" (existing paragraph 1910.36(b)(6)); OSHA did not revise the word "adequate" in the proposal because specifying a level of lighting could be viewed as a substantive change. However, OSHA has clarified in the final rule (paragraph 1910.37(b)(1)), to make it clear and performance-oriented. The revised provision requires that employees with normal vision be able to see their way along an exit route.

Therefore, OSHA has retained the word "adequate" but clarified its meaning in the final rule. Employers and employees can refer to NFPA 101-2000 for more detailed guidance.

Final paragraph 1910.37(b)(4) (proposed paragraphs 1910.37(c)(3) and (c)(4)), addresses the marking of the direction of travel to an exit. Signs would be redundant where the direction of travel is apparent. Therefore, OSHA has added the existing subpart E language to the final rule "where the direction of travel to the nearest exit is not immediately apparent" because such signs are needed only in that situation (Exs. 5-4, 14, 21, 64).

Final paragraph 1910.37(b)(5) (proposed paragraph 1910.37(c)(5)), requires that doors that could be mistaken for exit doors must be marked to indicate the actual use of the door. In the proposal, OSHA required the use of the term "Not an Exit" on such doors. Doing so eliminated the provision's performance nature. In the final rule OSHA has added the language currently found in subpart E (paragraph 1910.37(q)(2)) ("Not an Exit" or similar designation"). This change allows employers to comply with the current OSHA language or the NFPA language. (E.g., Exs. 5-14, 36).

In final paragraph 1910.37(b)(6) (proposed paragraph 1910.37(c)(6)), OSHA has restored the language from subpart E referring to the color of exit signs. In the proposal OSHA stated "An exit sign must show a designated color." OSHA has changed the language back to the current subpart E language, "distinctive in color" (paragraph 1910.37(q)(4)) at the request of several commenters (Exs. 5-30, 41). OSHA does not believe that the proposed language improved the provision and has accordingly changed it back to existing subpart E as recommended by commenters. This paragraph also retains the use of "electroluminescent" and "self-luminous" signs and has defined the terms in the definition section (Sec. 1910.34).

Paragraph 1910.37(b)(7) of the final rule was not in the proposed rule. OSHA proposed to delete the following requirement from current subpart E (paragraph 1910.37(q)(8)) "Every exit sign shall have the word `Exit' in plainly legible letters not less than 6 inches high, with the principal strokes of letters not less than three-fourths-inch wide." The Agency believed that this requirement could be handled without specifications (issue 5 in the hearing notice at 62 FR 9403).

Commenters disagreed and suggested that the current exit sign dimensions also be included in the final rule. For example, Donald R. Delano, P.E., (Ex. 5-36, p. 3) remarked:

Deletion of reference to design parameters for exit signs leaves no adequate frame of reference. Exit signs need to be of a minimum size and design, just as a national standard exists for a highway STOP sign.

Further, Tenneco Newport News Shipbuilding (NNS, Ex. 5-41, p.2) stated:

The exit signs as dictated by the current standard have become traditional and easily recognized by the general public. An employer's interpretation of `clearly visible' may not create an easily recognized sign. Therefore, in an emergency the lack of the traditional and consistent format may be detrimental. NNS suggests that the text from the current standard stay in effect.

(See also Exs. 5-5, 14, 18, 31, 39, 63.) OSHA agrees with these commenters and has included in the final rule new paragraph 1910.37(b)(7) specifying the height and stroke width of exit signs (as it appears in the existing subpart E, paragraph 1910.37(q)(8)).

Final paragraph 1910.37(c) (proposed paragraph 1910.37(d)), addresses the upkeep of fire-retardant properties of paints or solutions used in the workplace that might impact the safety of an exit route. In the proposal, OSHA stated that an employer must maintain the fire retardant properties of paints or other coatings used in the workplace. Commenters suggested that OSHA return to the existing subpart E language because the proposed language is vague and harder to understand than the existing language (e.g., Exs. 5-4, 18, 21, 43, 54). OSHA believes the language in the final rule has been made clearer by returning to the subpart E language fire-retardant

paints or "solutions," rather than "coatings." OSHA has further clarified the requirement by specifying that paints or solutions used in an exit route must be renewed as often as necessary to maintain the necessary flame retardant properties.

Final paragraph 1910.37(d) (proposed paragraph 1910.37(f)) addresses the maintenance of exit routes during construction, repairs, or alterations. "Alterations" were not included in the heading of the proposed provision; however, in the final rule, the heading has been modified to include "alterations." Both the proposal and final rule include the word "alterations" in the regulatory text.

The first paragraph concerning new construction remains the same as proposed and is now paragraph 1910.37(d)(1). Minor editorial changes have been made to final paragraph 1910.37(d)(2) that address repairs and alterations. Final paragraph 1910.37(d)(3) concerning flammable and explosive substances or equipment used during construction, repairs, or alterations, remains the same as proposed except for some minor changes. As discussed above OSHA has added the word "alterations" to the proposed language. In addition, the Agency returned to the use of "substances" instead of "materials." Finally, OSHA has added "equipment" to the paragraph. The words "substances" and "equipment" are in the present subpart E requirement (paragraph 1910.37(c)(3)) but were inadvertently left out of the proposal. OSHA has changed the proposed language "flammable or explosive materials used during construction or repair must not expose employees to hazards * * *" to "Employees must not be exposed to hazards of flammable or explosive substances or equipment used during construction, repairs, or alterations, that are beyond the normal permissible conditions in the workplace * * *."

Final rule paragraph 1910.37(e) (proposed paragraph 1910.37(g)), requires the installation and maintenance of an employee alarm system meeting Sec. 1910.165, unless employees can promptly see or smell a fire or other hazard. This requirement remains unchanged from the proposed rule.

Section 1910.38, Emergency Action Plans, and Section 1910.39, Fire Prevention Plans

In the final rule, OSHA has retained the separate sections for emergency action plans and fire prevention plans, Sec. Sec. 1910.38 and 1910.39 respectively. OSHA believes it is clearer for the plans and their requirements to be contained in separate sections. Because commenters tended to address both plans at the same time in their comments or their comments were quite similar about the plans, OSHA is discussing them together.

Final paragraph 1910.38(a) states that an emergency action plan is required, and final paragraph 1910.39(a) states that a fire prevention plan is required, when an OSHA standard requires such a plan. A number of commenters (Exs. 5-14, 20, 21, 23, 40, 49) recommended that OSHA include a listing of all OSHA standards that require an emergency action plan or a fire prevention plan. The Agency considered modifying the appendix to add a list of such standards. Instead, OSHA has issued a Compliance Directive that contains a list of current OSHA standards that require emergency action plans or fire prevention plans. The Agency has included this information in a Compliance Directive instead of an appendix to the standard because it is easier to amend the Compliance Directive as needed to keep it current.

For informational purposes, OSHA has identified the following general industry standards that require an emergency action plan or a fire prevention plan.

1. Process Safety Management of Highly Hazardous Chemicals, paragraph 1910.119(n), emergency action plan.
2. Hazardous Waste Operations and Emergency Response, paragraphs 1910.120(l)(1)(ii), (p)(8)(i), (q)(1), and (q)(11)(ii), emergency action plan.
3. Portable Fire Extinguishers, paragraphs 1910.157(a) and (b)(1), emergency action plan and fire prevention plan.
4. Grain Handling Facilities, paragraph 1910.272(d), emergency action plan.
5. Ethylene Oxide, paragraph 1910.1047(h)(1)(iii), emergency action plan and fire prevention plan.
6. Methylenedianiline, paragraph 1910.1050 (d)(1)(iii), emergency action plan and fire prevention plan.
7. 1,3-Butadiene, paragraph 1910.1051(j), emergency action plan and fire prevention plan.

Final paragraph 1910.38(b) and paragraph 1910.39(b) address written emergency action plans and fire prevention plans respectively. They require that the plans must be in writing and available; and for employers with 10 or fewer employees the plan may be transmitted orally rather than in writing. In the final rule, proposed paragraphs 1910.38(a)(2) and (a)(3) are combined into one paragraph, 1910.38(b), and proposed paragraphs 1910.39(a)(2) and (a)(3) become final paragraph 1910.39(b). Combining these paragraphs involved some minor editorial changes.

The Department of Energy (Ex. 5-11, p. 2) suggested that plans should be communicated orally to a "limited number" of employees rather than the 10 or fewer required by OSHA because the intent would be better served by not using an arbitrary number. OSHA disagrees with this suggestion. Since their promulgation in 1980, the emergency action plan and the fire prevention plan have used 10 as a reasonable number of employees for a plan to be communicated orally.

The International Brotherhood of Teamsters (IBT) (Ex. 5-31, p. 6) did not agree with the language in proposed paragraph 1910.38(a)(2) and paragraph 1910.39(a)(2), which stated that "the plan must be made available to employees on request." IBT asked the Agency to use the current language of subpart E, requiring the plans "be available for employees to review." The IBT believed the proposed language added an obstacle to employees by making them request to see the plan. OSHA agrees; in the proposal it had inadvertently changed the language from the current subpart E. OSHA fully believes that the plan should be available for employee review and in the final rule the language reflects this intent.

OSHA has reordered final paragraph 1910.38(c), containing the elements of an emergency action plan, to better reflect the order of an emergency response. Final paragraph 1910.38(c)(1) (proposed paragraph 1910.38(b)(3)) requires that the plan include procedures for reporting a fire or other emergency. OSHA believes reporting a fire or other emergency should be the first thing done in an emergency. The rest of the elements remain in the same order.

Final paragraphs 1910.38(c)(2), (3), and (4) remain for the most part the same as the proposed paragraphs—procedures for evacuation and exit route assignments, procedures to be followed by employees who remain to operate critical plant operations before they evacuate, and procedures to account for all employees after evacuation.

Final paragraph 1910.38(c)(3) concerning emergency operations or shutdown of plant equipment during an emergency has been changed back to the current subpart E language. This was done to clarify that this element of the plan does not apply to all employees and all plants, only to those plants that use employees for these emergency or shutdown procedures (Exs. 5-4, 18, 54).

Eastman Kodak Company (Ex. 5-21, p.3) suggested that OSHA delete the wording that addresses accounting for employees (final paragraph 1910.38(c)(4)):

[sbull] Procedures to assure that the fire area is clear of employees, visitors and contractors. Expectations to track employees such as maintenance personnel, service providers, or engineers is very burdensome. In today's work environment many transient employees work in multiple locations making it difficult to track who will be in any work area in an emergency. Hence, many emergency plans require the use of trained searchers to assure that the area being evacuated is clear of all personnel regardless of their normal work locations.

OSHA disagrees with this commenter and believes that accounting for employees after an emergency is critically important information to rescuers. Employees could, for example, be assigned designated locations away from the facility at which to meet.

In final paragraph 1910.38(c)(5), which requires that the plan include procedures for rescue or medical duties, OSHA has added language to clarify that the requirements only apply to those employees who will be performing such duties. This language parallels more closely the current subpart E language (paragraph 1910.38(a)(2)(iv)). The Agency has also changed "rescue and medical duties" in the proposal to "rescue or medical duties" (emphasis added) since employees may do one or the other but not necessarily both.

Final paragraph 1910.38(c)(6), which addresses names or job titles of employees to be contacted for more information or for an explanation of duties, has been revised from the proposal and is closer to the current language in subpart E (paragraph 1910.38(a)(2)(vi)). The change clarifies the requirement.

A few commenters (e.g., Ex. 5-4) contended that proposed paragraphs 1910.38(d) and 1910.37(g), are redundant. However, while both paragraphs require alarm systems, the two provisions are different. Proposed paragraph 1910.37(g) (paragraph 1910.37(e) in the final rule) requires that an employee alarm system be installed and maintained, unless employees can promptly see or smell a fire or other hazard. It applies regardless of whether the employer must have an emergency action plan. Paragraph 1910.38(d) requires that employers have and maintain an alarm system when an employer is required to have an emergency action plan by another OSHA standard. That alarm system must be provided even if employees can promptly see or smell a fire or other hazard. These paragraphs remain the same as proposed in the final rule.

Final paragraph 1910.38(e), regarding training of designated employees to assist in a safe and orderly evacuation of other employees, remains as proposed except for minor reorganization.

Final paragraph 1910.38(f) (proposed paragraph 1910.38(e)) requires that employers review the emergency action plan with each employee when the plan is developed or the employee is assigned initially to a job, when responsibility under the plan changes or the plan changes. Only minor editorial changes have been made to the final provision.

With regard to 29 CFR 1910.39, fire prevention plans, final paragraph 1910.39(c) (proposed paragraph 1910.39(b)) remains the same as proposed. Few comments were received with respect to the elements of the fire prevention plan.

Final rule paragraph 1910.39(d) (proposed rule paragraph 1910.39(c)) requires employers to inform employees of workplace fire hazards and review those parts of the fire prevention plan necessary for the employee's self-protection. Only minor editorial changes were made to this paragraph.

Miscellaneous Changes

OSHA is also amending the sections listed in the preamble's discussion of 1910.38 and 1910.39 above (e.g., 29 CFR 1910.120, 1910.157, etc.). These changes are necessary to conform with new section and paragraph designations for Emergency Action Plans and Fire Protection Plans found in this revised subpart E.

Other Hearing Issues

As discussed earlier in this preamble, OSHA asked a series of questions in its hearing notice (62 FR 9402). To the extent possible, OSHA has included the questions with the pertinent discussions in the preamble. For example, the use of performance-oriented language in the proposal was discussed earlier in this preamble (issue 3). "Are terms too technical" (issue 7) was discussed by commenters addressing the definitions of the standard or when commenters identified unclear language. However, some of the issues raised in the questions were more general and the vast majority of commenters did not definitively respond to these questions. These issues were numbered 3, 7, 8, 9, and 10 in the hearing notice (62 FR at 9403), and they asked: Would performance-oriented standards create compliance problems; are there terms that might be too technical; whether the revision imposes additional obligations; whether any requirements result in greater safety; and whether any requirements present technical feasibility problems. The questions raised in the hearing notice were intended to assure that various aspects of the proposal were fully considered. Some commenters addressed the issues through their comments regarding specific provisions of the proposal and did not respond to the questions specifically set forth in the hearing notice. To the extent that interested persons commented on these issues, OSHA has responded to these comments in the context of specific provisions of the proposed rule.

III. Legal Considerations

Because the final rule is only a plain language redrafting of a former Agency subpart, it is not necessary to determine significant risk or the extent to which the final rule reduces that risk. As noted above, most of the provisions of subpart E were adopted under section 6(a) of the Occupational Safety and Health Act, which gave the Secretary of Labor the authority, for a limited period of time, to adopt as occupational safety and health standards any established Federal Standard or national consensus standards unless the promulgation of such a standard would not result in improved safety and health for designated employees. By including section 6(a) in the OSH Act, Congress implicitly found that the promulgation of occupational safety and health standards was reasonably necessary or appropriate to provide safe or healthful employment and places of employment. In Industrial Union Department, AFL-CIO v. American Petroleum Institute, 448 U.S. 607 (1980), the Supreme Court ruled that before OSHA can increase the protection afforded by a standard, the Agency must find that the hazard being regulated poses a significant risk to employees and that a new, more protective standard is "reasonably necessary and appropriate" to reduce that risk. The final rule that replaces the Agency's former rules regulating means of egress, emergency action plans, and fire prevention plans does not directly increase or decrease the protection afforded to employees, nor does it increase employers' compliance obligations. Therefore, no finding of significant risk is necessary.

The Agency believes, however, that improved employee protection is likely to result from promulgation of the final rule because employers and employees who clearly understand a rule's requirements are more likely to comply with that rule. In addition, employers may find it easier to comply with the final rule because the final rule is more performance-oriented than the former rule.

IV. Economic Analysis

This final rule has been designated as significant and reviewed by the Office of Management and Budget under Executive Order 12866. It is not an economically significant rule under Executive Order 12866 or a major rule under the Unfunded Mandates Reform Act or section 801 of the Small Business Regulatory

Enforcement Fairness Act (SBREFA). The final rule imposes no additional costs on any private or public sector entity and does not meet any of the criteria for an economically significant or major rule specified by the Executive Order or the other statutes.

Certain provisions of the rule that add flexibility, such as permitting fire doors to remain open as long as they close automatically during an emergency and modifying the definition of exit route to reflect the acceptability of refuge areas, may even reduce costs for employers. Because the rule does not impose any additional costs on employers for exit routes, emergency action plans, and fire prevention plans, no economic or regulatory flexibility analysis of the final rule is required.

V. Regulatory Flexibility Certification

In accord with the Regulatory Flexibility act, 5 U.S.C. 601 et seq. (as amended), OSHA has examined the regulatory requirements of the final rule to determine if it will have a significant economic effect on a substantial number of small entities. As indicated in the previous section of this preamble, the final rule does not increase employers' compliance costs, and may even reduce the regulatory burden on all affected employers, both large and small. Accordingly, the Agency certifies that the final rule does not have a significant economic effect on a substantial number of small entities.

VI. Environmental Impact Assessment

OSHA has reviewed the final rule in accordance with the requirements of the National Environmental Policy Act (NEPA) of 1969 (42 U.S.C. 4321 et seq.), of the Council on Environmental Quality regulations (40 U.S.C. part 1500 et seq.), and the Department of Labor's NEPA regulations (29 CFR part 11). As noted earlier in this preamble, the final rule imposes the same requirements on employers as the standards it replaces. Consequently, the final rule has no additional impact beyond the impact imposed by OSHA's former standards for means of egress on the environment, including no impact on the release of materials that contaminate natural resources or the environment.

VII. Paperwork Reduction Act

The final rule contains no information collection requirements (paperwork) that are subject to the Paperwork Reduction Act. Therefore, approval under the Paperwork Reduction Act is unnecessary.

VIII. Unfunded Mandates

For the purposes of the Unfunded Mandates Reform Act of 1995, this rule does not include any Federal mandate that may result in increased expenditures by State, local, and tribal governments, or increased expenditures by the private sector of more than $100 million in any year.

IX. Federalism

OSHA has reviewed this final rule in accordance with the Executive Order on Federalism (Executive Order 13132, 64 FR 43255) which requires that agencies, to the extent possible, refrain from limiting state policy options, consult with states prior to taking any actions that would restrict state policy options, and take such actions only when there is clear constitutional authority and the presence of a problem of national scope. The Order provides for preemption of State law only if there is a clear Congressional intent for the Agency to do so. Any such preemption is to be limited to the extent possible.

Section 18 of the Occupational Safety and Health (OSH) Act (29 U.S.C. 651 et seq.) expresses Congress' intent to preempt state laws where OSHA has promulgated occupational safety and health standards. Under the OSH Act, a state can avoid preemption on issues covered by Federal standards only if it submits, and obtains Federal approval of, a plan for the development of such standards and their enforcement (State-Plan state). 29 U.S.C. 667. Occupational safety and health standards developed by such State-Plan states must, among other things, be at least as effective in providing safe and healthful employment and places of employment as the Federal standards.

Subject to these requirements, State-Plan states are free to develop and enforce their own requirements for exit routes, emergency action plans, and fire prevention plans. Having already adopted OSHA's former standards on means of egress, emergency action plans, and fire prevention plans, (or having developed alternative standards acceptable to OSHA), State-Plan states are not obligated to adopt the final rule; they may, however, choose to adopt the final rule, and OSHA encourages them to do so.

Although Congress has expressed a clear intent for OSHA standards to preempt State job safety and health rules in areas involving the safety and health rules of employees, this rule nevertheless limits State policy options to a minimal extent.

OSHA concludes that this action does not significantly limit State policy options.

X. State Plan States

OSHA encourages the 26 States and Territories with their own OSHA-approved occupational safety and health plans to revise their standards regulating means of egress, emergency action plans, and fire prevention plans according to the final rule that resulted from this rulemaking.

These states include Alaska, Arizona, California, Connecticut (state and local government employees only), Hawaii, Indiana, Iowa, Kentucky, Maryland, Michigan, Minnesota, Nevada, New Jersey (state and local government employees only), New Mexico, New York (state and local government employees only), North Carolina, Oregon, Puerto Rico, South Carolina, Tennessee, Utah, Vermont, Virginia, Virgin Islands, Washington, and Wyoming.

XI. Authority and Signature

This document was prepared under the direction of John L. Henshaw, Assistant Secretary of Labor for Occupational Safety and Health, U.S. Department of Labor, 200 Constitution Avenue, NW., Washington, DC 20210.

Signed in Washington, DC, this 21st day of October, 2002.
John L. Henshaw,
Assistant Secretary of Labor.
OSHA amends 29 CFR part 1910 as follows:

Part 1910—Occupational Safety and Health Standards
Subpart E—Exit Routes, Emergency Action Plans, and Fire Prevention Plans

Sec. 1910.33 Table of contents.
This section lists the sections and paragraph headings contained in Sec. Sec. 1910.34 through 1910.39.

Sec. 1910.34 Coverage and definitions.
(a) Every employer is covered.
(b) Exit routes are covered.
(c) Definitions.

Sec. 1910.35 Compliance with NFPA 101-2000, Life Safety Code.

Sec. 1910.36 Design and construction requirements for exit routes.
(a) Basic requirements.
(b) The number of exit routes must be adequate.
(c) Exit discharge.
(d) An exit door must be unlocked.
(e) A side-hinged exit door must be used.
(f) The capacity of an exit route must be adequate.
(g) An exit route must meet minimum height and width requirements.
(h) An outdoor exit route is permitted.

Sec. 1910.37 Maintenance, safeguards, and operational features for exit routes.
(a) The danger to employees must be minimized.
(b) Lighting and marking must be adequate and appropriate.
(c) The fire retardant properties of paints or solutions must be maintained.
(d) Exit routes must be maintained during construction, repairs, or alterations.
(e) An employee alarm system must be operable.

Sec. 1910.38 Emergency action plans.
(a) Application.
(b) Written and oral emergency action plans.

(c) Minimum elements of an emergency action plan.
(d) Employee alarm system.
(e) Training.
(f) Review of emergency action plan.

Sec. 1910.39 Fire prevention plans.
(a) Application.
(b) Written and oral fire prevention plans.
(c) Minimum elements of a fire prevention plan.
(d) Employee information.

Sec. 1910.34 Coverage and definitions.

(a) Every employer is covered. Sections 1910.34 through 1910.39 apply to workplaces in general industry except mobile workplaces such as vehicles or vessels.
(b) Exits routes are covered. The rules in Sec. Sec. 1910.34 through 1910.39 cover the minimum requirements for exit routes that employers must provide in their workplace so that employees may evacuate the workplace safely during an emergency. Sections 1910.34 through 1910.39 also cover the minimum requirements for emergency action plans and fire prevention plans.
(c) Definitions.

Electroluminescent means a light-emitting capacitor. Alternating current excites phosphor atoms when placed between the electrically conductive surfaces to produce light. This light source is typically contained inside the device.

Exit means that portion of an exit route that is generally separated from other areas to provide a protected way of travel to the exit discharge. An example of an exit is a two-hour fire resistance-rated enclosed stairway that leads from the fifth floor of an office building to the outside of the building.

Exit access means that portion of an exit route that leads to an exit. An example of an exit access is a corridor on the fifth floor of an office building that leads to a two-hour fire resistance-rated enclosed stairway (the Exit).

Exit discharge means the part of the exit route that leads directly outside or to a street, walkway, refuge area, public way, or open space with access to the outside. An example of an exit discharge is a door at the bottom of a two-hour fire resistance-rated enclosed stairway that discharges to a place of safety outside the building.

Exit route means a continuous and unobstructed path of exit travel from any point within a workplace to a place of safety (including refuge areas). An exit route consists of three parts: The exit access; the exit; and, the exit discharge. (An exit route includes all vertical and horizontal areas along the route.)

High hazard area means an area inside a workplace in which operations include high hazard materials, processes, or contents.

Occupant load means the total number of persons that may occupy a workplace or portion of a workplace at any one time. The occupant load of a workplace is calculated by dividing the gross floor area of the workplace or portion of a workplace by the occupant load factor for that particular type of workplace occupancy. Information regarding "Occupant load" is located in NFPA 101-2000, Life Safety Code.

Refuge area means either:
(1) A space along an exit route that is protected from the effects of fire by separation from other spaces within the building by a barrier with at least a one-hour fire resistance-rating; or
(2) A floor with at least two spaces, separated from each other by smoke-resistant partitions, in a building protected throughout by an automatic sprinkler system that complies with Sec. 1910.159 of this part.

Self-luminous means a light source that is illuminated by a self-contained power source (e.g., tritium) and that operates independently from external power sources. Batteries are not acceptable self-contained power sources. The light source is typically contained inside the device.

Sec. 1910.35 Compliance with NFPA 101-2000, Life Safety Code.

An employer who demonstrates compliance with the exit route provisions of NFPA 101-2000, the Life Safety Code, will be deemed to be in compliance with the corresponding requirements in Sec. Sec. 1910.34, 1910.36, and 1910.37.

Sec. 1910.36 Design and construction requirements for exit routes.

(a) **Basic requirements.** Exit routes must meet the following design and construction requirements:

(1) An exit route must be permanent. Each exit route must be a permanent part of the workplace.

(2) An exit must be separated by fire resistant materials. Construction materials used to separate an exit from other parts of the workplace must have a one-hour fire resistance-rating if the exit connects three or fewer stories and a two-hour fire resistance-rating if the exit connects four or more stories.

(3) Openings into an exit must be limited. An exit is permitted to have only those openings necessary to allow access to the exit from occupied areas of the workplace, or to the exit discharge. An opening into an exit must be protected by a self-closing fire door that remains closed or automatically closes in an emergency upon the sounding of a fire alarm or employee alarm system. Each fire door, including its frame and hardware, must be listed or approved by a nationally recognized testing laboratory. Section 1910.155(c)(3)(iv)(A) of this part defines "listed" and Sec. 1910.7 of this part defines a "nationally recognized testing laboratory."

(b) The number of exit routes must be adequate.

(1) **Two exit routes.** At least two exit routes must be available in a workplace to permit prompt evacuation of employees and other building occupants during an emergency, except as allowed in paragraph (b)(3) of this section. The exit routes must be located as far away as practical from each other so that if one exit route is blocked by fire or smoke, employees can evacuate using the second exit route.

(2) **More than two exit routes.** More than two exit routes must be available in a workplace if the number of employees, the size of the building, its occupancy, or the arrangement of the workplace is such that all employees would not be able to evacuate safely during an emergency.

(3) **A single exit route.** A single exit route is permitted where the number of employees, the size of the building, its occupancy, or the arrangement of the workplace is such that all employees would be able to evacuate safely during an emergency.

Note to paragraph 1910.36(b): For assistance in determining the number of exit routes necessary for your workplace, consult NFPA 101-2000, Life Safety Code.

(c) Exit discharge.

(1) Each exit discharge must lead directly outside or to a street, walkway, refuge area, public way, or open space with access to the outside.

(2) The street, walkway, refuge area, public way, or open space to which an exit discharge leads must be large enough to accommodate the building occupants likely to use the exit route.

(3) Exit stairs that continue beyond the level on which the exit discharge is located must be interrupted at that level by doors, partitions, or other effective means that clearly indicate the direction of travel leading to the exit discharge.

(d) An exit door must be unlocked.

(1) Employees must be able to open an exit route door from the inside at all times without keys, tools, or special knowledge. A device such as a panic bar that locks only from the outside is permitted on exit discharge doors.

(2) Exit route doors must be free of any device or alarm that could restrict emergency use of the exit route if the device or alarm fails.

(3) An exit route door may be locked from the inside only in mental, penal, or correctional facilities and then only if supervisory personnel are continuously on duty and the employer has a plan to remove occupants from the facility during an emergency.

(e) A side-hinged exit door must be used.

(1) A side-hinged door must be used to connect any room to an exit route.

(2) The door that connects any room to an exit route must swing out in the direc-

tion of exit travel if the room is designed to be occupied by more than 50 people or if the room is a high hazard area (i.e., contains contents that are likely to burn with extreme rapidity or explode).

(f) The capacity of an exit route must be adequate.

  (1) Exit routes must support the maximum permitted occupant load for each floor served.

  (2) The capacity of an exit route may not decrease in the direction of exit route travel to the exit discharge.

Note to paragraph 1910.36(f): Information regarding "Occupant load" is located in NFPA 101-2000, Life Safety Code.

(g) An exit route must meet minimum height and width requirements.

  (1) The ceiling of an exit route must be at least seven feet six inches (2.3 m) high. Any projection from the ceiling must not reach a point less than six feet eight inches (2.0 m) from the floor.

  (2) An exit access must be at least 28 inches (71.1 cm) wide at all points. Where there is only one exit access leading to an exit or exit discharge, the width of the exit and exit discharge must be at least equal to the width of the exit access.

  (3) The width of an exit route must be sufficient to accommodate the maximum permitted occupant load of each floor served by the exit route.

  (4) Objects that project into the exit route must not reduce the width of the exit route to less than the minimum width requirements for exit routes.

(h) An outdoor exit route is permitted. Each outdoor exit route must meet the minimum height and width requirements for indoor exit routes and must also meet the following requirements:

  (1) The outdoor exit route must have guardrails to protect unenclosed sides if a fall hazard exists;

  (2) The outdoor exit route must be covered if snow or ice is likely to accumulate along the route, unless the employer can demonstrate that any snow or ice accumula-

tion will be removed before it presents a slipping hazard;

  (3) The outdoor exit route must be reasonably straight and have smooth, solid, substantially level walkways; and

  (4) The outdoor exit route must not have a dead-end that is longer than 20 feet (6.2 m).

Sec. 1910.37 Maintenance, safeguards, and operational features for exit routes.

(a) The danger to employees must be minimized.

  (1) Exit routes must be kept free of explosive or highly flammable furnishings or other decorations.

  (2) Exit routes must be arranged so that employees will not have to travel toward a high hazard area, unless the path of travel is effectively shielded from the high hazard area by suitable partitions or other physical barriers.

  (3) Exit routes must be free and unobstructed. No materials or equipment may be placed, either permanently or temporarily, within the exit route. The exit access must not go through a room that can be locked, such as a bathroom, to reach an exit or exit discharge, nor may it lead into a dead-end corridor. Stairs or a ramp must be provided where the exit route is not substantially level.

  (4) Safeguards designed to protect employees during an emergency (e.g., sprinkler systems, alarm systems, fire doors, exit lighting) must be in proper working order at all times.

(b) Lighting and marking must be adequate and appropriate.

  (1) Each exit route must be adequately lighted so that an employee with normal vision can see along the exit route.

  (2) Each exit must be clearly visible and marked by a sign reading "Exit."

  (3) Each exit route door must be free of decorations or signs that obscure the visibility of the exit route door.

  (4) If the direction of travel to the exit or exit discharge is not immediately apparent, signs must be posted along the exit ac-

cess indicating the direction of travel to the nearest exit and exit discharge. Additionally, the line-of-sight to an exit sign must clearly be visible at all times.

(5) Each doorway or passage along an exit access that could be mistaken for an exit must be marked "Not an Exit" or similar designation, or be identified by a sign indicating its actual use (e.g., closet).

(6) Each exit sign must be illuminated to a surface value of at least five foot-candles (54 lux) by a reliable light source and be distinctive in color. Self-luminous or electroluminescent signs that have a minimum luminance surface value of at least .06 footlamberts (0.21 cd/m2) are permitted.

(7) Each exit sign must have the word "Exit" in plainly legible letters not less than six inches (15.2 cm) high, with the principal strokes of the letters in the word "Exit" not less than three-fourths of an inch (1.9 cm) wide.

(c) The fire retardant properties of paints or solutions must be maintained. Fire retardant paints or solutions must be renewed as often as necessary to maintain their fire retardant properties.

(d) Exit routes must be maintained during construction, repairs, or alterations.

(1) During new construction, employees must not occupy a workplace until the exit routes required by this subpart are completed and ready for employee use for the portion of the workplace they occupy.

(2) During repairs or alterations, employees must not occupy a workplace unless the exit routes required by this subpart are available and existing fire protections are maintained, or until alternate fire protection is furnished that provides an equivalent level of safety.

(3) Employees must not be exposed to hazards of flammable or explosive substances or equipment used during construction, repairs, or alterations, that are beyond the normal permissible conditions in the workplace, or that would impede exiting the workplace.

(e) An employee alarm system must be operable. Employers must install and maintain an operable employee alarm system that has a distinctive signal to warn employees of fire or other emergencies, unless employees can promptly see or smell a fire or other hazard in time to provide adequate warning to them. The employee alarm system must comply with Sec. 1910.165.

Sec. 1910.38 Emergency action plans.

(a) **Application.** An employer must have an emergency action plan whenever an OSHA standard in this part requires one. The requirements in this section apply to each such emergency action plan.

(b) **Written and oral emergency action plans.** An emergency action plan must be in writing, kept in the workplace, and available to employees for review. However, an employer with 10 or fewer employees may communicate the plan orally to employees.

(c) **Minimum elements of an emergency action plan.** An emergency action plan must include at a minimum:

(1) Procedures for reporting a fire or other emergency;

(2) Procedures for emergency evacuation, including type of evacuation and exit route assignments;

(3) Procedures to be followed by employees who remain to operate critical plant operations before they evacuate;

(4) Procedures to account for all employees after evacuation;

(5) Procedures to be followed by employees performing rescue or medical duties; and

(6) The name or job title of every employee who may be contacted by employees who need more information about the plan or an explanation of their duties under the plan.

(d) **Employee alarm system.** An employer must have and maintain an employee alarm system. The employee alarm system must use a distinctive signal for each purpose and comply with the requirements in Sec. 1910.165.

(e) **Training.** An employer must designate and train employees to assist in a safe and orderly evacuation of other employees.

(f) **Review of emergency action plan.** An employer must review the emergency action plan with each employee covered by the plan:

(1) When the plan is developed or the employee is assigned initially to a job;

(2) When the employee's responsibilities under the plan change; and

(3) When the plan is changed.

Sec. 1910.39 Fire prevention plans.

(a) **Application.** An employer must have a fire prevention plan when an OSHA standard in this part requires one. The requirements in this section apply to each such fire prevention plan.

(b) **Written and oral fire prevention plans.** A fire prevention plan must be in writing, be kept in the workplace, and be made available to employees for review. However, an employer with 10 or fewer employees may communicate the plan orally to employees.

(c) **Minimum elements of a fire prevention plan.** A fire prevention plan must include:

(1) A list of all major fire hazards, proper handling and storage procedures for hazardous materials, potential ignition sources and their control, and the type of fire protection equipment necessary to control each major hazard;

(2) Procedures to control accumulations of flammable and combustible waste materials;

(3) Procedures for regular maintenance of safeguards installed on heat-producing equipment to prevent the accidental ignition of combustible materials;

(4) The name or job title of employees responsible for maintaining equipment to prevent or control sources of ignition or fires; and

(5) The name or job title of employees responsible for the control of fuel source hazards.

(d) **Employee information.** An employer must inform employees upon initial assignment to a job of the fire hazards to which they are exposed. An employer must also review with each employee those parts of the fire prevention plan necessary for self-protection.

"Appendix E To Part 1910—Exit Routes, Emergency Action Plans, and Fire Prevention Plans."

* * * * *

Subpart H—Hazardous Materials

3. The authority citation for subpart H of part 1910 is revised to read as follows:

Sections 1910.103, 1910.106 through 1910.111, and 1910.119, 1910.120, and 190.122 through 126 also issued under 29 CFR part 1911.

Section 1910.119 also issued under section 304, Clean Air Act Amendments of 1990 (Pub. L. 101-549), reprinted at 29 U.S.C. 655 Note.

Section 1910.120 also issued under section 126, Superfund Amendments and Reauthorization Act of 1986 as amended (29 U.S.C. 655 Note), and 5 U.S.C. 553.

4. In Sec. 1910.119, the first sentence of paragraph (n) is revised to read as follows:

Sec. 1910.119 Process safety management of highly hazardous chemicals.

(n) Emergency planning and response. The employer shall establish and implement an emergency action plan for the entire plant in accordance with the provisions of 29 CFR 1910.38.* * * * * * *

5. In Sec. 1910.120, paragraphs (l)(1)(ii), (p)(8)(i), (q)(1), and the first sentence of paragraph (q)(11)(ii) are revised to read as follows:

Sec. 1910.120 Hazardous waste operations and emergency response.

(l) * * *

(1)(i) * * *

(ii) Employers who will evacuate their employees from the danger area when an emergency occurs, and who do not permit any of their employees to assist in handling the emergency, are exempt from the requirements of this paragraph if they provide an emergency action plan complying with 29 CFR 1910.38. * * * * * * *

(p) * * *

(8) * * *

(i) Emergency response plan. An emergency response plan shall be developed and implemented by all employers. Such plans need not duplicate any of the subjects fully addressed in the employer's contingency planning required by permits, such as those issued by the U.S. Environmental Protection Agency, provided that the contingency plan is made part of the emergency response plan. The emergency response plan shall be a written portion of the employer's safety and health program required in paragraph (p)(1) of this section. Employers who will evacuate their employees from the worksite location when an emergency occurs and who do not permit any of their employees to assist in handling the emergency are exempt from the requirements of paragraph (p)(8) if they provide an emergency action plan complying with 29 CFR 1910.38.* * * * *

(q) * * *

(1) **Emergency response plan.** An emergency response plan shall be developed and implemented to handle anticipated emergencies prior to the commencement of emergency response operations. The plan shall be in writing and available for inspection and copying by employees, their representatives and OSHA personnel. Employers who will evacuate their employees from the danger area when an emergency occurs, and who do not permit any of their employees to assist in handling the emergency, are exempt from the requirements of this paragraph if they provide an emergency action plan in accordance with 29 CFR 1910.38.* * * * *

(11) * * *

(i) * * *

(ii) Where the clean-up is done on plant property using plant or workplace employees, such employees shall have completed the training requirements of the following: 29 CFR 1910.38, 1910.134, 1910.1200, and other appropriate safety and health training made necessary by the tasks they are expected to perform such as personal protective equipment and decontamination procedures. * * * * * * * *

Subpart L—Fire Protection

6. The authority citation for subpart L of part 1910 is revised to read as follows:

7. In Sec. 1910.157, paragraphs (a) and (b)(1) are revised to read as follows:

Sec. 1910.157 Portable fire extinguishers.

(a) **Scope and application.** The requirements of this section apply to the placement, use, maintenance, and testing of portable fire extinguishers provided for the use of employees. Paragraph (d) of this section does not apply to extinguishers provided for employee use on the outside of workplace buildings or structures. Where extinguishers are provided but are not intended for employee use and the employer has an emergency action plan and a fire prevention plan that meet the requirements of 29 CFR 1910.38 and 29 CFR 1910.39 respectively, then only the requirements of paragraphs (e) and (f) of this section apply.

(b) **Exemptions.** (1) Where the employer has established and implemented a written fire safety policy which requires the immediate and total evacuation of employees from the workplace upon the sounding of a fire alarm signal and which includes an emergency action plan and a fire prevention plan which meet the requirements of 29 CFR 1910.38 and 29 CFR 1910.39 respectively, and when extinguishers are not available in the workplace, the employer is exempt from all requirements of this section unless a specific standard in part 1910 requires that a portable fire extinguisher be provided. * * * *

Subpart R—Special Industries

8. The authority citation for subpart R of part 1910 is revised to read as follows:

9. In Sec. 1910.268, paragraph (b)(1)(iii) is revised to read as follows:

Sec. 1910.268 Telecommunications.

(b) * * *

(1) * * *

(i) * * *

(ii) * * *

(iii) **Working spaces.** Maintenance aisles, or wiring aisles, between equipment frame

lineups are working spaces and are not an exit route for purposes of 29 CFR 1910.34.*
* * * *

10.a. In Sec. 1910.272, paragraph (d) is revised.

b. In Appendix A to Sec. 1910.272, under the heading "2. Emergency Action Plans" the second sentence is revised. The revised text is set forth as follows:

Sec. 1910.272 Grain handling facilities.

(d) Emergency action plan. The employer shall develop and implement an emergency action plan meeting the requirements contained in 29 CFR 1910.38.

* * * * *

Appendix A to Sec. 1910.272
Grain Handling Facilities

2. Emergency Action Plan

* * * The emergency action plan (Sec. 1910.38) covers those designated actions employers and employees are to take to ensure employee safety from fire and other emergencies. * * *
* * * * *

Subpart Z—Toxic and Hazardous Substances

11. The authority citation for subpart Z of part 1910 is revised to read as follows:

All of subpart Z issued under section 6(b) of the Occupational Safety and Health Act of 1970 (29 U.S.C 653), except those substances that have exposure limits in Tables Z-1, Z-2, and Z-3 of 29 CFR 1910.1000. Section 1910.1000 also issued under section (6)(a) of the Act (29 U.S.C. 655(a)). Section 1910.1000, Tables Z-1, Z-2, and Z-3 also issued under 5 U.S.C. 553, but not under 29 CFR part 1911, except for the inorganic arsenic, benzene, and cotton dust listings.

Section 1910.1001 also issued under section 107 of the Contract Work Hours and Safety Standards Act (40 U.S.C. 333) and 5 U.S.C. 553.

Section 1910.1002 also issued under 5 U.S.C. 553, but not under 29 U.S.C. 655 or 29 CFR part 1911. Sections 1910.1018, 1910.1029, and 1910.1200 also issued under 29 U.S.C. 653.

12. In Sec. 1910.1047, paragraph (h)(1)(iii) is revised to read as follows:

Sec. 1910.1047 Ethylene oxide.

(h) * * *

(1) * * *

(i) * * *

(ii) * * *

(iii) The plan shall include the elements prescribed in 29 CFR 1910.38 and 29 CFR 1910.39, "Emergency action plans" and "Fire prevention plans," respectively. * * * * *

13. In Sec. 1910.1050, paragraph (d)(1)(iii) is revised to read as follows:

Sec. 1910.1050 Methylenedianiline

(d) * * *

(1) * * *

(i) * * *

(ii) * * *

(iii) The plan shall specifically include provisions for alerting and evacuating affected employees as well as the elements prescribed in 29 CFR 1910.38 and 29 CFR 1910.39, "Emergency action plans" and "Fire prevention plans," respectively. * * * * *

14. In Sec. 1910.1051, paragraph (j) is revised to read as follows:

Sec. 1910.1051 1,3-Butadiene

(j) **Emergency situations.** Written plan. A written plan for emergency situations shall be developed, or an existing plan shall be modified, to contain the applicable elements specified in 29 CFR 1910.38 and 29 CFR 1910.39, "Emergency action plans" and "Fire prevention plans," respectively, and in 29 CFR 1910.120, "Hazardous Waste Operations and Emergency Response," for each workplace where there is the possibility of an emergency.

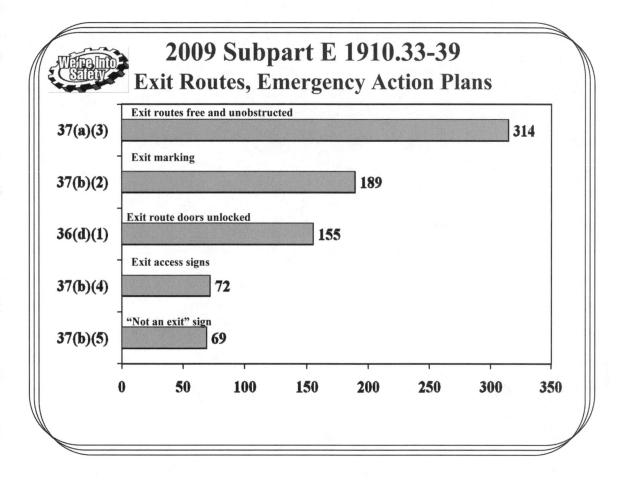

2009 Subpart E 1910.33-39
Exit Routes, Emergency Action Plans

37(a)(3)	Exit routes free and unobstructed — 314
37(b)(2)	Exit marking — 189
36(d)(1)	Exit route doors unlocked — 155
37(b)(4)	Exit access signs — 72
37(b)(5)	"Not an exit" sign — 69

CHAPTER
13

MACHINE GUARDING

Crushed hands and arms, severed fingers, blindness—the list of possible machinery-related injuries is as long as it is horrifying. There seem to be as many hazards created by moving machine parts as there are types of machines. Safeguards are essential for protecting workers from needless, preventable injuries. A good rule to remember is that any machine part, function or process that may cause injury must be safeguarded. Where the operation of a machine or accidental contact with it can injure the operator or others in the vicinity, the hazard must either be controlled or eliminated.

Where Mechanical Hazards Occur
Dangerous moving parts in these three basic areas need safeguarding:
- The point of operation: That point where work is performed on the material, such as cutting, shaping, boring or forming of stock.
- Power transmission apparatus: All components of the mechanical system that transmit energy to the part of the machine performing the work. These components include flywheels, pulleys, belts, connecting rods, couplings, cams, spindles, chains, cranks and gears.
- Other moving parts: All parts of the machine that move while the machine is working. These can include reciprocating, rotating and transverse moving parts as well as feed mechanisms and auxiliary parts of the machine.

Hazardous Mechanical Motions and Actions
A variety of mechanical motions and actions may present hazards to the worker. These can include the movement of rotating members, reciprocating arms, moving belts, meshing gears, cutting teeth and any parts that impact or shear. These types of hazardous mechanical motions and actions are basic to nearly all machines, and recognizing them is the first step toward protecting workers from the danger they present.

The basic types of hazardous mechanical motions and actions are:
- Rotating motions (including in-running nip points);
- Reciprocating motions
- Transverse actions
- Cutting
- Punching
- Shearing and
- Bending.

Motions

Rotating motion can be dangerous; even smooth, slowly rotating shafts can grip clothing and through mere skin contact force an arm or hand into a dangerous position. Injuries due to contact with rotating parts can be severe.

Collars, couplings, cams, clutches, flywheels, shaft ends, spindles and horizontal or vertical shafting are some examples of common rotating mechanisms that may be hazardous. There is added danger when bolts, nicks, abrasions and projecting keys or setscrews are exposed on rotating parts on machinery (See Exhibit 13-1.).

The rotating parts on machinery cause in-running nip point hazards. There are three main in-running types.

Parts can rotate in opposite directions while their axes are parallel to each other. These parts may be in contact (producing a nip point) or in close proximity to each other (See Exhibit 13-2.). In the latter case, the stock fed between the rolls produces the nip points. This danger is common on machinery with intermeshing gears, rolling mills and calendars.

Another type of nip point is created between rotating and tangentially moving parts. Examples include:

- The point of contact between a power transmission belt and its pulley;
- A chain and a sprocket; and
- A rack and pinion. (See Exhibit 13-3.)

Exhibit 13-2.
Nip points occur where rotating parts come in contact.

Exhibit 13-3.
Nip points can occur between rotating and tangentially moving parts.

Nip points also can occur between rotating and fixed parts that create a shearing, crushing, or abrading action (See Exhibit 13-4.). Examples include:

- Spoked hand wheels or flywheels;
- Screw conveyors;
- The periphery of an abrasive wheel; and
- An incorrectly adjusted work rest.

Exhibit 13-1.
Examples of rotating motion.

Exhibit 13-4.
Nip points can occur between rotating and fixed parts.

Reciprocating motions may be hazardous because during the back-and-forth or up-and-down motion, a worker may be struck by or caught between a moving and a stationary part (See Exhibit 13-5.).

Exhibit 13-5.
Example of a worker being struck by machine with reciprocating motion.

Transverse motion (movement in a straight, continuous line) creates a hazard because a worker may be struck or caught in a pinch or shear point by a moving part (See Exhibit 13-6.).

Exhibit 13-6.
Transverse Motion of Belt.

Actions

Cutting action involves rotating, reciprocating or transverse motion. The danger of cutting action exists at the point of operation where finger, head, and arm injuries can occur and flying chips or scrap material can strike the eyes or face. Such hazards are present at the point of operation in cutting wood, metal or other materials. Typical examples of mechanisms involving cutting hazards include bandsaws, circular saws, boring or drilling machines and turning machines, lathes or milling machines.

Punching action results when power is applied to a slide (ram) for the purpose of blanking, drawing or stamping metal or other materials. The danger of this type of action occurs at the point of operation where stock is inserted, held and withdrawn by hand. Typical machinery used for punching operations are power presses and ironworkers.

Shearing action involves applying power to a slide or knife in order to trim or shear metal or other materials. A hazard occurs at the point of operation where stock is actually inserted, held and withdrawn. Typical examples of machinery used for shearing operations are mechanically, hydraulically, or pneumatically powered shears.

Bending action results when power is applied to a slide in order to draw or stamp metal or other materials. A hazard occurs at the point of operation where stock is inserted, held and withdrawn. Equipment that uses bending actions include power presses, press brakes and tube benders.

Requirements for Safeguards

What must a safeguard do to protect workers against mechanical hazards? Safeguards must, at a minimum, meet the following general requirements:

Prevent contact. The safeguard must prevent hands, arms or any part of a worker's body or clothing from making contact with dangerous moving parts. A good safeguarding system eliminates the possibility of the operator or other workers placing parts of their bodies near hazardous moving parts.

Secure. Workers should not be able to easily remove or tamper with the safeguard because a safeguard that can easily be made ineffective is not much of a safeguard. Guards and safety devices should be made of durable material that will withstand the conditions of normal use. They must be firmly secured to the machine.

Protect from falling objects. The safeguard should ensure that no objects can fall into moving parts. A small tool that is dropped into a cycling machine could easily become a projectile that could strike and injure someone.

Create no new hazards. A safeguard defeats its own purpose if it creates a hazard of its own such as a shear point, jagged edge, or unfinished surface which can cause a laceration. The edges of guards, for instance, should be rolled or bolted in such a way that they eliminate sharp edges.

Create no interference. Any safeguard that impedes a worker from performing the job quickly and comfortably might soon be overridden or disregarded. Proper safeguarding can actually enhance efficiency since it can relieve the worker's apprehensions about injury.

Allow safe lubrication. If possible, one should be able to lubricate the machine without removing the safeguards. Locating oil reservoirs outside the guard, with a line leading to the lubrication point, will reduce the need for the operator or maintenance worker to enter the hazardous area.

Training

Even the most elaborate safeguarding system cannot offer effective protection unless the worker knows how to use it and why. Specific and detailed training is therefore a crucial part of any effort to provide safeguarding against machine-related hazards. This kind of safety training is necessary for new operators and maintenance or set-up personnel when any new or altered safeguards are put in service or when workers are assigned to a new machine or operation. Thorough operator training should involve instruction or hands-on training in the following:

- A description and identification of the hazards associated with particular machines;
- The safeguards themselves, how they provide protection and the hazards for which they are intended;
- How to use the safeguards and why;
- How and under what circumstances safeguards can be removed and by whom (in most cases, repair or maintenance personnel only); and
- What to do if a safeguard is damaged, missing, or unable to provide adequate protection (e.g., contact the supervisor).

Methods of Machine Safeguarding

There are many ways to safeguard machinery. The type of operation, size or shape of stock, method of handling, physical layout of the work area, type of material, and production requirements or limitations will help to determine the appropriate safeguarding method for the individual machine.

As a general rule, power transmission apparatus is best protected by fixed guards that enclose the danger area. For hazards at the point of operation, where moving parts actually perform work on stock, several kinds of safeguarding are possible. One must always choose the most effective and practical means available.

Safeguards are classified under five general categories:
1. **Guards**
   - Fixed
   - Interlocked
   - Adjustable
   - Self-adjusting
2. **Devices**
   - Presence Sensing
     - Photoelectrical (optical)
     - Radio frequency (capacitance)
     - Electromechanical
   - Pullback
   - Restraint
   - Safety Controls
     - Safety trip control
     - Pressure-sensitive body bar
     - Safety triprod
     - Safety tripwire cable
   - Two-hand control
   - Two-hand trip
   - Gates
     - Interlocked
     - Other
3. **Location/Distance**
4. **Potential Feeding and Ejection Methods to Improve Safety for the Operator**
   - Automatic feed
   - Semi-automatic feed
   - Automatic ejection
   - Semi-automatic ejection
   - Robot
5. **Miscellaneous Aids**
   - Awareness barriers
   - Miscellaneous protective shields
   - Hand-feeding tools and holding fixtures

Guards

Guards are barriers that prevent access to danger areas. There are four general types of guards.

Fixed

As its name implies, a fixed guard is a permanent part of the machine. It is not dependent upon moving parts to perform its intended function. It may be constructed of sheet metal, screen, wire cloth, bars, plastic or any other material that is substantial enough to withstand whatever impact it may receive and to endure prolonged use. This type of guard is usually preferable to all others because of its relative simplicity and permanence.

For example, a fixed guard on a power press completely encloses the point of operation. The stock is fed through the side of the guard into the die area, with the scrap stock exiting on the opposite side.

Exhibit 13-7 shows a fixed enclosure guard shielding the belt and pulley of a power transmission unit. An inspection panel is provided on top to minimize the need for removing the guard.

Exhibit 13-7
A fixed guard on a power transmission unit.

Fixed enclosure guards also may be seen on a bandsaw. These guards protect the operator from the turning wheels and moving saw blade. Normally, the only time for the guards to be opened or removed would be for a blade change or maintenance. It is very important that they be securely fastened while the saw is in use.

Interlocked

When this type of guard is opened or removed, the tripping mechanism and/or power automatically shuts off or disengages, and the machine cannot cycle or be started until the guard is back in place. An interlocked guard may use electrical, mechanical, hydraulic, or pneumatic power or any combination of these. Interlocks should not prevent "inching" by remote control, if required. Replacing the guard should not automatically restart the machine.

As illustrated in Exhibit 13-8, the beater mechanism of a picker machine (used in the textile industry) is covered by an interlocked barrier guard. This guard cannot be raised while the machine is running, nor can the machine be restarted with the guard in the raised position.

Exhibit 13-8.
A picker machine with an interlocked barrier guard.

Adjustable

Adjustable guards are useful because they allow flexibility in accommodating various sizes of stock (See Exhibit 13-9.).

Exhibit 13-9.
An example of an adjustable blade guard.

Self-Adjusting

The movement of the stock determines the openings of these barriers. As the operator moves the stock into the danger area, the guard is pushed away, providing an opening that is only large enough to admit the stock. After the stock is removed, the guard returns to the rest position. This guard protects the operator by placing a barrier between the danger area and the operator. The guards may be constructed of plastic, metal or other substantial material. Self-adjusting guards offer different degrees of protection.

Exhibit 13-10 shows a radial arm saw with a self-adjusting guard. As the blade is pulled across the stock, the guard moves up, staying in contact with the stock.

Exhibit 13-10.
A radial arm saw with a self-adjusting guard.

Devices

A safety device may perform one of several functions. It may:

- Stop the machine if a hand or any part of the body is inadvertently placed in the danger area;
- Restrain or withdraw the operator's hands from the danger area during operation;
- Require the operator to use both hands on machine controls thus keeping both hands and body out of danger; or
- Provide a barrier that is synchronized with the operating cycle of the machine to prevent entry to the danger area during the hazardous part of the cycle.

There are several types of devices available.

Presence-Sensing

The **photoelectric** (optical) presence-sensing device uses a system of light sources and controls that interrupt the machine's operating cycle (See Exhibit 13-11.). If the light field is broken, the machine stops and will not cycle. This device must be used only on machines that can be stopped before the worker can reach the danger area.

Exhibit 13-11.
A photoelectric presence-sensing device with a press brake.

The **radio frequency** (capacitance) presence-sensing device uses a radio beam that is part of the machine's control circuit (See Exhibit 13-12.). When the capacitance field is broken, the machine will stop or will not activate. Like the photoelectric device, this device shall only be used on machines that can be stopped before the worker can reach the danger area. This requires the machine to have a friction clutch or other reliable means for stopping.

Exhibit 13-12.
A radio frequency presence-sensing device mounted on a part-revolution power press.

The **electromechanical** sensing device has a probe or contact bar that descends to a predetermined distance when the operator initiates the machine cycle (See Exhibit 13-13.). If there is an obstruction preventing it from descending its full predetermined distance, the control circuit will not actuate the machine cycle.

Exhibit 13-13.
An electromechanical sensing device
on an eye-letting machine

Exhibit 13-14.
A pullback device on a small press.

Pullback

Pullback devices use a series of cables attached to the operator's hands, wrists and/or arms (See Exhibit 13-14.). This type of device is primarily used on machines with stroking action. When the side/ram is up, the operator is allowed access to the point of operation. When the side/ram begins to descend, a mechanical linkage automatically ensures withdrawal of the hands from the point of operation.

Restraint

The restraint (holdout) device in Exhibit 13-15 uses cables or straps that are attached to the operator's hands and a fixed point. The cables or straps must be adjusted to let the operator's hands travel within a predetermined safe area. There is no extending or retracting action involved. Consequently, hand-feeding tools are often necessary if the operation involves placing material into the danger area.

Exhibit 13-15.
A restraint device with wrist straps.

Safety Trip Control

Safety trip controls provide a quick means for deactivating the machine in an emergency situation (See Exhibit 13-16.).

Exhibit 13-16.
A pressure-sensitive body bar located on the front of a rubber mat.

A pressure-sensitive body bar, when depressed, will deactivate the machine. If the operator or anyone trips, loses balance or is drawn toward the machine, applying pressure to the bar will stop the operation. The positioning of the bar, therefore, is critical. It must stop the machine before a part of the employee's body reaches the danger area.

All tripwires, rods or other safety devices must be manually reset to restart the machine. When pressed by hand, the safety trip rod deactivates the machine. Because it has to be actuated by the operator during an emergency situation, its proper position is also critical. Exhibit 13-17 shows a trip-rod located above the rubber mill. Exhibit 13-18 shows safety tripwire cables are located around the perimeter of or near the danger area. The operator must be able to reach the cable with either hand to stop the machine.

Exhibit 13-17.
A triprod located above the rubber mill.

Exhibit 13-18.
Safety tripwire cables located on the perimeter of the danger area.

Two-Hand Control

The two-hand control requires constant, concurrent pressure by the operator to activate the machine. This kind of control requires a part-revolution clutch, brake and brake monitor if used on a power press as illustrated in Exhibit 13-19. With this type of device, the operator's hands are required to be at a safe location (on control buttons) and at a safe distance from the danger area while the machine completes its closing cycle.

Exhibit 13-19.
The two control buttons require the operator's hands to be a safe distance from the danger area.

Two-Hand Trip

The two-hand trip requires concurrent application of both of the operator's control buttons to activate the machine cycle, after which the hands are free. This device is usually used with machines equipped with full-revolution clutches. The trips must be placed far enough from the point of operation to make it impossible for the operator to move his or her hands from the trip buttons or handles into the point of operation before the first half of the cycle is completed. Thus, the operator's hands are kept far enough away to prevent them from being accidentally placed in the danger area prior to the slide/ram or blade reaching the full "down" position (See Exhibit 13-20.).

Exhibit 13-20.
The two-hand trip requires both hands to activate the machine cycle.

Gate

A gate is a movable barrier that protects the operator at the point of operation before the machine cycle can be started. Gates are usually designed to be operated with each machine cycle.

Exhibit 13-21 shows a gate on a power press. If the gate is not permitted to descend to the fully closed position, the press will not function.

Exhibit 13-21.
A gate on a power press.

Another potential application of this type of guard is where the gate is a component of a perimeter safeguarding system. In this case, the gate would provide protection to the operator as well as to pedestrian traffic.

Safeguarding by Location or Distance

The examples mentioned below are a few of the numerous applications of the principle of safeguarding by location or distance. A thorough hazard analysis of each machine and particular situation is absolutely essential before attempting this safeguarding technique.

To safeguard a machine by location, the machine or its dangerous moving parts must be so positioned that hazardous areas are not accessible or do not present a hazard to a worker during the normal operation of the machine. This may be accomplished by locating a machine so that a plant design feature, such as a wall, protects the worker and other personnel. Additionally, enclosure walls or fences can restrict access to machines. Another possible solution is to have dangerous parts located high enough to be out of the normal reach of any worker.

The feeding process can be safeguarded by location if a safe distance can be maintained to protect the worker's hands. The dimensions of the stock being worked on may provide adequate safety. For instance, if the stock is several feet long and only one end of the stock is being worked on, the operator may be able to hold the opposite end while the work is being performed. An example would be a single-end punching machine. However, depending upon the machine, protection might still be required for other personnel.

The positioning of the operator's control station provides another potential approach to safeguarding by location. Operator controls may be located at a safe distance from the machine if there is no reason for the operator to tend the controls during operation.

Feeding and Ejection Methods to Improve Operator Safety

Many feeding and ejection methods do not require the operator to place his or her hands in the danger area. In some cases, no operator involvement is necessary after the machine is set up. In other situations, operators can manually feed the stock with the assistance of a feeding mechanism. Properly designed ejection methods do not require any operator involvement after the machine starts to function.

However, some feeding and ejection methods may create hazards themselves. For instance, a robot may eliminate the need for an operator to be near the machine, but may create a new hazard when its arm moves.

Using feeding and ejection methods does not necessarily eliminate the need for guards and devices. Guards and devices must be used wherever practical to provide protection from exposure to hazards.

Automatic feed

Automatic feeds reduce the exposure of the operator during the work process and sometimes do not require any effort by the operator after the machine is set up and running.

In Exhibit 13-22, the power press has an automatic feeding mechanism. Notice the transparent fixed enclosure guard at the danger area.

Exhibit 13-22.
A power press with an automatic feeding mechanism.

Semi-automatic feed

With semi-automatic feeding, as in the case of a power press, the operator uses a mechanism to place the piece being processed under the ram at each stroke. The operator does not need to reach into the danger area, and the danger area is completely enclosed.

Exhibit 13-23 shows a chute feed. It may be either a horizontal or an inclined chute into which each piece is placed by hand. Using a chute feed on an inclined press not only helps center the piece as it slides into the die, but may also simplify the problem of ejection.

Exhibit 13-23.
A chute feed is one example of a semi-automatic feed.

Automatic Ejection

Automatic ejection may employ either an air-pressure or a mechanical apparatus to remove the completed part from a press. It may be interlocked with the operating controls to prevent operation until the part is ejected. This method requires additional safeguards for operator protection.

In Exhibit 13-24, the pan shuttle mechanism moves under the finished part as the slide moves toward the "up" position. The shuttle then catches the part stripped from the slide by the knockout pins and deflects it into a chute. When the ram moves down toward the next blank, the pan shuttle moves away from the die area.

Exhibit 13-24.
The pan shuttle mechanism automatically ejects the part once finished .

Exhibit 13-25.
The plunger handle and ejector leg work together to eject the part once finished.

Exhibit 13-26.
Robots may present new hazards to employees thus guards such as perimeter barriers should be used.

Semi-automatic Ejection

Exhibit 13-25 shows a semi-automatic ejection mechanism used on a power press. When the plunger is withdrawn from the die area, the ejector leg, which is mechanically coupled to the plunger, kicks out the completed work.

Robots

Robots are machines that load and unload stock, assemble parts, transfer objects or perform other tasks. Essentially, they perform work otherwise done by an operator. They are best used in high-production processes requiring repeated routines that present hazards to employees. However, robots may create hazards themselves, and, if they do, appropriate guards must be used.

Various techniques are available to prevent employee exposure to the hazards that can be imposed by robots. The most common technique is through the installation of perimeter guarding with interlocked gates (See Exhibit 13-26.). A critical parameter relates to the manner in which the interlocks function. Of major concern is whether the computer program, control circuit, or the primary power circuit, is interrupted when an interlock is activated. The various industry standards should be investigated for guidance; however, it is generally accepted that the interlock should interrupt the primary motive power to the robot.

The American National Standards Institute (ANSI) safety standard for industrial robots, ANSI/RIA R15.06-1986, is informative and presents certain basic requirements for protecting the worker. However, when a robot is to be used in a workplace, the employer should conduct a comprehensive operational safety/health hazard analysis and then devise and implement an effective safeguarding system that is fully responsive to the situation. (Various effective safeguarding techniques are described in ANSI B11.19-1990.)

Studies in Sweden and Japan indicate that many robot accidents have not occurred under normal operating conditions, but rather during programming, program touch-up, maintenance, repair, testing, setup or adjustment. During many of these operations, the operator, programmer or corrective maintenance worker may temporarily be within the robot's working envelope where unintended operations could result in injuries.

All industrial robots are either servo or non-servo controlled. Servo robots are controlled through the use of sensors that are employed to continually monitor the robot's axes for positional and velocity feedback information. This feedback information is compared on an ongoing basis to pre-taught information that has been programmed and stored in the robot's memory.

Non-servo robots do not have the feedback capability of monitoring its axes and velocity and comparing them with a pre-taught program. Their axes are controlled through a system of mechanical stops and limit switches to control the robot's movement.

Types of hazards associated with robots include:

Impact or collision hazards. Impact with the robot's arm or peripheral equipment as a result of unpredicted movements, component malfunctions or unpredicted program changes.

Crushing or trapping hazards. A hazard resulting in some part of a person's body being trapped between the robot's arm and other peripheral equipment or being crushed by peripheral equipment as a result of being impacted by the robot into the equipment.

Mechanical components hazards. Mechanical hazards result from the mechanical failure of components associated with the robot or its power source; drive components, tooling or end-effector and/or peripheral equipment. The failure of gripper mechanisms with resultant release of parts or the failure of end-effector power tools, such as grinding wheels, buffing wheels, de-burring tools, power screwdrivers and nut runners.

Human error. Human error results in hazards both to personnel and equipment. Errors in programming, interfacing peripheral equipment and connecting input/output sensors can result in unpredicted movement or action by the robot that can result in personnel injury or equipment breakage. Human error in judgment frequently results from incorrectly activating the teach pendant or control panel. The greatest human judgment error results from becoming so familiar with the robot's redundant motions that personnel are too trusting in assuming the nature of these motions and place themselves in hazardous positions while programming or performing maintenance within the robot's work envelope.

Miscellaneous Aids

While these aids do not give complete protection from machine hazards, they may provide the op-

erator with an extra margin of safety. Sound judgment is needed in their application and use.

Awareness barriers do not provide physical protection, but serve only to remind a person that he or she is approaching the danger area. Generally, awareness barriers are not considered adequate when continual exposure to the hazard exists.

For example, a rope may be used as an awareness barrier on the rear of a power-squaring shear, as shown in Exhibit 13-27. Although the barrier does not physically prevent a person from entering the danger area, it calls attention to it.

Awareness Barrier

Exhibit 13-27.
A rope being used as an awareness barrier on a power-squaring shear.

Shields may be used to provide protection from flying particles, splashing cutting oils or coolants (See Exhibit 13-28).

TRANSPARENT SHIELD

DRILL   LATHE

Exhibit 13-28.
Transparent shields provide protection from flying particles.

Holding tools can place and remove stock. A typical use would be for reaching into the danger area of a press or press brake. Holding tools should not be used instead of other machine safeguards; they are merely a supplement to the protection that other guards provide (See Exhibit 13-29). For example, a push stick or block may be used when feeding stock into a saw blade. When it becomes necessary for hands to be in close proximity to the blade, the push stick or block may provide a few inches of safety and prevent a severe injury. In the illustration, the push block fits over the fence.

Exhibit 13-29.
Holding tools can protect employees' hands
when inserting or removing stock.

Machinery and Machine Guarding

It is important to understand how Subpart 0 applies to machinery in the workplace. Section 212 is a general (or a horizontal) standard that applies to all machines not specifically mentioned elsewhere in other sections of Subpart 0. The other sections are specific (vertical) standards that apply to particular types of machines (e.g., Section 213 applies only to woodworking machinery).

General Requirements for All Machines—1910.212

Machine Guarding

One or more methods of machine guarding shall be provided to protect employees in the machine area from hazards, such as those created by point of operation, ingoing nip points, rotating parts, flying chips and sparks.

Guards shall be affixed to the machine where possible and secured elsewhere if not possible. A guard shall not offer an accident hazard in itself. The point of operation of machines whose operation exposes an employee to inquiry shall be guarded.

Revolving drums, barrels and containers shall be guarded by an enclosure that is interlocked with the drive mechanism

When the periphery of the blades of a fan is less than 7 ft. above the floor or working level, the blades shall be guarded with a guard having openings no larger than 1 in.

Anchoring Fixed Machinery

Machines designed for a fixed location shall be securely anchored to prevent walking or moving.

Woodworking Machinery Requirements—1910.213

Machine Construction, General

Each machine shall be so constructed as to be free from sensible (able to be felt) vibration when the largest size tool is mounted and run idle (no cutting load) at full speed.

Machine Controls and Equipment

A mechanical or electrical power control shall be provided on each machine to make it possible for operators to cut off the power from each machine without leaving their position at the point of operation.

On applications where injury to the operator might result if motors were to restart after power failures, provision shall be made to prevent machines from automatically restarting upon restoration of power.

Power controls and operating controls should be located within easy reach of the operators while they are at their regular work location, making it unnecessary for them to reach over the cutter to make adjustments. This does not apply to constant pressure controls used only for set-up purposes.

Specific Machine Requirements

The remaining paragraphs of Section 213 contain guarding requirements for specific woodworking machines. A discussion of some of these requirements follows.

All woodworking machinery such as table saws, swing saws, radial saws, band saws, jointers, tenoning machines, boring and mortising machines, shapers, planers, lathes, sanders, veneer cutters and other miscellaneous wood-working machinery shall be effectively guarded to protect the operator and other employees from hazards inherent to their operation.

Table Saws

Circular table saws shall have a hood over the portion of the saw above the table, so mounted that the hood will automatically adjust itself to the thickness of and remain in contact with the material being cut.

Circular table saws shall have a spreader aligned with the blade, spaced no more than ½ in. behind the largest blade mounted in the saw. The provision of a spreader in connection with grooving, dadoing or rabbeting is not required.

Circular table saws used for ripping shall have nonkick-back fingers or dogs.

Feed rolls and blades of self-feed circular saws shall be protected by a hood or guard to prevent the hand of the operator from coming into contact with the in-running rolls at any point.

Swing or Sliding Cut-Off Saws

All swing or sliding cut-off saws shall be provided with a guard that will completely enclose the upper half of the saw.

Limit stops shall be provided to prevent swing or sliding cut-off saws from extending beyond the front or back edges of the table.

Each swing or sliding cut-off saw shall be provided with an effective device to return the saw automatically to the back of the table when released at any point of its travel.

Inverted sawing or swing cut-off saws shall be provided with a hood that will cover the part of the saw that protrudes above the top of the table or material being cut.

Radial Saws

The upper hood shall completely enclose the upper portion of the blade down to a point that will include the end of the saw arbor.

The sides of the lower exposed portion of the blade shall be guarded to the full diameter of the blade by a device that will automatically adjust itself to the thickness of the stock and remain in contact with stock being cut (See Exhibit 13-30.). Radial saws used for ripping shall have nonkickback fingers or dogs.

Exhibit 13-30.
The guard extends over the full diameter of the radial saw.

An adjustable stop shall be provided to prevent the forward travel of the blade beyond the position necessary to complete the cut in repetitive operations.

Installation shall be in such a manner that the front end of the unit will be slightly higher than the rear, so as to cause the cutting head to return gently to the starting position when released by the operator.

Bandsaws and Band Resaws

All portions of the saw blade shall be enclosed or guarded, except for the working portion of the blade between the bottom of the guide rolls and the table. Bandsaw wheels shall be fully encased. The outside periphery of the enclosure shall be solid. The front and back shall be either solid or wire mesh or perforated metal.

Jointers

Each hand-fed jointer with horizontal cutting head shall be equipped with an automatic guard that will cover all the sections of the head on the working side of the fence or gauge (See Exhibit 13-31.).

Abrasive Wheel Machinery—1910.215

This section regulates only abrasive wheel machinery. It does not cover wire, buffing or similar wheels. An abrasive wheel is made up of individual particles that are bonded together to form a wheel. The hazard here is that if not properly mounted and used, the wheel can literally explode. Sections of the wheel may fly out at high speeds and strike the operator, causing serious injury or death.

Exhibit 13-31.
A Hand-fed jointer with automatic guard.

Exhibit 13-32.
**Work rests on grinding machines must
not open more than 1/8 in.**

Exhibit 13-33.
**Adjustable tongues should not extend
beyond ¼ in. from the wheel periphery.**

Machine Guarding

Abrasive wheels shall be used only on machines provided with safety guards with the following exceptions:

- Wheels used for internal work while within the work being ground;
- Mounted wheels, used in portable operations, 2 in. and smaller in diameter; and

- Type 16, 17, 18, 18R, and 19 cones, plugs and threaded hole pot balls where the work offers protection.

Guard Design

Abrasive wheel safety guards shall cover the spindle end, nut and flange projections, except:

- Safety guards on all operations where the work provides a suitable measure of protection to the operator may be so constructed that the spindle end, nut and outer flange are exposed;
- Where the nature of the work is such as to entirely cover the side of the wheel, the side covers of the guard may be omitted; and
- The spindle end, nut and outer flange may be exposed on machines designed as portable saws.

Work Rests

On off-hand grinding machines, adjustable work rests of rigid construction shall be used to support the work. Work rests shall be kept adjusted closely to the wheel with a maximum opening 1/8 in. to prevent the work from being jammed between the wheel and the rest, which may cause breakage (See Exhibit 13-32.).

Tongue Adjustment

The protecting member of the abrasive wheel safety guard shall be adjustable for variations in wheel size so that the distance between the wheel periphery and the adjustable tongue or the end of the peripheral member at the top shall never exceed ¼ in. (See Exhibit 13-33.).

Angular Exposure

Abrasive wheel safety guards for bench and floor stands and cylindrical grinders shall not expose the grinding wheel periphery for more than 65° above the horizontal plane of the wheel spindle.

Immediately before mounting, all wheels shall be closely inspected and sounded by the user (ring test) to make sure they have not been damaged.

The spindle speed of the machine shall be checked before mounting of the wheel to be certain that it does not exceed the maximum operating speed marked on the wheel.

Mills and Calendars—1910.216

This section regulates mills and calendars in the rubber and plastics industries. Due to the highly specialized nature of these rules, they are beyond the scope of this manual.

Mechanical Power Presses—1910.217

This section deals with mechanical power presses. This specialized topic is beyond the scope of this manual. However, there are some basic rules that provide insight into this potentially deadly operation.

- The employer shall provide and ensure the use of point-of-operation guards or properly applied and adjusted point-of-operation devices to prevent entry of hands or fingers into the point of operation by reaching through, over, under or around the guard on every operation performed on a mechanical power press. This requirement shall not apply when the point of operation opening is ¼ in. or smaller.
- A substantial guard shall be placed over the treadle on foot-operated presses.
- If the press has pedal counterweights, the path of travel of the weight shall be enclosed.
- Machines using full revolution clutches shall incorporate a single stroke mechanism, except where automatically fed in continuous operation and the points of operation are fully safeguarded by an affixed barrier guard.
- Employers shall establish a program of regular inspections of their power presses to ensure safe operating condition. They shall maintain a record of these inspections and maintenance work.
- All point-of-operation injuries involving a mechanical power press must be reported to OSHA or the state agency (in states with state plans) within 30 days of the injury.

Forging Machines—1910.218

This section regulates forging machines. Due to the highly specialized nature of these rules, they are beyond the scope of this manual.

Mechanical Power-Transmission Apparatus—1910.219

Mechanical power transmission apparatus refers to all components of the mechanical system that transmit energy from the prime source to the part of the machine performing the work. Examples of these components include pulleys, belts, connecting rods, flywheels, shafting, coupling, cams, spindles, chains, cranks and gears. The primary thrust of these regulations is to ensure that employees cannot be "caught" and injured by rotating members, in-running nip points, sprockets, pulleys and similar apparatus.

This section contains detailed requirements for safeguarding all of these components, including:

- Guards for mechanical power transmission equipment shall be made of metal or other suitable material. Wood guards may be used in the woodworking and chemical industries. In industries where atmospheric conditions would rapidly deteriorate metal guards or where extremes in temperature would make metal guards undesirable, wood guards may be used.
- All pulleys, belts, sprockets and chains, flywheels, shaft projections and shafting, gears, couplings or other rotating or reciprocating parts, or any portion thereof within 7 ft. of the floor or working platform shall be guarded effectively.
- All guards for inclined belts shall conform to the standards for construction of horizontal belts. They shall be arranged in such a manner that a minimum clearance of 7 ft. is maintained between the belt and floor at any point outside the guard.
- Flywheels protruding through a working floor shall be guarded.
- Where either runs of horizontal belts are 7 ft. or lower from the floor or working surface, the guard shall extend at least 15 in. above the belt.
- Where gears require a guard, the guard shall extend 6 in. above the mesh point by a bank guard covering the face or be completely enclosed.
- Couplings with bolts, nuts or setscrews that extend beyond the flange of the coupling shall be guarded by a safety sleeve.
- Belts, pulleys and shafting located in rooms used exclusively for power transmission apparatus need not be guarded when the following requirements are met:
  - The basement, tower or room occupied by transmission equipment is locked against unauthorized entrance.

- The vertical clearance in passageways between the floor and power transmission beams, ceiling or other objects is not less than 5 ft. 6 in.

- The intensity of illumination conforms to the requirements of ANSI A11.1-1965
- The route followed by the oiler is protected in such a manner as to prevent accidents.

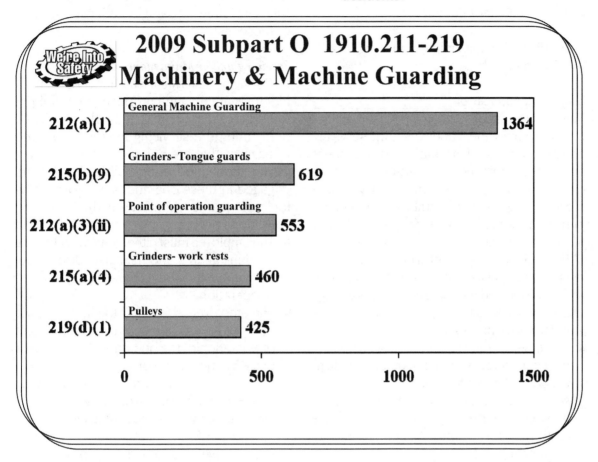

2009 Subpart O 1910.211-219
Machinery & Machine Guarding

We're Into Safety

212(a)(1) General Machine Guarding	1364
215(b)(9) Grinders- Tongue guards	619
212(a)(3)(ii) Point of operation guarding	553
215(a)(4) Grinders- work rests	460
219(d)(1) Pulleys	425

0   500   1000   1500

Control of Hazardous Energy (Lockout/Tagout)

This standard, which went into effect on January 2, 1990, helps safeguard employees from hazardous energy while they are performing service or maintenance on machines and equipment. The standard identifies the practices and procedures necessary to shut down and lock out or tag out machines and equipment, requires that employees receive training in their role in the lockout/tagout program, and mandates that periodic inspections be conducted to maintain or enhance the energy control program.

In the early 1970s, OSHA adopted various lockout-related provisions of the existing national consensus standards and federal standards that were developed for specific types of equip-

ment or industries. When the existing standards require lockout, the new rule supplements these existing standards' by requiring the development and utilization of written procedures, the training of employees, and periodic inspections of the use of the procedures. OSHA has determined that lockout is a more reliable means of deenergizing equipment than tagout and that it is the preferred method for employee use. OSHA contends that, except for limited situations, the use of lockout devices will provide a more secure and more effective means of protecting employees from the unexpected release of hazardous energy or startup of machines and equipment.

The following OSHA standards currently contain lockout/tagout related requirements:
- 1910.178—Powered Industrial Trucks;
- 1910.179—Overhead and Gantry Cranes;
- 1910.181—Derricks;

Machine Guarding

- 1910.213—Woodworking Machinery;
- 1910.217—Mechanical Power Presses;
- 1910.218—Forging Machines;
- 1910.252—Welding, Cutting and Brazing;
- 1910.262—Textiles;
- 1910.263—Bakery Equipment;
- 1910.265—Sawmills;
- 1910.272—Grain Handling; and
- 1910.305—Electrical.

Scope and Application

The lockout/tagout standard applies to general industry employment and covers the servicing and maintenance of machines and equipment in which the unexpected start-up or release of stored energy could cause injury to employees. The standard establishes minimum performance requirements for the control of hazardous energy.

If employees are performing service or maintenance tasks that do not expose them to the unexpected release of hazardous energy, the standard does not apply. For example, the standard does not apply:

- While servicing or maintaining cord- and plug-connected electrical equipment. (Unplugging the equipment from the energy source must control the hazards; the plug must be under the exclusive control of the employee performing the service and/or maintenance.)
- During hot tap operations that involve transmission and distribution systems for gas, steam, water or petroleum products when:
  - They are performed on pressurized pipelines;
  - Continuity of service is essential and shutdown of the system is impractical; and
  - Employees are provided with an alternative type of protection that is equally effective.

Normal Production Operations

OSHA recognizes that machines and equipment present many hazardous situations during normal production operations (i.e., whenever machines and equipment are used to perform their usual production function). These production hazards are covered by rules in other general industry standards, such as the requirements for general machine

guarding and guarding power transmission apparatus in 1910.212 and 1910.219. In certain circumstances, however, some hazards encountered during normal production operations may be covered by the lockout/tagout rule. The following paragraphs illustrate some of these instances.

Servicing and/or Maintenance Operations

If a servicing activity such as lubricating, cleaning or unjamming the production equipment takes place during production, the employee performing the servicing may be subjected to hazards that are not encountered as part of the production operation itself. Workers engaged in these operations are covered by lockout/tagout when any of the following conditions occurs:

- The employee must either remove or bypass machine guards or other safety devices, resulting in exposure to hazards at the point of operation;
- The employee is required to place any part of his or her body in contact with the point of operation of the operational machine or piece of equipment; or
- The employee is required to place any part of his or her body into a danger zone associated with a machine operating cycle.

In the above situations, the equipment must be deenergized and locks or tags must be applied to the energy-isolation devices.

In addition, when normal servicing tasks, such as setting equipment up and making significant adjustments to machines, do not occur during normal production operations, employees performing such tasks are required to lock out or tag out if they can be injured by unexpected energization of the equipment.

OSHA recognizes that some servicing operations must be performed with the power on. Making fine adjustments, such as centering the belt on conveyors or troubleshooting, such as identifying the source of the problem as well as checking to ensure that it has been corrected are examples. OSHA requires the employer to provide effective protection for employees performing such operations.

Minor Servicing Tasks

Employees performing minor tool changes, adjustments and other minor service activities during normal production operations that are routine, repetitive and integral to the use of the production equipment are not covered by the lockout/tagout standard, provided the work is performed using alternative measures that give effective protection.

Provisions of the Standard

The standard requires employers to establish procedures for isolating machines or equipment from the input of energy and affixing appropriate locks or tags to energy-isolating devices to prevent any unexpected energization, start-up or release of stored energy that could injure workers. When tags are used on energy-isolating devices capable of being locked out, the employer must provide additional means to ensure a level of protection equivalent to that of locks. The standard also requires employees be trained and periodic procedures periodically be inspected to maintain or improve their effectiveness.

Energy Control Program

The lockout/tagout rule requires that the employer establish an energy control program that includes:
1. Documented energy control procedures;
2. An employee-training program; and
3. Periodic inspections of the procedures.

The standard requires employers to establish a program to ensure that machines and equipment are isolated and inoperative before any employee performs service or maintenance where the unexpected energization, start up, or release of stored energy could occur and cause injury.

The purpose of the energy control program is to ensure that whenever the possibility of unexpected machine or equipment start-up exists or when the unexpected release of stored energy could occur and cause injury, the equipment is isolated from its energy source(s) and rendered inoperative prior to servicing or maintenance.

Employers have the flexibility to develop a program and procedures that meet the needs of their particular workplace and the particular types of machines and equipment being maintained or serviced.

Energy Control Procedure

This standard requires that energy control procedures be developed, documented and used to control potentially hazardous energy sources whenever workers perform activities covered by the standard.

The written procedures must identify the information that authorized employees must know in order to control hazardous energy during service or maintenance. If this information is the same for various machines or equipment or if other means of logical grouping exists, then a single energy control procedure may be sufficient. If there are other conditions, such as multiple energy sources, different connecting means or a particular sequence that must be followed to shut down the machine or equipment, the employer must develop separate energy control procedures.

The energy control procedure must outline the scope, purpose, authorization, rules and techniques that will be used to control hazardous energy sources as well as the means that will be used to enforce compliance. At a minimum, the procedure must include:
- A statement on how the procedure will be used;
- The steps needed to shut down, isolate, block and secure machines or equipment;
- The steps designating the safe placement, removal and transfer of lockout/tagout devices and who has the responsibility for them; and
- The specific requirements for testing machines or equipment to determine and verify the effectiveness of locks, tags and other energy control measures.

The procedure also must outline the following steps:
- Preparing for shutdown;
- Shutting down the machine(s) or equipment;
- Isolating the machine or equipment from the energy source(s);
- Applying the lockout or tagout device(s) to the energy-isolating device(s);
- Safely releasing all potentially hazardous stored or residual energy; and
- Verifying the isolation of the machine(s) or equipment prior to the start of service or maintenance work.

In addition, before lockout or tagout devices are removed and energy is restored to the machines or equipment, certain steps must be taken to reenergize equipment after service is completed, including:

- Ensuring that machines or equipment components are operationally intact;
- Notifying affected employees that lockout or tagout devices have been removed from each energy-isolating device by the employee who applied the device.

Energy-Isolating Devices

The employer's primary tool for providing protection under the standard is the energy-isolating device, which is the mechanism that prevents the transmission or release of energy and to which all locks or tags are attached. This device guards against accidental machine or equipment start-up or the unexpected reenergization of equipment during servicing or maintenance. There are two types of energy-isolating devices: those capable of being locked and those that are not. The standard differentiates between the existence of these two conditions and the employer and employee responsibilities in each case.

When the energy-isolating device cannot be locked out, the employer must use tagout. (The employer may, however, choose to modify or replace the device to make it capable of being locked.) When using tagout, the employer must comply with all tagout-related provisions of the standard and in addition to the normal training required for all employees, train employees in the following limitations of tags:

- Tags are essentially warning devices affixed to energy-isolating devices and do not provide the physical restraint of a lock.
- When a tag is attached to an isolating means, it is not to be removed except by the person who applied it and never to be bypassed, ignored or otherwise defeated.
- Tags must be legible and understandable by all employees.
- Tags and their means of attachment must be made of materials that will withstand the environmental conditions encountered in the work area.
- Tags may evoke a false sense of security. They are only one part of an overall energy control program.
- Tags must be securely attached to the energy-isolating devices so they cannot be detached accidentally during use.

Exhibit 13-34. A lockout/tagout board.

If the energy-isolating device is lockable, the employer shall use locks unless it can prove that the use of tags would provide protection at least as effective as locks and would ensure "full employee protection."

Full employee protection includes complying with all tagout-related provisions and implementing additional safety measures that can provide the level of safety equivalent to that obtained by using lockout. This might include removing and isolating a circuit element, blocking a controlling switch, opening an extra disconnecting device or removing a valve handle to reduce the potential for any inadvertent energization.

Although OSHA acknowledges the existence of energy-isolating devices that cannot be locked out, the standard clearly states that whenever major replacement, repair, renovation or modification of machines or equipment is performed and new machines or equipment are installed, the employer must ensure the energy-isolating devices for such machines or equipment are lockable. Such modifications and/or new purchases are most effectively and efficiently made as part of the normal equipment replacement cycle. All newly purchased equipment must be lockable.

Requirements for Lockout/Tagout Devices

When attached to an energy-isolating device, both lockout and tagout devices are tools that the employer can use in accordance with the requirements of the standard to help protect employees from hazardous energy. The lockout device provides protection by holding the energy-isolating device in the safe position thus preventing the machine or equipment from becoming energized. The tagout device provides protection by identifying the energy-isolating device as a source of potential danger and indicating that the energy-isolating device and the equipment being controlled may not be operated until the tagout device is removed. Whichever devices are used, they must be singularly identified and be the only devices used for controlling hazardous energy. They also must meet the following requirements.

Durable. Lockout and tagout devices must withstand the environment to which they are exposed for the maximum duration of the expected exposure. Tagout devices must be constructed and printed so that they do not deteriorate or become illegible, especially when used in corrosive (acid and alkali chemicals) or wet environments.

Standardized. Both lockout and tagout devices must be standardized according to either color, shape or size. Tagout devices must also be standardized according to print and format.

Substantial. Lockout and tagout devices must be substantial enough to minimize early or accidental removal. Locks must be substantial to prevent removal except by excessive force of special tools, such as bolt cutters or other metal cutting tools. Tag means of attachment must be non-reusable, attachable by hand, self-locking and non-releasable, with a minimum unlocking strength of no less than 50 lbs. The device for attaching the tag also must have the general design and basic characteristics equivalent to a one-piece nylon cable tie that can withstand all environments and conditions.

Identifiable. Locks and tags must clearly identify the employee who applies them. Tags must also warn against hazardous conditions if the machine or equipment is energized and must include a legend such as:

- DO NOT START;
- DO NOT OPEN;
- DO NOT CLOSE;
- DO NOT ENERGIZE; and
- DO NOT OPERATE.

Employee Training

The employer must provide effective initial training and retraining as necessary and certify that such training has been given to all employees covered by the standard. The certification must contain each employee's name and dates of training.

For the purposes of the standard, there are three types of employees: authorized, affected and other. The amount and kind of training that each employee receives is based upon the relationship of that employee's job to the machine or equipment being locked or tagged out and the degree of knowledge relevant to hazardous energy that he or she must possess.

For example, the employer's training program for authorized employees (those who are charged with the responsibility for implementing the energy control procedures and performing the service and maintenance) must cover, at minimum, details about the type and magnitude of the hazardous energy sources present in the workplace and the methods and means necessary to isolate and control those energy sources (i.e., the elements of the energy control procedure(s).)

By contrast, affected employees (usually the machine operators or users) and all other employees need only be able to recognize when the control procedure is being implemented and understand the purpose of the procedure and the importance of not attempting to start up or use the equipment that has been locked or tagged out.

Because an affected employee is not one who is performing the service of maintenance, that employee's responsibilities under the energy control program are simple: Whenever there is a lockout or tagout device in place on an energy isolating device, the affected employee must leave it alone and not attempt to operate the equipment.

Every training program must ensure that all employees understand the purpose, function and restrictions of the energy control program and that authorized employees possess the knowledge and skills necessary for the safe application, use and removal of energy controls. Training programs designed to comply with this standard, which is performance-oriented, should deal with the equipment, type(s) of energy and hazard(s) specific to the work area being covered.

Retraining must be provided whenever there is a change in:
- Job assignments;
- Machines, equipment or processes that present a new hazard; or
- Energy control procedures.

Additional retraining must be conducted when a periodic inspection reveals or the employer has reason to believe that there are deviations from or inadequacies in the employee's knowledge or use of the energy control procedure.

Periodic Inspections

Periodic inspections must be performed at least annually to ensure that the energy control procedures (locks and tags) continue to be implemented properly and that the employees are familiar with their responsibilities under those procedures. In addition, the employer must certify that the periodic inspections have been performed. The certification must identify the machine or equipment on which the energy control procedure was used, the date of the inspection, the employees included in the inspection and the name of the person who performed the inspection. For lockout procedures, the periodic inspection must include a review, between the inspector and each authorized employee, of that employee's responsibilities under the energy control procedure being inspected. When a tagout procedure is inspected, a review on the limitation of tags, in addition to the above requirements, must also be included with each affected and authorized employee.

Application of Controls and Lockout/Tagout Devices

The established procedure of applying energy controls includes the specific elements and actions that must be implemented in sequence.
- Prepare for shut down;
- Shut down the machine or equipment;
- Apply the lockout or tagout device;
- Render safe all stored or residual energy; and
- Verify the isolation and deenergization of the machine or equipment.

Removal of Locks and Tags

Before lockout or tagout devices are removed and energy is restored to the machine or equipment, the authorized employee(s) must take the following actions or observe the following procedures:
- Inspect the work area to ensure that non-essential items have been removed and that machine or equipment components are intact and capable of operating properly;
- Check the area around the machine or equipment to ensure that all employees have been safely positioned or removed;
- Notify affected employees immediately after removing locks or tags and before starting the equipment or machines; and

Make sure that only those employees who attached the locks or tags remove them. (In the very few instances when this is not possible, the device may be removed under the direction of the employer, provided that he or she strictly adheres to the specific procedures outlined in the standard.)

Additional Safety Requirements

Special circumstances exist when machines need to be tested or repositioned during servicing, outside (contractor) personnel are at the worksite, servicing or maintenance is performed by a group (rather than one specific person) and shift or personnel changes occur.

Testing or positioning of machines. OSHA allows the temporary removal of locks or tags and the reenergization of the machine or equipment only when necessary under special conditions (e.g., when power is needed for the testing or positioning of machines, equipment or components). The reenergization must be conducted in accordance with the sequence of steps listed below:

- Clear the machines or equipment of tools and materials;
- Remove employees from the machines or equipment area;
- Remove the lockout or tagout devices as specified in the standard;
- Energize and proceed with testing or positioning; and
- Deenergize all systems, isolate the machine or equipment from the energy source, and reapply lockout or tagout devices as specified.

Outside personnel (e.g., contractors). The onsite employer and the outside employer must inform each other of their respective lockout or tagout procedures. Each employer must ensure that his or her personnel understand and comply with all restrictions and/or prohibitions of the other employer's energy control program.

Group lockout or tagout. During all group lockout/tagout operations where the release of hazardous energy is possible, each authorized employee performing service or maintenance shall be protected by his or her personal lockout or tagout device or a comparable mechanism that provides equivalent protection.

Shift or personnel changes. Specific procedures must ensure the continuity of lockout or tagout protection during shift or personnel changes.

Lockout/Tagout Glossary

Affected employee. An employee who performs the duties of his or her job in an area in which the energy control procedure is implemented and servicing or maintenance operations are performed. An affected employee does not perform servicing or maintenance on machines or equipment and, consequently, is not responsible for implementing the energy control procedure. An affected employee becomes an "authorized" employee when he or she performs servicing or maintenance functions on machines or equipment that must be locked or tagged.

Authorized employee. An employee who performs servicing or maintenance on machines and equipment. Lockout or tagout is used by these employees for their own protection.

Capable of being locked out. An energy-isolating device is considered capable of being locked out if it meets one of the following requirements:

- It is designed with a clasp to which a lock can be attached;
- It is designed with any other integral part through which a lock can be affixed;
- It has a locking mechanism built into it; or
- It can be locked without dismantling, rebuilding, or replacing the energy isolating device or permanently altering its energy control capability.

Energized. Machines and equipment are energized when (1) they are connected to an energy source or (2) they contain residual or stored energy.

Energy-isolating device. Any mechanical device that physically prevents the transmission or release of energy. These include, but are not limited to, manually operated electrical circuit breakers, disconnect switches, line valves and blocks.

Energy source. Any source of electrical, mechanical, hydraulic, pneumatic, chemical, thermal or other energy.

Energy control procedure. A written document that contains those items of information

Machine Guarding

an authorized employee needs to know to safely control hazardous energy during servicing or maintenance of machines or equipment.

Energy control program. A program intended to prevent the unexpected energizing or the release of stored energy in machines or equipment on which servicing and maintenance is being performed by employees. The program consists of energy control procedures, an employee-training program and periodic inspections.

Lockout. The placement of a lockout device on an energy-isolating device, in accordance with an established procedure, ensuring that the energy-isolating device and the equipment being controlled cannot be operated until the lockout device is removed.

Lockout device. Any device that uses positive means such as a lock, either key or combination, to hold an energy-isolating device in a safe position, thereby preventing the energizing of machinery or equipment. When properly installed, a blank flange or bolted slip blind are considered equivalent to lockout devices.

Tagout. The placement of a tagout device on an energy-isolating device, in accordance with an established procedure, to indicate that the energy-isolating device and the equipment being controlled may not be operated until the tagout device is removed.

Tagout device. Any prominent warning device, such as a tag and a means of attachment that can be securely fastened to an energy-isolating device in accordance with an established procedure. The tag indicates that the machine or equipment to which it is attached is not to be operated until the tagout device is removed in accordance with the energy control procedure.

OSHA Instruction STD 1-7.3 SEP 11, 1990 Directorate of Compliance Programs

SUBJECT: 29 CFR 1910.147, the Control of Hazardous Energy (Lockout/Tagout)—Inspection Procedures and Interpretive Guidance

A. **Purpose.** This instruction establishes policies and provides clarification to ensure uniform enforcement of the Lockout/Tagout Standards.
B. **Scope.** This instruction applies OSHA-wide.
C. **References.**
 1. General Industry Standards, 29 CFR 1910, Subpart 0, Subpart S, and other specific subparts.
 2. OSHA Instruction CPL 2.45B, June 15, 1989, the Revised Field Operations Manual (FOM).
D. **Effective Date of Requirements.** All requirements of 29 CFR 1910.147 have an effective date of January 2, 1990. The information collection requirements contained in this section have been approved by the Office of Management and Budget (OMB) and listed under OMB control number 1218-0150, as announced at Federal Register, Volume, 54, No. 199, October 1989.
E. **Action.** Regional Administrators and Area Directors shall ensure that the guidelines and interpretive guidance in this instruction are followed and that compliance officers are familiar with the contents of the standard.
F. **Federal Program Change.** This instruction describes a Federal program change that affects State programs. Each Regional Administrator shall:
 1. Ensure that this change is forwarded to each State designee.
 2. Explain the technical content of this change to the State designee as requested.
 3. Ensure that State designees acknowledge receipt of this Federal program change in writing, within 30 days of notification, to the Regional Administrator. This acknowledgment should include the State's intention to follow the inspection guidelines described in this instruction, or a description of the State's alternative guidelines which are "at least as effective" as the Federal guidelines.
  a. If a State intends to follow the revised inspection guidelines described in this instruction, the State must submit either a revised version of this instruction, adapted as appropriate to reference State law, regulations and administrative structure, or a cover sheet describing how references in this instruction correspond to the State's structure. The State's acknowledgment letter may fulfill the plan supplement requirement if the appropriate documentation is provided.

b. Any alternative State inspection guidelines must be submitted as a State plan supplement within 6 months. If the State adopts an alternative to Federal guidelines, the State's submission must identify and provide a rationale for all substantial differences from Federal guidelines in order for OSHA to judge whether a different State guideline is as effective as a comparable Federal guideline.

4. After Regional review of the State plan supplement and resolution of any comments thereon, forward the State submission to the National Office in accordance with established procedures. The Regional Administrator shall provide a judgment on the relative effectiveness of each substantial difference in the State plan change and an overall assessment thereof with a recommendation for approval or disapproval by the Assistant Secretary.

5. Review policies, instructions and guidelines issued by the State to determine that this change has been communicated to State personnel.

G. **Background.** The Standard for Control of Hazardous Energy (Lockout/Tagout), 29 CFR 1910.147, was promulgated on September 1, 1989, at Federal Register, Volume 54, No. 169 (pages 36644-36696), and was effective on January 2, 1990, as announced at Federal Register, Volume 54, No. 213, November 6, 1989 (page 46610). Previously existing section 29 CFR 1910.147 was redesignated as 29 CFR 1910.150, Sources of Standards.

1. Since the inception of its enforcement program, OSHA has relied on the "General Duty Clause". (Section 5(a)(1) of the OSH Act) to ensure that employers safeguarded their maintenance and service employees through the use of lockout/tagout from the hazards involving the unintentional release of hazardous energy. Such violations reached a level so significant that the development and promulgation of a lockout/tagout standard was required.

2. The new rule addresses practices and procedures that are necessary to disable machinery or equipment and to prevent the release of potentially hazardous energy while maintenance and servicing activities are being performed.

3. The lockout/tagout provisions of this standard are for the protection of general industry workers while performing servicing and maintenance functions and augment the safeguards specified at Subparts 0, S, and other applicable portions of 29 CFR 1910.

H. **Inspection Guidelines.** The standard incorporates performance requirements which allow employers flexibility in developing lockout/tagout programs suitable for their particular facilities.

1. The compliance officer shall determine whether servicing and maintenance operations are performed by the employees. If so, the compliance officers shall further determine whether the servicing and maintenance operations are covered by 29 CFR 1910.147 or by the requirements of employee safeguarding specified by other standards as discussed in I.1.

2. Evaluations of compliance with 29 CFR 1910.147 shall be conducted during all general industry inspections within the scope of the standard in accordance with the FOM, Chapter III, D.7. and 8., Additional Information or Supplement Records Review. The review of records shall include special attention to injuries related to maintenance and servicing operations.

3. The compliance officer shall evaluate the employer's compliance with the specific requirements of the standard. The following guidance provides a general framework to assist the compliance officer during inspections:

a. Ask the employer for any hazard analysis or other basis on which the program related to the standard was developed. Although this is not a specific requirement of the standard, such information, when provided, will aid in determining the adequacy of the program. It should be noted that the absence of a hazard analysis does not indicate non-compliance with the standard.

b. Ask the employer for the documentation including: procedures for the control of hazardous energy including shutdown, equipment isolation, lockout/tagout application, release of stored energy, verification of isolation; certification of periodic inspections;

and certification of training. The documented procedure must identify the specific types of energy to be controlled and, in instances where a common procedure is to be used, the specific equipment covered by the common procedure must be identified at least by type and location. The identification of the energy to be controlled may be by magnitude and type of energy. Note the exception to documentation requirements at paragraph 1910.147(c)(4)(i), "Note". The employer need not document the required procedure for a particular machine or equipment when all eight(8) elements listed in the "Note" exist.

   c. Evaluate the employer's training programs for "authorized", "affected", and "other" employees. Interview a representative sampling of selected employees as a part of this evaluation (29 CFR 1910.147(c)(7)(i)).

     (1) Verify that the training of authorized employees includes:

       (a) Recognition of hazardous energy;

       (b) Type and magnitude of energy found in the workplace;

       (c) The means and methods of isolating and/or controlling energy; and

       (d) The means of verification of effective energy control, and the purpose of the procedures to be used.

     (2) Verify that affected employees have been instructed in the purpose and use of the energy control procedures.

     (3) Verify that all other employees who may be affected by the energy control procedures are instructed about the procedure and the prohibition relating to attempts to restart or reenergize such machines or equipment.

     (4) When the employer's procedures permit the use of tagout, the training of authorized, affected, and other employees shall include the provisions of 29 CFR 1910.147(c)(7)(ii) and (d)(4)(iii).

   d. Evaluate the employer's manner of enforcing the program (29 CFR 1910.147(c)(4)(ii)).

4. In the event that deficiencies are identified by following the guidelines in H.3. of this instruction, the compliance officer shall evaluate the employer's compliance with specific requirements of the standard, with particular attention to the interpretive guidance provided in section I. and to the following:

   a. Evaluate compliance with the requirements for periodic inspection of procedures.

   b. Ensure that the person performing the periodic inspection is an authorized employee other than the one(s) utilizing the procedure being inspected.

   c. Evaluate compliance with retraining requirements which result from the periodic inspection of procedures and practices, or from changes in equipment/processes.

   d. Evaluate the employer's procedures for assessment, and correction of deviations or inadequacies identified during periodic inspections of the energy control procedure.

   e. Identify the procedures for release from lockout/tagout, including:

     (1) Replacement of safeguards, machine or equipment inspection, and removal of non-essential tools and equipment;

     (2) Safe positioning of employees;

     (3) Removal of lockout/tagout device(s); and

     (4) Notification of affected employees that servicing and maintenance is completed.

   f. Ensure that when group lockout or tagout is used, it affords a level of protection equivalent to individual lockout or tagout as amplified in I.7. through I.9. of this instruction

5. The lockout/tagout standard is a performance standard; therefore, additional guidance is provided in Appendix C of this instruction to assist in effective implementation by employers and for uniform enforcement by OSHA field staff.

I. **Interpretive Guidance.** The following guidance relative to specific provisions of 29 CFR 1910.147 is provided to assist compliance officers in conducting inspections where the standard may be applicable:

1. **Scope of the Standard.**
   a. The standard as specified in 29 CFR 1910.147(b), applies to any source of mechanical, hydraulic, pneumatic, chemical, thermal, or other energy.
      (1) The standard applies to piping systems, and requires, at 29 CFR 1910.147(d)(5), that all potentially hazardous stored or residual energy be relieved, disconnected, restrained, and otherwise rendered safe. If there is a possibility of reaccumulation of stored energy to a hazardous level, continued monitoring shall be performed while a potential hazard exists.
      (2) The standard also applies to high intensity electromagnetic fields regulated at 29 CFR 1910.97, nonionizing radiation. Such electromagnetic devices shall be deenergized and held off whenever workers are present within a high intensity ambient field.
      (3) Servicing/maintenance of fire alarm and extinguishing systems and their components, upon which other employees are dependent for fire safety, are not required to meet the requirements of this standard if the workers performing servicing/maintenance upon fire extinguishing systems are protected from hazards related to the unexpected release of hazardous energy by appropriate alternative measures. (See 29 CFR 1910, Subpart L.)
   b. The standard does not apply to servicing and maintenance when employees are not exposed to the unexpected released of hazardous energy.
   c. Safeguarding workers from the hazards of contacting electrically live parts (exposure to electric current) continues to be regulated at Subpart S.
   d. Servicing and maintenance functions conducted during normal production operations are not regulated at 29 CFR 1910.147 if the safeguarding provisions of Subpart O or other applicable portions of 29 CFR 1910 prevent worker exposure to hazards created by the unexpected energization or start-up of the machine or equipment. However, lockout/tagout procedures are required if the production safeguards are rendered ineffective while an employee is exposed to hazardous portions of the machines or equipment.
   e. Generally, activities such as lubrication, cleaning or unjamming, servicing of machines or equipment, and making adjustments or tool changes, where the employee may be exposed to the UNEXPECTED energization of start-up of the equipment or release of hazardous energy, are covered by this standard. However, minor tool changes and adjustments, and other minor servicing activities, which take place during normal production operations, are not covered by this standard if they are routine, repetitive, and integral to the use of equipment for production, and if work is performed using alternative protective measures which provide effective employee protection. Thus, lockout or tagout is not required by this standard if the alternative protective measures enable the servicing employee to clean or unjam, or otherwise service the machine without being exposed to unexpected energization or activation of the equipment, or the release of stored energy.
   f. The exclusion of plug and cord connected electric equipment, at 29 CFR 1910.147(a)(2)(iii)(A), applies only when the equipment is unplugged and the plug is under the exclusive control of the employee performing the servicing and/or maintenance.
      (1) The plug is under the exclusive control of the employee if it is physically in the possession of the employee, or in arm's reach and in the line of sight of the employee, or if the employee has affixed a lockout/tagout device on the plug.
      (2) The company lockout/tagout procedures required by the standard at 29 CFR 1910.147(c)(4) shall specify the acceptable procedure for handling cord and plug connected equipment.

2. **Procedures.**
   a. The employer must develop and document procedures and techniques to be used for the control of hazardous energy. The standard, at 29 CFR 1910.147(c)(4)(i) "Note," identifies eight (8) conditions that must exist in order to excuse the employer's obligation to maintain a written procedure for a specific machine or piece of equipment.

b. 29 CFR 1910.147(d)(3) and (d)(5) provide that energy isolation be a mandatory part of employer's control procedure where either a lockout system or a tagout system is used.

c. Similar machines and/or equipment (such as those using the same type and magnitude of energy and the same or similar types of controls) can be covered with a single written procedure.

3. **Lockout vs. Tagout.**

a. OSHA has determined that lockout is a surer means of ensuring deenergization of equipment than tagout, and that it is the preferred method.

b. 29 CFR 1910.147(c)(3)(ii) provides that: When using a tagout program in those instances where the equipment is capable of being locked out, the employer shall demonstrate that the tagout program will provide a level of safety equivalent to the obtained when using a lockout program. Additional means beyond those necessary for lockout are required. (Additional means include: additional safety measures such as the removal of an isolating circuit element, blocking of a controlling switch, opening of an extra disconnecting device, or the removal of a valve handle to reduce the likelihood of inadvertent energization.)

c. 29 CFR 1910.147(c)(4)(ii) provides that: Where lockout/tagout programs are used, the employer is required to implement an effective means of enforcing the program.

d. 29 CFR 1910.147(c)(7)(ii)(A-F) provide that: Additional training of authorized, affected and other employees is required when tagout programs are used.

e. 29 CFR 1910.147(c)(5)(ii)(A) requires that lockout and tagout devices be capable of withstanding the environment to which they are exposed. Devices which are not exposed to harsh environments need not be capable of withstanding such exposure.

f. 29 CFR 1910.147(c)(5)(ii)(C)(2) requires that tagout devices having reusable, non-locking, easily detachable means of attachment (such as string, cord, or adhesive) are not permitted.

4. **Employees and Training.**

a. The standard recognized three types of employees: (1) "authorized" and (2) "affected", defined in 1910.147(b), and (3) "other", defined in 1910.147(c)(7)(ii)(C). Different levels of training are required based upon the respective roles of employees in the control of energy and the knowledge which they must possess to accomplish their tasks safely and to ensure the safety of fellow workers as related to the lockout/tagout procedures (1910.147(c)(7)(i)).

b. Employees who exclusively perform functions related to normal production operations, and who perform servicing and/or maintenance under the protection of normal machine safeguarding, need only be trained as "affected" (rather than "authorized") employees even if tagout procedures are used. (See I.1.d. and I.1.e. of this instruction.)

c. The employer's training program must cover, at a minimum, the following three areas: energy control program, elements of energy control procedures relevant to employee duties, and the pertinent requirements of the standard (1910.147(c)(7) and (d) through (f)).

d. The employer must provide:
   (1) Effective initial training;
   (2) Effective retraining as needed; and
   (3) Certification of training. The certification shall contain each employee's, name and dates of training (1910.147(c)(7)(iv)).

e. Retraining of authorized and affected employees is required:
   (1) Whenever there is a change in employee job assignments;
   (2) Whenever a new hazard is introduced due to a change in machines, equipment or process;
   (3) Whenever there is a change in the energy control procedures; or

(4) Whenever a periodic inspection by the employer reveals inadequacies in the company procedures or in the knowledge of the employees.

5.

a. At least annually, the employer shall ensure that an authorized employee other than the one(s) utilizing the energy control procedure being inspected, is required to inspect and verify the effectiveness of the company energy control procedures. These inspections shall at least provide for a demonstration of the procedures and may be implemented through random audits and planned visual observations. These inspections are intended to ensure that the energy control procedures are being properly implemented and to provide an essential check on the continued utilization of the procedures (29 CFR 1910.147(c)(6)(i)).

(1) When lockout is used, the employer's inspection shall include a review of the responsibilities of each authorized employee implementing the procedure with that employee. Group meetings between the authorized employee who is performing the inspection and all authorized employees who implement the procedure would constitute compliance with this requirement.

(2) When tagout is used, the employer shall conduct this review with each affected and authorized employee.

(3) Energy control procedures used less frequently than once a year need be inspected only when used.

b. The periodic inspection must provide for and ensure effective correction of identified deficiencies (29 CFR 1910.147(c)(6)(i)(B)).

c. The employer is required to certify that the prescribed periodic inspections have been performed (29 CFR 1910.147(c)(6)(ii)).

6. **Equipment Testing or Positioning.** Under 29 CFR 1910.147(f)(1), OSHA allows the temporary removal of lockout or tagout devices and the reenergization of the machine or equipment ONLY during the limited time necessary for the testing or positioning of machines, equipment or components. After the completion of the temporary reenergization, the authorized employees shall again deenergize the equipment and resume lockout/tagout procedures.

7. **Group Lockout/Tagout.** Group lockout/tagout procedures shall be tailored to the specific industrial operation and may be unique in the manner that employee protection from the release of hazardous energy is achieved. Irrespective of the situation, the requirements of this generic standard specify that each employee performing maintenance or servicing activities shall be in control of hazardous energy during his/her period of exposure.

a. Group operations normally require that a lockout/tagout program be implemented which ensures that each authorized employee is protected from the unexpected release of hazardous energy by his/her personal lockout/tagout device(s). No employee may affix the personal lockout/tagout device of another employee. Various group lockout/tagout procedures discussed in Appendix C provide for each authorized employee's use of his/her personal lockout/tagout device(s).

b. One of the most difficult problems addressed by the standard involves the servicing and maintenance of complex equipment. Such equipment is frequently used in the petrochemical and chemical industries. Acceptable group lockout/tagout procedures for complex equipment are discussed further at Appendix C.

8. **Compliance with Group Lockout/Tagout.** These operations shall, at a minimum, provide for the following:

a. Before the machine or equipment is shut down, each authorized employee who is to be involved during the servicing/maintenance operation shall be made aware by the employer of the type, magnitude, and hazards related to the energy to be controlled and of the method or means to control the energy. In the event that the machine or equipment is already shut down, the authorized employee shall be made aware of these elements before beginning his/her work (29 CFR 1910.147(d)(1)). Verification shall be performed as noted at I.8.f. of this instruction.

b. An orderly shutdown of the machine or equipment shall be conducted which conforms to the documented company procedure and which will not create hazards (29 CFR 1910.147(d)(2)).

c. All energy isolating devices needed to isolate the machine or equipment shall be effectively positioned and/or installed (29 CFR 1910.147(d)(3)).

d. The authorized employee(s) performing the servicing or maintenance (following the company procedure) shall personally affix a lock or tag upon each energy isolating device (29 CFR 1910.147(d)(4)(i)). The company procedure must ensure that no employee affixes a personal lockout/tagout device for another employee.

   (1) A single lock upon each energy isolating device, together with the use of a lockbox for retention of the keys and to which each authorized employee affixes his/her personal lock or tag, also satisfies the requirements (29 CFR 1910.147(f)(3)(i)).

   (2) Locks shall be affixed in a manner that will hold the energy isolating device in a safe (off) position (29 CFR 1910.147(d)(4)(ii)).

   (3) Tagout devices, where used, shall be affixed at the same location as would a lock if such fittings are provided, or shall be affixed in a manner that will clearly indicate that movement of the isolating device is prohibited (29 CFR 1910.147(d)(4)(iii)).

e. Following the application of locks or tags, all potentially hazardous stored energy or residual energy shall be relieved, disconnected, restrained, and otherwise rendered safe (29 CFR 1910.147(d)(5)(i)).

   (1) Verification of energy isolation shall be monitored as frequently as necessary if there is a possibility of reaccumulation of stored energy (29 CFR 1910.147(d)(5)(ii)).

   (2) Monitoring may be accomplished, for example, by observation or with the aid of a monitoring device which will sound an alarm if a hazardous energy level is being approached.
   Authorized employees shall verify that isolation and deenergization have been effectively accomplished before starting servicing/maintenance work. Verification is also necessary by each group of workers before starting work at shift changes.

g. Release from lockout/tagout shall be accomplished in compliance with the requirements of 29 CFR 1910.147(e).

   (1) The machine or equipment area shall be cleared of nonessential items to prevent malfunctions which could result in employee injuries (29 CFR 1910.147(e)(1)).

   (2) The authorized employees shall remove their respective locks or tags from the energy isolating devices or from the group lock-box(s) following the procedure established by the company (29 CFR 1910.147(e)(3)).

   (3) In all instances, the company procedure must provide a system which identifies each authorized employee involved in the servicing/maintenance operation.

   (4) Before reenergization, all employees in the machine or equipment area shall be safely positioned or moved from the area, and the affected employees shall be notified that the lockout/tagout devices have been removed (29 CFR 1910.147(e)(2)).

h. During all group lockout/tagout operations where the release of hazardous energy is possible, each authorized employee performing servicing or maintenance shall be protected by his/her personal lockout or tagout device and by the company procedure. As described at Appendix C, B.1.g., a master tag is a personal tagout device if each employee personally signs on and signs off on it and if the tag clearly identifies each authorized employee who is being protected by it.

9. **Compliance of Outside Personnel.** Outside servicing and maintenance personnel (contractors, etc.) engaged in activities regulated under 29 CFR 1910.147 are subject to the requirements of that standard.

a. The CSHO shall verify that the outside employer and the on-site employer have exchanged information regarding the lockout/tagout energy control procedures used by each employer's workers (29 CFR 1910.147(f)(2)(i)).

b. The CSHO shall verify that the on-site employer has effectively informed his/her personnel of the restrictions and prohibitions associated with the outside employer's energy control procedures (29 CFR 1910.147(f)(2)(ii)).

c. When an outside employer's is engaged in servicing and maintenance activities within an on-site employer's facility and if that contractor's activities are subject to the requirements of 29 CFR 1910.147, the CSHO shall coordinate with the Area Director to obtain permission to initiate an independent inspection of the outside contractor's activities.

10. Appendix B contains an example of a functional flow diagram to implement safe lockout/tagout procedures. This flow diagram is presented solely as an aid and does not constitute the exclusive or definitive means of complying with the standard in any particular situation.

J. **Classification of Violations.**

1. A deficiency in the employer's energy control program and/or procedure that could contribute to a potential exposure capable of producing serious physical harm or death shall be cited as a serious violation.

2. The failure to train "authorized", "affected", and "other" employees as required for their respective classification should normally be cited as a serious violation

3. Paperwork deficiencies in lockout/tagout programs where effective lockout/tagout work procedures are in place shall be cited as other-than-serious.

K. **Evaluation.** In keeping with agency policy, each Region shall evaluate the effectiveness of the guidance in this instruction annually. Each Regional Administrator shall submit a written evaluation report to the Directorate of Compliance Program within 30 day of the close of the fiscal year.

Gerard F. Scannell Assistant Secretary
DISTRIBUTION: National, Regional, and Area Offices All Compliance Officers State Designees NIOSH Regional Program Directors (7)(c)(1) Consultation Project Managers OSHA Training Institute

Appendix A

The following listing indicates a number of OSHA standards which currently impose lockout/tagout related requirements. The list does not necessarily include all lockout/tagout related OSHA 29 CFR 1910 standards.

Powered Industrial Trucks	1910.178(q)(4)
Overhead and Gantry Cranes	1910.179(g)(5)(i), (ii), (iii), 1910.179(l)(2)(i)(c), (d)
Derricks	1910.181(f)(2)(i)(c), (d)
Woodworking Machinery	1910.213(a)(10), 1910.213(b)(5)
Mechanical Power Presses	1910.217(b)(8)(i), 1910.217(d)(9)(iv)
Forging Machines	1910.218(a)(3)(iii), (v), 1910.218(d)(2)
	1910.218(e)(1)(ii), (iii), 1910.218(f)(1)(i), (ii), (iii), 1910.218(f)(2)(i), (ii), 1910.218(h)(2), (5), 1910.218(i)(1), (2), 1910.218(j)(1)
Welding, Cutting and Brazing	1910.252(c)(1)(i)
Pulp, Paper and Paperboard Mills	1910.261(b)(4), 1910.261(f)(6)(i), 1910.261(g)(15)(i)
	1910.261(g)(19)(iii), 1910.261(j)(4)(iii), 1910.261(j)(5)(iii), 1910.261(k)(2)(ii)
Textiles	1910.262(c)(1), 1910.262(n)(2), 1910.262(p)(1), 1910.262(q)(2)
Bakery Equipment	1910.263(l)(3)(iii)(b), 1910.263(l)(8)(iii)
Sawmills	1910.265(c)(12)(v), 1910.265(c)(13), 1910.265(c)(26)(v)
Grain Handling	1910.272(e)(1)(ii), 1910.272(g)(1)(ii), 1910.272(l)(4)
Electrical	1910.305(j)(4)(ii)(A), 1910.305(j)(4)(ii)(c)(1)

[Appendix B excluded.]

Appendix C

This appendix provides guidelines to assist the compliance officer during evaluations of employer operations.

A. **Normal Production Operations.** The lockout/tagout standard, 29 CFR 1910.147, addresses the safety of employees engaged in servicing and maintenance activities in general industry workplaces. The standard complements the requirements for machine and process operator safety prescribed by the various general industry standards in 29 CFR Part 1910. Subpart 0 of 29 CFR 1910 provides the principal, though not exclusive, machine guarding requirements.

1. Safeguarding of servicing and maintenance workers can be ensured either by:
   a. Effective machine safeguarding in compliance with Subpart 0, or
   b. Compliance with 29 CFR 1910.147 in situations where the normal production operations safeguards are rendered ineffective or do not protect the servicing/maintenance worker.

2. Activities which are routine, repetitive, and integral to the use of equipment for production are not covered by this standard if alternative measures provide effective worker protection from hazards associated with unexpected energization. Compliance with the machine guarding requirements of Subpart 0 is an example of such alternative measures. In addition, supplemental personal protective equipment may be necessary during a servicing or maintenance operation when a toxic substance is to be isolated. Under such circumstances, the requirements of applicable standards, such as 29 CFR 1910.134 and Subpart Z, also must be met.

3. An employer who requires employees to perform routine maintenance and/or servicing while a machine or process is operating in the production mode, must provide employee safeguarding under the applicable requirements of Subpart 0. (Ref. 29 CFR 1910.212(a)(1)). Operations such as lubricating, draining sumps, servicing of filters, and inspection for leaks and/or mechanical malfunction are examples of routine operations which can be

accomplished with effective production-mode safeguards. However, the replacement of machine or process equipment components such as valves, gauges, linkages, support structure, etc., is not considered to be normal routine maintenance function which can safely be accomplished during machine or process equipment operation. Such maintenance requires energy isolation and should be evaluated by OSHA field staff. They also may be an appropriate subject of a variance request.

4. Several alternative means of safeguarding the hazardous portions of machines and equipment are presented by the national consensus standard, ANSI B11.19-1990. Although that standard is not all inclusive, it describes effective safeguarding alternatives for the protection of employees. The safeguards described include: interlocked barrier guards, presence sensing devices and various devices under the exclusive control of the employee. Such devices or guards, properly applied, may be used in clearing minor jams and performing other minor servicing functions which occur during normal production operations and which meet the criteria described in paragraph A.2. of this appendix.

B. **Group Lockout/Tagout.** The group lockout/tagout procedures described in this instruction at paragraph I.8. require each authorized employee to be in control of potentially hazardous energy release during their servicing/maintenance work assignments. Under most circumstances, where servicing/maintenance is to be conducted during only one shift by an individual or a small number of persons working together, the installation of each individual's lockout/tagout device upon each energy isolating device would not be a burdensome procedure. However, when many energy sources or many persons are involved, and/or the procedure is to extend over more than one shift, (possibly several days, or weeks) consideration must be given to the implementation of a lockout/tagout procedure that will ensure the safety of the employees involved and will provide for each individual's control of the energy hazards. The following procedures are presented as examples to illustrate the implementation of a group lockout/tagout procedure involving many energy isolating devices and/or many servicing/maintenance personnel. They illustrate several alternatives for having authorized employees affix personal lockout/tagout devices in a group lockout/tagout setting. Theses examples are not intended to represent the only acceptable procedures for conducting group operations.

1. **Definitions.** Various terms used in the examples are defined below.

    a. PRIMARY AUTHORIZED EMPLOYEE is the authorized employee who exercises overall responsibility for adherence to the company lockout/tagout procedures. (See 29 CFR 1910.147(f)(3)(ii)(A).)

    b. PRINCIPAL AUTHORIZED EMPLOYEE is an authorized employee who oversees or leads a group of servicing/maintenance workers (e.g., plumbers, carpenters, electricians, metal workers, mechanics).

    c. JOB-LOCK is a device used to ensure the continuity of energy isolation during a multi-shift operation. It is placed upon a lock-box. A key to the job-lock is controlled by each assigned primary authorized employee from each shift.

    d. JOB-TAG with TAB is a special tag for tagout of energy isolating devices during group lockout/tagout procedures. The tab of the tag is removed for insertion into the lock-box. The company procedure would require that the tagout job-tag cannot be removed until the tab is rejoined to it.

    e. MASTER LOCKBOX is the lockbox into which all keys and tabs from the lockout or, tagout devices securing the machine or equipment are inserted and which would be secured by a "job-lock" during multi-shift operations.

    f. SATELLITE LOCKBOX is a secondary lockbox or lock-boxes to which each authorized employee affixes his/her personal lock or tag.

    g. MASTER TAG is a document used as an administrative control and accountability device. This device is normally controlled by the operations department personnel and is a personal tagout device if each employee personally signs on and signs off on it and if the tag clearly identifies each authorized employee who is being protected by it.

    h. WORK PERMIT is a control document which authorizes specific tasks and procedures to be accomplished.

2. **Organization.** A group lockout/tagout procedure might provide the following basic organizational structure:

    a. A primary authorized employee would be designated. This employee would exercise primary responsibility for implementation and coordination of the lockout/tagout of hazardous energy sources, for the equipment to be serviced.

    b. The primary authorized employee would coordinate with equipment operators before and after completion of servicing and maintenance operations which require lockout/tagout.

    c. A verification system would be implemented to ensure the continued isolation and deenergization of hazardous energy sources during maintenance and servicing operations.

    d. Each authorized employee would be assured of his/her right to verify individually that the hazardous energy has been isolated and/or deenergized.

    e. When more than one crew, craft, department, etc., is involved, each separate group of servicing/maintenance personnel would be accounted for by a principal authorized employee from each group. Each principal employee is responsible to the primary authorized employee for maintaining accountability of each worker in that specific group in conformance with the company procedure. No person may sign on or sign off for another person, or attach or remove another person's lockout/tagout device, unless the provisions of the exception to 29 CFR 1910.147(e)(3) are met.

3. **Examples of Procedures for Group Lockout/Tagout.** Examples are presented for the various methods of lockout/tagout using lockbox procedures. An example of an applicable method for complex process equipment is also presented.

    a. The following procedures address circumstances ranging from a small group of servicing/maintenance employees during a one-shift operation to a comprehensive operation involving many over a longer period.

        (1) *Type A.* Each authorized employee places his/her personal lock or tag upon each energy isolating device and removes it upon departure from that assignment. Each authorized employee verifies or observes the deenergization of the equipment.

        (2) *Type B.* Under a lockbox procedure, a lock or job-tag with tab is placed upon each energy isolation device after deenergization. The key(s) and removed tab(s) are then placed into a lockbox. Each authorized employee assigned to the job then affixes his/her personal lock or tag to the lockbox. As a member of a group, each assigned authorized employee verifies that all hazardous energy has been rendered safe. The lockout/tagout devices cannot be removed or the energy isolating device turned on until the appropriate key or tab is matched to its lock or tag.

        (3) *Type C.* After each energy isolating device is locked/tagged out and the keys/tabs placed into a master lockbox, each servicing/maintenance group "principal" authorized employee places his/her personal lock or tag upon the master lockbox. Then each principal authorized employee inserts his/her key into a satellite lockbox to which each authorized employee in that specific group affixes his/her personal lock or tag. As a member of a group, each assigned authorized employee verifies that all hazardous energy has been rendered safe. Only after the servicing/maintenance functions of the specific subgroup have been concluded and the personal locks or tags of the respective employees have been removed from the satellite lockbox can the principal authorized employee remove his/her lock from the master lockbox.

        (4) *Type D.* During operations to be conducted over more than one shift or even many days or weeks) a system such as described here might be used. Single locks/tags are affixed upon a lockbox by each authorized employee as described at Type B or Type C above. The master lockbox is first secured with a job-lock before subsequent

locks by the principal authorized employees are put in place on the master lockbox. The job-lock may have multiple keys if they are in the sole possession of the various primary authorized employees (one on each shift). As a member of a group, each assigned authorized employee verifies that all hazardous energy has been rendered safe. In this manner, the security provisions of the energy control system are maintained across shift changes while permitting reenergization of the equipment at any appropriate time or shift.

b. Normal group lockout/tagout procedures require the affixing of individual lockout/tagout devices by each authorized employee to a group lockout device, as discussed in paragraph B.3.a. of this appendix. However, in the servicing and maintenance of sophisticated and complex equipment, such as process equipment in petroleum refining, petroleum production, and chemical production, there may be a need for adaptation and modification of normal group lockout/tagout procedures in order to ensure the safety of the employees performing the servicing and maintenance. To provide greater worker safety through implementation of a more feasible system, and to accommodate the special constraints of the standard's requirement for ensuring employees a level of protection equivalent to that provided by the use of a personal lockout or tagout device, an alternative procedure may be implemented if the company documentation justifies it. Lockout/tagout, blanking, blocking, etc., is often supplemented in these situations by the use of work permits and a system of continuous worker accountability. In evaluating whether the equipment being serviced or maintained is so complex as to necessitate a departure from the normal group lockout/tagout procedures (discussed in paragraph B.3.a.), to the use of an alternative procedures as set forth below, the following (often occurring simultaneously) are some of those which must be evaluated: physical size and extent of the equipment being serviced/maintained; the relative inaccessibility of the energy isolating devices; the number of employees performing the servicing/maintenance; the number of energy isolating devices to be locked/tagged out; and the interdependence and interrelationship of the components in the system or between different systems.

(1) Once the equipment is shut down and the hazardous energy has been controlled, maintenance/servicing personnel, together with operations personnel, must verify that the isolation of the equipment is effective. The workers may walk through the affected work area to verify isolation. If there is a potential for the release or re-accumulation of hazardous energy, verification of isolation must be continued. The servicing/maintenance workers may further verify the effectiveness of the isolation by the procedures that are used in doing the work (e.g., using a bleeder valve to verify depressurization, flange-breaking techniques, etc.). Throughout the maintenance and/or servicing activity, operations personnel normally maintain control of the equipment. The use of the work permit or "master tag" system (with each employee personally signing on and signing off the job to ensure continual employee accountability and control), combined with verification of hazardous energy control, work procedures, and walk-through, is an acceptable approach to compliance with the group lockout/tagout and shift transfer provisions of the standard. (Note, B.1.g. of this appendix.)

(2) Specific issues related to the control of hazardous energy in complex process equipment are described below in a typical situation which could be found at any facility. This discussion is intended only as an example and is not anticipated to reflect operations at any specific facility.

(a) Complex process equipment which is scheduled for servicing/maintenance operations is generally identified by plant supervision. Plant supervision would issue specific work orders regarding the operations to be performed.

(b) In most instances where complex process equipment is to be serviced or maintained, the process equipment operators can be expected to conduct the shutdown procedure. This is generally due to their in-depth knowledge of the equipment and the need to conduct the shut-down procedure in a safe, economic and specific sequence.

(c) The operations personnel will normally prepare the equipment for lockout/tagout as they proceed and will identify the locations for blanks, blocks, etc., by placing "operations locks and/or tags" on the equipment. The operations personnel can be expected to isolate the hazardous energy, and drain and flush fluids from the process equipment following a standard procedure or a specific work permit procedure.

(d) Upon completion of shutdown, the operations personnel would review the intended job with the servicing and maintenance crew(s) and would ensure their full comprehension of the energy controls necessary to conduct the servicing or maintenance safely. During or immediately after the review of the job, the servicing and maintenance crews would install locks, tags and/or special isolating devices at previously identified equipment locations following the specified work permit procedure.

(e) Line openings necessary for the isolation of the equipment would normally be permitted only by special work permits issued by operations personnel. (Such line openings should be monitored by operations personnel as an added safety measure.)

(f) All of the previous steps should have been documented by a master system of accountability and retained at the primary equipment control station for the duration of the job. The master system of accountability may manifest itself as a Master Tag which is subsequently signed by all of the maintenance/servicing workers if they fully comprehend the details of the job and the energy isolation devices actuated or put in place. This signing by the respective workers further verifies that energy isolation training relative to this operation has been conducted.

(g) After the system has been rendered safe, the authorized employees verify energy controls as described in B.3.b.(1) of the appendix.

(h) Specific work functions are controlled by work permits which are issued for each shift. Each day each authorized employee assigned must sign in on the work permit at the time of arrival to the job and sign out at departure. Signature, date, and time for sign-in and sign-out would be recorded and retained by the applicable crew supervisor who upon completion of the permit requirements would return the permit to the operations supervisor. Work permits could extended beyond a single shift and may subsequently be the responsibility of several supervisors.

(i) Upon completion of the tasks required by the work permit, the authorized employees' names can be signed off the Master Tag by this supervisor once all employees have signed off the work permit. The work permit is then attached to the Master Tag. (Accountability of exposed workers is maintained.)

(j) As the work is completed by the various crews, the work permits and the accountability of personnel are reconciled jointly by the primary authorized employee and the operations supervisor.

(k) During the progress of the work, inspection audits are conducted.

(l) Upon completion of all work, the equipment is returned to the operation personnel after the maintenance and servicing crews have removed their locks, tags, and/or special isolating devices following the company procedure.

(m) At this time all authorized employees who were assigned to the tasks are again accounted for and verified to be clear from the equipment area.

(n) After the completion of the servicing/maintenance work, operations personnel remove the tags originally placed to identify energy isolation.

(o) Operations personnel then begin check-out, verification and testing of the equipment prior to being returned to production service.

c. It should be noted that the purpose of the lockout/tagout standard is to reduce the likelihood of worker injuries and fatalities during servicing/maintenance operations. Therefore, when compliance officers inspect workplaces, they should evaluate the potential for employee exposure to the unexpected release of hazardous energy during servicing/maintenance operations. When a hazard is noted, the various requirements of the standard should be applied in a manner which will result in abatement of the hazardous circumstances.

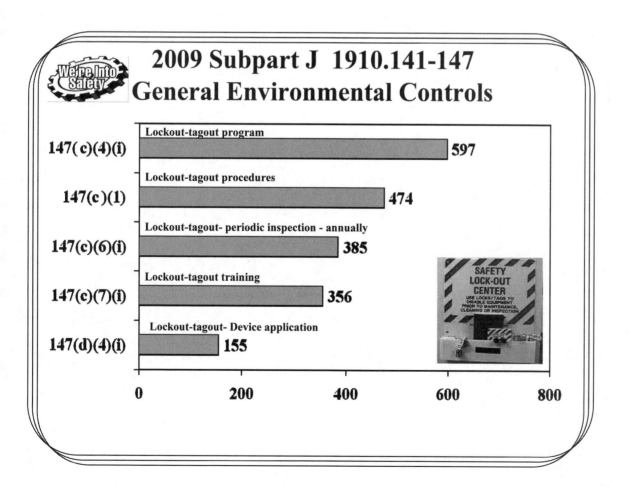

2009 Subpart J 1910.141-147
General Environmental Controls

Standard	Description	Value
147(c)(4)(i)	Lockout-tagout program	597
147(c)(1)	Lockout-tagout procedures	474
147(c)(6)(i)	Lockout-tagout- periodic inspection - annually	385
147(c)(7)(i)	Lockout-tagout training	356
147(d)(4)(i)	Lockout-tagout- Device application	155

HAND AND PORTABLE POWERED TOOLS

Each employer shall be responsible for the safe condition of tools and equipment used by employees, including tools and equipment that may be furnished by employees. All tools shall be restricted to the use for which they are intended and unsafe hand tools shall not be used.

Employees who use hand and power tools and who are exposed to the hazards of falling, flying, abrasive and splashing objects, or exposed to harmful dusts, fumes, mists, vapors or gases must be provided with the particular personal protective equipment necessary to protect them from the hazard.

Following five basic safety rules can prevent all hazards involved in the use of power tools:
- Keep all tools in good condition with regular maintenance;
- Use the right tool for the job;
- Examine each tool for damage before use;
- Operate according to the manufacturer's instructions; and
- Provide and use the proper protective equipment.

Employees and employers have a responsibility to work together to establish safe working, procedures. If a hazardous situation is encountered, it should be brought to the attention of the proper individual immediately.

Hand Tools

Hand tools are non-powered. They include anything from axes to wrenches. The greatest hazards posed by hand tools result from misuse and improper maintenance.

Some examples of misuse and improper maintenance include:
- Using a screwdriver as a chisel may cause the tip of the screwdriver to break and fly, hitting the user or other employees.
- If a wooden handle on a tool such as a hammer or an ax is loose, splintered or cracked, the head of the tool may fly off and strike the user or another worker.
- A wrench must not be used if its jaws are sprung because it might slip.
- Impact tools such as chisels, wedges or drift pins are unsafe if they have mushroomed heads. The heads might shatter on impact, sending sharp fragments flying.

The employer is responsible for the safe condition of tools and equipment used by employees but the employees are responsible for the proper use and maintenance of the tools.

Employers should caution employees to direct saw blades, knives or other tools away from aisle areas and away from other employees working in close proximity. Knives and scissors must be sharp; dull tools can be more hazardous than sharp ones.

Appropriate personal protective equipment (e.g., safety goggles, gloves) should be worn due to hazards that may be encountered while using portable power tools and hand tools. Floors should be kept as clean and dry as possible to prevent accidental slips with or around dangerous hand tools. Sparks produced by iron and steel hand tools can be a dangerous ignition source around flammable substances. Where this hazard exists, spark-resistant tools made from brass, plastic, aluminum or wood will provide safety.

Power Tools

Power tools can be hazardous when improperly used. There are several types of power tools, based on the power source they use: electric, pneumatic, liquid fuel, hydraulic, and powder-actuated.

Employees should be trained in the use of all tools—not just power tools. They should understand the potential hazards as well as the safety precautions to prevent those hazards from occurring.

Power tool users should observe the following general precautions:

- Never carry a tool by its cord or hose.
- Never yank the cord or the hose to disconnect it from the receptacle.
- Keep cords and hoses away from heat, oil and sharp edges.
- Disconnect tools when not in use, before servicing and when changing accessories such as blades, bits and cutters.
- All observers should be kept at a safe distance from the work area.
- Secure work with clamps or a vise, freeing both hands to operate the tool.
- Avoid accidental starting. The worker should not hold a finger on the switch button while carrying a plugged-in tool.
- Tools should be maintained with care. They should be kept sharp and clean for the best performance.
- Follow instructions in the user's manual for lubricating and changing accessories.

- Be sure to keep good footing and maintain good balance.
- The proper apparel should be worn. Loose clothing, ties or jewelry can become caught in moving parts.
- All portable electric tools that are damaged shall be removed from use and tagged "Do Not Use."

Guards

Hazardous moving parts of a power tool need to be safeguarded. For example, belts, gears, shafts, pulleys, sprockets, spindles, drums, flywheels, chains or other reciprocating, rotating or moving parts of equipment must be guarded if such parts are exposed to contact by employees.

Guards, as necessary, should be provided to protect the operator and others from:

- Point of operation
- In-running nip points
- Rotating parts
- Flying chips and sparks.

Safety Switches

All hand-held powered circular saws having a blade diameter greater than 2 in., electric, hydraulic or pneumatic chain saws, and percussion tools without positive accessory holding means shall be equipped with a constant pressure switch or control that will shut off the power when the pressure is released. All hand-held gasoline-powered chain saws shall be equipped with a constant pressure throttle control that will shut off the power to the saw chain when the pressure is released.

All other hand-held powered drills, tappers, fastener drivers, horizontal, vertical and angle grinders with wheels greater than 2 in. in diameter; disc sanders with discs greater than 2 in. in diameter; belt sanders, reciprocating saws, saber, scroll, and jig saws with blade shanks greater than a nominal ¼ in.; and other similarly operated powered tools shall be equipped with a constant pressure switch or control and may have a lock-on control, provided that turn-off can be accomplished with a single motion of the same finger or fingers that turn it on.

All other hand-held powered tools, such as, but not limited to, platen sanders, grinders with wheels 2 in. in diameter or smaller, disc sanders with discs 2 in. in diameter or smaller; routers, planers, laminate trimmers, nibblers, shears, saber, scroll, and jigsaws with blade shanks a nominal ¼ in. wide or smaller, may be equipped with either a positive "on-off" control or other controls as described in this section.

The operating control on hand-held power tools shall be so located as to minimize the possibility of its accidental operation if such accidental operation would constitute a hazard to employees.

The following hand-held powered tools must be equipped with a momentary contact "on-off" control switch:

- Drills
- Tappers
- Fastener drivers;
- Horizontal, vertical and angle grinders with wheels larger than 2 in. in diameter and
- Disc and belt sanders, reciprocating saws, saber saws and other similar tools.

These tools also may be equipped with a lock-on control, provided that turn-off can be accomplished with a single motion of the same finger or fingers that turn it on.

The following hand-held powered tools may be equipped with only a positive "on-off" control: switch-platen sanders; disc sanders with discs 2 in. or less in diameter; grinders with wheels 2 in. or smaller in diameter; and routers, planers, laminate trimmers, nibblers, shears, scroll saws and jigsaws with blade shanks ¼ in. wide or smaller.

Other hand-held power tools, such as circular saws having a blade diameter of more than 2 in., chain saws, and percussion tools without positive accessory holding means, must be equipped with a constant pressure switch that will shut off the power when the pressure is released.

Electric Tools

Among the chief hazards of electric-powered tools are burns and electric shocks, which can lead to injuries or even heart failure. Under certain conditions, even a small amount of current can result in fibrillation of the heart and eventual death. A shock also can cause the user to fall off a ladder or other elevated work surface.

To protect the user from shock, tools must either have a three-wire cord with ground and be grounded, be double insulated, or be powered by a low-voltage isolation transformer.

Three-wire cords contain two current-carrying conductors and a grounding conductor. One end of the grounding conductor connects to the tool's metal housing. The other end is grounded through a prong on the plug. Anytime an adapter is used to accommodate a two-hole receptacle, the adapter wire must be attached to a known ground. The third prong should never be removed from the plug.

Double insulation is more convenient. The user and the tools are protected in two ways: by normal insulation on the wires inside and by a housing that cannot conduct electricity to the operator in the event of a malfunction.

A ground-fault circuit interrupter (GFCI) can provide protection against fatal electrical shocks. A GFCI is not an overcurrent device like a fuse or circuit breaker. GFCIs are designed to sense an imbalance in current flow over the normal path and turn off power within 1/40 second. GFCIs can provide electrical shock protection beyond what a grounded circuit or double insulated tools can provide.

These general practices should be followed when using electric tools:

- Electric tools should be operated within their design limitations;
- Gloves and safety footwear are recommended during use of electric tools;
- When not in use, tools should be stored in a dry place;
- Electric tools should not be used in damp or wet locations;
- Work areas should be well lighted;
- Use a GFCI whenever possible; and
- Never use a tool with damaged cord or missing ground prong.

Powered Abrasive Wheel Tools

Powered abrasive grinding, cutting, polishing, and wire buffing wheels create special safety problems because they may throw off flying fragments. Before an abrasive wheel is mounted, it should be inspected closely and sound, or ring, tested to ensure that it is free from cracks or defects. To test, wheels should be tapped gently with a light non-metallic instrument. If they sound cracked or dead, they could fly apart in operation and must not be used. A sound and undamaged wheel will give a clear metallic tone or ring.

To prevent the wheel from cracking, the user should be sure it fits freely on the spindle. The spindle nut must be tightened enough to hold the wheel in place, but not enough to distort the flange. Follow the manufacturer's recommendations. Care must be taken to ensure that the spindle wheel will not exceed the abrasive wheel specifications.

Due to the possibility of a wheel disintegrating (exploding) during start-up, the employee should never stand directly in front of the wheel as it accelerates to full operating speed.

Portable grinding tools need to be equipped with safety guards to protect workers not only from the moving wheel surface, but also from flying fragments in case of breakage. In addition, when using a grinder, employees should:

- Always use eye protection;
- Turn off power when not in use; and
- Never clamp a hand-held grinder in a vise.

Pneumatic Tools

Pneumatic tools are powered by compressed air. Common pneumatic tools include chippers, drills, hammers and sanders. There are several dangers encountered in the use of pneumatic tools. The main one is the danger of getting hit by one of the tool's attachments or by some kind of fastener the worker is using with the tool.

Eye protection is required and face protection is recommended for employees who work with pneumatic tools. Noise is another hazard. Working with noisy tools such as jackhammers requires proper, effective use of hearing protection.

When using pneumatic tools, employees must check to see that they are fastened securely to the hose to prevent them from becoming disconnected. A short wire or positive locking device that attaches the air hose to the tool will serve as an added safeguard.

A safety clip or retainer must be installed to prevent attachments, (e.g., chisels on chipping hammers) from being unintentionally shot from the barrel.

Screens must be set up to protect nearby workers from being struck by flying fragments around chippers, riveting guns, staplers or air drills. Compressed air guns should never be pointed toward anyone. Users should never "dead-end" it against themselves or anyone else.

Powder-Actuated Tools

Powder-actuated tools operate like a loaded gun and should be treated with the same respect and precautions. In fact, they are so dangerous that only specially trained employees must operate them.

Safety precautions to remember include the following:

- These tools should not be used in an explosive or flammable atmosphere.
- Before using the tool, the worker should inspect it to determine that it is clean, all moving parts operate freely and the barrel is free from obstructions.
- The tool should not be loaded unless it is to be used immediately. A loaded tool should not be left unattended, especially where it would be available to unauthorized persons.
- Hands should be kept clear of the barrel end. To prevent the tool from firing accidentally, two separate motions are required for firing: one to bring the tool into position and another to pull the trigger. The tools must not be able to operate until they are pressed against the work surface with a force of at least 5 lbs. greater than the total weight of the tool.

If a powder-actuated tool misfires, the employee should wait at least 30 seconds before trying to fire it again. If it still will not fire, the user should wait another 30 seconds so that the faulty cartridge is less likely to explode, then carefully remove the load. The bad cartridge should be put in water.

Suitable eye and face protection are essential when using a powder-actuated tool. The muzzle end of the tool must have a protective shield or guard centered perpendicularly on the barrel to confine any flying fragments or particles that might otherwise create a hazard when the tool is fired. The tool must be designed so that it will not fire unless it has this kind of safety device.

All powder-actuated tools must be designed for varying powder charges so the user can select a powder level necessary to do the work without excessive force. If the tool develops a defect during use, it should be tagged and taken out of service immediately until it is properly repaired.

Fasteners

When using powder-actuated tools to apply fasteners, there are some precautions to consider. Fasteners must not be fired into material that would let them pass through to the other side.

In steel, the fastener must not come any closer than ½ in. from a corner or edge. Fasteners must not be driven into very hard or brittle materials that might chip, splatter or make the fastener ricochet.

An alignment guide must be used when shooting a fastener into an existing hole. A fastener must not be driven into a spalled area caused by an unsatisfactory fastening.

Hydraulic Power Tools

The fluid used in hydraulic power tools must be an approved fire-resistant fluid and must retain its operating characteristics at the most extreme temperatures to which it will be exposed. The manufacturer's recommended safe operating pressure for hoses, valves, pipe fitters and other fittings must not be exceeded.

Jacks

All jacks (i.e., lever and ratchet jacks, screw jacks, hydraulic jacks) must have a device that stops them from jacking up too high.

Also, the manufacturer's load limit must be permanently marked in a prominent place on the jack and should not be exceeded. A jack should never be used to support a lifted load. Once the load has been lifted, it must immediately be blocked up.

Use wooden blocking under the base if necessary to make the jack level and secure. If the lift surface is metal, place a 1-in. thick hardwood block or equivalent between the lift surface and the metal jack head to reduce the danger of slippage.

When setting up a jack, make certain of the following:
- The base rests on a firm level surface;
- The jack is correctly centered;
- The jack head bears against a level surface; and
- The lift force is applied evenly.

Proper maintenance of jacks is essential for safety. All jacks must be inspected before each use and lubricated regularly. If a jack is subjected to an abnormal load or shock, it should be thoroughly examined to make sure it has not been damaged. Hydraulic jacks exposed to freezing temperatures must be filled with an adequate antifreeze liquid.

OSHA INSTRUCTION STD 1-13.4 AUGUST 5, 1981 OFFICE OF COMPLIANCE PROGRAMMING

SUBJECT: Portable Belt Sanding Machines as Covered by 29 CFR 1910.243(a)(3) and 29 CFR 1926.304(f)

A. Purpose. This instruction provides guidance to allow equitable enforcement of 29 CFR 1910.243 (a)(3) and 29 CFR 1926.304(f) as they pertain to the guarding of portable belt sanders.

B. Scope. This instruction applies OSHA-wide.

C. Action. OSHA Regional Administrators/Area Directors shall classify violations of 29 CFR 1910.243(a)(3) and 29 CFR 1926.304(f) as de minimis violations where the employer has complied with appropriate safeguarding precautions as follows:

  1. Portable belt sanding machines shall be provided with guarding on one side at the nip point where the sanding belt runs into a pulley,
  2. Handles shall be so located that a barrier interrupts any straight line path between the gripping surface of a handle and the nip point of a pulley, and
  3. The unused run of the sanding belt shall be guarded on one side and at the rear.

D. Federal Program Change. This instruction describes a Federal program change which affects State Programs. Each Regional Administrator shall:
  1. Ensure that this change is forwarded to each State designee.
  2. Explain the technical content of the change to the State designee as requested.
  3. Ensure that State designees are asked to acknowledge receipt of this Federal program change in writing, within 30 days of notification, to the Regional Administrator. This acknowledgment should include a description either of the State's plan to implement the change or of the reasons why the change should not apply to that State.
  4. Review policies, instructions and guidelines issued by the State to determine if this change has been communicated to State program personnel. Routine monitoring activities (accompanied inspections and case file reviews) shall also be used to determine if this change has been implemented in actual performance.

E. Background. Revision of 29 CFR 1910.243(a)(3) and 29 CFR 1926.304(f) are under consideration by the Mechanical Engineering and Construction Standards Divisions. The standards presently in effect prescribe guarding requirements which essentially prevent flush sanding at corners, and important feature and an application of portable belt sanders. The modified form of guarding , as presented by this instruction, permits flush sanding at corners and provides for operator safety.

Thorne G. Auchter Assistant Secretary

DISTRIBUTION: National, Regional and Area Offices All Compliance Officers State Designees NIOSH Regional Program Directors

OSHA INSTRUCTION STD 1-13.2A DEC 9 1985 DIRECTORATE OF FIELD OPERATIONS

SUBJECT: Explosive Actuated Fastening Tools

A. Purpose. This instruction provides specific interpretation as to when magazine-fed, explosive power operated hand tools are loaded.
B. Scope. This Instruction applies OSHA-wide.
C. Cancellation. OSHA Instruction STD 1-13.2, October 30, 1978, is canceled.
D. Action. OSHA Regional Administrators and Area Directors shall ensure that when magazine-fed tools covered by these standards are inspected, the tool is not considered loaded until the magazine feeds the tool, even though the magazine is in the tool. The operator's instructions shall provide for removing the magazine when the tool is left unattended.
E. Federal Program Change. This instruction describes a Federal program change which affects State programs. Each Regional Administrator shall:
   1. Ensure that this change is promptly forwarded to each State designee.
   2. Explain the technical content of this change to the State designee as requested.
   3. Ensure that State designees are asked to acknowledge receipt of this Federal program change in writing, within 30 days of notification, to the Regional Administrator. This acknowledgment should include a description either of the State's plan to implement the change or of the reasons why the change should not apply to that State.
   4. Review policies, instructions, and guidelines issued by the State to determine that this change has been communicated to State program personnel. Routine monitoring shall also be used to determine if this change has been implemented in actual performance.
F. Application. For the General Industry, Construction and Maritime industries, the following standards shall apply:

General Industry, 29 CFR 1910.243(d)(4)(iv).
Construction, 29 CFR 1926.302(e)(5) and (6).
Maritime, 29 CFR 1915.135(c)(3).

G. Explanation. In developing and promulgating the standards, the magazine or clip-fed explosive power load was not considered. The magazine contains several explosive power loads and single loads are fed into the ram (firing chamber) as needed. Until such time as single loads are fed into the ram, explosive power loads, are not a part of the firing cycle. A separate operation on the part of the operator has to be made to place the load into the firing position.

John B. Miles, Office Director Directorate of Field Operations

DISTRIBUTION National, Regional and Area Offices Compliance Officers State Designees 7(c)(1) Project Managers NIOSH Regional Program Directors

2009 Subpart P 1910.241-244
Hand & Portable Powered Tools

Citation	Description	Value
242(b)	Compressed air used for cleaning	447
242(c)(1)	Guards on portable abrasive wheels	55
242(a)	Condition of tools and equipment	32
243(c)(3)	Vertical portable grinders - Guarding	29
244(a)(1)	Rated Load Markings on Jacks	7

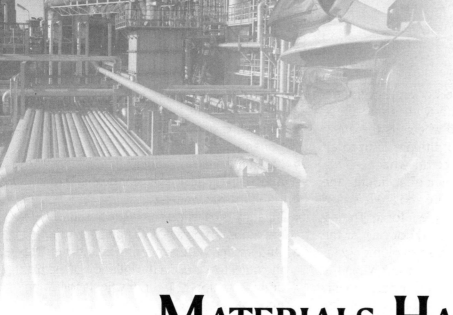

MATERIALS HANDLING

More employees are injured in industry while moving materials than while performing any other single function. In everyday operations, workers handle, transport and store materials. They may do so by hand, by manually operated materials handling equipment or by power operated equipment.

Handling Material—General—1910.176

Where mechanical handling equipment is used, sufficient, safe clearance shall be allowed for aisles, at loading docks, through doorways and wherever turns or passage must be made. Permanent aisles and passageways shall be appropriately marked. Storage of material shall not create a hazard. All materials stored in tiers shall be stacked, blocked, interlocked and limited in height so that they are secure against sliding or collapse. Storage areas shall be kept free from accumulation of materials that constitute hazards from tripping, fire, explosion or pest harborage. Vegetation control will be exercised when necessary.

Servicing Multi-Piece and Single-Piece Rim Wheels—1910.177

Approximately 322,000 employees in more than 100,000 workplaces service large vehicle tires that are mounted on multi-piece or single-piece wheels. OSHA requires:

- Training for all tire-servicing employees;
- The use of industry-accepted procedures that minimize the potential for employee injury;
- The use of proper equipment, such as clip-on chucks, restraining devices or barriers, to retain the wheel components in the event of an incident during the inflation of tires; and
- The use of compatible components.

Types of Wheels/Tires

A rim wheel is the component assembly of wheel (either multi-piece or single-piece), tire and tube and other components. A single-piece wheel is the component of the assembly used to hold the tire, form part of the air chamber (with tubeless wheels) and provide the assembly's means of attachment to the vehicle axle. A multi-piece wheel is a vehicle wheel consisting of two or more parts, one of which is a side- or locking-ring that holds the tire and other components on the rim wheel by interlocking the components when the tire is inflated.

The standard does not apply to the servicing of rim wheels using automobile tires or truck tires designated "LT."

Hazards

The principal difference between accidents involving single-piece rim wheels and those involving multi-piece rim wheels is the effect of the sudden release of the pressurized air contained in a single-piece rim wheel.

In a multi-piece rim wheel accident, the wheel components separate and are released from the rim wheel with violent force. The severity of the hazard is related not only to the air pressure, but also to the air volume.

Single-rim wheel accidents occur when the pressurized air contained in the tire is suddenly released, whether by the bead breaking or slipping over the rim flange. The principal hazards involve pressurized air, which, once released, can either pick up and hurl an employee across the shop if he or she is in close proximity to the rim wheel and within the trajectory; propel the rim wheel in any potential path or route that a rim wheel component may travel during an explosive separation.

Employee Training

The employer must provide a program to train all employees who service rim wheels about the hazards involved and the safety procedures to be followed. The employer must ensure that no employee services any rim wheel unless the worker has been instructed in the correct procedures for mounting, demounting and servicing the wheel as well as the safe operating precautions for the type of wheel being serviced. The employer must regularly evaluate each employee's performance and provide additional training as necessary to ensure that each employee maintains his or her proficiency.

At a minimum, the training program must include the contents of the OSHA standard and the information in the manufacturer's rim manuals or the OSHA charts. Charts are available from OSHA regional, area or national offices.

The instruction must be conducted in an intelligible way. Employees who are unable to read the charts or rim manuals must be trained in the subject matter. The employer must regularly evaluate each employee's performance and provide additional training, as necessary, to ensure each employee maintains his or her proficiency. The employer must ensure each worker demonstrates and maintains the abil-ity to service rim wheels safely by correctly performing the following tasks:

- Demounting tires, including deflation;
- Inspecting and identifying rim wheel components;
- Mounting tires, including inflating them with a restraining device or other safeguard
- Handling rim wheels;
- Inflating tires when single-piece rim wheels are mounted on a vehicle; and
- Understanding the need to stand outside the trajectory during the inflation of the tire and inspection of the rim wheels following inflation.

The Servicing Equipment

The employer must furnish a restraining device for inflating a tire on a multi-piece wheel and must provide a restraining device or barrier for inflating a tire on a single-piece wheel, unless the single-piece rim wheel is bolted onto a vehicle during inflation. The restraining device can be a cage, rack or an assemblage of bars and other parts that will constrain all rim wheel components during an explosive separation of the multi-piece rim wheel or the sudden release of the contained air of a single-piece rim wheel.

A barrier can be a fence, wall, or other structure or object placed between a single-piece rim wheel and an employee during tire inflation to contain the rim wheel components in the event of the sudden release of contained air. Each barrier or restraining device must be able to withstand the maximum force of an explosive rim wheel separation or release of the pressurized air occurring at 150 percent of the maximum tire specification pressure for the rim wheel being serviced.

Restraining devices showing any of the following defects must be immediately removed from service:

- Cracks at welds;
- Cracked or broken components;
- Bent or sprung components caused by mishandling, abuse, tire explosion or rim wheel separation; or
- Component pitted due to corrosion or other structural damage that would decrease its effectiveness.

Restraining devices or barriers removed from service must not be returned to service until they are repaired and inspected. Restraining devices or barriers requiring structural repair such as component replacement or re-welding must not be returned to service until they are certified by either the manufacturer or a Registered Professional Engineer as meeting the strength requirements as stated above (the force of 150 percent of the maximum tire specification pressure).

Current charts or rim manuals containing instructions for the types of wheels being serviced must be available in the service area, including a mobile service unit. Only tools that are recommended in the rim manual may be used for the type of wheel being serviced. The employer must also supply airline equipment with a clip-on chuck with sufficient length of hose between the chuck and in-line valve or regulator to allow the employee to stand outside the trajectory, as well as an in-line valve with a pressure gauge or a pre-settable regulator.

The size (bead diameter and tire/wheel width) and type of both the tire and wheel must be checked for compatibility prior to assembly of the rim wheel. Mismatching of half sizes such as 16-inch and 16.5-inch tires and wheel must be avoided.

Multi-piece wheel components must not be interchanged except as indicated in the applicable charts or rim manuals. Multi-piece wheel components and single-piece wheels must be inspected prior to assembly. Any wheel or wheel component that is bent out of shape, pitted from corrosion, broken or cracked must be marked or tagged "unserviceable" and removed from the service area. Damaged or leaky valves must be replaced.

Rim flanges, rim gutters, rings, and the bead-seating areas of wheels must be free of any dirt, surface rust, scale, or loose or flaked rubber build-up prior to tire mounting and inflation.

Safe Operating Procedures: Multi-Piece Rim Wheels

Employers must instruct employees to use the following steps for safe operating procedures:
1. The tire must be completely deflated by removing the valve core before a rim wheel is removed from the axle in the following situations:
   - When the tire has been driven under inflated at 80 percent or less of its recommended pressure, or
   - When there is obvious or suspected damage to the tire or wheel components.
2. The tire must be completely deflated by removing the valve core before demounting.
3. A rubber lubricant must be applied to the bead and rim mating surfaces when assembling the wheel and inflating the tire, unless the tire or wheel manufacturer recommends against its use.
4. If a tire on a vehicle is underinflated, but has more than 80 percent of the recommended pressure, the tire may be inflated while the rim wheel is on the vehicle, provided remote control inflation equipment is used and no employee remains in the trajectory during inflation.
5. The tire shall be inflated outside a restraining device only to a pressure sufficient to force the tire bead onto the rim ledge and create an airtight seal with the tire and bead.
6. Whenever a rim wheel is in a restraining device, the employee must not rest or lean any part of his or her body or equipment on or against the restraining device.
7. After tire inflation, the tire and wheel must be inspected while still within the restraining device to make sure that they are properly seated and locked. If further adjustment to the tire or wheel components is necessary, the tire shall be deflated by removal of the valve core before the adjustment is made.
8. An attempt must not be made to correct the seating of side and lock rings by hammering, shielding or forcing the components while the tire is pressurized.
9. Cracked, broken, bent or otherwise damaged wheel components must not be reworked, welded, brazed or otherwise heated. Heat must not be applied to a multi-piece wheel.
10. Whenever multi-piece rim wheels are being handled, employees must stay out of the trajectory unless the employer can show that performance of the servicing makes the employee's presence in the trajectory necessary.

Safe Operating Procedures: Single-Piece Rim Wheels

Employees must be instructed in and use the following steps for safe operating procedures with single-piece wheels:

1. The tire must be completely deflated by removing the valve core before demounting.
2. Mounting and demounting of the tire must be performed only from the narrow ledge side of the wheel. Care must be taken to avoid damaging the tire beads, and the tire must be mounted only on a compatible wheel of mating bead diameter and width.
3. A nonflammable rubber lubricant must be applied to bead and wheel mating surfaces before assembling the rim wheel, unless the tire or wheel manufacturer recommends against the use of any rubber lubricant.
4. If a tire-changing machine is used, the tire may be inflated only to the minimum pressure necessary to force the tire bead onto the rim ledge and create an airtight seal before it can be removed from the tire-changing machine.
5. If a bead expander is used, it must be removed before the valve core is installed and as soon as the rim wheel becomes airtight (when the bead slips onto the bead seat).
6. The tire may be inflated only when contained within a restraining device, positioned behind a barrier or bolted on the vehicle with the lug nuts fully tightened.
7. The tire must not be inflated when any flat, solid surface is in the trajectory and within 1 ft. of the sidewall.
8. The tire must not be inflated to more than the inflation pressure stamped in the sidewall, unless the manufacturer recommends a higher pressure.
9. Employees must stay out of the trajectory when a tire is being inflated.
10. Heat must not be applied to a single-piece wheel.
11. Cracked, broken, bent or otherwise damaged wheels must not be reworked, welded, brazed or otherwise heated.

Powered Industrial Trucks—1910.178

This section contains safety requirements relating to fire protection, design, maintenance and use of fork trucks, tractors, platform lift trucks, motorized hand trucks and other specialized industrial trucks powered by electric motors or internal combustion engines. This section does not apply to compressed air or nonflammable compressed gas-operated industrial trucks, farm vehicles or vehicles intended primarily for earth moving or over-the-road hauling.

Approved powered industrial trucks shall bear a label or some other identifying mark indicating approval by the testing laboratory. The user shall not perform modifications and additions that affect capacity and safe operation of trucks without the manufacturer's prior written approval. The term "approved truck" or "approved industrial truck" means a truck that is listed or approved for fire safety purposes for the intended use by a nationally recognized testing laboratory, using nationally recognized testing standards.

Designations

For this standard, there are 11 designations of industrial trucks or tractors:

1. D. Diesel engine-powered units having minimum acceptable safeguards against inherent fire hazards.
2. DS. Diesel-powered units that are provided with additional safeguards to the exhaust, fuel and electrical systems.
3. DY. Diesel-powered units that have all the safeguards of the DS, but do not have any electrical equipment, including the ignition and are equipped with temperature limitation features.
4. E. Electrically powered units that have minimum acceptable safeguards against inherent fire hazards.
5. ES. Electrically powered units that, in addition to all the requirements for E units, are provided with additional safeguards to the electrical system to prevent emission of hazardous sparks and limit surface temperatures.
6. EE. Electrically powered units that have, in addition to all of the requirements for the E and ES units, the electric motors and all other electrical equipment completely enclosed.

7. EX. Electrically powered units that differ from the E, ES, and EE units in that the electrical fittings and equipment are so designed, constructed and assembled that the units may be used in certain atmospheres containing flammable vapors or dusts.
8. G. Gasoline-powered units that have minimum acceptable safeguards against inherent fire hazards.
9. GS. Gasoline-powered units that are provided with additional safeguards to the exhaust, fuel and electrical systems.
10. LP. Liquefied petroleum gas-powered units that are similar to G units, except that liquefied petroleum gas is used for fuel instead of gasoline.
11. LPS. Liquefied petroleum gas-powered units that are provided with additional safeguards to the exhaust, fuel and electrical systems.

Atmospheres or locations throughout the plant must be classified hazardous or nonhazardous before the use of industrial trucks can even be considered. Refer to Table N-1 of 1910.178(c)(2), which is a summary table on the use of industrial trucks in various locations.

Safety Guards

All high-lift rider trucks shall be fitted with overhead guards where overhead lifting is performed unless operating conditions do not permit. In those cases where a high-lift rider truck must enter a structure and the overhead guard will not permit this entry (e.g., truck trailer), the guard may be removed or a powered industrial truck without a guard may be used.

If a powered industrial fork truck carries a load that presents a hazard of falling back onto the operator, the fork truck shall be equipped with a vertical load backrest extension.

Changing and Charging Storage Batteries

Workplaces using electrically powered industrial trucks will have battery-charging areas somewhere in the plant. In many cases, depending on the number of electrically powered industrial trucks, there will be more than one changing and charging area. This sec-

tion only applies to storage battery changing and charging areas associated with powered industrial trucks. It does not apply to areas where other batteries, such as those used in motor vehicles (cars or trucks), are charged, although some of the same hazardous conditions may exist.

Some of the requirements specified in the regulation include:
- Battery-charging installations shall be located in areas designated for that purpose;
- Facilities shall be provided for:
  - Flushing and neutralizing spilled electrolyte;
  - Fire protection;
  - Protecting charging apparatus from damage by trucks; and
  - Adequate ventilation for dispersal of air contaminants from gassing batteries.
- A conveyor, overhead hoist or equivalent material handling equipment shall be provided for handling batteries.
- Smoking shall be prohibited in the charging area.
- Precautions shall be taken to prevent open flames, sparks or electric arcs in battery charging areas.

Exhibit 15-1.
A battery-charging area.

Trucks and Railroad Cars

In plant receiving and shipping areas, powered industrial trucks are often used to load and unload materials from trucks and railroad cars. The brakes of highway trucks shall be set and wheel chocks placed under the rear wheels to prevent trucks from rolling while they are boarded with powered industrial trucks (See Exhibit 15-2.).

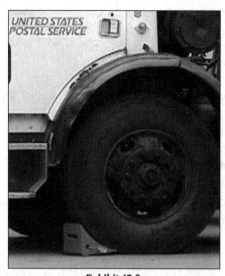

Exhibit 15-2.
Wheel chucks must be used, in addition to truck brakes, to prevent trucks from rolling while being boarded.]

Wheel stops or other positive protection shall be provided to prevent railroad cars from moving during loading or unloading operations.

Fixed jacks may be necessary to support a semi trailer and prevent unending during the loading or unloading when the trailer is not coupled to a tractor.

Operator Training

No employee, including supervisory personnel, is permitted to operate a powered industrial truck unless properly trained and authorized to do so.

Operators must pass a written test in a classroom setting as well as demonstrate hands-on capability.

This training must be certified with the name of the operator, the trainer and the date of training. Training is good for three years or until the operator demonstrates a lack of competency.

Truck Operations

Some of the requirements regarding industrial truck operations include:

- No person shall be allowed to stand or pass under the elevated portion of any truck, whether loaded or empty.
- Unauthorized personnel shall not be permitted to ride on powered industrial trucks. A safe place to ride shall be provided where riding of trucks is authorized.
- When a powered industrial truck is left unattended, load-engaging means shall be fully lowered, controls shall be neutralized, power

shall be shut off, and brakes set. (A powered industrial truck is "unattended" when the operator is 25 ft. or more away from a vehicle that remains in his or her view or whenever the operator leaves the vehicle and it is not in his or her view.)

Traveling

This section contains requirements for traveling in powered industrial trucks. Some of these requirements include:

- All traffic regulations shall be observed, including authorized plant speed limits.
- The driver shall be required to slow down and sound the horn at cross aisles and other locations where vision is obstructed. If the load being carried obstructs forward view, the driver shall be required to travel with the load trailing.
- Railroad tracks shall be crossed diagonally whenever possible. Parking closer than 8 ft. from the center of railroad tracks is prohibited.
- When ascending or descending grades in excess of 10 percent, loaded trucks shall be driven with the load upgrade.
- Dockboards or bridge plates shall be properly secured before they are driven over. Dockboards or bridge plates shall be driven over carefully, slowly and their rated capacity never exceeded.

Loading

Only stable or safely arranged loads shall be handled. Caution shall be exercised when handling off-center loads that cannot be centered. Only loads within the rated capacity of the truck shall be handled.

Operation of the Truck

If at any time a powered industrial truck is found to be in need of repair, defective or in any way unsafe, the truck shall be taken out of service until it has been restored to safe operating condition. Fuel tanks shall not be filled while the engine is running. Spillage shall be avoided. Any spillage of oil or fuel shall be carefully washed away or completely evaporated and the fuel cap replaced before restarting the engine. Open flames shall not be used for checking electrolyte levels in storage batteries or gasoline levels in fuel tanks.

Maintenance of Industrial Trucks

Any powered industrial truck not in safe operating condition shall be removed from service. Authorized personnel shall make all repairs. No repairs shall be made in Class I, II or III locations. Those repairs to the fuel and ignition systems that involve fire hazards shall be conducted only in locations designated for such repairs.

Industrial trucks shall be examined before being placed in service and shall not be placed in service if the examination shows any condition adversely affecting the safety of the vehicle. Examinations shall be made at least daily. Where trucks are used on a round-the-clock basis, they shall be examined after each shift.

Overhead and Gantry Cranes— 1910.179

General Requirements

This section applies to overhead and gantry cranes, including semi-gantry, cantilever gantry, wall cranes, storage bridge cranes and others having the same fundamental characteristics.

Overhead and gantry cranes may not be modified and re-rated unless a qualified engineer or the equipment manufacturer checks the modifications and the supporting structure thoroughly for the new rated load. It is not unusual to find overhead or gantry cranes where it is claimed that the lifting capacity was increased simply by installing a new rated load sign on the bridge of the crane.

The rated loads of the crane shall be plainly marked on each side of the crane. If the crane has more than one hoisting unit, each hoist shall have its rated load marked on it or on its load block.

The potential for overloading the crane increases if the hook-up man or the operator does not know the rated capacity. Only employees selected or assigned by the employer or the employer's representative as being qualified to operate a crane shall be permitted to do so.

Cabs

A cab-operated crane is an overhead or gantry crane controlled by an operator in a cab located on the bridge or trolley. The general arrangement of the cab and the location of control and protective equipment shall be such that all operating handles are within convenient reach of the operator when facing the area to be served by the load hook or while facing the direction of travel of the cab. The arrangement shall allow a view of the load hook in all positions.

The access to all cab-operated cranes shall be checked thoroughly. Serious injuries have occurred because of the following three conditions:

1. There was no conveniently placed fixed ladder, stairs or platform provided to reach the cab or bridge footwalk. It is unacceptable and poses a significant hazard to allow employees to board a crane or climb over guardrails or over, under and around building structures, energized hot rails, portable ladders or movable platforms.
2. There was a gap exceeding 12 in. between a fixed ladder, stairs or platform and access to the cab or bridge footwalk.
3. The fixed ladder used as access to the crane did not meet the American National Standard Safety Code for Fixed Ladders, ANSI A14.3-1956. Common citations include that there were no cages provided for ladders more than 20 ft. in unbroken length, offset platforms were not provided and the ladders themselves were not maintained in a safe condition.

Footwalks and Ladders

Where sufficient headroom is available on cab-operated cranes, a footwalk shall be provided on the drive side along the end length of the bridge of all cranes having the trolley running on the top of the girders.

Significant hazards exist for maintenance and inspection personnel if no footwalk is provided, including work being performed:
- From portable ladders;
- Off the main bridge girder without protection against falling to the floor; or
- From the trolley platform with the same potential for falling to the floor.

Maintenance managers and supervisors shall check very thoroughly the maintenance procedures followed in those cases where cab-operated cranes are not provided with bridge footwalks. This, of course, also applies to all other types of cranes where no footwalk is provided and those cases where bridge footwalks cannot be provided because sufficient headroom is not available.

Bridge footwalks, where provided, shall be of rigid construction and designed to sustain a distributed load of at least 50 lbs. per square foot. In many older workplaces, serious hazards are associated with the bridge footwalk itself. This area cannot be inspected from the floor, and safety people must climb onto the crane to properly document the hazardous conditions. It is quite common to find bridge footwalks not continuous or permanently secured. Although no employees may be on the bridge footwalks or cranes during an inspection, maintenance employees, inspection personnel and the crane operator will be required to go on the bridge footwalk at various times. A common and serious hazard is one where standard railings have not been provided on all open sides of the bridge footwalk. In addition, toe boards shall be installed. The standard railing provisions apply to all sides of the bridge footwalk, including the inside edge next to the bridge girders if a fall potential exists.

All gantry cranes shall be provided with a ladder or a stair that extends from the ground to the footwalk or the cab platform. It is not permitted to board a gantry crane via portable ladders, the structure of the crane or any other method.

Any ladder provided on an overhead or gantry crane shall be permanently and securely fastened in place and also shall be in compliance with 29 CFR 1910.27. Damaged, loose, improperly maintained or unguarded fixed ladders are common.

Stops, Bumpers, Rail Sweeps and Guards

A "stop" is a device to limit travel of a trolley. This device normally is attached to a fixed structure and does not have energy-absorbing ability. Every overhead or gantry crane where the trolley runs on top of the bridge girder shall be provided with stops at either end of the limits of the travel of the trolley. These stops shall be fastened to resist forces applied when contacted, and if the stop engages the tread of the wheel of the trolley, it shall be of a height at least equal to the radius of the wheel.

The obvious hazard concerned with improperly applied trolley stops or no trolley stops

at all is that the trolley could be rolled off the trolley runway. The hazards associated with this condition are numerous and present serious injury potential to the employees on the floor below. The trolley itself could fall to the floor, parts of the trolley could come off the crane structure and hit employees below, the load itself could be dumped, or at a minimum, cause unexpected movement of the load, and finally, if the trolley contacted the bridge runway conductors, the entire crane could itself be energized. Again, the only practical method to inspect for this condition is the boarding of the overhead or gantry crane and walking out on the bridge footwalk to look and see if trolley stops are present and installed properly.

Modern cranes must meet or exceed the design specifications of the American National Standard Safety Code for Overhead and Gantry Cranes, ANSI B30.2.0–1967. Another similar hazardous condition is the failure to reinstall crane runway stops at the ends of the limits of travel of the runway. A common problem with overhead crane installations is that the controllers have malfunctioned and become stuck in the open position, after which the crane has run off the ends of the bridge runway—many times through the building wall.

Bridge and Trolley Bumpers

A "bumper"(buffer) is an energy-absorbing device for reducing impact when a moving crane or trolley reaches the end of its permitted travel or when two moving cranes or trolleys come in contact.

Overhead or gantry crane bridges shall be provided with bumpers unless the crane:

- Travels at a slow rate of speed and has a faster deceleration rate due to the use of sleeve bearings;
- Is not operated near the end of bridge travel; or
- Is restricted to a limited distance by the nature of the crane operation and there is no hazard of striking any object in this limited distance.

A common condition that will be observed on many overhead or gantry cranes is that bumpers were not provided where required. However, many times bumpers will be provided that do not have sufficient energy-absorbing capacity to stop the crane when traveling at a speed of at least 40 percent of the rated load speed or the bumpers are not designed and installed as to minimize parts falling from the crane in case of breakage. The hazards of not providing bridge bumpers with energy-absorbing capacities are that when an overhead or gantry crane contacts another crane on the same runway or contacts the bridge stops at the ends of the runway, a shock load is transmitted to the lifting mechanisms that could cause the load to be dropped. In addition, the constant striking of a crane against another object without energy-absorption buffers causes the bridge and end structures to weaken, which could cause cracks in the webbing and lead to the failure of the crane structure.

Trolleys shall also be provided with bumpers, unless the trolley:

- Travels at a slow rate of speed;
- Is not operated near the ends of the trolley travel; or
- Is restricted to a limited distance on the trolley runway and there is no hazard of striking any object in this limited distance.

If there is more than one trolley operated on the same trolley runway, each trolley shall be provided with bumpers on its adjacent ends. If bumpers are installed on the trolley, they shall be designed and installed to minimize parts falling from the trolley in case of breakage and shall be energy absorbing. It must be emphasized that both trolley stops and bumpers shall be provided where required.

Rail Sweeps

Bridge end truck wheels shall be provided with sweeps that extend below the top of the rail and project in front of the truck wheels. Their omission is a common violation. This requirement does not apply to the trolley end truck wheels. By not having rail sweeps, maintenance equipment could be left on the bridge runway rails and as the crane travels into the area, the equipment could derail, causing the movement of the load, a shock load, or dropping of the load. This also applies to gantry and semi-gantry cranes where the truck wheels run on a rail usually located on the floor or working surface.

Guards

Hoisting ropes on overhead and gantry cranes must be closely inspected to ensure they do not run near enough to other parts to make fouling or chafing possible. If a hoisting rope is chafing over a long period of time, the rope will eventually wear through or break and the load will drop to the floor. If the ropes do not run near other parts, guards shall be installed to prevent fouling and chafing. Guards also shall be provided to prevent contact between bridge conductors and hoisting ropes if they could come into contact. Bridge conductors are almost always located on the inside flange of the bridge girders and provide the power to the trolley.

Another very common hazard on overhead or gantry cranes is that exposed moving parts are not properly guarded. For example, gears on or near the bridge footwalk shaft ends on bridge motors usually located on the bridge footwalks, and chain and chain sprockets. There have been several reported fatalities where maintenance employees working on bridge footwalks have been drawn into open gears, projecting shaft ends, and chain and sprocket drives.

Brakes

Each independent hoisting unit of all cranes shall be provided with a holding brake applied directly to the motor shaft or some part of the gear grain. On cab-operated cranes with the cab on the bridge, a bridge brake shall be provided. On occasion, operators of cab-operated overhead cranes that are not equipped with bridge brakes will stop the bridge by plugging—where the operator uses the controller to reverse the direction of the motor. This can be a hazardous practice, especially if it is the only method of stopping cranes. If power to the crane is lost for any reason, the crane will be unstoppable.

All floor, remote and pulpit-operated crane bridge devices shall be provided with a brake or noncoasting mechanical drive (i.e., the crane must be able to stop quickly). It should be noted that overhead or gantry cranes with a cab on the trolley should also be provided with a trolley brake. However, under most conditions trolleys will not be required to have a brake.

Electrical Equipment

All wiring and equipment on overhead or gantry cranes shall comply with the applicable electrical sections of Subpart S.

On floor-operated cranes where a multiple conductor cable is used with a suspended push-button station, the station shall be supported in some manner that will protect the electrical conductor against strain. Simply installing a chair or cable from an upper support to the push-button station to take the strain off the conductor can abate this condition.

Pendant control boxes also shall be clearly marked for identification of functions. Lack of clear labeling is quite common. The hazard is that inexperienced operators or supervisory personnel operating the pendant crane may not know the various functions of the push-button station and could cause an unexpected movement of the crane. Only designated personnel are permitted to operate a crane per § 1910.179(b)(8).

One of the most serious hazards associated with cranes concerns the provision that the hoisting motion of all electric traveling cranes shall be provided with an over-travel limit switch in the hoisting direction. A "limit switch" is a switch that disconnects the power to the drive motor and stops the load if that load is raised above a certain point. Many fatalities and serious injuries have occurred because a crane was not provided with a limit switch or the limit switch malfunctioned.

If a limit switch is not provided or if the limit switch malfunctions, the hoist block could run up into the lifting beam or rope drum, severing the cable and dropping the entire assembly and any load on the hook to the floor below. All inspections of an overhead crane shall include the verification of the presence of a functioning limit switch.

Hoisting Equipment

Sheaves are grooved pulleys that carry the hoisting ropes on overhead cranes. Sheave grooves shall be smooth and free from surface defects.

Sheaves in the bottom blocks shall be equipped with close-fitting guards that will prevent ropes from becoming fouled when the block is lying on the ground with the rope loose. This common condition can be readily observed while watching the crane in operation. The hazard, if the guards are not installed, is that the hoisting rope can come off the sheave groove and become entangled on the shaft, creating binding or shaving of the hoisting rope.

Rope fouling can also occur when there is a slack cable condition, such as when a load block rests on top of a load. It is required that the hoisting ropes have no less than two wraps remaining on the hoist drum when the hook is in its lowest position.

Inspection

Prior to initial use, all new and altered cranes shall be inspected to ensure they are in compliance with the provisions of this section. The inspection procedure for cranes in regular service is divided into two classifications: frequent inspection (daily to monthly intervals) and periodic inspection (one- to 12-month intervals).

Equipment Inspection

All functional operating mechanisms, air and hydraulic systems, chains, rope slings, hooks and other lifting equipment shall be visually inspected daily. Chains, cables, ropes, hooks, etc. on overhead and gantry cranes shall be visually inspected for problems, including deformation, cracks, excessive wear, twists and stretching. Defective gear shall be replaced or repaired. In addition, hooks and chains shall be visually inspected monthly and a certification record kept that includes the date of inspection, the signature of the person who performed the inspection and the serial number or other identifier of the equipment. Running ropes shall be inspected monthly with a certification record that includes the date of inspection the signature of the person who performed the inspection, and the serial number or other identifier of each rope.

Periodic Inspection

Complete inspection of the crane shall be performed at one-month to 12-month intervals, depending on its activity, severity of service and environmental conditions. The inspection shall include the following areas:
- Deformed, cracked, corroded, worn, or loose members or parts;

- The brake system;
- Limit indicators (e.g., wind, load);
- Power plant; and
- Electrical apparatus.

Testing

Prior to initial use, all new and altered cranes shall be tested, including the following functions:
- Hoisting and lowering;
- Trolley travel;
- Bridge travel; and
- Limit switches, locking and safety devices

The trip setting of hoist limit switches shall be determined by tests with an empty hook traveling in increasing speeds up to the maximum speed. The actuating mechanism of the limit switch shall be located so that it will trip the switch, under all conditions, in sufficient time to prevent contact of the hook or hook block with any part of the trolley. A preventive maintenance program based on the crane manufacturer's recommendations shall be established.

Handling the Load

One of the most significant hazards associated with cranes is overloading. A crane shall not be loaded beyond its rated load capacity for any reason except test purposes. "Rated load" means the maximum load for which a crane or individual hoist is designed and built by the manufacturer as shown on the equipment nameplate.

A common misconception is that a safety factor is built in and that an employer may exceed the rated load up to this safety factor. *This is not true.* A load means the total superimposed weight on the load block or hooks and includes lifting devices, such as magnets, spreader bars, chains and slings.

Every load lifted by a crane shall be well secured and properly balanced in the sling or lifting device before it is lifted more than a few inches. In some instances, workers may have balanced, but not secured the load. This is a violation.

To prevent swinging of a load, the hook shall be brought directly over the load when the attachment is made. In addition, no employee is permitted on the load, hook or lifting device while the load is being hoisted, lowered or traveling.

The operator of a crane shall avoid carrying loads over other personnel. This hazard is increased significantly when using a magnet or a vacuum device to lift scrap material. Operators of cranes are not permitted to leave their position at the controls while loads are suspended. This includes suspended lifting devices such as magnets or vacuum lifts.

At the beginning of each operator's shift, the upper limit switch of each hoist shall be tried out under no-load conditions. Additionally, the hoist limit switch, which controls the upper limit of travel of the load block, shall never be used as an operating control.

Crawler Locomotive and Truck Cranes—1910.180

This section applies to crawler cranes, locomotive cranes, wheel-mounted cranes of both truck and self-propelled wheel type, and any variations thereof that retain the same fundamental characteristics. It includes only cranes of the above types, which are powered by internal combustion engines or electric motors and use drums and ropes. Cranes designed for railway and automobile wreck clearances are exceptions. The requirements of this section are applicable only to machines when used as lifting cranes.

All modern crawler, locomotive and truck cranes shall meet the design specifications of the American National Standard Safety Code for Crawler, Locomotive, and Truck Cranes, ANSI B30-1-1968. Only employees selected or assigned by the employer or the employer's representative as being qualified shall be permitted to operate a crane covered by this section.

Load Ratings

Where stability governs lifting performance, load ratings have been established for various types of mounting and are given in a table in 1910.180. A substantial and durable rating chart with clearly legible letters and figures shall be securely fixed in each crane cab in a location easily visible to the operator while seated at the control station.

Inspection

Prior to initial use, all new and altered cranes shall be inspected to ensure compliance with the provisions of this section. The inspection procedure for cranes in regular service is divided into two classifications: frequent inspection (daily to monthly intervals) and periodic inspection (one- to 12-month intervals).

Equipment Inspection

All functional operating mechanisms, control systems, safety devices, air and hydraulic systems, chains, rope slings, hooks, and other lifting equipment shall be visually inspected daily. Items such as cables, ropes and hooks shall be visually inspected daily for problems, including deformation, cracks, excessive wear, twists and stretches. Defective gear shall be replaced or repaired. Running ropes shall be inspected monthly and a certification record kept that includes the date of inspection, the signature of the person who performed the inspection, and the serial number or other identifier of each rope.

Periodic Inspection

Complete inspection of the crane shall be performed at one-month to 12-month intervals, depending on its activity, severity of service and environmental conditions. The inspection shall include the following areas:

- Deformed, cracked, corroded, worn or loose members or parts;
- The brake system;
- Limit indicators (e.g., wind, load);
- Power plant;
- Electrical apparatus; and
- Travel steering, braking and locking devices.

Inspection Records

Certification records that include the date of inspection, signature of the person who performed the inspection, and the serial number or other identifier of the crane that was inspected shall be made monthly on critical items in use, such as brakes, crane hooks and ropes. This certification record shall be kept on file where readily available to appointed personnel.

Testing

Prior to initial use, all new production cranes shall be tested to ensure compliance with the provisions of this section, including the following functions:

- Hoisting and lowering mechanisms;
- Swinging mechanism;
- Travel mechanism; and
- Safety devices.

Maintenance

After adjustments and repairs have been made, the crane shall not be operated until all guards have been reinstalled, safety devices reactivated and maintenance equipment removed.

Handling the Load

One of the most significant hazards associated with cranes is overloading. A crane shall not be loaded beyond its rated load capacity for any reason except test purposes. "Rated load" means the maximum load for which a crane or individual hoist is designed and built by the manufacturer as shown on the equipment nameplate. A load means the total superimposed weight on the load block or hooks and includes lifting devices such as magnets, spreader bars, chains and slings. The hoist rope shall not be wrapped around the load. The load shall be attached to the hook by means of slings or other approved devices.

The employer shall ensure:

- The crane is level and, where necessary, blocked properly;
- The load is well secured and properly balanced in the sling or lifting device before it is lifted more than a few inches;
- Before starting to hoist, the following conditions shall be noted:
  - Hoist rope shall not be kinked;
  - Multiple part lines shall not be twisted around one another; and
  - The hook should be brought over the load in such a manner as to prevent swinging;
- During hoisting, care shall be taken that there is no sudden acceleration or deceleration of the moving load and that the load does not contact any obstructions.

Side loading of booms shall be limited to freely suspended loads. Cranes shall not be used for dragging loads sideways. The operator shall test the brakes each time a load approaching the rated load is handled by raising it a few inches and applying the brakes.

Outriggers shall be used when the load to be handled at that particular radius exceeds the rated load without outriggers as given by the crane manufacturer. Neither the load nor the boom shall be lowered below the point where less than two full wraps of rope remain on their respective drums.

Before traveling a crane with a load, a designated person shall be responsible for determining and controlling safety. When rotating the crane, sudden starts and stops shall be avoided.

When a crane is to be operated at a fixed radius, the boom-hoist pawl or other positive locking device shall be engaged.

Holding the Load
Operators shall not be permitted to leave their position at the controls while the load is suspended. No person shall be permitted to pass under a load on the hook. If the load must remain suspended for considerable time, the operator shall hold the drum from rotating in the lowering direction by activating the positive controllable means of the operator's station.

Operating Near Electric Power Lines

Clearances
Except where the electrical distribution and transmission lines have been deenergized and visibly grounded at the point of work or when insulating barriers not part of the crane have been erected to prevent physical contact with the lines, the minimum clearance between the lines and any part of the crane or load shall be:
- For lines rated 50 kV or below, 10 ft.;
- For lines rated over 50 kV, 10 ft. plus 0.4 inch for every kV over 50 kV or twice the length of the fine insulator, but never less than 10 ft.; and
- In transit with no load and boom lowered, a minimum of 4 ft.

Notification
Before operations near electrical lines begin, the owners of the lines or their authorized representatives shall be notified and provided with all pertinent information.

Overhead Wire
Any overhead wire shall be considered to be an energized line unless and until the owner of the line or the electrical utility authorities indicate that it is not an energized line.

Derricks—1910.181
A derrick is an apparatus consisting of a mast or equivalent member held at the head by guys or braces, with or without a boom, for use with a hoisting mechanism and operating ropes.

This section applies to guy, stiffleg, basket, breast, gin pole, Chicago boom, and A-frame derricks of the stationary type, capable of handling loads at variable reaches and powered by hoists through systems of rope reeling, used to perform lifting hook work, single or multiple line bucket work, grab, grapple and magnet work. Derricks may be permanently installed for temporary use as in construction work. This section also applies to any modification of these types that retain their fundamental features, except for floating derricks.

All modern derricks shall meet the design specifications of the American National Standard Safety Code for Derricks, ANSI B30.6-1969. Only employees designated by the employer or employee's representatives as being qualified shall be permitted to operate these derricks.

Load Ratings

Permanent Installations
For permanently installed derricks with fixed lengths of boom, guy and mast, a durable and clearly legible rating chart shall be securely affixed where it is visible to the operators. The chart shall include:
- Manufacturer's approval load ratings at corresponding ranges of boom angle or operating radii;
- Specific lengths of components on which the load ratings are based; and
- Required parts for hoist reeling.

Nonpermanent Installations
For nonpermanent installations, the manufacturer shall provide sufficient information from which capacity charts can be prepared for the particular installation. The capacity charts shall be located at the derricks or the job site office.

Inspection

Prior to initial use, all new and altered derricks shall be inspected to ensure compliance with the provisions of this section. The inspection procedures for derricks in regular service is divided into two general classifications: frequent inspection (daily to monthly intervals) and periodic inspection (one- to 12-month intervals).

Frequent Inspection

All functional operating systems, control systems, safety devices, cords and lacing, tension in guys, plumb of the mast, air and hydraulic systems, rope reeling, hooks and electrical apparatus shall be visually inspected daily. Running ropes shall be inspected monthly and a certification record shall be kept on file where readily available.

Periodic Inspection

Complete inspection of the derrick shall be performed at one-month to 12-month intervals, depending on its activity, severity of service and environmental conditions. The inspection shall include the following areas:

- Deformed, cracked, corroded, worn or loose members or parts;
- Power plant; and
- Foundation or supports.

Testing

The appointed person shall approve all anchorage. Rock and hairpin anchorage may require special testing. Prior to initial use, all new and altered derricks shall be tested by hoisting and lowering the load and moving the boom up and down. The operator also must inspect the swing and operation of all clutches and brakes of the hoist.

Maintenance

A preventive maintenance program based on the derrick manufacturer's recommendations shall be established.

Handling the Load

No derrick shall be loaded beyond the rated load and the hoist rope shall not be wrapped around the load. The load shall be attached to the hook by means of slings or other suitable devices.

Moving the Load

Some of the requirements for moving loads are stated below:

- The load shall be well secured and properly balanced in the sling or lifting device before it is lifted more than a few inches.
- Before starting to hoist, the following conditions shall be noted:
  - Hoist rope shall not be kinked;
  - Multiple part lines shall not be twisted around each other; and
  - The hook shall be brought over the load in such a manner as to prevent swinging.
- During hoisting, care shall be taken that:
  - There is no sudden acceleration or deceleration of the moving load;
  - Load does not contact any obstructions; and
  - The operator shall test the brakes each time a load approaching the rated load is handled by raising it a few inches and applying the brakes.
- Neither the load nor the boom shall be lowered below the point where less than two full wraps of rope remain on their respective drums.

The operator shall not be allowed to leave his or her position at the controls while the load is suspended. If the load must remain suspended for any considerable length of time, a dog, or pawl and ratchet, or other equivalent means, rather than the brake alone, shall be used to hold the load.

Dogs, pawls or other positive holding mechanism on the hoist shall be engaged. When not in use, the derrick boom shall be:

- Laid down;
- Secured to a stationary member, as nearly under the head as possible, by attachment of a sling to the load block; or
- Hoisted to a vertical position and secured to the mast.

Guards

Exposed moving parts, such as gears, ropes, setscrews, chains, chain sprockets and reciprocating components that constitute a hazard under normal operating conditions shall be guarded.

Operating Near Electrical Power Lines

Except where the electrical distribution and transmission lines have been deenergized and visibly grounded at the point of work or when insulating barriers not part of the derrick have been erected to prevent physical contact with the lines, the minimum clearance between the lines and any part of the derrick or load shall be:

- For lines rated 50 kV or below, 10 ft.; and
- For lines rated over 50 kV, 10 ft. plus 0.4 inch for every kV over 50 kV, or twice the length of the fine insulator but never less than 10 ft.

Notification

Before operations near electrical lines begin, the owners of the lines or their authorized representatives shall be notified and provided with all pertinent information.

Overhead Wire

Any overhead wire shall be considered to be an energized line unless and until the owner of the line or the electrical utility indicates that it is not an energized line.

Helicopters—1910.183

Helicopter cranes shall comply with any applicable regulations of the Federal Aviation Administration. Prior to each day's operation, a briefing shall be conducted that sets forth the plan of operation for the pilot and ground personnel.

Slings and Tag Lines

Loads shall be properly slung. Tag lines shall be of a length that will not permit their being drawn up into the rotors.

Cargo Hooks

All electrically operated cargo hooks shall have the electrical activating device designed and installed so as to prevent inadvertent operation. In addition, cargo hooks shall be equipped with an emergency mechanical control for releasing the load.

The cargo hooks must be tested prior to each day's operation by a competent person to determine that the release functions properly, both electrically and mechanically.

Personal Protective Equipment

Personal protective equipment (i.e., complete eye protection and hard hats secured by chin straps) shall be provided by the employer and used by employees receiving the load.

Loose-fitting clothing likely to flap in rotor downwash and be snagged on the hoist lines may not be worn.

Loose Gear and Housekeeping

All loose gear within 100 ft. of the place of lifting the load or depositing the load or within all other areas susceptible to rotor downwash shall be secured or removed.

Good housekeeping shall be maintained in all helicopter loading and unloading areas.

Hooking and Unhooking Loads

Employees are not permitted to perform work under hovering aircraft except when necessary to hook or unhook loads.

Static Charge

Static charge on the suspended load shall be dissipated with a grounding device before ground personnel touch the suspended load, unless all ground personnel who may be required to touch are wearing protective rubber gloves.

Signal Systems

The employer shall instruct the aircrew and ground personnel on the signal systems to be used and shall review the systems with the employees before hoisting the load. This applies to both radio and hand signal systems. Hand signals, where used, are to be in conformance with Figure N-1 of 1910.183.

Approach Distance

No employees shall be permitted to approach within 50 ft. of the helicopter when the rotor blades are turning, unless their work duties require their presence in that area.

Communications

There shall be constant, reliable communication between the pilot and a designated employee of the ground crew who acts as a signalman during the period of loading and unloading. The signalman shall be clearly distinguishable from other ground personnel.

Slings—1910.184

This section applies to slings used in conjunction with other material handling equipment for the movement of material by hoisting as covered elsewhere by this part. The types of slings covered are those made from alloy steel chain, wire rope, metal mesh, natural or synthetic fiber rope (conventional three-strand construction) and synthetic web (nylon, polyester, polypropylene).

Safe Operating Practices

Whenever any sling is used, the following practices shall be observed:

- Slings that are damaged or defective shall not be used.
- Slings shall not be shortened with knots or bolts or other makeshift devices.
- Sling legs shall not be kinked.
- Slings shall not be loaded in excess of their rated capacities.
- Slings used in a basket hitch shall have the loads balanced to prevent slippage.
- Slings shall be securely attached to their loads and padded to protect sharp edges.
- Suspended loads shall be kept clear of all obstructions.
- All employees shall be kept clear of loads about to be lifted and of suspended loads.
- Hands or fingers shall not be placed between the sling and its load while the sling is being tightened around the load.
- Shock loading is prohibited.
- A sling shall not be pulled from under a load when the load is resting on the sling.

Inspections

Each day before being used, the sling and all fastenings and attachments shall be inspected for damage or defects by a competent person designated by the employer. Additional inspections shall be performed during sling use, where service conditions warrant. Damaged or defective slings shall be immediately removed from service.

Alloy Steel Chain Slings

Alloy steel chain slings shall have permanently affixed, durable identification stating size, grade, rated capacity and reach.

Sling Use

Alloy steel chain slings shall not be used with loads in excess of the rated capacities prescribed in Table N-184-1 of 1910.184. Slings not included in this table shall be used only in accordance with the manufacturer's recommendations.

Safe Operating Temperatures

Alloy steel chain slings shall be permanently removed from service if they are heated above 1000°F. When exposed to temperatures in excess of 600°F, maximum working load limits permitted in Table N-184-1 of 1910.18.4 shall be reduced in accordance with the chain or sling manufacturer's recommendations.

Repairing Slings

Worn or damaged alloy steel chain slings or attachments shall not be used until repaired. If the chain size at any point of any link is less than that stated in Table N-1 84-2 of 1910.184, the sling shall be removed from service. Alloy steel chain slings with cracked or deformed master links, coupling links or other components shall be removed from service.

Wire Rope Slings

Sling Use

Wire rope slings shall not be used with loads in excess of the rated capacities shown in Tables N-184-3 through N-184-14 of § 1910.184. Slings not included in these tables shall be used only in accordance with the manufacturer's recommendations.

Safe Operating Temperatures

Fiber core wire rope slings of all grades shall be permanently removed from service if they are exposed to temperatures in excess of 200°F. When non-fiber core wire rope slings of any kind are used at temperatures above 40°F, or below -60°F, recommendations of the sling manufacturer regarding use at that temperature shall be followed.

Removal from Service

Wire rope slings shall be immediately removed from service if any of the following conditions are present:

- There are 10 randomly distributed broken wires in one rope lay or five broken wires in one strand in one rope lay;
- There is wear or scraping of one-third the original diameter of outside individual wires;

- There is kinking, crushing, bird caging or any other damage;
- There is evidence of heat damage;
- There are end attachments that are cracked, deformed or worn;
- There are hooks that have been opened more than 15 percent of the normal throat opening, measured at the narrowest point, or twisted more than 10° from the plane of the unbent hook; or
- The rope or end attachments are corroded.

Metal Mesh Slings

Each metal mesh sling shall have permanently affixed to it a durable marking that states the rated capacity for vertical basket hitch and choker hitch loadings. Handles shall have a rated capacity at least equal to the metal fabric and exhibit no deformation after proof testing. The fabric and handles shall be joined so that:

- The rated capacity of the sling is not reduced.
- The load is evenly distributed across the width of the fabric.
- Sharp edges will not damage the fabric.

Coatings that diminish the rated capacity of a sling shall not be applied.

Sling Test

All new and repaired metal mesh slings, including handles, shall not be used unless proof tested by the manufacturer or equivalent.

Sling Use

Metal mesh slings shall not be used to lift loads in excess of their rated capacities as prescribed in Table N-184-15 of 1910.184. Slings not included in this table shall be used only in accordance with the manufacturer's recommendations.

Safe Operating Temperatures

Metal mesh slings that are not impregnated with elastomers may be used in a temperature range from –20°F to 550°F without decreasing the working load limit. Metal mesh slings impregnated with polyvinyl chloride or neoprene may be used only in a temperature range from 0° to 200°F. For operations outside these temperature ranges or for metal mesh slings impregnated with other materials, the manufacturer's recommendations shall be followed.

Repair

Metal mesh slings that have been repaired, shall not be used unless they were repaired by a metal mesh sling manufacturer or an equivalent entity. Once repaired, records shall be maintained to indicate the date and nature of repairs and the person or organization that performed the repairs.

Removal from Service

Metal mesh slings shall be immediately removed from service if there is a:

- Broken weld or brazed joint along the sling edge;
- Reduction in wire diameter of 25 percent due to abrasion or 15 percent due to corrosion;
- Lack of flexibility due to distortion of the fabric;
- Distortion of the female handle so that the depth of the slot is increased more than 10 percent;
- Distortion of either handle so that the width of the eye is decreased more than 10 percent;
- Fifteen percent reduction of the original cross sectional area of metal at any point around the handle eye; or
- Distortion of either handle out of its plane.

Natural and Synthetic Fiber Rope Slings

Sling Use

Fiber rope slings made from conventional three-strand construction fiber rope shall not be used with loads in excess of the rated capacities prescribed in Tables N-184-16 through N-184-19 of 1910.184. Fiber rope slings shall have a diameter of curvature meeting at least the minimums specified in Figures N-184-4 and N-184-5 of 1910.184.

Slings not included in these tables shall be used only in accordance with the manufacturer's recommendations.

Safe Operating Temperature

Natural and synthetic fiber rope slings, except for wet frozen slings, may be used in a temperature range from –20°F to 180°F without decreasing the working load limit. For operations outside this temperature range and for wet frozen slings, the sling manufacturer's recommendations shall be followed.

Splicing
Spliced fiber rope slings shall not be used unless they have been spliced in accordance with the minimum requirements specified in 1910.184 and with any additional recommendations of the manufacturer.

Removal from Service
Natural and synthetic fiber rope slings shall be immediately removed from service if there is:
- Abnormal wear;
- Powdered fiber between strands;
- Variations in the size or roundness of strands;
- Discoloration or rotting; or
- Distortion of hardware in the sling.

Only fiber rope slings made from new rope shall be used. Use of repaired or reconditioned fiber rope slings is prohibited.

Synthetic Web Slings

Sling Identification
Each sling shall be marked or coded to show the rated capacities for each type of hitch and type of synthetic web material.

Sling Use
Synthetic web slings illustrated in Figure N-184-6 shall not be used with loads in excess of the rated capacities specified in Tables N-184-20 through N-184-22 of §1910.184. Slings not included in these tables shall be used only in accordance with the manufacturer's recommendations.

When synthetic web slings are used, the following precautions shall be taken:
- Nylon web slings shall not be used where fumes, vapors, sprays, dusts or liquids of acids or phenolics are present;
- Polyester and polypropylene web slings shall not be used where fumes, vapors, sprays, dusts or liquids of caustics are present; and
- Web slings with aluminum fittings shall not be used where fumes, vapors, sprays, dusts or liquids of caustics are present.

Safe Operating Temperature
Synthetic web slings of polyester and nylon shall not be used at temperatures in excess of 180°F. Polypropylene web slings shall not be used at temperatures in excess of 200°F.

Repair
Repaired synthetic web slings shall not be used unless repaired by a sling manufacturer or an equivalent entity.

Removal from Service
Synthetic web slings shall be immediately removed from service if any of the following conditions are present:
- Acid or caustic burns;
- Melting or charring of any part of the sling surface;
- Snags, punctures, tears or cuts;
- Broken or worn stitches; or
- Distortion of fittings.

Sling Safety
Whenever possible, mechanical means should be used to move materials in order to avoid employee injuries such as muscle pulls, strains, and sprains. In addition, many loads are too heavy or bulky to be safely moved manually. Therefore, various types of equipment have been designed specifically to aid in the movement of materials. They include cranes, derricks, hoists, powered industrial trucks, and conveyors. Because cranes, derricks, and hoists rely upon slings to hold their suspended loads, slings are the most commonly used piece of materials-handling apparatus.

Sling Types
The dominant characteristics of a sling are determined by the components of that sling. For example, the strengths and weaknesses of a wire rope sling are essentially the same as the strengths and weaknesses of the wire rope of which it is made.

Slings are generally one of six types:
1. Chain,
2. Wire rope,
3. Metal mesh,
4. Natural fiber rope,
5. Synthetic fiber rope, or
6. Synthetic web.

In general, use and inspection procedures tend to place these slings into three groups:
1. Chain;
2. Wire rope and mesh; and
3. Fiber rope web.

Each type has its own particular advantages and disadvantages. Factors that should be taken into consideration when choosing the best sling for the job include the size, weight, shape, temperature and sensitivity of the material to be moved, as well as the environmental conditions under which the sling will be used.

Chains

Chains are commonly used because of their strength and ability to adapt to the shape of the load. Care should be taken, however, when using alloy chain slings because they are subject to damage by sudden shocks. Misuse of chain slings could damage the sling, resulting in sling failure and possible injury to an employee.

Chain slings are the best choice for lifting materials that are very hot. They can be heated to temperatures of up to 1000°F; however, when alloy chain slings are consistently exposed to service temperatures in excess of 600°F, operators must reduce the working load limits in accordance with the manufacturer's recommendations.

All sling types must be visually inspected prior to use. When inspecting alloy steel chain slings, pay special attention to any stretching, wear in excess of the allowances made by the manufacturer, and nicks and gouges. These are all indications that the sling may be unsafe and should immediately be removed from service.

Wire Rope

A second type of sling is made of wire rope. Wire rope is composed of wire individual wires that have been twisted core to form strands (See Exhibit 15-3.). The strands are then twisted to form a wire rope. When wire rope has a fiber core, it is usually more flexible but less resistant to environmental damage. Conversely, a core that is made of a wire rope strand tends to have greater strength and be more resistant to heat damage.

Exhibit 15-3.
Wipe rope is composed of individual wires twisted around a core.

Rope Lay

Wire rope may be further defined by the "lay." The lay of a wire rope can mean any of three things:
1. *One complete wrap of a strand around the core.* One rope lay is one complete wrap of a strand around the core (See Exhibit 15-4.).

Exhibit 15-4.
An example of one rope lay.

2. The direction the strands are wound around the core. Wire rope is referred to as right lay or left lay. A right lay rope is one in which the strands are wound in a right-hand direction like a conventional screw thread (See Exhibit 15-5.). A left lay rope is just the opposite.

Exhibit 15-5.
An example of right lay rope.

3. *The direction the wires are wound in the strands in relation to the direction of the strands around the core.* In regular lay rope, the wires in the strands are laid in one direction, while the strands in the rope are laid in the opposite direction. In lang lay rope, the wires are twisted in the same direction as the strands. (See Exhibit 15-6.)

In *regular lay ropes*, the wires in the strands are laid in one direction, while the strands in the rope are laid in the opposite direction. The result is that the wire crown runs approximately parallel to the longitudinal axis of the rope. These ropes have good resistance to kinking and twisting and are easy to handle. They are also able to withstand considerable crushing and distortion due to the short length of exposed wires. This type of rope has the widest range of applications.

Lang lay (where the wires are twisted in the *same* direction as the strands) is recommended for such excavating, construction and mining applications, including draglines, hoist lines, dredge lines and other similar lines.

Lang lay ropes are more flexible and have greater wearing surface per wire than regular lay ropes. In addition, because the outside wires in lang lay rope lie at an angle to the rope axis, internal stress due to bending over sheaves and drums is reduced, causing lang lay ropes to be more resistant to bending fatigue.

A *left lay rope* is one in which the strands form a left-hand helix similar to the threads of a left-hand screw thread. Left lay rope has its greatest use in oil fields on rod and tubing lines, blast hole rigs and spudders where rotation of right lay would loosen couplings. The rotation of a left lay rope tightens a standard coupling.

Exhibit 15-6.
Examples of regular lay and lang lay ropes.

Wire Rope Sling Selection
When selecting a wire rope to give the best service, there are four characteristics to consider:
1. Strength;
2. Ability to bend without distortion;
3. Ability to withstand abrasive wear; and
4. Ability to withstand abuse.

Strength. The strength of a wire rope is a function of its size, grade and construction. It must be sufficient to accommodate the maximum load that will be applied. The maximum load limit is determined by means of an appropriate multiplier. This multiplier is the number by which the ultimate strength of a wire rope is divided to determine the working load limit. Thus, a wire rope sling with the strength of 10,000 lbs. and a total working load of 2,000 lbs. has a design factor (multiplier) of 5. New wire rope slings have a design factor of 5. As a sling suffers from the rigors of continued service; however, both the design factor and the sling's ultimate strength will be proportionately reduced. If a sling is loaded beyond its ultimate strength, it will fail. For this reason, older slings must be more rigorously inspected to ensure that rope conditions adversely affecting the strength of the sling are considered when determining whether a wire rope sling should be allowed to continue in service.

Fatigue. A wire rope must have the ability to withstand repeated bending without the failure of the wires from fatigue. Fatigue failure of the wires in a wire rope is the result of the development of small cracks under repeated applications of bending loads (See Exhibit 15-7.). It occurs when ropes make small radius bends. The best means of preventing fatigue failure of wire rope slings is to use blocking or padding to increase the radius of the bend.

Exhibit 15-7.
Example of wire rope fatigue failure.

Abrasive Wear. The ability of a wire rope to withstand abrasion is determined by the size, number of wires and construction of the rope. Smaller wires bend more readily and therefore offer greater flexibility but are less able to withstand abrasive wear. Conversely, the larger wires of less flexible ropes are better able to withstand abrasion than smaller wires of more flexible ropes.

Abuse. All other factors being equal, misuse or abuse of wire rope will cause a wire rope sling to become unsafe long before any other factor. Abusing a wire rope sling can cause serious structural damage to the wire rope, such as kinking or bird caging, which reduces the strength of the wire rope. (In bird caging, the wire rope strands are forcibly untwisted and become spread outward (See Exhibit 15-8.).) Therefore, to prolong the life of the sling and protect the lives of employees, the manufacturer's suggestion for safe and proper use of wire rope slings must be strictly followed.

Wire Rope "Bird Cage"

Exhibit 15-8.
Example of wire rope "bird cage."

Wire Rope Life

Many operating conditions affect wire rope life, including bending, stresses, loading conditions, speed of load application, jerking, abrasions, corrosion, sling design, materials handled, environmental conditions and history of previous use.

In addition to the above operating conditions, the weight, size and shape of the loads to be handled also affect the service life of a wire rope sling. Flexibility is also a factor. Generally, more flexible ropes are selected when smaller radius bending is required. Less flexible ropes should be used when the rope must move through or over abrasive materials.

Wire Rope Sling Inspection

Wire rope slings must be visually inspected before each use. The operator should check the twists or lay of the sling. If 10 randomly distributed wires in one lay are broken or five wires in one strand of a rope lay are damaged, the sling must not be used. It is not sufficient, however, to check only the condition of the wire rope. End fittings and other components should also be inspected for any damage that could make the sling unsafe.

To ensure safe sling usage between scheduled inspections, all workers must participate in a safety awareness program. Each operator must keep a close watch on the slings he or she is using. If any accident involving the movement of materials occurs, the operator must immediately shut down the equipment and report the accident to a supervisor. The cause of the accident must be determined and corrected before operations can resume.

Field Lubrication

Although every rope sling is lubricated during manufacture, to lengthen its useful service life it must also be lubricated in the field. There is no set rule on how much or how often this should be done. It depends on the conditions under which the sling is used; the more adverse the conditions under which the sling operates, the more frequently lubrication will be required.

Storage

Wire rope slings should be stored in a well-ventilated, dry building or shed. They should never be stored on the ground or continuously exposed to the elements because this will make them vulnerable to corrosion and rust. If it is necessary to store wire rope slings outside, they must be set off the ground and protected.

Note: Using the sling several times a week, even at a light load, is a good practice. Records show that slings that are used frequently or continuously give useful service far longer than those that are idle.

Discarding Slings

Wire rope slings can provide a margin of safety by showing early signs of failure. Factors requiring that a wire sling be discarded include:

- Severe corrosion;
- Localized wear (shiny worn spots) on the outside;
- A one-third reduction in outer wire diameter;
- Damage or displacement of end fittings, hooks, rings, links or collars by overload or misapplication;
- Distortion, kinking, bird caging or other evidence of damage to the wire rope structure; or
- Excessive broken wires.

Fiber Rope and Synthetic Web
Fiber rope and synthetic web slings are used primarily for temporary work, such as construction and painting jobs, and in marine operations. They are also the best choice for use on expensive loads, highly finished parts, fragile parts and delicate equipment.

Fiber Rope
Fiber rope slings are preferred for some applications because they are pliant, grip the load well and do not mar the surface of the load. They should be used only on light loads, however, and must not be used on objects that have sharp edges capable of cutting the rope or in applications where the sling will be exposed to high temperatures, severe abrasion or acids.

The choice of rope type and size will depend upon the application, the weight to be lifted and the sling angle. Before lifting any load with a fiber rope sling, the sling should be inspected carefully because they deteriorate far more rapidly than wire rope slings and their actual strength is very difficult to estimate.

When inspecting a fiber rope sling prior to using it, look first at its surface. Look for dry, brittle, scorched or discolored fibers. If any of these conditions are found, the supervisor must be notified and a determination made regarding the safety of the sling. If the sling is found to be unsafe, it must be discarded.

Next, check the interior of the sling. It should be as clean as when the rope was new. A build-up of powder-like sawdust on the inside of the fiber rope indicates excessive internal wear and is an indication that the sling is unsafe.

Finally, scratch the fibers with a fingernail. If the fibers come apart easily, the fiber sling has suffered some kind of chemical damage and must be discarded.

Synthetic Web Slings
Synthetic web slings offer a number of advantages for rigging purposes. The most commonly used synthetic web slings are made of nylon, dacron and polyester. They have the following properties in common:
- Strength: can handle load of up to 300,000 lbs.;
- Convenience: can conform to any shape;
- Safety: will adjust to the load contour and hold it with a tight, nonslip grip;
- Load protection: will not mar, deface, or scratch highly polished or delicate surfaces;
- Long life: are unaffected by mildew, rot, or bacteria; resist some chemical action and have excellent abrasion resistance;
- Economy: have low initial cost plus long service life;
- Shock absorbency: can absorb heavy shocks without damage; and
- Temperature resistance: are unaffected by temperatures up to 180°F.

Each synthetic material has its own unique properties. Nylon must be used wherever alkaline or greasy conditions exist. It is also preferable when neutral conditions prevail and resistance to chemicals and solvents is important. Dacron must be used where high concentrations of acid solutions, such as sulfuric, hydrochloric, nitric and formic acids, and high-temperature bleach solutions are prevalent. (Nylon will deteriorate under these conditions.) Dacron should not be used in alkaline conditions because it will deteriorate; nylon or polypropylene should be used instead. Polyester must be used where acids or bleaching agents are present and is also ideal for applications where a minimum of stretching is important.

Possible Defects. Synthetic web slings must be removed from service if any of the following defects exist:
- Acid or caustic burns;
- Melting or charring of any part of the surface;
- Snags, punctures, tears or cuts;
- Broken or worn stitches;
- Wear or elongation exceeding the amount recommended by the manufacturer; or
- Distortion of fittings.

Safe Lifting Practices
After the sling has been selected (based upon the characteristics of the load and the environmental conditions surrounding the lift) and inspected prior to use, it can be used—safely. There are four primary factors to take into consideration when safely lifting a load:
- The size, weight and center of gravity of the load;

- The number of legs and the angle the sling makes with the horizontal line;
- The rated capacity of the sling; and
- The history of the care and use of the sling.

Size, Weight and Center of Gravity

The center of gravity of an object is that point at which the entire weight may be considered as concentrated. In order to make a level lift, the crane hook must be directly above this point. While slight variations are usually permissible, if the crane hook is too far to one side of the center of gravity, dangerous tilting will result, causing unequal stresses in the different sling legs. This imbalance must be compensated for at once.

Number of Legs and Angle with the Horizontal

As the angle formed by the sling leg and the horizontal line decreases, the rated capacity of the sling also decreases. In other words, the smaller the angle between the sling leg and the horizontal, the greater the stress on the sling leg and the smaller (lighter) the load the sling can safely support. Larger (heavier) loads can be safely moved if the weight of the load is distributed among more sling legs.

Rated Capacity of the Sling

The rated capacity of a sling varies depending upon the shape of sling, the size of the sling and the type of hitch. Operators must know the capacity of the sling. Charts or tables that contain this information generally are available from sling manufacturers. However, the values given are for *new* slings; older slings must be used with additional caution. Under no circumstances shall a sling's rated capacity be exceeded.

History of Care and Usage

The mishandling and misuse of slings are the leading causes of accidents involving their use. The majority of injuries and accidents, however, can be avoided by becoming familiar with the essentials of proper sling care and use.

Proper care and usage are essential for maximum service and safety. Slings must be protected from sharp bends and cutting edges by means of cover saddles, burlap padding or wood blocking, as well as from unsafe lifting procedures such as overloading.

Before making a lift, check to be certain that the sling is properly secured around the load and that the weight and balance of the load have been accurately determined if the load is on the ground. Do not allow the load to drag along the ground; this could damage the sling if the load is already resting on the sling. Then ensure that there is no sling damage prior to making the lift.

Next, position the hook directly over the load and seat the sling squarely within the hook bowl. This gives the operator maximum lifting efficiency without bending the hook or overstressing the sling.

Wire rope slings are also subject to damage resulting from contact with sharp edges of the loads being lifted. These edges can be blocked or padded to minimize damage to the sling. After the sling is properly attached to the load, there are a number of good lifting techniques that are common to all slings:

- Make sure the load is not clamped or bolted to the floor.
- Guard against shock loading by taking up the slack in the sling slowly.
- Apply power cautiously so as to prevent jerking at the beginning of the lift and accelerate or decelerate slowly.
- Check the tension on the sling.
- Raise the load a few inches, stop, and check for proper balance and that all items are clear of the path of travel.
- Never allow anyone to ride on the hood or load.
- Keep all personnel clear while the load is being raised, moved or lowered.
- Crane or hoist operators should watch the load at all times when it is in motion. Obey the following "nevers":
- Never allow more than one person to control a lift;
- Never allow more than on person to give signals to a crane operator;
- Never raise the load more than necessary;
- Never leave the load suspended in the air; and
- Never work under a suspended load or allow anyone else to do so.

Once the lift has been completed, clean the sling, check it for damage and store it in a clean, dry, airy place. It is best to hang it on a rack or wall. Safe and proper use and storage of slings will increase their service life.

Maintenance of Slings

Chains

Chain slings must be cleaned prior to each inspection, as dirt or oil may hide damage. The operator must be certain to inspect the total length of the sling, periodically looking for stretching, binding, wear, or nicks and gouges. If a sling has stretched so that it is now more than 3 percent longer than it was when new, it is unsafe and must be discarded.

Binding is the term used to describe the condition that exists when a sling has become deformed to the extent that its individual links cannot move within each other freely. It is also an indication that the sling is unsafe. Generally, wear occurs on the load-bearing inside ends of the links. Pushing links together so that the inside surface becomes clearly visible is the best way to check for this type of wear. Wear may also occur, however, on the outside of links when the chain is dragged along abrasive surfaces or pulled out from under heavy loads. Either type of wear weakens slings and makes accidents more likely.

Heavy nicks and gouges must be filed smooth, measured with calipers, and then compared with the manufacturer's minimum allowable safe dimensions. When in doubt or in borderline situations, do not use the sling. In addition, never attempt to repair the welded components on a sling. If the sling needs repair of this nature, the supervisor must be notified.

Wire Rope

Wire rope slings, like chain slings, must be cleaned prior to each inspection because they are also subject to damage hidden by dirt or oil. In addition, they must be lubricated according to the manufacturer's instructions. Lubrication prevents or reduces corrosion and wear due to friction and abrasion. Before applying any lubricant, however, the sling user should make certain that the sling is dry. Applying lubricant to a wet or damp sling traps moisture against the metal and hastens corrosion, which deteriorates wire rope. Pitting may indicate it, but it is sometimes hard to detect. Therefore, if a wire rope sling shows any sign of significant deterioration, that sling must be removed until a person who is qualified to determine the extent of the damage can examine it.

Fiber Ropes and Synthetic Webs

In general, fiber ropes and synthetic webs should be discarded rather than serviced or repaired. Operators must always follow manufacturer's recommendations.

Summary

There are good practices to follow to protect employees while using slings to move materials. First, an employee should learn as much as he or she can about the materials with which he or she will be working. Slings come in many different types; analyze the load to be moved—in terms of size, weight, shape, temperature and sensitivity - then choose the sling which best meets those needs. Next, always inspect all the equipment before and after a move. Always be sure to give equipment whatever "in service" maintenance it may need. Finally, use safe lifting practices. Use the proper lifting technique for the type of sling and the type of load.

2009 Subpart N 1910.176-184
Materials Handling & Storage

178(l)(1)(i) — Powered Industrial Trucks – Operator competency — 525

178(l)(4) — Powered Industrial Trucks – Operator Evaluation — 243

178(p)(1) — Powered Industrial Trucks – Safe operating condition — 221

178(q)(7) — Powered Industrial Trucks – Examination for defects — 161

178(l)(6) — Powered Industrial Trucks- Operator certification — 156

WELDING, CUTTING, AND BRAZING

Many welding and cutting operations require the use of compressed gases. When compressed gases are consumed in the welding process, such as oxygen fuel gas welding, requirements for their handling, storage and use are contained in Subpart Q.

General requirements for the handling, storage, and use of compressed gases are contained in Subpart H, Hazardous Materials, 1910.101 to 1910.105. Certain welding and cutting operations require the use of compressed gases other than those consumed in the welding process. For example, gas metal arc welding uses compressed gases for shielding. Handling, storage and use of compressed gases in situations such as these require compliance with the requirements contained in Subpart H.

Many hazards are involved in compressed gas handling, storage and use. Compressed gases are stores of potential energy and it takes energy to compress and confine the gas. That energy is stored until purposely released to perform useful work or until accidental release by container failure or other causes.

Some compressed gases (e.g., acetylene) have high flammability characteristics. Flammable compressed gases, therefore, have additional stored energy besides simple compression-release energy. Other compressed gases, such as nitrogen, have simple asphyxiating properties. Some compressed gases, such as oxygen, can augment or compound fire hazards.

Compressed Gases General Requirements—1910.101

Cylinder Inspection

Employers shall determine that compressed gas cylinders under their control are in a safe condition to the extent that this can be determined by visual inspection. Visual and "other" inspections are required, but "other" inspections are not defined. These inspections must be conducted as prescribed in the Hazardous Materials Regulations of the Department of Transportation (DOT) contained in 49 CFR Parts 171 to 179 and 14 CFR Part 103. Where these regulations are not applicable, these inspections shall be conducted in accordance with Compressed Gas Association (CGA) Pamphlets C-6 and C-8. According to DOT regulations:

A cylinder that leaks, is bulged, has defective valves or safety devices, bears evidence of physical abuse, fire or heat damage, or detrimental rusting or corrosion, must not be used unless it is properly repaired and requalified as prescribed in these regulations.

The term "cylinder" is defined as a pressure vessel designed for pressures higher than 40 psia (pounds per square inch absolute) and having a circular cross section. It does not include a portable tank, multi-unit tank car tank, cargo tank or tank car.

The Department of Transportation (DOT) requires basic information markings on all cylinders. Each required marking on a cylinder must be maintained so that it is legible (See Exhibit 16-1.).

Exhibit 16-1.
The Department of Transportation requires legible markings on all containers.

1. DOT or ICC marking may appear—new manufacture must read "DOT" (49 CFR 171.14). "3AA" indicates specification found in 49 CFR 178.37. "2015" is the marked service pressure.
2. Serial number—no duplications permitted with any particular symbol-serial number combinations.
3. Symbol of manufacturer, user or purchaser.
4. "6 56" date of manufacture. Month and year. "O" is a disinterested inspector's official mark.
5. Plus mark (+) indicates cylinder may be 10% overcharged (49 CFR 173.302(c)).
6. Retest dates.
7. A five-pointed star indicates a 10-year retest interval (49 CFR 173.34(e)(15)).

Handling, Storage and Utilization

The in-plant handling, storage and utilization of all compressed gases in cylinders, portable tanks, rail tank cars or motor vehicle cargo tanks shall be in accordance with Compressed Gas Association (CGA) Pamphlet P-1.

Safety Relief Devices

Compressed gas cylinders, portable tanks and cargo tanks shall have pressure relief devices installed and maintained in accordance with CGA Pamphlets S-1.1 and S-1.2.

Special gases
The OSHA regulations contain some sections regulating specific compressed gases, including acetylene, hydrogen, oxygen, nitrous oxide, anhydrous ammonia and liquefied petroleum gases.

There are many compressed gases that are in common use that fall under regulation 1910.101. Examples include chlorine, vinyl chloride, sulfur dioxide, methyl chloride, hydrogen sulfide, ethane, compressed air and nitrogen.

These compressed gases do not receive explicit coverage by the OSHA regulations, but are covered by the requirements of 1910.101.

Welding, Cutting, and Brazing General Requirements—1910.252
Fire Prevention and Protection

Basic Precautions
The basic precautions for fire prevention in welding or cutting work are:
- If the object to be welded or cut cannot readily be moved, all movable fire hazards in the vicinity shall be taken to a safe place.
- If the object to be welded or cut cannot be moved and if all the fire hazards cannot be removed, then guards shall be used to confine the heat, sparks, and slag and to protect the immovable fire hazards.
- If the above requirements cannot be met, then welding and cutting shall not be performed.

Special Precautions
Suitable fire extinguishing equipment shall be maintained in a state of readiness for instant use. Such equipment may consist of pails of water, buckets of sand, hose or portable extinguishers, depending upon the nature and quantity of the combustible material exposed.

Fire watchers are required whenever welding or cutting is performed in locations where other than a minor fire might develop and if the following conditions exist:
- Appreciable combustible materials, in building construction or contents, are closer than 35 ft. to the point of operation; or
- Appreciable combustibles are more than 35 ft. away, but are easily ignited by sparks.

A fire watch also shall be maintained for at least a half hour after the completion of welding or cutting operations to detect and extinguish possible smoldering fires.

Cutting or welding shall not be permitted in the following situations:

- In areas not authorized by management;
- In sprinklered buildings while such protection is impaired;
- In the presence of explosive atmospheres (e.g., mixtures of flammable gases, vapors, liquids, dusts with air), or in explosive atmospheres that may develop inside uncleaned or improperly prepared tanks or equipment that have previously contained such materials or that may develop in areas with an accumulation of combustible dusts.

Welding or Cutting Containers

No welding, cutting or other hot work shall be performed on used drums, barrels, tanks or other containers until they have been cleaned so thoroughly as to make absolutely certain that there are no flammable materials present or any substances such as greases, tars, acids or other materials that when subjected to heat, might produce flammable or toxic vapors. Any pipelines or connections to the drum or vessel shall be disconnected or blanked.

Confined Spaces

When arc welding is to be suspended for any substantial period of time, such as during lunch or overnight, all electrodes shall be removed from the holders and the holders carefully located so that accidental contact cannot occur. The machine also shall be disconnected from the power source.

In order to eliminate the possibility of gas escaping through leaks or improperly closed valves when gas welding or cutting, the torch valves shall be closed and the gas supply to the torch positively shut off at some point outside the confined area whenever the torch is not to be used for a substantial period of time, such as during lunch or overnight. Where practical,

the torch and hose shall also be removed from the confined space.

Protection of Personnel

A welder or helper working on platforms, scaffolds or runways shall be protected against falling through the use of railings, safety belts, lifelines or some equally effective safeguard.

Eye Protection

Helmets or hand shields shall be used during all arc welding or arc cutting operations, excluding submerged arc welding. Helpers or attendants shall be provided with proper eye protection.

Helmets and hand shields shall be made of a material that is an insulator for heat and electricity. Helmets, shields and goggles shall not be readily flammable and shall be capable of withstanding sterilization.

Helmets and hand shields shall be arranged to protect the face, neck and ears from direct radiant energy from the arc.

Where the work permits, the welder should be enclosed in an individual booth painted with a finish of low reflectivity such as zinc oxide (an important factor for absorbing ultra-violet radiations) and lamp black or shall be enclosed with non-combustible screens similarly painted. Booths and screens shall permit circulation of air at floor level. Workers or other persons adjacent to the welding areas shall be protected from the rays by noncombustible or flameproof screens or shields or shall be required to wear appropriate goggles.

Protective Clothing

Employees exposed to the hazards created by welding, cutting or brazing operations shall be protected by personal protective equipment in accordance with the requirements of 1910.132. Appropriate protective clothing required for any welding operation will vary with the size, nature and location of the work to be performed (See Exhibit 16-2.).

Exhibit 16-2. Filter Lens Shade Number Guide

Welding Operation	Shade Number
Shielded Metal-Arc Welding, up to 5/32" (4 mm) electrodes	10
Shielded Metal-Arc Welding, 3/16 to ¼" (4.8 to 6.4 mm) electrodes	12
Shielded Metal-Arc Welding, over ¼" (6.4 mm) electrodes	14
Gas Metal-Arc Welding (Nonferrous)	11
Gas Metal-Arc Welding (Ferrous)	12
Gas Tungsten-Arc Welding	12
Atomic Hydrogen Welding	14
Carbon Arc Welding	10-14
Torch Soldering	2
Torch Brazing	3 or 4
Light Cutting, up to 1" (25 mm)	3 or 4
Medium Cutting, 1 to 6" (25 to 150 mm)	4 or 5
Heavy Cutting, more than 6" (150 mm)	5 or 6
Gas Welding (light), up to 1/8" (3.2 mm)	4 or 5
Gas Welding (medium), 1/8 to ½" (3.2 to 12.7 mm)	5 or 6
Gas Welding (heavy), more than ½" (12.7 mm)	6 or 8

Note: In gas welding or oxygen cutting where the torch produces a high yellow light, it is desirable to use a filter lens that absorbs the yellow or sodium line in the visible light of the operation spectrum.

Welders should always select clothing materials that will provide maximum protection from sparks and hot metal. Protective eye wear, safety shoes, clean fire-resistant clothing, and fire-resistant gauntlet gloves are recommended.

In addition, shirts should have full sleeves, no pockets and should be worn outside the trousers with their collars buttoned. Trousers should have no cuffs and should extend well down to the safety shoes.

Work in Confined Spaces

A confined space is defined in this regulation to be a relatively small or restricted space such as a tank, boiler, pressure vessel or small compartment of a ship. Adequate ventilation is a prerequisite to work in confined spaces. Ventilation requirements are discussed later in this section.

When welding or cutting is being performed in any confined space, the gas cylinders and welding machines shall be left outside the space. Where welders must enter a confined space through a manhole or other small opening, means shall be provided for quickly removing them in case of emergency. An atten-dant with a pre-planned rescue procedure shall be stationed outside to observe the welder at all times and be capable of putting rescue operations into effect.

When arc welding is to be suspended for any substantial period of time, such as during lunch or overnight, all electrodes shall be removed from the holders and the holders carefully located so that accidental contact cannot occur. The machine also shall be disconnected from the power source.

In order to eliminate the possibility of gas escaping through leaks of improperly closed valves when gas welding or cutting, the torch valves shall be closed and the fuel-gas and oxygen supply to the torch positively shut off at some point outside the confined area whenever the torch is not to be used for a substantial period of time, such as during lunch or overnight. Where practical, the torch and hose also shall be removed from the confined space.

Health Protection and Ventilation

Mechanical ventilation is required when welding or cutting is done with materials not specifically mentioned in this section. These materials—fluorine compounds, zinc, lead, beryllium, cadmium, mercury, cleaning compounds and stainless steel—are particularly hazardous and have specific control requirements.

Oxygen-Fuel Gas Welding and Cutting— 1910.253

Under no conditions shall acetylene be generated, piped (except in approved cylinder manifolds) or used at a pressure in excess of 15 psig (pounds per square inch gauge) or 30 psia (pounds per square inch absolute). The

30-psia limit is intended to prevent unsafe use of acetylene in pressurized chambers, such as caissons, underground excavations or tunnel construction. (Absolute pressure equal to gauge pressure plus atmospheric pressure, which at sea level averages 14.7 psi. Thus, at sea level a gauge pressure reading of 15 psi is equal to an absolute pressure of 29.7 psi.) This requirement is not intended to apply to storage of acetylene dissolved in a suitable solvent in cylinders manufactured and maintained according to U.S. Department of Transportation requirements or to acetylene for chemical use.

Using acetylene at pressures in excess of 15-psi gauge pressure (or about 30 psi absolute pressure) is a hazardous practice. Free gaseous acetylene is potentially unstable at pressures above 15 psig and could decompose with explosive violence. Experience indicates that 15 psig is generally acceptable as a safe upper pressure limit.

Keeping the gas in liquid solution and storing it in cylinders of unique construction avoids the decomposition characteristics of acetylene gas. Internally, acetylene cylinders are not designed like other kinds of compressed gas cylinders. Acetylene cylinders are never hollow. These cylinders contain a porous, calcium silicate filler and a suitable solvent, usually acetone, because under pressure, acetylene by itself is unstable. Acetone is used because it has the ability to absorb more than 400 times its own volume of acetylene at 70°F.

Millions of microscopic pores make up the calcium silicate filler. Although it appears to fill the steel shell, approximately 90 percent of the filler's volume consists of "pore space" for holding and evenly distributing the acetylene/acetone solution. When absorbed in this filler, the acetylene is divided into such small units that should acetylene decomposition take place in one pore, the heat released is not enough to raise the temperature of the acetylene in surrounding pores to the point where it too will decompose. Acetylene is usually supplied in cylinders that have a capacity of up to 300 cu. ft. of dissolved gas under pressure of 250 psig at 70°F.

Cylinders and Containers

Approval and Marking
All portable cylinders used for the storage and shipment of compressed gases shall be constructed and maintained in accordance with the regulations of the U.S. Department of Transportation (49 CFR Parts 171 to 179).

Compressed gas cylinders shall be legibly marked, for the purpose of identifying the gas content, with either the chemical or trade name of the gas. Such marking shall be by means of stenciling, stamping or labeling and shall not be readily removable. Whenever practical, the marking shall be located on the shoulder of the cylinder.

Storage of Cylinders—General
- Cylinders shall be kept away from radiators and other sources of heat.
- Inside of buildings, cylinders shall be stored in a well-protected, well-ventilated dry location, at least 20 ft. (6.1 m) from highly combustible materials.
- Cylinders should be stored in definitely assigned places away from elevators, stairs, or gangways or other areas where they might be knocked over or damaged by passing or falling objects or subject to tampering.
- Empty cylinders shall have their valves closed.
- Valve protection caps, where the cylinder is designed to accept a cap, shall always be in place, hand-tight, except when cylinders are in use or connected for use. The valve protection cap is designed to take the blow in case the cylinder falls.

Fuel-Gas Cylinder Storage
Inside a building, cylinders, except those in actual use or attached ready for use, shall be limited to a total gas capacity of 2,000 cu. ft. or 300 lbs. of liquefied petroleum gas.

Acetylene cylinders shall be stored valve end up. If the cylinder is on its side, acetone may leak out and create a dangerous condition.

Oxygen Storage
Oxygen cylinders in storage shall be separated from fuel-gas cylinders or combustible materials (especially oil or grease), by a minimum

distance of 20 ft. (6.1 m) or by a noncombustible barrier at least 5 ft. (1.5 m) high having a fire resistance rating of at least one-half hour (See Exhibit 16-3.). This requirement is intended to reduce the possibility of any fire support when a fire occurs among the fuel-gas storage.

Exhibit 16-3.
Oxygen cylinders in storage shall be separated from fuel-gas cylinders or combustible materials by the distances shown below.

Operating Procedures

Cylinders, cylinder valves, couplings, regulators, hose and apparatus shall be kept free from oily or greasy substances. Oxygen cylinders or apparatus shall not be handled with oily hands or gloves. A jet of oxygen must never be permitted to strike an oily surface, greasy clothes, or enter a fuel oil or other storage tank.

Valve-protection caps shall not be used for lifting cylinders from one vertical position to another. The cap may accidentally and suddenly come loose. Should the cylinder fall or be knocked over, the valve may be damaged or sheared off, causing a sudden release of pressure.

Should the valve outlet of a cylinder become clogged with ice, it should be thawed with warm, not boiling, water.

Unless cylinders are secured on a special truck, regulators shall be removed and valve-protection caps, when provided for, shall be put in place before cylinders are moved.

Cylinders not having fixed hand wheels shall have keys, handles or nonadjustable wrenches on valve stems while they are in service.

Unless connected to a manifold, oxygen from a cylinder shall not be used without first attaching an oxygen regulator to the cylinder valve. In addition, operators must make sure the regulator is proper for the particular gas or service. The regulator also should be clean and have a clean filter installed in its inlet nipple.

Before attaching the regulator, the protective cap should be removed from the cylinder. The valve also should be opened slightly for an instant and then closed. Always stand to one side of the outlet when opening the cylinder valve. This "cracking" of the cylinder valve will clean the valve of dust or dirt that may have accumulated during storage. Dirt can damage critical parts of a regulator and may cause a fire or explosion.

Before a regulator is removed from a cylinder valve, the valve shall be closed and the gas released from the regulator. An acetylene cylinder valve shall not be opened more than one and one-half turns of the spindle. This permits adequate flow of acetylene and allows ready closing of the valve in an emergency situation.

Exhibit 16-4.
Ten Basic Rules for Oxyacetylene Welding

1. Blow out the cylinder valve before you connect the regulator.
2. Release the adjusting screw on the regulator before opening the cylinder valve.
3. Stand to one side of the regulator before you open the cylinder valve.
4. Open the cylinder valve slowly.
5. Do not use or compress acetylene in a free state at pressures more than 15 psig.
6. Purge your acetylene and oxygen passages individually before lighting the torch.
7. Light the acetylene before opening the oxygen on the torch.
8. Never use oil or grease on regulators, tips, etc., in contact with oxygen.
9. Do not use oxygen as a substitute for air.
10. Keep your work area clear of anything that will burn.

Manifolding of Cylinders

Portable Outlet Headers

Portable outlet headers shall not be used indoors except for temporary service where the conditions preclude a direct supply from outlets located on the service piping system.

Each outlet on the service piping from which oxygen or fuel gas is withdrawn to supply a portable outlet header shall be equipped with a readily accessible shut-off valve.

Each service outlet on portable outlet headers shall be provided with a valve assembly that includes a detachable outlet seal cap, chained or otherwise attached to the body of the valve.

The primary reason for using a seal cap is to protect the outlet pipe thread from damage and to prevent the deposit of oil or grease on the threads. However, many times the caps are not used. Damage to threads and ground seals can cause leaky connections.

Service Piping Systems

Materials and Design

Pipe shall be at least Schedule 40 and fittings shall be at least standard weight in sizes up to and including 6-in. nominal.

Schedule 40 pipe is standard black iron pipe that has a working pressure of up to 125 psi and is always tested before use. Problems might arise when line extensions are made with other types of pipe or aluminum tubing. Therefore, a close inspection is necessary.

When oxygen is supplied to a service piping system from a low-pressure oxygen manifold without an intervening pressure regulating device, the piping system shall have a minimum design pressure of 250 psig. A pressure-regulating device shall be used at each station outlet when the connected equipment is for use at pressures less than 250 psig.

Piping for acetylene or acetylenic compounds shall be steel or wrought iron. Unalloyed copper shall not be used for acetylene or acetylenic compounds except in listed equipment. Under certain conditions, acetylene forms explosive compounds with copper (as well as with silver and mercury).

Installation

All piping shall be run as directly as practical and protected against physical damage, with proper allowance being made for expansion and contraction, jarring and vibration. Pipe laid underground shall be located below the frost line and protected against corrosion. After assembly, piping shall be thoroughly blown out with air, nitrogen, or carbon dioxide to remove foreign materials. For oxygen piping, only oil-free air, oil-free nitrogen or oil-free carbon dioxide shall be used.

Low points in piping carrying moist gas shall be drained into drip pots that have been constructed to permit pumping or draining out the condensate at necessary intervals. Drain valves shall be installed for this purpose, having outlets normally closed with screw caps or plugs. No open-end valves or petcocks shall be used. However, when drips are located outdoors or underground, and are not readily accessible, valves may be used at such points if they are equipped with means to secure them in the closed position. Pipes leading to the surface of the ground shall be cased or jacketed where necessary to prevent loosening or breaking.

Piping from overhead lines shall have drip pots at each station. These drip pots either have a plug or petcock on the bottom. Underground installations have no draining system. Pipes leading to the surface from underground lines have to be secured to prevent breaking or to avoid other damage.

Painting

Underground pipe and tubing and outdoor ferrous pipe and tubing shall be covered or painted with a suitable material for protection against corrosion.

Testing

Piping systems shall be tested and proved gas tight at all times during the maximum operating pressure and shall be thoroughly purged of air before being placed in service. The material used for testing oxygen shall be oil free and noncombustible. Flames shall not be used to detect leaks.

Welding, Cutting, and Brazing

Protective Equipment, Hose and Regulators

Pressure Relief Devices

Service piping systems shall be protected by pressure relief devices set to function at not more than the design pressure of the systems and discharge upwards to a safe location. Pressure relief valves are required in fuel-gas piping systems to prevent excessive pressure build-up within the system. Relief valves will vent automatically at preset pressures or may be manually operated to relieve pressure in the system (See Exhibit 16-5.).

Exhibit 16-5.
Pressure relief valves are required to prevents excessive pressure build-up.

Personal Protective Equipment

Approved protective equipment shall be installed on fuel-gas piping to prevent:

- Backflow of oxygen into the fuel-gas supply system;
- Passage of a flashback into the fuel-gas supply system; and
- Excessive back pressure of oxygen in the fuel-gas supply system.

The three functions of the protective equipment may be combined in one device or may be provided by separate devices.

Exhibit 16-6 illustrates the accepted location of approved protective equipment in fuel-gas piping systems. The protective equipment shall be located in the main supply line, as in Fig. Q-1 or at the head of each branch line as in Fig. Q-2 or withdrawn as shown in Fig. Q-3.

The first system has the most protection; that is, protective equipment is installed in the main supply and one check valve is installed before each outlet. System Q-2 has protective equipment in each branch circuit plus check valves at each outlet. System Q-3 has protective equipment at the fuel gas outlet and check valves at each outlet.

Exhibit 16-6.
Accepted locations of approved protective equipment in fuel-gas systems.

Hose and Hose Connections

Operators must use the proper hose. A fuel-gas hose is usually red (sometimes black) and has a left-hand threaded nut for connecting to the torch. An oxygen hose is green and has a right-hand threaded nut for connecting to the torch (See Exhibit 16-7.).

Exhibit 16-7.
Hose and hose connections are color-coded.

Hose and hose connections shall be clamped or otherwise securely fastened in a manner that will withstand, without leakage, twice the pressure to which they are normally subjected in service, but in no case less than a pressure of 300 psi. Oil-free air or an oil-free inert gas shall be used for the test.

Hoses showing leaks, burns, worn places or other defects rendering it unfit for service shall be repaired or replaced. When inspecting hoses, look for charred sections close to the torch. These may have been caused by flashback. Also check that hoses are not taped to cover leaks.

Pressure-Reducing Regulators

Pressure-reducing regulators shall be used only for the gas and pressures for which they are intended. When regulators or parts of regulators, including gauges, need repair, the work shall be performed by skilled mechanics that have been properly instructed. Most production shops do not have the proper equipment to make such repairs. For any equipment repairs or if there are questions about performance reliability, contact the manufacturer.

Gauges on oxygen regulators shall be marked "USE NO OIL."

Arc Welding and Cutting—1910.254

In the arc welding process, an electric current passing through the welding rod, or electrode, is forced to jump, or arc, across a gap. The resulting arc produces the intense heat necessary for the welding or cutting operation. Arc welding is used to fabricate nearly all types of carbon or alloy steels, the common nonferrous metals, and is indispensable in the repair and reclamation of metallic machine parts.

Arc cutting is primarily used for rough cuts or for scrapping because of the unevenness of the cut obtained. It has also been used for underwater cutting in salvaging operations. While most precautions and safe practices are common to oxygen-fuel gas welding, there are some that are unique to either gas or arc welding.

Shielding

It has long been known that welds will have better chemical and physical properties if the air can be kept away from the weld puddle. Such gases as oxygen, hydrogen, nitrogen and water vapor (i.e., moisture) all tend to reduce the quality of the weld. Dirt, dust, and metal oxides (i.e., contaminants) also reduce the weld quality. Shielding of the arc is normally provided in order to preserve the integrity of the weld joint. Shielding is provided either by decomposition of the electrode covering, known as the flux, or by a gas (or gas mixture) that may or may not be inert.

Common Arc Welding and Cutting Processes

Some of the more common arc welding and cutting processes are briefly discussed below.

Shielded metal arc welding (SMAW). This is the most widely used of arc welding, commonly referred to as "stick" welding. In this process, coalescence is achieved by heating with an electric arc between a covered (or coated) electrode and the work surface (See Exhibit 16-8.). Shielding is provided by decomposition of the electrode covering, known as the flux, while filler metal is obtained from the electrode's metal core.

Exhibit 16-8.
Shielded Metal Arc Welding (SMAW).

Gas metal arc welding (GMAW). Commonly known as "MIG" welding. In the gas metal arc welding process, the heat of an electric arc maintained between the end of an electrode and the work surface achieves coalescence (See Exhibit 16-9.). Shielding of the arc is provided by a gas (or gas mixture) that may or may not be inert. The electrode is fed continuously to the weld where it is melted in the intense heat of the arc and deposited as weld metal.

Exhibit 16-9.
Gas Metal Arc Welding (GMAW).

Gas tungsten arc welding (GTAW). Commonly known as "TIG" welding.

In gas tungsten arc welding, coalescence is achieved by the same arc and electrode method as in GMAW, except that the tungsten electrode is not consumed (See Exhibit 16-10.). Shielding is provided by an inert gas. This process offers high precision welds.

Exhibit 16-10.
Gas Tungsten Arc Welding.

Flux cored arc welding (FCAW). Flux cored arc welding is a process that produces coalescence by means of an arc between a continuous consumable electrode and the work surface. Shielding is provided by flux contained within the tubular electrode. Additional shielding may be obtained from a gas or gas mixture.

Submerged arc welding (SAW). In this process, heating produces coalescence with an arc between a bare metal electrode and the work surface. A blanket of granular, fusible flux shields the arc. The tip of the electrode and the welding zone

are surrounded and shielded by the molten flux and a layer of unused flux in the granular state. In this process, there is no visible evidence of the passage of current between the electrode and the work surface. This eliminates the sparks, spatter and smoke ordinarily seen in other arc welding processes. Fumes are still produced, but not in quantities generated by other processes.

Arc cutting. Arc cutting is the general process in which the cutting or removal of metals is done by melting with the heat of an arc between an electrode and the base metal.

Plasma arc cutting (PAC). In plasma arc cutting, the metal is cut by melting a localized area with a constricted arc and removing the molten material with a high velocity jet of hot, ionized gas.

Air carbon-arc cutting (AAC). Air carbon-arc is a type of arc cutting in which the metal is cut by melting with the heat of an arc, with use of an air stream to facilitate cutting.

Arc gouging. Arc gouging is an application of arc cutting used to produce a groove or bevel in the metal surface (See Exhibit 16-11.).

Voltage
The following limits shall not be exceeded:

	Alternating Current (AC)	Direct Current (DC)
Manual	80 Volts	100 Volts
Automatic	100 Volts	100 Volts

For AC welding under wet conditions or warm surroundings where perspiration is a factor, the use of reliable automatic controls for reducing no-load voltage is recommended to reduce the hazard of shock. Some of the older AC machines do not have an automatic control and are on load all the time. It is easy to receive an electric shock when the equipment is not handled properly.

Installation

Grounding
The frame or case of the welding machine (except engine-driven machines) shall be grounded under the conditions and according to the methods prescribed in Subpart S, Electrical. Conduits containing electrical conductors shall

not be used for completing a work-lead circuit. Pipelines shall not be used as a permanent part of a work-lead circuit, but may be used during construction, extension or repair, providing current is not carried through threaded joints, flanged bolted joints or caulked joints and that special precautions are used to avoid sparking at connection of the work-lead cable.

Operation and Maintenance

Machine Hook Up
Before starting operations, all connections to the machine shall be checked to make certain they are properly made. The work-lead shall be firmly attached to the work; magnetic work clamps shall be freed from adherent metal particles of spatter on contact surfaces. Coiled welding cable shall be spread out before use to avoid serious overheating and damage to insulation.

Electric Shock
Cables with splices within 10 ft. (3 m) of the holder shall not be used. Welders should not coil or loop welding electrode cable around parts of their body.

Maintenance
Cables with damaged insulation or exposed bare conductors shall be replaced. Joining lengths of

work and electrode cables shall be done by the use of connecting means specifically intended for the purpose. The connecting means shall have insulation adequate for the service conditions.

Resistance Welding—1910.255
A qualified electrician in conformance with Subpart S, Electrical, shall install all equipment.

Spot and Seam Welding Machines

Interlocks
All doors and access panels of all resistance welding machines and control panels shall be kept locked and interlocked to prevent access by unauthorized persons to live portions of the equipment.

Guarding
All press welding operations, where there is a possibility of the operator's fingers being under the point of operation, shall be effectively guarded by the use of a device such as an electronic eye safety circuit, two hand controls or protection similar to that prescribed for punch press operations.

Shields
Installing a shield guard of safety glass or suitable fire-resistant plastic at the point of operation shall, wherever practical, eliminate the hazard of flying sparks. Additional shields

COMMON WELDING PROCESSES

Process	Used For	Shielding	Smoke/Fume	Light/Radiation	Specific Hazard
Stick (SMAW)	General purpose; more than 50% of all welding	Electrode coating	High	moderate-variable	Depends on electrode, e.g., low hydrogen-flourides, stainless steel-nickel
MIG (GMAW)	High production/ automation	Inert gas (argon, helium, CO_2)	Moderate	High-especially with reflective metal and argon shield	Ozone, CO (CO_2 shield), stainless steel-chromium and nickel
TIG (GTAW)	High precision	Inert gas	Low	High	Ozone, light
Plasma (PAW)	Process can be used to weld, cut, metal spray	Gas	Moderate/high	Moderate/high	Noise, electrical shock, potential X-radiation
Sub Arc (SAW)	Horizontal welds, high production	Granular flux	Low	No visible arc unless have "breathrough"	Generally low hazard
Air Arc (AAW)	"Gouging," weld preparation	None	Very high	High	Noise, high fume levels
Flux Core (FCW)	High production/ automation, e.g., MIG with flux filled wire	Wire filling with or without gas	High	Moderate/high	High fume levels
Oxyacetylene (OAW)	Thin to medium thickness metals, steel and nonferrous in all positions	Filler rod coating	Low/moderate	Low	Compressed gas cylinders; depends on filler rod, e.g., silver brazing-cadmium

or curtains shall be installed as necessary to protect passing persons from flying sparks.

Foot Switches
All foot switches shall be guarded to prevent accidental operation of the machine.

Stop Buttons
Two or more safety emergency stop buttons shall be provided on all special multi-spot-welding machines, including two-post and four-post weld presses.

Welding Health Hazards

I. CHEMICAL AGENTS
ZINC. Zinc is used in large quantities in the manufacture of brass, galvanized metals, and various other alloys. Inhalation of zinc oxide fumes can occur when welding or cutting on zinc-coated metals. Exposure to these fumes is known to cause metal fume fever. Symptoms of metal fume fever are very similar to those of common influenza. They include fever (rarely exceeding 102°F), chills, nausea, dryness of the throat, cough, fatigue, and general weakness and aching of the head and body. The victim may sweat profusely for a few hours, after which the body temperature begins to return to normal. The symptoms of metal fume fever have rarely, if ever, lasted beyond 24 hours. The subject can then appear to be more susceptible to the onset of this condition on Mondays or on weekdays following a holiday than they are on other days.

CADMIUM. Cadmium is used frequently as a rust-preventive coating on steel and also as an alloying element. Acute exposures to high concentrations of cadmium fumes can produce severe lung irritation, pulmonary edema, and in some cases, death. Long-term exposure to low levels of cadmium in air can result in emphysema (a disease affecting the ability of the lung to absorb oxygen) and can damage the kidneys. Cadmium is classified by OSHA, NIOSH, and EPA as a potential human carcinogen.

BERYLLIUM. Beryllium is sometimes used as an alloying element with copper and other base metals. Acute exposure to high concentrations of beryllium can result in chemical pneumonia.

Portable Welding Machines

Safety Chains
All portable welding guns, transformers and related equipment suspended from overhead structures, beams, trolleys, etc., shall be equipped with safety chains or cables. Safety chains or cables shall be capable of supporting the total shock load in the event of failure of any component of the supporting system.

Long-term exposure can result in shortness of breath, chronic cough, and significant weight loss, accompanied by fatigue and general weakness.

IRON OXIDE. Iron is the principal alloying element in steel manufacture. During the welding process, iron oxide fumes arise from both the base metal and the electrode. The primary acute effect of this exposure is irritation of nasal passages, throat, and lungs. Although long-term exposure to iron oxide fumes may result in iron pigmentation of the lungs, most authorities agree that these iron deposits in the lung are not dangerous.

MERCURY. Mercury compounds are used to coat metals to prevent rust or inhibit foliage growth (marine paints). Under the intense heat of the arc or gas flame, mercury vapors will be produced. Exposure to these vapors may produce stomach pain, diarrhea, kidney damage, or respiratory failure. Long-term exposure may produce tremors, emotional instability, and hearing damage.

LEAD. The welding and cutting of lead-bearing alloys or metals whose surfaces have been painted with lead-based paint can generate lead oxide fumes. Inhalation and ingestion of lead oxide fumes and other lead compounds will cause lead poisoning. Symptoms include metallic taste in the mouth, loss of appetite, nausea, abdominal cramps, and insomnia. In time, anemia and general weakness, chiefly in the muscles of the wrists, develop. Lead adversely affects the brain, central nervous system, circulatory system, reproductive system, kidneys, and muscles.

FLUORIDES. Fluoride compounds are found in the coatings of several types of fluxes used in welding. Exposure to these fluxes may irritate the eyes, nose, and throat. Repeated exposure to high concentrations of fluorides in air over a long period may cause pulmonary edema (fluid in the lungs) and bone damage. Exposure to fluoride dusts and fumes has also produced skin rashes.

CHLORINATED HYDROCARBON SOLVENTS. Various chlorinated hydrocarbons are used in degreasing or other cleaning operations. The vapors of these solvents are a concern in welding and cutting because the heat and ultraviolet radiation from the arc will decompose the vapors and form highly toxic and irritating phosgene gas. (See Phosgene.)

PHOSGENE. Phosgene is formed by decomposition of chlorinated hydrocarbon solvents by ultraviolet radiation. It reacts with moisture in the lungs to produce hydrogen chloride, which in turn destroys lung tissue. For this reason, any use of chlorinated solvents should be well away from welding operations or any operation in which ultraviolet radiation or intense heat is generated.

CARBON MONOXIDE. Carbon monoxide is a gas usually formed by the incomplete combustion of various fuels. Welding and cutting may produce significant amounts of carbon monoxide. In addition, welding operations that use carbon dioxide as the inert gas shield may produce hazardous concentrations of carbon monoxide in poorly ventilated areas. This is caused by a "breakdown" of shielding gas. Carbon monoxide is odorless, colorless and tasteless and cannot be readily detected by the senses. Common symptoms of overexposure include pounding of the heart, a dull headache, flashes before the eyes, dizziness, ringing in the ears, and nausea.

OZONE. Ozone (O_3) is produced by ultraviolet light from the welding arc. Ozone is produced in greater quantities by gas metal arc welding (GMAW or short-arc), gas tungsten arc welding (GTAW or heli-arc), and plasma arc cutting. Ozone is a highly active form of oxygen and can cause great irritation to all mucous membranes. Symptoms of ozone exposure include headache, chest pain, and dryness of the upper respiratory tract. Excessive exposure can cause fluid in the lungs (pulmonary edema). Both nitrogen dioxide and ozone are thought to have long-term effects on the lungs.

NITROGEN OXIDES. The ultraviolet light of the arc can produce nitrogen oxides (NO, NO_2), from the nitrogen (N) and oxygen (O_2) in the air. Nitrogen oxides are produced by gas metal arc welding (GMAW or short-arc), gas tungsten arc welding (GTAW or heli-arc), and plasma arc cutting. Even greater quantities are formed if the shielding gas contains nitrogen. Nitrogen dioxide (NO_2), one of the oxides formed, has the greatest health effect. This gas is irritating to the eyes, nose and throat but dangerous concentrations can be inhaled without any immediate discomfort. High concentrations can cause shortness of breath, chest pain, and fluid in the lungs (pulmonary edema).

II. PHYSICAL AGENTS

ULTRAVIOLET RADIATION. Ultraviolet radiation (UV) is generated by the electric arc in the welding process. Skin exposure to UV can result in severe burns, in many cases without prior warning. UV radiation can also damage the lens of the eye. Many arc welders are aware of the condition known as "arc-eye," a sensation of sand in the eyes. This condition is caused by excessive eye exposure to UV. Exposure to ultraviolet rays may also increase the skin effects of some industrial chemicals (coal tar and cresol compounds, for example).

INFRARED RADIATION. Exposure to infrared radiation (IR), produced by the electric arc and other flame cutting equipment may heat the skin surface and the tissues immediately below the surface. Except for this effect, which can progress to thermal burns in some situations, infrared radiation is not dangerous to welders. Most welders protect themselves from IR (and UV) with a welder's helmet (or glasses) and protective clothing.

INTENSE VISIBLE LIGHT. Exposure of the human eye to intense visible light can produce adaptation, pupillary reflex, and shading of the eyes. Such actions are protective mechanisms to prevent excessive light from being focused on the retina. In the arc welding process, eye exposure to intense visible light is prevented for the most part by the welder's helmet. However, some individuals have sustained retinal damage due to careless "viewing" of the arc. At no time should the arc be observed without eye protection.

Care of Gas Cylinders

Acetylene

Acetylene is a compound of the elements carbon and hydrogen. At atmospheric temperatures and pressures, acetylene is a colorless gas that is slightly lighter than air. Acetylene of 100% purity is odorless, but gas of ordinary commercial purity has a distinctive, garlic-like odor. In air at atmospheric pressure, the upper explosive limit is about 80% acetylene and 20% air. The lower explosive limit is 2.5% acetylene in air.

The maximum safe working pressure of acetylene is 15 psig, yet most gauges available in the field permit higher unsafe pressures. The hydrogen and carbon components of acetylene will come apart (dissociate) explosively when pressures-are too high. At 1435°F, or at 30 psig, acetylene can explode by itself.

Acetylene cylinders avoid the decomposition characteristics of the gas by providing a porous mass packing material having minute cellular spaces so that no pockets of appreciable size remain where "free" acetylene in gaseous form can collect. This porous filler is saturated with liquid acetone. Acetone has the ability to hold 400 times its own volume of acetylene at the working pressure of 250 psig. The acetylene is dissolved within the acetone, making it stable. A small air space at the top of the cylinder is the only place where gas is permitted to collect. Acetylene cylinders should always be stored, transported and used in a vertical position. If the cylinder is on its side, acetone may leak out and dissolve the rubber hose, permitting a dangerous build-up of acetylene gas in the atmosphere. Another potential hazard exists during heavy cutting or use of large tips. When demands exceed 42 cu. ft. per hour, acetone may be sucked out and burned. Under these conditions, some of the acetylene gas may come free inside the cylinder, creating a potential hazard. Heavy gas volume demands require that more than one tank be manifolded together. Appropriate reverse flow check valves and flashback arresters add safety to any system and become important whenever cylinders are manifolded together.

Oxygen

Oxygen cylinders are pressurized to 2200 psig. If the valve protection cap is not in place and the cylinder is not secured, there is potential for damage to the valve stem. The fastest drag racer can reach 30 mph in 1 to 2 seconds. A compressed oxygen cylinder can reach 30 mph in less than 0.01 second. This is enough momentum to make it rocket through a cinder block wall over 200 ft. away. Consequently, the valve stem must be protected at all times.

An employee's clothing can become saturated with oxygen if he or she uses the torch to blow dust off of his or her clothing. A lit cigarette or any accidental spark will then cause that employee to catch fire. Do not permit oil or grease to come into contact with (or even near) regulators, hoses or torches for oxygen. Oxygen and oils or greases are an explosive combination.

Cylinder Storage For Acetylene

Acetylene gas may be stored in cylinders specifically designed for this purpose. The gas is first passed through filters and purifiers and then compressed into cylinders to a pressure of approximately 250 psig. The storage of acetylene in its gaseous form under pressure is not safe at pressures above 15 psig. The method used to safely store acetylene in cylinders follows:

The cylinders are filled with a substance such as pith from cornstalk, fuller's earth, lime silica or similar substances that absorb acetone. The cylinders are then charged with acetone that absorbs acetylene. The theory is that the acetylene molecules fit in between the acetone molecules. Using both of these techniques prevents the accumulation of a pocket of high-pressure acetylene.

Safety fuse plugs have a metal center that will melt at a temperature of approximately 212°F. If the cylinder should be subjected to a high temperature, the plugs will melt and allow the gas to escape before the pressure builds up enough to burst the cylinder. These precautions are necessary as the pressure in an acetylene cylinder builds up rapidly with an increase of temperature.

Acetylene cylinder valves come in two types. A common type is provided with a 3/8-in. square shank. It is turned by means of a

3/8-in. square box socket wrench. It is recommended that this cylinder valve be opened only 1/4 to 1-1/2 turns. The wrench should be left on the valve stem at all times that the valve is open so that the valve may be closed quickly in emergencies.

Another type of acetylene cylinder valve is fitted with a hand wheel. The regulator fitting is a female fitting.

The pressure in the cylinder cannot estimate the amount of acetylene in a cylinder because the gas discharge pressure will remain fairly constant (depending on the temperature) until most of the gas is consumed.

Oxygen Cylinder—Fuel-Gas Cylinder
Do not drop or strike an electric arc against a cylinder or heat it with an open flame. Recap it whenever gauges and regulators are removed. Never transport a cylinder without safeguards against shifting or falling. Cylinders should not be allowed to stand alone without being secured with lashing or chain to prevent them from toppling over. Avoid laying an acetylene cylinder on its side. Never use choker slings or magnets, nor hook into the protection cap to hoist a cylinder. Instead, use "racks" or "baskets."

Regulator (Oxygen And Fuel Gas)
Inspect to be sure there are no ignition sources in the immediate area; then "crack" the valve to blow out any dust or dirt before connecting the regulator. When setting up a rig, be sure to install a regulator in the line. Screw the regulator stem all the way out before placing pressure on the regulator. Before removing the regulator, close the cylinder valve and vent regulator of any residual gas.

Line And Cylinder Pressure Gauges (Oxygen And Fuel Gas)
Make sure these gauges are made up properly the oxygen gauge to the oxygen cylinder and the fuel-gas gauge to the fuel-gas cylinder. The difference in the thread sizes will prevent exchanging the connections. Observe each gauge frequently to note any trouble, such as unusual movement or sticking of the pointer. When any trouble sign is noted, close the cylinder valve and discontinue use of the rig until the trouble is located and corrected. Never lubricate gauges,

regulators, valves, connections or open valves while wearing greasy gloves. Lubricant can react violently with oxygen. Note: The gauge for acetylene line pressure should register less than 15 psi; higher pressures are unstable.

Cylinder Cap Threads
Avoid striking or scoring the cylinder cap threads or distorting the caps or they will not screw on properly. Never lubricate them with oil or grease.

Cylinder Shut-off Valves (Oxygen And Fuel Gas)
If you hear a leak around the stem after opening the valve, try to stop the leak by tightening the gland nut. If you are not immediately successful, close the valve and tag the cylinder. Then have the cylinder removed from service. The wrench used to open a cylinder valve should be left in position on the stem to permit quick shut-off of the gas flow in case of emergency. For manifold or coupled cylinders, at least one such wrench should be available for immediate use.

Torch
Before beginning work, check torches for leaks in shut-off valves, hose couplings or tip connections. Never use a defective torch. Inspect torch tips for clogging. Clear blockages with proper cleaning tools before beginning work. Never light a torch from hot work or with matches; use a friction lighter.

Torch Shut-off Valves (Oxygen And Fuel Gas)
Inspect frequently for leaks. Do not depend on the valves to prevent gas leakage when torch is left unattended at the worksite for extended periods of time. Always remove torch and hose from enclosed spaces when work is interrupted or concluded. As an additional precaution, close shut-off valves on cylinders.

Hose (Oxygen And Fuel Gas)
Hoses, probably the most fragile part of any burning or welding system, should be inspected frequently, especially before being used. Never use a system that does not distinguish (by color or other means) between the hose carrying oxygen from the one carrying fuel-gas. Couplings are designed so as not to

be interchangeable; fuel-gas couplings are left-hand threaded, while oxygen hose couplings are right-hand threaded.

Never use a hose that carries fuel-gas and oxygen simultaneously (having a common wall construction to separate them). Should a breakdown occur in the separation wall, the two gases could mix, with serious results. Connections that can be joined by being pushed or separated by a straight pull motion should not be used. Only couplings that require a rotary motion to be joined should be used. Pressure test any hose that has a flashback or that shows excessive wear upon inspection.

Fuel-gas and oxygen hoses that have been disconnected from the torch or other gas-consuming device should be removed immediately from a confined space.

OSHA Instruction STD 1-13.1 October 30, 1978 Office of Program Operations
February 14, 1972
OSHA PROGRAM DIRECTIVE #100-1

TO: National and Field Offices
SUBJECT: Reduction of Air Pressure Below 30 psi for Cleaning Purposes
ATTACHMENT: Acceptable Methods for Complying with 41 CFR 50.204.8 and 29 CFR 1910.242(b)

1.   Purpose. To provide guidance and examples of what alternate systems will meet the requirements of this section, and to clarify its intent.
2.   Background. A number of inquiries have been received requesting a clarification of the meaning of 1910.242(b) also known as 41 CFR 50-2048 under the Walsh-Healey Act.
3.   Interpretation. The phrase "reduce to less than 30 psi" means that the downstream pressure of the air at the nozzle (nozzle pressure) or opening of a gun, pipe, cleaning lance, etc., used for cleaning purposes will remain at a pressure level below 30 psi for all static conditions. The requirements for dynamic flow are such that in the case when dead ending occurs a static pressure at the main orifice shall not exceed 30 psi. This requirement is necessary in order to prevent a back pressure buildup in case the nozzle is obstructed or dead ended. See enclosure (1) for two acceptable methods of meeting this requirement. Also, there is no intent to restrict the diameter of the nozzle orifice or the volume (CFM) flowing from it.

"Effective chip guarding" means any method or equipment which will prevent a chip or particle (of whatever size) from being blown into the eyes or unbroken skin of the operator or other workers. Effective chip guarding may be separate from the air nozzle as in the case where screens or barriers are used. The use of protective cone air nozzles are acceptable in general for protection of the operator but barriers, baffles or screens may be required to protect other workers if they are exposed to flying chips or particles.
4.   Action. Inquiries about subject section should be handled in accordance with this instruction.
5.   Effective Date. This instruction is effective immediately, and will remain in effect until canceled or superseded.

Director, of Program Operations

DISTRIBUTION: National Field Office A/SEC. (3) Regional Administrators (6) Dep. A/Sec (2) Area/District Offices (3) Spec. Asst. (1) Training Institute (1) Directors (3) RAO (2) SOL (1) Professional Staff (1) BLS (1) Review Commission (6)
Originator: OCSDG

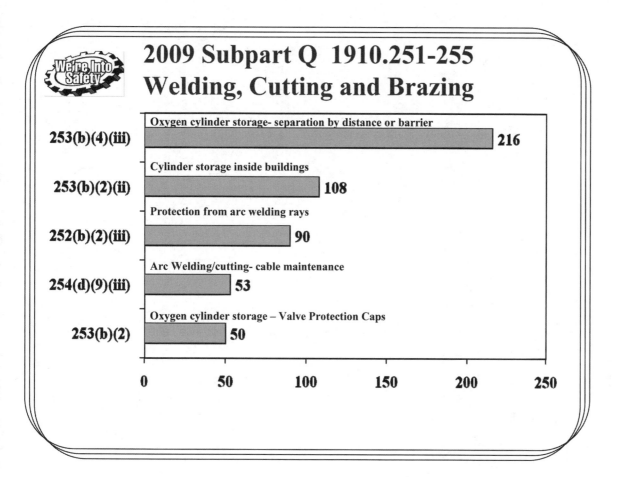

2009 Subpart Q 1910.251-255
Welding, Cutting and Brazing

We're Into Safety

253(b)(4)(iii) — Oxygen cylinder storage- separation by distance or barrier — 216

253(b)(2)(ii) — Cylinder storage inside buildings — 108

252(b)(2)(iii) — Protection from arc welding rays — 90

254(d)(9)(iii) — Arc Welding/cutting- cable maintenance — 53

253(b)(2) — Oxygen cylinder storage – Valve Protection Caps — 50

0   50   100   150   200   250

Welding, Cutting, and Brazing

SAFETY PROGRAMS

To effectively control hazards on work sites, companies recognize the need for a safety and health program. This program addresses work-related hazards including *potential* hazards that can result from changes in work conditions or practices whether or not they are regulated by government standards. A good safety and health program makes a big impact on loss prevention, worker productivity and the bottom line of a company.

OSHA has found that those companies with an effective safety and health program are rewarded with fewer and less severe accidents. Employee morale and productivity also are increased, and there is a significant reduction in workers' compensation costs and other costs associated with on the job injuries. The key components of any safety and health program consist of:

- Hazard analysis—Assessment of the hazard;
- Hazard prevention—Steps taken to keep workers safe;
- Polices and procedures—Rules that can be used by workers and subcontractors;
- Employee training—Type and frequency of training for all workers;
- Follow-up inspections—Audits or walk around inspections of the work site; and
- Enforcement—What specific steps are taken when a worker violates a safety rule.

A safety and health program describes the policies, procedures and practices that an organization uses to provide effective safety protection on the job. These guidelines are normally performance oriented. A large number of worksites lack the professional resources to develop this type of program on their own. Most small and medium-sized business do not have a full time safety staff to create such guidelines and this task often falls to a worker who picks up the additional job as a "collateral duty." In these cases it is even more important to have a written document to guide the safety program.

The safety program should spell out the authority, responsibility and accountability of all parties concerned. It also should be documented in writing to prevent confusion and uncertainty. Understanding the practices can be too easily confused considering, personnel turnover, cultural differences, and other factors that influence the work performance on any job. Written guidance is needed to cover basic polices, practices, procedures, emergency plans, posted signs, performance objectives and disciplinary actions.

An effective program includes provisions for the systematic identification and control of hazards in the workplace. The system must go beyond mere regulatory compliance to address all hazards.

Safety programs can be described as a system. Individual parts of the system work together to achieve a common goal. Companies often develop a baseline comprehensive worksite audit and then perform surveys on a routine basis to update that audit. Safety teams or committees work with those audits to correct unsafe conditions. Management and employees must work together to make the system work and they should review the safety program annually to make sure it still fits the needs of the organization.

Major Elements of a Safety Program

OSHA established voluntary guidelines for safety programs in 1989. These rules are guidelines and are not enforceable by OSHA in the general industry sector. However, they have been used by successful companies to develop programs that have reduced their number of accidents significantly. Firms that are involved with the Voluntary Protection Program consistently report that safety programs that follow federal guidelines work very well. There are common elements in any safety program, including:

- Commitment by management;
- Involvement of the workforce;
- Analysis of the work area to identify and control hazardous situations;
- Safety training; and
- Enforcement of the rules.

Management Commitment and Employee Involvement

Safety is a team effort where management is convinced that on-the-job safety is just as important as productivity and cost control. Managers demonstrate their safety leadership by communicating freely with their staff on safety matters. The legal responsibility for safety and health lies with the employer. The employer establishes the program and is responsible for decision making in the facility.

A clearly stated safety policy involves top management and is understood by all workers on a site. An example of demonstrated commitment on the part of management can be found in a company letter from the senior manager explaining that safety is of the utmost importance and is a requirement for the job. The person in charge of a facility often signs a policy statement on safety and health protection.

The role of management in the safety system is to create the needed resources so that responsible workers have the authority and ability to react to safety needs. Management must also hold supervisors accountable for enforcing the safety standards.

Individual workers have a right to a safe and healthy workplace. In successful safety programs, individuals feel that they are involved in the overall safety culture, accept responsibility for their workplace and realize that they have an active role in the safety of others. Safety programs should have committees that meet periodically. Hazard analysis teams or other worker-led groups should assist in inspections or the revision of safety rules as well as accident investigations. This will encourage employees to report workplace conditions that appear to be hazardous.

When workers are involved in decisions that affect safety the results are better management decisions, more effective safety protection and increased employee support for the safety program. A work site that solicits safety suggestions is a better place to work. This type of solicitation should be systematic and workers should feel that they are protected from reprisal for reporting an unsafe condition, and they should be provided with the appropriate response to their suggestion in a timely fashion. Workers will support a company where they know that management wants to be made aware of safety issues and will take action to correct them.

A key part of any program is fixing responsibility at the correct level. Both management and workers share responsibility for safety. Management establishes and enforces the rules and provides financial support for safety training and equipment. When the disciplinary procedures are fairly enforced and clearly understood, and management is held accountable for enforcing those standards, there is little opportunity to push workers into taking short cuts. Management must be held accountable for enforcing safety rules.

Workers are required to follow the rules. They must understand that there is no tolerance for unsafe behavior. Discipline is an indispensable piece of the whole approach to safety and health protection. Safe work procedures must be enforced and must cover all personnel, from site manager to hourly employee.

Accountability can be demonstrated by a written human resource policy that provides for corrective actions to be taken when a safety rule is ignored. This may involve a verbal reprimand, a written reprimand, suspension without pay or even termination. A clearly communicated system of progressive discipline lets all workers and supervisors know what is expected of them as well as the consequences for failing to meet those expectations. By using readily available counseling forms from the Human Resources department to accomplish counseling for safety misconduct, the supervisors reinforce the company's commitment to safety.

Work Site Analysis

Companies should examine the work site to identify existing hazards or conditions that could create hazards. Dangerous operations should be analyzed in such a way that hazards can be anticipated. This involves time and resources that must be approved by management. Safety committees, hazard evaluation teams, insurance carriers or outside consultants can assist in a workplace analysis. The people performing the inspections should be familiar with the safety program and applicable regulations for the work site.

The analysis can take the form of a comprehensive walk-through audit to establish a baseline for future safety audits. Some companies conduct a Job Hazard Analysis that involves reviewing each step of a job in a systematic method to determine the safest way to perform that task. Safety inspections should be performed on a periodic basis. A weekly inspection is recommended, although some companies perform a walk-around inspection every other week. Checklists can be developed that identify regulations that apply to the operation or safety challenges that have developed in the past. A review of accident records or injury reports often provides an insight into hazardous operations. The safety team should review new facilities and processes, materials, and equipment that may be brought into the facilities. The team should also look into accidents and even "near-miss" incidents to find ways to prevent future accidents from occurring.

Workers who report safety problems should be able to notify management or committees about unsafe conditions without fear of reprisal. They should receive feedback in a timely manner and should be encouraged to use the system.

Hazard Prevention and Control

Armed with a list of hazardous operations, the employees can begin a systematic method of controlling the hazards. Effective design or engineering controls often eliminate the hazard at the source. The most effective method of controlling hazards is to establish an engineering control. If that is not feasible, some form of administrative control, personal protective equipment, or another form of work safety practice may be used. Such things as installing a guardrail or electrical insulation often are cost-effective ways of eliminating the hazard. This must be done in a timely manner to minimize the exposure of workers to the danger.

If the hazard cannot be eliminated, workers may have to use some form of hazard control, such as using a spotter or wearing personal protective equipment to continue to work in a safe manner. Sometimes the hazard is the result of poor maintenance or use or abuse of the facility and normal maintenance procedures correct the problem. In other cases, an emergency event such as the release of chlorine gas or reaction to a fire require special training for the workers.

The best preventive measure for controlling unsafe conditions is to create an engineered solution, such as a guardrail or a physical system to protect the worker. Sometimes a feasible physical solution cannot be found. In these cases a procedure for safe work can be established. These procedures may not be as effective at ensuring a safe workplace as building engineered controls, but with the right type of training, positive reinforcement and correction of unsafe worker performance, the workplace can be made significantly safer. Firms should consider the use of a clearly

Safety Programs

communicated disciplinary system to enforce worker safety performance. In the event that the unsafe act cannot be engineered to a safe degree, or procedures do not provide sufficient safety, the firm may rely on personal protective equipment that can protect the workers. If none of these protective systems are deemed sufficient, the firm may rely on administrative controls to maintain safety. In this event, the facility may rotate workers through the hazardous area in order to minimize the amount of time that the employees are exposed to a hazard.

For example, imagine there is a wastewater treatment facility that has a lot of toxic gases being vented into an area. The first thing to do is try an engineering control, such as installing a ventilation system. If that is not feasible, the second best system is to develop procedures for safe work. In this case, workers may be required to manually vent the area prior to entering the work area. If that procedure is not feasible, the company may elect to use personal protective equipment and require the workers to wear respirators when they are in that area. Finally, if none of those solutions are feasible, the firm may rotate workers through that area so that no single worker is exposed to toxic gases for more than 30 minutes at a time, based on the maximum amount of exposure listed for short-term exposures on the material safety data sheet.

Safety and Health Training

Training is a key element in any business. In order to maximize the human element, workers must be trained in new and productive techniques. Maintaining a safety system is no different than maintaining a production system. Some training is required by federal or state regulations, while other safety training topics enhance the overall safety of the job.

The safety program should identify the types of training required, the personnel who need the training and the frequency of that training. A test should be given to ensure that workers understand the training material. This test can be a written quiz or a hands-on demonstration. It is important to provide sufficient training for safety so that responding to emergencies becomes second nature to the workers. Workers must understand the hazards to which they may be exposed and the training must ensure that they understand how to prevent themselves from getting injured as a result of those hazards.

Training can easily be broken into two areas: initial training and refresher training. When new employees are brought into the job site, they must be taught about the hazards of their new position. If a new machine or process is brought into place, the workers must receive initial training so that they can perform their required tasks safely.

Once they have been on the job for a while, refresher training helps to improve their performance and update the worker regarding any changes in policy or procedures.

Workers need to understand the hazards associated with their jobs, how to identify hazards and how to use the safety equipment that is provided to them. This training should be incorporated into their other training. Contractors and short-term workers must receive orientation training to prepare them to work in the area safely in an environment that may be new to them or hazards that they normally do not encounter. All workers must be trained on how to report incidents and accidents that may require posting in the OSHA 300 log.

Supervisors must understand company polices and procedures, hazard detection and control, how to conduct accident investigations, how to handle emergencies and how to reinforce training. Management training should be different than training that is provided to new hires, contract workers and other employees. It is important to stress to management that their role is to guide the safety program and provide support so that the workers can accomplish the job in a safe and efficient manner.

Elements of a Written Safety Program

These safety programs can be published as a written document and stored in a three-ring binder for easy updating. There are some topics that are common in any safety and health program. The basic plan sets the safety policy of the company and establishes responsibility, accountability and disciplinary procedures. Some topics included in the basic plan are:

- Safety policy
- Management responsibilities
- Supervisor responsibilities
- Employee responsibilities
- Safety committee or safety team (employee participation)
- Safety meetings
- Hazard recognition
- Incident investigation
- Elimination of workplace hazards
- Basic safety rules
- Job related safety rules
- Disciplinary policy
- Emergency planning
- Reporting accidents and incidents (OSHA 300 log)
- Training
  - Initial (new employee)
  - Refresher
  - Specialized
  - Supervisory

Appendices can then be added to the basic program to provide specific guidance on site-specific hazards that workers will encounter. This allows a company or a facility to personalize the plan to handle situations that may be unique to that area. Some examples of appendices that may be added to the safety program are:

- Personal protective equipment hazard analysis and program
- Respirator program
- Lockout/tagout (control of hazardous energy)
- Permit-required confined space entry
- Electrical safety
- First-aid plan
- Hazard communication program
- Hearing conservation program
- Welding hot work program
- Bloodborne pathogen plan
- Violence in the workplace plan
- Emergency action plan
- Hazardous waste operations plan

State Programs

States often develop regulations that provide safety for their workers that are as effective or even more so than the federal regulations. Two such states are Washington and California. California enacted Senate Bill 198, a worker safety bill that applies to all employers in the state of California. Washington State requires that all companies have an "Accident Prevention Program." Both states require that the document be written and meet certain criteria.

California Requirements

The State of California passed S.B. 198 requiring that all California employers have a safety program. California compares workers' compensation data to target employers for safety inspections. S.B. 198 requires employers to:

- Designate a responsible person;
- Periodically conduct inspections and accident investigations, as necessary;
- Identify workplace hazards;
- Correct safety deficiencies or hazards;
- Train employees;
- Establish a system for employee communication; and
- Establish a disciplinary system.

California requires that a person be designated as a "responsible person" who has the authority to allocate resources of the company to ensure compliance with the rules and regulations. This person should be at the management level in order to be effective. In order to ensure accountability for the program, this responsible person is personally liable and if it is found that he or she concealed danger in a product or business practice, he or she can incur fines and imprisonment.

Any time new equipment is installed or new material or chemicals are introduced to a work area, workers must be trained on those hazards. A list of workplace hazards must be maintained. The list should include such recognized hazards as employees in a company vehicle, operation of dangerous machinery, exposure to electricity, air quality, environmental noise, walking and working surfaces, chemical fumes, mists, vapors, and smoke.

Hazards must be corrected on a timely basis. Employers should identify every possible hazard and establish a priority to correct the deficiency based on the severity of the hazard. Those hazards that can kill, maim, or cause injury to people should be corrected first. If the hazard cannot be eliminated, the area or equipment must be clearly labeled with a sign that informs employees of the danger involved. All employees who might enter the danger area must be given instructions about the hazard. Both the corrective action and the employee training must be documented.

Trained personnel must conduct periodic inspections on a scheduled basis. The person conducting the inspection must be able to identify new potential hazards or investigate workplace safety. Those unsafe conditions and practices that can be corrected on the spot should be immediately corrected. It is a good idea to document these inspections and the corrective actions that result from them.

Before any worker is assigned to a job, he or she must be trained on the general safety procedures for that job. This includes workers on their initial assignment to the work area and workers who are transferred to new positions or the acquisition of new equipment. California requires that this training be accomplished by a trainer and documented. Workers may not be "self-taught" on the job.

Refresher training also should be provided to ensure proficiency in the safety area. Safety training should be incorporated into regular department meetings and routine employee training. Some training topics to regularly cover include:

- The location and operation of firefighting equipment;
- Proper lifting techniques;
- Defensive driving techniques;
- Chemical hazards;
- Electrocution hazards; and
- General housekeeping, which can help reduce slip and fall hazards.

California requires that employers and employees communicate with one another. This communication can be in the form of posters, meetings, training sessions, and labor unions. The intent of the communication is to ensure workers have a way to inform management of unsafe conditions so management can correct them. A company discipline policy for safety violations also must be established, posted, documented, and enforced by management.

Washington State Requirements

The State of Washington requires companies to develop an accident prevention plan (APP) in writing. This plan must be tailored to the workplace. The written plan must contain an orientation and a description of the company safety program. The plan should detail the requirement for a safety committee as well as how to report injuries and unsafe conditions.

Washington's plan requires specific training for employees, such as the initial on-the-job orientation; use and care of personal protective equipment; emergency actions to be taken to evacuate the workplace; and how to identify, store and use hazardous gases, chemicals and materials. Other training topics should include materials-handling equipment, machine tool operations, toxic materials and the operation of utility systems. The plan should require employers to enforce training programs to ensure that the work is performed in a safe manner. Washington companies must establish, supervise and enforce accident prevention programs in a manner that is effective.

A large part of the APP is the establishment of a safety committee and the use of safety meetings. Companies with more than 11 employees at the same location in the same shift are required to have a safety committee. The committee should have an equal number of employee-elected and employer-selected members. It also is important to include union members in the selection of the committee if a union is present. The committee should serve for a maximum of one year. The group must elect a chairperson of the committee and decide how often, when, and where to meet. The committee meetings should not last longer than one hour.

Firms with less than 10 employees may elect to have safety meetings instead of a safety committee. These safety meetings must be held monthly and there must be at least one representative of management at the meetings. The purpose of these meetings should be to review safety inspections, evaluate accident investigations and the overall performance of the APP. A record of the meeting must be made and include the names of the attendees and the subjects discussed.

The safety committee shall:

- Document the attendance at the meeting;
- Record subjects discussed;
- Review safety inspection reports;
- Evaluate accident investigations;
- Evaluate the workplace APP; and
- Maintain meeting records for one year.

The State of Washington allows companies to establish additional programs, plans and other rules that go beyond the APP described in order to develop a total safety and health plan.

Sample Plan

The federal program and the two state programs that have been reviewed provide an insight into how organizations are expected to respond with safety programs. By combining the intent of those programs into one document, a sample safety program that companies can use to meet the requirements of the overall safety program can be created. Companies can use this form by filling in the blank spaces with the pertinent information. It is important to review the plan once it is completed with the management and staff to ensure that the plan is workable for the facility as well as understood by all.

The safety plan provided here is a sample that can be used to develop a facility safety program. The base document describes roles and responsibilities and sets forth guidelines for the effective operation of a safety system. The guidelines may be modified to include more specific details as necessary.

With the overall plan in place, the facility should add appendices as needed to establish site-specific safety operations for detailed tasks. These appendices can be added or deleted as the facility establishes or discontinues procedures.

Sample Safety and Health Policy

It is the policy of _____ to provide a safe and healthy workplace for all of our employees. We feel that all accidents are preventable and that safety is a team effort involving the workforce, supervisors and management.

This company has established a safety and health program that is designed to involve all workers in the identification and reduction of hazards on each of our work sites. This program is designed to protect our most valuable resource, our workers, as well as meet federal and state regulations.

Safety is a key element in all workers' jobs. Unsafe behavior will not be tolerated and supervisors are required to enforce safety rules the same as they would enforce quality and timeliness issues with the employees. Active participation and adherence to our Safety Program is a condition of employment. No worker is allowed to work on a job that he or she knows is not safe. That includes our contractors and subcontractors.

Our goal is to eliminate accidents and injuries. There is no excuse or reason to take a shortcut or cut corners when they could result in an unsafe condition or action.

We're all in this together. If we work together, we will all go home safe and sound.

_____
Senior person

Responsibilities

Safety is a team effort and all employees and subcontractors of _____ are responsible for ensuring that the work area is safe. Different levels of management hold levels of responsibility. The person identified to maintain this program is _____, who is the head of _____ and can be reached at telephone extension _____.

Management is responsible to ensure that a safety committee is formed, staffed and resourced to allow it to complete its task of assisting the safety program. Managers will ensure that workers have sufficient time, resources and support from their supervisors to carry out the program. Managers will include an evaluation of safety performance in the annual review of workers' performance. Managers are responsible to ensure that all incidents (accidents and close calls) are investigated within five days and that corrective action is taken to prevent hazardous conditions from recurring.

Managers will ensure that the OSHA 300 form is maintained in an up-to-date, accurate manner with all recordable incidents being posted within seven calendar days of their occurrence. Managers are expected to report unsafe practices and to take action to correct unsafe behavior when they see it.

Managers of this facility are required to set a good example by following established safety rules, attending required safety training and encouraging all workers to do the same. Managers must enforce the disciplinary rules established in this safety program by ensuring that supervisors counsel workers as necessary.

Supervisors are responsible for the workers entrusted to their care. They must ensure that workers receive initial safety training prior to being allowed to work. Such training should be documented and evaluated to ensure that the worker understands what is expected of him or her. Supervisors are responsible for ensuring workers have the correct personal protective equipment and that the equipment is maintained correctly and used in the correct manner.

Supervisors are required to conduct a daily walk-around safety check of the work area and to direct the correction of any safety deficiencies found. In the event that the safety deficiency is caused by worker misconduct or non-compliance with established safety rules, the supervisor is required to counsel the individual and record that counseling on the employee's work record as outlined in the section on discipline.

Supervisors are not allowed to remove or defeat any safety device or to encourage workers by word or example to take short cuts that could result in an unsafe condition. Supervisors are required to support the safety committee by allowing workers the time needed to participate in safety activities.

Employees are required to comply with the safety rules established by the facility, federal or state law, safety training and any actions directed by their supervisors with regard to safety. When employees identify unsafe conditions, they are to report those to their supervisors or the safety committee promptly. All injuries or accidents are to be reported immediately to supervisors. All personal protective equipment should be maintained in good working condition and used correctly. Workers may not remove or defeat any safety device nor encourage coworkers by word or deed to take short cuts that may lead to an unsafe condition.

The Safety Committee has been formed to help employees and management work together to resolve safety problems and develop solutions identified to ensure that the safety program works smoothly. The safety committee consists of an equal number from management and employees. The union is invited to sit on the safety committee. The leader of the safety committee reports directly to _____ who has responsibility for the safety program. The leader is elected from the group. Members of the safety committee serve for one year and the group meets once a quarter on company time. The committee will review the OSHA 300 log and any accident reports or audits that have occurred during that time. The Safety Committee will conduct a monthly safety audit of the facility and the results of the audit will be posted on the company safety bulletin board.

The Safety Committee meets for one hour on the first Tuesday of the month in the employee lunchroom. The minutes of each meeting will be posted on the company's safety bulletin board and kept on file for two years.

Safety meetings for all employees will be held monthly by the supervisor. All employees are required to attend these meetings to enhance safety-related communication in the facility.

Employees are required to report any injury or work-related illness to their immediate supervisor regardless of how serious. Minor injuries such as cuts and scrapes can be entered on the minor injury log that is posted at _____.

The site supervisor will:

- Investigate a serious injury or illness using procedures in the "Incident Investigation" section below. Complete an "Incident Investigation Report" form. Give the "Employee's Report" and the "Incident Investigation Report" to _____, who is responsible for this form.
- Determine from the Employee's Report, Incident Investigation Report, and any loss and injury claim form associated with the incident, whether it must be recorded on the OSHA Injury and Illness Log and Summary according to the instructions for that form.
- Enter a recordable incident within six days after the company becomes aware of it.
- If the injury is not recorded on the OSHA log, add it to a separate incident report log, which is used to record non-OSHA recordable injuries and near misses.
- Each month before the scheduled safety committee meeting, make any new injury reports and investigations available to the safety committee for review, along with an updated OSHA and incident report log.

The safety committee will review the log for trends and may decide to conduct a separate investigation of any incident.

The management will post a signed copy of the OSHA log summary for the previous year on the safety bulletin board each February 1 until April 30. The log will be kept on file for at least five years. Any employee can view an OSHA log upon request at any time during the year.

Incident Investigation

If an employee dies while working or is not expected to survive, or when three or more employees are admitted to a hospital as a result of the same work-related incident the management will contact the OSHA representative (federal or state) within eight hours after becoming aware of the incident. The scene of the incident should not be disturbed except to aid in rescue or make the scene safe.

Whenever there is an incident that results in death or serious injuries that have immediate symptoms, a preliminary investigation should be conducted by the immediate supervisor of the injured person(s), a person designated by management, an employee representative of the safety committee, and any other persons whose expertise would help the investigation.

The investigation team should take written statements from witnesses and photograph the incident scene and equipment involved. The team also should document as soon as possible after the incident, the condition of the equipment and any anything else in the work area that may be relevant. The team should make a written report of its findings. The report also should include a sequence of events leading up to the incident, conclusions about the incident and any recommendations to prevent a similar incident in the future. The safety committee should review the report at its next regularly scheduled meeting.

When a supervisor becomes aware of an employee injury where the injury was not serious enough to warrant a team investigation as described above, the supervisor should write an Incident Report to accompany the "Employee's Injury/Illness Report Form" and forward them to _____, who maintains the OSHA 300 log.

Whenever there is an incident that did not but could have resulted in serious injury to an employee (a near-miss), the incident should be investigated by the supervisor or a team depending on the seriousness of the injury that would have occurred. The "Incident Investigation Report" form should be used to investigate the near miss. The form should be clearly marked to indicate that it was a near miss and that no actual injury occurred. The report should be forwarded to the bookkeeper to record on the incident log.

Safety Inspection Procedures

This company is committed to aggressively identifying hazardous conditions and practices that are likely to result in injury or illness to employees. We will take prompt action to eliminate any hazards we find. In addition to reviewing injury records and investigating incidents for their causes, management and the safety committee will regularly check the workplace for hazards as described below:

Annual Site Survey—An inspection team made up of members of the safety committee will do a wall-to-wall, walk-through inspection of the entire worksite. They will write down any safety hazards or potential hazards they find. The results of this inspection will be used to eliminate or control obvious hazards, target specific work areas for more intensive investigation, assist in revising the checklists used during regular monthly safety inspections and as part of the annual review of the effectiveness of our accident prevention program.

Weekly Safety Inspection—Each week, safety representatives will inspect their areas for hazards using the standard safety inspection checklist. They will talk to employees about their safety concerns. Committee members will report any hazards or concerns to the whole committee for consideration. The results of the area inspection and any action taken will be posted in the affected area. Occasionally, committee representatives may agree to inspect each other's area rather than their own.

Job Hazard Analysis—As a part of our on-going safety program, we will use a "Job Hazard Analysis" form to look at each type of job task our employees perform. The supervisor of that job task or a member of the safety committee will conduct this analysis. We will change how the job is performed as needed to eliminate or control any hazards. We will also determine whether the employee needs to use personal protective equipment (PPE) while performing the job. Employees will be trained in the revised operation and to use any required PPE. The results will be reported to the safety committee. Each job task will be analyzed at least once every two years, whenever there is a change in how the task is performed or if a serious injury occurs while the task is being performed.

Hazard Prevention and Control

This company is committed to eliminating or controlling workplace hazards that could cause injury or illness to our employees. We will meet the requirements of federal and state safety standards where there are specific rules about a hazard or potential hazard in our workplace. Whenever possible we will design our facilities and equipment to eliminate employee exposure to hazards. Where these engineering controls are not possible, work rules that effectively prevent employee exposure to the hazard will be established. When the above methods of control are not possible or are not fully effective, we will require employees to use personal protective equipment (PPE) such as safety glasses, hearing protection, and foot and hand protection.

Basic Safety Rules

The following basic safety rules have been established to help make our company a safe and efficient place to work. These rules are in addition to safety rules that must be followed when doing particular jobs or operating certain equipment. Those rules are listed elsewhere in this program. Failure to comply with these rules will result in disciplinary action.

- Never do anything that is unsafe in order to get the job done. If a job is unsafe, report it to your supervisor or safety committee representative. We will find a safer way to do that job.
- Do not remove or disable any safety device! Keep guards in place at all times when machinery is operating.
- Never operate a piece of equipment unless you have been trained on it and are authorized to use it.
- Use your personal protective equipment whenever it is required.
- Obey all safety-warning signs.
- Working under the influence of alcohol or illegal drugs or using them at work is prohibited and will not be tolerated.
- Do not bring firearms or explosives onto company property.
- Smoking is only permitted in designated areas.
- Horseplay, running and fighting are prohibited
- Clean up spills immediately. Replace all tools and supplies after use. Do not allow scraps to accumulate where they will become a hazard. Good housekeeping helps prevent injuries.

Disciplinary Policy

This facility has established a disciplinary policy to provide appropriate consequences for failure to follow safety rules. This policy is designed not so much to punish as to bring unacceptable behavior to the employee's attention in a way that the employee will be motivated to make corrections. The following consequences apply to the violation of the same rule or the same unacceptable behavior:

- First instance—Verbal warning, notation in employee file, and instruction on proper actions.
- Second instance—One-day suspension, written reprimand, and instruction on proper actions.
- Third instance—One-week suspension, written reprimand, and instruction on proper actions.
- Fourth instance—Termination of employment.

An employee may be subject to immediate termination when a safety violation places the employee or his or her coworkers at risk of permanent disability or death.

If an Injury Occurs

A first-aid kit is maintained at _____ _____. Each company vehicle is equipped with a first-aid kit located in the glove box or under the driver's seat. Members of the safety committee check these kits monthly. An inventory of each kit is taped to the inside cover of the box. If you are injured, promptly report it to any supervisor.

All supervisors are required to have first-aid cards. Other employees may have been certified. A list of current first-aid and CPR-certified supervisors and employees is posted on the company safety bulletin board along with the expiration dates of their cards.

In case of serious injury, do not move the injured person unless absolutely necessary. Only provide assistance to the level of your training. Call for help. If there is no response, call 911.

Safety Training

Training is an essential part of our plan to provide a safe workplace at this facility. To ensure that all employees are trained *before* they start a task that requires training, we have a training coordinator whose name is posted on the company safety bulletin board. Our safety-training supervisor is _____ _____.

That person is responsible for verifying that each employee has received an initial orientation by his or her supervisor has received any training needed to do the job safely and that the employee file includes documentation of the training. The coordinator will make sure that an outline and materials list is available for each training course we provide:

Course	Who must attend
Basic Orientation	All employees (given by the employee's supervisor)
Chemical Hazards (General)	All employees
Chemical Hazards (Specific)	An employee who uses or is exposed to a particular chemical
Fire extinguisher Safety	All employees
Respirator Training	Employees who use respirators
Forklift Training	Employees who operate forklifts
Electrical Safety	Employees who work with electricity
Power Tool Safety	Employees who use power tools

How This Safety Program Meets Federal and State Requirements

	Federal Guidelines	California	Washington
Written Plan	X	X	X
Policy Statement by Management	X		
Responsible Person		X	
Accountability	X	X	
Employee Involvement	X	X	X
Hazard Identification	X	X	
Hazard Control	X	X	
Training	X	X	X
Safety Committee	X	X	
Safety Rule Enforcement		X	X
Disciplinary Guides		X	X

Checklist to Assess Your Safety Program

- ❏ Title, signature and phone number of Responsible Person
- ❏ Policy statement of company safety and health
- ❏ Administrative responsibilities for implementing the plan
- ❏ Identification and accountability of worksite personnel responsible for accident prevention
- ❏ Means for controlling work activities of subcontractors and suppliers
- ❏ Responsibilities of subcontractors and vendors
- ❏ Plans for safety indoctrination of new employees
- ❏ Plans for continued safety training
- ❏ Provisions for safety inspections
- ❏ Responsibilities for investigation and reporting accidents/exposure
- ❏ Responsibilities for maintaining accident data, reports and logs
- ❏ Emergency response plan for disasters
- ❏ Public safety requirements (e.g., fencing/signs)
- ❏ Plans for monthly safety meetings and weekly employee safety meetings.
- ❏ Meetings shall be documented, including the date, attendance, subjects, and the names of the individuals who conducted the meeting.
- ❏ Documents shall be available for inspection on the job site.

Appendices and Local Requirements as Needed for the Job

- ❑ First-aid procedures—local emergency phone numbers posted
- ❑ Personal protective equipment—warning signs posted
- ❑ Hazard communications—list of chemicals on the job site/container labels
- ❑ Confined space entry—identification, entry procedures, rescue procedures
- ❑ Hearing conservation
- ❑ Respirator program
- ❑ Hot work program (welding)
- ❑ Bloodborne pathogens
- ❑ Violence in the workplace
- ❑ Emergency action plan
- ❑ Hazardous waste operations
- ❑ Fire prevention/protection
- ❑ Electrical safety
- ❑ Machinery and mechanized equipment
- ❑ Hand and power tools
- ❑ Fall protection
- ❑ Working over water or liquids

RISK MANAGEMENT

INTRODUCTION:

WHY USE A RISK MANAGEMENT APPROACH

The risk management process and the benefits and opportunities it provides have given companies a way to fix responsibility and accountability at the appropriate level. It requires managers and supervisors to accept responsibility for safety actions in a written form that reinforces their responsibility and liability, resulting in more safe decision making.

Risk Management enhances the workplace environment by eliminating or controlling hazards before they result in losses, whether personnel or materiel, losses that can degrade or halt the operation.

Effective use of Risk Management techniques provides worker, manager and leader with a workplace for which the risks are acceptable, in fact, a safe workplace. The Occupational Health and Safety Act mandates that every workplace be free of recognized hazards. This 'general duty' clause is used when there are no specific standards applicable to a particular hazard.

WHAT IS RISK MANAGEMENT?

Risk Management is a disciplined, organized, and logical decision making process to identify, evaluate and control hazards. With training and practice, personnel will be better able to spot hazards, analyze risk and make risk decisions at the appropriate level of control.

All work and daily routines involve risk. All job tasks and daily living require decisions that include assessing and managing hazards. Each supervisor, along with every individual, is responsible for identifying potential risks and adjusting or compensating appropriately. Decisions must then be made at a level of responsibility that corresponds to the degree of risk and the ability to apply resources, taking into consideration the significance of the task and the timeliness of the required decision. The decision-making techniques apply to all operations.

Risk Management is a process that gives an added edge to those with a long history of meeting "minimum" requirements, or, of meeting standards. It is an opportunity to go beyond the minimum, to reach greater effectiveness in any task or operation. Its prerequisite is a firm foundation in standards. One must understand the standards well enough to know the consequences of compromising them, and therefore how to control the task with a new set of 'standards' that provide risk controls or that the decision authority accepts the risk of loss.

Managers, supervisors and individuals must:

- Take ownership of workplace hazards.
- Not allow uncontrolled hazards.

Risk management is not a radical new way of doing business. Each of us manages risk on a daily basis, while working, driving, shopping, investing, etc. Most decisions are automatic, guided by years of experience coping with the same or similar situations. In a sense, we are all experienced "Risk Managers".

Simply put, Risk Management is an organized framework for decision-making. The aim is to minimize losses, whether associated with money, equipment or personnel safety, while maximizing operation success. It is the rational decision process: Weigh expected costs against expected benefits; if benefits outweigh costs—go for it; otherwise don't. The dilemma most often is how to quantify expected costs and benefits.

WHAT ABOUT COMPLIANCE?

Meeting OSHA standards is required in the workplace. It's important to understand there is no conflict between standards and the application of Risk Management techniques. The OSHA standards provide a foundation for hazard identification and control. Knowledge of OSHA standards provides valuable insight into understanding and implementing safety programs and systems. Application of OSHA standards provides safe workplaces from recognized hazards. However OSHA standards don't cover all hazards. Risk Management provides a process to make the workplace safer by reviewing and prioritizing tasks and operations either not covered, or not covered effectively, by OSHA standards.

HOW DOES IT WORK?

The basic decision making principles are applied before any job, action, or operation is executed. As an operation progresses and evolves, risk management controls are continuously reevaluated. Risk Management requires that owners and CEOs accept the process and take an active part in it. This is done by enforcing its use and establishing the amount of risk that workers can accept. For example, a low risk task, such as setting up a ladder and

changing a light bulb can be approved by the worker doing the task. On the other hand, if the light bulb has electrical wiring that is shorting out and exposing that worker to an electrical shock, and it is in a wet environment, the task may be defined as a high risk task. The CEO may require that all high risk tasks be approved by the plant manager, thereby shifting the authority and acceptance of liability to the plant manager. This is an important concept that eliminates the situation where a plant manager tells a subordinate to engage in a risky task with impunity. Under the Risk Management system, the worker would be required by company policy to inform the supervisor that as performed, this is a highly dangerous risk that cannot be accepted by the worker or the supervisor. It must be sent up the chain of command to someone who can accept the risk and liability. This protects the company, its officers and the workers by forcing a process to be enacted.

Integrate into planning.

- Risks are more easily assessed and managed in the early planning stages.
- The acceptable plans are in proportion to risks and worth the anticipated cost.
- Operation is accomplished without incurring excessive losses in personnel, equipment, time, or position.

Accept no Unnecessary Risk.

- Unnecessary risk has no payback in terms of real benefits or available opportunities.
- RM provides tools to determine which risk or what level of risk is unnecessary. CEOs

FIGURE 1.
COST AND BENEFIT SCALES

must make this decision to protect their company from lawsuits.

Make Risk Decisions at the Appropriate Level.
- Appropriate level for risk decisions is the one that can allocate the resources to reduce the risk or eliminate the hazard and implement controls.

Accept Risk When Benefits Outweigh the Costs.
- All identified benefits should be compared to all identified costs.
- Figure 1 depicts this principle. Balancing costs and benefits may be a subjective process and open to interpretation.

Ultimately, the balance may have to be determined by the appropriate decision authority.

Integrate RM into Company Doctrine and Planning at all Levels.
Risks are more easily assessed and managed in the planning stages of an operation. Integrating risk management into planning as early as possible provides the decision maker the greatest opportunity to apply RM principles.

Five-Step Risk Management Process. RM is a continuous process designed to detect, assess, and control risk while enhancing performance and maximizing capabilities. Figure 2 depicts the five-step process.
- **Identify Hazards.** A hazard is any real or potential condition that can cause (mission degradation) injury, illness, death to personnel or damage to or loss of equipment or property. Experience, common sense, and specific risk management tools help identify real or potential hazards.
- **Assess the Hazards.** Risk is the probability and severity of loss from exposure to the hazard. Assessment is the application of quantitative or qualitative measures to determine the level of risk associated with a specific hazard. The assessment step in the process defines the probability and severity of a mishap that could result from the hazard and determines the exposure of personnel or assets to that hazard.
- **Develop Control Measures and Make Risk Decision.** Investigate specific strategies and tools that reduce, mitigate, or eliminate the risk. Effective control measures reduce one or more of the three components (probability, severity, or exposure) of risk. Decision makers at the appropriate level choose controls based on the analysis of overall costs and benefits.
- **Implement Controls.** Once control strategies have been selected, an implementation strategy needs to be developed and then applied by management and the work force. Implementation requires commitment of time and resources.
- **Supervise and Evaluate.** Risk management is a process that continues throughout the life cycle of the system, mission, or activity. Once controls are in place, the process must be scrutinized and reevaluated to determine its effectiveness. Mission performance is periodically evaluated to determine the effectiveness of risk control measures.

WHAT IS RISK?
The following chart depicts risk: as risk is evaluated some emerge as clearly unacceptable. The unacceptable risk will either be controlled or the task will not be performed as planned. Some risk is not identified until later in the planning process or in the actual operation phase. That risk is evaluated as it's identified and additional controls either put into place or the risk is accepted or eliminated. Risk perception, risk tolerance, and risk acceptance play major roles in an individual's definition of "risk". Diversity of age, experience, and training are among the filters individuals use to consider risk. Level of experience with the specific mission or task adds another dimension to each individual's concept of "risk".

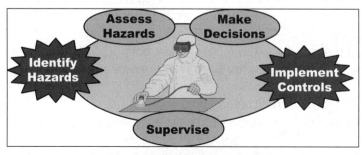

FIGURE 2.
FIVE-STEP PROCESS OF RISK MANAGEMENT

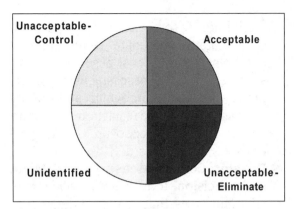

**FIGURE 3.
TYPES OF RISK**

WHAT ARE THE BENEFITS?

Benefits are not limited to reduced accident rates or decreased injuries, but may be actual increases in efficiency or job effectiveness. Examples of potential benefits include:

- Improved ability to protect the workforce by minimizing accidents—analysis of current processes may reduce risks.
- Enhanced job efficiency—reducing hazards by placing controls may make the task flow decisions are based on a reasoned and repeatable process instead of guess work or intuition.
- Improved confidence in capabilities—adequate risk analysis provides a clear picture of workforce strengths and weaknesses.

WHAT IS UNNECESSARY RISK?

Applying risk management requires a clear understanding of what constitutes "unnecessary risk", when benefits actually outweigh costs, and some guidance as to the appropriate level. Accepting risk is a function of both risk assessment and risk management. Risk acceptance is not as simple a matter as it may first appear. Several points must be kept in mind.

- Some risk is a fundamental reality.
- Risk management is a process of tradeoffs.
- Quantifying risk doesn't ensure safety.

General risk management guidelines are:

- Many activities involving a technical device or complex process entail some risk during their execution.
- Weigh risks and make judgments according to knowledge, experience, and mission requirements.
- Encourage other disciplines to adopt risk management principles. Hazard analysis

and risk assessment do not free us from reliance on good judgment.

- It is more important to establish clear objectives and parameters for risk assessment than to find a "cookbook" approach and procedure.
- There may be no "best solution." There are a variety of directions to go. Each of these directions may produce some degree of risk reduction.
- Point out improvements to established controls rather than to say their approach will not work.
- Complete risk control is not the goal; total risk elimination is seldom achieved in a practical manner.

WHO DOES WHAT?

CEOs/plant managers:

- Set the example
- Establish the acceptable level of risk for subordinates..
- Establish, endorse, and enforce established standards.
- Reinforce personal accountability.
- Accept responsibility for effective management of risk.
- Select from risk reduction options provided by the staff.
- Accept or reject risk based on the benefit to be derived.
- Train and motivate leaders to use risk management.
- Elevate to the appropriate decision maker; based on clearly defined risk levels.

Supervisors:

- Apply the risk management process and direct personnel to use it both on and off duty.
- Consistently apply effective risk management concepts and methods to operations and tasks.
- Elevate risk issues beyond their control or authority to superiors for resolution.

Individuals:

- Understand, accept, and implement risk management processes.
- Maintain a constant awareness of the hazards associated with a task.

- Make supervisors immediately aware of any unrealistic risk reduction measures or high risk procedures.

HOW MUCH IS ENOUGH?

Somewhere between the back of an envelope and a multi-year, multi-million dollar, contractor-engineered PERT chart lies the right amount of risk management for the task or mission at hand. How much is enough? How do you advise the CEO or manager as to the most appropriate level of detail for a particular task or operation? What criteria would you use to make your recommendation?

- We've talked about "effective application of the Risk Management process". It means that "hands on", not just following the "fine print", defines an efficient and effective process when it comes to Risk Management. It's easy to fall into using some format that soon becomes a thoughtless process. That road may be efficient; but it's rarely effective and it's full of potholes. We've talked about Risk Management providing insights into balancing cost and benefit. Some of the costs and benefits are subjective. The question arises "What 'criteria' would you use to advise the CEO on how much Risk Management is enough?" There is no easy answer. We recognize that the cost benefit of effective Risk Management for a major mobilization would likely be greater than for an everyday delivery of goods and services already in the pipeline. "Enough" Risk Management for continued operations is different than "enough" for an office staff with little change in their day to day operations.

Some suggested criteria:

- Is hasty or is deliberate decision making underway?
- Is time available to plan?
- What's the Importance of operation success—100% OK? 75%, 50%? What if it fails completely?
- Is the operation or task a new one or an old familiar one?
- Are personnel involved new to the operation or task? Unit? Experienced/Inexperienced?
- What's been their operation tempo recently?

HOW DO I EVALUATE OUR PROGRAM?

Use structured internal and external assessments. Leaders and managers take advantage of the entrepreneurial genius of the people within the organization to develop better ways of helping people and getting work done. It is a process which encourages ideas and initiatives to float upward. Embedding the risk management process into organizational processes is one way to help achieve better results. The idea behind risk management is to identify strengths and weaknesses in planning and execution with emphasis on hazard control. The value of self-assessments is the awakening of self awareness. With this self awareness, change is more readily accepted.

Risk management integration and self assessment can help change the thinking from "minimal essential" to "maximum possible" philosophies in providing support to workers. Employees are deserving of nothing less than excellence. Authority and responsibility must be pushed down into the organization.

WHERE DOES THE SAFETY PROFESSIONAL FIT IN?

The safety professional is the link between the compliance world and the world of uncontrolled risk. The first step the safety professional makes is to help leaders recognize that risks can be controlled, that accidental losses need not be the cost of doing business. Whether an individual views a task or operation as having group or individual risk plays a major role in whether the individual believes he can take action to reduce the risk. The safety professional can facilitate a change of attitude from the idea that "warehousemen have back injuries", or group risk about which little can be done; to the reality of individual risk, where worksite redesign, individual work-hardening, or use of manual materials handling equipment and eliminate the hazard. Once leaders believe that losses are unnecessary, the next step is that the safety professional can provide the Risk Management process as a deliberative, logical decision making methodology to control the hazards that lead to unnecessary losses. Now, the safety professional must advise leaders on how much Risk Management is appropriate to the task at hand and facilitate the process.

Professional safety personnel provide knowledge of Occupational Health and Safety standards, application of safety practices to recognize, avoid/eliminate hazards, and for hazard control and evaluation techniques that provide the foundation of a safe workplace. Safety professionals are investigators when hazardous conditions turn into accidents or incidents related to inadequately controlled hazards. Safety offices assist in training, program management and coordinating with health and safety related offices; to include preventive medicine, engineers, security and others.

AUDITS. Measurements are necessary to ensure accurate evaluations of how effectively controls eliminated hazards or reduced risks. After action reports, surveys, and in progress reviews provide great starting places for measurements. To be meaningful, measurements must quantitatively or qualitatively identify reductions of risk, improvements in operation success, or enhancement of capabilities. The Risk Management Evaluation Profile (an adaptation of OSHA's Program Evaluation Profile) in appendix B, provides an audit process of a safety program's overall effectiveness. Benefits of conducting an audit include:

- Formally going through the internal audit process with managers and employees,
- Formally reviewing the elements of a safety and health program,
- Getting managers involved in the audit process,
- Making managers, supervisors and employees aware of the scope and complexity of a formal safety and health program, and of their roles and responsibilities in the programs success.

After finishing your audit share the results with managers and legal personnel since the process of doing an audit creates a paper trail of the program's weaknesses. The audit is a formal tool to uncover weak points in the management system that create unsafe work practices and unsafe conditions that can injure workers, diminish their health, interrupt production, or damage products and property.

CONCLUSION. Risk management provides a logical and systematic means of organizing information for rational decision-making, to identify and control risk. Risk management is a process that requires individuals, supervisors and leaders to support and implement the basic principles, along with the discipline to apply them on a continuing basis. Risk management offers individuals and organizations a powerful tool for eliminating accidents and increasing effectiveness. This process has the unique advantage of being accessible to and usable by everyone in every conceivable setting or scenario.

Appendix A: Risk Management Steps

Tools to accomplish the various steps are explained and examples are given in, The Risk Manager's *Hazard Identification Tool Box*.

Step 1. IDENTIFY THE HAZARDS.

Hazards lead to risk, so the first step is to identify relevant hazards. Consider all aspects of current and future situations, environment, and known historical problems.

In identifying hazards, experience and training cannot be overemphasized; it is the most effective tool available. Those who have experience must use it, if an organization is to effectively use the RM process. Still, everyone is responsible for, and should be involved in finding potential hazards and informing their supervisor.

Visualization is an effective method to identify hazards. Picture the planned operation, think of what could go wrong—**ask yourself what if**? This can be done by an individual or a group, and can also use quality techniques such as brainstorming, "five whys", mental imaging, affinity diagrams, or cause-effect diagrams. The bottom line is: Honestly assess the planned procedure—**Think of what could go wrong, no matter how unlikely**.

Recognize Hazards: The Activity Hazard Analysis and Job Hazard Analysis (JHA) are both excellent tools to help identify risk as you think through a course of action to be examined. This is accomplished by reviewing current and planned operations describing the task. The supervisor defines what is required to accomplish the tasks and the conditions under which these tasks are to be conducted.

Construct a list or chart depicting the major steps in the job process, normally in time

RESOURCE

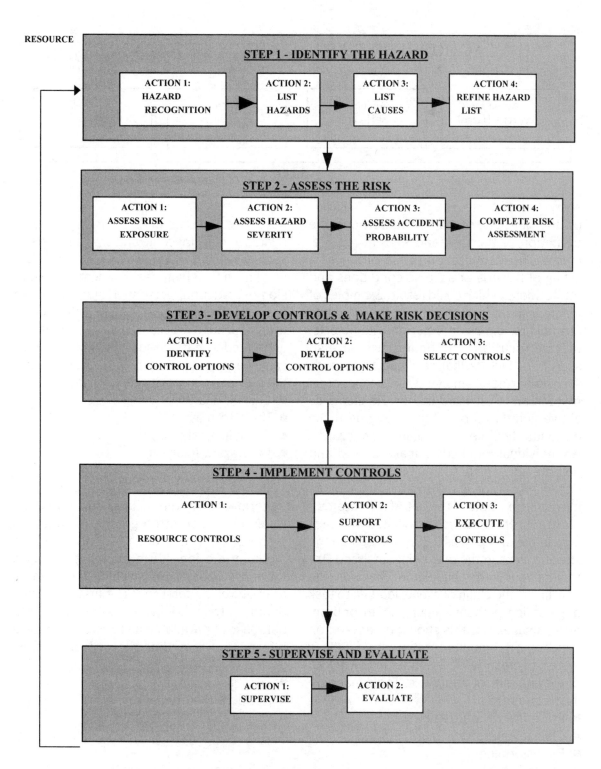

**FIGURE 4
RISK MANAGEMENT STEPS**

sequence. Break the operation down into 'bite size' chunks.

Some tools that will help perform mission/task analysis are:

- Activity Hazard Analysis
- Job Hazard Analysis
- Flow Diagram
- Multilinear Event Sequence (MES)
- Sequentially Timed Event Plot (STEP)

List Hazards: Hazards, and factors that could generate hazards, are identified based

FIGURE 5
STEP 1 ACTIONS

on the deficiency to be corrected and the definition of the task and system requirements. The identification phase produces a listing of hazards or adverse conditions and the accidents which could result. Examples of inherent hazards in any one of the elements include fire, explosion, collision with objects, or electrocution. The analysis must also search for factors that can lead to hazards such as alertness, ambiguity, or escape route. In addition to a hazard list for the elements above, interfaces between or among these elements should be investigated for hazards. An individual required to make critical and delicate adjustment to equipment on a cold, dark night may be at risk to a frost-bite injury, maybe an example of the "interface hazards." Make a list of the hazards associated with each step in the task process. Stay focused on the specific steps in the task being analyzed. Try to limit your list to "big picture" hazards (the final link in the chain of events leading to task degradation, personnel injury, death, or property damage). Hazards should be tracked on paper or in a computer spreadsheet/database system to organize ideas and serve as a record of the analysis for future use. Tools that help list hazards are:

- Preliminary Hazard Analysis.
- Change Analysis.
- Brainstorming.
- "What if" Analysis.

Identify hazards associated with these three categories:

- Task Degradation.
- Personal Injury or Death.
- Property Damage.

List Causes: Make a list of the causes associated with each hazard identified in the hazard list. A hazard may have multiple causes related to man, machine and environments. In each case, try to identify the root cause (the first link in the chain of events leading to mission degradation, personnel injury, death, or property damage). Risk controls can be effectively applied to root causes. Causes should be annotated with the associated hazards in the same paper or computer record mentioned in the previous action. Suggested tools are:

- Change Analysis.
- Brainstorming.
- "What if" Analysis.
- Job Hazard Analysis.

Refine Hazard Lists: If time and resources permit, and additional hazard information is required, use strategic hazard analysis techniques. These are normally used for medium and long term planning, complex tasks, or operations in which the hazards are not well understood. The first step of in-depth analysis should be to examine existing databases or available historical and hazard information regarding the operation. Suggested tools are:

- Database analysis.
- Accident History.
- Cause and effect diagrams.
- Tree Diagrams

The following tools are particularly useful for complex, coordinated operations in which multiple units, participants, and system components and simultaneous events are involved: Complex operations risk management tools are:

- Sequentially timed event plot.
- Multilinear event sequence.
- Interface analysis.
- Failure mode and effect analysis.

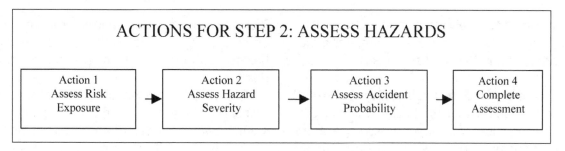

FIGURE 6
STEP 2 ACTIONS

There are many additional tools that can help identify hazards. One of the best is through a group process involving representatives directly from the workplace. A simple brainstorming process with a trained facilitator is very productive. The following is a partial list of sources of hazard identification:

- *Accident Reports*: These can come from within the organization, from tenants, within the chain of command, the safety department, etc. Other sources might be medical reports, maintenance records, and fire and police reports.
- *Quality reports*: Quality audits provide important feedback and written documentation on local process management.
- *Accident Databases*: The OSHA 300 and insurance claims are information resources.
- *Surveys*: These can be unit generated. Target an audience and ask some very simple questions related to such topics as: What will your next accident be? Who will have it? What task will cause it? When will it happen? The survey can be a powerful tool because it pinpoints people in the workplace with first hand knowledge of the job. Often, first line supervisors in the same workplace won't have as good an understanding of risk as those who confront it every day.
- *Inspections*: Safety inspections can consist of spot checks, walk-throughs, checklist inspections, site surveys, and mandatory inspections. Use onsite workers to provide input beyond the standard third-party inspection.

Step 2. ASSESS HAZARDS.
For each hazard identified in the previous step:

Assess Hazards. Once hazards are found, the next step is to analyze the associated risk—how likely and how big a loss is possible? **Recognition and assessment is the core of the Risk Management process.** Risk Management process depends on doing good analyses at each step in the process.

Assess Hazard Exposure: Probability is effected by exposure. Repeated exposure to a hazard greatly increases the total likelihood of an accident. This can be expressed in terms of time, proximity, volume, or repetition. Does it happen often, or near personnel or equipment? Does the event happen to a lot of people or equipment? This level can aid in determining the severity or the probability of the event. Additionally, it may serve as a guide for devising control measures to limit exposure. Another important concept is **interaction**. Interaction occurs when two (or more) hazards are present and their total risk is much greater than simply adding their separate risks. It's more like multiplying than adding. Often it is the combination of several factors that make a situation hazardous, rather than any single factor. Experience and clear thinking are the best ways to consistently assess interaction.

Assess Hazard Severity: Determine the severity of the hazard in terms of its potential impact on the people, equipment, or mission. Cause and effect diagrams, scenarios and "What-If" analysis are some of the best tools for assessing the hazard severity. Severity assessment should be based upon the worst possible outcome that can reasonably be expected. Severity categories are defined to provide a qualitative measure of the worst credible accident resulting from personnel error,environmental FIGURE 7conditions; design inadequacies; procedural deficiencies; or system, subsystem, or component failure or malfunction. Using severity categories provide guidance to a wide variety of missions and systems.

Assess Accident Probability: Determine the probability that the hazard will cause an accident or loss of the severity assessed above. Accident probability is proportional to the cumulative probability of the identified causes for the hazard. Probability may be determined through estimates or actual numbers, if they are available. Assigning a quantitative accident probability to a new mission or system may not be possible early in the planning process.

A qualitative accident probability may be derived from research, analysis, and evaluation of historical safety data from similar missions and systems. The typical accident sequence is much more complicated than a single line of erect dominos where tipping the first domino (hazard) triggers a clearly predictable reaction. Supporting rationale for assigning a accident probability should be documented for future reference.

Complete Risk Assessment: Combine severity and probability estimates to form a risk assessment for each hazard. By combining the probability of occurrence with severity, a matrix is created where intersecting rows and columns define a Risk Assessment Index (RAI), table 3-3, AR 385-10. The Risk Assessment Index forms the basis for judging both the acceptability of a risk and the management level at which the decision of acceptance will be made.

The index may also be used to prioritize resources to resolve risks due to hazards or to standardize hazard notification or response actions. Severity, probability, and risk assessment should be recorded to serve as a record of the analysis for future use. Existing databases,

Risk Assessment Index matrix, or a panel of personnel experienced with the mission and hazards can be used to help complete the risk assessment.

The following are some analytical pitfalls that should be avoided in the assessment:

- *Overoptimism*: "It can't happen to us. We're already doing it." This pitfall results from not being totally honest and not looking for root causes of risk.
- *Misrepresentation*: Individual perspectives may distort data.
- *Alarmist*: "The sky's falling" approach, or "worst case" estimates are used.
- *Indiscrimination*: All data is given equal weight.
- *Prejudice*: Subjectivity and/or hidden agendas are used, rather than facts.
- *Inaccuracy*: Bad or misunderstood data nullifies accurate risk assessment.
  - It is difficult to assign a numerical value to human behavior.

SEVERITY	PROBABILITY				
	Frequent	Likely	Occasional	Seldom	Unlikely
Catastrophic	E	E	H	H	M
Critical	E	H	H	M	L
Marginal	H	M	M	L	L
Negligible	M	L	L	L	L

Risk Level: E-Extremely High, H-High, M-Moderate, L-Low

PROBABILITY- The likelihood that an event will occur.
FREQUENT- Occurs often, continuously experienced.
LIKELY- Occurs several times.
OCCASIONAL- Occurs sporadically.
SELDOM- Unlikely, but could occur at some time.
UNLIKELY- Can assume it will not occur.

SEVERITY- The expected consequence of an event in terms of degree of injury, property damage, or other mission-impairing factors.
CATASTROPHIC- Death or permanent total disability, system loss, major property damage, not able to accomplish mission.
CRITICAL- Permanent partial disability, temporary total disability in excess of 3 months, major system damage, significant property damage, significantly degrades mission capability.
MARGINAL- Minor injury, lost workday accident, minor system damage, minor property damage, some degradation of mission capability.
NEGLIGIBLE- First aid or minor medical treatment, minor system impairment, little/no impact on accomplishment of mission.

FIGURE 7

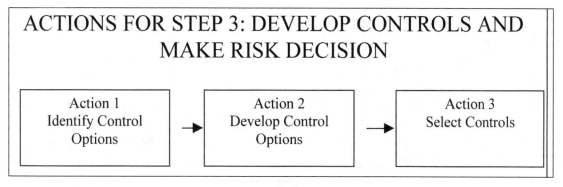

ACTIONS FOR STEP 3: DEVELOP CONTROLS AND MAKE RISK DECISION

FIGURE 8
STEP 3 ACTIONS

- Numbers may oversimplify real life situations.
- It may be difficult to get enough applicable data, which could force inaccurate estimates.
- Oftentimes simple numbers take the place of reasoned judgment.
- Risk can be unrealistically traded off against benefit by relying solely on numbers.

Step 3. DEVELOP CONTROLS & MAKE RISK DECISIONS.

In this area, one must "develop control measures that eliminate the hazard or reduce its risk. As control measures are developed, risks are re-evaluated until all risks are reduced to a level where benefits outweigh potential cost."

Identify Control Options: The process of developing controls starts by taking the risk levels determined in Step 2, then identifying as many risk control options as possible for all hazards which exceed an acceptable level of risk. Refer to the list of possible causes from Step 1 for control ideas. Brainstorming, mission accident analysis and "What-If" analysis are excellent tools to identify control options. Risk control options include: **avoidance, reduction, spreading** and **transference**.

Avoiding risk altogether requires canceling or delaying the job, mission, or operation, but is an option that is rarely exercised due to mission importance. However, it may be possible to avoid specific risks: like wearing proper personal protective equipment can reduce risks in most job areas.

Risk can be **reduced**. The overall goal of risk management is to plan missions or design systems that do not contain uncontrolled hazards. A proven order of precedence for dealing with hazards and reducing the resulting risks is:

- **Plan or Design for Minimum Risk.** From the first, plan the mission or design the system to eliminate hazards. Without a hazard there is no probability, severity or exposure. If an identified hazard cannot be eliminated, reduce the associated risk to an acceptable level.
- **Incorporate Safety Devices.** If identified hazards cannot be eliminated or their associated risk adequately reduced by modifying the mission or system elements or their inputs, that risk should be reduced to an acceptable level through the use of safety design features or devices. Safety devices usually do not effect probability but reduce severity: an automobile seat belt doesn't prevent a collision but reduces the severity of injuries. Nomex gloves and steel toed boots won't prevent the hazardous event, or even change the probability of one occurring, but they prevent, or decrease the severity of, injury. Physical barriers fall into this category.
- **Provide Warning Devices.** When mission planning, system design, and safety devices cannot effectively eliminate identified hazards or adequately reduce associated risk, devices should be used to detect the condition and warn personnel of the hazard. Warning signals and their application should be designed to minimize the probability of the incorrect personnel reaction to the signals and should be standardized. Flashing red lights or sirens are a common warning device that most people understand.

ACTIONS FOR STEP 4: IMPLEMENT CONTROLS

```
+------------------+         +------------------+
|     Action 1     |  ---->  |     Action 2     |
| Identify Control |         | Develop Control  |
|     Options      |         |     Options      |
+------------------+         +------------------+
```

FIGURE 9
STEP 4. CONTROL ACTION

■ **Develop Procedures and Training.** Where it is impractical to eliminate hazards through design selection or adequately reduce the associated risk with safety and warning devices, procedures and training should be used. If the system is well designed and the mission well planned, the only remaining risk reduction strategies may be procedures and training. *Emergency procedure training and disaster preparedness exercises improve human response to hazardous situations.*

Risk is commonly **spread** out by either increasing the exposure distance or by lengthening the time between exposure events. Administratively controlling exposure events, substitution of less hazardous chemicals or re-engineering an operation to reduce exposures to chemicals or toxic agents are examples.

Risk **transference** does not change probability or severity, however, possible losses or costs are shifted to another entity. An example is locating a remote sensing device in a high risk environment instead of risking personnel.

COMMON WAYS TO CONTROL RISK
■ Protective equipment, clothing, or safety devices (PPE)
■ Highlight hazards for extra care and handling
■ Warnings (signs, color coding, audio/visual alarms)
■ Repair hazards or build new facilities
■ Limit exposure consistent with mission needs
■ Train and educate
■ Incorporate firm, fail-safe go/no-go criteria
■ Select experienced or specialized personnel
■ Increase and /or select more highly qualified and experienced supervision

■ New policy—formal/informal, written/unwritten
■ Develop new procedures

Develop Control Options: Determine the controls for the risk associated with the hazard. A computer spread sheet or data form (Job Hazard Analysis) may be used to list control ideas and indicate control effects. The estimated value(s) for severity and/or probability after implementation of control measures and the change in overall risk assessed from the Risk Assessment Index should be recorded. Scenario building and next accident assessment provide the greatest ability to determine control effects.

Select Controls: For each hazard, select those risk controls that will reduce the risk to an acceptable level.. The decision maker selects the control options after being briefed on all the possible controls. The best controls will be consistent with mission objectives and optimum use of available resources (manpower, material, equipment, money, time. It is not an ad hoc decision, but rather a logical, sequenced part of the risk management process. Decisions are made with awareness of hazards and how important hazard control is to success or failure of the mission (cost versus benefit).

Step 4. IMPLEMENT CONTROLS.
The decision maker must allocate resources to control risk. Control decisions must be made at the appropriate level. The standard for risk management is leadership at the appropriate level of authority making informed decisions control hazards or accept risks.

Safety advisors and consultants do not control the necessary resources to implement the

ACTIONS FOR STEP 5: SUPERVISE AND EVALUATE

```
┌─────────────────┐                    ┌─────────────────┐
│    Action 1     │                    │    Action 2     │
│    Supervise    │ ─────────────────▶ │    Evaluate     │
│                 │                    │                 │
└─────────────────┘                    └─────────────────┘
```

FIGURE 10
STEP 5 ACTIONS

control decisions. Appropriate levels of decisions making reflect the ability of the decision maker to resource the controls.

Resource Controls: For each identified hazard, resource controls that will reduce the risk to an acceptable level. The best controls will be consistent with mission objectives and optimum use of available resources (manpower, material, equipment, money, and time). Record implementation decisions for future reference. Should management determine that the controls require resources beyond their authority, they should elevate the risk decision to higher authority.

Order Controls: To be successful, command must support the control measures put in place. Then, explore appropriate ways to demonstrate command commitment. Provide the personnel and resources necessary to implement the control measures. Design in sustainability from the beginning. Deploy the control measure with a feedback mechanism that provides information on whether the control measure is achieving the intended purpose.

Step 5. SUPERVISE AND EVALUATE.

Supervise: Monitor the operation to ensure:
- The controls are effective and remain in place.
- Changes which require further risk management are identified.
- Action is taken when necessary to correct ineffective risk controls and reinitiate the risk management steps in response to new hazards.

Any time personnel, equipment or operations change or new operations are anticipated in an environment not covered in the initial risk management analysis, the risks and control measures should be reevaluated. The goal of measurement is to answer the question of whether the control measure in fact controlled the associated hazard. The best tool for accomplishing this action of supervision is Change Analysis.

Evaluation: The process review must be systematic. After assets are expended to control risks, then a cost benefit analysis must be accomplished to see if risk and cost are in balance. Any changes in the system (the flow charts from the earlier steps provide convenient benchmarks to compare the present system to the original) are recognized and appropriate risk management controls are applied

To accomplish an effective review:
- Identify whether the actual cost is in line with expectations.
- What effect the control measure has had on mission performance.

Provide operation feedback to ensure that the corrective or preventive action taken was effective and that any new hazards identified during the mission are analyzed and corrective action taken.

Audits: Measurements are necessary to ensure accurate evaluations of how effectively controls eliminated hazards or reduced risks. After action reports, surveys, and in progress reviews provide great starting places for measurements. To be meaningful, measurements must quantitatively or qualitatively identify reductions of risk, improvements in operation success, or enhancement of capabilities. The Risk Management Evaluation Profile (OSHA's PEP) in appendix B, provides an audit process of a programs overall effectiveness.

Benefits of conducting an audit includes:

- Formally going through the internal audit process with managers and employees,
- Formally reviewing the elements of a safety and health program,
- Getting managers involved in the audit process,
- Making managers, supervisors and employees aware of the scope and complexity of a formal safety and health program, and of their roles and responsibilities in the programs success.

After finishing your audit share the results with managers and legal personnel. However the process of doing an audit creates a paper trail of the programs weaknesses. The audit is a formal tool to uncover weak points in the management system that create unsafe work practices and unsafe conditions that can injure workers, diminish their health, interrupt production, or damage products and property.

Conclusion. Risk management provides a logical and systematic means of organizing information for rational decision-making, to identify and control risk. Risk management is a process that requires individuals, supervisors and leaders to support and implement the basic principles, along with the discipline to apply them on a continuing basis. Risk management offers individuals and organizations a powerful tool for eliminating accidents and increasing effectiveness. This process has the unique advantage of being accessible to and usable by everyone in every conceivable setting or scenario.

Appendix B: The Risk Management Evaluation Profile (RMEP)

Subject: The Risk Management Evaluation Profile (RMEP)

A. **Purpose.** To establish policies and procedures for the Risk Management Evaluation Profile (RMEP), the RMEP form, which can be used in assessing safety and health programs in general workplaces.

B. **Scope.** The RMEP is applicable to all company workplaces.

C. **References.**
   1. AR 385-10, Army Safety Program.
   2. OSHA Instruction CPL 2.103, September 26, 1994, Field Inspection Reference Manual (FIRM).

D. **Action.** CEOs, directors and managers should ensure that the guidelines and procedures set forth here are followed in using the RMEP.

E. **Background.** Assessment of safety and health conditions in the workplace depends on a clear understanding of the programs and management systems that an employer is using for safety and health compliance. The organization places a high priority on safety and health programs and mandates their implementation.

F. **Application.**
   1. The RMEP should be completed for a general evaluation of workplace safety and health programs.
      a. The RMEP is an educational document for workers and employers, as well as a source of information for use in the inspection process.
      b. In multi-employer workplaces, a RMEP shall be completed for the safety and health program of the host organization. This RMEP will normally apply to all subordinate organizations, and individual RMEPs need not be completed for them.
      c. The RMEP shall be used in experimental programs that require evaluation of an organizations safety and health program, except where other program evaluation methods/tools are specifically approved.
   2. The evaluation of the safety and health program contained in the RMEP shall be shared with the employer and with employee representatives.

G. **Using the RMEP.** The RMEP will be used as a source of safety and health program evaluation for the employer, employees.
   1. **Gathering Information for the RMEP** begins during the opening conference

and continues through the inspection process.

a. The evaluator shall explain the purpose of the RMEP and obtain information about the employer's safety and health program in order to make an initial assessment about the program.

b. This initial assessment shall be verified—or modified—based on information obtained in interviews of an appropriately representative number of employees and by observation of actual safety and health conditions during the inspection process.

2. **Recording the Score.** The program elements in the RMEP correspond generally to the major elements of the Guidelines.

a. **Elements.** The **six** elements to be scored in the RMEP are:
   (1) Management.
   (2) Leadership.
   (3) Employee Participation.
   (4) Hazard Identification.
   (5) Hazard Control.
   (6) Training.

b. **Factors.** These elements will also be scored. The score for an element will be determined by the factor scores. The factors are:
   - Management
   - Leadership.
     - Employee participation.
     - Contractor safety.
     - Survey and hazard identification.
     - Reporting.
     - Investigation of accidents and near-miss incidents
     - Data analysis.
     - Hazard control.
     - Maintenance.
   - Medical program.
   - Training (as a whole).

c. **Scoring.** The evaluator shall objectively score the organization on each of the individual factors and elements after obtaining the necessary information to do so. These shall be given a score of 1, 2, 3, 4, or 5. If the element or factor does not apply to the worksite being inspected, a notation of **"Not Applicable"** shall be made in the space provided. This shall not affect the score.

(1) The attachment contains the **RMEP Tables**, which provide verbal descriptors of workplace characteristics for each factor for each of the five levels. Evaluators shall refer to these tables as appropriate to ensure that the score they assign to a factor corresponds to the descriptor that best fits the worksite.

(2) Determine scores for each of the six elements as follows:

NOTE: The factors of "Management", "Leadership" and "Employee Participation" are given greater weight because they are considered the foundation of a safety and health program.

(a) For each of the other elements, **average** the scores for the factors.

(b) In **averaging** factor scores, round to the nearest whole number (1, 2, 3, 4, or 5). Round up from one-half (.5) or greater; round down from less than one-half (.5).

3. **Program Levels.** The Overall Score on the RMEP constitutes the "level" at which the establishment's safety and health program is scored. **Remember: This level is a relatively informal assessment.** The following chart summarizes the levels:

Score	Level of Safety and Health Program
5	Outstanding program
4	Superior program
3	Basic program
2	Developmental program
1	No program or ineffective program

4. **Specific Scoring Guidance.** The following shall be taken into account in assessing specific factors:

a. **Written Programs.** Employer safety and health programs should be in writing in order to be effectively implemented and communicated.

  (1) Nevertheless, a program's **effectiveness** is more important than whether it is in writing.

    (a) An employer's failure to comply with a paperwork requirement is normally penalized only when there is a serious hazard related to this requirement.

    (b) An employer's failure to comply with a written program requirement is normally not penalized if the employer is actually taking the actions that are the subject of the requirement.

  (2) Thus, evaluators should follow the general principle that "performance counts more than paperwork." In using the RMEP, the evaluator is responsible for evaluating the organizations actual management of safety and health in the workplace, not just the organizations documentation of a safety and health program.

b. **Employee Participation.**

  (1) Employee involvement in an establishment's safety and health program is essential to its effectiveness. Thus, evaluation of safety and health programs must include objective assessment of the ways in which workers' rights and responsibilities are addressed in form and practice.

  (2) Employee involvement should also include participation walk-around inspections, interviews, informal conferences, and formal settlement discussions, as may be appropriate. Many methods of employee involvement may be encountered in individual workplaces.

c. **Comprehensiveness.** The importance of a safety and health program's comprehensiveness is implicitly addressed in Hazard Identification under both hazard identification and Data analysis. An effective safety and health program shall address all known and potential sources of workplace injuries and illnesses, whether or not they are covered by a specific OSHA standard.

d. **Consistency with Violations/Hazards Found.** The RMEP evaluation and the scores assigned to the individual elements and factors should be consistent with the types and numbers of violations or hazards found during the inspection.

5. **Scope of the RMEP Review.** The duration of the RMEP review will vary depending on the circumstances of the workplace and the inspection. In all cases, however, this review shall include:

a. A review of any appropriate employer documentation relating to the safety and health program.

b. A walk-around inspection of pertinent areas of the workplace.

c. Interviews with an appropriate number of employer and employee representatives.

The RMEP Tables

- The text in each block provides a description of the program element or factor that corresponds to the level of program that the employer has implemented in the workplace.
- To avoid duplicative language, each level should be understood as containing all positive factors included in the level below it.

MANAGEMENT, LEADERSHIP and EMPLOYEE PARTICIPATION	
Management	
Visible management provides the motivating force for an effective safety and health program.	
1	Management demonstrates no policy, goals, objectives, or interest in safety and health issues at this worksite.
2	Management sets and communicates safety and health policy and goals, but remains detached from all other safety and health efforts.
3	Management follows all safety and health rules, and gives | visible support to the safety and health efforts of others.
4	Management participates in significant aspects of the site's safety and health program, such as site inspections, incident reviews, and program reviews. Incentive programs that discourage reporting of accidents, symptoms, injuries, or hazards are absent. Other incentive programs may be present.
5	Site safety and health issues are regularly included on agendas of management operations meetings. Management clearly demonstrates—by involvement, support, and example—the primary importance of safety and health for everyone on the worksite. Performance is consistent and sustained or has improved over time.
Notes:	

Employee Participation

Employee participation provides the means through which workers identify hazards, recommend and monitor abatement, and otherwise participate in their own protection.

1	Worker participation in workplace safety and health concerns is not encouraged. Incentive programs are present which have the effect of discouraging reporting of incidents, injuries, potential hazards or symptoms. Employees/employee representatives are not involved in the safety and health program.
2	Workers and their representatives can participate freely in safety and health activities at the worksite without fear of reprisal. Procedures are in place for communication between employer and workers on safety and health matters. Worker rights under the Occupational Safety and Health Act to refuse or stop work that they reasonably believe involves imminent danger are understood by workers and honored by management. Workers are paid while performing safety activities.
3	Workers and their representatives are involved in the safety and health program, involved in inspection of work area, and are permitted to observe monitoring and receive results. Workers' and representatives' right of access to information is understood by workers and recognized by management. A documented procedure is in place for raising complaints of hazards or discrimination and receiving timely employer responses.
4	Workers and their representatives participate in hazard identification analysis, inspections and investigations, and development of control strategies throughout facility, and have necessary training and education to participate in such activities. Workers and their representatives have access to all pertinent health and safety information, including safety reports and audits. Workers are informed of their right to refuse job assignments that pose serious hazards to themselves pending management response.
5	Workers and their representatives participate fully in development of the safety and health program and conduct of training and education. Workers participate in audits, program reviews conducted by management or third parties, and collection of samples for monitoring purposes, and have necessary training and education to participate in such activities. Employer encourages and authorizes employees to stop activities that present potentially serious safety and health hazards.
Notes:	

LEADERSHIP
Implementation
Implementation means tools, provided by management, that include: — budget — information — personnel — assigned responsibility — adequate expertise and authority — means to hold responsible persons accountable (line accountability) — program review procedures.

1	Tools to implement a safety and health program are inadequate or missing.
2	Some tools to implement a safety and health program are adequate and effectively used; others are ineffective or inadequate. Management assigns responsibility for implementing a safety and health program to identified person(s). Management's designated representative has authority to direct abatement of hazards that can be corrected without major capital expenditure.
3	Tools to implement a safety and health program are adequate, but are not all effectively used. Safety representative is knowledgeable in hazard recognition and applicable OSHA requirements. Management keeps or has access to applicable OSHA standards at the facility, and seeks appropriate guidance information for interpretation of OSHA standards. Management representative has authority to order/purchase safety and health equipment.
4	All tools to implement a safety and health program are more than adequate and effectively used. Written safety procedures, policies, and interpretations are updated based on reviews of the safety and health program. Safety and health expenditures, including training costs and personnel, are identified in the facility budget. Hazard abatement is an element in management performance evaluation.
5	All tools necessary to implement a good safety and health program are more than adequate and effectively used. Management safety and health representative has expertise appropriate to facility size and process, and has access to professional advice when needed. Safety and health budgets and funding procedures are reviewed periodically for adequacy.

Notes:

Hazard Identification
Hazard Recognition and Evaluation
Survey and hazard analysis: An effective, proactive safety and health program will seek to identify and evaluate all hazards. In large or complex workplaces, components of such analysis are the **comprehensive survey** and **evaluations of job hazards and changes in conditions**.

1	No system or requirement exists for hazard review of planned/changed/new operations. There is no evidence of a comprehensive survey for safety or health hazards or for routine job hazard analysis.
2	Surveys for violations of standards are conducted by knowledgeable person(s), but only in response to accidents or complaints. The employer has identified principal OSHA standards which apply to the worksite.
3	Process, task, and environmental surveys are conducted by knowledgeable person(s) and updated as needed and as required by applicable standards. Current hazard analyses are written (where appropriate) for all high-hazard jobs and processes; analyses are communicated to and understood by affected employees. Hazard analyses are conducted for jobs/tasks/workstations where injury or illnesses have been recorded.
4	Methodical surveys are conducted periodically and drive appropriate corrective action. Initial surveys are conducted by a qualified professional. Current hazard analyses are documented for all work areas and are communicated and available to all the workforce; knowledgeable persons review all planned/changed/new facilities, processes, materials, or equipment.
5	Regular surveys including documented comprehensive workplace hazard evaluations are conducted by certified safety and health professional or professional engineer, etc. Corrective action is documented and hazard inventories are updated. Hazard analysis is integrated into the design, development, implementation, and changing of all processes and work practices.
Notes:	

	WORKPLACE ANALYSIS
	Hazard Assessment
	Inspection: To identify new or previously missed hazards and failures in hazard controls, an effective safety and health program will include regular **site inspections.**
1	No routine physical inspection of the workplace and equipment is conducted.
2	Supervisors dedicate time to observing work practices and other safety and health conditions in work areas where they have responsibility.
3	Competent personnel conduct inspections with appropriate involvement of employees. Items in need of correction are documented. Inspections include compliance with relevant OSHA standards. Time periods for correction are set.
4	Inspections are conducted by specifically trained employees, and all items are corrected promptly and appropriately. Workplace inspections are planned, with key observations or check points defined and results documented. Persons conducting inspections have specific training in hazard identification applicable to the facility. Corrections are documented through follow-up inspections. Results are available to workers.
5	Inspections are planned and overseen by certified safety or health professionals. Statistically valid random audits of compliance with all elements of the safety and health program are conducted. Observations are analyzed to evaluate progress.
	Notes:

Risk Management

WORKPLACE ANALYSIS	
Hazard Reporting	
A reliable **hazard reporting system** enables employees, without fear of reprisal, to notify management of conditions that appear hazardous and to receive timely and appropriate responses. [Guidelines, (c)(2)(iii)]	
1	No formal hazard reporting system exists, or employees are reluctant to report hazards.
2	Employees are instructed to report hazards to management. Supervisors are instructed and are aware of a procedure for evaluating and responding to such reports. Employees use the system with no risk of reprisals.
3	A formal system for hazard reporting exists. Employee reports of hazards are documented, corrective action is scheduled, and records maintained.
4	Employees are periodically instructed in hazard identification and reporting procedures. Management conducts surveys of employee observations of hazards to ensure that the system is working. Results are documented.
5	Management responds to reports of hazards in writing within specified time frames. The workforce readily identifies and self-corrects hazards; they are supported by management when they do so.
Notes:	

	WORKPLACE ANALYSIS
	Accident Investigation
	Accident investigation: An effective program will provide for **investigation of accidents and "near miss" incidents**, so that their causes, and the means for their prevention, are identified. [Guidelines, (c)(2)(iv)]
1	No investigation of accidents, injuries, near misses, or other incidents is conducted.
2	Some investigation of incidents takes place, but root cause may not be identified, and correction may be inconsistent. Supervisors prepare injury reports for lost time cases.
3	OSHA-101 is completed for all recordable incidents. Reports are generally prepared with cause identification and corrective measures prescribed.
4	OSHA-recordable incidents are always investigated, and effective prevention is implemented. Reports and recommendations are available to employees. Quality and completeness of investigations are systematically reviewed by trained safety personnel.
5	All loss-producing accidents and "near-misses" are investigated for root causes by teams or individuals that include trained safety personnel and employees.
	Notes:

Risk Management

	WORKPLACE ANALYSIS
	Data Analysis

Data analysis: An effective program will **analyze injury and illness records** for indications of sources and locations of hazards, and jobs that experience higher numbers of injuries. By analyzing injury and illness trends over time, patterns with common causes can be identified and prevented.

1	Little or no analysis of injury/illness records; exposure monitoring) are kept or conducted.
2	Data is collected and analyzed, but not widely used for prevention. Reports are completed for all recordable cases. Exposure records and analyses are organized and are available to safety personnel.
3	Injury/illness logs and exposure records are kept correctly, are audited by facility personnel, and are essentially accurate and complete. Rates are calculated so as to identify high risk areas and jobs. Workers compensation claim records are analyzed and the results used in the program. Significant analytical findings are used for prevention.
4	Employer can identify the frequent and most severe problem areas, the high risk areas and job classifications, and any exposures responsible for OSHA recordable cases. Data are fully analyzed and effectively communicated to employees. Illness/injury data are audited and certified by a responsible person.
5	All levels of management and the workforce are aware of results of data analyses and resulting preventive activity. External audits of accuracy of injury and illness data, including review of all available data sources are conducted. Scientific analysis of health information, including non-occupational data bases is included where appropriate in the program.

Notes:

	HAZARD CONTROL
	Hazard Control

Hazard Control: Workforce exposure to all current and potential hazards should be prevented or controlled by using **engineering controls** wherever feasible and appropriate, **work practices** and **administrative controls**, and **personal protective equipment** (PPE).

1	Hazard controls are seriously lacking or absent from the facility.
2	Hazard controls are generally in place, but effectiveness and completeness vary. Serious hazards may still exist. Employer has achieved general compliance with applicable OSHA standards regarding hazards with a significant probability of causing serious physical harm. Hazards that have caused past injuries in the facility have been corrected.
3	Appropriate controls (engineering, work practice, and administrative controls, and PPE) are in place for significant hazards. Some serious hazards may exist. Employer is generally in compliance with voluntary standards, industry practices, and manufacturers, and suppliers' safety recommendations. Documented reviews of needs for machine guarding, energy lockout, ergonomics, materials handling, bloodborne pathogens, confined space, hazard communication, and other generally applicable standards have been conducted. The overall program tolerates occasional deviations.
4	Hazard controls are fully in place, and are known and supported by the workforce. Few serious hazards exist. The employer requires strict and complete compliance with all OSHA, consensus, and industry standards and recommendations. All deviations are identified and causes determined.
5	Hazard controls are fully in place and continually improved upon based on workplace experience and general knowledge. Documented reviews of needs are conducted by certified health and safety professionals or professional engineers, etc.

Notes:

Risk Management

HAZARD CONTROL	
Maintenance	

Maintenance: An effective safety and health program will provide for **facility and equipment maintenanc**e, so that hazardous breakdowns are prevented.

1	No preventive maintenance program is in place; break-down maintenance is the rule.
2	There is a preventive maintenance schedule, but it does not cover everything and may be allowed to slide or performance is not documented. Safety devices on machinery and equipment are generally checked before each production shift.
3	A preventive maintenance schedule is implemented for areas where it is most needed; it is followed under normal circumstances. Manufacturers' and industry recommendations and consensus standards for maintenance frequency are complied with. Breakdown repairs for safety related items are expedited. Safety device checks are documented. Ventilation system function is observed periodically.
4	The employer has effectively implemented a preventive maintenance schedule that applies to all equipment. Facility experience is used to improve safety-related preventative maintenance scheduling.
5	There is a comprehensive safety and preventive maintenance program that maximizes equipment reliability.

Notes:

	HAZARD CONTROL
	Medical Program

An effective safety and health program will include a suitable **medical program** where it is appropriate for the size and nature of the workplace and its hazards.

1	Employer is unaware of, or unresponsive to medical needs. Required medical surveillance, monitoring, and reporting are absent or inadequate.
2	Required medical surveillance, monitoring, removal, and reporting responsibilities for applicable standards are assigned and carried out, but results may be incomplete or inadequate.
3	Medical surveillance, removal, monitoring, and reporting comply with applicable standards. Employees report early signs/symptoms of job-related injury or illness and receive appropriate treatment.
4	Health care providers provide follow-up on employee treatment protocols and are involved in hazard identification and control in the workplace. Medical surveillance addresses conditions not covered by specific standards. Employee concerns about medical treatment are documented and responded to.
5	Health care providers are on-site for all production shifts and are involved in hazard identification and training. Health care providers periodically observe the work areas and activities and are fully involved in hazard identification and training.

Notes:

TRAINING	
Safety and health training should cover the safety and health responsibilities of all personnel who work at the site or affect its operations. It is most effective when incorporated into other training about performance requirements and job practices. It should include all subjects and areas necessary to address the hazards at the site.	
1	Facility depends on experience and peer training to meet needs. Managers/supervisors demonstrate little or no involvement in safety and health training responsibilities.
2	Some orientation training is given to new hires. Some safety training materials (e.g., pamphlets, posters, videotapes) are available or are used periodically at safety meetings, but there is little or no documentation of training or assessment of worker knowledge in this area. Managers generally demonstrate awareness of safety and health responsibilities, but have limited training themselves or involvement in the site's training program.
3	Training includes OSHA rights and access to information. Training required by applicable standards is provided to all site employees. Supervisors and managers attend training in all subjects provided to employees under their direction. Employees can generally demonstrate the skills/knowledge necessary to perform their jobs safely. Records of training are kept and training is evaluated to ensure that it is effective.
4	Knowledgeable persons conduct safety and health training that is scheduled, assessed, and documented, and addresses all necessary technical topics. Employees are trained to recognize hazards, violations of OSHA standards, and facility practices. Employees are trained to report violations to management. All site employees—including supervisors and managers—can generally demonstrate preparedness for participation in the overall safety and health program. There are easily retrievable scheduling and record keeping systems.
5	Knowledgeable persons conduct safety and health training that is scheduled, assessed, and documented. Training covers all necessary topics and situations, and includes all persons working at the site (hourly employees, supervisors, managers, contractors, part-time and temporary employees). Employees participate in creating site-specific training methods and materials. Employees are trained to recognize inadequate responses to reported program violations. Retrievable record keeping system provides for appropriate retraining, makeup training, and modifications to training as the result of evaluations.
Notes:	

1. Site Location:

2. Page [1] of [1]

3. Task:

4. Date Begin:

5. Date End:

6. Date Form Prepared:

7. Operational Phase in which the Task will be conducted:

8. Prepared by: (Name /Duty Position)

9. Identified Hazards:	10. Assess Hazards: Initial Risk: (Must Be Filled In By Hand)				11. Develop Control Measures for Identified Hazards: (measures to reduce probability and severity of a hazard)	12. Make Risk Decisions: Remaining Risk: (Must Be Filled In By Hand)				13. How to Implement the Controls: (Include SOPs, PPE etc.)	14. Supervision and Evaluation by: (Name of Supervisor, worker, team, etc.)
	L	M	H	E		L	M	H	E		
(Be Specific)					(Be Specific)					(Be Specific)	(Be Specific)

15. Remaining Risk Level After Countermeasures Are Implemented: (CIRCLE HIGHEST REMAINING RISK LEVEL) →

LOW	MEDIUM	HIGH	EXTREMELY HIGH
Employee doing the Job	Immediate Supervisor	Site Supervisor	CEO/OWNER

16. RISK AUTHORITY: Signature of the employee accepting the risk and liability for the operation
(Signature indicates only that the appropriate risk decision authority was notified of the initial risk level, control measures taken and appropriate resources requested)

Risk Management

SAFETY AND HEALTH HAZARDS IN THE OFFICE

Despite common beliefs that the office provides a safe environment to work in, many hazards exist that cause thousands of injuries and health problems each year among office workers. Since one-third of the workforce is in offices, even low rates of work-related injuries and illnesses can have an immense impact on employee safety and health.

Modern offices today are substantially different from the office environment of 20 years ago. Sweeping changes have occurred in the U.S. workplaces as a result of new office technology and the automation of office equipment. Unfortunately, office workers are now faced with many more hazards.

In addition to obvious hazards such as a slippery floor or an open file drawer, an office also may contain hazards such as poor lighting, noise, poorly designed furniture and equipment, and machines that emit noxious gases and fumes. Even the nature of office work itself has produced a host of stress-related symptoms and musculoskeletal strains. For example, long hours at the visual display terminal can cause pains in the neck and back, eyestrain, and a general feeling of tension and irritability.

Leading Types of Disabling Accidents

It is estimated that office workers sustain 76,000 fractures, dislocations, sprains, strains and contusions each year. The leading types of disabling accidents that occur within the office are:

- Falls, strains and overexertion;
- Struck by or striking against objects; and
- Caught in or between objects.

Office workers also are injured as a result of foreign substances in the eye, spilled hot liquids, and burns from fire and electric shock.

In recent years, illness has increased among the office worker population This may be attributed, in part, to the increased presence of environmental toxins within the office and to stress-producing factors associated with the automated office. Resulting illnesses may include respiratory problems, skin diseases and stress-related conditions.

Common Safety and Health Hazards in the Office

There are several types of safety and health hazards common to the office environment; however, there also are control measures that can reduce or eliminate these hazards.

Ventilation

Sources of air pollution in the office include both natural agents (e.g., carbon monoxide, microorganisms, radon) and synthetic chemicals (e.g., formaldehyde, cleaning fluids, cigarette smoke, asbestos).

An adequate ventilation system that delivers quality indoor air and provides for comfortable humidity and temperature is a necessity for the office. Where printing or copying machines are present, an exhaust ventilation system that draws fumes away from the employees' breathing zone should be present. Office machines and ventilation system components should be checked and maintained on a regular basis.

Illumination

Lighting problems in the office include glare, shadows and visual problems (e.g., eyestrain, fatigue, double vision). Poor lighting can also be a contributing factor in accidents.

Controls to prevent poor lighting conditions include:

- Regular maintenance of the lighting system;
- Light-colored matte finish on walls, ceilings and floors to reduce glare;
- Adjustable shades on windows; and
- Indirect lighting.

Noise

In an office, workers are subjected to many noise sources, such as video display terminals, high-speed printers, telephones and human voices. Noise can produce tension and stress as well as damage to hearing. A variety of measures to control unwanted noise is available.

- Noisy machines should be placed in an enclosed space;
- Carpeting, draperies and acoustical ceiling tiles should be used to muffle noise;
- Telephone volume should be adjusted to its lowest level; and
- Traffic routes within the office should be rearranged to reduce traffic within and between work areas.

Physical Layout and Housekeeping

Poor design and/or poor housekeeping can lead to crowding, lack of privacy, and slips, trips and falls. Important factors related to office layout and orderliness include:

- At least 3 ft. distance between desks and at least 50 sq. ft. per employee;
- Keep telephone and electrical cords out of aisles;
- Group employees who use the same machines;
- Office machines should be kept away from edges of desks and tables;
- Regular inspection, repair and replacement of faulty carpets;
- Place mats inside building entrances; and
- Proper placement of electrical and telephone wires.

Exits/Egress

Blocked or improperly planned means of egress can lead to injuries as a result of slips, trips and falls. If during an emergency, employees become trapped due to improper egress, more serious injuries or fatalities may result.

Controls to ensure proper means of egress include providing:

- Access to exits with a minimum width of 28 in.;
- Two exits, if possible;
- Exits and access to exits that are clearly marked;
- Means of egress, including stairways used for emergency exit, that are free of obstructions and adequately lit; and
- Employees with training on the locations of exits and procedures for evacuation.

Fire Hazards

A serious problem associated with office design is the potential for creating fire hazards. Another danger found in modern offices is combustible materials (e.g., furniture, rugs, fibers) that can easily ignite and emit toxic fumes.

A number of steps can be taken to reduce office fire hazards:

- Store unused records or papers in fire-resistant files or vaults;
- Use flame-retardant materials;
- Allow smoking in designated areas only and provide proper ashtrays; and
- Place fire extinguishers and alarms in conspicuous, easily accessible locations.

Handling and Storage Hazards

The improper lifting of materials can cause musculoskeletal disorders such as sprains, strains and inflamed joints. Office materials that are improperly stored can lead to hazards such as objects falling on workers, poor visibility and fires.

There are several controls that can reduce handling and storage hazards:

- An effective control program incorporating employee awareness and training and ergonomic design of work tasks can reduce back injuries.
- Materials should not be stored on top of cabinets.
- Heavy objects should be stored on lower shelves and materials neatly stacked.
- Materials should be stored inside cabinets, files or lockers.
- There should be no storage of materials in aisles, corners or passageways.
- Fire equipment should remain unobstructed.
- Flammable and combustible materials and liquids should be identified and stored properly.
- Material safety data sheets must be provided for each hazardous chemical identified.

Electrical Equipment

Electrical accidents in an office usually occur as a result of faulty or defective equipment, unsafe installation or misuse of equipment. The following guidelines should be adhered to when installing or using electrical equipment:

- Equipment must be properly grounded to prevent shock injuries;
- A sufficient number of outlets will prevent overloading of circuits;
- The use of poorly maintained or nonapproved equipment should be avoided;
- Cords should not be dragged over nails, hooks or other sharp objects;
- Receptacles should be installed and electric equipment maintained so that no live parts are exposed; and
- Machines should be disconnected before cleaning or adjusting. Generally, machines and equipment should be locked or tagged out during maintenance.

Office Furniture

Defective furniture or the misuse of chairs or file cabinets by office workers can lead to serious injuries. Controls related to chairs and cabinets include:

- Chairs should be properly designed and regularly inspected for missing casters, shaky legs and loose parts;
- Employees should not lean back in a chair with feet on a desk;
- Employees should not scoot across the floor while sitting on a chair;
- Employees should never stand on a chair to reach an overhead object;
- Employees should open only one file drawer at a time and use drawer handles to close file drawers; and
- File cabinets should not be located close to doorways or in aisles.

Office Machinery

Machines with ingoing nip points or rotating parts, if not adequately guarded, can cause lacerations, abrasions, fractures and amputations. Machines such as conveyors, electric hole punches and paper shredders with hazardous moving parts must be guarded so that office workers cannot contact the moving parts. Fans must have substantial bases and fan blades must be properly guarded.

Ladders, Stands and Stools

Improper use of ladders, ladder stands and stools can lead to falls. To reduce related injuries include workers should:

- Always face the ladder when climbing up or down;
- Ensure ladders are in good condition and inspected regularly;
- Never use the top of a ladder as a step; and
- Ensure the ladder is fully open and the spreaders are locked before climbing on it.

Office Tools

Misuse of office tools, such as pens, pencils, paper, letter openers, scissors and staplers, can cause cuts, punctures and related infections. Precautions when using these materials can prevent such injuries. Precautions include:

- The blade on a paper cutter should be closed when not in use. A guard also should be provided. Employees should never place their fingers near the blade.
- Employees should always use a staple remover to remove staples. An employee also

should never test a jammed stapler with his or her fingers.

- Employees should store sharp objects (e.g., scissors, pen, pencil) in a drawer or with the point down. Employees should never hand someone a sharp object point first.

Photocopying Machines

Potential health hazards associated with photocopying machines include toxic chemicals, excessive noise and intense light. They can also be a source of indoor air pollution when used in offices that are not well ventilated.

Controls to reduce these hazards include:

- Keeping the document cover closed;
- Reducing noise exposure by isolating the machine;
- Placing machines in well-ventilated rooms away from workers' desks;
- Having machines routinely serviced to prevent chemical emissions;
- Avoiding skin contact with photocopying chemicals; and
- Cleaning all spills immediately and disposing of waste properly.

Video Display Terminals (VDTs)

Health concerns relating to VDT, or computer monitor, use involve radiation, noise, eye irritation, stress and low back, neck and shoulder pain.

Studies have shown that the radiation levels emitted from VDTs are well below those allowed by current standards. However, to minimize any potential exposure, only equipment for which the manufacturer will supply data on emissions should be used.

To minimize noise, VDTs should not be clustered and sound absorbent screens can be used if needed.

Proper ergonomic design, including the relation of the operator to the screen, the operator's posture, lighting and background, should be carefully tailored to prevent discomfort. The keyboard position, document holder, screen design, characters, and color are other factors to consider.

Vision testing should be conducted before office workers operate VDTs and annually thereafter. Work breaks and variation of tasks enable VDT operators to rest their eyes. Pos-

tural strain related to VDT use can be relieved by performing simple exercises. Finally, a training program to inform workers of the capabilities of the equipment they are using should be conducted.

Some Do's and Dont's of Office Safety

1. Glass doors should have some conspicuous design, either painted or decal, about 4 ft. above the floor and centered on the door so people will not walk into them.
2. Frosted glass in doors gives a view through for accident prevention, but still preserves privacy. The see-through feature also prevents collisions.
3. If it is necessary that a door be solid, the hazardous area that the door swings over can be marked by yellow and black tape or painted a bright color, or the path of the swinging door can be outlined by colored plastic circles. On carpeted floors, a quarter or half-circle of different colored carpet can be used.
4. Employees should not face windows, unshielded lamps or other sources of glare. Many factors associated with poor illumination are contributing causes of office accidents. Some of these causes are direct glare, reflected glare from the work and harsh shadows. Excessive visual fatigue may be an element leading toward accidents. Accidents may also be prompted by the delayed eye adaptation that a person experiences when moving from bright to dark. Some accidents that are attributed to the individual's "carelessness" actually can be traced to difficulty in seeing.
5. Fans in the office should be placed where they cannot fall on anybody and they should be secured in place.
6. Where possible, outlets (receptacles) should be installed to eliminate extension cords. If cords must cross the floors, they should be covered with rubber channels designed for this purpose.
7. A policy should be adopted to prevent the use of poorly maintained or unsafe, poor quality coffee makers, radios, lamps, hot plates etc., provided by or used by employees, particularly in out-of-the-way locations. Such appliances create fire and shock hazards.

8. Switches should be provided, either in the equipment or in the cords, so that it is not necessary to pull the plugs to shut off the power.
9. Outlets should not only be located under desks to eliminate tripping hazards but they should also be placed where they will not accidentally be kicked or used as a footrest. When they loosen or wear, outlets can become sources of electric shock.
10. Where materials are stored on shelves, the heavy objects should be on the lower shelves.
11. Rolling ladders and stands used for reaching high storage should have brakes that automatically operate when weight is applied to them.
12. Good housekeeping is essential to prevent falls. Wipe up spilled liquid immediately and pick up pieces of paper, paper clips, rubber bands and pencils as soon as they are spotted.
13. Broken glass should be swept up immediately. It should not be placed loose in a waste paper basket but it should be carefully wrapped in heavy paper and marked "Broken Glass." Glass that shatters into fine pieces should be blotted up with damp paper towels.
14. Leaning back in the chair and placing the feet on the desk should not be allowed.
15. Chairs should have at least four legs on the ground whenever they are being occupied.
16. Only one file drawer should be opened at a time to prevent the cabinet from toppling over. File cabinets should be bolted together or otherwise secured to prevent tipping.
17. Desks or files should never be moved by office personnel; they should be moved by maintenance people using special dollies or trucks.

18. Do not pile boxes, papers, books or other heavy objects on top of file cabinets. This could cause the cabinet to tip and the materials to fall on to the employee.
19. Stacks of materials should not be carried on stairs; the elevator should be used instead.
20. Accident records are absolutely necessary if an office safety program is to succeed. Office employees should report every accident, no matter how minor the injury. Near-miss accidents should be reported because they often serve as warnings of worse accidents to come.
21. To develop proper safety attitudes, safety instructions should be properly given to new office employees.
22. A company safety program cannot succeed unless it has the wholehearted backing of top management. The supervisor must know that his or her accident prevention performance is watched and that good performance is appreciated.
23. Supervisors should personally investigate each accidental injury and they should report what caused the accident as well as what steps have been taken to prevent a recurrence.
24. When safety inspections are made and accident hazards are found, the report of these hazards should go to the vice president or other top officers in charge of the department. This top executive should then request a report of corrective measures directly from the supervisor responsible for the hazard. This procedure will go along way in making a safety expert of every office manager and supervisor and reducing the problem of office accidents to a negligible size.

Checklist for Office Safety Concerns

- ❐ Exit safety
- ❐ Condition of furniture and ladders
- ❐ Housekeeping and aisles
- ❐ Grounding
- ❐ Toolbox power tools
- ❐ Floor cleaning equipment
- ❐ Cleaning supplies (corrosives)
- ❐ Guarding of equipment
- ❐ Flammable materials
- ❐ Minimize quantities
- ❐ Proper Cans and Cabinets

Emergency Action Plan

- ❐ Written plan (written for more than 10 employees)
- ❐ Alarm system
- ❐ Evacuation
- ❐ Training

Plan Elements

- ❐ Escape procedure and routes
- ❐ Critical operation (control or shutdown)
- ❐ Accounting for employees
- ❐ Rescue duties
- ❐ Medical duties
- ❐ Preferred method of reporting emergency
- ❐ Authorities

Fire Prevention Plans

- ❐ Hazard lists (written for more than 10 employees)
- ❐ Responsible persons
- ❐ Trash and waste control
- ❐ Training
- ❐ Maintenance of combustion controls

Personal Office Safety and Health Checklist

☐ Is there an active safety and health program in your office?

☐ Is one person clearly responsible for the overall activities of the safety and health program?

☐ Is there a procedure for handling complaints regarding safety and health?

☐ Do you know how to locate the nearest doctor or hospital?

☐ Are emergency numbers posted?

☐ Are first-aid kits easily accessible to each work area?

☐ Are you familiar with basic first-aid procedures in case of an emergency?

☐ Are all work areas clean and orderly?

☐ Are floor surfaces clean, dry, level and in good condition?

☐ Are carpets secured to the floor and in good condition?

☐ Are aisles and doorways free from obstructions to permit visibility and movement?

☐ Are there sufficient exits to permit prompt escape in case of emergency?

☐ Are all exits clearly marked and visible?

☐ Are emergency exits adequately lighted and free of debris?

☐ Do you know where emergency exits are and how to reach them?

☐ Are stairways in good condition and covered with skid-resistant materials?

☐ Do you know where fire extinguishers are and how to use them?

☐ Do you know where fire alarms are?

☐ Are you familiar with fire evacuation procedures for your building and what to do in case of fire in your area?

☐ Are electrical appliances and equipment in good condition and properly grounded?

☐ Are a sufficient number of outlets available to eliminate overloading of circuits?

☐ Are file cabinets arranged so that drawers do not open into aisles? Can only one drawer be opened at a time?

☐ Are chairs in good condition with no loose casters? Is furniture free from sharp edges, points and splinters?

☐ Is your office equipped with a step stool or ladder so that you can safely reach overhead objects? Are you familiar with the correct way to use a ladder?

☐ Are photocopying machines placed in well-ventilated rooms away from workers' desks? Are machines serviced routinely?

☐ If you work with hazardous substances such as cleaning fluids, are you aware of the related hazards?

☐ Are hazardous substances properly stored?

☐ Are work areas properly illuminated?

☐ Does the ventilation system deliver quality indoor air?

☐ Are noise levels within acceptable levels?

☐ If you use a video display terminal (VDT), are the keyboard, table, screen and chair adjustable?

☐ For VDT users, are work breaks and variation of tasks incorporated into work schedules?

☐ Are you trained in proper lifting techniques?

OSHA
OUTREACH PROGRAMS

Voluntary Protection Programs

The Voluntary Protection Programs (VPP) is designed to recognize and promote effective safety and health management. In the VPP, management, labor, and OSHA establish a cooperative relationship at a workplace that has implemented a strong program. Management agrees to operate an effective program that meets an established set of criteria, while employees agree to participate in the program and work with management to ensure a safe and healthful workplace. OSHA verifies that the program meets VPP criteria and then publicly recognizes the site's exemplary program. OSHA also removes the site from its scheduled routine inspection lists. To confirm the site continues to meet VPP criteria, OSHA reassesses periodically the site program (e.g., every three years or every year).

The VPP concept recognizes that compliance enforcement alone cannot fully achieve the objectives of the Occupational Safety and Health Act. Good safety management programs that go beyond OSHA standards can protect workers more effectively than simple compliance.

VPP participants are a select group of employers that have designed and implemented outstanding health and safety programs. Star Program participants meet all VPP requirements. Merit Program participants have demonstrated the potential and willingness to achieve Star Program status and are implementing planned steps to fully meet all Star requirements.

Participants in the VPP enjoy benefits, such as:

- Improved employee motivation to work safely, which leads to better quality and productivity;
- Reduced workers' compensation costs;
- Recognition in the community;
- Improvement of programs that are already good, through the internal and external review that is part of the VPP application process; and
- Fewer lost-workday injuries (VPP participants generally experience from 60 percent to 80 percent fewer lost-workday injuries than average sites of the same size and industry).

Companies that would like to participate in the VPP must submit a written application to OSHA. The application guideline is included in the VPP information kit. After OSHA has reviewed the written application, an Onsite Review will be scheduled. "What Happens When OSHA Comes Onsite," included in the VPP information kit, describes the onsite review.

Participants provide OSHA with examples of the most effective way to protect workers in their industries, often in ways that exceed the requirements of OSHA standards. Participants from several companies help provide OSHA compliance and program personnel training in safety and health program management. Many participants in the petro-chemical industry provided OSHA standards setters with models of effective process safety management. For example, Mobil Oil Company's Joliet, Ill. refinery provides OSHA compliance officers with hands-on training in process safety management.

The experience with the VPP has led to the issuance of OSHA's Voluntary Safety and Health Program Management Guidelines. CIBA Inc.'s McIntosh, Ala. site and Dow Chemical's Freeport, Texas facility have provided OSHA standards setters with demonstrations of effective 100 percent fall protection. Participation in VPP onsite evaluations provides OSHA with model plants that can be shown to others. As one compliance officer said at an evaluation closing conference, "I've always felt it could be done this way, and now I've seen that it can be done right. So no one will ever be able to tell me again that it can't be done."

The three VPPs—Star, Merit, and Demonstration—are designed to:
- Recognize outstanding achievement of those who have successfully incorporated comprehensive safety and health programs into their total management systems;
- Motivate others to achieve excellent safety and health results in the same outstanding way; and
- Establish a relationship between employers, employees, and OSHA that is based on cooperation rather than coercion.

Star Program. This program is the most demanding and the most prestigious. It is open to employers in any industry who have successfully managed a comprehensive safety and health program to reduce injury rates below the national average for that industry. Specific requirements for the program include:
- Management commitment and employee participation;
- A high quality worksite analysis program;
- Hazard prevention and control programs; and
- Comprehensive safety and health training for all employees.

These requirements must all be in place and operating effectively.

Merit Program. This program is primarily a stepping stone to Star Program. An employer with a basic safety and health program built around the Star requirement who is committed to improving the company's program and has the resources to do so within a specified period of time may work with OSHA to meet Star qualifications.

Demonstration Program. This program is for companies that provide Star-quality worker protection in industries where certain Star requirements may not be appropriate or effective. It allows OSHA both the opportunity to recognize outstanding safety and health programs that would otherwise be unreached by the VPP and to determine if general Star requirements can be changed to include these companies as Star participants.

OSHA reviews an employer's VPP application and conducts an onsite review to verify that the safety and health program described is in operation at the site. Evaluations are conducted on a regular basis: annually for Merit and Demonstration programs and triennially for Star. All participants must send their injury information annually to their OSHA regional office. Sites participating in the VPP are not scheduled for programmed inspection; however, any employee complaints, serious accidents or significant chemical releases that may occur are handled according to routine enforcement procedures.

An employer may make application for any VPP at the nearest OSHA regional office. Once OSHA is satisfied that, on paper, the employer qualifies for the program, an onsite review will be scheduled. The review team will present its findings in a written report for the company's review prior to submission to the Assistant Secretary of Labor, who heads OSHA. If approved, the employer will receive a letter from the Assistant Secretary informing the site of its participation in the VPP. A certificate of approval and flag are presented at a ceremony held at or near the approved worksite. Star sites receiving reapproval after each triennial evaluation receive plaques at similar ceremonies.

The VPPs described are available in states under federal jurisdiction. Some state-plan states have similar programs. Interested employers in these states should contact the appropriate state designee for more information.

Additional information on VPPs is available from OSHA national, regional, and area offices.

OSHA Outreach Program

The OSHA Outreach Training Program is a primary way to train workers in the basics of occupational safety and health. Through the program, individuals who complete a one-week OSHA trainer course are authorized to teach 10-hour or 30-hour courses in construction or general industry safety and health standards. Authorized trainers can receive OSHA course completion cards for their students. Current policy and rules regarding OSHA's Outreach Program can be found on the OSHA website at: www.osha.gov/dte/outreach/construction_generalindustry/index.html

Becoming an Authorized Trainer

To become an authorized trainer, you must complete the required Course 501, Trainer Course in Occupational Safety and Health Standards for General Industry, and pass a test at the end of the course. This course provides an overview of the most hazardous and referenced standards. It is conducted by the OSHA Training Institute and OSHA Training Institute Education Centers located around the country. When you complete the course, you are authorized to train for four years. Before the end of four years, you must take Course 503, Update for General Industry Outreach Trainers, to renew your authorization for another four years. Trainers also may also retake Course 500 to maintain their trainer status. If the trainer authorization status has expired, taking a 500 course available through the OSHA Training Institute Education Centers for course scheduling information can reinstate it.

General industry outreach trainers are authorized to conduct 10- and 30-hour general industry outreach courses and receive OSHA course completion cards to issue to the students.

Outreach Training Program Guidelines

Designated Training Topics

Training must cover the designated topics for the 10-or 30-hour General Industry Outreach Training Program. The 10-hour program is intended to provide a variety of instruction on general industry safety and health standards to entry-level workers. Of the topics listed below, four hours are mandatory and three hours must be chosen from the options provided. For the remainder of the class, you may teach any other general industry standards and policies and/or expand on the required topics.

The following course topics are required:
- Introduction to OSHA, OSH Act/General Duty Clause 5(a)(1), Inspections, Citations, and Penalties (CFR Part 1903);
- Subpart D, Walking and Working Surfaces;
- Subparts E and L, Exit Routes and Fire Protection; and
- Subpart S, Electrical.

Trainers must cover at least three of the following topics:
- Subpart H, Flammable and Combustible Liquids;
- Subpart I, Personal Protective Equipment;
- Subpart O, Machine Guarding;
- Subpart Z, Hazard Communication; or
- Subpart Z, Introduction to Industrial Hygiene, Bloodborne Pathogens and/or Ergonomics
- Safety and Health Programs.

Additional Topics

By tailoring your 10 hours to meet the needs of all industries, you can easily develop two-day seminars for specific industries. For example, when developing separate seminars for maintenance workers and medical workers, the core material (required topics) will remain the same. The medical workers may not need to know about machine guarding or flammable liquid storage, so you can include that information in the maintenance seminar, but substitute it with hazard communication and bloodborne pathogens for the medical seminar.

Additional topics for specific industries could include:
- **Medical/Healthcare**
  - Introduction to Industrial Hygiene, Bloodborne Pathogens (two hours); and
  - Ergonomics, Personal Protective Equipment, Hazard Communication, and Workplace Violence (at least two hours).

- **Maintenance**
  - Ergonomics;
  - Hazard Communication; and
  - Powered Industrial Trucks.
- **Utility**
  - Ergonomics;
  - Power Generation;
  - Confined Spaces; and
  - Ladder Safety.
- **General Office**
  - Ergonomics;
  - Office Safety; and
  - Hazard Communication.

Topic Length
Training sessions for each course topic should last for at least one hour. In most cases, one hour is the least amount of time necessary to cover a topic adequately. The minimum amount of time spent on any topic is 30 minutes.

Trainers must spend at least 10 or 30 class hours covering course topics. Breaks and lunch periods are not counted as class time.

Conducting a class over a period of time. Trainers may teach classes in segments. Each segment must be at least one hour and the course must be completed within six months.

Guest trainers. Trainers may have other trainers help conduct classes. An authorized outreach trainer must design and coordinate the course, teach more of the class than anyone else, and attend all sessions to answer questions and ensure the topics are adequately covered and all students are in attendance.

In-person training. Outreach training must be delivered in person, unless the trainer has received an individual exception. Trainers considering using other training methods, such as online, CDROM, and video conferencing, must contact the OSHA Outreach Coordinator. The basic guidelines for video conferencing are that the trainer be able to ensure the full attendance of all trainees, that off-site locations have a training monitor, and that there is a setup to answer trainee questions quickly and effectively.

Class size. If class will exceed 50 students, contact the OSHA Outreach Coordinator before the class begins to get permission for the class to be considered an outreach training class. Trainers must have a way for students to ask questions apart from the classroom. E-mail is the usual method. It is a good idea to have more than one trainer in large classes and to break the class into work groups whenever possible. Small classes encourage trainee involvement through discussion and group participation and through sharing of knowledge and experiences.

10 + 20 Hours = 30 hours. If a student that was trained in the 10-hour training course is interested in taking the 30-hour course, trainers may supplement the training with 20 additional hours and receive a 30-hour card for the trainee. The limitations are that the same trainer must do the training and all the training must take place within six months. Trainees who do this should only receive the 30-hour card.

Combined 10-hour construction and general industry class. A person who is authorized as a trainer in Construction and General Industry may *not* receive 10-hour student cards for both Construction and General Industry when holding a class for less than 20 full hours.

Outreach Training Tips

Worker Emphasis
The outreach classes are designed to be presented to workers; therefore, they must emphasize hazard identification, avoidance, control, and prevention—not OSHA standards. Trainers must tailor their presentations to the needs and understanding of their audience.

Site-Specific Training
The most rewarding classes for students are the ones they can relate to because the trainer uses examples, pictures, and scenarios that come from the students' workplaces.

Homogenous Class
The ideal class to teach is one in which students have similar needs because they hold comparable positions. Therefore, it is best to conduct separate training for supervisors, managers, and workers. Also, separate workers into like groups (e.g., office personnel, machine operators, and maintenance staff).

Use Objectives
Inform students what is expected of them after receiving training on each topic. Describe the

skills and abilities the students should have or exhibit, be specific, and relate the objectives to the students' work if possible.

Presentation Assortment

Students learn in different manners and get tired of one style of training over a lengthy period. Use different trainers, computer presentations, videos, case studies, exercises, and graphics to make the course interesting and enjoyable. By doing this you will be employing the three levels of training techniques:

- Presentation (presenting the material in a variety of ways);
- Discussion (getting the students involved in the learning); and
- Performance (students practice the material they have learned).

Testing

Use quizzes and tests to ensure the students understand key objectives of the training. Students should receive feedback on incorrect answers.

Student Evaluations

Have students evaluate the class. This feedback will help the trainer determine whether the course is accomplishing its goals and provide input that can be used to improve the training.

Monitoring

Staff from the OSHA Office of Training and Education periodically attend outreach training classes to observe training, obtain feedback from the trainer and the students on the training, and to ensure awareness of the outreach guidelines and the materials and assistance that are available to help trainers conduct classes. Through these visits, OSHA aims to help trainers, improve the outreach-training program, ensure consistent program implementation, and assist the trainer in designing the class to meet the needs of the audience.

Advertising

When advertising outreach-training courses, trainers must take the proper care to correctly describe their outreach trainer designation and outreach courses. Trainer authorization is limited to conducting the 10- and 30-hour General Industry outreach training courses.

Outreach advertising restrictions include the following:

- **Certified.** Neither the trainer, the students, nor the curriculum is certified or accredited. The trainer is authorized, the students receive course completion cards, and the OSHA-produced curriculum is approved.
- **OSHA.** Do not make it appear that you are an OSHA employee or that the course is an OSHA course.
- **Course 501.** Do not refer to your outreach course as a 501 course. The 501 course is the train-the-trainer course that is conducted by the OSHA Training Institute or its OSHA Training Institute Education Centers.
- **Department of Labor Logo.** Do not use the logo that you see on outreach cards in your advertising.
- **Train-the-Trainer Course.** Students who complete the 10- or 30-hour training are not entitled to receive cards for students they may train.

If OSHA notifies a trainer that their advertising appears false or misleading and the advertising is not corrected, that trainer will be removed from the program.

Program Administration

Obtaining Student Course Completion Cards

After the class has been conducted, trainers must submit documentation about the course to the OSHA Training Institute to receive OSHA student course completion cards. Prepare a separate packet for each class taught that contains the Outreach Training Program Report, a list of the topics that were taught, and the student roster.

- Submit course documentation within six months of course completion.
- Send one list of legible student names; do not send multiple sign-in sheets.
- You may send more than one class submission in one envelope.
- Do not staple the documentation.

For each outreach class you complete, send the following, in this order, to OSHA (**Note:** OSHA may return submittals that are not complete):

- The OSHA Outreach Training Program Report, which includes information on the course and the trainer. Make sure you include your most recent trainer date and the address to send the cards. (An excerpt of the format is shown on the following pages.)

- A copy of your course certificate/trainer card (note the place you took the training) if:
  - This is your first outreach training class; or
  - You are a trainer with an ID number, but you have taken a more recent trainer course than the one shown on your preprinted Outreach Training Program Report.
- The names of students who completed the course. Keep a copy of the students' names and addresses before sending them to OSHA. You will need them to complete and distribute the cards
- A topic outline that lists the topics taught and the amount of time spent on each. For 10-hour classes, you may complete the topic outline on the bottom of the OSHA Outreach Training Program Report or send a separate outline. For 30-hour classes, you must send a separate outline.

Mail your course documentation to the Education Center that issued you your trainer card. The OSHA Training Institute oversees the program and can be reached at:

Construction (or General Industry)
Outreach Program Coordinator
OSHA Training Institute
2020 S. Arlington Heights Road
Arlington Heights, IL 60005

Student course completion cards are sent to the trainer for completion and distribution.

The trainer completes the card by listing the student's name, the end date of the course, and signing it. If the trainer is unavailable, the trainer's name may be typed in (See Exhibit 18-1.).

Cards may be laminated. Trainers may use the back of the cards for other identification or training information purposes, but no other alterations are permitted.

The student course completion cards do not expire.

Trainers may provide students with a certificate of training. This may help students have proof they took the training before they receive their pocket student cards. The advertising restrictions also apply to a certificate.

The OSHA Training Institute will send a few extra cards to trainers for each class completed in case of card errors or to enable trainers to replace lost student cards for students trained.

OSHA recommends Outreach Training Program courses as an orientation to occupational safety and health for workers. Participation is voluntary. Workers must receive additional training on specific hazards of their job.

Replacing Lost or Damaged Trainer or Student Cards
Trainer cards. Contact the organization that issued the card. Inform them what course you took and when you took it. After they validate the class was taken and the test was passed, they will issue a replacement card.

Student cards. Trainers receive a few extra cards when OSHA sends them student cards. Trainers can use these cards to replace student cards, after the proper verification is made. If you do not have an extra card, you or the student may contact OSHA for the replacement. You must provide the following information:
- Student name;
- Trainer name;
- Training date; and
- Type of class (10- or 30-hour, construction or general industry).

OSHA training records are only kept for five years plus the present year. If the training took place prior to this, OSHA will not be able to issue a new card.

Shortcut Procedures for Outreach Trainers with ID Numbers

OSHA will accept student card requests by e-mail and fax if the trainer has an ID number.

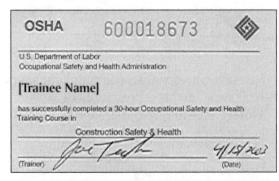

Exhibit 20-1. Sample completed student card.

OSHA also will accept a short mail-in format, which lessens the paperwork required. These procedures are only available to trainers with ID numbers. Trainers should carefully read the instructions below before using these procedures.

General Industry
Outreach Training Program
I. Background

The Occupational Safety and Health Administration's (OSHA) Outreach Training Program is a voluntary program to train workers in the basics of safety and health hazard recognition and prevention. OSHA authorizes trainers who complete construction and general industry train-the-trainer courses to conduct occupational safety and health classes for workers. OSHA has promoted workplace safety and health by authorizing trainers since 1971.

The Outreach Training Program has grown rapidly in recent years. From fiscal year (FY) 2004 through FY2008, 2.3 million workers have received outreach training; the number of workers trained more than doubled. In 2008, OSHA distributed nearly 680,000 student cards to trainers who held over 43,000 classes – an average of almost 850 classes per week. The number of students completing 30-hour construction training tripled from 2005 to 2008; however, 10-hour classes still comprise over 80% of the overall program. Construction outreach training comprises 80% of outreach training. On any day, approximately 2,700 workers attend OSHA outreach training.

OSHA Outreach Training Program

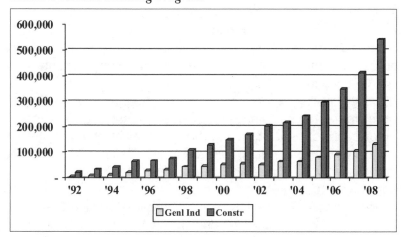

This growth is a result of industry-wide acceptance. Many employers use the Outreach Training Program to provide training for their employees. Groups who have integrated the program into their overall safety and health training plans include the building trades, general contractors, employer associations, insurance companies, and manufacturing firms. The endorsement of outreach training to serve as a foundation of occupational safety and health training within an organization has often resulted in the requirement of the training as a condition of employment for these workers or members.

Recent State laws enacted in Massachusetts, Rhode Island, Connecticut, New Hampshire, Missouri and New York require 10-hour construction training for workers on various sized publicly funded construction projects.

II. The General Industry
Outreach Training Program

General industry outreach trainers are authorized to conduct 10- and 30-hour general industry outreach courses and receive OSHA course completion cards to issue to their students. To become an authorized trainer, you must complete Course #501, *Trainer Course in Occupational Safety and Health Standards for General Industry*. You must pass a final test to receive your trainer authorization.

Update Requirement. To stay current on relevant OSHA matters, General Industry outreach trainers are required to attend Course #503, *Update for General Industry Outreach Trainers*, every four years to remain authorized. The OSHA course #501 may also be used to maintain a trainer's authorized status. If a trainer's authorization status has expired, the trainer has a three month grace period after their expiration to take the update course. After the three month period, a trainer's authorization status may only be reinstated by retaking the OSHA #501 course.

The trainer courses are primarily offered at the OSHA

Training Institute Education Centers (OTIECs), see Attachment A. These courses may also be available at the OSHA Training Institute.

III. Outreach Training Program Guidelines

This section contains information on the rules and procedures for conduction an outreach training course. Trainers are responsible for understanding these requirements when planning and conduction their outreach classes.

Training Topics. See the Designated Training Topics (sections V and VI) for what must be covered in a 10- and 30-hour general industry class. The objective of all OSHA General Industry Outreach Training Program training is to provide workers with information on recognizing and preventing hazards on a general industry site. If you have a question concerning whether your outreach training meets the needs of specific OSHA standards or requirements, contact your OSHA regional or local office (see section VII). CPR and First Aid can be added to your training, but you can't count this time as part of your 10- or 30-hour class.

Topic Length. OSHA has assigned minimum lengths of one hour to the required course topics; see the Designated Training Topics (sections V and VI). One-half hour is the minimum a trainer may spend on any topic. OSHA recommends spending an hour on each elective or optional topic. In the 10-hour class, a trainer may not cover any topic for more than four hours. In the 30-hour class, a trainer may not spend more than six hours on any topic.

Training Materials. Trainers compile materials for their training from a variety of sources, including products OSHA has available under "Teaching Aids" at the OSHA Outreach Training Program web site, *www.osha.gov/dte/outreach/ construction_generalindustry/aids.html*. Trainers are provided a CD-ROM in their trainer course. The CD-ROM contains 10-hour PowerPoint presentations and lesson plans that may be used in full or in part in conducting an outreach class. Course materials provided in the train-the-trainer classes are not designed for outreach students. Trainers should provide their students with reference materials, at least a fact sheet, on each topic covered, which highlights the key training points. See section VII, Further Assistance, for additional information.

Class Time. Breaks and lunch periods are not counted as class time. Instructional time must be at least 10 or 30-hours, as applicable.

Classes Over a Period of Time. Trainers may break classes into segments. Each segment must be at least one hour and the entire course must be completed within six months.

Guest Trainers. Authorized trainers may use others who have topic expertise to help conduct classes. The authorized outreach trainer must design and coordinate the course, teach more contact hours than anyone else, attend all sessions to answer questions, ensure topics are adequately covered, and document students' attendance.

Records. Trainers must retain outreach class files for five years. The file for each class must include:

- Student sign-in sheets for each class day
- Student addresses
- Copy of the documentation sent in to request cards, including a list of the topics taught and the amount of time spent on each
- Records which indicate the card number dispensed to each student. One way to accomplish this is to make a copy of all the cards you issue.

OSHA reserves the right to request copies of class records for verification purposes.

Class Size. If a planned training class will exceed 50 students, contact your Outreach Training Program Coordinator (Attachment B) prior to the class to receive permission to hold the class and receive student cards. The coordinator will need to know:

- How students will be able to ask questions when the class is not in session. Methods include e-mail, answering questions after class, and a Q & A session.
- What materials, in general, you are providing to the students. At a minimum, trainers must provide students with a fact sheet on each topic covered.
- That you will take attendance at the beginning and end of each class day. Only those students who are on all attendance sheets may receive cards. Trainers must retain these sign-in sheets in their class files.

OSHA recommends using more than one trainer, holding the 10-hour course over more than one day, and breaking the class into work groups. Small classes encourage student involvement through discussion and group participation and through sharing of knowledge and experiences.

Training Delivery. Outreach training must be done in-person, unless an exemption is given.

Online Training. OSHA has specific online training guidelines. OSHA has only accepted a few online programs. If you're considering developing online training, contact the OSHA Outreach Training Program coordinator at outreach@dol.gov. The online guidelines include the following:

- Testing and reporting test scores for each topic and a final test
- Removal of anyone scoring less than 70% after three tries on any program topic
- Mandatory page views of each content page
- Easy trainer availability built into the system
- Printable online materials for each topic
- The course must be interactive
- Tracking students' time in the course (including a timing-out mechanism)
- Providing required reports and evaluations

Video Conferencing. If you're considering using video conferencing, contact your Outreach Training Program Coordinator (Attachment B) prior to the video conference to receive permission. The guidelines for video conferencing are as follows:

- The trainer can ensure the full attendance of all students
- Off-site locations have a training monitor
- There is a setup to answer students questions quickly and effectively
- Explain what materials you will provide to the students – at a minimum they must receive a fact sheet on each topic covered

Combining 10-hour Construction and General Industry Classes. Trainers may not combine a 10-hour Construction and a 10-hour General Industry class in less than 20 hours in order to receive both types of student cards.

10 + 20 Hours = 30. If a student you trained in the 10-hour course wants to take the 30-hour course at a later time, you may provide 20 more training hours and receive a 30-hour card for the student. The limitations are as follows:

- The same trainer must do all the training
- All the training must be completed, from start to finish, within six months
- You must return the 10-hour cards to receive the 30-hour cards.

Advertising. When advertising outreach training, trainers must take the proper care to correctly describe their outreach trainer designation and outreach courses. Trainer authorization is limited to conducting the 10- and 30-hour General Industry outreach training courses.

Follow these restrictions when advertising General Industry Outreach Training Program courses:

Certified	Neither the trainer, the students, nor the curriculum is certified or approved. The trainer is authorized and the students receive course completion cards.
OSHA	"OSHA" may be used in advertising, but not in a manner which would imply that the trainer is an OSHA employee or that the course is being conducted by OSHA
Course #501	Authorized outreach trainers cannot conduct the #501 course. Don't refer to any outreach course as a #501 course. The #501 course is the trainer course that is conducted by OTI and the OTIECs.
Department of Labor Logo	Don't use the logo that is on the outreach cards or the front cover of this guide
Train-the-Trainer Course	Do not combine the use of "OSHA" and "Train-the-Trainer" in advertising. Students who complete outreach training are not entitled to receive cards for students they may train.

If OSHA notifies a trainer that their advertising appears false or misleading and it is not promptly corrected, the trainer will be removed from the Outreach Training Program and will no longer be able to receive student completion cards.

Monitoring. OSHA periodically conducts training observations of outreach classes. The purpose is to:
- Observe training
- Obtain feedback from the trainer and the students on the training

- Ensure awareness of the Outreach Training Program guidelines and the materials and assistance that are available to help trainers

Through these visits, OSHA aims to help trainers, improve the Outreach Training Program, and ensure consistent program implementation.

To request a training observation by OSHA, send the following information to *outreach@dol.gov*:

- Course date
- Type of class: 10- hour or 30-hour, Construction or General Industry
- Location
- Contact information

IV. Outreach Training Tips

This section is intended to provide trainers with suggestions on how to conduct more productive and effective outreach training classes.

Worker Emphasis. Outreach classes are designed to be presented to workers, therefore they must emphasize hazard identification, avoidance, control and prevention, not OSHA standards. Trainers must tailor their presentations to the needs and understanding of their audience.

Importance of Safety and Health Training. Explain early in the class that safety and health training isn't a bureaucratic exercise – it may save their life and help them continue to provide for their family.

- Highlight local stories that students will recognize
- Discuss personal experiences
- Provide information on injury and fatality statistics and OSHA Fatal Facts. For more information, see section VII, Further Assistance.
- Explain that safety and health training adds value to the company, the workplace and their life. See *www.osha.gov/dcsp/smallbusiness/safetypays/index.html*.

Site-Specific Training. The most rewarding classes for students are the ones they can relate to because the trainer uses examples, pictures, and real-life scenarios from their workplace, or one similar to it.

Homogenous Class. The ideal class is one where students have similar positions and needs. Hold separate sessions for supervisors, managers, and workers, when possible. Try to train workers from similar groups, such as trade groups, office personnel, machine operators, and maintenance staff.

Train Workers in Their Language. Ensure that you know your audience, including whether there are language barriers. To the extent possible, teach non-English speaking workers separately. Use translators, easy to understand photos, videos in their language, and hands-on activities. Also emphasize real-life examples. OSHA and the Outreach Training Program have Spanish-speaking trainers, references, publications, dictionaries and e-tools available at www.osha.gov. See section VII (Further Assistance) for additional details. Also, see the "OSHA training Standards Policy Statement", which reiterates OSHA's policy that employee training be presented in a manner that employees can understand, *www.osha.gov/pls/oshaweb/owadisp.show_document?p_table=INTERPRETATIONS&p_id=25658*.

Use Objectives. Describe the skills and abilities the students should have or exhibit for each topic. Relate the objectives to the students' work, if possible.

Presentation Assortment. Students learn in different manners and benefit from multiple training styles. Use different trainers, computer presentations, videos, case studies, exercises and graphics to make the course interesting and enjoyable. By doing so, trainers will be employing the three levels of training techniques: presentation (presenting the material in a variety of ways), discussion (getting the students involved in the learning), and performance (students practice the material they learned).

Testing. OSHA recommends using quizzes and tests to ensure students remain focused and understand key objectives. Trainers may set passing scores. Provide feedback to the students on the exam questions.

Evaluations. OSHA recommends having students complete a class evaluation. Trainers should use this feedback to determine whether the course is accomplishing its goals and how to improve the training.

V. Designated Training Topics

- 10-Hour General Industry Outreach Training Program

The 10-hour General Industry Outreach Training Program is intended to provide entry level general industry workers broad awareness on recognizing and preventing hazards on a general industry site. The training covers a variety of safety and health hazards which a worker may encounter at a general industry site. OSHA recommends this training as an orientation to occupational safety and health. Workers must receive additional training on hazards specific to their job. Training should emphasize hazard identification, avoidance, control and prevention, not OSHA standards. Learning objectives on many of these topics are on the 10-hour CD-ROM which is distributed in the train-the-trainer class, and is also available for download at the Outreach Training Program website. Instructional time must be a minimum of 10 hours.

Breakdown of topics as follows:

- **Mandatory - 6 hours (left column):** Six topics to be taught, for one hour each
- **Elective - 2 hours (right column top):** Choose at least two of these topics to teach, for a minimum of one-half hour each. Must cover at least two hours.
- **Optional - 2 hours (right column bottom):** Teach any other general industry hazards or policies and/or expand on the mandatory or elective topics, minimum of one-half hour each

10-Hour General Industry Required Course Topics

OSHA subpart references are provided for informational purposes; training should emphasize hazard awareness	
Mandatory – 6 hours	**Elective – 2 hours**
Two Hours - **Introduction to OSHA**, including: • OSH Act, General Duty Clause, Employer and • Employee Rights and Responsibilities, • Whistleblower Rights, Recordkeeping basics • Inspections, Citations, and Penalties • Value of Safety and Health • OSHA Website and available resources • OSHA 800 number	Choose at least two of the following elective topics: These topics must add up to at least two hours: *- Minimum One-half hour each -*
One Hour **Walking and Working Surfaces**, Subpart D *– including fall protection*	**Hazardous Materials**, Subpart H **Materials Handling**, Subpart N **Machine Guarding**, Subpart O **Introduction to Industrial Hygiene**, Subpart Z **Bloodborne Pathogens**, Subpart Z
One Hour **Exit Routes, Emergency Action Plans, Fire Prevention Plans, and Fire Protection**, Subparts E & L	**Ergonomics** Safety and Health Program Fall Protection
One Hour - **Electrical**, Subpart S	**Optional – 2 hours**
One Hour - **Personal Protective Equipment**, Subpart I	**For the remaining two class hours:** Teach any other general industry hazards or policies and/or expand on the mandatory or elective topics
One Hour - **Hazard Communication**, Subpart Z	

Special Industry Recommendations:

In addition to the six mandatory hours, the groups noted below should also teach the following:

- **Medical / Health Care** – 1 hour each - Introduction to Industrial Hygiene, Bloodborne Pathogens
- **At least ½ hour each** — Ergonomics and Workplace Violence
- **Maintenance** — Ergonomics and (if applicable) Powered Industrial Trucks
- **Utility** — Ergonomics, Power Generation, and Confined Spaces
- **Office** — Ergonomics

VI. Designated Training Topics

- 30-Hour General Industry Outreach Training Program

The 30-hour General Industry Outreach Training Program is intended to provide a variety of training to people with some safety responsibility. Workers must receive additional training on hazards specific to their job. Training should emphasize hazard identification, avoidance, control and prevention, not OSHA standards. Instructional time must be a minimum of 30 hours.

Breakdown of topics as follows:

- **Mandatory - 11 hours:** Seven topics to be taught, ranging from one to two hours each
- **Elective - 10 hours:** Choose at least five of these topics to teach, for a minimum of one-half hour each
- **Optional - 9 hours:** Teach any other general industry hazards or policies and/or expand on the mandatory or elective topics, minimum of one-half hour each

30-Hour Mandatory Course Topics

Introduction to OSHA — at least Two Hours

- OSH Act, General Duty Clause, Employer and Employee Rights and Responsibilities, Whistleblower Rights, Recordkeeping basics
- Inspections, Citations, and Penalties
- Value of Safety and Health
- OSHA Website, OSHA 800 number and available resources

Walking and Working Surfaces – including fall protection, Subpart D — at least One Hour

Exit Routes, Emergency Action Plans, Fire Prevention Plans, and Fire Protection, Subparts E & L — at least Two Hours

Electrical, Subpart S — at least Two Hours

Personal Protective Equipment (PPE), Subpart I — at least One Hour

Materials Handling, Subpart N — at least Two Hours

Hazard Communication, Subpart Z — at least One Hour

30-Hour Elective Course Topics

Choose at least 5 of the following topics — Must add up to at least 10 hours

- Hazardous Materials (Flammable and Combustible Liquids, Spray Finishing, Compressed Gases, Dipping and Coating Operations), Subpart H
- Permit-Required Confined Spaces, Subpart J
- Lockout / Tagout, Subpart J
- Machine Guarding, Subpart O
- Welding, Cutting, and Brazing, Subpart Q

- Introduction to Industrial Hygiene, Subpart Z
- Bloodborne Pathogens, Subpart Z
- Ergonomics
- Fall Protection
- Safety and Health Programs
- Powered Industrial Vehicles

VII. Further Assistance

This section provides resource information that trainers can use to help them to prepare and conduct outreach training courses

Main OSHA Web Sites

- OSHA Home Page - *www.osha.gov*
- OSHA Outreach Training Program Page — *www.osha.gov/dte/outreach/construction_general-industry/index.html*. The site includes:
  - Teaching Aids, including the 10-hour PowerPoint provided in the trainer class
  - Program Guidelines
  - How to get OSHA student course completion cards
  - Frequently Asked Questions (FAQs)
  - Special Announcements

OSHA Teaching / Materials Assistance Web Sites

- Training and Reference Materials Library. This library contains training and reference materials developed by OSHA as well as links to other related sites. *www.osha.gov/dcsp/ote/materials_library.html*
- Resource Center Loan Service. Outreach trainers may borrow videos from OSHA's Resource Center. This collection of videos covers many occupational safety and health subjects. The catalog contains borrowing information and a list of videos, including various Spanish titles. *www.osha.gov/dcsp/ote/resource-center/loan.html*
- Multimedia — Videos and Slide presentations — *www.osha.gov/SLTC/multimedia.html*
- Alliance Program Participants Developed Products — *www.osha.gov/dcsp/alliances/alliance_products.html*
- Compliance Assistance — Resources and Specialists — *www.osha.gov/dcsp/compliance_assistance/index.html*
- OSHA Small Business Page — *www.osha.gov/dcsp/smallbusiness/index.html*
- Teen Workers — *www.osha.gov/SLTC/teenworkers/index.html*

- Spanish References and Trainers *www.osha. gov/dte/outreach/construction_generalindustry/ spanish_training.html, www.osha.gov/dte/outreach/ construction_generalindustry/spanish_outreach_ trainers.html*
- Making the Business Case for Safety and Health — *www.osha.gov/dcsp/products/topics/ businesscase/*
- Quick Takes. At the OSHA Home Page, sign up for OSHA's bi-weekly e-news memo with information, updates, and results about safety and health in America's workplaces.

General Industry and Training Web Sites
- Safety and Health Topics Index — *www.osha. gov/SLTC/index.html*
- Industry-Specific Resources — *www.osha.gov/ dcsp/compliance_assistance/industry.html*
  - Agriculture and Forestry — Agricultural Operations, Grain Handling, Logging
  - Health Care — Dentistry, Health Care Facilities, Nursing Homes, Hospitals
  - Manufacturing — Apparel & Footwear, Battery Manufacturing, Chemical Manufacturing, Concrete and Concrete Products, Fireworks, Food Processing, Lead Smelters, Lubricant Manufacturing, Meat Packing, Metal Manufacturing, Plastics, Poultry Processing, Preserved Fruits & Vegetables, Printing, Pulp, Paper, and Paperboard Mills, Semiconductors, Textiles, Wood Products
  - Retail and Wholesale — Retail Sale, Lumber and Building Materials, Restaurants, Fireworks
  - Services — Automotive, Diving, Dry Cleaning, Fireworks Display, Labs, Landscaping/Tree Service
  - Transportation and Warehousing — Airlines, Beverage Delivery, Taxi Drivers, Trucking, Warehousing and Storage
  - Utilities — Electric Power Generation, Transmission, and Distribution Industry
- Health Care Industry Quick Start. Forms, publications, resources, and sample programs. *www.osha.gov/dcsp/compliance_assistance/ quickstarts/health_care/hc_library.html*
- Alliance Program Participants Developed Products *www.osha.gov/dcsp/alliances/alliance_products.html*
- Printing Industry Health and Safety *www.osha. gov/SLTC/printing_industry/recognition.html*

- OSHA Small Business Page — *www.osha.gov/ dcsp/smallbusiness/index.html*
- OSHA eTools — Web-based training tools, includes Hospital and Powered Industrial Trucks *www.osha.gov/dts/osta/oshasoft/index. html#eTools*
- Spanish PowerPoint Presentations — *www. consultationconnection.org/oti/*
- NIOSH Safety and Health Topics — *www.cdc. gov/niosh/topics/*
- General Safety and Health References — Other Internet Sites *www.osha.gov/SLTC/ generalshreferences/otherresources.html*
- General Safety and Health References — *www. osha.gov/SLTC/generalshreferences/index.html*

OSHA Publications. OSHA has many helpful publications, forms, posters, and fact sheets. See *www.osha.gov/pls/publications/pubindex.list*. Publications are available in HTML and PDF formats. Publications may also be available from the nearest OSHA Area or Regional Office.

A few significant publications are noted below.
- **All About OSHA**, OSHA 3302
- **OSHA Publications and Audiovisual Programs**, OSHA 2019
- **Training Requirements in OSHA Standards and Training Guidelines**, OSHA 2254
- **OSHA Handbook for Small Businesses**, OSHA 2209. Assists small business employers in implementing OSHA's recommended safety and health program management guidelines.

OSHA Quick Cards
Students will benefit from these cards, many of which are available in both English and Spanish. These are straightforward reference materials which focus on specific safety and health topics. See *www.osha.gov/OshDoc/quickcards.html*.

U.S. Government Bookstores
These bookstores offer OSHA standards and publications, at *http://bookstore.gpo.gov*

How to Find Outreach Trainers and Training
- **Outreach Trainer Website** — OSHA encourages all authorized outreach trainers to add their trainer profile and training schedules to *www.OutreachTrainers.org*. The site allows individuals and organizations

OSHA OUTREACH PROGRAMS

to search by type of training or geographically for trainers and training to assist them in meeting their training needs. OSHA is referencing the website to persons looking for outreach training.

- **Active Outreach Trainer Lists** — OSHA distributes lists of active trainers (two or more classes conducted within a year), by state, to persons looking for 10- or 30-hour outreach training and to trainers who need assistance in conducting their training. To obtain a state list(s):

Contact: *outreach@dol.gov*, (847) 759-7780, fax (847) 297-6636 or see Attachment B

Provide: 1) State(s) you are looking for
2) Whether you want the list(s) for Construction or General Industry
3) Your e-mail, fax number or mailing address

OSHA Technical Support

- For support related to enforcement and the OSHA standards, contact the Regional Office or the Area Office near you. These offices also provide publications and other helpful references. At the Regional Office ask for technical support. See *www.osha.gov/html/RAmap.html*.
- OSHA also has Compliance Assistance Specialists in each Area Office in states under federal jurisdiction. They're available for seminars, workshops, and speaking events. See *www.osha.gov/dcsp/compliance_assistance/cas.html*.

Outreach Training Program Contacts

- OSHA Outreach Training Program Coordinator. For online training information and help on matters that are not found in this guide or at the OSHA web site, including annual PowerPoint charts on OSHA's Most Frequently Cited Serious Violations in Construction or General Industry, contact:
  - e-mail: *outreach@dol.gov*
  - (847) 759-7735
- OSHA and OSHA Training Institute Education Centers. For matters relating to general program administration, contact your representative from the organization responsible

for your training. The contact list is included in Attachment B.

- Resource Center Loan Program. For further information on borrowing videos through this program, contact the OSHA librarian:
  - e-mail: *otiresourceloan@dol.gov*
  - (847) 759-7736

VIII. Program Administration

This section contains information on outreach cards. The section informs trainers how to receive student completion cards for the training they have conducted.

A. Obtaining Student Course Completion Cards

After conducting an outreach class, follow the instructions below to document your class to receive OSHA student course completion cards. Your responsible training office may also issue specific instructions.

New Trainers, and trainers who have updated their trainer status. To receive student completion cards for training you have conducted, send these items:

1. OSHA Outreach Training Program Report. Use our format or create your own. This includes trainer and course information. Provide an address that goes directly to you, because OSHA can't replace card packages that are not received.
2. A copy of your OSHA General Industry trainer card
3. A list of the students who completed the training. Use the area on the back to list your students, or send a separate list. The list must be legible. Only send one list, not all of the sign-in sheets.
4. Topic Outline. List the topics taught and the amount of time spent on each. Complete the topic outline on the bottom of the report (10-hour) or on the back (30-hour) or send a separate outline.

Existing Trainers. If you have previously received student completion cards, you have been issued an ID number. Use this ID to document your training. Send these items:

1. OSHA Outreach Training Program Report. Use our format or create your own. This includes your trainer ID number, name, and course information. Provide an address that goes directly to you, because OSHA

can't replace card packages that are not received. If you complete this report in its entirety, it is all you need to document your outreach training.

2. A list of the students who completed the training. Use the area on the back of the form to list your students, or send a separate list. The list must be legible. Only send one list, not all of the sign-in sheets.

3. Topic Outline. List the topics taught and the amount of time spent on each. Complete the topic outline on the bottom of the report (10-hour) or on the back (30-hour) or send a separate outline.

B. Other Key Points on Submitting Course Documentation

- Trainers must sign the statement of certification attesting that they have conducted the training in accordance with the guidelines and have submitted accurate documentation.
- Trainers must document training within six months of class completion
- Trainers must report classes separately. Each class should be reported individually and contain each of the items indicated above.
- Existing trainers with ID numbers may e-mail or fax their course documentation. See Attachment C.

C. Records Trainers Must Retain for Five Years

1. Student sign-in sheets for each class day
2. Student addresses
3. Copy of the documentation sent in to request cards, including a list of the topics taught and the amount of time spent on each
4. Records which indicate the card number dispensed to each student. One way to do this is to make a copy of the cards you issue.

D. Where to Send Documentation

See Attachment B for the training organization responsible for processing your requests for student cards. This is where you will send your course documentation. If you are unsure, the name of your responsible training office is typed in on the front of your trainer card, below "OSHA, U.S. Department of Labor."

E. ID Number Information

- All trainers who have received student cards will get an ID number. Trainers receive an ID number in their card package AFTER submitting their first card request. The trainer ID is provided on the letter or the preprinted Outreach Training Program Report that are returned with your student cards. Some responsible training offices issue an ID upon course registration or completion.
- A trainer who has received Construction and General Industry training from different organizations will have two ID numbers and will request cards from two different organizations.
- If you misplaced your ID number, note on the report that you were issued one but misplaced it.

F. Information on Student Course Completion Cards

- For legibility, trainers complete student cards by printing or typing:
  1. Student's name
  2. Course end date
  3. Trainer's name (the trainer may also sign the card)
- Trainers may not alter the cards or use white out on the cards. If you misprint or mistype the cards, you may return the cards to your responsible training organization and receive replacements.
- Student course completion cards don't expire. However, employers and other organizations may have different requirements than OSHA on this. Some states have enacted laws mandating the training. OSHA recommends Outreach Training Program courses as an orientation to occupational safety and health for workers. Participation is voluntary. Workers must receive additional training on specific hazards of their job.
- Trainers may provide training certificates to students. This often helps them verify that they took the training prior to receiving their card. Advertising restrictions also apply here.

- Trainers can use the back of the cards for other identification or training information. This may be helpful and appropriate if your outreach class is targeted to a specific industry or audience.
- The cards may be laminated.
- Use Avery 5371 label style to print on the cards. Practice by using a copy of the card sheet. Feed one sheet at a time.
- Processing card requests takes two to four weeks. Please wait this amount of time before inquiring about the status of a request.

G. Replacing Lost, Damaged, or Misprinted Cards

Extra Cards. Trainers are sent a few extra cards for each class completed in case of card errors and to allow them to replace lost student cards for students they have trained. Trainers are not to use these extra cards for any other purpose.

Trainer Card. Contact your responsible training organization (Attachment B) where you took your trainer course if you need your trainer card replaced.

Student Cards
- OSHA rarely replaces a batch of cards from an entire class.
- Use the extra cards provided to you for replacements, after you make the proper verification.
- If you don't have an extra card, contact your responsible training organization (Attachment B) for a replacement. Provide them the student's name, your name, the training date, and the type of class (10- or 30-hour, construction or general industry).
- If the training took place more than five years ago, no replacement cards will be issued.
- Trainers must maintain records which indicate the card number dispensed to each student.

Misprinted Cards: Return all misprinted cards for replacements. Do not attempt to correct and use misprinted cards.

Attachment A — OSHA Training Institute Education Centers

OSHA has authorized these educational institutions to conduct selected OSHA courses, including:

Course #500   Trainer Course in Occupational Safety and Health Standards for the Construction Industry

Course #501   Trainer Course in Occupational Safety and Health Standards for General Industry

Course #502   Update for Construction Industry Outreach Trainers

Course #503   Update for General Industry Outreach Trainers

Course #510   Occupational Safety and Health Standards for Construction

Course #511   Occupational Safety and Health Standards for General Industry

For Schedules, locations, and tuition see www.osha.gov/fso/ote/training/edcenters/index.html		
OTI Education Centers	**Lead Center: City / State**	**Phone**
Keene State College	Manchester, NH	800-449-6742
Rochester Institute of Technology	Rochester, NY	866-385-7470x2919
Atlantic OSHA Training Center (Univ. of Medicine & Dentistry of NJ, State University of New York at Buffalo, Universidad Metropolitana, San Juan, PR)	New Brunswick, NJ	732-235-9450
National Resource Center for OSHA Training (West Virginia University, National Labor College, Center to Protect Workers' Rights)	Morgantown, WV	800-626-4748
Mid-Atlantic OTI Education Center (ECRI Institute, Chesapeake Region Safety Council, Mid-Atlantic Construction Safety Council, Johns Hopkins University and Health System)	Plymouth Meeting, PA	800-875-4770
Georgia Tech Research Institute	Atlanta, GA	404-385-3500
University of South Florida	Tampa, FL	866-697-0975
Eastern Kentucky University	Richmond, KY	877-358-6742
Southeastern OTI Education Center (North Carolina State University, University of Tennessee)	Raleigh, NC	800-227-0264
University of Alabama	Tuscaloosa, AL	877-508-7246
Great Lakes OSHA Training Consortium (Univ. of Cincinnati, Eastern Michigan University, United Auto Workers)	Cincinnati, OH	800-207-9399
The National Safety Education Center (Northern Illinois University, Construction Safety Council, National Safety Council)	Chicago area, IL	800-656-5317
Mid-America OSHA Training Institute (Ohio Valley Construction Education Foundation, Sinclair Community College)	Springboro, OH	866-444-4412
Heartland Safety and Health OTI Education Center (Indiana University, University of Wisconsin-Whitewater)	Bloomington, IN	866-563-4820
Texas Engineering Extension Service, Texas A & M Univ.	Mesquite, TX	800-723-3811
The University of Texas at Arlington	Houston, TX	866-906-9190
Metropolitan Community Colleges	Kansas City, MO	800-841-7158
Midwest OSHA Education Centers (Kirkwood Community College, St. Louis University, Safety and Health Council of Greater Omaha)	Cedar Rapids, IA	800-464-6874
Red Rocks Community College	Lakewood, CO	800-933-8394
Mountain West OSHA Training & Outreach Center (University of Utah, Salt Lake City Community College, Uintah Basin Applied Technology College)	Salt Lake City, UT	801-581-4055
University of California - San Diego	San Diego, CA	800-358-9206
California State University Dominguez Hills	Carson, CA	888-4LA-OSHA
Chabot-Las Positas Community College District	Pleasanton, CA	866-936-OSHA
College of Southern Nevada	Las Vegas, NV	877-651-OSHA
University of Washington	Seattle, WA	800-326-7568

Attachment B — OSHA Outreach Training Program Fact Sheet

Where To Send Documentation:
- If an OSHA Education Center conducted or sponsored your training, see the following pages on where and how (mail, e-mail, fax) to submit requests.
- If you are unsure of the your responsible training location:
  - It is typed in on the front of the trainer card, below "OSHA, U.S. Department of Labor".
  - See the below chart which lists where each of the OSHA Training Institute Education Centers conducted their training
- Trainers taking their Construction and General Industry trainer courses from different organizations will send their student card requests to different organizations
- For persons who took their training at the OSHA Training Institute (OTI) send your requests to:

OSHA Construction (or General Industry) Outreach Training Program
2020 S. Arlington Heights Road
Arlington Heights, IL 60005
Fax: (847) 297-6636
E-mail: *outreach@dol.gov*

What To Send In:
1. OSHA Outreach Training Program report
2. Copy of trainer card if this is your first request or you have updated your trainer status
3. Student names
4. Course topic list and the time spent on each

What To Retain In Your Records (for five years):
1. Student sign-in sheets for each class day
2. Student addresses
3. Copy of the documentation submitted for card request (be sure this includes the topic outline)
4. Records which indicate the card number dispensed to each student

Requests are reviewed to ensure:
- Trainer is currently authorized
- Complies with guidelines (topics, time, etc.)
- Documentation is complete

Questions:
- For OSHA, see above
- For OSHA Training Institute Education Centers, see the list below

Where — Specifics
The following list is organized by OSHA Regions 1-10. Here are the Regional Office locations in each of the regions.
1 ~ Boston
2 ~ New York
3 ~ Philadelphia
4 ~ Atlanta
5 ~ Chicago
6 ~ Dallas
7 ~ Kansas City
8 ~ Denver
9 ~ San Francisco
10 ~ Seattle

Region 1 – Northeast, including NH, ME, RI, MA, CT, VT	
If you took the training from - OTI Education Center, Manchester, NH - Keene State College, Keene, NH - Associated Builders and Contractors, Rocky Hill, CT - Survival Systems USA, Inc., Groton, CT - Associated General Contractors of Mass., Wellesley, MA - Safety Council of Western Massachusetts, Springfield, MA - Williams College, Williamstown, MA - New England Institute of Technology, Warwick, RI - Central Maine Community College (CMCC), Auburn, ME - Maine Dept. of Transportation Safety & Performance, Fairfield, ME - Associated General Contractors of Maine, Augusta, ME - Associated General Contractors of Vermont, Montpelier, VT - Champlain College Conference & Event Center, Burlington, VT	Send your card requests to OSHA Training Institute Education Center Keene State College 175 Ammon Drive Manchester, NH 03103-3308 For questions: • (800) 449-6742 or (603) 465-0050 • Fax (603) 645-0080 • e-mail: oshaed@keene.edu Leslie Singleton ~ Outreach Coordinator lsingleton@keene.edu Outreach information and course schedule at: www.keene.edu/conted/osha.cfm

Region 2 – Northeast, including NJ, NY, and Puerto Rico

If you took the training from	Send your card requests to
- Univ. of Medicine and Dentistry of NJ, New Brunswick, NJ - State Univ. of New York at Buffalo, Toxicology Research Center, Buffalo, NY - Universidad Metropolitana, San Juan, PR	UMDNJ- School of Public Health Attn: Janet Crooks, Registrar Atlantic OSHA Training Center Office of Public Health Practice 683 Hoes Lane West, 1st Floor Piscataway, NJ, 08854 • Fax (732) 235-9460 • e-mail: crooksje@umdnj.edu • Online request form http://sph.ophp.umdnj.edu For questions Koshy Koshy (732) 235-9459, koshyko@umdnj.edu Janet Crooks (732) 235-9455, crooksje@umdnj.edu

Region 2 – New York

If you took the training from	Send your card requests to
- Rochester Institute of Technology OSHA Education Center, Rochester, NY - Rochester Builder's Exchange, Rochester, NY - General Building Contractors' Safety Training Facility in Spencerport, NY and Albany, NY - Total Safety Consulting, Long Island City, NY - Oneida Indian Nation Building Annex, Oneida, NY	Rochester Institute of Technology OSHA Education Center Attn: Donna Winter 31 Lomb Memorial Dr. Rochester, NY 14623-5603 • Fax (585) 475-6292 • e-mail: dlwtpo@rit.edu For questions: Donna Winter (866) 385-7470 ext. 2919

Region 3 – East and Building Trades, including WV, MD, PA, VA, DC

If you took the training from	Send your card requests to
Center to Protect Workers' Rights/BCTD - Building and Construction Trades Unions - Building and Construction Trades Councils - Building and Construction Trades Contractors	Center to Protect Workers' Rights 815 16th Street NW Washington, DC 20006 Fax (202) 756-4675 e-mail: Janice Wheeler Questions: Janice Wheeler (202) 756-4636
West Virginia University - Morgantown, WV, Charleston, WV, Huntington, WV - Operating Engineers, Beckley, WV - Contractors Association, Parkersburg, WV, Pittsburgh, PA, Richmond, VA - and others served with on-site training	West Virginia University Safety & Health Extension P. O. Box 6615 - 130 Tower Lane Morgantown, WV 26506 Fax (304) 293-5905 e-mail: Missy Stewart missy.stewart@mail.wvu.edu Questions: Tom Stockdale (800) 626-4748
National Labor College - College Park, MD; Philadelphia PA; Silver Spring MD; Washington DC; Wilkes-Barre PA, Harrisburg PA, Richmond VA & Roanoke VA - and others served with special programs or on-site training	
Indiana University of Pennsylvania (former OTI Education Center) - Indiana University Training Center, Indiana & Monroeville, PA - High Training Center, Lancaster, PA - Wilkes University, Wilkes Barre, PA - Graduate Business Center, West Chester Univ., West Chester, PA - Montgomery County Public Safety Training Campus Fire Academy, Conshohocken, PA (Philadelphia) - Dixon Center, Harrisburg, PA - New Castle School of Trades, New Castle, PA - Bedford County Workforce Development and CE Center, Everett, PA - Lucerne County Community College, Nantycoke, PA	

Region 3 – Mid Atlantic - including WV, MD, PA, VA, DE, DC	
If you took the training from - ECRI Institute, Plymouth Meeting, PA - High Training Center, Lancaster, PA - Hanover Wellness Center, Hanover, PA - Montgomery County Public Safety Training Campus Fire Academy, Conshohocken, PA - Associated Builders and Contractors Eastern Pennsylvania Chapter, Inc. (ABC), Allentown, PA - Priscilla Pane-Hurd Pavilion at St. Luke's Hospital & Health Network, Bethlehem, PA - Health and Technology Center at Good Shepherd Rehabilitation Network, Allentown, PA - Lackawanna County Center for Public Safety, Jessup, PA - Chesapeake Region Safety Council, Baltimore, MD - Chesapeake College, Wye Mills, MD - Howard Johnson Plaza, Ocean City, MD - Johns Hopkins Medical Institutions - The Johns Hopkins Bayview Campus - The Johns Hopkins University Homewood campus - Johns Hopkins at Mt. Washington - Johns Hopkins Howard County General Hospital - Johns Hopkins University Montgomery County campus - The Johns Hopkins University Columbia Campus	Send your card requests to ECRI Institute – Center for Education and Training 5200 Butler Pike Plymouth Meeting, PA 19462 • Fax (610) 834-0240 • e-mail: lpetosa@ecri.org For questions: Luke A. Petosa (610) 825-6000 ext 5330 or (800) 640-7421

Region 4 – South, including GA, NC, SC, MS, KY, AL, FL, TN	

If you took the training from
- Georgia Tech / Georgia Institute of Technology, Atlanta, GA
- Georgia Tech OTI Education Center in these cities:
  GA – Atlanta, Savannah
  FL - Orlando, Ft. Lauderdale, Destin, Jacksonville
  NC – Raleigh
  AL – Birmingham, Huntsville
  SC - Charleston
  MS - Biloxi
  TN – Nashville, Knoxville, Memphis
	Send your card requests to
	Georgia Tech OTI Education Center
	ATTN: Diane Knobloch
	430 Tenth Street, NW
	Atlanta, GA 30332-0837
	• Fax (404) 407-9024
	• e-mail: diane.knobloch@gtri.gatech.edu
	• Online request form - www.oshainfo.gatech.edu
	
	For questions: Diane Knobloch (404) 407-7024
	            Myrtle Turner (404) 407-8066

Region 4 – Florida	
If you took the training from University of South Florida, Tampa, FL Host Training Sites: - Associated Builders and Contractors, Orlando, FL - Caribbean Legal and Professional Institute, Kingston, Jamaica - Indian River Community College, Fort Pierce, FL - Florida International College, Fort Myers, FL - Florida Safety Council, Orlando, FL - North East Florida Safety Council, Jacksonville, FL - Safety Council of Palm Beach County, West Palm Beach, FL - Safety Management Internatl Co., Couva, Trinidad, West Indies - Suncoast Safety Council, Clearwater, FL - Suncoast Safety Council, St Petersburg, FL - Sunshine Safety Council, Daytona, FL	Send your card requests to University of South Florida OTI Education Center ATTN: Diane Ray 13201 Bruce B. Downs Blvd., MDC 56 Tampa, FL 33612-3805 • Fax (813) 974-9972 • e-mail: dray@health.usf.edu For questions: Diane Ray (813) 974-7782

Region 4 – Kentucky	
If you took the training from - Eastern Kentucky University, Richmond, KY - McCulley, Eastham & Associates, Inc., Greenup, KY - Corbin Center for Technology & Community Activities, Corbin, KY	Send your card requests to Bobby Spurlock Eastern Kentucky University OSHA Training Institute Education Center Workforce Education 521 Lancaster Ave, Perkins 202 Richmond, KY 40475-3100 e-mail: Bobby.Spurlock@eku.edu For questions: (859) 622-2961

Region 4 – South, including AL, MS, TN, FL	
If you took the training from The University of Alabama, Tuscaloosa, AL or Host Training Sites: - The University of Alabama Birmingham, Birmingham, AL - The University of Alabama Huntsville, Huntsville, AL - Other host locations	Send your card requests to The University of Alabama CCS-DEIP ATTN: June Vance Box 870388 624 Paul Bryant Drive Tuscaloosa, AL 35487 • Fax (205) 348-3049 • e-mail: jvance@ccs.ua.edu For questions: June Vance (877) 508-7246 toll free or (205) 348-4585

Region 4 – Southeast, including NC, TN, GA, SC, MS, KY, AL, FL	
If you took the training from • Southeastern OTI Education Center, North Carolina State University, Raleigh, NC and other host sites • Southeastern OTI Education Center, University of Tennessee, Nashville, TN, Knoxville, TN and other host sites	Send your card requests to Southeastern OTI Education Center NC State University Campus Box 7902 Raleigh, NC 27695-7902 • Fax (919) 515-8585 • E-mail: Anna Mangum anna_mangum@ncsu.edu For Questions: Wendy Laing (919) 515-9430 or Anna Mangum (919) 515-1080

Region 5 – Midwest, IL and WI, IN	
If you took the training from - NIU-DeKalb, IL - NIU-Naperville, IL - NIU Education Center, Hoffman Estates, IL - NIU Rockford Center, Rockford, IL - National Safety Council, Itasca, IL - Construction Safety Council, Hillside, IL - Richland Community College, Decatur, IL - Northeast Wisconsin Technical College, Green Bay, WI - Fox Valley Technical College, Appleton, WI - Dawson Technical Institute, Chicago, IL - University of Southern Indiana, Evansville, IN - and other safety councils, organizations, and companies served with on-site contract training.	Send your card requests to The National Safety Education Center College of Engineering & Engineering Technology Northern Illinois University 590 Garden Road, EB 318 DeKalb, IL 60115 Fax: (815) 753-4203 Email: nsec_outreach@niu.edu Online request form available at: www.earnyourcard.com For questions: (815) 753-6902 or (800) 656-5317, or engineeringoutreach@niu.edu

Region 5 – Midwest, including OH, MI, MN, IN, WI

If you took the training from	Send your card requests to
- University of Cincinnati, Cincinnati, OH - Eastern Michigan University, Ypsilanti, MI - Eastern Michigan University, Livonia, MI - Eastern Michigan University-Web Based Training - South Central Tech, Mankato, MN - M-TEC, Kalamazoo, MI - University of Findlay, Findlay, OH - University of Minnesota, Minneapolis, MN - Hennepin Technical College, Eden Prairie, MN - Safety Alliance, LLC, Springboro, OH - Varga-Wilson, Consulting, Columbus, OH - Purdue University North Central, Indianapolis IN	Great Lakes Regional OTI Education Center ATTN: Marianne Kautz Genome Research Institute University of Cincinnati 2180 E. Galbraith, 3rd Floor Cincinnati, OH 45237-1625 • Fax (513) 558-1756 • e-mail: kautzm@uc.edu For questions: Marianne Kautz (800) 207-9399 or (513) 558-1730

Region 5 – Ohio

If you took the training from	Send your card requests to
Mid-America OSHA Education Center, Springboro, OH	Mid-America OSHA Education Center ATTN: Susan White 33 Greenwood Lane Springboro, OH 45066 • Fax (937) 704-9394 • e-mail: ovabc@ovabc.org • Online request form available www.midamericaosha.org For questions: (937) 521-1570 or (866) 444-4412

Region 5, IN and WI

If you took your training from	Send your card requests to
- Heartland OTI Education Center, Bloomington, Indianapolis New Albany, IN - Heartland OTI Education Center, Milwaukee, Oshkosh, Whitewater, WI	Heartland OSHA Training Institute Education Center Outreach Trainer Card Requests Attn: Cheryl Holmes Indiana University Poplars, Room 629 400 E. 7th Street Bloomington, IN 47405 • Fax 812-855-7092 • e-mail: clholmes@indiana.edu For questions: Toll Free: (866) 563-4820 Website: www.heartland.indiana.edu

Region 6 – South, TX, and NM, LA, OK, AR

If you took the training from - TEEX – North Texas Regional Training Center, Mesquite, TX - TEEX – Houston Regional Training Center, Houston, TX - TEEX – South Central TX Reg'l Training Center, San Antonio, TX - TEEX – Corpus Christi Regional Training Center, Corpus Christi, TX - TEEX – South Presa Training Center, San Antonio, TX - TEEX – Marine Safety Center, Galveston, TX - State of New Mexico Occup. Health & Safety Bureau, Santa Fe, NM - Safety Counseling Inc., Albuquerque, NM - Safety Matters, Albuquerque, NM - Acadian Integrated Solutions, Maurice, LA - U.S. Army Safety Center, Ft. Rucker, AL - U.S. Air Force Safety Center, Albuquerque, NM - Francis Tuttle Tech. Center, Oklahoma City, OK - NATCO Training Center, Midland, TX - Pioneer Tech. Center, Ponca City, OK - National Park Community College, Hot Springs, AR - Texas State Tech. College, Harlingen, TX - TAMU – Corpus Christi, TX - KTech, Inc., Albuquerque, NM - Eastern New Mexico University, Roswell, NM - CEHMM, Carlsbad, NM - Permian Basin Regional Training Center, Carlsbad, NM - United Space Alliance, Houston, TX - San Juan College, Farmington, NM - Arkansas Construction Education Foundation, Little Rock, AR - Bossier Parish Community College, Shreveport, LA - Alford Safety Services, Houma, LA - Del Mar College, Corpus Christi, TX - David Carrasco Job Corp Center, El Paso, TX - New Mexico State University, Las Cruces, NM	Send your card requests to OTI Southwest Education Center Texas Engineering Extension Service ATTN: Registrar 15515 IH 20 at Lumley Mesquite, TX 75181 Fax (972) 222-2978 e-mail: OTISEC@teexmail.tamu.edu For questions: Therese Paterka or Pam Pendleton (972) 222-1300 or (800) 723-3811

Region 6 – South, TX, and NM, LA, OK, AR

If you took the training from - The University of Texas at Arlington - Louisiana Technical College Region 8 - City of Houston E. B. Cape Training Center - Austin Community College - Rose State College - North West Arkansas Community College	Send your card requests to Region VI OSHA Education Center The University of Texas at Arlington ATTN: Star Connell Box 19197 140 West Mitchell Arlington, Texas 76019-0197 Fax (817) 272-2556 e-mail: osha@uta.edu For Questions: Star Connell (817) 272-2581 or (866) 906-9190

Region 7 – Missouri

If you took the training from - Metropolitan Community College, Kansas City, MO - Maple Woods Community College, Kansas City, MO - Business & Technology Center, Kansas City, MO	Send your card requests to Region VII OTI Education Center Metropolitan Community Colleges ATTN: Dick Day, Program Manager 1775 Universal Avenue Kansas City, MO 64120 • Fax 816-482-5454 • e-mail: dick.day@mcckc.edu For questions: Dick Day (816) 482-5282

Region 7 – Midwest, including MO, IA, NE

If you took the training from - Saint Louis University, St. Louis, MO - Saint Louis University, Springfield, MO - Kirkwood Community College, Cedar Rapids, IA - National Safety Council, Omaha, NE	Send your card requests to Kirkwood Community College Midwest OSHA Education Center ATTN: Marsha Willox 6301 Kirkwood Blvd. SW Cedar Rapids, IA 52406 • Fax (319) 398-5894 • e-mail: mwillox@kirkwood.edu • Online request form at: http://moec.slu.edu For questions : ~ Marsha Willox (319) 398-5893 ~ Edgar Thornton (319) 398-1029

Region 8 – Mountain, Colorado, and also UT, MT

If you took the training from - Rocky Mountain Education Center, Lakewood, CO - Red Rocks Community College, Lakewood, CO - Ogden Weber Applied Technology College, Salt Lake City, UT - Montana Dept of Labor and Industry Occupational Safety & Health Bureau, Missoula, MT	Send your card requests to Rocky Mountain Education Center ATTN: Jeannine Kreller 13300 W. 6th Ave, Box 41 Lakewood, CO 80228-1255 Fax (303) 914-8997 e-mail: outreach@rrcc.edu For questions: Jeannine Kreller (800) 933-8394

Region 8 – Utah

If you took the training from - Mountain West OSHA Training and Outreach Center, Salt Lake City, UT - Salt Lake Community College, Salt Lake City, UT - Uintah Basin Applied Technology College, Vernal, UT	Send your card requests to Mountain West OSHA Training and Outreach Center University of Utah ATTN: Registrar 391 Chipeta Way, Suite C Salt Lake City, UT 84108 • Fax (801) 585-5275 • e-mail: luz.dominguez@hsc.utah.edu For questions: ~ Connie Crandall (801)581-7182, connie.crandall@hsc.utah.edu ~ Luz Dominguez (801)581-7909, luz.dominguez@hsc.utah.edu

Region 9 – West, CA, and also NV, HI, and AZ

If you took training from University of California, San Diego OSHA Training Institute in Region IX Arizona California Hawaii Nevada	Send your card requests to UCSD OSHA Training Institute ATTN: Outreach Training Coordinator 11770 Bernardo Plaza Court, Suite 270 San Diego, CA 92128 Fax (858) 485-7390 e-mail: OTI-Outreach@ucsd.edu Forms available online at: http://osha.ucsd.edu/outreach.htm For questions: OTI-Outreach@ucsd.edu, (858) 485-5371

Region 9 – West, CA, also NV, AZ and Guam

If you took the training from	Send your card requests to
- California State University Dominguez Hills, Carson CA WESTEC (former OTI Education Center) - WESTEC, North Kern Training Center, Shafter, CA - Community College of Southern Nevada, Henderson, NV - Truckee Meadows Community College, Reno, NV - Guam Community College, Mangilao, Guam	CSUDH OSHA Training Institute College of Extended and International Education Attn: Outreach Training Coordinator 1000 E.Victoria St. Carson, CA 90747 • Fax (310) 516-3753 • e-mail: OSHA@csudh.edu • Forms can be found at: www.csudh.edu/osha For questions: (888) 4LA-OSHA

Region 9 – West, CA, also NV and AZ

If you took the training from	Send your card requests to
- The College of Southern Nevada, Las Vegas, NV	College of Southern Nevada Attn: Abigail Rakvica 2409 Las Verdes St. K1B Las Vegas, NV 89102 • Fax (702) 651-4538 • e-mail: abigail.rakvica@csn.edu For questions: Abigail Rakvica (702) 651-4551 abigail.rakvica@csn.edu

Region 9 – West, CA, also NV and AZ

If you took the training from	Send your card requests to
- Chabot-Las Positas Community College District OSHA Training Institute	Chabot-Las Positas Community College District (CLPCCD) OTI - Contract Education 5020 Franklin Drive Pleasanton, CA 94588 • Fax (925) 485-5211 • e-mail: cpaczocha@clpccd.org For questions: (866) 936-OSHA

Region 10 – West, WA, and also OR, ID, and AK

If you took the training from	Send your card requests to
- UW/Denali Safety Council – Anchorage, AK - UW – Boise State University - Boise, ID - UW/HVAC Metals Institute – Portland, OR - UW/Portland Community College – Portland, OR - UW/HAMMER Facility – Richland, WA - UW/EnergX Facility – Richland, WA - UW – Seattle, WA - UW – Spokane, WA - UW – Cruise to Alaska	Region X OSHA Training Institute Education Center University of Washington ATTN: Registrar 4225 Roosevelt Way NE #100 Seattle, WA 98105 • Fax Fax (206) 685-3872 • e-mail: Terumi Capeling capeling@u.washington.edu • Online requests form available at: www.osha.washington.edu For questions: Terumi Capeling (206) 685-3089

OSHA Outreach Programs

Attachment C — E-mail or Fax Procedures

For Outreach Trainers With Id Numbers

Student card requests are accepted by e-mail, or fax, if a trainer has an ID number
* *Carefully read the instructions below before using these procedures.*

1. **Who is eligible to send e-mails or faxes?** Outreach Trainers with ID Numbers
   - Trainers receive an ID number in their card package AFTER submitting their first card request
   - The trainer ID is provided on the letter or the preprinted Outreach Training Program Report that are returned with your student cards

2. **Sending Requests for Student Cards**
   a. **E-mail**
      - See Attachment B for e-mail addresses
      - Subject: 10- or 30-Hour // Construction or General Industry
      - Send your e-mail request based on the format which follows these procedures. Include all of the information that is shown.
   b. **Fax**
      - See Attachment B for fax numbers
      - Send a cover page and indicate the number of pages you're sending
      - Subject: 10- or 30-hour; Construction or General Industry
      - Send your fax request based on the format which follows these procedures. Include all of the information that is shown.

3. **Instructions**
   a. Use your ID Number
   b. For each class - send a separate e-mail, or fax
   c. Keep a file (for five years) on each course which includes:
      1) Student sign-in sheets for each class day
      2) Student addresses
      3) Copy of the documentation sent in to request cards, including the topic outline list of the topics taught and the amount of time spent on each
      4) Records which indicate the card number dispensed to each student

4. **Monitoring.** At times, OSHA may ask for a copy of your class records. When OSHA conducts monitoring visits for the OSHA Outreach Training Program, you may need to provide these training records.

E-Mail Format – Request for Outreach Training Cards -- For Trainers with ID Numbers

— Below is a sample of the e-mail format.
— Send a separate e-mail for each class.

TO: See Attachment B for e-mail address

SUBJECT: 10-hour Construction or 30-hour Construction
                 10-hour General Industry or 30-hour General Industry

Statement of Certification. I certify that I have conducted this outreach training class in accordance with the OSHA Outreach Training Program guidelines. I have maintained the training records as required by these guidelines and I will provide these records to the OSHA Directorate of Training and Education (or their designee) upon request. I understand that I will be subject to immediate dismissal from the OSHA Outreach Training Program if information provided herein is not true and correct. I further understand that providing false information herein may subject me to civil and criminal penalties under Federal law, including section 17(g) of the Occupational Safety and Health Act, 29 U.S.C.666(g), which provides criminal penalties for making false statements or representations in any document filed pursuant to that Act. I hereby attest that the information on this form is true and correct.

_____   _____
Trainer Signature   Date

___ *If submitting this application by electronic means, by checking the box to the left or affixing a signature, I attest that all information provided in this submission is true and accurate.*

Course Information (check all that apply):
__ Spanish
__ Language other than English or Spanish (specify: _____)
__ Youth (age 18 or less)
__ Training conducted outside US
__ OSHA Alliance or Partnership related (specify: _____)

State in which training was held (or country if outside of US): _____

Course End Date: _____ / _____ / _____ (Requests cannot be older than 6 months)

Number of Students: _____ (More than 50 requires prior permission)

Trainer Name: _____
  Trainer ID: _____
  Your Responsible Training Organization (which OTI Education Center, or OSHA) _____
       Construction   __ #500 __ #502   Expiration Date ___/___/___
       General Industry   __ #501 __ #503   Expiration Date ___/___/___

Trainer Address / Phone / E-mail (Only needed if address has changed):

Student Names

Topic Outline - Include a list of the topics taught and the amount of time spent on each

Fax – Request for Outreach Training Cards -- For Trainers with ID Numbers

See Attachment B for fax numbers for your responsible training organization

Course: 10-hour Construction   10-hour General Industry
                30-hour Construction   30-hour General Industry

Statement of Certification. I certify that I have conducted this outreach training class in accordance with the OSHA Outreach Training Program guidelines. I have maintained the training records as required by these guidelines and I will provide these records to the OSHA Directorate of Training and Education (or their designee) upon request. I understand that I will be subject to immediate dismissal from the OSHA Outreach Training Program if information provided herein is not true and correct. I further understand that providing false information herein may subject me to civil and criminal penalties under Federal law, including section 17(g) of the Occupational Safety and Health Act, 29 U.S.C.666(g), which provides criminal penalties for making false statements or representations in any document filed pursuant to that Act. I hereby attest that the information on this form is true and correct.

_____   _____
                Trainer Signature   Date

___ *If submitting this application by electronic means, by checking the box to the left or affixing a signature, I attest that all information provided in this submission is true and accurate.*

Course Information (check all that apply):
__ Spanish
__ Language other than English or Spanish (specify: _____)
__ Youth (age 18 or less)
__ Training conducted outside US
__ OSHA Alliance or Partnership related (specify: _____)

State in which training was training held (or country if outside of US): _____
Course End Date: _____ / _____ / _____ (Requests cannot be older than 6 months)
Number of Students: _____ (More than 50 requires prior permission)

Trainer Name: _____
  Trainer ID: _____
  Your Responsible Training Organization (which OTI Education Center, or OSHA) _____
       Construction   __ #500 __ #502   Expiration Date __/__/__
       General Industry __ #501 __ #503   Expiration Date __/__/__
  Trainer Address / Phone / E-mail (Only needed if your address has changed):
       _____
       _____
       _____
       _____

Topic Outline – Include a list of the topics taught and the amount of time spent on each

Student Names
1 _____   11 _____
2 _____   12 _____
3 _____   13 _____
4 _____   14 _____
5 _____   15 _____
6 _____   16 _____
7 _____   17 _____
8 _____   18 _____
9 _____   19 _____
10 _____   20 _____

TRAINING TECHNIQUES

As an OSHA Outreach trainer you are a key player in helping OSHA's goal to reduce accidents and injuries. Workers do not want to get hurt and employers want to provide a safe workplace. Unfortunately, many safety training sessions are conducted in a manner that leaves the worker with a less-than-enthusiastic regard for safety training. It is necessary to liven up the topic to keep workers' attention. A good training philosophy is to present the material three different times in three different ways so the student is not bored, and yet the material is emphasized in such a way that he or she cannot forget it. A good trainer will establish the climate for training by introducing him or herself to the class as well as any guest speakers. Group discussions and workshops enhance training. A good rule to follow when setting up a class is to stress the key points of the topic.

- Tell them what you are going to teach them.
- Teach them.
- Tell them what you have taught them.

Presenting the material in a lecture is one way of presenting the material. Then have the students refer to written material that you have provided in a handout. Finally, show them a video of the subject as a third method of instruction. This allows different learners to obtain information in different ways and helps to break up the monotony of a class.

Good trainers realize that they are working with an adult audience that has needs and expectations. These trainers also realize that they are the key element in the company safety training program. Trainers must be confident of their own skills and technical knowledge to provide benefit to the learners. This confidence enhances the importance of the message.

Children versus Adult Learners

We've learned that children rely on others for information and tend to accept the material presented to them at face value. They are looking for a return on their educational investment some time in the distant future. They know that without a high school education they aren't going to succeed easily, and that an investment in some college, or even getting a college degree, will increase their ability to earn an income in the long run. Still, they have little experience in these matters and usually do not contribute to class discussions. Children generally:

- Rely on others
- Accept the lessons at face value
- Look for long term payback

- Little experience
- Seldom contribute to class

Adult learners, on the other hand, have generally graduated from the school of hard knocks already. They rely on their own experiences, question facts that you present and will challenge what you are presenting. They are very experienced with the topic material and contribute on a regular basis to the class discussions. This sometimes makes it a challenge to keep the class on track and trainers must be ever watchful that they do not "take off on a tangent" discussion.

Adult learners want a quick return on their investment. They are paying for the course and want to be able to use the information today. Adult learners generally:
- Are self reliant
- Question facts
- Are very experienced
- Can contribute significantly to the class
- Expect quick return on their investment

If you attempt to treat adult learners as children, you will lose them. Your class will suffer and your evaluations will reflect that. So remember to treat all learners as adults. Find out what their goals are for the class. A good technique is to introduce yourself and the class topic, then ask the students to stand up, introduce themselves and to mention what they would want to get out of this class. Capture their goals on a sheet of display paper and leave it taped to the wall during the class. This will allow your class to focus on the real world as perceived by the students.

Emphasize how the training can be applied. Talk to the students about how OSHA is enforcing the regulations strictly using recent newspaper articles to illustrate this point. Relate the course topics to the students' experiences and learn from the experiences and opinions of your students. Always encourage discussion.

Treat learners as adults and identify the goals of the learners in the class.

Focus on "real world" situations instead of academic solutions, emphasize how the training can be applied to their day to day jobs and relate the material to their experiences.

Encourage discussion within the group and listen to and respect their opinions.

When it comes to the actual learning process, psychologists have found that we learn information through sight, then by hearing, then by smell and finally by touch. By combining these senses in a class setting you can compound the learning process.

Students learn with their senses:
Touch ....(1.5%)
Smell...(3.5%)
Hearing......................................(11%)
Sight...(83%)

Psychologists also conducted tests to find out how different methods of learning affected the ability to remember and recall material later on. While we learn using sight 83% of the time students were found to recall only 10% of what they read. They recall 20% of what they hear and 30% of what they see. Instructors who combine the training techniques have discovered that students recall 50% of what they see and hear. Compare that to 10% of what they read in a safety flyer, or 30% of what they see in the worksite.

If students repeat what they've just heard, they will recall 80% of the information, and if they repeat what they've heard and take action, such as building a scaffold and explaining the procedures as they do it, they recall 90% of the information.

That's why hands on training is so very important in the safety field as the numbers show:
What they read ....(10%)
What they hear ....(20%)
What they see ....(30%)
What they see AND hear ....(50%)
What they SAY............................(80%)
What they say AND act ....(90%)

Studies reveal that only 30% of the students are actually listening to you. The other 70% are thinking about what they have to do after class is over, wondering how the company is doing without them, or what they should get as a gift for someone important to them. So your class must be vibrant enough to bring them back from their mental vacation to concentrate on the task at hand: learning safety. Remember that only 30% of your students are listening to you at any time during the class. Seventy percent are taking mental vacations, thinking of a past event or planning a future one.

Human beings have a natural potential for learning. Trainers must understand that people are naturally curious, yet they are simultaneously eager and *not* eager to learn. The tendency to learn is more likely to appear when people see relevance to themselves in the learning process.

Significant learning takes place when the subject matter is perceived by students as being meaningful for their own purposes.

Confronting students with practical, social, and ethical problems is effective in promoting learning. Brief, intensive experiences for individuals facing immediate problems are especially effective.

Learning is facilitated when the student participates responsively in the learning process. When students set their own goals, locate and learn to use their resources, and take responsibility for their actions, they tend to learn quickly. Students should be involved in and participate in the class to enhance their educational experience.

Classroom Training in General

Students will not normally pursue the learning objectives on their own and must be prompted to do so. Tests and quizzes can be used as motivators to get students focused on the learning objectives. These evaluations are part of the education itself as students learn what they need to master and build upon their skill levels "one brick at a time."

Instructors must assign projects and tasks to the students and supervise the work to ensure it is completed. The facilitator must provide guidance to the learners and some form of evaluation.

As a trainer, you are expected to know the subject inside and out, as well as the objective of the training session. Prepare your materials the day before the training session and be prepared to teach an outstanding class. The reason that many instructors carry their own LCD projectors and laptop computers with them is that often different brands are not compatible and simply do not work together. Check out your equipment so that you know how it works. Do a function check of the equipment to ensure your material works with your equipment. Do not wait until the last minute to plan, prepare, and practice.

It is the trainer's responsibility to set the initial mood of the group and establish a climate of learning. Students may be motivated by allowing them to have input into the learning structure. One way of doing this is to have the students introduce themselves at the beginning of a class and identify one particular problem that they seek to have resolved during this class. The trainer can write those concerns on a chalkboard and tailor the session to ensure that those concerns are met. Facilitators can provide a range of resources for the students, including the instructor. Facilitators should keep a close eye on the climate of the class and modify the presentation to maximize class learning.

Confidence comes from being thoroughly prepared. Instructors can expect to be nervous. Some instructors use acting skills and exercises to overcome this natural nervousness. They realize that trainers who *act* enthusiastic will *be* enthusiastic. Keep a positive attitude when you are training and commit yourself to the training session preparation and the class time itself. Speak loudly and clearly. Your clothes say a lot about you, so dress appropriately. Wear comfortable shoes and match your dress to your audience. An executive briefing may require a coat and tie, while the same set of clothes would not be appropriate for forklift operator training.

Understand how long you have to conduct the class and meet that time expectation. Start and finish the class on time. This may require that the class be rehearsed and timed. Understanding the audience is also important. Giving a presentation to new employees is different than giving a presentation to experienced workers or job foremen. Executive briefings and seminars require an entirely different presentation.

What you hear, you forget.
What you hear and see, you remember.
Use PowerPoints, videos, flipcharts
What you do, you understand
and remember.
Use field trips, demonstrations, hands-on activities

There are several ways that training can be presented. Each of these methods has its own advantages and disadvantages. The simplest form of education is the lecture, where the instructor talks to the students about the subject. A foreman getting the workers together and talking to them about how to set up and use a ladder can accomplish ladder safety training.

Using a chalkboard or easel and paper to show the workers the 1:4 pitch, how to tie off the ladder, and the 3-ft. extension can enhance a ladder presentation.

The presentation could be further enhanced by using PowerPoint slides to show photographs of ladders being used correctly and incorrectly. Pictures help to maintain focus on the material. Another teaching aid is a videotape or DVD that brings in sound and action. Other things that can add to the class are personal experiences of the instructor or the students, case studies, and handouts (available from OSHA's web page www.osha.gov) as well as diagrams and sketches. Training is always enhanced when the students receive a handout to refer to after the class. Use a variety of teaching techniques to present your materials to keep the information interesting.

In some cases, students cannot be brought together in one location for the training. In these cases a remote broadcast or teleconference may be used to provide training over long distances. Some companies use computer-based training via CD-ROM or the Internet. Both of these systems provide sound, action, and student interactions so that the training is effective.

About Your Session

It is all about you! You are the instructor and your personal style is what sets you apart from the thousands of other instructors out there. Learn what your strengths and weaknesses are and work to correct and minimize the weak parts of your style. Use your strong points to your advantage.

If you are getting ready for a class and don't feel nervous, you are unusual. In other words, everyone gets butterflies in their stomach from time to time. It's natural. To counter this feeling, realize that you are the expert in this subject and have a positive attitude. Don't try to be someone else, their tricks and jokes may not work for you.

The best thing to do is to be prepared. Study the slides the night before, go over what you are going to present. Wear the right clothes. If it's a construction class, you don't want to wear a suit and tie, but if you are presenting a class to executives blue jeans and a flannel shirt probably won't fit the occasion.

Be enthusiastic about the subject and don't forget to project your voice to the student sitting in the last row. That way all the students will hear you.

- Expect to be nervous
- Have a positive attitude and be yourself, be flexible, be accessible
- Be prepared and speak loudly to be heard
- Dress appropriately and show enthusiasm

Use a three step procedure for training. Tell the student what you are going to teach them, teach them, and then tell them what you've taught them. More formal institutions have developed a five step method, but the procedure is the same. Review the material you are going to present with the class, giving them the reasons why the topic is important. Give the student an overview of the material that you are going to present. Then present the material in a more detailed manner. Provide some form of activity or exercise to reinforce the learning points you presented and finally, summarize what you've taught them. Use the following five steps to organize your training plan:

- Review
- Overview
- Presentation
- Exercise
- Summary

In this first step of the five step process you should introduce the topic that you are going to present. Demonstrate why such training is important, such as the fact that it saves lives, reduces fines and could keep the employee from losing a finger. Ask students if they have any compliance inspection stories to share with the group. Identify any person or group in the class that has experiences that make the topic a valuable lesson.

- Introduce the topic
- Ask students to share experiences
- Recognize resources within the group

Explain the learning objectives of the module that you are going to present. Tell them that in this class we are going to discuss these five points that are the most popular points that OSHA cites when they walk onto a worksite.

- Discuss the learning objectives
- Establish why this material is important
- Explain the most frequently cited violations

During the presentation of the module, try to make the slides and conversation flow into the next module. Don't load the class up with superfluous information when a few short points are all that they are really going to remember.

It's a good idea to reinforce your lecture with real life stories or newspaper clippings. OSHA publishes FATAL FACTS, which are nice handouts for a class since they detail what happened, what should have happened and why the person died in the accident. You can also hand out and discuss letters of interpretation that are available on the OSHA website at www.osha.gov or in the OSHA CD ROM. Other realistic training aids are statistics or court decisions. When presenting the module, lead into the topic from the overview and explain to the students that you are going to cover the material that they need to know. Provide realistic examples of incidents from a number of sources, including:

- Stories or quotes
- Newspaper clippings
- Fatal Facts from OSHA
- Letters of Interpretation
- Statistics or court decisions

Let the students play with handout materials, tools, mock ups. Involve the students by having them relate their experiences with the topic. Often students will learn more by doing something, so get them involved in committee or team activity, have them build a scaffold or put on safety equipment. Even if it is simply a matter of taking a highlighter and having the students highlight a section in the manual

and put a tab on the page, they will remember the session! Always give positive feedback to students. Telling students "Yes, that's right", or "You are on the right track, let's explore this further" is a very strong method of keeping students happy and motivated. Students best remember what they do as opposed to what they observe. Involve the students. Have them:

- Relate personal experiences
- Handle safety equipment
- Demonstrate how to do something
- Highlight and tab the applicable regulations

Take a few minutes at the end of each module to summarize key points for the students. These key points are often brought up again in a quiz or test, so this is an important time to make sure that all students got the same information out of the last hour. Ask the students if they have any questions pertaining to the subject matter. Finally, use these moments to get the students' minds ready for the next lesson. If you are discussing walking and working surfaces and the next topic is scaffolding, tell the students something like "Now that we know how to work safely on level surfaces, let's take it up a notch. When we get back from break we'll get into working surfaces at a higher elevation as we study scaffolds."

- Stressing key points, summarize the lesson
- Answer any question students may present
- Use this as a transition to the next lesson

It cannot be said often enough: Rehearsal is the key to building an excellent class. Act enthusiastically and your students will become enthusiastic about the class as well. Speak to the student in the last row so that your voice will be heard, and move around in the class so that you are accessible to the students. Make eye contact with each student in the class and hold it for a few seconds when you are teaching. And don't forget to smile.

- Be prepared – rehearse your "show"
- Be positive and show enthusiasm
- Speak loud enough to be heard
- Be flexible and accessible
- Make eye contact

When you are preparing for your class, commit yourself and your time to the class.

Analyze the audience and prepare for each day as if it was the only day you had the student under your control. Think of what you can do to improve the sight and sound of your class. If the props you are using are getting old and worn, replace them. Practice moves that you use in the class in front of a mirror to make sure that you have all the moves down. And remember that the class is a presentation. Present it, deliver it to your students as if it were a gift. It is a gift of knowledge, after all.

- Commit yourself to the class
- Analyze the audience
- Prepare
- Think "Sight and Sound"
- Practice and time yourself
- Deliver the class

When you show up at the class, check out the room. You should normally try to check out the classroom the night before the class if it is at a hotel. If it is at a company training center make sure you check in at least an hour or two before the class. That way you can re-arrange any seating or chairs and tables, find out where the electrical outlets are, light controls, etc. Find out where the restrooms and telephones are so that you can remind the class. It's important to establish a refreshment and smoking area as well as finding out where students need to go to be contacted by their company in case of emergencies.

- Table and chair arrangement
- Electrical outlets (you may need an extension cord, power strip)
- Light and heating controls
- Restrooms and telephones
- Refreshment area
- Point of contact for emergencies

Safety training doesn't have to be boring and extremely serious all the time. The students know that the subject is deadly serious, so in the class you can have fun, lighten up the session by telling amusing stories and quotations. Remind students of the gravity of the topic by using recent court decisions and statistics as well as real life experiences.

- Stories
- Quotations
- Court Decisions
- Statistics
- Life Experiences

There are all sorts of training aids that you can use, but remember that they are just that, training aids. The purpose of the class is to get knowledge from the instructor into the mind of the student. If your training aid detracts from the learning process, you have to ask yourself why are you using int. Flip charts and blackboards are easy to use and are just about everywhere. Write large enough so that the student in the back can read the printing without their glasses. Overhead transparencies are nice, easy to create and keep current. You can make overhead transparencies using PowerPoint slides, your computer and a printer. Once the ink is dry, you can place the transparency inside a clear document protector to keep the slide from getting scratched or damaged. Keep the modules in a three ring binder for ease of transportation and filing. Laptop computers and a projector make presentations easy, too. They are state of the art for presenters. Models of industrial plants and equipment can be shown in the class, and the best way to make a point about safety equipment is the safety equipment itself. Hand out eyeglasses, hard hats, gloves and test equipment in the classes so that the students can touch and feel the equipment that they'll be using.

- Flip chart/Blackboard
- Overhead Transparency
- Slides, Movies
- Computer LCD with power point
- Models
- Actual tools and instruments

Whenever there is a change in the flow of education, introduce that change. If you are coming on platform, take a moment to introduce yourself. If you are being followed by another speaker, introduce that speaker, talk about any awards or credentials that you or the next speaker have. If you are going to show a film or video, introduce that as well, saying, "Now we'll take a look at a short film that reinforces the things we've been talking about." Remember how important introductions are and introduce yourself with some background that makes you credible. Always do the same for the guest speaker or the speaker who will follow you. Films and videos should also be introduced so that students can get into the right frame of mind and be more receptive to the video since they know why it is being shown.

Students in groups learn better when there is an informal structure that is relaxed and comfortable. Make sure that discussions within the groups remain fixed on the topic at hand, and make sure that everyone participates in the discussions. It is natural for a leader to emerge in the group, and you may have to rotate among the groups, quietly involving the student who is more shy than the others by asking them what they think about the task. Make sure that the group members listen to each other to get the most of their collective experiences.

- Atmosphere is informal, comfortable and relaxed
- Center discussions on pertinent issues
- Everyone participates in discussions
- Members of the group listen to each other

The biggest mistake that trainers make is not being prepared. No matter how good you are, how well you know the material, always practice and review your material. Make sure that your equipment is checked and functional before the students arrive. Batteries die and liquids dry up, so check your laser pointers, equipment and markers to make sure that they all work.

Be natural. Don't try to copy someone else if their method is drastically different from yours. Relax, this is your class. Keep control of the class and never, never embarrass a student or belittle them. If the student asks a question and you don't know the answer, it's all right to say that you don't know, but that you'll check and get the answer to the student by the end of the class.

- Don't try to "wing it"
  - Be prepared
  - Check your equipment before class starts
- Don't try to be someone you are not
  - Be yourself, natural
  - Relax
- Don't lose control
- Try not to embarrass students

- Don't be afraid to say that you don't know Tell the student you'll get the answer to them.

Don't apologize for your lack of preparedness, the room conditions or the lunch. Don't bring up something that is negative for the students to dwell on. Watch out for those human traits that creep up on us, like rattling your keys in your pocket or jingling change when you walk. Shuffling papers and the repeating phrase "uh", "well" should be trained out of your vocabulary.

- Don't apologize
  - "Your friends don't need it, your enemies won't believe it" Mark Twain
- Distracting mannerisms
  - Rattling keys or change
  - Shuffling papers
  - Verbal annoyances ("uh", "you know")

You may find that you need to be more forceful when leading a group so the students do not get out of control. Or you may find that you need to speak more deliberately, slowly, or loudly. Gestures work for some instructors and are a disaster for others. Stress the point that everyone involved in the session is going to learn from each other, instructor and student alike. Most adult students have experiences to share with the class, so stress the equality of the group as opposed to the superiority of any one person. Focus on solving problems that the group has identified and try to avoid ego trips of individual students...and the instructor.

Involve the students as much as possible using your personal style, attitude, and philosophy. Be open and honest with the students and do not be afraid to display your weaknesses as well as your strengths. This allows the group to open up. When students realize that everyone has foibles and shortcomings, they tend to become more involved. Make eye contact with the students and smile.

Some in the group may initially be a little defensive. They may be a little tense, wondering what they have gotten into and what demands will be made on them. The instructor must allay their fears and lower their tension levels by creating a climate that is open and positive and encourages discussion. Remind the group that their combined experience is far greater than yours and that the instructor is there to serve as a guide to help them use the resources of the group constructively and positively. Mention that quite often they will learn more from one another than they will from the programmed course of instruction.

Handling Problem Situations

When you find a student who talks incessantly, you should realize that they may be eager to demonstrate their skills. On the other hand, some students just like to talk.

Don't embarrass the student or use sarcasm. Slow them down by giving them challenges to solve. Try to involve the group in the handling of the constant talker. When they make a point, steer the attention to the group by asking how the group feels about that point.

- Why
  - May be eager to show off
  - May be well informed and want to show it
  - Some folks are just naturally talkative
- What to do
  - Don't embarrass them or use sarcasm
  - Slow them down with challenging questions
  - Try to let the group handle it -"Hmm, that's interesting, how does the group feel about it?"

Sometimes there are student personalities that mix about the same as oil and water, and this can divide the group into different factions. This occurrence can be the result of different personalities or experiences that the students have. In these cases, emphasize the points that the parties do agree on. Minimize those parts that they don't agree on, and remind the class that it is alright to disagree. Keep the topic and discussion focused on the class objectives, and invite the students to be frank, but note that personalities should be left out of the discussion.

- Why
  - Two or more personalities/experiences
  - Can divide group into factions
- What to do
  - Emphasize points of agreement
  - Minimize disagreements

- Keep focused on objectives
- Be frank, ask that personalities be left out

Side conversations can be disconcerting to the instructor, and you won't find out until the end of the class that those conversations were keeping other students from hearing what you had to say. When those conversations take place, and they will, ask the participants if they could leave the class to conclude their discussion without your interrupting them. Ask easy questions, and call on the side conversationalist by name to answer the question. Move towards them when you are making a point and your presence within their personal space is usually enough to disrupt their conversation.

- What
  - May be personal, may be related to the topic, but is usually distracting
- What to do
  - Never embarrass
  - Ask an easy question, call one of them by name
  - Move over towards the group that is talking so that your presence disrupts them

Students who tend to ramble get lost in their own conversation, linking related topics to unrelated topics until you don't know where they are going. They seem to want to talk about everything but the topic you are trying to teach. When they pause to take a breath, thank them for their comments, restate their positive points and move on with your lecture. Smile, and remind them that the class only has one hour to master this particular topic and let him know that you'd love to chat after class or during lunch, but that the class must be focused on the training material at hand.

- What
  - Get lost, use far fetched analogies
  - Talk about everything BUT the topic
- What to do
  - When they pause to breath, thank them for their comments, restate the relevant points and move on
  - Smile, tell them its an interesting point, but mention that we only have one hour to complete this topic
  - Ask them to continue this discussion during lunch or after class

Obstinate people are usually prejudiced and refuse to see your point. Try to use the group and stories to swing the obstinate student around to your way of thinking. Ask the student to keep an open mind, that you see his point, too.

- What
  - Won't budge, Prejudiced, can't see your point
- What to do
  - Use the group to straighten out the student
  - Ask the student to keep an open mind and see this point for the time being

Some students just won't participate. They won't talk. They may be bored, timid, insecure or they may feel superior to you as an expert in this field. You have to find out why they are not speaking and try to arouse their interest by asking them direct questions that they can answer. Try to draw out the person next to the timid person, and then ask the shy student to comment on the response. Make eye contact with them and smile to make them feel comfortable.

- What
  - Bored, indifferent, timid, insecure or feels superior
- What to do
  - Find the motivation for non speaking
  - Arouse interest by asking direct questions
  - Draw out the person next to him, then ask the shy person to comment on the response
  - Smile at them a lot

There are students who really know their field, but they can't convey the meaning with the spoken word. When the student speaks and the words come out wrong, rephrase the words and ask the student if that's their meaning, or if they agree with you. It is important to make them feel a part of the class because they want to contribute. Some of us just don't have a lot of opportunity to speak publicly and get nervous. Tell them to take a deep breath, pause, and then make their point.

- What
  - Cannot put thoughts into words
  - Get the idea, cannot convey it

- What to do
  - Say "Let me repeat that for the class" and restate it more clearly

When a student is heading off on the wrong track, you have to get him back on track. You can say that perhaps you misled the conversation and then restate what you are saying, or use one of the responses below to try to get the person back. One instructor who told a student, "You are absolutely incorrect and this is why..." disoriented the student, who became quiet for the rest of the class, spoke with the other students about how terrible the instructor was, and wrote a scathing letter about the instructor's lack of educational skills to the program director. This situation has to be handled delicately.

- What
  - Student offers a comment that is obviously incorrect
- What to do
  - "I can see how you feel" or "That is one way of looking at it"
  - "Hmm, good point, let's look at it from another direction"

Handling Questions

Skillfully used questions help guide discussions and extract and develop information. Questions invite participation and test the effectiveness of the communication. Questions should motivate student thought and opinion and should be directed to everyone in the group. The purpose of questions is to get the students to participate and think.

There are several types of questions that instructors can ask:

- Open. Allows great freedom, is less threatening, and the student controls the amount of detail in answer.
- Closed. The instructor limits the response length and allows for re-direction of the discussion.
- Direct. Directed at one student.
- Overhead. Covers the class as a whole.
- Return. Redirects the question back to the person who asked it.
- Relay. Takes a question from one student and redirects it at another.

Good questions require the students to think so after you ask a question, allow adequate time for answer formulation and response. Be patient. As a rule of thumb, count to 12 before asking the class another question.

Presenting Material

You have had time to prepare, but most people in the group are hearing the material for the first time. Understanding this new material can be difficult. Presenting it in a way that others understand is even more difficult.

Preparation enables you to organize your thoughts, plan your approach, expand your understanding and develop illustrations, examples and analogies. Only preparation will give you the skill and confidence you need to achieve your goals. Rehearsal is difficult, but it is one of the key tools of good preparation. So run through your act before you go on stage. Concentrate on the things you will say and go over it a few times.

Make sure you allow students time to become familiar with a topic before moving on to the next topic. Stress how the concepts can be applied to add value for the students in their own lives. Increase their understanding by relating concepts presented to their own experiences.

Stories hold a group's interest a lot more than explaining something. Everybody loves a story; they are "the propelling power of persuasion". Good stories are real, vital, timely, specific, and about people. The best stories are drawn from your own experience and tailored to fit the topic. Variety keeps them interested and can make a good program outstanding.

OSHA 501 —
Effective Training Techniques

Instructions:

This exercise is designed to get trainers in front of a live audience to develop their training skills using a variety of methods. Power point slides, chart boards and demonstrations are strong teaching tools that you should strive to incorporate into the exercise. Each topic of the course will be assigned to an individual or a group.

Preparation time will be allocated in class, but you will find that some "homework" will be required to adequately perform this task.

You have been provided with a sample powerpoint presentation on CD. This CD comes from the OSHA Training Institute in Arlington, Illinois. You probably want to go through the slides and modify them for your presentation. Remember the six by six rule which states that a slide should have no more than six lines on it and no more than six words per line. Feel free to import your own photographs and images onto your demo slides. Save your presentation as the OLDER version of powerpoint, not the VISTA system since it tends to confuse computers using the XP system. Put your presentation on a USB drive and have your instructor load it onto his computer in a special file for this class. If you are using a video or something else on the computer, include that in your file on the USB drive.

Feel free to bring in examples of equipment from your company or ask the instructor for assistance. Some examples of things you may want to use in your presentation are listed on your sheet. Some student bring on models, fall arrest systems... one student actually brought in a mobile crane for his demonstration!

You will present your material in a twenty minute time frame. During your twenty minute presentation each person on the team must present part of the lesson plan. Use a variety of methods to get the message across to your target audience (new employees of the company who are going through the 10 hour OSHA Outreach Program).

Upon completion of your presentation one group will provide direct feedback, then the entire class will critique your performance. Finally, the instructor will address any topics that you missed or may have provided incorrect information on as well as a critique of your performance.

Topics not used by the student groups will be taught by the OTIEC instructor.

Tips that students may use to enhance their presentation

- Museum Walk
- White Board/Easel Tips
- Power Point Tips
- Demonstration Tips

Assigned Group Topic: HAZARD COMMUNICATION

Presenters Name:
Presenters Name:
Presenters Name:
Presenters Name:

Training Objectives (see the OSHA Outreach Guide) that must be emphasized during your short presentation include:
- Hazard Communication regulations in construction are identical to those used in general industry.
- Elements of a Hazard Communication Program include a Written Program, Labels, MSDS and Training
- How to read an MSDS
- Requirements for labels
- Elements of a written program
- Requirements for training

Suggested Items to use:
- Regulation (highlight/point out the teaching point) 1910.1200 (in back of regulation)
- Sample Equipment
- Student Handout – MSDS

Notes for your presentation

Introduction

Main Topic

Sub Topics
A.

B.

C.

D.

Summary and Conclusion

Trainer Feedback

Time Started: _____ Time Stopped: _____ Total Time: _____

Item being evaluated	Needs Improvement			OK	Excellent
Voice Projection:	1	2	3	4	5
Introduction of material/following speaker:	1	2	3	4	5
Control of class/use of time:	1	2	3	4	5
Use of handouts:	1	2	3	4	5
Use of demonstrations:	1	2	3	4	5
Appearance:	1	2	3	4	5
Attention Getting Step:	1	2	3	4	5
Humor:	1	2	3	4	5
Clarity of topic presentation:	1	2	3	4	5
Continuity: (Did it flow?) 1	2	3	4	5	
Technical Accuracy:	1	2	3	4	5

Things I Liked About Your Presentation:

Things To Make Your Presentation Even Better:

General Comments:

Assigned Group Topic: HEALTH HAZARDS

Presenters Name:
Presenters Name:
Presenters Name:
Presenters Name:

Training Objectives (see the OSHA Outreach Guide) that must be emphasized during your short presentation include:

- Terminology ~ TLV/TWA/PEL/IDLH
- PELs found in Table Z are based on 8 hour TWA
- How to compute Time Weighted Average

Suggested Items to use:

- Regulation (highlight/point out the teaching point)
- Sample Equipment
- Student Handout

Notes for your presentation

Introduction

Main Topic

Sub Topics

A.

B.

C.

D.

Summary and Conclusion

512

Trainer Feedback

Time Started: _____ Time Stopped: _____ Total Time: _____

Item being evaluated	Needs Improvement			OK	Excellent
Voice Projection:	1	2	3	4	5
Introduction of material/following speaker:	1	2	3	4	5
Control of class/use of time:	1	2	3	4	5
Use of handouts:	1	2	3	4	5
Use of demonstrations:	1	2	3	4	5
Appearance:	1	2	3	4	5
Attention Getting Step:	1	2	3	4	5
Humor:	1	2	3	4	5
Clarity of topic presentation:	1	2	3	4	5
Continuity: (Did it flow?) 1	2	3	4	5	
Technical Accuracy:	1	2	3	4	5

Things I Liked About Your Presentation: _____

Things To Make Your Presentation Even Better: _____

General Comments: _____

Assigned Group Topic: PERSONAL PROTECTIVE EQUIPMENT
Presenters Name:
Presenters Name:
Presenters Name:
Presenters Name:

Training Objectives (see the OSHA Outreach Guide) that must be emphasized during your short presentation include:
- When is PPE required
- ANSI standards for PPE
- Head Protection
- Eye Protection
- Foot Protection
- Respirators Medical Eval/fit testing
- Hearing Protection How to wear ear plugs

Suggested Items to use:
- Regulation (highlight/point out the teaching point)
- Sample Equipment – Hard hat/safety glasses/gloves
- Student Handout

Notes for your presentation

Introduction

Main Topic

Sub Topics
A.

B.

C.

D.

Summary and Conclusion

Trainer Feedback

Time Started: _____   Time Stopped: _____   Total Time: _____

Item being evaluated	Needs Improvement			OK	Excellent
Voice Projection:	1	2	3	4	5
Introduction of material/following speaker:	1	2	3	4	5
Control of class/use of time:	1	2	3	4	5
Use of handouts:	1	2	3	4	5
Use of demonstrations:	1	2	3	4	5
Appearance:	1	2	3	4	5
Attention Getting Step:	1	2	3	4	5
Humor:	1	2	3	4	5
Clarity of topic presentation:	1	2	3	4	5
Continuity: (Did it flow?) 1	2	3	4	5	
Technical Accuracy:	1	2	3	4	5

Things I Liked About Your Presentation: _____

Things To Make Your Presentation Even Better: _____

General Comments: _____

Assigned Group Topic: FIRE PREVENTION

Presenters Name:
Presenters Name:
Presenters Name:
Presenters Name:

Training Objectives (see the OSHA Outreach Guide) that must be emphasized during your short presentation include:

■ Different types of Fires A/B/C/D/K
■ Fire extinguisher selection and placement
■ Fire extinguisher use

Suggested Items to use:

■ Regulation (highlight/point out the teaching point)
■ Sample Equipment – Fire extinguisher
■ Student Handout

Notes for your presentation

Introduction

Main Topic

Sub Topics

A.

B.

C.

D.

Summary and Conclusion

Trainer Feedback
Time Started: _____ Time Stopped: _____ Total Time: _____

Item being evaluated	Needs Improvement			OK	Excellent
Voice Projection:	1	2	3	4	5
Introduction of material/following speaker:	1	2	3	4	5
Control of class/use of time:	1	2	3	4	5
Use of handouts:	1	2	3	4	5
Use of demonstrations:	1	2	3	4	5
Appearance:	1	2	3	4	5
Attention Getting Step:	1	2	3	4	5
Humor:	1	2	3	4	5
Clarity of topic presentation:	1	2	3	4	5
Continuity: (Did it flow?) 1	2	3	4	5	
Technical Accuracy:	1	2	3	4	5

Things I Liked About Your Presentation:

Things To Make Your Presentation Even Better:

General Comments:

Assigned Group Topic: VEHICLES AND EQUIPMENT

Presenters Name:

Presenters Name:

Presenters Name:

Presenters Name:

Training Objectives (see the OSHA Outreach Guide) that must be emphasized during your short presentation include:

- Vehicle backing hazards and requirements
- Barricades

Suggested Items to use:

- Regulation (highlight/point out the teaching point)
- Sample Equipment –safety vest
- Student Handout

Notes for your presentation

Introduction

Main Topic

Sub Topics

A.

B.

C.

D.

Summary and Conclusion

Trainer Feedback

Time Started: _____ Time Stopped: _____ Total Time: _____

Item being evaluated	Needs Improvement			OK	Excellent
Voice Projection:	1	2	3	4	5
Introduction of material/following speaker:	1	2	3	4	5
Control of class/use of time:	1	2	3	4	5
Use of handouts:	1	2	3	4	5
Use of demonstrations:	1	2	3	4	5
Appearance:	1	2	3	4	5
Attention Getting Step:	1	2	3	4	5
Humor:	1	2	3	4	5
Clarity of topic presentation:	1	2	3	4	5
Continuity: (Did it flow?) 1	2	3	4	5	
Technical Accuracy:	1	2	3	4	5

Things I Liked About Your Presentation: _____

Things To Make Your Presentation Even Better: _____

General Comments: _____

Assigned Group Topic: TOOLS

Presenters Name:

Presenters Name:

Presenters Name:

Presenters Name:

Training Objectives (see the OSHA Outreach Guide) that must be emphasized during your short presentation include:

- Regardless of who provided the tools (employer, employee, union) the employer is responsible for ensuring the safety of such tools.
- Demonstrate the "ring test" for abrasive wheels

Suggested Items to use:

- Regulation (highlight/point out the teaching point)
- Sample Equipment - Grinding wheel to demonstrate the ring test
- Student Handout

Notes for your presentation

Introduction

Main Topic

Sub Topics

A.

B.

C.

D.

Summary and Conclusion

Trainer Feedback

Time Started: _____ Time Stopped: _____ Total Time: _____

Item being evaluated	Needs Improvement			OK	Excellent
Voice Projection:	1	2	3	4	5
Introduction of material/following speaker:	1	2	3	4	5
Control of class/use of time:	1	2	3	4	5
Use of handouts:	1	2	3	4	5
Use of demonstrations:	1	2	3	4	5
Appearance:	1	2	3	4	5
Attention Getting Step:	1	2	3	4	5
Humor:	1	2	3	4	5
Clarity of topic presentation:	1	2	3	4	5
Continuity: (Did it flow?) 1	2	3	4	5	
Technical Accuracy:	1	2	3	4	5

Things I Liked About Your Presentation: _____

Things To Make Your Presentation Even Better: _____

General Comments: _____

Assigned Group Topic: ELECTRICAL

Presenters Name:
Presenters Name:
Presenters Name:
Presenters Name:

Training Objectives (see the OSHA Outreach Guide) that must be emphasized during your short presentation include:

- The minimum safe distance from energized overhead lines is ten feet!
- Requirements for electrical grounding
- Requirements for guarding over 50Volts
- Assured Grounding Program

Suggested Items to use:

- Regulation (highlight/point out the teaching point)
- Sample Equipment – Electrical test equipment/damaged extension cords
- Student Handout

Notes for your presentation

Introduction

Main Topic

Sub Topics
A.

B.

C.

D.

Summary and Conclusion

Trainer Feedback

Time Started: _____ Time Stopped: _____ Total Time: _____

Item being evaluated	Needs Improvement			OK	Excellent
Voice Projection:	1	2	3	4	5
Introduction of material/following speaker:	1	2	3	4	5
Control of class/use of time:	1	2	3	4	5
Use of handouts:	1	2	3	4	5
Use of demonstrations:	1	2	3	4	5
Appearance:	1	2	3	4	5
Attention Getting Step:	1	2	3	4	5
Humor:	1	2	3	4	5
Clarity of topic presentation:	1	2	3	4	5
Continuity: (Did it flow?) 1	2	3	4	5	
Technical Accuracy:	1	2	3	4	5

Things I Liked About Your Presentation: _____

Things To Make Your Presentation Even Better: _____

General Comments: _____

Assigned Group Topic: FORKLIFT

Presenters Name:
Presenters Name:
Presenters Name:
Presenters Name:

Training Objectives (see the OSHA Outreach Guide) that must be emphasized during your short presentation include:

- Training requires a classroom session, a written test, a hands on performance test and certification of the training.
- Explain Center of Balance/Stability Triangle
- Steps to take in the event of a tip over
- Operation of forklifts

Suggested Items to use:

- Regulation (highlight/point out the teaching point)
- Sample Equipment – Toy forklift (you can paint/draw the stability triangle on the bottom)
- Student Handout

Notes for your presentation

Introduction

Main Topic

Sub Topics

A.

B.

C.

D.

Summary and Conclusion

Trainer Feedback

Time Started: _____ Time Stopped: _____ Total Time: _____

Item being evaluated	Needs Improvement			OK	Excellent
Voice Projection:	1	2	3	4	5
Introduction of material/following speaker:	1	2	3	4	5
Control of class/use of time:	1	2	3	4	5
Use of handouts:	1	2	3	4	5
Use of demonstrations:	1	2	3	4	5
Appearance:	1	2	3	4	5
Attention Getting Step:	1	2	3	4	5
Humor:	1	2	3	4	5
Clarity of topic presentation:	1	2	3	4	5
Continuity: (Did it flow?) 1	2	3	4	5	
Technical Accuracy:	1	2	3	4	5

Things I Liked About Your Presentation: _____

Things To Make Your Presentation Even Better: _____

General Comments: _____

Assigned Group Topic: EXCAVATIONS

Presenters Name:
Presenters Name:
Presenters Name:
Presenters Name:

Training Objectives (see the OSHA Outreach Guide) that must be emphasized during your short presentation include:

- Spoil piles (dirt removed from the trench/excavation) must be at least two feet from the edge of the excavation.
- Acceptable fall protection systems include sloping, benching or shoring.
- Explain different types of soil (A,B,C)
- Role and definition of a competent person
- Access/Egress requirements

Suggested Items to use:

- Regulation (highlight/point out the teaching point)
- Sample Equipment ~ various samples of soil
- Student Handout

Notes for your presentation

Introduction

Main Topic

Sub Topics

A.

B.

C.

D.

Summary and Conclusion

Trainer Feedback

Time Started: _____ Time Stopped: _____ Total Time: _____

Item being evaluated	Needs Improvement			OK	Excellent
Voice Projection:	1	2	3	4	5
Introduction of material/following speaker:	1	2	3	4	5
Control of class/use of time:	1	2	3	4	5
Use of handouts:	1	2	3	4	5
Use of demonstrations:	1	2	3	4	5
Appearance:	1	2	3	4	5
Attention Getting Step:	1	2	3	4	5
Humor:	1	2	3	4	5
Clarity of topic presentation:	1	2	3	4	5
Continuity: (Did it flow?) 1	2	3	4	5	
Technical Accuracy:	1	2	3	4	5

Things I Liked About Your Presentation:

Things To Make Your Presentation Even Better:

General Comments:

Assigned Group Topic: CONCRETE AND MASONRY

Presenters Name:
Presenters Name:
Presenters Name:
Presenters Name:

Training Objectives (see the OSHA Outreach Guide) that must be emphasized during your short presentation include:

- Prior to placing a load on concrete it must be determined that the structure is capable of supporting the anticipated load.
- Rebar must be capped
- Controlled Access Zone

Suggested Items to use:

- Regulation (highlight/point out the teaching point)
- Sample Equipment- rebar protection caps (old mushroom vs new flat top)
- Student Handout

Notes for your presentation

Introduction

Main Topic

Sub Topics
A.

B.

C.

D.

Summary and Conclusion

Trainer Feedback

Time Started: _____   Time Stopped: _____   Total Time: _____

Item being evaluated	Needs Improvement			OK	Excellent
Voice Projection:	1	2	3	4	5
Introduction of material/following speaker:	1	2	3	4	5
Control of class/use of time:	1	2	3	4	5
Use of handouts:	1	2	3	4	5
Use of demonstrations:	1	2	3	4	5
Appearance:	1	2	3	4	5
Attention Getting Step:	1	2	3	4	5
Humor:	1	2	3	4	5
Clarity of topic presentation:	1	2	3	4	5
Continuity: (Did it flow?) 1	2	3	4	5	
Technical Accuracy:	1	2	3	4	5

Things I Liked About Your Presentation: _____

Things To Make Your Presentation Even Better: _____

General Comments: _____

Assigned Group Topic: CONFINED SPACE ENTRY

Presenters Name:
Presenters Name:
Presenters Name:
Presenters Name:

Training Objectives (see the OSHA Outreach Guide) that must be emphasized during your short presentation include:

- Define Confined Space/Permit Space/Non-Permit Space
- Evaluate a space to select correct entry procedures
- Entry Procedures
- Rescue
- Reclassification
- Alternate Procedures

Suggested Items to use:

- Regulation (highlight/point out the teaching point)
- Sample Equipment – Gas monitor
- Student Handout

Notes for your presentation

Introduction

Main Topic

Sub Topics

A.

B.

C.

D.

Summary and Conclusion

Trainer Feedback

Time Started: _____ Time Stopped: _____ Total Time: _____

Item being evaluated	Needs Improvement			OK	Excellent
Voice Projection:	1	2	3	4	5
Introduction of material/following speaker:	1	2	3	4	5
Control of class/use of time:	1	2	3	4	5
Use of handouts:	1	2	3	4	5
Use of demonstrations:	1	2	3	4	5
Appearance:	1	2	3	4	5
Attention Getting Step:	1	2	3	4	5
Humor:	1	2	3	4	5
Clarity of topic presentation:	1	2	3	4	5
Continuity: (Did it flow?) 1	2	3	4	5	
Technical Accuracy:	1	2	3	4	5

Things I Liked About Your Presentation: _____

Things To Make Your Presentation Even Better: _____

General Comments: _____

Assigned Group Topic: WELDING

Presenters Name:
Presenters Name:
Presenters Name:
Presenters Name:

Training Objectives (see the OSHA Outreach Guide) that must be emphasized during your short presentation include:

- When gas welding cylinders are being transported they must be in a vertical position.
- Compressed gas cylinders used in welding must be kept at least 20 feet from flammable material.
- PPE requirements
- Fire Safety
- When can welding be performed (hot work permit)

Suggested Items to use:

- Regulation (highlight/point out the teaching point)
- Sample Equipment – Welding tips/rods/helmet
- Student Handout

Notes for your presentation

Introduction

Main Topic

Sub Topics
A.

B.

C.

D.

Summary and Conclusion

Trainer Feedback

Time Started: _____ Time Stopped: _____ Total Time: _____

Item being evaluated	Needs Improvement			OK	Excellent
Voice Projection:	1	2	3	4	5
Introduction of material/following speaker:	1	2	3	4	5
Control of class/use of time:	1	2	3	4	5
Use of handouts:	1	2	3	4	5
Use of demonstrations:	1	2	3	4	5
Appearance:	1	2	3	4	5
Attention Getting Step:	1	2	3	4	5
Humor:	1	2	3	4	5
Clarity of topic presentation:	1	2	3	4	5
Continuity: (Did it flow?) 1	2	3	4	5	
Technical Accuracy:	1	2	3	4	5

Things I Liked About Your Presentation: _____

Things To Make Your Presentation Even Better: _____

General Comments: _____

Assigned Group Topic: CRANES

Presenters Name:
Presenters Name:
Presenters Name:
Presenters Name:

Training Objectives (see the OSHA Outreach Guide) that must be emphasized during your short presentation include:

■ When a mobile crane is in transit mode, it may be closer than ten feet to an energized power line. The closes it can be is four feet only when in transit!

■ The accessible area within the swing radius of any crane must be barricaded to keep workers from being struck by the crane as it moves.

■ Inspections

Suggested Items to use:

■ Regulation (highlight/point out the teaching point)
■ Sample Equipment – Toy crane
■ Student Handout

Notes for your presentation

Introduction

Main Topic

Sub Topics

A.

B.

C.

D.

Summary and Conclusion

Trainer Feedback

Time Started: _____ Time Stopped: _____ Total Time: _____

Item being evaluated	Needs Improvement			OK	Excellent
Voice Projection:	1	2	3	4	5
Introduction of material/following speaker:	1	2	3	4	5
Control of class/use of time:	1	2	3	4	5
Use of handouts:	1	2	3	4	5
Use of demonstrations:	1	2	3	4	5
Appearance:	1	2	3	4	5
Attention Getting Step:	1	2	3	4	5
Humor:	1	2	3	4	5
Clarity of topic presentation:	1	2	3	4	5
Continuity: (Did it flow?) 1	2	3	4	5	
Technical Accuracy:	1	2	3	4	5

Things I Liked About Your Presentation: _____

Things To Make Your Presentation Even Better: _____

General Comments: _____

Assigned Group Topic: RIGGING

Presenters Name:

Presenters Name:

Presenters Name:

Presenters Name:

Training Objectives (see the OSHA Outreach Guide) that must be emphasized during your short presentation include:

- Types of rigging equipment
- Never saddle a dead horse
- Cable inspection

Suggested Items to use:

- Regulation (highlight/point out the teaching point)
- Sample Equipment- Rigging cables/hooks
- Student Handout

Notes for your presentation

Introduction

Main Topic

Sub Topics

A.

B.

C.

D.

Summary and Conclusion

Trainer Feedback

Time Started: _____ Time Stopped: _____ Total Time: _____

Item being evaluated	Needs Improvement			OK	Excellent
Voice Projection:	1	2	3	4	5
Introduction of material/following speaker:	1	2	3	4	5
Control of class/use of time:	1	2	3	4	5
Use of handouts:	1	2	3	4	5
Use of demonstrations:	1	2	3	4	5
Appearance:	1	2	3	4	5
Attention Getting Step:	1	2	3	4	5
Humor:	1	2	3	4	5
Clarity of topic presentation:	1	2	3	4	5
Continuity: (Did it flow?) 1	2	3	4	5	
Technical Accuracy:	1	2	3	4	5

Things I Liked About Your Presentation: _____

Things To Make Your Presentation Even Better: _____

General Comments: _____

Assigned Group Topic: STEEL ERECTION

Presenters Name:

Presenters Name:

Presenters Name:

Presenters Name:

Training Objectives (see the OSHA Outreach Guide) that must be emphasized during your short presentation include:

- When any repairs, modifications or replacements have been made to anchor bolts the controlling contractor must provide written notification to the affect contractors.
- The maximum number of members that can be hoisted per lift in multiple lift rigging (Christmas Treeing/Luggaging) is five.
- Fall protection for connectors when doing connecting is 15-30 feet.

Suggested Items to use:

- Regulation (highlight/point out the teaching point)
- Sample Equipment ~ mock up of a multi lift system using pencils and string
- Student Handout

Notes for your presentation

Introduction

Main Topic

Sub Topics

A.

B.

C.

D.

Summary and Conclusion

Trainer Feedback

Time Started: _____ Time Stopped: _____ Total Time: _____

Item being evaluated	Needs Improvement			OK	Excellent
Voice Projection:	1	2	3	4	5
Introduction of material/following speaker:	1	2	3	4	5
Control of class/use of time:	1	2	3	4	5
Use of handouts:	1	2	3	4	5
Use of demonstrations:	1	2	3	4	5
Appearance:	1	2	3	4	5
Attention Getting Step:	1	2	3	4	5
Humor:	1	2	3	4	5
Clarity of topic presentation:	1	2	3	4	5
Continuity: (Did it flow?)	1	2	3	4	5
Technical Accuracy:	1	2	3	4	5

Things I Liked About Your Presentation: _____

Things To Make Your Presentation Even Better: _____

General Comments: _____

Assigned Group Topic: SCAFFOLDS

Presenters Name:

Presenters Name:

Presenters Name:

Presenters Name:

Training Objectives (see the OSHA Outreach Guide) that must be emphasized during your short presentation include:

- Fall protection is required on all scaffolds over ten feet tall.
- On suspended scaffolds counterweights must be specifically designed for the system. Don't use sandbags or bags of concrete to support the scaffold counterweight!
- Competent person definition and duties
- Assembly and disassembly
- Fall protection during assembly and disassembly
- Use

Suggested Items to use:

- Regulation (highlight/point out the teaching point)
- Sample Equipment
- Student Handout

Notes for your presentation

Introduction

Main Topic

Sub Topics

A.

B.

C.

D.

Summary and Conclusion

Trainer Feedback

Time Started: _____   Time Stopped: _____   Total Time: _____

Item being evaluated	Needs Improvement			OK	Excellent
Voice Projection:	1	2	3	4	5
Introduction of material/following speaker:	1	2	3	4	5
Control of class/use of time:	1	2	3	4	5
Use of handouts:	1	2	3	4	5
Use of demonstrations:	1	2	3	4	5
Appearance:	1	2	3	4	5
Attention Getting Step:	1	2	3	4	5
Humor:	1	2	3	4	5
Clarity of topic presentation:	1	2	3	4	5
Continuity: (Did it flow?) 1	2	3	4	5	
Technical Accuracy:	1	2	3	4	5

Things I Liked About Your Presentation:

Things To Make Your Presentation Even Better:

General Comments:

Assigned Group Topic: FALL PROTECTION

Presenters Name:
Presenters Name:
Presenters Name:
Presenters Name:

Training Objectives (see the OSHA Outreach Guide) that must be emphasized during your short presentation include:

- Conventional fall protection is considered to be the use of guardrails, safety nets or personal fall arrest systems.
- Body belts as a form of fall arrest is prohibited.
- Definition and use of competent person
- Guardrail requirements
- Personal Fall Arrest System requirements

Suggested Items to use:

- Regulation (highlight/point out the teaching point)
- Sample Equipment- PFAS/Rope Grab
- Student Handout

Notes for your presentation

Introduction

Main Topic

Sub Topics

A.

B.

C.

D.

Summary and Conclusion

Trainer Feedback

Time Started: _____ Time Stopped: _____ Total Time: _____

Item being evaluated	Needs Improvement			OK	Excellent
Voice Projection:	1	2	3	4	5
Introduction of material/following speaker:	1	2	3	4	5
Control of class/use of time:	1	2	3	4	5
Use of handouts:	1	2	3	4	5
Use of demonstrations:	1	2	3	4	5
Appearance:	1	2	3	4	5
Attention Getting Step:	1	2	3	4	5
Humor:	1	2	3	4	5
Clarity of topic presentation:	1	2	3	4	5
Continuity: (Did it flow?) 1	2	3	4	5	
Technical Accuracy:	1	2	3	4	5

Things I Liked About Your Presentation:

Things To Make Your Presentation Even Better:

General Comments:

Assigned Group Topic: STAIRS AND LADDERS

Presenters Name:
Presenters Name:
Presenters Name:
Presenters Name:

Training Objectives (see the OSHA Outreach Guide) that must be emphasized during your short presentation include:
- Training requirements
- Proper use of ladders
- Inspection requirements

Suggested Items to use:
- Regulation (highlight/point out the teaching point)
- Sample Equipment
- Student Handout

Notes for your presentation

Introduction

Main Topic

Sub Topics
A.

B.

C.

D.

Summary and Conclusion

Trainer Feedback

Time Started: _____ Time Stopped: _____ Total Time: _____

Item being evaluated	Needs Improvement			OK	Excellent
Voice Projection:	1	2	3	4	5
Introduction of material/following speaker:	1	2	3	4	5
Control of class/use of time:	1	2	3	4	5
Use of handouts:	1	2	3	4	5
Use of demonstrations:	1	2	3	4	5
Appearance:	1	2	3	4	5
Attention Getting Step:	1	2	3	4	5
Humor:	1	2	3	4	5
Clarity of topic presentation:	1	2	3	4	5
Continuity: (Did it flow?) 1	2	3	4	5	
Technical Accuracy:	1	2	3	4	5

Things I Liked About Your Presentation: _____

Things To Make Your Presentation Even Better: _____

General Comments: _____

INSPECTION PROCEDURES

Purpose of the Inspection
- Uncover unsafe acts and conditions.
- Reveal the need for specific guards for workers, machines and materials.
- Help "sell" safety program to workers.
- Encourage supervisors to inspect their own areas, tools, equipment, materials, and work practices.
- Bring about a closer liaison between safety personnel and line personnel.
- Provide an additional set of eyes to identify unsafe conditions before an accident occurs.

Preparation for the Inspection
- The person making inspection should acquire and digest all pertinent information available on the type of operation to be inspected.
- He or she should review and acquaint himself or herself with details of these functions, generally and specifically, in relation to one another.
- He or she should determine which standards will apply.
- He or she should define the work area.
- He or she should plan the inspection route.
- He or she should review previous inspections and results, looking for any outstanding work orders.
- He or she should learn what OSHA is inspecting for similar industries (go to www.osha.gov and use the Establishment Search).
- He or she should make or obtain checklists (if they are to be used).

Conduct of the Inspection
- Inspect while employees are working (if possible).
- Use simple forms or notes during the inspection process.
- Be alert for all hazards and conditions.
- Record all unsafe practices and conditions.
- Check for specific items as well as general conditions.
- Check all areas; do not be steered away.
- Do not be a disturbing influence.
- Be constructive.
- Look for "why" conditions exist.

- Advise supervisors; do not argue with them.
- Discuss recommendations with supervisors.
- Try to "sell" your recommendations to ensure early abatement.

Examples of What to Check in a Safety Inspection

Receiving, Shipping, Storage
Equipment, job planning, layout, heights, floor loads, projection of materials, material-handling methods. Dockboards on trucks securely fastened, guardrails in place to keep workers from walking off the docks. Forklift operations require seat belts for operators and 18-wheel trucks must have at least one wheel chocked when forklifts are inside them.

Building Conditions
Floors, walls, ceilings, exits, stairs, walkways, ramps, platforms, driveways, and aisles. Exit signs, markings, and emergency lighting systems.

Housekeeping
Waste disposal, tools, objects, materials, leakage and spillage, methods, schedules, work areas, remote areas, windows, and ledges.

Electricity
Equipment, switches, breakers, fuses, switchboards, junctions, special fixtures, circuits, insulation, extensions, tools, motors, grounding and code compliance. Access to circuit breakers and fuse panels, unguarded electrical wiring. Overused extension cords or extension cords used in place of permanent wiring.

Lighting
Type, intensity, controls, condition, diffusion, location, glare and shadow control, and standards applied.

Heating And Ventilation
Type, effectiveness, temperature, humidity, controls, natural and artificial ventilation and exhausting.

Machines
Points of operation, flywheels, gears, shafts, pulleys, key ways, belts, couplings, sprockets, chains, frames, controls, lighting, tools and equipment, brakes, exhausting, feeding, oiling, adjusting, maintenance, grounding, how attached, workspace, and location.

Personnel
Training, experience, methods of checking machines before use, methods of cleaning, oiling, or adjusting machinery, type of clothing, personal protective equipment, use of guards, tool storage, and work practices.

Hand and Power Tools
Purchasing standards, inspection, storage, repair, types, maintenance, grounding, use and handling, guards in place on tools.

Chemicals
Storage, handling, transportation, amounts used, warning signs, supervision, training, protective clothing and equipment. Hazard communication plan, list of current hazardous chemicals, MSDS for each chemical onsite, all containers labeled.

Fire Prevention
Extinguishers, alarms, sprinklers, smoking rules, exits, personnel assigned, separation of flammable materials and dangerous operations, explosion-proof fixtures, and waste disposal.

Maintenance
Regularity, effectiveness, training of personnel, materials, and equipment used, method of locking out machinery and general methods. Lockout/tagout and confined space entry programs.

Personal Protective Equipment
Type, size, maintenance, repair, storage, assignment of responsibility, purchasing methods, standards observed, rules of use and method of assignment. ANSI standards on equipment. Head, eye, face, and foot protection. Use of respirators and respirator program.

Common Occupational Safety Inconsistencies Found During Inspections

Inconsistency	Part Subpart	Risk Code
EXIT ROUTES		
Fire exit doors do not operate	29CFR1910.37 (d) (2)	3
Two means of egress as required	29CFR1910.36 (b) (1)	3
Exit routes free of obstruction	29CFR1910.37 (a) (3)	3
Locked exit door	29CFR1910.36 (d)(1)	3
Exits route 28 inches wide	29CFR1910.36 (g) (2)	3
All exits marked with signs	29CFR1910.37 (b) (2)	3
All NON EXIT's labeled as such	29CFR1910.37 (b) (5)	3
Direction signs to exits not marked	29CFR1910.37 (b) (4)	3
Exit lights not illuminated	29CFR1910.37 (b) (1)	3
Exit letters s six inches by ¾ inch	29CFR1910.37 (b) (7)	3
Emergency Action Plan	29CFR1910.38 (b)	3
ELECTRICAL		
No ground fault circuit interrupters	29CFR1910.304(b)(3)	3
Circuit breakers not labeled	29CFR1910.303 (f) (1)	3
Grounding path missing	29CFR1910.304 (g) (5)	3
Ungrounded outlet	29CFR1910.304 (b) (2)	3
Loose or broken electrical outlet	29CFR1910.305 (j) (2)	3
Guarding of live wires over 50 volts	29CFR1910.303 (g) (2)	2
Flexible cords through doors/windows	29CFR1910.305 (g) (1) (iv) (C)	3
Temporary wiring used as permanent	29CFR1910.305 (g) (1) (iv)(A)	4
Overcurrent devices not accessible	291910.304 (f) (1) (iv)	3
Unused opening in box not closed	291910.303 (b) (7) (i)	3
FIRE		
Extinguishers mounted, accessible	29CFR1910.157 (c) (1)	3
Extinguishers fully charged	29CFR1910.157 (c) (4)	3
Extinguishers of the correct type	29CFR1910.157 (d) (1)	3
Extinguishers within 75 feet	29CFR1910.157 (d) (2)	3
Extinguishers monthly inspection	29CFR1910.157 (e) (2)	3
Extinguishers annual inspection	29CFR1910.157 (e) (3)	3
Fire alarms readily accessible	29CFR1910.164 (e)	3
Emergency phone numbers posted	29CFR1910.165 (b) (4)	3
Flammable liquid storage	29CFR1910.106	3
HAZMAT		
Bulk combustibles in storage cabinet	29CFR1910.106 (d) (3)	3
Combustibles in storage room	29CFR1910.106 (d) (3)	3
Flammable liquids in office	29CFR1910.106 (d) (5) (iii)	3
Hazard Communication Program	29CFR1910.1200	3

Inconsistency	Part Subpart	Risk Code
SANITATION		
Proper housekeeping	29CFR1910.141 (a) (3) (i)	3
Adequate toilet facilities	29CFR1910.141 (c) (1) (i)	3
Toilets with privacy	29CFR1910.141 (c) (2) (i)	3
Adequate washing facilities	29CFR1910.141 (d) (2) (iii)	3
Emergency eye wash station	29CFR1910.151 (c)	3
SHOP		
Grinding wheel rest not 1/8 inch	29CFR1910.215 (a) (4)	3
Tongue guard adjusted to ¼ inch	29CFR1910.215 (a) (9)	3
All wheels ring tested prior to mounting	29CFR1910.215 (d) (1)	3
Lockout Tagout Program	29CFR1910.147	3
Machine guards in place	29CFR1910.212(a)(1)	3
Eye and face protection	29CFR1910.133	3
Eyewash stations	29CFR1910.151(c)	3
WALKING/WORKING		
Roof/pipe leaks- wet floor	29CFR1910.22 (a) (2)	3
Slip hazard/broken door	29CFR1910.22 (b) (1)	3
Aisles clear and in good repair	29CFR1910.22 (b) (1)	3
Fixed ladder over 20 feet without cage	29CFR1910.27 (d) (1) (iii)	3
Guarding Floor and wall openings	29CFR1910.23	3
WELDING		
Gas cylinder caps in place	29CFR1910.253 (a) (2) (iii)	3
Gas cylinders marked	29CFR1910.253 (b) (1) (ii)	3
Gas cylinders 20 feet from combustibles	29CFR1910.253 (b) (2) (ii)	3
Acetylene cylinders stored upright	29CFR1910.253 (b) (3) (ii)	3
Oxygen cylinders near oil or grease	29CFR1910.253 (4) (i)	3
Oxygen cylinders separated from fuel	29CFR1910.253 (4) (iii)	3
MISC		
General Duty Clause	PL 91-156	3
Forklift Seat belt in use	General Duty Clause	3
Respiratory Protection when required	29CFR1910.134	2
Forklift Training	29CFR1910.178(l)	3
Record keeping	29CFR1904	3

Sample Inspection Form

Location	Discrepancy	OSHA Citation	Corrective Action

Comments: How many citations did your team find? _____
What was the single most important item to fix?

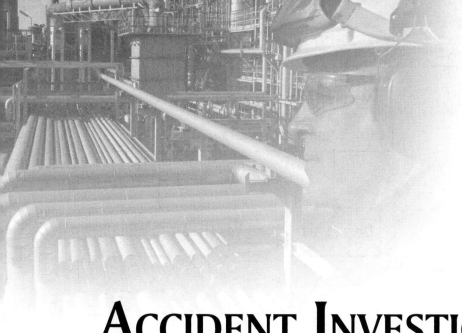

ACCIDENT INVESTIGATION

Thousands of workplace accidents occur throughout the United States every day. The failure of people, equipment, supplies or surroundings to behave or react as expected cause most accidents. Accident investigations determine how and why these failures occur. By using the information gained through an investigation, a similar or perhaps more disastrous accident may be prevented. Conduct accident investigations with accident prevention in mind. Investigations are *not* to place blame.

An accident is any unplanned event that results in personal injury or property damage. When the personal injury requires little or no treatment, it is minor. If it results in a fatality or in a permanent total, permanent partial or temporary total (lost-time) disability, it is serious. Similarly, property damage may be minor or serious. Investigate all accidents regardless of the extent of injury or damage.

Accidents are part of a broad group of events that adversely affect the completion of a task. These events are incidents. For simplicity, the procedures discussed in later sections refer only to accidents. They are, however, also applicable to incidents.

Accident Prevention

Accidents are usually complex. An accident may have 10 or more events that can be causes. A detailed analysis of an accident will normally reveal three cause levels: basic, indirect and direct. At the lowest level, an accident results only when a person or object receives an amount of energy or hazardous material that cannot be absorbed safely. This energy or hazardous material is the *direct cause* of the accident. The direct cause is usually the result of one or more unsafe acts, unsafe conditions or both. Unsafe acts and conditions are the *indirect causes* or symptoms. In turn, indirect causes are usually traceable to poor management policies and decisions or to personal or environmental factors. These are the *basic causes*.

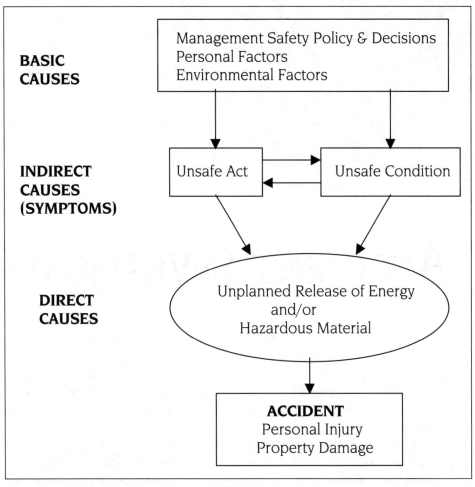

BASIC CAUSES

Management Safety Policy & Decisions
Personal Factors
Environmental Factors

INDIRECT CAUSES (SYMPTOMS)

Unsafe Act ⟷ Unsafe Condition

DIRECT CAUSES

Unplanned Release of Energy
and/or
Hazardous Material

ACCIDENT
Personal Injury
Property Damage

Exhibit 23-1.
A detailed analysis of an accident will normally reveal three cause levels: basic, indirect and direct.

Despite their complexity, most accidents can be prevented by eliminating one or more causes. Accident investigations determine not only what happened, but also how and why. Accident investigators are interested in each event as well as in the sequence of events that led to an accident. The accident type is also important to the investigator. The recurrence of accidents of a particular type or those with common causes shows areas needing special accident-prevention emphasis.

Investigative Procedures

The actual procedures used in a particular investigation depend on the nature and results of the accident. The agency having jurisdiction over the location determines the administrative procedures. In general, responsible officials will appoint an individual to be in charge of the investigation. The investigator uses most of the following steps:

1. Define the scope of the investigation.
2. Select the investigators. Assign specific tasks to each (preferably in writing).
3. Present a preliminary briefing to the investigating team, including:
   a. Description of the accident, with damage estimates.
   b. Normal operating procedures.
   c. Maps (local and general).
   d. Location of the accident site.
   e. List of witnesses.
   f. Events that preceded the accident.
4. Visit the accident site to get updated information.
5. Inspect the accident site:
   a. Secure the area. Do not disturb the scene unless a hazard exists.
   b. Prepare the necessary sketches and photographs. Label each carefully and keep accurate records.
6. Interview each victim and witness. Also interview those who were present before

the accident and those who arrived at the site shortly after the accident. Keep accurate records of each interview. Use a tape recorder if desired and approved.

7. Determine:
   a. What was not normal before the accident.
   b. Where the abnormality occurred.
   c. When it was first noted.
   d. How it occurred.
8. Analyze the data obtained in step 7. Repeat any of the prior steps, if necessary.
9. Determine:
   a. Why the accident occurred.
   b. A likely sequence of events and probable causes (direct, indirect, basic).
   c. Alternative sequences.
10. Check each sequence against the data from step 7.
11. Determine the most likely sequence of events and the most probable causes.
12. Conduct a post-investigation briefing.
13. Prepare a summary report, including the recommended actions to prevent a recurrence. Distribute the report according to applicable instructions.

An investigation is not complete until all data is analyzed and a final report is completed. In practice, the investigative work, data analysis and report preparation often occur simultaneously.

Fact-Finding

The investigator should gather evidence from many sources during an investigation, obtaining information from witnesses and reports as well as by observation. Interview witnesses as soon as possible after an accident. Inspect the accident site before any changes occur. Take photographs and draw sketches of the accident scene. Record all pertinent data on maps. Get copies of all reports. Documents containing normal operating procedures, flow diagrams, maintenance charts, or reports of difficulties or abnormalities are particularly useful. Record pre-accident conditions, the accident sequence, and post-accident conditions. In addition, document the location of victims, witnesses, machinery, energy sources, and hazardous materials. Keep complete and accurate notes in a bound notebook.

In some investigations, a particular physical or chemical law, principle or property may explain a sequence of events. Include laws in the notes taken during the investigation or in the later analysis of data. In addition, gather data during the investigation that may lend itself to analysis by these laws, principles or properties. An appendix in the final report can include an extended discussion.

Interviews

In general, experienced personnel should conduct interviews. If possible, the team assigned to this task should include an individual with a legal background. In conducting interviews, the team should:

1. Appoint a speaker for the group.
2. Get preliminary statements as soon as possible from all witnesses.
3. Locate the position of each witness on a master chart (including the direction of view).
4. Arrange for a convenient time and place to talk to each witness.
5. Explain the purpose of the investigation (accident prevention) and put each witness at ease.
6. Listen. Let each witness speak freely, and be courteous and considerate.
7. Take notes without distracting the witness. Use a tape recorder only with the consent of the witness.
8. Use sketches and diagrams to help the witness.
9. Emphasize areas of direct observation. Label hearsay accordingly.
10. Be sincere and do not argue with the witness.
11. Record the exact words used by the witness to describe each observation. Do not "put words into a witness's mouth."
12. Word each question carefully and be sure the witness understands.
13. Identify the qualifications of each witness (e.g., name, address, occupation, years of experience).
14. Supply each witness with a copy of his or her statements. Have each witness sign his or her statement if possible.

After interviewing all witnesses, the team should analyze each witness statement. They may wish to re-interview one or more witnesses to confirm or clarify key points. While there may be inconsistencies in witnesses' statements, investigators should assemble the available testimony into a logical order. Analyze this information along with data from the accident site.

Not all people react in the same manner to a particular stimulus. For example, a witness within close proximity to the accident may have an entirely different story from one who saw it at a distance. Some witnesses may also change their stories after they have discussed it with others. The reason for the change may be an additional clue.

A witness who has had a traumatic experience may not be able to recall the details of the accident. A witness who has a vested interest in the results of the investigation may offer biased testimony. Finally, eyesight, hearing, reaction time and the general condition of each witness may affect his or her powers of observation. A witness may omit entire sequences because of a failure to observe them or because their importance was not realized.

Problem Solving Techniques

Accidents represent problems that must be solved through investigations. Several formal procedures solve problems of any degree of complexity. This section considers these problem-solving procedures.

The Scientific Method

The scientific method forms the basis of nearly all problem-solving techniques. It is used for conducting research. In its simplest form, it involves the following sequence: making observations, developing hypotheses and testing the hypotheses.

Even a simple research project may involve many observations. A researcher records all observations immediately. A good investigator must do the same thing. Where possible, the observations should involve quantitative measurements. Quantitative data is often important in later development and testing of the hypotheses. Such measurements may require the use of many instruments in the field as well as in the laboratory.

When making observations, the investigator develops one or more hypotheses that explain the observations. The hypothesis may explain only a few of the observations or it may try to explain all of them. At this stage, the hypothesis is merely a preliminary idea. Even if later rejected, the investigator has a goal toward which to proceed.

Test the hypothesis against the original observations. A series of controlled experiments is often useful in performing this evaluation. If the hypothesis explains all of the observations, testing may be a simple process. If not, either make additional observations, change the hypothesis or develop additional hypotheses.

As with scientific research, the most difficult part of any investigation is the formulation of worthwhile hypotheses. Use the following three principles to simplify this step:

- **The principle of agreement.** An investigator uses this principle to find one factor that associates with each observation.
- **The principle of differences.** This principle is based on the idea that variations in observations are due only to differences in one or more factors and no other factors.
- **The principle of concomitant variation.** This principle is the most important because it combines the ideas of both of the preceding principles. In using this principle, the investigator is interested in the factors that are common as well as those that are different in the observations.

In using the scientific method, the investigator must be careful to eliminate personal bias. The investigator must be willing to consider a range of alternatives. Finally, he or she must recognize that accidents often result from the chance occurrence of factors that are too numerous to evaluate fully.

Change Analysis

As its name implies, this technique emphasizes change. To solve a problem, an investigator must look for deviations from the norm. As with the scientific method, change analysis also follows a logical sequence. It is based on the principle of differences described in the discussion of the scientific method. Consider all problems to result from some unanticipated change. Make an analysis of the change to determine its causes. Use the following steps in this method:

- Define the problem (What happened?).
- Establish the norm (What should have happened?).

- Identify, locate and describe the change (What, where, when and to what extent?).
- Specify what was and what was not affected.
- Identify the distinctive features of the change.
- List the possible causes.
- Select the most likely causes.

Sequence Diagrams

Gantt charts are sequence diagrams. Use them for scheduling investigative procedures. They can also aid in the development of the most probable sequence of events that led to the accident. Such a chart is especially useful in depicting events that occurred simultaneously.

Gross Hazard Analysis

Perform a gross hazard analysis (GHA) to get a rough assessment of the risks involved in performing a task. It is "gross" because it requires further study. It is particularly useful in the early stages of an accident investigation in developing hypotheses. A GHA will usually take the form of a logic diagram or table. In either case, it will contain a brief description of the problem or accident and a list of the situations that can lead to the problem. In some cases, analysis goes a step further to determine how the problem could occur. A GHA diagram or table thus shows at a glance the potential causes of an accident. One of the following analysis techniques can then expand upon a GHA.

Job Safety Analysis

Job safety analysis (JSA) is part of many existing accident prevention programs. In general, a JSA breaks a job into basic steps and identifies the hazards associated with each step. The JSA also prescribes controls for each hazard. A JSA is a chart listing these steps, hazards and controls. If available, review the JSA during the investigation. If not available, perform a JSA if one is not available. Perform a JSA as a part of the investigation to determine the events and conditions that led to the accident.

Failure Mode and Effect Analysis

Failure mode and effect analysis (FMEA) determines where failures occurred. Consider all items used in the task involved in the accident (e.g., people, equipment, machine parts, materials). In the usual procedure, FMEA lists each item on a chart. The chart lists the manner or mode in which each item can fail and determines the effects of each failure. Included in the analysis are the effects on other items and on overall task performance. In addition, make evaluations about the risks associated with each failure. That is, project the chance of each failure and the severity of its effects. Determine the most likely failures that led to the accident. Comparing these projected effects and risks with actual accident results does this.

Fault Tree Analysis

Fault tree analysis (FTA) is a logic diagram. It shows all the potential causes of an accident or other undesired event. The undesired event is at the top of the "tree." Reasoning backward from this event, determine the circumstances that can lead to the problem. These circumstances are then broken down into the events that can lead to them and so on. Continue the process until the identification of all events can produce the undesired event. Use a logic tree to describe each of these events and the manner in which they combine. This information determines the most probable sequence of events that led to the accident.

Report of Investigation

As noted earlier, an accident investigation is not complete until a report is prepared and submitted to proper authorities. Special report forms are available in many cases. Other instances may require a more extended report. Such reports are often very elaborate and may include a cover page, title page, abstract, table of contents, commentary or narrative portion, discussion of probable causes and a section on conclusions and recommendations.

The following outline is useful when developing the formal report:

1. Background information
   a. Where and when the accident occurred
   b. Who and what were involved
   c. Operating personnel and other witnesses
2. Account of the accident (What happened?)
   a. Sequence of events
   b. Extent of damage

  c. Accident type

  d. Agency or source (of energy or hazardous material)

3. Discussion (Analysis of the accident—how, why?)

  a. Direct causes (energy sources, hazardous materials)

  b. Indirect causes (unsafe acts, conditions)

  c. Basic causes (management policies, personal or environmental factors)

4. Recommendations (to prevent a recurrence) for immediate and long-range action to remedy

  a. Basic causes

  b. Indirect causes

  c. Direct causes (e.g., reduced quantities, protective equipment, structures)

Summary

A successful accident investigation determines not only what happened, but also finds how and why the accident occurred. Investigations are an effort to prevent a similar or perhaps more disastrous sequence of events.

Accident investigations involve gathering and analyzing facts, and developing hypotheses to explain these facts. Each hypothesis must then be tested against the facts. An investigation is not complete, however, until a final report is written. Responsible officials can then use the resulting information and recommendations to prevent future accidents.

FIELD
OPERATIONS MANUAL

Abstract

Purpose: This Instruction implements the OSHA Field Operations Manual (FOM), and replaces the September 26, 1994 Instruction that implemented the Field Inspection Reference Manual (FIRM). The FOM is a revision of OSHA's enforcement policies and procedures manual that provides the field offices a reference document for identifying the responsibilities associated with the majority of their inspection duties.

Scope: OSHA-wide.

References: Title 29 Code of Federal Regulations §1903.6, Advance Notice of Inspections; 29 Code of Federal Regulations §1903.14, Policy Regarding Employee Rescue Activities; 29 Code of Federal Regulations §1903.19, Abatement Verification; 29 Code of Federal Regulations §1904.39, Reporting Fatalities and Multiple Hospitalizations to OSHA; and Housing for Agricultural Workers: Final Rule, Federal Register, March 4, 1980 (45 FR 14180).

Cancellations: OSHA Instruction ADM 01-00-002, Administrative Subpoenas, August 19, 1991; OSHA Instruction CPL 02-00-045, Field Operations Manual, Chapter VI, Sections D, Handling Monies Received from Employers, and E, Debt Collection Procedures, March 3, 1995; OSHA Instruction CPL 02-00-045, Field Operations Manual, Chapter XI, Migrant Labor Camps, March 3, 1995; OSHA Instruction CPL 02-00-103, Field Inspection Reference Manual (FIRM), September 26, 1994; and OSHA Instruction CPL 02-00-112, National Quick-Fix Program, August 2, 1996.

State Impact: Notice of Intent and Adoption required. See paragraph VI.

Action Offices: National, Regional, and Area Offices

Originating Office: Directorate of Enforcement Programs

Contact: Directorate of Enforcement Programs Office of General Industry Enforcement 200 Constitution Avenue, NW, N3119 Washington, DC 20210 202-693-1850

By and Under the Authority of Donald G. Shalhoub Deputy Assistant Secretary

Executive Summary

This Instruction cancels and replaces OSHA Instruction CPL 02-00-103, Field Inspection Reference Manual (FIRM), issued September 26, 1994, and two of the three remaining parts of the prior Field Operations Manual, CPL 02-00-045, which are still in effect. The one remaining part of the prior Field Operations Manual, the chapter on Disclosure, will be added at a later date. This Instruction constitutes OSHA's general enforcement policies and procedures manual for use by the field offices in conducting inspections, issuing citations and proposing penalties.

Significant Changes

- Cancels and replaces the Field Inspection Reference Manual (FIRM).
- Cancels sections D. and E. of Chapter VI of the prior Field Operations Manual.
- Cancels Chapter XII of the prior Field Operations Manual.

Chapter 1 — Introduction

I.   **Purpose.** This Instruction implements the Field Operations Manual (FOM), and replaces OSHA Instruction CPL 02-00-103, Field Inspection Reference Manual (FIRM), issued September 26, 1994. This Instruction also replaces two of the three remaining parts of the prior Field Operations Manual (CPL 02-00-045) that are still in effect. The one remaining part, the chapter on Disclosure, will be added at a later date. This FOM is a revision of OSHA's enforcement policies and procedures as stated in the FIRM, which provides the field offices a reference document for identifying the responsibilities associated with the majority of their inspection duties.

II.   **Scope.** This Instruction applies OSHA-wide.

III.   **References.**

A.   Title 5 *United States Code* 504, The Equal Access to Justice Act.

B.   Title 18 *United States Code* 601, Small Business Regulatory Enforcement Fairness Act.

C.   Title 18 *United States Code* 1905, Disclosure of Confidential Information.

D.   Title 28 *United States Code* 2412, Rules Implementing the Equal Access to Justice Act; Costs and Fees.

E.   Title 29 *United States Code* 651, Occupational Safety and Health Act of 1970.

F.   Title 29 *United States Code* 1802, Migrant and Seasonal Agricultural Worker Protection Act.

G.   Title 31 *United States Code* 3717, Debt Collection Improvement Act.

H.   Title 39 *United States Code* 101, The Postal Employee Safety Enhancement Act of 1998.

I.   29 *Code of Federal Regulations* 2.21 and 2.22, Employees Served with Subpoenas.

J.   29 *Code of Federal Regulations* Part 20, Federal Claims Collection.

K.   29 *Code of Federal Regulations* 500.132, Applicable Federal Standards: ETA and OSHA Housing Standards.

L.   29 *Code of Federal Regulations* Part 654, Social Responsibilities of the Employment Service System.

M.   29 *Code of Federal Regulations* 1903.6, Advance Notice of Inspections.

N.   29 *Code of Federal Regulations* 1903.14, Policy Regarding Employee Rescue Activities.

O.   29 *Code of Federal Regulations* 1903.19, Abatement Verification.

P.   29 *Code of Federal Regulations* 1904.39, Reporting Fatalities and Multiple Hospitalizations to OSHA.

Q.   29 *Code of Federal Regulations* Part 1908, Consultation Agreements.

R.   29 *Code of Federal Regulations* Part 1910, Occupational Safety and Health Standards.

S.   29 *Code of Federal Regulations* Part 1915, Occupational Safety and Health for Shipyard Employment.

T.   29 *Code of Federal Regulations* Part 1926, Safety and Health Regulations for Construction.

U.   29 *Code of Federal Regulations* Part 1928, Occupational Safety and Health Standards for Agriculture.

V.   29 *Code of Federal Regulations* Part 1960, Basic Program Elements for Federal Employee Occupational Safety and Health Programs.

W.   29 *Code of Federal Regulations* 1975.4(*b*)(2), Coverage – Agricultural Employers.

X.   29 *Code of Federal Regulations* Part 2200, Rules of Procedure.

Y.   40 *Code of Federal Regulations* Part 170, Worker Protection Standard.

Z.   Housing for Agricultural Workers: Final Rule, *Federal Register*, March 4, 1980 (45 FR 14180).

AA.   Incorporation of General Industry Safety and Health Standards Applicable to Construction Work, *Federal Register*, August 12, 1996 (61 FR 41738).

BB.   Delegation of Authorities and Assignment of Responsibilities to the Assistant Secretary for Employment Standards and Other Officials in the Employment Standards Administration, *Federal Register*, January 2, 1997 (62 FR 107).

CC.   Safety and Health Program Management Guidelines; Issuance of Voluntary Guidelines, *Federal Register*, January 16, 1989 (54 FR 3904).

DD.   Final Rule on State Plans Coverage of the U.S. Postal Service (*Federal Register*, June 9, 2000 (65 FR 36618).

EE.   Final Policy Concerning the Occupational Safety and Health Administration's Treatment of Voluntary Employer Safety and Health Self-Audits, *Federal Register*, July 28, 2000 (65 FR 46498).

FF.   Secretary's Order 5-2002; Delegation of Authority and Assignment of Responsibility to the Assistant Secretary for Occupational Safety and Health, *Federal Register*, October 22, 2002 (67 FR 65007).

GG.   OSHA Instruction ADM 01-00-003, Redelegation of Authority and Responsibility of the Assistant Secretary for Occupational Safety and Health, March 6, 2003.

HH.   OSHA Instruction ADM 03-01-005, OSHA Compliance Records, August 3, 1998.

II.   OSHA Instruction CPL 02-00-025, Scheduling System for Programmed Inspections, January 4, 1995.

JJ.   OSHA Instruction CPL 02-00-028, Compliance Assistance the Powered Industrial Truck Operator Training Standards, November 30, 2000.

KK.   OSHA Instruction CPL 02-00-051, Enforcement and Limitations under the Appropriations Act, May 28, 1998.

LL.   OSHA Instruction CPL 02-00-080, Handling of Cases to be Proposed for Violation-By-Violation Penalties, October 21, 1990.

MM.   OSHA Instruction CPL 02-00-090, Guidelines for Administration of Corporate-Wide Settlement Agreements, June 3, 1991.

NN. OSHA Instruction CPL 02-00-094, OSHA Response to Significant Events of Potentially Catastrophic Consequences, July 22, 1991.

OO. OSHA Instruction CPL 02-00-098, Guidelines for Case File Documentation for use with Videotapes and Audiotapes, October 12, 1993.

PP. OSHA Instruction CPL 02-00-111, Citation Policy for Paperwork and Written Program Requirement Violations, November 27, 1995.

QQ. OSHA Instruction CPL 02-00-120, Inspection procedures for the Respiratory Protection Standard, September 25, 1998.

RR. OSHA Instruction CPL 02-00-121, Providing Assistance to Smaller Employers, March 12, 1998.

SS. OSHA Instruction CPL 02-00-122, Enforcement Guidance for the U.S. Postal Service, April 16, 1999.

TT. OSHA Instruction CPL 02-00-124, Multi-Employer Citation Policy, December 10, 1999.

UU. OSHA Instruction CPL 02-00-125, Home-Based Worksites, February 25, 2000.

VV. OSHA Instruction CPL 02-00-135, Recordkeeping Policies and Procedures Manual (RKM), December 30, 2004.

WW. OSHA Instruction CPL 02-00-136, OSHA's National Emphasis Program (NEP) on Shipbreaking, March 16, 2005.

XX. OSHA Instruction CPL 02-00-139, Longshoring and Marine Terminals "Tool Shed" Directive, May 23, 2006.

YY. OSHA Instruction CPL 02-00-141, Inspection Scheduling for Construction, July 14, 2006.

ZZ. OSHA Instruction CPL 02-00-142, Shipyard Employment "Tool Bag" Directive, August 3, 2006.

AAA. OSHA Instruction CPL 02-00-145, Enhanced Enforcement Program (EEP), January 1, 2008.

BBB. OSHA Instruction CPL 02-02-035, 29 CFR 1910.95(b)(1), Guidelines for Noise Enforcement; Appendix A, December 19, 1983.

CCC. OSHA Instruction CPL 02-02-038, Inspection Procedures for the Hazard Communication Standard, March 20, 1998.

DDD. OSHA Instruction CPL 02-02-043, Chemical Information Manual, July 1, 1991.

EEE. OSHA Instruction CPL 02-02-054, Respiratory Protection Program Guidelines, July 14, 2000.

FFF. OSHA Instruction CPL 02-02-072, Rules of Agency Practice and Procedure Concerning OSHA Access to Employee Medical Records, August 22, 2007.

GGG. OSHA Instruction CPL 02-02-073, Inspection Procedures for 29 CFR 1910.120 and 1926.65, Paragraph (q): Emergency Response to Hazardous Substance Releases, August 27, 2007.

HHH. OSHA Instruction CPL 03-00-004, Petroleum Refinery Process Safety Management National Emphasis Program, June 7, 2007.

III. OSHA Instruction CPL 04-00-001, Procedures for Approval of Local Emphasis Programs (LEPs), November 10, 1999.

JJJ. OSHA Instruction CSP 01-00-002, State Plan Policies and Procedures Manual, March 21, 2001.

KKK. OSHA Instruction CSP 02-00-002, Consultation Policies and Procedures Manual, January 18, 2008.

LLL. OSHA Instruction CSP 03-01-003, Voluntary Protection Programs (VPP) Policies and Procedures Manual, April 18, 2008.

MMM. OSHA Instruction CSP 03-02-002, OSHA Strategic Partnership Program for Worker Safety and Health, February 10, 2005.

NNN. OSHA Instruction CSP 04-01-001, OSHA Alliance Program, June 10, 2004.

OOO. OSHA Instruction FAP 01-00-003, Federal Agency Safety and Health Programs, May 17, 1996.

PPP. OSHA Instruction HSO 01-00-001, National Emergency Management Plan (NEMP), dated December 18, 2003.

QQQ. OSHA Instruction IRT 01-00-007, The IMIS Enforcement Data Processing Manual for Use with the NCR Computer System, dated September 20, 1993.

RRR. OSHA Instruction TED 01-00-015, OSHA *Technical Manual*, January 20, 1999.

SSS. Memoranda dated September 12 and 13, 2000 to the Regional Administrators from H. Berrien Zettler, Deputy Director, Directorate of Construction (via email) regarding transmittal of information on construction fatalities to the University of Tennessee.

TTT. Memoranda dated May 14, 2003 and February 18, 2004 to the Regional Administrators from Deputy Assistant Secretary R. Davis Layne regarding transmittal of information on construction fatalities to the University of Tennessee.

UUU. *Memorandum* dated December 16, 2003, to the Regional Administrators from Deputy Assistant Secretary R. Davis Layne regarding IMMLANG Procedures (available on the OSHA Intranet).

VVV. *Memorandum* dated March 24, 2004 to Regional Administrators from Deputy Assistant Secretary R. Davis Layne regarding Procedures for Significant Enforcement Cases (available on the OSHA Intranet).

WWW. *Frank Diehl Farms v. Secretary of Labor*, 696 F.2d 1325 (11th Cir. 1983).

XXX. *Int. Union UAW v. General Dynamics Land Systems Division*, 815 F.2d 1570 (D.D. Cir. 1987).

YYY. *Marion Stevens dba Chapman & Stephens Company*, 5 BNA OSHC 1395 (No. 13535, 1977).

ZZZ. *Darragh Company*, 9 BNA OSHC 1205, (Nos. 77-2555, 77-3074, and 773075, 1980).

AAAA. J. C. *Watson Company*, 22 BNA OSHC 1235 (Nos. 05-0175 and 050176, 2008).

IV. Cancellations.

A. OSHA Instruction ADM 01-00-002, Administrative Subpoenas, August 19, 1991.

B. OSHA Instruction CPL 02-00-045, Field Operations Manual, Chapter VI, Sections D. Handling Monies Received from Employers, and E. Debt Collection Procedures, March 3, 1995.

C. OSHA Instruction CPL 02-00-045, Field Operations Manual, Chapter XI, Migrant Labor Camps, March 3, 1995.

D. OSHA Instruction CPL 02-00-103, Field Inspection Reference Manual (FIRM), September 26, 1994.

E. OSHA Instruction CPL 02-00-112, National Quick-Fix Program, August 2, 1996.

F. OSHA Instruction CPL 02-00-114 Abatement Verification Regulation Enforcement Policies and Procedures, May 28, 1998.

G. OSHA Instruction CPL 02-00-137, Fatality/Catastrophe Investigation Procedures, April 14, 2005.

H. OSHA Instruction CPL 02-00-140, Complaint Policies and Procedures, June 23, 2006.

I. Memorandum dated March 23, 1995, to the Regional Administrators from Deputy Assistant Secretary James W. Stanley regarding FIRM Change: Minimum Serious Willful Penalty.

J. Memorandum dated June 21, 1996 to the Regional Administrators from Deputy Assistant Secretary Michael G. Connors regarding FIRM Change: Mandatory Collection of OSHA-200 and Lost Workday Injury and Illness (LWDII) Data During Inspections.

K. Memorandum dated July 13, 1999 to the Regional Administrators from Assistant Secretary Charles N. Jeffress regarding Child Labor: Probability Assessment and Good Faith Penalty Adjustment Considerations.

V. Action Information.

A. **Responsible Office.** Directorate of Enforcement Programs (DEP).

B. **Action Offices.** National, Regional, and Area Offices.

C. **Information Offices.** State Plan States, OSHA Training Institute, Consultation Project Managers, VPP Managers and Coordinators, OSHA Strategic Partnership Coordinators, Compliance Assistance Coordinators, Compliance Assistance Specialists, and Regional EEP Coordinators.

VI. State Impact.

A. Notice of Intent, Adoption, and Submission of a Plan Change Supplement are required.

B. This instruction describes a Federal Program Change which consolidates and updates OSHA's field enforcement policies and procedures. States must have, as a part of their State plan, formal written policies and procedures on all aspects of their compliance program, including inspections, targeting, citations, penalties, and post citation processes, which are at least as effective as the procedures in this revised Field Operations Manual (FOM). In adopting equivalent policies and procedures States must address each chapter and/or policy area in this manual. Significant changes to this manual are listed in section VII of this chapter.

    States need not adopt the internal OSHA administrative procedures set out in this manual, such as those relating to organizational structure and such matters as penalty collection, but must include documentation of their own comparable internal administrative procedures and processes. These will necessarily differ from those of Federal OSHA.

C. States must notify OSHA within 60 days whether their enforcement policies will be identical to or different from those in this Instruction. State policies and procedures must be adopted within 6 months of issuance of this Instruction. Each State must both submit a copy of its revised Field Operations Manual as a plan change supplement to OSHA, preferably in electronic format, with a comparison document clearly identifying any differences from the revised FOM, within 60 days of adoption, and either post its equivalent State Field Operations Manual on its State plan website and provide the link to OSHA or provide OSHA with information on how the public may obtain a copy. OSHA will post information on the State responses to this Instruction on its website.

VII. Significant Changes.

A. **Chapter 2. Program Planning.**

1. The title of this chapter has been changed from Pre-Inspection Procedures to Program Planning.

2. Section II: Area Office responsibilities have been expanded.

3. Section III: A section has been added to cover OSHA Cooperative Programs Overview.

4. Specific information regarding Complaints and Referrals has been removed from this chapter.

5. Specific information regarding Inspection Preparation has been removed from this chapter.

6. Paragraph IV.D.. A section has been added to address Enforcement Exemptions and Limitations.

7. Paragraph IV.E.: A section has been added to address Preemption by Another Federal Agency.

8. Paragraph IV.F.: A section has been added to address enforcement activity at the United States Postal Service.

9. Paragraph IV.G.: A section has been added to address Home-Based Worksites.

10. Section VI.H.4.a.: A note has been added defining "other critical inspections as determined by the Assistant Secretary" to include referrals, although not limit only to referrals.

B. **Chapter 3. Inspection Procedures.**

1. This replaces the majority of Chapter II of the FIRM, Inspection Procedures.

2. Paragraph II.A.1.: Inspection planning requires an establishment search using the IMIS database.

3. Paragraph II.A.2.: State plan citation history **may** be used to document employer knowledge to support a willful violation, and to determine eligibility for the history penalty reduction factor. It **may not** be used to support a repeat violation.

4. Paragraph II.D.: Expanded guidance is provided on compliance officer safety and health.

5. Paragraph III.A.: The definition of a comprehensive inspection is revised to "a substantially complete and thorough inspection of all potentially hazardous areas of the establishment."

6. Paragraph IV.H.: The strike or labor dispute section has been revised to emphasize that CSHOs must make every effort to ensure that their actions are not interpreted as supporting either side.

7. Paragraph V.A.: The CSHO is required to review any written hazard assessment that the employer has made in compliance with §1910.132(d) to determine appropriate personal protective equipment.

8. Paragraph V.D.: Expanded guidance is provided on review of voluntary compliance programs, including on-site consultation, SHARP, and VPP.

9. Paragraph VI.A.: Revised guidance is provided on collection of employer injury and illness data and calculation of the DART rate.

10. Paragraph VIII.B.2.: Extensive guidance is provided on interviews of non-managerial employees.

C. **Chapter 4. Violations.**

1. This chapter replaces section C, Violations, of Chapter III of the FIRM.

2. Paragraphs I.A.3. and 4: The definition and application of horizontal and vertical standards have been revised and clarified.

3. Paragraph II.C.: The discussion of the four factors involved in determining a serious violation has been expanded and clarified, with examples.

4. Section III: The elements of a general duty clause violation are given an expanded discussion, with examples.

5. Paragraph III.D.: Additional clarification is provided on limitations of use of the general duty clause, with examples.

6. Section V: Expanded and clarified guidance is provided on willful violations, with examples.

7. Section VI: Updated guidance is provided for criminal/willful violations.

8.   Paragraph VII.A.2.: Violations cited by State Plan States cannot be used as a basis of OSHA repeat violations by Federal OSHA, even if the same standards are cited by a State agency. Only violations that have become a final order of the Review Commission are to be considered.

9.   Paragraph. VII.E.1.: Clarification is provided on time limitations for citing repeat violations.

10.   Paragraph VII.G.: Responsibilities of the Area Director in citing repeat violations are clarified.

11.   Section VIII: De minimis *violations* are corrected to de minimis *conditions*.

12.   Paragraph X.C.: Clarifies when not to group or combine violations.

13.   Sections XI., XII., XIII., and XIV: Guidance on citing health standard violations has been updated.

D.   **Chapter 5. Case File Preparation and Documentation.**

1.   This chapter replaces section A., Four Stage Case File Documentation, and section B., Specific Forms, of Chapter III, and section C., Citations, of Chapter IV of the FIRM.

2.   Paragraph X.A.: Expanded guidance is provided on Inspection Case File Activity Diary Sheet.

3.   Paragraph XI: Clarification is provided on Statute of Limitation for issuance of citations.

4.   Paragraph XII.C.: Expanded guidance is provided on Classified and Trade Secret Information.

E.   **Chapter 6. Penalties and Debt Collection.**

1.   This chapter replaces Section C. of Chapter IV of the FIRM.

2.   Paragraph III.B.2.c.: A provision requiring documentation in the case file if the Area Director approves a partial reduction for *Size* for small employers (1-25 employees) is added.

3.   Paragraph III.B.3.d.: A provision allowing some OSHA Strategic Partnership (OSP) sites to qualify for an extra 10% *Good Faith* reduction is added.

4.   Paragraph III.B.4.a.: A provision clarifying that the H*istory* reduction factor is to be applied nationwide, and to include State Plan state history as well, is added.

5.   Paragraphs III.B.4.c. second bullet and X.C.2.c.: A H*istory* reduction will no longer be given to employers being cited for failure to certify abatement.

6.   Paragraph IV.C.1. and Table 6-5: The Quick-Fix policy has been modified to allow it to apply to medium gravity serious violations.

7.   Paragraph VI.B.: A note has been added to clarify that the second *Size* chart applies only to serious willful violations.

8.   Paragraph VI.C.2.: The reduction factor for H*istory* is allowed for penalties for regulatory violations that are classified as willful; this is in addition to the reduction factor for Size that has been allowed.

9.   Paragraph X.C.2.c. and 3.b.: A change has been made to abatement verification policy to not allow a H*istory* reduction to employers being cited for failure to certify abatement or for failure to notify employees and tagging movable equipment.

10.   Paragraph X.D.2.: A clarification has been added to the Part 1904 provision that the Repeated and Willful penalty policies of paragraphs V.D. and VI.C., respectively, are applicable to recordkeeping violations.

11.   Section XIII replaces section D of Chapter VI of the prior Field Operations Manual (FOM), CPL 02-00-045, regarding Handling Monies Received from Employers.

12.   Section XIV replaces section E. of Chapter VI of the prior Field Operations Manual (FOM), CPL 02-00-045, regarding Debt Collection Procedures.

13.   All references to the Office of Management Data Systems (OMDS) have been replaced with the Debt Collection Accountability Team (DCAT).

14.   Paragraph XIII.B.3.: Adjustment to Payments – If a check is unsigned it should be forwarded to the lockbox instead of being returned to the employer.

15.   Paragraph XIII.B.4.a., fourth bullet: If a payment instrument is dated more than six months prior to the current date, it should be returned to the employer via a certified delivery service.

16.   Paragraph XIII.C.: Returning Penalty Payments – Refund requests should go to DCAT instead of the Office of Financial Management.

17.   Paragraph XIV.C.: Notification Procedures – Referencing the "Notice" as the first demand letter has been removed. All subsequent references to second or third demand letters have also been removed.

18.   Paragraph XIV.D.: Notification of Overdue Debt – Demand letters do not have to be mailed via certified mail. They may be mailed using regular mail. Also, demand letters may be faxed if it is verified that the company received the fax.

19.   Paragraph XIV.D.2.: Contested Case with Penalties – Instead of sending a demand letter with late fees to the employer, the Area Director may send a letter, without assessing late fees, which notifies the employer that the debt is now past due. This "notification" letter is a substitute for the demand letter requirement and allows the Area Director some lee way in contested cases with special circumstances, i.e. not receiving or acting on the Final Order Document in a timely manner.

20.   Paragraph XIV.F.6.: If the Area Office receives a check for a case that was referred to DCAT, the check should not be forwarded to the National Office. Instead, DCAT should be notified immediately so proper action can be determined.

21.   Paragraph XIV.H.: Uncollectible Penalties – A provision is added for dealing with debts that the Area Office may deem as uncollectible.

22.   Paragraph XIV.I.: National Office Debt Collection Procedures are updated to reflect the current procedures and processes for referring uncollected debts to the Department of Treasury.

23.   Paragraph XIV.I.5.: Compromise of Debts over $100,000 – Instead of the Solicitor, DCAT will obtain Department of Treasury or Justice approval for waiving these debts.

24.   Paragraph XIV.I.6.: Return to the Area Office – The requirement that the Area Director forward cases to the RSOL for legal action to collect debts returned by DCAT as uncollectible has been removed.

Field Operations Manual

F. **Chapter 7. Post-Citation Procedures and Abatement Verification.**
1. Paragraph I.A.: Procedures for accepting and handling electronic (e-mail) notices of contest are provided.
2. Section II: Provides policies and procedures for informal conferences; policies and procedures for settlement of cases is in Chapter 8.
3. Paragraph II.B.: Provides guidance on the attendance of the employer's attorney at the informal conference.
4. Paragraph II.F.2.b.: Specifically prohibits any discussion of possible criminal referrals in fatality cases during the informal conference.
5. Section III: Provides updated policies and procedures on Petitions for Modification of Abatement Date.
6. Sections IV through XVI: Replace the current directive on abatement verification, OSHA Instruction CPL 02-00-114, Abatement Verification Regulation Enforcement Policies and Procedures, May 28, 1998.
7. Paragraph IV.A.: Provides an expanded definitions section, including definitions of the terms *Abatement* and *Abatement Dates*.
8. Sections V through VIII: Provide expanded guidance on citations for violations of § 1903.19.
9. Paragraph XI.C. and paragraph XII: Provide policy on follow-up inspections for employer failure to verify abatement under § 1903.19, including follow-up inspections under the Enhanced Enforcement Program.

G. **Chapter 8. Settlements.** This chapter incorporates the Settlement policies and procedures that currently exist in the FIRM as updated, except that Section 17 settlements will be handled in accordance with established agency procedures, including approval by the National Office.

H. **Chapter 9. Complaint and Referral Processing.**
1. This incorporates and replaces the current directive on this subject, OSHA Instruction CPL 02-00-140, Complaint Policies and Procedures, June 23, 2006.
2. Paragraph I.A.1.: The definition of *complaint* has been clarified to include only present employees, not past employees.
3. Paragraph I.A.2.a.: The potential harm necessary to file a complaint has been clarified to include health harm as well as physical harm.
4. Paragraph I.A.8.: The OSHA-90 form has been identified as the proper form in which to use the coding identified under the referral sources.
5. Paragraph I.F.2.b.: This paragraph explicitly states that information received via telephone from a current employee or representative of employees is considered a non-formal complaint until a signed copy of the information is received.

I. **Chapter 10. Industry Sectors.**
1. **Agriculture.**
   a. OSHA's main policies and procedures in the agriculture industry are gathered together for the first time.
   b. Paragraph I.E: Coverage of pesticides by OSHA and EPA are addressed, including use of the Hazard Communication standard.
   c. Paragraph I.F: OSHA's shared authority with the Wage and Hour Division of ESA is discussed.
2. **Construction.** [Reserved]
3. **Maritime.** [Reserved]

J. **Chapter 11. Imminent Danger, Fatality, Catastrophe and Emergency Response.**
1. This chapter incorporates and replaces OSHA Instruction CPL 02-00-137, Fatality/Catastrophe Investigation Procedures, April 14, 2005.
2. Section III. A section on rescue operations and emergency response has been added.

K. **Chapter 12. Specialized Inspection Procedures.**
1. **Multi-Employer Workplace/site Policy.** [Reserved]
2. **Temporary Labor Camps.**
   a. This section cancels Chapter XI of OSHA Instruction CPL 2.45B, Field Operations Manual (the old FOM). Chapter XI was not cancelled by CPL 02-00-103, Field Inspection Reference Manual (FIRM), when it was issued September 26, 1994.
   b. Paragraph II.A.: A provision has been added to clarify that OSHA's § 1910.142 Temporary Labor Camp standards apply to non-agriculture workplaces as well as to agriculture workplaces.
   c. Paragraph II.C.: A section has been added describing the shared responsibility between OSHA and the Wage and Hour Division.
   d. Paragraph II.E.: A provision has been added that discusses when other Part 1910 standards may be cited for hazards that are not covered by § 1910.142 for non-agriculture housing.

L. **Chapter 13. Federal Agency Safety and Health Programs.** [Reserved]

M. **Chapter 14. Health Inspection Enforcement Policy.** [Reserved]

N. **Chapter 15. Legal Issues.**
1. Section IV: Equal Access to Justice Act explains the application of this Act to OSHA enforcement proceedings.
2. Section XII: Commission Simplified Proceedings gives an explanation of the OSHRC's simplified proceedings and some of its rules.
3. Section XIV: Federal Court Enforcement under Section 11(b) of the Act adds enforcement instruction regarding Federal summary enforcement orders previously stated in the Enhanced Enforcement Program directive.

O. **Chapter 16. Disclosure under the Freedom of Information Act (FOIA).** [Reserved]

VIII. Background. The Field Inspection Reference Manual (FIRM) was issued September 26, 1994 and replaced most of the previous Field Operations Manual (FOM). Since that time, the FIRM has never revised, but has been supplemented and modified by numerous additional directives, memorandums, and interpretations.

This Instruction, the OSHA Field Operations Manual, incorporates and replaces the FIRM and many of the subsequent directives and memoranda, and provides a single, updated source of instruction on general OSHA enforcement policies and procedures.

The FOM is designed to be updated on a regular basis by amending chapters or sections thereof to embody modifications and clarifications to OSHA's general enforcement policies and procedures.

IX. **Definitions and Terminology.**
   A. **The Act.** This term refers to the Occupational Safety and Health Act of 1970 (29 United States Code 651).
   B. **Compliance Safety and Health Officer (CSHO).** This term refers to Safety Engineers, Safety Compliance Officers, and Industrial Hygienists.
   C. **He/She** and **His/Hers.** The terms *he* and *she*, as well as *his* or *her*, when used throughout this manual, are interchangeable. That is, male(s) applies to female(s), and vice versa.
   D. **Professional Judgment.** All OSHA employees are expected to exercise their best judgment as safety and health professionals and as representatives of the United States Department of Labor in every aspect of carrying out their duties.
   E. **Workplace** and **Worksite.** The terms *workplace* and *worksite* are interchangeable. *Workplace* is used more frequently in general industry, while *worksite* is more commonly used in the construction industry.

Chapter 2 — Program Planning

I. **Introduction.** OSHA's mission is to assure the safety and health of America's working men and women by promulgating and enforcing standards and regulations; providing training, outreach, and education; establishing partnerships; and encouraging continual improvement in workplace safety and health as well as the development of comprehensive safety and health management systems. Effective and efficient use of resources requires careful, flexible planning. In this way, the overall goal of hazard abatement and employee protection is best served.

II. **Area Office Responsibilities.**
   A. **Providing Assistance to Small Employers.**
      1. In 1996, the Congress passed the Small Business Regulatory Enforcement Fairness Act (SBREFA) to respond to the concern expressed by the small business community that Federal regulations were too numerous and complex, and that small business needed special assistance in understanding and complying with those regulations.
      2. All Federal agencies regulating small businesses are required to have in place programs to provide guidance and compliance assistance. These programs must contain procedures to answer inquiries by small entities (small businesses). These programs also provide information on and advice about compliance with the statutes and regulations; interpretations; and applications of the law to specific sets of facts supplied by the small entity.
   B. **Area Office Outreach Program.** The Area Director or designee will ensure that the Area Office maintains an outreach program appropriate to local conditions and the needs of the service area. The plan may include Regional and National Office support services, compliance assistance services including assistance in developing compliance safety and health management systems, training and education services, referral services, cooperative programs, abatement assistance, and technical services.
   C. **Responding to Requests for Assistance.** All requests from employers or employees for compliance information or assistance shall receive timely, accurate, and helpful responses from OSHA. See the section on *Information Requests* in this chapter for additional information.

III. **OSHA Cooperative Programs Overview.** OSHA offers a number of avenues for businesses and organizations to work cooperatively with the Agency. Compliance Officers should discuss the various cooperative programs with employers.
   A. **Voluntary Protection Program (VPP).** The Voluntary Protection Program (VPP) is designed to recognize and promote effective safety and health management. A hallmark of VPP is the principle that management, labor, and OSHA can work together in pursuit of a safe and healthy workplace. A VPP participant is an employer that has successfully designed and implemented a health and safety management system at its worksite.
   B. **Onsite Consultation Program.**
      1. OSHA onsite consultation programs are available in all 50 states as well as the District of Columbia, Guam, Northern Marianas Islands, Puerto Rico and the Virgin Islands under Section 21(d) and 23(g) agreements with Federal OSHA or under State plans approved by OSHA.
         a. The State Onsite Consultation Program offers a variety of services at no cost to employers. These services include assisting in the development and implementation of an effective safety and health management system, and offering training and education to the employer and employees at the worksite. Smaller businesses in high hazard industries or those involved in hazardous operations receive priority.
         b. The State Onsite Consultation Program is separate from OSHA's enforcement efforts. Under onsite consultation programs, no citations are issued, nor are penalties proposed.
      2. **Safety and Health Achievement Recognition Program (SHARP).**
         a. Another program that recognizes employers' efforts to create a safe workplace and exempts them from inspection is the Safety and Health Achievement Recognition Program (SHARP). This program is administered by the State Onsite Consultation Program but is funded under Section 21(d) of the Act.
         b. SHARP is designed to provide incentives and support those employers that implement and continuously improve effective safety and health management system(s) at their worksite. SHARP participants are exempted from OSHA programmed inspections.
   C. **Strategic Partnerships.** Organizations can enter into Strategic Partnerships with OSHA to address specific safety and health issues. In these partnerships, OSHA enters into extended, voluntary, cooperative relationships with groups of employers, employees, and employee representatives (sometimes including other stakeholders, and sometimes involving only one employer) in order to encourage, assist, and recognize efforts to eliminate serious hazards and to achieve a high level of employee safety and health.
   D. **Alliance Program.** Through the Alliance Program, OSHA works with groups committed to safety and health, including businesses, trade or professional organizations, unions and educational institutions, to leverage resources and expertise to develop compliance assistance tools and resources and share information with employers and employees to help prevent injuries, illnesses and fatalities in the workplace. OSHA and the organization sign a formal agreement with goals that address training and education, outreach and communication, and promote the national dialogue on workplace safety and health.

IV. **Enforcement Program Scheduling.**
  A. **General.**
    1. OSHA's priority system for conducting inspections is designed to allocate available OSHA resources as effectively as possible to ensure that maximum feasible protection is provided to working men and women. The Area Director or designee will ensure that inspections are scheduled within the framework of this chapter, that they are consistent with the objectives of the Agency, and that appropriate documentation of scheduling practices is maintained.
    2. The Area Director or designee will also ensure that OSHA resources are effectively distributed during inspection activities. If an inspection is of a complex nature, the Area Director or designee may consider utilizing additional OSHA resources (e.g., the Health Response Team). In other circumstances, the use of outside resources may aid the Area or District Office to deploy available resources more effectively. The Area Office will retain control of the inspection.
  B. **Inspection Priority Criteria.** Generally, priority of accomplishment and of assigning staff resources for inspection categories is as shown in Table 2-1 below:

Table 2-1: Inspection Priorities

Priority	Category
First	Imminent Danger
Second	Fatality/Catastrophe
Third	Complaints/Referrals
Fourth	Programmed Inspections

    1. **Efficient Use of Resources.** Deviations from this priority list are allowed so long as they are justifiable, lead to the efficient use of resources, and promote effective employee protection. An example of such a deviation would be when the Agency, Regional Administrator or an Area 2-4 Director commits a certain percentage of resources to programmed Special Emphasis Program (SEP) inspections such as a National Emphasis Program (NEP), a Local Emphasis Program (LEP), or Regional Emphasis Program (REP). Inspection scheduling deviations must be documented in the case file.
    2. **Follow-up Inspections.** In cases where follow-up inspections are necessary, they shall be conducted as promptly as resources permit. In general, follow-up inspections shall take priority over all programmed inspections and any unprogrammed inspection in which the hazards are anticipated to be other-than-serious.
    3. **Monitoring Inspections.** When a monitoring inspection is necessary, the priority is the same as for a follow-up inspection.
       NOTE: *See Chapter 7, Post-Citation Procedures and Abatement Verification, for additional information.*
    4. **Employer Information Requests.** Contacts for technical information initiated by employers or their representatives will not trigger an inspection, nor will such employer inquiries protect the requesting employer against inspections conducted pursuant to existing policy, scheduling guidelines and inspection programs established by the Agency.
    5. **Reporting of Imminent Danger, Catastrophe, Fatality, Amputations, Accidents, Referrals or Complaints.** The Area Director or designee will act in accordance with established inspection priority procedures.
  C. **Effect of Contest.** If an employer has contested a citation and/or a penalty from a previous inspection at a specific worksite, and the case is still pending before the Review Commission, the following guidelines apply to additional inspections of the employer at that worksite:
    1. If the employer has contested the penalty only, the inspection will be scheduled as if there were no contest;
    2. If the employer has contested the citation itself or any items therein, then programmed and unprogrammed inspections will be scheduled, but all under contest will be excluded from the inspection unless a potential imminent danger is involved.
  D. **Enforcement Exemptions and Limitations.**
    1. In providing funding for OSHA, Congress has consistently placed restrictions on enforcement activities for two categories of employers: small farming operations and small employers in low-hazard industries. Congress may place exemptions and limitations on OSHA activities through the annual Appropriations Act.
    2. Before initiating an inspection of an employer in these categories the Area Office will evaluate whether the Appropriations Act for the fiscal year would prohibit the inspection. Where this determination cannot be made beforehand, the CSHO will determine the status of the small farming operation or a small employer in a low-hazard industry upon arrival at the workplace. If the prohibition applies, the inspection shall immediately be discontinued.
  E. **Preemption by Another Federal Agency.**
    1. Section 4(b)(1) of the Act states that the Act does not apply to working conditions over which other federal agencies exercise statutory responsibility to prescribe standards for safety and health. The determination of preemption by another Federal agency is, in many cases, a highly complex matter.
    2. If a question arises, usually upon receipt of a complaint, referral, or other inquiry, consult the list of *Memorandums of Understanding* (MOU) on the OSHA website to determine if the issue has been previously addressed. A MOU is an agreement created to address/resolve coverage issues and to improve the working relationships between other Federal agencies and organizations regarding employee safety and health.
    3. At times, an inspection may have already begun when the coverage jurisdiction question arises. Any such situation will be brought to the attention of the Area Director or designee as soon as they arise, and dealt with on a case-by-case basis.
    4. Two examples of MOUs include the following:
      a. *Mine Safety and Health Administration* - Interagency Agreement between the Mine Safety and Health Administration and OSHA, dated March 29, 1979.

b.   *United States Coast Guard/U.S. Department of Transportation* -Authority of Coast Guard and OSHA regarding enforcement of safety and health standards aboard vessels inspected and certified by the Coast Guard, dated March 4, 1983.

F.   **United States Postal Service.**
1.   *The Postal Employee Safety Enhancement Act of* 1998 applies the Act to the U.S. Postal Service in the same manner as the Act applies to a private sector employer.
2.   All State Plan States elected not to cover the U.S. Postal Service. Thus, Federal OSHA retains authority to cover the U.S. Postal Service nationwide. Federal coverage in State Plan States encompasses U.S. Postal Service employees and contract employees engaged in U.S. Postal Service mail operations. Coverage includes contractor-operated facilities engaged in mail operations and postal stations in public or commercial facilities. State Plan States continue to exercise jurisdiction over all other private sector contractors working on U.S. Postal Service sites who are not engaged in U.S. Postal Service mail operations, such as building maintenance and construction employees. See the Final Rule on State Plans Coverage of the U.S. Postal Service (*Federal Register*, June 9, 2000 (65 FR 36618))
3.   Violations documented during inspections initiated at a U.S. Postal Service site will be cited with penalties in accordance with the FOM and other applicable OSHA policies for the private sector.

G.   **Home-Based Worksites.**
1.   The agency will not perform any inspections of employees' home offices. A home office is defined as office work activities in a home-based setting/worksite (e.g., filing, keyboarding, computer research, reading, writing) and may include the use of office equipment (e.g., telephone, facsimile machine, computer, scanner, copy machine, desk, file cabinet).
2.   OSHA will only conduct inspections of other home-based worksites, such as home manufacturing operations, when it receives a complaint or referral alleging that a violation of a safety or health standard exists that threatens physical harm, that an imminent danger is present, or that there was a work-related fatality.

H.   **Inspection/Investigation Types.**
1.   **Unprogrammed.**
a.   Inspections scheduled in response to alleged hazardous working conditions identified at a specific worksite are classified as unprogrammed. This type of inspection responds to:
   ■   Imminent Dangers;
   ■   Fatalities/catastrophes;
   ■   Complaints; and
   ■   Referrals.
b.   It also includes follow-up and monitoring inspections scheduled by the Area Office.
2.   **Unprogrammed Related.**
a.   Inspections of employers at multi-employer worksites whose operations are not directly addressed by the subject of the conditions identified in a complaint, accident, or referral are designated as unprogrammed related.
b.   An example would be: A trenching inspection conducted at the unprogrammed worksite where the trenching hazard was not identified in the complaint, accident report, or referral.
3.   **Programmed.** Inspections of worksites which have been scheduled based upon objective or neutral selection criteria are programmed inspections, such as the Site Specific Targeting (SST) Program. The worksites are selected according to national scheduling plans for safety and for health or under local, regional, and national special emphasis programs.
4.   **Program Related.** Inspections of employers at multi-employer worksites whose activities were not included in the programmed assignment, such as a low injury rate employer at a worksite where programmed inspections are being conducted for all high rate employers.

V.   **Unprogrammed Activity – Hazard Evaluation and Inspection Scheduling.** Enforcement procedures relating to unprogrammed activity are located in subject specific chapters of this manual:
   ■   Imminent Danger, see Chapter 11, Imminent Danger, Fatality, Catastrophe, and Emergency Response.
   ■   Fatality/Catastrophe, see Chapter 11, Imminent Danger, Fatality, Catastrophe, and Emergency Response.
   ■   Emergency Response, see Chapter 11, Imminent Danger, Fatality, Catastrophe, and Emergency Response.
   ■   Complaint/Referral Processing, see Chapter 9, Complaint and Referral Processing.
   ■   Whistleblower Complaints, see Chapter 9, Complaint and Referral Processing..
   ■   Follow-ups and Monitoring, see Chapter 7, Post-Citation Procedures and Abatement Verification.

VI.   **Programmed Inspections.**
A.   **Site-Specific Targeting (SST) Program.** In order to achieve OSHA's goal of reducing the number of injuries and illnesses that occur at individual worksites, the Site-Specific Targeting (SST) program directs enforcement resources to those worksites where the highest rate of injuries and illness have occurred. The SST is OSHA's primary programmed inspection plan for non-construction worksites that have 40 or more employees. The SST Program is based on the data collected by the OSHA Data Initiative (ODI). The ODI collects injury and illness data from approximately 80,000 employers.
B.   **Scheduling for Construction Inspections.** Due to the mobility of the construction industry, the transitory nature of construction worksites, and the fact that construction worksites frequently involve more than one employer, inspections are scheduled from a list of construction worksites rather than construction employers. The University of Tennessee will provide to each Area/District Office a randomly selected list of construction projects from identified or known covered active projects. This list will contain the projected number of sites which the field office has reported it plans on inspecting during the next month. Projects are selected in accordance with the inspection schedule for construction.

C. **Scheduling for Maritime Inspections.** Marine inspection activities will be covered in greater detail in *Chapter 10, Section III, Maritime* [Reserved].

1. **Marine Cargo Handling Industry.** The marine cargo handling industry is made up of longshoring activities (i.e., cargo handing aboard vessels) and activities within marine terminals (i.e., cargo handling ashore). Due to the unique differences among these activities, several scheduling methods are necessary. Consequently, marine cargo handling industry inspections can be scheduled as National Emphasis Programs (NEPs), Site-Specific Targeting (SST), Local Emphasis Programs (LEPs), or from lists developed in accordance with CPL 02-00-025, *Scheduling System for Programmed Inspections*, dated January 4, 1995.

2. **Shipbreaking.** CPL 02-00-136, OSHA's *National Emphasis Program (NEP) on Shipbreaking*, dated March 16, 2005, describes policies and procedures to reduce or eliminate workplace hazards associated with shipbreaking operations.

    Also, OSHA has entered into a *Memorandum of Agreement* (MOA) on Interagency Coordination and Cooperation for Ship Scrapping (i.e., shipbreaking) between DOD, DOT, EPA, and DOL-OSHA, dated November 16, 1999.

3. **Shipyard Employment.** The shipyard employment industry is made up of several industrial activities and due to the unique differences among these activities, several scheduling methods are necessary. Consequently, shipyard employment inspections can be scheduled under NEPs, SST, LEPs, or from lists developed in accordance with CPL 02-00-025, *Scheduling System for Programmed Inspections*, dated January 4, 1995.

D. **Special Emphasis Programs (SEPs).** Special Emphasis Programs provide for programmed inspections of establishments in industries with potentially high injury or illness rates that are not covered by other programmed inspection scheduling systems or, if covered, where the potentially high injury or illness rates are not addressed to the extent considered adequate under the specific circumstances. SEPs are also based on potential exposure to health hazards. Special emphasis programs may also be used to develop and implement alternative scheduling procedures or other departures from national procedures. Special emphasis programs can include National Emphasis Programs, Regional Emphasis Programs and Local Emphasis Programs.

1. **Identification of Special Emphasis Programs.** The description of the particular Special Emphasis Program shall be identified by one or more of the following:
    a. Specific industry;
    b. Trade/craft;
    c. Substance or other hazard;
    d. Type of workplace operation;
    e. Type/kind of equipment; and
    f. Other identifying characteristic.

2. **Special Emphasis Program Scope.** The reasons for and the scope of a Special Emphasis Program shall be described; and may be limited by geographic boundaries, size of worksite, or similar considerations.

3. **Pilot Programs.** National or local pilot programs may also be established under Special Emphasis Programs. Such programs may be conducted for the purpose of assessing the actual extent of suspected or potential hazards, determining the feasibility of new or experimental compliance procedures, or for any other legitimate reason.

E. **National Emphasis Programs (NEPs).** OSHA develops National Emphasis Programs to focus outreach efforts and inspections on specific hazards in a workplace.

F. **Local Emphasis Programs (LEPs) and Regional Emphasis Programs (REPs).**

1. LEPs and REPs are types of special emphasis program in which one or more Area Offices of a Region participate. LEPs and REPs are generally based on knowledge of local industry hazards or local industry injury/illness experience. LEPs and REPs must be developed and approved when one or more Area Offices within a Region target inspections to a specific industry(ies), hazard(s), or other workplace characteristic(s), e.g., as part of, or in conjunction with, a local initiative or problem-solving project. A list of LEPs may be found on the OSHA website under the Directorate of Enforcement Programs.

2. OSHA directives include topic specific scheduling procedures in addition to the general information provided in this section.

G. **Other Special Programs.** The Agency may develop programs to cover special categories of inspections which are not covered under the SST Program or under a Special Emphasis Program.

H. **Inspection Scheduling and Interface with Cooperative Program Participants.**

1. Employers who participate in voluntary compliance programs may be exempt from programmed inspections and eligible for inspection deferrals or other enforcement incentives. The Area Director or designee will determine whether the employer is actively participating in a Cooperative Program that would impact inspection and enforcement activity at the worksite being considered for inspection. Where possible, this determination should be made prior to scheduling the inspection.

2. Information regarding a facility's participation in the following programs should be available prior to scheduling inspection activity:
    a. VPP Program;
    b. Pre-SHARP and SHARP Participants;
    c. OSHA Strategic Partnerships; and
    d. Consultation 90-Day Deferrals.

3. **Voluntary Protection Program.**
    a. **Regional VPP Manager Responsibilities.** The Regional VPP managers must keep the Area Director or his/her designee informed regarding VPP applicants and the status of participants in the VPP. This will prevent unnecessary scheduling of programmed inspections at VPP sites and ensure efficient use of resources. Area Directors or his/her designee should be informed:
        - That the site can be removed from the programmed inspection list. Such removal may occur no more than 75 days prior to the onsite evaluation;
        - Of the site's approval for the VPP program;

- Of the site's withdrawal or termination from the VPP program; and
- If the Regional VPP Manager is the first person notified by the site of an event requiring enforcement, the VPP Manager must instruct the site to contact the appropriate Area Office.

    b. **Programmed Inspections and VPP Participation.**

- **Inspection Deferral.** Approved sites must be removed from any programmed inspection lists for the duration of participation, unless a site chooses otherwise. The applicant worksite will be deferred starting no more than 75 calendar days prior to the commencement of its scheduled pre-approval onsite review.
- **Inspection Exemption.** The exemption from programmed inspections for approved VPP sites will continue for as long as they continue to meet VPP requirements. Sites that have withdrawn or have been terminated from VPP will be returned to the programmed inspection list, if applicable, at the time of the next inspection cycle.

    c. **Unprogrammed Enforcement Activities at VPP Sites.** When an Area Office receives a complaint, or a referral other than from the OSHA VPP onsite team, or is notified of a fatality, catastrophe, or other event requiring an enforcement inspection at a VPP site, the Area Director or designee must initiate the inspection following normal OSHA enforcement procedures.

- The Area Office must immediately notify the Regional VPP Manager of any fatalities, catastrophes or other accidents or incidents occurring at a VPP worksite that require an enforcement inspection; as well as of a referral or complaint that concerns a VPP worksite, including complaint inquiries that would receive a letter response. If the VPP is a national VPP, the National Office should be notified.
- If the Regional VPP Manager is the first person notified by the site of an event requiring an enforcement inspection, the VPP Manager must instruct the site to contact the appropriate Area Office and the National Office if the fatality is on a National VPP site.
- The inspection will be limited to the specific issue of the unprogrammed activity. If citations are issued as a result of the inspection, a copy of the citation will be sent to the Regional VPP Manager. See CSP 03-01-003, *Voluntary Protection Programs (VPP): Policies and Procedures Manual*, dated March 25, 2003.
- The Area Director will send the VPP Manager a copy of any report resulting from an enforcement case.

4. **Consultation.**

    a. **Consultation Visit in Progress.**

- If an onsite consultation visit is in progress, it will take priority over OSHA programmed inspections. An onsite consultation visit will be considered "in progress" in relation to the working conditions, hazards, or situations covered by the visit from the beginning of the opening conference through the end of the correction due dates and any extensions thereof. If an onsite consultation visit is already in progress it will terminate when the following kind of OSHA compliance inspection is about to take place:

    a. Imminent danger inspection;

    b. Fatality/catastrophe inspection;

    c. Complaint inspections; and/or

    d. Other critical inspections, as determined by the Assistant Secretary.

    NOTE: *Other "such critical inspections" may include, but are not limited to, referrals as defined in Chapter 9, Complaint and Referral Processing. Following an evaluation of the hazards alleged in a referral, if the Assistant Secretary determines that enforcement action is required prior to the end of an abatement period established by the state consultation project, the consultation visit in progress shall be immediately terminated to allow for an enforcement inspection.*

- For purposes of efficiency and expediency, an employer's worksite shall not be subject to concurrent consultation and enforcement-related visits. The following excerpts from CSP 02-00-002, *Consultation Policies and Procedures Manual, Chapter 7: Relationship to Enforcement*, dated January 18, 2008, to clarify the interface between enforcement and consultation activity at the worksite:
- **Full Service OnSite Consultation Visits.** While a worksite is undergoing a full service onsite consultation visit for safety and health, programmed enforcement activity may not occur until after the end of the worksite's visit "In Progress" status.
- **Full Service Safety or Health OnSite Consultation Visits.** An onsite consultation visit "in Progress" is discipline-related, whether for safety or health; programmed enforcement activity may not proceed until after the end of the worksite's visit "in Progress" status, and is limited to the discipline examined, safety or health.
- **Limited Service OnSite Consultation Visits.** If a worksite is undergoing a limited service onsite consultation visit, whether focused on a particular type of work process or a hazard, programmed enforcement activity may not proceed while the consultant is at the worksite. The re-scheduled enforcement activity must be limited only to those areas that were not addressed by the scope of the consultative visit (posted List of Hazards).
- **Enforcement Follow-Up and Monitoring Inspections.** If an enforcement follow-up or monitoring inspection is scheduled while a worksite is undergoing an onsite consultation visit, the inspection shall not be deferred; however, its scope shall be limited only to those areas required to be covered by the follow-up or monitoring inspection. In such instances, the consultant must halt the onsite visit until the enforcement inspection is completed. In the event OSHA issues a citation(s) as a result of the follow-up or monitoring inspection, an onsite consultation visit may not proceed until the citation(s) becomes a final order(s).

b.   **OnSite Consultation and 90-Day Deferral.**

■   If an establishment has requested an initial full-service comprehensive consultation visit for safety or health from the State OSHA Consultation Program, and that visit has been scheduled by the State Program, a SST inspection may be deferred for 90 calendar days from the date of the notification by the State Program to the Regional Office. No extension of the deferral beyond the 90 calendar days is possible, unless the consultation visit is "in progress."

■   OSHA may, however, in exercising its authority to schedule inspections, assign a lower priority to worksites where consultation visits are scheduled.

5.   **Pre-Safety and Health Achievement Recognition Program (Pre-SHARP) Status.**

a.   Those employers who do not meet the SHARP requirements, but who exhibit a reasonable promise of achieving agreed-upon milestones and time frames for SHARP participation, may be granted Pre-SHARP status. Pre-SHARP participants receive a full service, comprehensive consultation visit that involves a complete safety and health hazard identification survey, including a comprehensive assessment of the worksite's safety and health management system.

b.   The deferral time frame recommended by the State Consultation Project Manager must not exceed a total of 18 months from the expiration of the latest hazard correction due date(s), including extensions. Upon achieving Pre-SHARP status, employers may be granted a deferral from OSHA programmed inspections. The following types of incidents can trigger an OSHA enforcement inspection at Pre-SHARP sites:

■   Imminent danger;

■   Fatality/catastrophe; and

■   Formal complaints.

6.   **Safety and Health Achievement Recognition Program (SHARP).** SHARP is designed to provide support and incentives to those employers that implement and continuously improve effective safety and health management system(s) at their worksite. SHARP participants are exempted from OSHA programmed inspections, see § 1908.7(b)(4).

a.   **Duration of SHARP Status.** All initial approvals of SHARP status will be for a period of up to two years, commencing with the date the Regional Office approves an employer's SHARP application. After the initial approval, all SHARP renewals will be for a period of up to three years.

b.   **OSHA Inspection(s) at SHARP Worksites.** As noted above, employers that meet all the requirements for SHARP status will have the names of their establishments deleted from OSHA's Programmed Inspection Schedule. However, pursuant to § 1908.7(b)(4)(ii), the following types of incidents can trigger an OSHA enforcement inspection at SHARP sites: imminent danger; fatality/catastrophe; or formal complaints.

NOTE: *See* CSP 02-00-002, *Consultation Policies and Procedures Manual, Chapter 8: OSHA's Safety and Health Achievement Recognition Program (SHARP) and Pre-SHARP, dated January 18, 2008, for additional information.*

7.   **OSHA Strategic Partnership Program (OSP).**

a.   **Deferral from Programmed Inspection List for Non-Construction OSPs.**

■   OSHA may offer up to a six-month deferral from programmed inspections to OSHA Strategic Partnership (OSP) participants upon their entry into a partnership. During the deferral period, the partner must commit to make workplace safety and health improvements or seek compliance assistance to improve workplace safety and health in accordance with its responsibilities under the Act.

■   For a majority of OSP agreements, the beginning of the deferral period will be the effective date of the partnership agreement. However, in situations where sites join the partnership on a staggered basis, the deferral period begins at the site's actual entry into the partnership. The partnership agreement should clearly address the issue of OSP participant effective/entry dates.

b.   **Programmed Inspection with a Limited Scope.**

■   At OSHA's discretion, an establishment operated by a partner may receive an inspection in which the focus is limited to hazardous areas, operations, conditions or practices at the establishment. The limited scope inspection must focus on the significant worksite and industry-specific hazards based on an analysis of information available, such as:

a.   BLS injury and illness data;

b.   Site and corporate injury and illness data;

c.   Site accident audit and inspection data; and

d.   OSHA Target Industry Profiles.

■   For inspections with limited scope, the workplace hazards to be addressed will be determined by OSHA with input from the partner(s). OSHA may expand the scope of the inspection based on information gathered during the inspection process.

■   To gain a limited scope inspection as a benefit, the establishment must have undergone an onsite non-enforcement verification inspection within one year of the date of the programmed inspection.

c.   **Deletion from Programmed Inspection List.**

■   **Non-Construction.** Following a comprehensive onsite enforcement inspection conducted to meet OSP verification requirements, an establishment operated by an OSP partner will be deleted from programmed inspection lists for the period of time established for deletions in the then-current OSHA Site-Specific Targeting directive.

e.   If the OSP is designed to comprehensively address a hazard covered by the Act, the Area Director or designee, with the approval of the Regional Administrator, may extend the deletion for one year if the partner continues to meet the conditions of the OSP agreement and demonstrates improved performance in areas measured by the OSP.

■   **Construction.**

f.   An OSP agreement may provide that following an appropriate number of comprehensive onsite enforcement inspections conducted to verify satisfaction of OSP requirements, the sites, or portions of sites, over which the employer/partner exercises control is exempt from programmed inspection for a period of up to one year. This exemption is limited to the terms of the specific OSP agreement between the employer and OSHA, which are limited to the geographical boundaries of the OSHA office with whom the partnership was formed (Area, Regional, or National), if not otherwise specified in the agreement. However, it should be noted that if a serious or imminent danger condition is observed by enforcement personnel or reported to OSHA, the partner should be inspected and cited (per Agency policy).

    o   This program is available only where the partner has an effective safety and health management system fully compliant with §1926.20 and §1926.21, and the effectiveness of the system has been confirmed during the verification inspections described above. For recordkeeping purposes, the official date of the comprehensive onsite enforcement (verification) inspection is the opening conference. Therefore, the beginning of the deletion period is the date of the opening conference of the verification inspection(s).

See CSP 03-02-002, OSHA *Strategic Partnership Program for Worker Safety and Health*, dated February 10, 2005, for additional information. This verification process is sometimes referred to as the "tiered approach."

    g.   One such alternative to the "tiered approach" is described in the June 1, 2006 memorandum, *Clarification of Verification and Exemption Policies for OSHA Strategic Partnership Program Construction Participants*. Where the partner has advised the appropriate Area/Regional office of the number and location of all worksites covered by the partnership, the RA or AD has discretion to select an appropriate number of verification visits per year. The number should not be more than the number of programmed inspections the RA/AD determines would be conducted during the same time frame. Other criteria include the number of inspections needed to cover all types of work performed by the contractor; the quality of the contractor's safety and health management system; the phases of construction and the nature of associated hazards; and other factors which may affect OSHA's ability to fully and accurately assess the effectiveness of the participant's safety and health management system.

8.   **Alliances.** Unlike OSHA's OSP, VPP, and SHARP programs, Alliances do not require applications, data collection, verification, or evaluation. Alliances also do not offer incentives, such as focused inspections or inspection deferral, to their signatories.

Chapter 3 — Inspection Procedures

I.   **Inspection Preparation.** The conduct of effective inspections requires judgment in the identification, evaluation, and documentation of safety and health conditions and practices. Inspections may vary considerably in scope and detail depending on the circumstances of each case.

II.   **Inspection Planning.** It is important that the Compliance Officer (CSHO) adequately prepare for each inspection. Due to the wide variety of industries and associated hazards likely to be encountered, pre-inspection preparation is essential to the conduct of a quality inspection.

    A.   **Review of Inspection History.**

        1.   Compliance Officers will carefully review data available at the Area Office for information relevant to the establishment scheduled for inspection. This may include inspection files and source reference material relevant to the industry. CSHOs will also conduct an establishment search by accessing the IMIS database. CSHOs should use name variations and address-matching in their establishment search to maximize their efforts due to possible company name changes and status (e.g., LLC, Inc.).

        2.   If an establishment has an inspection history that includes citations received while performing work in a State Plan State, CSHOs should be aware of this information. This inspection history may be used to document an employer's heightened awareness of a hazard and/or standard in order to support the development of a willful citation and may be considered in determining eligibility for the history penalty reduction. However, the state plan citation may not be used to support a repeat violation.

    B.   **Review of Cooperative Program Participation.** CSHOs will access the Regional Homepage to obtain information about employers who are currently participating in cooperative programs. CSHOs will verify whether the employer is a current program participant during the opening conference. CSHOs will be mindful of whether they are preparing for a programmed or unprogrammed inspection, as this may affect whether the inspection should be conducted and/or its scope. See Paragraph V.D. of this chapter, *Review of Voluntary Compliance Programs*.

    C.   **OSHA Data Initiative (ODI) Data Review.** The CSHO must obtain ODI survey information for SST inspections, which is available from *http://www.ergweb3.com* (this site is available only to OSHA field personnel and requires a user name and password). If assistance is needed, contact the OSHA Regional Recordkeeping Coordinator for assistance. See CPL 02-00-135, *Recordkeeping Policies and Procedures Manual*, dated December 30, 2004.

    D.   **Safety and Health Issues Relating to CSHOs.**

        1.   **Hazard Assessment.** If the employer has a written certification that a hazard assessment has been performed pursuant to §1910.132(d), the CSHO shall request a copy. If the hazard assessment itself is not in writing, the CSHO shall ask the person who signed the certification to describe all potential workplace hazards and then select appropriate protective equipment. If there is no hazard assessment, the CSHO will determine potential hazards from sources such as the OSHA 300 Log of injuries and illnesses and shall select personal protective equipment accordingly.

        2.   **Respiratory Protection.** CSHOs must wear respirators when and where required, and must care for and maintain respirators in accordance with the CSHO training provided.

           a.   CSHOs should conduct a pre-inspection evaluation for potential exposure to chemicals. Prior to entering any hazardous areas, the CSHO should identify those work areas, processes, or tasks that require respiratory protection. The hazard assessment requirement in §1910.132(d) does not apply to respirators; see CPL 02-02-054, *Respiratory Protection Program Guidelines*, dated July 14, 2000. CSHOs should review all pertinent information contained in the establishment file and appropriate reference sources to become knowledgeable about the industrial processes and potential respiratory hazards that may be encountered. During the opening conference, a list of hazardous substances should be obtained or identified, along with any air monitoring results. CSHOs should determine if they have the appropriate respirator to protect against chemicals present at the work site.

    b.   CSHOs must notify their supervisor or the respiratory protection program administrator:

- If a respirator no longer fits well (CSHOs should request a replacement that fits properly);
- If CSHOs encounter any respiratory hazards during inspections or on-site visits that they believe have not been previously or adequately addressed during the site visit; or
- If there are any other concerns regarding the program.

3.   **Safety and Health Rules and Practices.** Section 1903.7(c) requires that CSHOs comply with all safety and health rules and practices at the establishment and wear or use the safety clothing or protective equipment required by OSHA standards or by the employer for the protection of employees.

4.   **Restrictions.** CSHOs will not enter any area where special entrance restrictions apply until the required precautions have been taken. It shall be the Area Director's responsibility to determine that an inspection may be conducted without exposing the CSHO to hazardous situations and to procure whatever materials and equipment are needed for the safe conduct of the inspection.

E.   **Advance Notice.**

    1.   **Policy.**

        a.   Section 17(f) of the Act and §1903.6 contain a general prohibition against the giving of advance notice of inspections, except as authorized by the Secretary or the Secretary's designee. The Act regulates many conditions that are subject to speedy alteration and disguise by employers. To forestall such changes in worksite conditions, the Act prohibits unauthorized advance notice.

        b.   **Advance Notice Exceptions.** There may be occasions when advance notice is necessary to conduct an effective investigation. These occasions are narrow exceptions to the statutory prohibition against advance notice. Advance notice of inspections may be given only with the authorization of the Area Director or designee and only in the following situations:

- In cases of apparent imminent danger to enable the employer to correct the danger as quickly as possible;
- When the inspection can most effectively be conducted after regular business hours or when special preparations are necessary;
- To ensure the presence of employer and employee representatives or other appropriate personnel who are needed to aid in the inspection; and
- When giving advance notice would enhance the probability of an effective and thorough inspection; e.g., in complex fatality investigations.

        c.   **Delays.** Advance notice exists whenever the Area Office sets up a specific date or time with the employer for the CSHO to begin an inspection. Any delays in the conduct of the inspection shall be kept to an absolute minimum. Lengthy or unreasonable delays shall be brought to the attention of the Area Director or designee. Advance notice generally does not include non-specific indications of potential future inspections.

In unusual circumstances, the Area Director or designee may decide that a delay is necessary. In those cases the employer or the CSHO shall notify affected employee representatives, if any, of the delay and shall keep them informed of the status of the inspection.

    2.   **Documentation.** The conditions requiring advance notice and the procedures followed shall be documented in the case file.

F.   **Pre-Inspection Compulsory Process.**

    1.   Section 1903.4 authorizes the agency to seek a warrant in advance of an attempted inspection if circumstances are such that "preinspection process (is) desirable or necessary." Section 8(b) of the Act authorizes the agency to issue administrative subpoenas to obtain relevant information.

    2.   Although the agency generally does not seek warrants without evidence that the employer is likely to refuse entry, the Area Director or designee may seek compulsory process in advance of an attempt to inspect or investigate whenever circumstances indicate the desirability of such warrants.

        NOTE: *Examples of such circumstances include evidence of denied entry in previous inspections, or awareness that a job will only last a short time or that job processes will be changing rapidly.*

    3.   Administrative subpoenas may also be issued prior to any attempt to contact the employer or other person for evidence related to an OSHA inspection or investigation. See Chapter 15, *Legal Issues*.

G.   **Personal Security Clearance.** Some establishments have areas that contain material or processes that are classified by the U.S. Government in the interest of national security. Whenever an inspection is scheduled for an establishment containing classified areas, the Area Director or designee shall assign a CSHO who has the appropriate security clearances. The Regional Administrator shall ensure that an adequate number of CSHOs with appropriate security clearances are available within the Region and that the security clearances are current.

H.   **Expert Assistance.**

    1.   The Area Director or designee shall arrange for a specialist and/or specialized training, preferably from within OSHA, to assist in an inspection or investigation when the need for such expertise is identified.

    2.   OSHA specialists may accompany CSHOs or perform their tasks separately. CSHOs must accompany outside consultants. OSHA specialists and outside consultants shall be briefed on the purpose of the inspection and personal protective equipment to be utilized.

III. Inspection Scope. Inspections, either programmed or unprogrammed, fall into one of two categories depending on the scope of the inspection:

A.   **Comprehensive.** A comprehensive inspection is a substantially complete and thorough inspection of all potentially hazardous areas of the establishment. An inspection may be deemed comprehensive even though, as a result of professional judgment, not all potentially hazardous conditions or practices within those areas are inspected.

B.   **Partial.** A partial inspection is one whose focus is limited to certain potentially hazardous areas, operations, conditions or practices at the establishment.

1. A partial inspection may be expanded based on information gathered by the CSHO during the inspection process consistent with the Act and Area Office priorities.
2. CSHOs shall use pre-determined criteria from their offices to determine the necessity for expanding the scope of an inspection, based on information gathered during records or program review and walkaround inspection.

IV. Conduct of Inspection.

A. Time of Inspection.
1. Inspections shall be made during regular working hours of the establishment except when special circumstances indicate otherwise.
2. The Area Director or designee and the CSHO shall determine if alternate work schedules are necessary regarding entry into an inspection site during other than normal working hours.

B. Presenting Credentials.
1. At the beginning of the inspection, the CSHO shall locate the owner representative, operator or agent in charge at the workplace and present credentials. On construction sites this will most often be the representative of the general contractor.
2. When neither the person in charge nor a management official is present, contact may be made with the employer to request the presence of the owner, operator or management official. The inspection shall not be delayed unreasonably to await the arrival of the employer representative. This delay should normally not exceed one hour. On occasions when the CSHO is waiting for the employer representative, the workforce may begin to leave the jobsite. In this situation the CSHO should contact the Area Director or designee for guidance. If the person in charge at the workplace cannot be determined, record the extent of the inquiry in the case file and proceed with the physical inspection.

C. Refusal to Permit Inspection and Interference.
Section 8 of the Act provides that CSHOs may enter without delay and at reasonable times any establishment covered under the Act for the purpose of conducting an inspection. Unless the circumstances constitute a recognized exception to the warrant requirement (i.e., consent, third party consent, plain view, open field, or exigent circumstances) an employer has a right to require that the CSHO seek an inspection warrant prior to entering an establishment and may refuse entry without such a warrant.

NOTE: *On a military base or other Federal Government facility, the following guidelines do not apply. Instead, a representative of the controlling authority shall be informed of the contractor's refusal and asked to take appropriate action to obtain cooperation.*

1. **Refusal of Entry or Inspection.**
   a. When the employer refuses to permit entry upon being presented proper credentials, or allows entry but then refuses to permit or hinders the inspection in some way, an attempt shall be made to obtain as much information as possible about the establishment. See Chapter 15, *Legal Issues*, for additional information.
   b. If the employer refuses to allow an inspection of the establishment to proceed, the CSHO shall leave the premises and immediately report the refusal to the Area Director or designee. The Area Director shall notify the RSOL.
   c. If the employer raises no objection to inspection of certain portions of the workplace but objects to inspection of other portions, this shall be documented. Normally, the CSHO shall continue the inspection, confining it only to those certain portions to which the employer has raised no objections.
   d. In either case, the CSHO shall advise the employer that the refusal will be reported to the Area Director or designee and that the agency may take further action, which may include obtaining legal process.
   e. On multi-employer worksites, valid consent can be granted by the owner, or another employer with employees at the worksite, for site entry.
2. **Employer Interference.** Where entry has been allowed but the employer interferes with or limits any important aspect of the inspection, the CSHO shall determine whether or not to consider this action as a refusal. Examples of interference are refusals to permit the walkaround, the examination of records essential to the inspection, the taking of essential photographs and/or videotapes, the inspection of a particular part of the premises, private employee interviews, or the refusal to allow attachment of sampling devices. See §1903.7(b).
3. **Forcible Interference with Conduct of Inspection or Other Office Duties.** Whenever an OSHA official or employee encounters forcible resistance, opposition, interference, etc., or is assaulted or threatened with assault while engaged in the performance of official duties, all investigative activity shall cease.
   a. If a CSHO is assaulted while attempting to conduct an inspection, they shall contact the proper authorities such as the Federal Protective Services or local police and immediately notify the Area Director.
   b. Upon receiving a report of such forcible interference, the Area Director or designee shall immediately notify the Regional Administrator.
   c. If working at an offsite location, CSHOs should leave the site immediately pending further instructions from the Area Director or designee.
4. **Obtaining Compulsory Process.** If it is determined, upon refusal of entry or refusal to produce evidence required by subpoena, that a warrant will be sought, the Area Director shall proceed according to guidelines and procedures established in the Region for warrant applications. See Chapter 15, *Legal Issues*.

D. Employee Participation.
CSHOs shall advise employers that Section 8(e) of the Act and §1903.8 require that an employee representative be given an opportunity to participate in the inspection.
1. CSHOs shall determine as soon as possible after arrival whether the employees at the inspected worksite are represented and, if so, shall ensure that employee representatives are afforded the opportunity to participate in all phases of the inspection.
2. If an employer resists or interferes with participation by employee representatives in an inspection and the interference cannot be resolved by the CSHO, the resistance shall be construed as a refusal to permit the inspection and the Area Director or designee shall be contacted.

E. Release for Entry.
1. CSHOs shall not sign any form or release or agree to any waiver. This includes any employer forms concerned with trade secret information.

2.   CSHOs may obtain a pass or sign a visitor's register, or any other book or form used by the establishment to control the entry and movement of persons upon its premises. Such signature shall not constitute any form of a release or waiver of prosecution of liability under the Act.

F.   **Bankrupt or Out of Business.**

1.   If the establishment scheduled for inspection is found to have ceased business and there is no known successor, the CSHO shall report the facts to the Area Director or designee.

2.   If an employer, although bankrupt, is continuing to operate on the date of the scheduled inspection, the inspection shall proceed.

3.   An employer must comply with the Act until the day the business actually ceases to operate.

G.   **Employee Responsibilities.**

1.   Section 5(b) of the Act states: "Each employee shall comply with occupational safety and health standards and all rules, regulations, and orders issued pursuant to the Act which are applicable to his own actions and conduct." The Act does not provide for the issuance of citations or the proposal of penalties against employees. Employers are responsible for employee compliance with the standards.

2.   In cases where CSHOs determine that employees are systematically refusing to comply with a standard applicable to their own action and conduct, the matter shall be referred to the Area Director who shall consult with the Regional Administrator.

3.   Under no circumstances are CSHOs to become involved in an onsite dispute involving labor-management issues or interpretation of collective-bargaining agreements. CSHOs are expected to obtain sufficient information to assess whether the employer is using its authority to ensure employee compliance with the Act. Concerted refusals to comply by employees will not bar the issuance of a citation if the employer has failed to exercise its control to the maximum extent reasonable, including discipline and discharge.

H.   **Strike or Labor Dispute.** Plants or establishments may be inspected regardless of the existence of labor disputes, such as work stoppages, strikes or picketing. If the CSHO identifies an unanticipated labor dispute at a proposed inspection site, the Area Director or designee shall be consulted before any contact is made.

1.   **Programmed Inspections.** Programmed inspections may be deferred during a strike or labor dispute, either between a recognized union and the employer or between two unions competing for bargaining rights in the establishment.

2.   **Unprogrammed Inspections.**

a.   Unprogrammed inspections (complaints, fatalities, referrals, etc.) will be performed during strikes or labor disputes. However, the credibility and veracity of any complaint shall be thoroughly assessed by the Area Director or designee prior to scheduling an inspection.

b.   If there is a picket line at the establishment, CSHOs shall attempt to locate and inform the appropriate union official of the reason for the inspection prior to initiating the inspection.

c.   During the inspection, CSHOs will make every effort to ensure that their actions are not interpreted as supporting either party to the labor dispute.

I.   **Variances.** The employer's requirement to comply with a standard may be modified through granting of a variance, as outlined in Section 6 of the Act.

1.   An employer will not be subject to citation if the observed condition is in compliance with an existing variance issued to that employer.

2.   In the event that an employer is not in compliance with the requirement(s) of the issued variance, a violation of the applicable standard shall be cited with a reference in the citation to the variance provision that has not been met.

V.   **Opening Conference.**

A.   **General.** CSHOs shall attempt to inform all affected employers of the purpose of the inspection, provide a copy of the complaint if applicable, and include any employee representatives, unless the employer objects. The opening conference should be brief so that the compliance officer may quickly proceed to the walkaround. Conditions of the worksite shall be noted upon arrival, as well as any changes that may occur during the opening conference. At the start of the opening conference, CSHOs will provide both the employer and the employee representative(s) copies of their rights during the inspection, including the opportunity to participate in the physical inspection of the workplace.

CSHOs shall request a copy of the written certification that a hazard assessment has been performed by the employer in accordance with §1910.132(d). CSHOs should then ask the person who signed the certification about any potential worksite exposures and select appropriate personal protective equipment.

1.   **Attendance at Opening Conference.**

a.   CSHOs shall conduct a joint opening conference with employer and employee representatives unless either party objects.

b.   If there is objection to a joint conference, the CSHO shall conduct separate conferences with employer and employee representatives.

2.   **Scope of Inspection.** CSHOs shall outline in general terms the scope of the inspection, including the need for private employee interviews, physical inspection of the workplace and records, possible referrals, rights during an inspection, discrimination complaints, and the closing conference(s).

3.   **Video/Audio Recording.** CSHOs shall inform participants that a video camera and/or an audio recorder may be used to provide a visual and/or audio record, and that the videotape and audiotape may be used in the same manner as handwritten notes and photographs in OSHA inspections.

NOTE: *If an employer clearly refuses to allow videotaping during an inspection, CSHOs shall contact the Area Director to determine if videotaping is critical to documenting the case. If it is, this may be treated as a denial of entry.*

4.   **Immediate Abatement.** CSHOs should explain to employers the advantages of immediate abatement, including that there are no certification requirements for violations quickly corrected during the inspection. See Chapter 7, *Post-Inspection Procedures and Abatement Verification.*

5.   **Quick-Fix Penalty Reduction.** CSHOs shall advise both the employer and employee representatives, if applicable, that the Quick-Fix penalty reduction may be applied to each qualified violation (i.e., those which meet the criteria

noted in Chapter 6), which the employer immediately abates during the inspection and is visually verified by the CSHO. CSHOs shall explain the Quick-Fix criteria and answer any questions concerning the program. See Chapter 6, *Penalties and Debt Collection*.

6. **Abbreviated Opening Conference.** An abbreviated opening conference shall be conducted whenever the CSHO believes that circumstances at the worksite dictate the walkaround begin as promptly as possible.

    a.   In such cases, the opening conference shall be limited to presenting credentials, purpose of the visit, explanation of rights, and a request for employer and employee representatives. All other elements shall be fully addressed in the closing conference.

    b.   Pursuant to §1903.8, the employer and the employee representatives shall be informed of the opportunity to participate in the physical inspection of the workplace.

B. **Review of Appropriation Act Exemptions and Limitation.** CSHOs shall determine if the employer is covered by any exemptions or limitations noted in the current Appropriations Act. See CPL 02-00-051, *Enforcement Exemptions and Limitations under the Appropriations Act*, dated May 28, 1998.

C. **Review Screening for Process Safety Management (PSM) Coverage.** CSHOs shall request a list of the chemicals on site and their respective maximum intended inventories. CSHOs shall review the list of chemicals and quantities, and determine if there are highly hazardous chemicals (HHCs) listed in §1910.119, Appendix A or flammable liquids or gases at or above the specified threshold quantity. CSHOs may ask questions, conduct interviews, or a walkaround to confirm the information on the list of chemicals and maximum intended inventories.

    1.   If there is an HHC present at or above threshold quantities, CSHOs shall use the following criteria to determine if any exemptions apply:

        a.   CSHOs shall confirm that the facility is not a retail facility, oil or gas well drilling or servicing operation, or normally unoccupied remote facility (§1910.119(a)(2)). If the facility is one of these types of establishments, PSM does not apply.

        b.   If management believes that the process is exempt, CSHOs shall ask the employer to provide documentation or other information to support that claim.

    2.   According to §1910.119 (a)(1)(ii), a process could be exempt if the employer can demonstrate that the covered chemical(s) are:

        a.   Hydrocarbon fuels used solely for workplace consumption as a fuel (e.g., propane used for comfort heating, gasoline for vehicle refueling), if such fuels are not a part of a process containing another highly hazardous chemical covered by the standard, or

        b.   Flammable liquids stored in atmospheric tanks or transferred, which are kept below their normal boiling point without the benefit of chilling or refrigeration.

        NOTE: *Current agency policies for applying exemptions can be found on the OSHA website. See CPL 03-00-004, Petroleum Refinery Process Safety Management National Emphasis Program, dated June 7, 2007.*

D. **Review of Voluntary Compliance Programs.** Employers who participate in selected voluntary compliance programs may be exempted from programmed inspections. CSHOs shall determine whether the employer falls under such an exemption during the opening conference.

    1.   **OSHA On-Site Consultation Visits.**

        a.   In accordance with §1908.7 and Chapter VII of CSP 02-00-002, *The Consultation Policies and Procedures Manual*, CSHOs shall ascertain at the opening conference whether an OSHA-funded consultation visit is in progress. A consultation Visit in Progress extends from the beginning of the opening conference to the end of the correction due dates (including extensions).

        b.   An on-site consultation Visit in Progress has priority over programmed inspections except for imminent danger investigations, fatality/catastrophe investigations, complaint investigations, and other critical inspections as determined by the Assistant Secretary as noted in §1908.7(b)(2).

    2.   **Safety and Health Achievement Recognition Program (SHARP).**

        a.   Upon verifying that the employer is a current participant, the CSHO shall notify the Area Director or designee so that the company can be removed from the OSHA General Programmed Inspection Schedule for the approved exemption period, which begins on the date the Regional Office approves the employer's participation in SHARP.

        b.   The initial exemption period is one year. The renewal exemption period is one or two years, based on the recommendation of the Consultation Project Manager.

    3.   **Voluntary Protection Program (VPP).** Inspections at a VPP site may be conducted in response to referrals, formal complaints, fatalities, and catastrophes.

        NOTE: *A Compliance Officer who was previously a VPP on-site team member cannot conduct an enforcement inspection at that VPP site for the following 2 years or until the site is no longer a VPP participant, whichever occurs first. See CSP 03-01-003, Voluntary Protection Programs (VPP): Policies and Procedures Manual, dated April 18, 2008.*

E. **Disruptive Conduct.** CSHOs may deny the right of accompaniment to any person whose conduct interferes with a full and orderly inspection. See §1903.8(d). If disruption or interference occurs, the CSHO shall contact the Area Director or designee as to whether to suspend the walkaround or take other action. The employee representative shall be advised that during the inspection matters unrelated to the inspection shall not be discussed with employees.

F. **Classified Areas.** In areas containing information classified by an agency of the U.S. Government in the interest of national security, only persons authorized to have access to such information may accompany a CSHO on the inspection. See §1903.8(d).

VI. **Review of Records.**

A. **Injury and Illness Records.**

    1.   **Collection of Data.**

        a.   At the start of each inspection, the CSHO shall review the employer's injury and illness records for three prior calendar years, record the information on a copy of the OSHA300 screen, and enter the employer's data using the IMIS Application on the NCR (micro). This shall be done for all general industry, construction, maritime, and agriculture inspections and investigations.

    b.   CSHOs shall use these data to calculate the Days Away, Restricted, or Transferred (DART) rate and to observe trends, potential hazards, types of operations and work-related injuries

2. **Information to be Obtained.**
   a. CSHOs shall request copies of the OSHA-300 Logs, the total hours worked and the average number of employees for each year, and a roster of current employees.
   b. If CSHOs have questions regarding a specific case on the log, they shall request the OSHA-301s or equivalent form for that case.
   c. CSHOs shall check if the establishment has an on-site medical facility and/or the location of the nearest emergency room where employees may be treated.
   NOTE: *The total hours worked and the average number of employees for each year can be found on the OSHA-300A for all past years.*

3. **Automatic DART Rate Calculation.** CSHOs will not normally need to calculate the Days Away, Restricted, or Transferred (DART) rate since it is automatically calculated when the OSHA-300 data are entered into the micro. If one of the three years is a partial year, so indicate and the software will calculate accordingly.

4. **Manual DART Rate Calculation.** If it is necessary to calculate rates manually, the CSHO will calculate the DART Rates onsite using the following procedures. The DART rate includes cases involving days away from work, restricted work activity, and transfers to another job.
   The formula is:
   (N/EH) x (200,000) where:
   - N is the number of cases involving days away and/or restricted work activity and job transfers.
   - EH is the total number of hours worked by all employees during the calendar year; and
   - 200,000 is the base number of hours worked for 100 full-time equivalent employees.

EXAMPLE 3-1: Employees of an establishment (XYZ Company), including management, temporary and leased workers, worked 645,089 hours at XYZ company. There were 22 injury and illness cases involving days away and/or restricted work activity and/or job transfer from the OSHA-300 Log (total of column H plus column I). The DART rate would be (22÷645,089) x (200,000) = 6.8.

5. **Construction.** For construction inspections/investigations, only the OSHA-300 information for the prime/general contractor need be recorded where such records exist and are maintained. It will be left to the discretion of the Area Director or the CSHO as to whether OSHA300 data should also be recorded for any of the subcontractors.

6. **Federal Agencies.** Federal agency injury and illness recording and reporting requirements shall comply with the requirements under § 1904, subparts C, D, E, and G, except that the definition of "establishment" found in § 1960.2(h) will remain applicable to Federal agencies.

B. **Recording Criteria.** Employers must record new work-related injuries and illnesses that meet one or more of the general recording criteria or meet the recording criteria for specific types of conditions.
   1. Death;
   2. Days Away from Work;
   3. Restricted Work;
   4. Transfer to another job;
   5. Medical treatment beyond first aid;
   6. Loss of consciousness;
   7. Diagnosis of a significant injury or illness; or
   8. Meet the recording criteria for Specific Cases noted in § 1904.8 through § 1904.11.

C. **Recordkeeping Deficiencies.**
   1. If recordkeeping deficiencies are suspected, the CSHO and the Area Director or designee may request assistance from the Regional Recordkeeping Coordinator. If there is evidence that the deficiencies or inaccuracies in the employer's records impairs the ability to assess hazards, injuries and/or illnesses at the workplace, a comprehensive records review shall be performed.
   2. Other information related to this topic:
      a. See CPL 02-00-135, *Recordkeeping Policies and Procedures Manual*, dated September 3, 2004, and CPL 02-02-072, *Rules of Agency Practice and Procedure concerning OSHA Access to Employee Medical Records for Policy Regarding Review of Medical and Exposure Records*, dated August 22, 2007.
      b. Other OSHA programs and records will be reviewed including hazard communication, lockout/tagout, emergency evacuation and personal protective equipment. Additional programs will be reviewed as necessary.
      c. Many standard-specific directives provide additional instruction to CSHOs requesting certain records and/or documents at the opening conference.

VII. **Walkaround Inspection.** The main purpose of the walkaround inspection is to identify potential safety and/or health hazards in the workplace. CSHOs shall conduct the inspection in such a manner as to avoid unnecessary personal exposure to hazards and to minimize unavoidable personal exposure to the extent possible.

A. **Walkaround Representatives.** Persons designated to accompany CSHOs during the walkaround are considered walkaround representatives, and will generally include those designated by the employer and employee. At establishments where more than one employer is present or in situations where groups of employees have different representatives, it is acceptable to have a different employer/employee representative for different phases of the inspection. More than one employer and/or employee representative may accompany the CSHO throughout or during any phase of an inspection if the CSHO determines that such additional representatives will aid, and not interfere with, the inspection. See § 1903.8(a).
   1. **Employees Represented by a Certified or Recognized Bargaining Agent.** During the opening conference, the highest ranking union official or union employee representative onsite shall designate who will participate in the walkaround. OSHA regulation § 1903.8(b) gives the CSHO the authority to resolve all disputes as to whom is the representative authorized by the employer and employees. Section 1903.8(c) states that the representative

authorized by the employees shall be an employee of the employer. If in the judgment of the CSHO, good cause has been shown why accompaniment by a third party who is not an employee of the employer (such as an industrial hygienist or a safety engineer) is reasonably necessary to the conduct of an effective and thorough physical inspection of the workplace, such third party may accompany CSHOs during the inspection.

2. **No Certified or Recognized Bargaining Agent.** Where employees are not represented by an authorized representative, there is no established safety committee, or employees have not chosen or agreed to an employee representative for OSHA inspection purposes (regardless of the existence of a safety committee), CSHOs shall determine if other employees would suitably represent the interests of employees on the walkaround. If selection of such an employee is impractical, CSHOs shall conduct interviews with a reasonable number of employees during the walkaround.

3. **Safety Committee.** Employee members of an established plant safety committee or employees at large may designate an employee representative for OSHA inspection purposes,

B. **Evaluation of Safety and Health System.** The employer's safety and health system shall be evaluated to determine its good faith for the purposes of penalty calculation. See Chapter 6, *Penalties and Debt Collection*.

C. **Record All Facts Pertinent to a Violation.**
1. Safety and health violations shall be brought to the attention of employer and employee representatives at the time they are documented.
2. CSHOs shall record, at a minimum, the identity of the exposed employee(s), the hazard to which the employee(s) was exposed, the employee's proximity to the hazard, the employer's knowledge of the condition, and the manner in which important measurements were obtained and how long the condition has existed.
3. CSHOs will document interview statements in a thorough and accurate manner; including names, dates, times, locations, type of materials, positions of pertinent articles, witnesses, etc.
   NOTE: *If employee exposure to hazards is not observed, the CSHO shall document facts on which the determination is made that an employee has been or could be exposed. See Chapter 4, Violations and Chapter 5, Case File Preparation and Documentation.*

D. **Testifying in Hearings.** CSHOs may be required to testify in hearings on OSHA's behalf, and shall be mindful of this fact when recording observations during inspections. The case file shall reflect conditions observed in the workplace as accurately and detailed as possible.

E. **Trade Secrets.** A trade secret, as referenced in Section 15 of the Act, includes information concerning or related to processes, operations, style of work, or apparatus, or to the identity, confidential statistical data, amount or source of any income, profits, losses, or expenditures of any person, firm, partnership, corporation, or association. See 18 USC 1905.
1. **Policy.** It is essential to the effective enforcement of the Act that CSHOs and OSHA personnel preserve the confidentiality of all information and investigations which might reveal a trade secret.
2. **Restriction and Controls.** When the employer identifies an operation or condition as a trade secret, it shall be treated as such. Information obtained in such areas, including all negatives, photographs, videotapes, and OSHA documentation forms, shall be labeled:
   "ADMINISTRATIVELY CONTROLLED INFORMATION" "RESTRICTED TRADE INFORMATION"
   a. Under Section 15 of the Act, all information reported to or obtained by CSHOs in connection with any inspection or other activity which contains or which might reveal a trade secret shall be kept confidential. Such information shall not be disclosed except to other OSHA officials concerned with the enforcement of the Act or, when relevant, in any proceeding under the Act.
   b. Title 18 USC 1905 provides criminal penalties for Federal employees who disclose such information. These penalties include fines of up to $1,000 or imprisonment of up to one year, or both, and removal from office or employment.
   c. Trade secret materials shall not be labeled as "Top Secret," "Secret," or "Confidential," nor shall these security classification designations be used in conjunction with other words unless the trade secrets are also classified by an agency of the U.S. Government in the interest of national security.
3. If the employer objects to the taking of photographs and/or videotapes because trade secrets would or may be disclosed, CSHOs should advise the employer of the protection against such disclosure afforded by Section 15 of the Act and § 1903.9. If the employer still objects, CSHOs shall contact the Area Director or designee.

F. **Collecting Samples.**
1. CSHOs shall determine early in the inspection whether sampling such as, but not limited to, air sampling and surface sampling is required, by utilizing the information collected during the walk around and from the pre-inspection review.
2. Summaries of the results shall be provided on request to the appropriate employees, including those exposed or likely to be exposed to a hazard, employer representatives and employee representatives.

G. **Photographs and Videotapes.**
1. Photographs and/or videotapes, whether digital or otherwise, shall be taken whenever CSHOs determine there is a need.
   a. Photographs that support violations shall be properly labeled, and may be attached to the appropriate OSHA-1B.
   b. CSHO shall ensure that any photographs relating to confidential or trade secret information are identified as such and are kept separate from other evidence.
2. All film and photographs or videotape shall be retained in the case file. If lack of storage space does not permit retaining the film, photographs or videotapes with the file, they may be stored elsewhere with a reference to the corresponding inspection. Videotapes shall be properly labeled. For more information regarding guidelines for case file documentation with video, audio and digital media, see OSHA Instruction CPL 02-00-098,
   Guidelines for Case File Documentation for Use with Videotapes and Audiotapes, dated October 12, 1993, and any other directives related to photograph and videotape retention.

H. **Violations of Other Laws.** If a CSHO observes apparent violations of laws enforced by other government agencies, such cases shall be referred to the appropriate agency. Referrals shall be made using appropriate Regional procedures.

I. **Interviews of Non-Managerial Employees.** A free and open exchange of information between CSHOs and employees is essential to an effective inspection. Interviews provide an opportunity for employees to supply valuable factual information concerning hazardous conditions, including information on how long workplace conditions have existed, the number and extent of employee exposure(s) to a hazardous condition, and the actions of management regarding correction of a hazardous condition.

1. **Background.**

   a. Section 8(a)(2) of the Act authorizes CSHOs to question **any employee privately** during regular working hours or at other reasonable times during the course of an OSHA inspection. The purpose of such interviews is to obtain whatever information CSHOs deem necessary or useful in carrying out inspections effectively. The mandate to interview employees in private is OSHA's right.

   b. Employee interviews are an effective means to determine if an advance notice of inspection has adversely affected the inspection conditions, as well as to obtain information regarding the employer's knowledge of the workplace conditions or work practices in effect prior to, and at the time of, the inspection. During interviews with employees, CSHOs should ask about these matters.

   c. CSHOs should also obtain information concerning the presence and/or implementation of a safety and health system to prevent or control workplace hazards.

   d. If an employee refuses to be interviewed, the CSHO shall use professional judgment, in consultation with the Area Director or designee, in determining the need for the statement.

2. **Employee Right of Complaint.** CSHOs may consult with any employee who desires to discuss a potential violation. Upon receipt of such information, CSHOs shall investigate the alleged hazard, where possible, and record the findings.

3. **Time and Location of Interview.** CSHOs are authorized to conduct interviews during regular working hours and at other reasonable times, and in a reasonable manner at the workplace. Interviews often occur during the walkaround, but may be conducted at any time during an inspection. If necessary, interviews may be conducted at locations other than the workplace. CSHOs should consult with the Area Director if an interview is to be conducted someplace other than the workplace. Where appropriate, OSHA has the authority to subpoena an employee to appear at the Area Office for an interview.

4. **Conducting Interviews of Non-Managerial Employees in Private.** CSHOs shall inform employers that interviews of non-managerial employees will be conducted in private. CSHOs are entitled to question such employees in private regardless of employer preference. If an employer interferes with a CSHOs ability to do so, the CSHO should request that the AD consult with RSOL to determine appropriate legal action. Interference with a CSHO's ability to conduct private interviews with non-managerial employees includes, but is not limited to, attempts by management officials or representatives to be present during interviews.

5. **Conducting Employee Interviews.**

   a. **General Protocols.**
      - At the beginning of the interview CSHOs should identify themselves to the employee by showing their credentials, and provide the employee with a business card. This allows employees to contact CSHOs if they have further information at a later time.
      - CSHOs should explain to employees that the reason for the interview is to gather factual information relevant to a safety and health inspection. It is not appropriate to assume that employees already know or understand the agency's purpose. Particular sensitivity is required when interviewing a non-English speaking employee. In such instances, CSHOs should initially determine whether the employee's comprehension of English is sufficient to permit conducting an effective interview. If an interpreter is needed, CSHOs should contact the General Services Administration (GSA) tele-interpreter or use the Area Office's protocol for interpreters.
      - Every employee should be asked to provide his or her name, home address and phone number. CSHOs should request identification and make clear the reason for asking for this information.
      - CSHOs shall inform employees that OSHA has the right to interview them in private and of the protections afforded under Section 11(c) of the Act.
      - In the event an employee requests that a representative of the union be present, CSHOs shall make a reasonable effort to honor the request.
      - If an employee requests that his/her personal attorney be present during the interview, CSHOs should honor the request and, before continuing with the interview, consult with the Area Director for guidance.
      - Rarely, an attorney for the employer may claim that individual employees have also authorized the attorney to represent them. Such a situation creates a potential conflict of interest. CSHOs should ask the affected employees whether they have agreed to be represented by the attorney. If the employees indicate that they have, CSHOs should consult with the Area Director, who will contact RSOL.

   b. **Interview Statements.** Interview statements of employees or other persons shall be obtained whenever CSHOs determine that such statements would be useful in documenting potential violations. Interviews shall normally be reduced to writing and written in the first person in the language of the individual. Employees shall be encouraged to sign and date the statement.
      - Any changes or corrections to the statement shall be initialed by the individual. Statements shall not otherwise be changed or altered in any manner.
      - Statements shall include the words, "I request that my statement be held confidential to the extent allowed by law" and end with the following; "I have read the above, and it is true to the best of my knowledge."
      - If the person making the declaration refuses to sign, the CSHO shall note the refusal on the statement. The statement shall, nevertheless, be read back to the person in an attempt to obtain agreement and noted in the case file.
      - A transcription of any recorded statement shall be made when necessary to the case.

- Upon request, if a management employee requests a copy of his/her interview statement, one shall be given to them.

C. **The Informant Privilege.**

- The informant privilege allows the government to withhold the **identity** of individuals who provide information about the violation of laws, including OSHA rules and regulations. CSHOs shall inform employees that their statements will remain confidential to the extent permitted by law. However, each employee giving a statement should be informed that disclosure of his or her identity may be necessary in connection with enforcement or court actions.

    NOTE: *Whenever CSHOs make an assurance of confidentiality as part of an investigation (i.e. informs the person giving the statement that their identity will be protected), the pledge shall be reduced to writing and included in the case file.*

- The privilege also protects the contents of statements to the extent that disclosure may reveal the witness's identity. Where the contents of a statement will not disclose the identity of the informant (i.e., does not reveal the witness' job title, work area, job duties, or other information that would tend to reveal the individual's identity), the privilege does not apply. Interviewed employees shall be told that they are under no legal obligation to inform anyone, including employers, that they provided information to OSHA. Interviewed employees shall also be informed that if they voluntarily disclose such information to others, it may impair the agency's ability to invoke the privilege.

J. **Multi-Employer Worksites.** On multi-employer worksites (in all industry sectors), more than one employer may be cited for a hazardous condition that violates an OSHA standard. A two-step process must be followed in determining whether more than one employer is to be cited. See CPL 02-00-124, *Multi-Employer Citation Policy*, dated December 10, 1999, for further guidance.

K. **Administrative Subpoena.** Whenever there is a reasonable need for records, documents, testimony and/or other supporting evidence necessary for completing an inspection scheduled in accordance with any current and approved inspection scheduling system or an investigation of any matter properly falling within the statutory authority of the agency, the Regional Administrator, or authorized Area Director or designee, may issue an administrative subpoena. See Chapter 15, *Legal Issues.*

L. **Employer Abatement Assistance.**

1. **Policy.** CSHOs shall offer appropriate abatement assistance during the walkaround as to how workplace hazards might be eliminated. The information shall provide guidance to the employer in developing acceptable abatement methods or in seeking appropriate professional assistance. CSHOs shall not imply OSHA endorsement of any product through use of specific product names when recommending abatement measures. The issuance of citations shall not be delayed.

2. **Disclaimers.** The employer shall be informed that:

    a. The employer is not limited to the abatement methods suggested by OSHA;

    b. The methods explained are general and may not be effective in all cases; and

    c. The employer is responsible for selecting and carrying out an effective abatement method, and maintaining the appropriate documentation.

VIII. Closing Conference.

A. **Participants.** At the conclusion of an inspection, CSHOs shall conduct a closing conference with the employer and the employee representatives, jointly or separately, as circumstances dictate. The closing conference may be conducted on-site or by telephone as CSHOs deem appropriate. If the employer refuses to allow a closing conference, the circumstances of the refusal shall be documented in the OSHA-1A narrative and the case shall be processed as if a closing conference had been held.

    NOTE: *When conducting separate closing conferences for employers and labor representatives (where the employer has declined to have a joint closing conference with employee representatives), CSHOs shall normally hold the conference with employee representatives first, unless the employee representative requests otherwise. This procedure will ensure that worker input is received before employers are informed of violations and proposed citations.*

B. **Discussion Items.**

1. CSHOs shall discuss the apparent violations and other pertinent issues found during the inspection and note relevant comments on the OSHA-1B, including input for establishing correction dates.

2. CSHOs shall give employers the publication, "Employer Rights and Responsibilities Following an OSHA Inspection," (OSHA3000) which explains the responsibilities and courses of action available to the employer if a citation is issued, including their rights under the Small Business Regulatory Enforcement Fairness Act (SBREFA). (See SBREFA on OSHA's public webpage.) They shall then briefly discuss the information in the booklet and answer any questions. All matters discussed during the closing conference shall be documented in the case file, including a note describing printed materials distributed.

3. CSHOs shall discuss the strengths and weaknesses of the employer's occupational safety and health system and any other applicable programs, and advise the employer of the benefits of an effective program(s) and provide information, such as, OSHA's website, describing program elements.

4. Both the employer and employee representatives shall be advised of their rights to participate in any subsequent conferences, meeting or discussions, and their contest rights. Any unusual circumstances noted during the closing conference shall be documented in the case file.

5. Since CSHOs may not have all pertinent information at the time of the first closing conference, a second closing conference may be held by telephone or in person.

6. CSHOs shall advise employee representatives that:

    a. Under §2200.20 of the Occupational Safety and Health Review Commission regulations, if an employer contests a citation, the employees have a right to elect "party status" before the Review Commission;

    b. The employer should notify them if a notice of contest or a petition for modification of abatement date is filed;

    c. They have Section 11(c) rights; and

    d.   They have a right to contest the abatement date. Such contests must be in writing and must be postmarked within 15 working days after receipt of the citation.

C.   **Advice to Attendees.**

    1.   The CSHO shall advise those attending the closing conference that a request for an informal conference with the OSHA Area Director is encouraged as it provides an opportunity to:

        a.   Resolve disputed citations and penalties without the need for litigation which can be time consuming and costly;

        b.   Obtain a more complete understanding of the specific safety or health standards which apply;

        c.   Discuss ways to correct the violations;

        d.   Discuss issues concerning proposed penalties;

        e.   Discuss proposed abatement dates;

        f.   Discuss issues regarding employee safety and health practices; and

        g.   Learn more of other OSHA programs and services available.

    2.   If a citation is issued, an informal conference or the request for one does not extend the 15 working-day period in which the employer or employee representatives may contest.

    3.   Verbal disagreement with, or intent to, contest a citation, penalty or abatement date during an informal conference does not replace the required written Notice of Intent to Contest.

    4.   Employee representatives have the right to participate in informal conferences or negotiations between the Area Director and the employer in accordance with the guidelines given in Chapter 7, Section II., *Informal Conferences*.

D.   **Penalties.** CSHOs shall explain that penalties must be paid within 15 working days after the employer receives a citation and notification of penalty. If, however, an employer contests the citation and/or the penalty, penalties need not be paid for the contested items until the final order date.

E.   **Feasible Administrative, Work Practice and Engineering Controls.** Where appropriate, CSHOs will discuss control methodology with the employer during the closing conference.

    1.   **Definitions.**

        a.   **Engineering Controls.** Consist of substitution, isolation, ventilation and equipment modification.

        b.   **Administrative Controls.** Any procedure which significantly limits daily exposure by control or manipulation of the work schedule or manner in which work is performed is considered a means of administrative control. The use of personal protective equipment is not considered a means of administrative control.

        c.   **Work Practice Controls.** A type of administrative controls by which the employer modifies the manner in which the employee performs assigned work. Such modification may result in a reduction of exposure through such methods as changing work habits, improving sanitation and hygiene practices, or making other changes in the way the employee performs the job.

        d.   **Feasibility.** Abatement measures required to correct a citation item are feasible when they can be accomplished by the employer. The CSHO, following current directions and guidelines, shall inform the employer, where appropriate, that a determination will be made as to whether engineering or administrative controls are feasible.

        e.   **Technical Feasibility.** The existence of technical know-how as to materials and methods available or adaptable to specific circumstances, which can be applied to a cited violation with a reasonable possibility that employee exposure to occupational hazards will be reduced.

        f.   **Economic Feasibility.** Means that the employer is financially able to undertake the measures necessary to abate the citations received.

        NOTE: *If an employer's level of compliance lags significantly behind that of its industry, allegations of economic infeasibility will not be accepted.*

    2.   **Documenting Claims of Infeasibility.**

        a.   CSHOs shall document the underlying facts which give rise to an employer's claim of infeasibility.

        b.   When economic infeasibility is claimed, the CSHO shall inform the employer that, although the cost of corrective measures to be taken will generally not be considered as a factor in the issuance of a citation, it may be considered during an informal conference or during settlement negotiations.

        c.   Complex issues regarding feasibility should be referred to the Area Director or designee for determination.

F.   **Reducing Employee Exposure.** Employers shall be advised that, whenever feasible, engineering, administrative or work practice controls must be instituted, even if they are not sufficient to eliminate the hazard (or to reduce exposure to or below the permissible exposure limit). They are required in conjunction with personal protective equipment to further reduce exposure to the lowest practical level.

G.   **Abatement Verification.** During the closing conference the Compliance Officer should thoroughly explain to the employer the abatement verification requirements. See Chapter 7, *Post Inspection Procedures and Abatement Verification.*

    1.   **Abatement Certification.** Abatement certification is required for all citation item(s) which the employer received except for those citation items which are identified as "Corrected During Inspection."

    2.   **Corrected During Inspection (CDI).** The violation(s) that will reflect on-site abatement and will be identified in the citations as "Corrected During Inspection" shall be reviewed at the closing conference.

    3.   **Abatement Documentation.** Abatement documentation, the employer's physical proof of abatement, is required to be submitted along with each willful, repeat and designated serious violation. To minimize confusion, the distinction between abatement certification and abatement documentation should be discussed.

    4.   **Placement of Abatement Verification Tags.** The required placement of abatement verification tags or the citation must also be discussed at the closing conference, if it has not been discussed during the walkaround portion of the inspection. See § 1903.19(i).

    5.   **Requirements for Extended Abatement Periods.** Where extended abatement periods are involved, the requirements for abatement plans and progress reports shall be discussed.

H.   **Employee Discrimination.** The CSHO shall emphasize that the Act prohibits employers from discharging or discriminating in any way against an employee who has exercised any right under the Act, including the right to make safety or health complaints or to request an OSHA inspection.

IX. Special Inspection Procedures.

A. Follow-up and Monitoring Inspections.

1. The primary purpose of a follow-up inspection is to determine if the previously cited violations have been corrected. Monitoring inspections are conducted to ensure that hazards are being abated and employees protected, whenever a long period of time is needed for an establishment to come into compliance (or to verify compliance with the terms of granted variances). Issuance of willful, repeated and high gravity serious violations, failure to abate notifications, and/or citations related to imminent danger situations are examples of prime candidates for follow-up or monitoring inspections. These type of inspections will not normally be conducted when evidence of abatement is provided by the employer or employee representatives.

2. **Failure to Abate.**

   a. A failure to abate exists when a previously cited violation continues unabated and the abatement date has passed or the abatement date is covered under a settlement agreement, or the employer has not complied with interim measures within the allotted time specified in a long-term abatement plan.

   b. If previously cited items have not been corrected, a Notice of Failure to Abate Alleged Violation shall normally be issued. If a subsequent inspection indicates the condition has still not been abated, the RSOL shall be consulted for further guidance.

      NOTE: *If the employer has demonstrated a good faith effort to comply, a late Petition for Modification of Abatement (PMA) may be considered in accordance with Chapter 7, Section III, Petition for Modification of Abatement (PMA).*

   c. If an originally cited violation has at one point been abated but subsequently recurs, a citation for a repeated violation may be appropriate.

3. **Reports.**

   a. For any items found to be abated, a copy of the previous OSHA-1B, OSHA-1B-IH, or citation can be notated with "corrected" written on it, along with a brief explanation of the abatement measures taken,. This information may alternately be included in the narrative of the investigative file.

   b. In the event that any item has not been abated, complete documentation shall be included on an OSHA-1B.

4. **Follow-up Files.** Follow-up inspection reports shall be included with the original (parent) case file.

B. Construction Inspections.

1. **Standards Applicability.** The standards published as 29 CFR Part 1926 have been adopted as occupational safety and health standards under Section 6(a) of the Act and §1910.12. They shall apply to every employment and place of employment of every employee engaged in construction work, including non-contract construction.

2. **Definition.** The term "construction work" as defined by §1926.32(g) means work for construction, alteration, and/or repair, including painting and decorating. These terms are also discussed in §1926.13. If any question arises as to whether an activity is deemed to be construction for purposes of the Act, the Director of the Directorate of Construction shall be consulted.

3. **Employer Worksite.**

   a. Inspections of employers in the construction industry are not easily separable into distinct worksites. The worksite is generally the site where the construction is being performed (e.g., the building site, the dam site). Where the construction site extends over a large geographical area (e.g., road building), the entire job will be considered a single worksite. In cases when such large geographical areas overlap between Area Offices, generally only operations of the employer within the jurisdiction of any Area Office will be considered as the worksite of the employer.

   b. When a construction worksite extends beyond a single Area Office and the CSHO believes that the inspection should be extended, the affected Area Directors shall consult with each other and take appropriate action.

4. **Upon Entering the Workplace.**

   a. CSHOs shall ascertain whether there is a representative of a Federal contracting agency at the worksite. If so, they shall contact the representative, advise him/her of the inspection and request that they attend the opening conference.

   b. If the inspection is being conducted as a result of a complaint, a copy of the complaint is to be furnished to the general contractor and any affected sub-contractors.

5. **Closing Conference.** Upon completion of the inspection, the CSHO shall confer with the general contractors and all appropriate subcontractors or their representatives, together or separately, and advise each one of all the apparent violations disclosed by the inspection to which each one's employees were exposed, or violations which the employer created or controlled. Employee representatives participating in the inspection shall also be afforded the right to participate in the closing conference(s).

C. Federal Agency Inspections.
Policies and procedures for Federal agencies are to be the same as those followed in the private sector. See FAP 01-00-003, *Federal Agency Safety and Health Programs*, dated May 17, 1996, for additional guidance.

Chapter 4 — Violations

I. Basis of Violations.

A. Standards and Regulations.

1. Section 5(a)(2) of the Act states that each employer has a responsibility to comply with occupational safety and health standards promulgated under the Act, which includes standards incorporated by reference. For example, the American National Standard Institute (ANSI) standard A92.2 – 1969, "Vehicle Mounted Elevating and Rotating Work Platforms," including appendix, is incorporated by reference as specified in §1910.67. Only the mandatory provisions, i.e., those containing the word "shall" or other mandatory language of standards incorporated by reference, are adopted as standards under the Act.

2. The specific standards and regulations are found in Title 29 Code of Federal Regulations (CFR) 1900 series. Subparts A and B of 29 CFR 1910 specifically establish the source of all the standards, which serve as the basis of violations. Standards are subdivided as follows per the preferred Federal Register nomenclature:

Subdivision Naming Convention	Example
Title	29
Part	1910
Subpart	D
Section	1910.23
Paragraph	1910.23(c)
Paragraph	1910.23(c)(1)
Paragraph	1910.23(c)(1)(i)

NOTE: *The most specific provision of a standard shall be used for citing violations.*

3.   **Definition and Application of Vertical and Horizontal Standards.** Vertical standards are standards that apply to a particular industry or to particular operations, practices, conditions, processes, means, methods, equipment, or installations. Horizontal standards are other (more general) standards applicable to multiple industries. See § 1910.5(c).

4.   **Application of Horizontal and Vertical Standards.** If a CSHO is uncertain whether to cite under a horizontal or a vertical standard when both may be applicable, the supervisor or the Area Director shall be consulted. The following guidelines shall be considered:

   a.   When a hazard in a particular industry is covered by both a vertical (e.g., 29 CFR 1915) and a horizontal (e.g., 29 CFR 1910) standard, the vertical standard shall take precedence even if the horizontal standard is more stringent.

   b.   In situations covered by both a horizontal (general) and a vertical (specific) standard where the horizontal standard appears to offer greater protection, the horizontal (general) standard may be cited only if its requirements are not inconsistent or in conflict with the requirements of the vertical (specific) standard. To determine whether there is a conflict or inconsistency between the standards, an analysis of the intent of the two standards must be performed. For the horizontal standard to apply, the analysis must show that the vertical standard does not address the precise hazard involved, even though it may address related or similar hazards.

EXAMPLE 4-1: When employees are connecting structural steel, § 1926.501(b)(15) may not be cited for fall hazards above 6 feet since that specific situation is covered by § 1926.760(b)(1) for fall distances of more than 30 feet.

   c.   If the particular industry does not have a vertical standard that covers the hazard, then the CSHO shall use the horizontal (general industry) standard.

   d.   When determining whether a horizontal or a vertical standard is applicable to a work situation, the CSHO shall focus attention on the particular activity an employer is engaged in rather than on the nature of the employer's general business.

   e.   Hazards found in construction work that are not covered by a specific 29 CFR 1926 standard shall not normally be cited under 29 CFR 1910 unless that standard has been identified as being applicable to construction. See Incorporation of General Industry Safety and Health Standards Applicable to Construction Work, 58 FR 35076 (June 30, 1993).

   f.   If a question arises as to whether an activity is deemed construction for purposes of the Act, contact the Directorate of Construction (DOC). See § 1910.12, Construction Work.

5.   **Violation of Variances.** The employer's requirement to comply with a standard may be modified through granting of a variance, as outlined in Section 6(d) of the Act.

   a.   In the event that the employer is not in compliance with the requirements of the variance, a violation of the controlling standard shall be cited with a reference in the citation to the variance provision that has not been met.

   b.   If, during an inspection, CSHOs discover that an employer has filed a variance application regarding a condition that is an apparent violation of a standard, the Area Director or designee shall determine whether the variance request has been granted. If the variance has not been granted, a citation for the violative condition may be issued.

B.   **Employee Exposure.** A hazardous condition that violates an OSHA standard or the general duty clause shall be cited only when employee exposure can be documented. The exposure(s) must have occurred within the six months immediately preceding the issuance of the citation to serve as a basis for a violation, except where the employer has concealed the violative condition or misled OSHA, in which case the citation must be issued within six months from the date when OSHA learns, or should have known, of the condition. The RSOL should be consulted in such cases.

1.   **Determination of Employer/Employee Relationship.** Whether or not exposed persons are employees of a particular employer depends on several factors, the most important of which is who controls the manner in which employees perform their assigned work. The question of who pays these employees may not be the key factor. Determining the employer of exposed employees may be a complex issue, in which case the Area Director shall seek the advice of the RSOL.

2.   **Proximity to the Hazard.** The actual and/or potential proximity of the employees to a hazard shall be thoroughly documented. (i.e., photos, measurements, employee interviews).

3.   **Observed Exposure.**

   a.   Employee exposure is established if CSHOs witness, observe, or monitor the proximity or access of an employee to the hazard or potentially hazardous condition.

   b.   The use of personal protective equipment may not, in itself, adequately prevent employee exposures to a hazardous condition. Such exposures may be cited where the applicable standard requires the additional use of engineering and/or administrative (including work practice) controls, or where the personal protective equipment used is inadequate.

4. **Unobserved Exposure.** Where employee exposure is not observed, witnessed, or monitored by CSHOs, employee exposure may be established through witness statements or other evidence that exposure to a hazardous condition has occurred or may continue to occur.

    a. **Past Exposure.** In fatality/catastrophe (or other "accident/incident") investigations, prior employee exposure(s) may be established if CSHOs establish, through written statements or other evidence, that exposure(s) to a hazardous condition occurred at the time of the accident/incident. Additionally, prior exposures may serve as the basis for a violation when:
- The hazardous condition continues to exist, or it is reasonably predictable that the same or similar condition could recur;
- It is reasonably predictable that employee exposure to a hazardous condition could recur when:
    - o The employee exposure has occurred in the previous six months;
    - o The hazardous condition is an integral part of an employer's normal operations; and
    - o The employer has not established a policy or program to ensure that exposure to the hazardous condition will not recur.

    b. **Potential Exposure.** Potential exposure to a hazardous condition may be established if there is evidence that employees have access to the hazard, and may include one or more of the following:
- When a hazard has existed and could recur because of work patterns, circumstances, or anticipated work requirements;
- When a hazard would pose a danger to employees simply by their presence in an area and it is reasonably predictable that they could come into that area during the course of the work, to rest or to eat, or to enter or exit from an assigned work area; or
- When a hazard is associated with the use of unsafe machinery or equipment or arises from the presence of hazardous materials and it is reasonably predictable that an employee could again use the equipment or be exposed to the materials in the course of work; *however*
- If the inspection reveals an adequately communicated *and* effectively enforced safety policy or program that would prevent or minimize employee exposure, including accidental exposure to the hazardous condition, it would not be reasonably predictable that employee exposure could occur. In such circumstances, no citation should be issued in relation to the condition.

    c. **Documenting Employee Exposure.** CSHOs shall thoroughly document exposure, both observed and unobserved, for each potential violation. This includes:
- Statements by the exposed employees, the employer (particularly the immediate supervisor of the exposed employee), other witnesses (other employees who have observed exposure to the hazardous condition), union representatives, engineering personnel, management, or members of the exposed employee's family;
- Recorded statements or signed written statements;
- Photographs, videotapes, and/or measurements; and
- All relevant documents (e.g., autopsy reports, police reports, job specifications, site plans, OSHA-300/301, equipment manuals, employer work rules, employer sampling results, employer safety and health programs, and employer disciplinary policies, etc.).

C. **Regulatory Requirements.** Violations of 29 CFR Part 1903 and Part 1904 shall be documented and cited when an employer does not comply with posting, recordkeeping, and reporting requirements of the regulations contained in these parts as provided by agency policy. See also CPL 02-00-111, *Citation Policy for Paperwork and Written Program Violations*, dated November 27, 1995.

NOTE: *If prior to the lapse of the 8-hour reporting period, the Area Director becomes aware of an incident required to be reported under §1904.39 through means other than an employer report, there is no violation for failure to report.*

D. **Hazard Communication.** Section 1910.1200 requires chemical manufacturers and importers to assess the hazards of chemicals they produce or import, and applies to these employers even though they may not have their own employees exposed. Violations of this standard by manufacturers or importers shall be documented and cited, irrespective of any employee exposure at the manufacturing or importing location. See CPL 02-02-038, *Inspection Procedures for the Hazard Communication Standard*, dated March 20, 1998.

E. **Employer/Employee Responsibilities.**

1. **Employer Responsibilities.** Section 5(a) of the Act states: "Each employer shall furnish to each of his employees employment and a place of employment which are free from recognized hazards that are causing or are likely to cause death or serious physical harm to his employees." This section also states "The employer shall comply with occupational safety and health standards promulgated under this Act."

2. **Employee Responsibilities.**

    a. Section 5(b) of the Act states: "Each employee shall comply with occupational safety and health standards and all rules, regulations, and orders issued pursuant to the Act which are applicable to his own actions and conduct." The Act does not provide for the issuance of citations or the proposal of penalties against employees. Employers are responsible for employee compliance with the standards.

    b. In cases where the CSHO determines that employees are systematically refusing to comply with a standard applicable to their own actions and conduct, the matter shall be referred to the Area Director who shall consult with the Regional Administrator or designee.

    c. The CSHO is expected to obtain information to ascertain whether the employer is exercising appropriate oversight of the workplace to ensure compliance with the Act. Concerted refusals by employees to comply will not ordinarily bar the issuance of a citation where the employer has failed to exercise its authority to adequately supervise employees, including taking appropriate disciplinary action.

3. **Affirmative Defenses.** An affirmative defense is a claim which, if established by the employer, will excuse it from a violation which has otherwise been documented by the CSHO. Although affirmative defenses must be proved by the employer at the time of the hearing, CSHOs should preliminarily gather evidence to rebut an employer's potential argument supporting any such defenses. See Chapter 5, Section VI, *Affirmative Defenses*, for additional information.

4. **Multi-Employer Worksites.** On multi-employer worksites in all industry sectors, more than one employer may be cited for a hazardous condition that violates an OSHA standard. For specific and detailed guidance, see the multi-employer policy contained in CPL 02-00-124, *Multi-Employer Citation Policy*, dated December 10, 1999.

II. Serious Violations.

A. **Section 17(k).** Section 17(k) of the Act provides that "a serious violation shall be deemed to exist in a place of employment if there is a substantial probability that death or serious physical harm could result from a condition which exists, or from one or more practices, means, methods, operations, or processes which have been adopted or are in use, in such place of employment unless the employer did not, and could not with the exercise of reasonable diligence, know of the presence of the violation."

B. **Establishing Serious Violations.**
1. CSHOs shall consider four factors in determining whether a violation is to be classified as serious. The first three factors address whether there is a substantial probability that death or serious physical harm could result from an accident/incident or exposure relating to the violative condition. The **probability** that an incident or illness will occur is not to be considered in determining whether a violation is serious, but is considered in determining the relative gravity of the violation. The fourth factor addresses whether the employer knew or could have known of the violative condition.
2. The classification of a violation need not be completed for each instance. It should be done once for each citation or, if violation items are grouped in a citation, once for the group.
3. If the citation consists of multiple instances or grouped violations, the overall classification shall normally be based on the most serious item.
4. The four-factor analysis outlined below shall be followed in making the determination whether a violation is serious. Potential violations of the general duty clause shall also be evaluated on the basis of these steps to establish whether they may cause death or serious physical harm.

C. **Four Steps to be Documented.**
1. **Type of Hazardous Exposure(s).** The first step is to identify the type of potential exposures to a hazard that the violated standard or the general duty clause is designed to prevent.
   a. CSHOs need not establish the exact manner in which an exposure to a hazard could occur. However, CSHOs shall note all facts which could affect the probability of an injury or illness **resulting** from a potential accident or hazardous exposure.
   b. If more than one type of hazardous exposure exists, CSHOs shall determine which hazard could reasonably be predicted to result in the most severe injury or illness and shall base the classification of the violation on that hazard.
   c. The following are examples of some types of hazardous exposures that a standard is designed to prevent:

EXAMPLE 4-2: Employees are observed working at the unguarded edge of an open-sided floor 30 feet above the ground in apparent violation of §1926.501(b)(1). The regulation requires that the edge of the open-sided floor be guarded by standard guardrail systems. The type of hazard the standard is designed to prevent is a fall from the edge of the floor to the ground below.

EXAMPLE 4-3: Employees are observed working in an area in which debris is located in apparent violation of §1915.91(b). The type of hazard the standard is designed to prevent here is employees tripping on debris.

EXAMPLE 4-4: An 8-hour time-weighted average sample reveals regular, ongoing employee overexposure to methylene chloride at 100 ppm in apparent violation of §1910.1052. This is 75 ppm above the PEL mandated by the standard.

2. **The Type of Injury or Illness.** The second step is to identify the most serious injury or illness that could reasonably be expected to result from the potential hazardous exposure identified in Step 1.
   a. In making this determination, CSHOs shall consider all factors that would affect the severity of the injury or illness that could reasonably result from the exposure to the hazard. CSHOs shall not give consideration at this point to factors relating to the **probability** that an injury or illness will occur.
   b. The following are examples of types of injuries that could reasonably be predicted to result from exposure to a particular hazard:

EXAMPLE 4-5: If an employee falls from the edge of an open-sided floor 30 feet to the ground below, the employee could die, break bones, suffer a concussion, or experience other serious injuries that would substantially impair a body function.

EXAMPLE 4-6: If an employee trips on debris, the trip may cause abrasions or bruises, but it is only marginally predictable that the employee could suffer a substantial impairment of a bodily function. If, however, the area is littered with broken glass or other sharp objects, it is reasonably predictable that an employee who tripped on debris could suffer deep cuts which could require suturing.

   c. For conditions involving exposure to air contaminants or harmful physical agents, the CSHO shall consider the concentration levels of the contaminant or physical agent in determining the types of illness that could reasonably result from the exposure. CPL 02-02-043, *The Chemical Information Manual*, dated July 1, 1991, shall be used to determine both toxicological properties of substances listed and a Health Code Number.

d. In order to support a classification of serious, a determination must be made that exposure(s) at the sampled level could lead to illness. Thus, CSHOs must document all evidence demonstrating that the sampled exposure(s) is representative of employee exposure(s) under normal working conditions, including identifying and recording the frequency and duration of employee exposure(s). Evidence to be considered includes:

- The nature of the operation from which the exposure results;
- Whether the exposure is regular and on-going or is of limited frequency and duration;
- How long employees have worked at the operation in the past;
- Whether employees are performing functions which can be expected to continue; and
- Whether work practices, engineering controls, production levels, and other operating parameters are typical of normal operations.

e. Where such evidence is difficult to obtain or inconclusive, CSHOs shall estimate frequency and duration of exposures from any evidence available. In general, if it is reasonable to infer that regular, ongoing exposures could occur, CSHOs shall consider such potential exposures in determining the types of illness that could result from the violative condition. The following are some examples of illnesses that could reasonably result from exposure to a health hazard:

EXAMPLE 4-7: If an employee is exposed regularly to methylene chloride at 100 ppm, it is reasonable to predict that cancer could result.

EXAMPLE 4-8: If an employee is exposed regularly to acetic acid at 20 ppm, it is reasonable that the resulting illnesses would be irritation to eyes, nose and throat, or occupational asthma with chronic rhinitis and sinusitis.

3. **Potential for Death or Serious Physical Harm.** The third step is to determine whether the type of injury or illness identified in Step 2 could include death or a form of serious physical harm. In making this determination, the CSHO shall utilize the following definition of "serious physical harm:"

Impairment of the body in which part of the body is made functionally useless or is substantially reduced in efficiency on or off the job. Such impairment may be permanent or temporary, chronic or acute. Injuries involving such impairment would usually require treatment by a medical doctor or other licensed health care professional.

a. Injuries that constitute serious physical harm include, but are not limited, to:

- Amputations (loss of all or part of a bodily appendage);
- Concussion;
- Crushing (internal, even though skin surface may be intact);
- Fractures (simple or compound);
- Burns or scalds, including electric and chemical burns;
- Cuts, lacerations, or punctures involving significant bleeding and/or requiring suturing;
- Sprains and strains; and
- Musculoskeletal disorders.

b. Illnesses that constitute serious physical harm include, but are not limited, to:

- Cancer;
- Respiratory illnesses (silicosis, asbestosis, byssinosis, etc.);
- Hearing impairment;
- Central nervous system impairment;
- Visual impairment; and
- Poisoning.

c. The following are examples of injuries or illnesses that could reasonably result from an accident/incident or exposure and lead to death or serious physical harm:

EXAMPLE 4-9: If an employee falls 15 feet to the ground, suffers broken bones or a concussion, and experiences substantial impairment of a part of the body requiring treatment by a medical doctor, the injury would constitute serious physical harm.

EXAMPLE 4-10: If an employee trips on debris and because of the presence of sharp debris or equipment suffers a deep cut to the hand requiring suturing, the use of the hand could be substantially reduced. This injury would be classified as serious.

EXAMPLE 4-11: An employee develops chronic beryllium disease after long-term exposure to beryllium at a concentration in air of 0.004 mg/m3, and his or her breathing capacity is significantly reduced. This illness would constitute serious physical harm.

NOTE: *The key determination is the likelihood that death or serious harm will result IF an accident or exposure occurs. The likelihood of an accident occurring is addressed in penalty assessments and not by the classification.*

4. **Knowledge of Hazardous Condition.** The fourth step is to determine whether the employer knew or, with the exercise of reasonable diligence, could have known, of the presence of the **hazardous condition**.

a. The knowledge requirement is met if it is established that the employer actually knew of the hazardous condition constituting the apparent violation. Examples include the employer saw the condition, an employee or employee representative reported it to the employer, or an employee was previously injured by the condition and the employer knew of the injury. CSHOs shall record any/all evidence that establishes employer knowledge of the condition or practice.

b. If it cannot be determined that the employer has actual knowledge of a hazardous condition, the knowledge requirement may be established if there is evidence that the employer could have known of it through the exercise of reasonable diligence. CSHOs shall record any evidence that substantiates that the employer could have known of the hazardous condition. Examples of such evidence include:

- The violation/hazard was in plain view and obvious;
- The duration of the hazardous condition was not brief;
- The employer failed to regularly inspect the workplace for readily identifiable hazards; and
- The employer failed to train and supervise employees regarding the particular hazard.

c. The actual or constructive knowledge of a supervisor who is aware of a violative condition or practice can usually be imputed to the employer for purposes of establishing knowledge. In cases where the employer contends that the supervisor's own conduct constituted an isolated event of employee misconduct, the CSHO shall attempt to determine whether the supervisor violated an established work rule, and the extent to which the supervisor was trained in the rule and supervised regarding compliance to prevent such conduct.

III. **General Duty Requirements.** Section 5(a)(1) of the Act requires that "Each employer shall furnish to each of his employees employment and a place of employment which are free from recognized hazards that are causing or are likely to cause death or serious physical harm to his employees." The general duty requirement also exists for federal agencies. See §1960.8.

A. **Evaluation of General Duty Requirements.** In general, Review Commission and court precedent have established that the following elements are necessary to prove a violation of the general duty clause:

- The employer failed to keep the workplace free of a hazard to which employees of that employer were exposed;
- The hazard was recognized;
- The hazard was causing or was likely to cause death or serious physical harm; and
- There was a feasible and useful method to correct the hazard.

A general duty citation must involve both the presence of a serious hazard and exposure of the cited employer's **own** employees.

B. **Elements of a General Duty Requirement Violation.**

1. **Definition of a Hazard.**

a. The hazard in a Section 5(a)(1) citation is a *workplace condition* or practice to which employees are exposed, creating the *potential for death or serious physical harm* to employees.

b. These conditions or practices must be **clearly stated in a citation** so as to apprise employers of their obligations and must be ones the employer can reasonably be expected to prevent. The hazard must therefore be defined in terms of the **presence of hazardous conditions or** practices that present a particular danger to employees.

2. **Do Not Cite the Lack of a Particular Abatement Method.**

a. General duty clause citations are not intended to allege that the violation is a failure to implement certain precautions, corrective actions, or other abatement measures but rather addresses the failure to prevent or remove a particular hazard. Section 5(a)(1) therefore does not mandate a particular abatement measure but only requires an employer to render the workplace free of recognized hazards by any feasible and effective means the employer wishes to utilize.

b. In situations where a question arises regarding distinguishing between a dangerous workplace condition or practice and the lack of an abatement method, the Area Director shall consult with the Regional Administrator or designee, or RSOL for assistance in correctly identifying the hazard.

EXAMPLE 4-12: Employees are conducting sanding operations that create sparks in the proximity of magnesium dust (workplace condition or practice) exposing them to the serious injury of burns from a fire (potential for physical harm). One proposed method of abatement may be engineering controls such as adequate ventilation. The "hazard" is sanding that creates sparks in the presence of magnesium that may result in a fire capable of seriously injuring employees, not the lack of adequate ventilation.

EXAMPLE 4-13: Employees are operating tools that generate sparks in the presence of an ignitable gas (workplace condition) exposing them to the danger of an explosion (physical harm). The hazard is use of tools that create sparks in a volatile atmosphere that may cause an explosion capable of seriously injuring employees, not the lack of approved equipment.

EXAMPLE 4-14: In a workplace situation involving high-pressure machinery that vents gases next to a work area where the employer has not installed proper high-pressure equipment, has improperly installed the equipment that is in place, and does not have adequate work rules addressing the dangers of high pressure gas, there are three abatement measures the employer has failed to take. However, there is only one hazard (i.e., employee exposure to the venting of high-pressure gases into a work area that may cause serious burns from steam discharges).

3. **The Hazard is Not a Particular Accident/Incident.**

a. The occurrence of an accident/incident does not necessarily mean that the employer has violated Section 5(a)(1), although the accident/incident may be evidence of a hazard. In some cases a Section 5(a)(1) violation may be unrelated to the cause of the accident/incident. Although accident/incident facts may be relevant and shall be documented, the citation shall address the **hazard in the workplace that existed prior to the accident/incident**, not the particular facts that led to the occurrence of the accident/incident.

EXAMPLE 4-15: A fire occurred in a workplace where flammable materials were present. No one was injured by the fire but an employee, disregarding the clear instructions of his supervisor to use an available exit, jumped out of a window and broke a leg. The danger of fire due to the presence of flammable materials may be a recognized hazard causing or likely to cause death or serious physical harm, but the action of the employee may be an instance of unpreventable employee misconduct. The citation must address the underlying workplace fire hazard, not the accident/incident involving the employee.

  f. State and local laws or regulations that apply in the jurisdiction where the violation is alleged to have occurred and which currently are enforced against the industry in question. In such cases, however, corroborating evidence of recognition is recommended; and/or

  g. If the relevant industry participated in the committees drafting national consensus standards such as the American National Standards Institute (ANSI), the National Fire Protection Association (NFPA), and other private standard-setting organizations, this can constitute industry recognition. Otherwise, such private standards normally shall be used only as corroborating evidence of recognition. Preambles to these standards that discuss the hazards involved may show hazard recognition as much as, or more than, the actual standards. However, these private standards **cannot** be enforced as OSHA standards, but they may be used to provide evidence of industry recognition, seriousness of the hazard or feasibility of abatement methods.

■ In cases where State and local government agencies have codes or regulations covering hazards not addressed by OSHA standards, the Area Director, upon consultation with the Regional Administrator or designee, shall determine whether the hazard is to be cited under Section 5(a)(1) or referred to the appropriate local agency for enforcement.

EXAMPLE 4-18: A safety hazard on a personnel elevator in a factory is documented during an inspection. It is determined that the hazard may not be cited under Section 5(a)(1), but there is a local code that addresses this hazard and a local agency actively enforces the code. The situation normally shall be referred to the local enforcement agency in lieu of citing 5(a)(1).

■ References that may be used to supplement other evidence to help demonstrate industry recognition include the following:
 a. NIOSH criteria documents.
 b. EPA publications.
 c. National Cancer Institute and other agency publications.
 d. OSHA Hazard Alerts.
 e. OSHA Technical Manual.

 c. **Common Sense Recognition.** If industry or employer recognition of the hazard cannot be established in accordance with (a) and (b), hazard recognition can still be established if a hazardous condition is so obvious that any reasonable person would have recognized it. This form of recognition should only be used in flagrant or obvious cases.

EXAMPLE 4-19: In a general industry situation, courts have held that any reasonable person would recognize that it is hazardous to use an unenclosed chute to dump bricks into an alleyway 26 feet below where unwarned employees worked. In construction, Section 5(a)(1) could not be cited in this situation because §1926.252 or §1926.852 applies. In the context of a chemical processing plant, common sense recognition was established where hazardous substances were being vented into a work area.

7. **The Hazard Was Causing or Likely to Cause Death or Serious Physical Harm.**
 a. This element of a Section 5(a)(1) violation is virtually identical to the substantial probability element of a serious violation under Section 17(k) of the Act. Serious physical harm is defined in Paragraph II.C.3. of this chapter.
 b. This element of a Section 5(a)(1) violation can be established by showing that:
  ■ An actual death or serious injury resulted from the recognized hazard, whether immediately prior to the inspection or at other times and places; or
  ■ If an accident/incident occurred, the likely result would be death or serious physical harm.

EXAMPLE 4-20: An employee is standing at the edge of an unguarded floor 25 feet above the ground. If a fall occurred, death or serious physical harm (e.g., broken bones) is likely to result.

 c. In the health context, establishing serious physical harm at the cited levels may be challenging if the potential for illness/harm requires the passage of a substantial period of time. In such cases, expert testimony is crucial to establish there is probability that long-term serious physical harm will occur. It will generally be less difficult to establish this element for acute illnesses, since the immediacy of the effects will make the causal relationship clearer. In general, the following must be shown to establish that the hazard causes, or is likely to cause, death or serious physical harm when such illness or death will occur only after the passage of time:
  ■ Regular and continuing employee exposure at the workplace to the toxic substance at the measured levels could reasonably occur;
  ■ An illness reasonably could result from such regular and continuing employee exposures; and
  ■ If illness does occur, its likely result is death or serious physical harm.

8. **The Hazard May be Corrected by a Feasible and Useful Method.**
 a. To establish a Section 5(a)(1) violation, the agency must also identify the existence of a measure(s) that is feasible, available, and likely to correct the hazard. Evidence regarding feasible abatement measures shall indicate that the recognized hazard, rather than a particular accident/incident, is preventable.
 b. If the proposed abatement method would eliminate or significantly reduce the hazard beyond whatever measures the employer may be taking, a Section 5(a)(1) citation may be issued. A citation will not be issued merely because the agency is aware of an abatement method different from that of the employer, if the proposed method would not reduce the hazard significantly more than the employer's method. In some cases, only a series of abatement methods will materially reduce a hazard and then all potential abatement methods shall be listed. For example, an abatement note shall be included on the OSHA-1b and -2 such as "Among other methods, one feasible and acceptable means of abatement would be to ___." (Fill in the blank with the specified abatement recommendation.)

c. Examples of such feasible and acceptable means of abatement include, but are not limited, to:
- The employer's own abatement method,/ which existed prior to the inspection but was not implemented;
- The implementation of feasible abatement measures by the employer after the accident/incident or inspection;
- The implementation of abatement measures by other employers/companies; and
- Recommendations made by the manufacturer addressing safety measures for the hazardous equipment involved, as well as suggested abatement methods contained in trade journals, national consensus standards and individual employer work rules. National consensus standards shall not solely be relied on to mandate specific abatement methods.

EXAMPLE 4-21: An ANSI standard addresses the hazard of exposure to hydrogen sulfide gas and refers to various abatement methods, such as the prevention of the buildup of materials that create the gas and the provision of ventilation. The ANSI standard may be used as general evidence of the existence of feasible abatement measures.

In this example, the citation shall state that the recognized hazard of exposure to hydrogen sulfide gas was present in the workplace and that a feasible and useful abatement method existed; e.g., preventing the buildup of gas by providing an adequate ventilation system. It would not be correct to base the citation on the employer's failure to prevent the buildup of materials that could create the gas and to provide a ventilation system as both of these are abatement methods, not recognized hazards.

d. Evidence provided by expert witnesses may be used to demonstrate feasibility of abatement methods. In addition, although it is not necessary to establish that an industry recognizes a particular abatement measure, such evidence may be used if available.

C. **Use of the General Duty Clause.**
1. The general duty clause shall be used only where there is no standard that applies to the particular hazard and in situations where a recognized hazard is created in whole or in part by conditions not covered by a standard. See §1910.5(f).

EXAMPLE 4-22: A hazard covered only partially by a standard would be construction employees exposed to a collapse hazard because of a failure to properly install reinforcing steel. Construction standards contain requirements for reinforcing steel in wall, piers, columns, and similar vertical structures, but do not contain requirements for steel placement in horizontal planes, e.g., a concrete floor. A failure to properly install reinforcing steel in a floor in accordance with industry standards and/or structural drawings could be cited under the general duty clause.

EXAMPLE 4-23: The powered industrial truck standard at §1910.178 does not address all potential hazards associated with forklift use. For instance, while that standard deals with the hazards associated with a forklift operator leaving his vehicle unattended or dismounting the vehicle and working in its vicinity, it does not contain requirements for the use of operator restraint systems. An employer's failure to address the hazard of a tipover (forklifts are particularly susceptible to tipovers) by requiring operators of powered industrial trucks equipped with restraint devices or seat belts to use those devices could be cited under the general duty clause. See CPL 02-01-028, *Compliance Assistance for the Powered Industrial Truck Operator Training Standards*, dated November 30, 2000, for additional guidance.

2. The general duty clause may also be applicable to some types of employment that are inherently dangerous (fire brigades, emergency rescue operations, confined space entry, etc.).
a. Employers involved in such occupations must take the necessary steps to eliminate or minimize employee exposure to all recognized hazards that are likely to cause death or serious physical harm. These steps include an assessment of hazards that may be encountered, providing appropriate protective equipment, and any training, instruction, or necessary equipment.
b. An employer, who has failed to take such steps and allows its employees to be exposed to a hazard, may be cited under the general duty clause.

D. **Limitations of Use of the General Duty Clause.** Section 5(a)(1) is to be used only within the guidelines given in this chapter.
1. **Section 5(a)(1) Shall Not be Used When a Standard Applies to a Hazard.** As discussed above, Section 5(a)(1) may not be cited if an OSHA standard applies to the hazardous working condition. If there is a question as to whether a standard applies, the Area Director shall consult with the Regional Administrator or designee. The RSOL will assist the Regional Administrator or designee in determining the applicability of a standard prior to the issuance of a citation.

EXAMPLE 4-24: Section 5(a)(1) shall not be cited for electrical hazards as §1910.303(b) and §1926.403(b) require that electrical equipment is to be kept free from recognized hazards that are likely to cause death or serious physical hard to employees.

2. **Section 5(a)(1) Shall Normally Not be Used to Impose a Stricter Requirement than that Required by the Standard.**

EXAMPLE 4-25: A standard provides for a permissible exposure limit (PEL) of 5 ppm. Even if data establish that a 3 ppm level is a recognized hazard, Section 5(a)(1) shall not be cited to require that the lower level be achieved. If the standard has only a time-weighted average permissible exposure level and the hazard involves exposure above a recognized ceiling level, the Area Director shall consult with the Regional Administrator or designee, who shall discuss any proposed citation with the RSOL.

NOTE: *An exception to this rule may apply if it can be proven that "an employer knows a particular safety or heath standard is inadequate to protect his employees against the specific hazard it is intended to address." See, Int. Union UAW v. General Dynamics Land Systems Division, 815 F.2d 1570 (D.C. Cir. 1987). Such cases shall be subject to pre-citation review.*

3. **Section 5(a)(1) Shall Normally Not be Used to Require Additional Abatement Methods not Set Forth in an Existing Standard.** If a toxic substance standard covers engineering control requirements but not requirements for medical surveillance, Section 5(a)(1) shall not be cited to additionally require medical surveillance. Area Directors shall evaluate the circumstances of special situations in accord with guidelines stated herein and consult with the Regional Administrator or designee to determine whether a 5(a)(1) citation can be issued in those special cases.

4. **Alternative Standards.** The following standards shall be considered carefully before issuing a Section 5(a)(1) citation for a health hazard.

   a. There are a number of general standards that shall be considered rather than Section 5(a)(1) in situations where the hazard is not covered by a particular standard. If a hazard not covered by a specific standard can be substantially corrected by compliance with a personal protective equipment (PPE) standard, the PPE standard shall be cited. In general industry, § 1910.132(a) may be appropriate where exposure to a hazard may be prevented by the wearing of PPE.

   b. For a health hazard, the particular toxic substance standard, such as asbestos and coke oven emissions, shall be cited where appropriate. If those particular standards do not apply, however, other standards may be applicable; e.g., the air contaminant levels contained in § 1910.1000 in general industry and in § 1926.55 for construction.

   c. Another general standard is § 1910.134(a), which addresses the hazards of breathing harmful air contaminants not covered under § 1910.1000 or another specific standard, and which may be cited for failure to use feasible engineering controls or respirators.

   d. Violations of § 1910.141(g)(2) may be cited when employees are allowed to consume food or beverages in an area exposed to a toxic material, and § 1910.132(a) where there is a potential for toxic materials to be absorbed through the skin.

E. **Classification of Violations Cited Under the General Duty Clause.** Only hazards presenting serious physical harm or death may be cited under the general duty clause (including willful and/or repeated violations that would otherwise qualify as serious violations). Other-than-serious citations shall not be issued for general duty clause violations.

F. **Procedures for Implementation of Section 5(a)(1) Enforcement.** To ensure that citations of the general duty clause are defensible, the following procedures shall be followed:

1. **Gathering Evidence and Preparing the File.**

   a. The evidence necessary to establish each element of a Section 5(a)(1) violation shall be documented in the file. This includes all photographs, videotapes, sampling data, witness statements, and other documentary and physical evidence necessary to establish the violation. Additional documentation includes evidence of specific and/or general awareness of a hazard, why it was detectable and recognized, and any supporting statements or reference materials.

   b. If copies of documents relied on to establish the various Section 5(a)(1) elements cannot be obtained before issuing the citation, these documents shall be accurately cited and identified in the file so they can be obtained later if necessary.

   c. If experts are necessary to establish any element(s) of a Section 5(a)(1) violation, such experts and RSOL shall be consulted **prior to the citation being issued** and their opinions noted in the file.

2. **Pre-Citation Review.** The Area Director shall review and approve all proposed Section 5(a)(1) citations. These citations shall undergo additional pre-citation review as follows:

   a. The Regional Administrator or designee and RSOL shall be consulted prior to the issuance of all Section 5(a)(1) citations where complex issues or exceptions to the outlined procedures are involved; and

   b. If a standard does not apply and all criteria for issuing a Section 5(a)(1) citation are not met, yet the Area Director determines that the hazard warrants some type of notification, a Hazard Alert Letter shall be sent to the employer and employee representative describing the hazard and suggesting corrective action.

IV. **Other-than-Serious Violations.** This type of violation shall be cited in situations where the accident/incident or illness that would be most likely result from a hazardous condition would probably not cause death or serious physical harm, but would have a direct and immediate relationship to the safety and health of employees.

V. **Willful Violations.** A willful violation exists under the Act where an employer has demonstrated either an intentional disregard for the requirements of the Act or a plain indifference to employee safety and health. Area Directors are encouraged to consult with RSOL when developing willful citations. The following guidance and procedures apply whenever there is evidence that a willful violation may exist:

A. **Intentional Disregard Violations.** An employer commits an intentional and knowing violation if:

1. An employer was aware of the requirements of the Act or of an applicable standard or regulation and was also aware of a condition or practice in violation of those requirements, but did not abate the hazard; or

2. An employer was not aware of the requirements of the Act or standards, but had knowledge of a comparable legal requirement (e.g., state or local law) and was also aware of a condition or practice in violation of that requirement. **NOTE:** *Good faith efforts made by the employer to minimize or abate a hazard may sometimes preclude the issuance of a willful violation. In such cases, CSHOs should consult the Area Director or designee if a willful classification is under consideration.*

3. A willful citation also may be issued where an employer knows that specific steps must be taken to address a hazard, but substitutes its judgment for the requirements of the standard. See the internal memorandum on Procedures for Significant Cases, and CPL 02-00-080, Handling of Cases to be Proposed for Violation-by-Violation, dated October 21, 1990.

EXAMPLE 4-26: The employer was issued repeated citations addressing the same or similar conditions, but did not take corrective action.

B.   **Plain Indifference Violations.**
1.   An employer commits a violation with plain indifference to employee safety and health where:
a.   Management officials were aware of an OSHA requirement applicable to the employer's business but made little or no effort to communicate the requirement to lower level supervisors and employees.
b.   Company officials were aware of a plainly obvious hazardous condition but made little or no effort to prevent violations from occurring.

EXAMPLE 4-27: The employer is aware of the existence of unguarded power presses that have caused near misses, lacerations and amputations in the past and does nothing to abate the hazard.

c.   An employer was not aware of any legal requirement, but knows that a condition or practice in the workplace is a serious hazard to the safety or health of employees and makes little or no effort to determine the extent of the problem or to take the corrective action. Knowledge of a hazard may be gained from such means as insurance company reports, safety committee or other internal reports, the occurrence of illnesses or injuries, or complaints of employees or their representatives.
     NOTE: *Voluntary employer self-audits that assess workplace safety and health conditions shall not normally be used as a basis of a willful violation. However, once an employer's self-audit identifies a hazardous condition, the employer must promptly take appropriate measures to correct a violative condition and provide interim employee protection. See OSHA's Policy on Voluntary Employer Safety and Health Self-Audits (Federal Register, July 28, 2000 (65 FR 46498)).*
d.   Willfulness may also be established despite lack of knowledge of a legal requirement if circumstances show that the employer would have placed no importance on such knowledge.

EXAMPLE 4-28: An employer sends employees into a deep unprotected excavation containing a hazardous atmosphere without ever inspecting for potential hazards.

2.   It is not necessary that the violation be committed with a bad purpose or malicious intent to be deemed "willful." It is sufficient that the violation was deliberate, voluntary or intentional as distinguished from inadvertent, accidental or ordinarily negligent.
3.   CSHOs shall develop and record on the OSHA-1B all evidence that indicates employer knowledge of the requirements of a standard, and any reasons for why it disregarded statutory or other legal obligations to protect employees against a hazardous condition. Willfulness may exist if an employer is informed by employees or employee representatives regarding an alleged hazardous condition and does not make a reasonable effort to verify or correct the hazard. Additional factors to consider in determining whether to characterize a violation as willful include:
a.   The nature of the employer's business and the knowledge regarding safety and health matters that could reasonably be expected in the industry;
b.   Any precautions taken by the employer to limit the hazardous conditions;
c.   The employer's awareness of the Act and of its responsibility to provide safe and healthful working conditions; and
d.   Whether similar violations and/or hazardous conditions have been brought to the attention of the employer through prior citations, accidents, warnings from OSHA or officials from other government agencies or an employee safety committee regarding the requirements of a standard.
     NOTE: *This includes prior citations or warnings from OSHA State Plan officials.*
4.   Also, include facts showing that even if the employer was not consciously violating the Act, it was aware that the violative condition existed and made no reasonable effort to eliminate it.

VI.   **Criminal/Willful Violations.** Section 17(e) of the Act, as amended, provides that: "Any employer who willfully violates any standard, rule or order promulgated pursuant to Section 6 of this Act, or of any regulations prescribed pursuant to this Act, and that violation caused death to any employee, shall, upon conviction, be punished by a fine" of not more than $250,000 for an individual and $500,000 for an organization or by imprisonment for not more than six months nor less than 30 days, or by both. Note that this provision of the Act does not apply to Section 5(a)(1) violations classified as willful. See Chapter 6, Section XIII, *Penalties and Debt Collection*, regarding criminal penalties.
A.   **Area Director Coordination.** The Area Director, in coordination with the RSOL, shall carefully evaluate all willful cases involving employee deaths to determine whether they may involve criminal violations of Section 17(e) of the Act. Because the quality of the evidence available is of paramount importance in these investigations, there shall be early and close discussions between the CSHO, the Area Director, the Regional Administrator, and the RSOL in developing all evidence when there is a potential Section 17(e) violation.
B.   **Criteria for Investigating Possible Criminal/Willful Violations.** The following criteria shall be considered in investigating possible criminal/willful violations:
1.   In order to establish a criminal/willful violation OSHA must prove that:
a.   The employer violated an OSHA standard. A criminal/willful violation cannot be based on violation of Section 5(a)(1).
b.   The violation was willful in nature.
c.   The violation of the standard caused the death of an employee. In order to prove that the violation caused the death of an employee, there must be evidence which clearly demonstrates that the violation of the standard was the direct cause of, or a contributing factor to, an employee's death.
2.   If asked during an investigation, CSHOs should inform employers that any violation found to be willful that has caused or contributed to the death of an employee is evaluated for potential criminal referral to the U.S. Department of Justice.
3.   Following the investigation, if the Area Director decides to recommend criminal prosecution, a memorandum shall be forwarded promptly to the Regional Administrator. It shall include an evaluation of the possible criminal charges, taking into consideration the burden of proof requiring that the Government's case be proven beyond a reasonable doubt. In addition, if correction of the hazardous condition is at issue, this shall be noted in the

transmittal memorandum, because in most cases prosecution of a criminal/willful case stays the resolution of the civil case and its abatement requirements.

    4.   The Area Director shall normally issue a civil citation in accordance with current procedures even if the citation involves charges under consideration for criminal prosecution. The Regional Administrator shall be notified of such cases. In addition, the case shall be promptly forwarded to the RSOL for possible referral to the U.S. Department of Justice.

    C.   **Willful Violations Related to a Fatality** Where a willful violation is related to a fatality and a decision is made not to recommend a criminal referral, the Area Director shall ensure the case file contains documentation justifying that conclusion. The file documentation should indicate which elements of a potential criminal violation make the case unsuitable for referral.

VII. Repeated Violations.

    A.   **Federal and State Plan Violations.**

        1.   An employer may be cited for a repeated violation if that employer has been cited previously for the same or substantially similar condition or hazard **and the citation has become a final order of the Review Commission**. A citation may become a final order by operation of law when an employer does not contest the citation, or pursuant to court decision or settlement.

        2.   Prior citations by State Plan States cannot be used as a basis for Federal OSHA repeated violations. Only violations that have become final orders of the Review Commission may be considered.

    B.   **Identical Standards.** Generally, similar workplace conditions or hazards can be demonstrated by showing that in both situations the identical standard was violated, but there are exceptions.

EXAMPLE 4-28: A citation was previously issued for a violation of §1910.132(a) for not requiring the use of safety-toe footwear for employees. A recent inspection of the same establishment revealed a violation of §1910.132(a) for not requiring the use of head protection (hardhats). Although the same standard was involved, the hazardous conditions in each case are not substantially similar and therefore a repeated violation would not be appropriate.

    C.   **Different Standards.** In some circumstances, similar conditions or hazards can be demonstrated even when different standards are violated.

EXAMPLE 4-29: A citation was previously issued for a violation of §1910.28(d)(7) for not installing standard guardrails on a tubular welded frame scaffold platform. A recent inspection of the same employer reveals a violation of §1910.28(c)(14) for not installing guardrails on a tube and coupler scaffold platform. Although different standards are involved, the conditions and hazards (falls) present during both inspections were substantially similar, and therefore a repeated violation would be appropriate.

NOTE: *There is no requirement that the previous and current violations occur at the same workplace or under the same supervisor.*

    D.   **Obtaining Inspection History.** For purposes of determining whether a violation is repeated, the following criteria shall apply:

        1.   **High Gravity Serious Violations.**

            a.   When high gravity serious violations are to be cited, the Area Director shall obtain a history of citations previously issued to this employer at all of its identified establishments nationwide, within the same two digit Standard Industrial Classification (SIC) or three digit North American Industry Classification System (NAICS) code. Note that for repeated violations at federal agencies, the history of citations is limited to region-wide.

            b.   If these violations have been previously cited within the time limitations (described in Paragraph VII.E. of this chapter) and have become final orders of the Review Commission, a repeated citation may be issued.

            c.   Under special circumstances, the Area Director, in consultation with the RSOL, may also issue citations for repeated violations without regard for the SIC code.

        2.   **Violations of Lesser Gravity.** When violations are of lesser gravity than high gravity serious, Area Directors should obtain a national inspection history whenever the circumstances of the current inspection would result in multiple serious, repeat, or willful citations. This is particularly essential if the employer is known to have establishments nationwide and has been subject to a significant case in other areas or at other mobile worksites.

    E.   **Time Limitations.**

        1.   Although there are no statutory limitations on the length of time that a prior citation was issued as a basis for a repeated violation, the following policy shall generally be followed. A citation will be issued as a repeated violation if:

            a.   The citation is issued within 3 years of the final order date of the previous citation or within 3 years of the final abatement date, whichever is later; and

            b.   If the previous citation was contested, within 3 years of the Review Commission's final order or the Court of Appeals final mandate.

        2.   When a violation is found during an inspection and a repeated citation has previously been issued for a substantially similar condition, the violation may be classified as a second instance repeated violation with a corresponding increase in penalty.

EXAMPLE 4-30: An inspection is conducted in an establishment and a violation of §1910.217(c)(1)(i) is found. That citation is not contested by the employer and becomes a final order of the Commission on October 17, 2006. On December 8, 2008, a citation for repeated violation of the same standard was issued. The violation found during the current inspection may be treated as a second instance repeated.

        3.   In cases of multiple prior repeated citations, the Regional Administrator or designee shall be consulted for guidance.

    F.   **Repeated v. Failure to Abate.** A failure to abate exists when a previously cited hazardous condition, practice or non-complying equipment has not been brought into compliance since the prior inspection (i.e., the violation is continuously present) and is discovered at a later inspection. If, however, the violation was corrected, but later reoccurs, the subsequent occurrence is a repeated violation.

G. **Area Director Responsibilities.** After the CSHO makes a recommendation that a violation should be cited as repeated, the Area Director shall:

1. Ensure that the violation meets the criteria outlined in the preceding subparagraphs of this section;

2. Ensure that the case file includes a copy of the citation for the prior violation, the OSHA-1Bs describing the prior violation that serves as the basis for the repeated citation, and any other supporting evidence that describes the violation. If the prior violation citation is not available, the basis for the repeated citation shall, nevertheless, be adequately documented in the case file. The file shall also include all documents showing that the citation is a final order and on what date it became final (i.e., if the case was not contested, the **certified mail card** (final 15 working days from employer's receipt of the citation), **signed Informal Settlement** (final 15 working days from when **both** parties signed) or **Formal Settlement Agreements and Notice of Docketing** (final 30 days after docketing date), or **Judge's Decision and Notice of Docketing** (final 30 days after docketing));

3. IMIS information shall not be used as the sole means to establish that a prior violation has been issued.

4. In circumstances when it is not clear that the violation meets the criteria outlined in this section, consult with the Regional Administrator or designee before issuing a repeated citation; and

5. If a repeated citation is issued, ensure that the cited employer is fully informed of the previous violations serving as a basis for the repeated citation by notation in the Alleged Violation Description (AVD) portion of the citation, using the following or similar language:

   The (employer name) was previously cited for a violation of this occupational safety and health standard or its equivalent standard (name previously cited standard), which was contained in OSHA inspection number_____, citation number_____, item number_____ and was affirmed as a final order on (date), with respect to a workplace located at_____.

VIII. **De Minimis Conditions.** De minimis conditions are those where an employer has implemented a measure different than one specified in a standard, that has no direct or immediate relationship to safety or health. Whenever de minimis conditions are found during an inspection, they shall be documented in the same manner as violations.

A. **Criteria.** The criteria for finding a de minimis condition are as follows:

1. An employer complies with the intent of the standard, yet deviates from its particular requirements in a manner that has no direct or immediate impact on employee safety or health. These deviations may involve, for example, distance specifications, construction material requirements, use of incorrect color, minor variations from record-keeping, testing, or inspection regulations.

EXAMPLE 4-31: § 1910.27(b)(1)(ii) allows 12 inches as the maximum distance between ladder rungs. Where the rungs are 13 inches apart, the condition is de minimis.

EXAMPLE 4-32: § 1910.217(e)(1)(ii) requires that mechanical power presses be inspected and tested at least weekly. If the machinery is seldom used, inspection and testing prior to each use is adequate to meet the intent of the standard.

2. An employer complies with a proposed OSHA standard or amendment or a consensus standard rather than with the standard in effect at the time of the inspection and the employer's action clearly provides equal or greater employee protection.

3. An employer complies with a written interpretation issued by the OSHA National Office or an OSHA Regional Office.

4. An employer's workplace protections are "state of the art" and technically more enhanced than the requirements of the applicable standard and provides equivalent or more effective employee safety or health protection.

B. **Professional Judgment.** Professional judgment should be exercised in determining whether noncompliance with a standard constitutes a de minimis condition.

C. **Area Director Responsibilities.** Area Directors shall ensure that all proposed de minimis notices meet the criteria set out above.

IX. **Citing in the Alternative.** In rare cases, the same factual situation may present a possible violation of more than one standard.

EXAMPLE 4-33: The facts which support a violation of § 1910.28(a)(1) may also support a violation of § 1910.132(a), if no scaffolding is provided and the use of safety belts is not required by the employer.

Where it appears that more than one standard is applicable to a given factual situation and that compliance with any of the applicable standards would effectively eliminate the hazard, it is permissible to cite alternative standards using the words "in the alternative." A reference in the citation to each of the standards involved shall be accompanied by a separate AVD that clearly alleges all of the necessary elements of a violation of that standard. Only one penalty shall be proposed for the violative condition.

X. **Combining and Grouping Violations.**

A. **Combining.** Separate violations of a single standard, for example § 1910.212(a)(3)(ii), having the same classification found during the inspection of an establishment or worksite generally shall be combined into one alleged citation item. Different options presented in the SAVEs of the same standard shall normally also be combined. Each instance of the violation shall be separately set out within that item of the citation.

NOTE: *Except for standards which deal with multiple hazards (e.g., Tables Z-1, Z-2 and Z-3 cited under § 1910.1000 (a), (b), or (c)), the same standard may not normally be cited more than once on a single citation. However, the same standard may be cited on different citations based on separate classifications and facts on the same inspection.*

B. **Grouping.** When a source of a hazard is identified which involves interrelated violations of different standards, the violations may be grouped into a single violation. The following situations normally call for grouping violations:

1. **Grouping Related Violations.** If violations classified either as serious or other than serious are so closely related they may constitute as a single hazardous condition, such violations shall be grouped and the overall classification shall normally be based on the most serious item.

2. **Grouping Other-than-Serious Violation Where Grouping Results in a Serious Violation.** When two or more violations are found which, if considered individually, represent other than serious violations, but together create a substantial probability of death or serious physical harm, the violations shall be grouped as a serious violation.

3. **Where Grouping Results in High Gravity Other-than-Serious Violation.** Where the CSHO finds, during the course of the inspection, that a number of other-than-serious violations are present, the violations shall be considered in relation to each other to determine the overall gravity of possible injury resulting from an accident or incident involving the hazardous condition.

4. **Penalties for Grouped Violations.** If penalties are to be proposed for grouped violations, the penalty shall be written across from the first violation item appearing on the OSHA-2.

C. **When Not to Group or Combine.**

1. **Multiple Inspections.** Violations discovered during multiple inspections of a single establishment or worksite may not be grouped. Where only one OSHA-1 has been completed, an inspection at the same establishment or worksite shall be considered a single inspection even if it continues for a period of more than one day, or is discontinued with the intention of later resuming it.

2. **Separate Establishments of the Same Employer.** The employer shall be issued separate citations for each establishment or worksite where inspections are conducted, either simultaneously or at different times. If CSHOs conduct inspections at two establishments belonging to the same employer and instances of the same violation are discovered during each inspection, the violations shall not be grouped.

3. **General Duty Clause.** Because a Section 5(a)(1) citation covers all aspects of a serious hazard where no standard exists, there shall be no grouping of separate Section 5(a)(1) violations. This policy, however, does not prohibit grouping a Section 5(a)(1) violation with a related violation of a specific standard.

4. **Egregious Violations.** Violations, which are proposed as instance-by-instance citations, shall not normally be combined or grouped. See CPL 02-00-080, *Handling of Cases to be Proposed for Violation-by-Violation Penalties*, dated October 21, 1990.

XI. **Health Standard Violations.**

A. **Citation of Ventilation Standards.** In cases where a citation of a ventilation standard is appropriate, consideration shall be given to standards intended to control exposure to hazardous levels of air contaminants, prevent fire or explosions, or regulate operations that may involve confined spaces or specific hazardous conditions. In such cases, the following guidelines shall be observed:

1. **Health-Related Ventilation Standards.**

   a. Where an over-exposure to an airborne contaminant is present, the appropriate air contaminant engineering control requirement shall be cited; e.g., §1910.1000(e). Citations of this standard shall not be issued to require specific volumes of air to reduce such exposures.

   b. Other requirements contained in health-related ventilation standards shall be evaluated without regard to the concentration of airborne contaminants. Where a specific standard has been violated and an actual or potential hazard has been documented, a citation shall be issued.

2. **Fire and Explosion-Related Ventilation Standards.** Although not normally considered health violations, the following guidelines shall be observed when citing fire and explosion related ventilation standards:

   a. **Adequate Ventilation.** An operation is considered to have **adequate** ventilation when **both** of the following criteria are present:

   - The requirement(s) of the specific standard has been met.
   - The concentration of flammable vapors is 25 percent or less of the lower explosive limit (LEL).

   EXCEPTION: Some maritime standards require that levels be kept to 10 percent of the LEL (e.g. §1915.36(a)).

   b. **Citation Policy.** If 25 percent (10 percent when specified for maritime operations) of the LEL has been exceeded and:

   - The standard's requirements have not been met, violations of the applicable ventilation standard normally shall be cited as serious.
   - If there is no applicable ventilation standard, Section 5(a)(1) of the Act shall be cited in accordance with the guidelines in Section III of this chapter, General Duty Requirement.

B. **Violations of the Noise Standard.** Current enforcement policy regarding §1910.95(b)(1) allows employers to rely on personal protective equipment and a hearing conservation program, rather than engineering and/or administrative controls, when hearing protectors will effectively attenuate the noise to which employees are exposed to acceptable levels. (See Tables G-16 or G-16a of the standard).

1. Citations for violations of §1910.95(b)(1) shall be issued when technologically and economically feasible engineering and/or administrative controls have not been implemented; and

   a. Employee exposure levels are so elevated that hearing protectors alone may not reliably reduce noise levels received to levels specified in Tables G-16 or G-16a of the standard. (e.g., Hearing protectors which offer the greatest attenuation may reliably be used to protect employees when their exposure levels border on 100 dba). See CPL 02-02-035, 29 CFR 1910.95(b)(1), *Guidelines for Noise Enforcement; Appendix A*, dated December 19, 1983; or

   b. The costs of engineering and/or administrative controls are less than the cost of an effective hearing conservation program.

2. When an employer has an ongoing hearing conservation program and the results of audiometric testing indicate that existing controls and hearing protectors are adequately protecting employees, no additional controls may be necessary. In making this assessment, factors such as exposure levels present, number of employees tested, and duration of the testing program shall be considered.

3. When employee noise exposures are less than 100 dBA but the employer does not have an ongoing hearing conservation program, or results of audiometric testing indicate that the employer's existing program is inadequate, the CSHO shall consider whether:

   a. Reliance on an effective hearing conservation program would be less costly than engineering and/or administrative controls.

b. An effective hearing conservation program can be established or improvements made in an existing program which could bring the employer into compliance with Tables G-16 or G-16a.

c. Engineering and/or administrative controls are both technically and economically feasible.

4. If noise workplace levels can be reduced to the levels specified in Tables G-16 or 16a by means of hearing protectors along with an effective hearing conservation program, a citation for any missing program elements shall be issued rather than for lack of engineering controls. If improvements in the hearing conservation program cannot be made or, if made, cannot reasonably be expected to reduce exposures, but feasible controls exist to address the hazard, then § 1910.95(b)(1) shall be cited.

5. When hearing protection is required but not used and employee exposures exceed the limits of Table G-16, § 1910.95(i)(2)(i) shall be cited and classified as serious (see (8), below) whether or not the employer has instituted a hearing conservation program. § 1910.95(a) shall no longer be cited except in the case of the oil and gas drilling industry. **NOTE:** *Citations of § 1910.95(i)(2)(ii)(b) shall also be classified as serious.*

6. Where an employer has instituted a hearing conservation program and a violation of one or more elements (other than § 1910.95(i)(2)(ii)(b) or (i)(2)(ii)(b)) is found, citations for the deficient elements of the noise standard shall be issued if exposures equal or exceed an 8-hour time-weighted average of 85 dB.

7. If an employer has not instituted a hearing conservation program and employee exposures equal or exceed an 8-hour time-weighted average of 85 dB, a citation for § 1910.95(c) only shall be issued.

8. Violations of § 1910.95(i)(2)(i) may be grouped with violations of § 1910.95(b)(1) and classified as serious when employees are exposed to noise levels above the limits of Table G-16 and:

a. Hearing protection is not utilized or is not adequate to prevent overexposures; or

b. There is evidence of hearing loss that could reasonably be considered:
■ To be work-related, and
■ To have been preventable, if the employer had been in compliance with the cited provisions.

9. No citation shall be issued where, in the absence of feasible engineering or administrative controls, employees are exposed to elevated noise levels, but effective hearing protection is being provided and used, and the employer has implemented a hearing conservation program.

XII. Violations of the Respiratory Protection Standard (§ 1910.134). If an inspection reveals the presence of potential respirator violations, CPL 02-00-120, *Inspection Procedures for the Respiratory Protection Standard*, dated September 25, 1998, shall be followed.

XIII. Violations of Air Contaminant Standards (§ 1910.1000).

A. **Requirements under the standard:**

1. Section 1910.1000(a) through (d) provide ceiling values and 8-hour time – weighted averages applicable to employee exposure to air contaminants.

2. Section 1910.1000(e) provides that to achieve compliance with those exposure limits, administrative or engineering controls shall first be identified and implemented to the extent feasible. When such controls do not achieve full compliance, personal protective equipment shall be used. Whenever respirators are used, their use shall comply with § 1910.134.

3. Section § 1910.134(a) provides that when effective engineering controls are not feasible, or while they are being instituted, appropriate respirators shall be used.

4. There may be cases where workplace conditions require that employers provide engineering controls as well as administrative controls (including work practice controls) and personal protective equipment. Section 1910.1000(e) allows employers to implement feasible engineering controls and/or administrative and work practice controls in any combination, provided the selected abatement means eliminates the overexposure.

5. Where engineering and/or administrative controls are feasible but do not, or would not, reduce air contaminant levels below applicable ceiling values or threshold limit values, an employer must nevertheless institute such controls to reduce the exposure levels. In cases where the implementation of all feasible engineering and administrative controls fails to reduce the level of air contaminants below applicable levels, employers must additionally provide personal protective equipment to reduce exposures.

B. **Classification of Violations of Air Contaminant Standards.** Where employees are exposed to a toxic substance in excess of the PEL established by OSHA standards (without regard to the use of respirator protection), a citation for exceeding the air contaminant standard shall be issued. The violation shall be classified as serious or other-than-serious on the criteria set forth in the Chemical Sampling Information web page and based on whether respirators are being used. Classification of these violations is dependent upon the determination that an illness is reasonably predictable at the measured exposure level.

1. **Classification Considerations.** Exposure to regulated substances shall be characterized as serious if exposures could cause impairment to the body as described in Paragraph II.C.3. of this chapter.

a. In general, substances having a single health code of 13 or less shall be considered as posing a serious health hazard at any level above the Permissible Exposure Limit (PEL). Substances in categories 6, 8 and 12, however, are not considered serious at levels where only mild, temporary effects would be expected to occur.

b. Substances causing irritation (i.e., categories 14 and 15) shall be considered other-than-serious up to levels at which "moderate" irritation could be expected.

c. For a substance having multiple health codes covering both serious and other-than-serious effects (e.g., cyclohexanol), a classification of other-than-serious is appropriate up to levels where serious a health effect(s) could be expected to occur.

d. For a substance having an ACGIH Threshold Limit Value (TLV) or a NIOSH recommended value, but no OSHA PEL, a citation for exposure in excess of the recommended value may be considered under Section 5(a)(1) of the Act. Prior to citing a Section 5(a)(1) violation under these circumstances, it is essential that CSHOs document that a *hazardous exposure* is occurring or has occurred at the workplace, not just that a recognized occupational exposure recommendation has been exceeded. See instructions in Section III of this chapter, *General Duty Requirements*.

e. If an employee is exposed to concentrations of a substance below the PEL, but in excess of a recommended value (e.g., ACGIH TLV or NIOSH recommended value), citations will not normally be issued. CSHOs shall advise employers that a reduction of the PEL has been recommended.

NOTE: *An exception to this may apply if it can be documented that an employer knows that a particular safety or health standard fails to protect his workers against the specific hazard it is intended to address.*

   f.   For a substance having an 8-hour PEL with no ceiling PEL but ACGIH or NIOSH has recommended a ceiling value, the case shall be referred to the Regional Administrator in accordance with Paragraph III.D.2. of this chapter. If no citation is issued, CSHO shall advise employers that a ceiling value is recommended.

2.   **Additive and Synergistic Effects.**

   a.   Substances which have a known additive effect and, therefore, result in a greater probability/severity of risk when found in combination with each other shall be evaluated using the formula found in §1910.1000(d)(2). Use of this formula requires that exposures have an additive effect on the same body organ or system.

   b.   If CSHOs suspect that synergistic effects are possible they shall consult with their supervisor, who shall then refer the question to the Regional Administrator. If a synergistic effect of the cited substances is determined to be present, violations shall be grouped to accurately reflect severity and/or penalty.

XIV. Citing Improper Personal Hygiene Practices. The following guidelines apply when citing personal hygiene violations:

A.   **Ingestion Hazards.** A citation under §1910.141(g)(2) and (4) shall be issued where there is reasonable probability that, in areas where employees consume food or beverages (including drinking fountains), a significant quantity of a toxic material may be ingested and subsequently absorbed.

   1.   For citations under §1910.141(g)(2) and (4), wipe sampling results shall be taken to establish the potential for a serious hazard.

   2.   Where, for any substance, a serious hazard is determined to exist due to potential for ingestion or absorption for reasons other than the consumption of contaminated food or drink (e.g., smoking materials contaminated with the toxic substance), a serious citation shall be considered under Section 5(a)(1) of the Act.

B.   **Absorption Hazards.** A citation for exposure to materials that may be absorbed through the skin or can cause a skin effect (e.g., dermatitis) shall be issued where appropriate personal protective clothing is necessary, but is not provided or worn. If a serious skin absorption or dermatitis hazard exists that cannot be eliminated with protective clothing, a Section 5(a)(1) citation may be considered. Engineering or administrative (including work practice) controls may be required in these cases to prevent the hazard. See §1910.132(a).

C.   **Wipe Sampling.** In general, wipe samples, not measurements for air concentrations, will be necessary to establish the presence of a toxic substance posing a potential absorption or ingestion hazard. (See TED 01-00-015, OSHA *Technical Manual*, dated January 20, 1999, for sampling procedures.)

D.   **Citation Policy.** The following criteria should be considered prior to issuing a citation for ingestion or absorption hazards:

   1.   A health risk exist as demonstrated by one of the following:

     a.   A potential for an illness, such as dermatitis, and/or

     b.   The presence of a toxic substance that may be potentially ingested or absorbed through the skin. (See the *Chemical Sampling Information* web page.)

   2.   The potential for employee exposure by ingestion or absorption may be established by taking both qualitative and quantitative wipe samples. The substance must be present on surfaces that employees contact (such as lunch tables, water fountains, work areas etc.) or on other surfaces, which, if contaminated, present the potential for ingestion or absorption.

   3.   The sampling results must reveal that the substance has properties and exists in quantities that pose a serious hazard.

XV. Biological Monitoring. If an employer has been conducting biological monitoring, CSHOs shall evaluate the results of such testing. These results may assist in determining whether a significant quantity of the toxic substance is being ingested or absorbed through the skin

Chapter 5 — Case File Preparation and Documentation

I.   Introduction. These instructions are provided to assist CSHOs in determining the minimum level of written documentation necessary in preparation of an inspection case file. All necessary information relative to documentation of violations shall be obtained during the inspection, (including but not limited to notes, audio/videotapes, photographs, employer and employee interviews and employer maintained records). CSHOs shall develop detailed information for the case file to establish the specific elements of each violation.

CSHOs and Area Directors shall follow all Regional consultation procedures, including those established by the RSOL's Office, when an inspection involves important or novel facts or presents potentially complex litigation issues. If consultation is necessary, it shall be conducted at the earliest possible stage of the inspection.

II.   Inspection Conducted, Citations Being Issued. All case files must include the following forms and documents.

A.   **OSHA-1.** The CSHO shall obtain available information to complete the OSHA-1 and other appropriate forms.

B.   **OSHA-1A.** The OSHA-1A shall list the following:

   1.   Establishment Name;

   2.   Inspection Number;

   3.   Additional Citation Mailing Addresses;

   4.   Names and Addresses of all Organized Employee Groups;

   5.   Names, Addresses and Phone Numbers of Authorized Representatives of Employees;

   6.   Employer Representatives contacted and the extent of their participation in the inspection;

   7.   CSHO's evaluation of the Employer's Safety and Health System, and if applicable, a discussion of any penalty reduction for good faith;

   8.   A written narrative containing accurate and concise information about the employer and the worksite;

   9.   Date the closing conference(s) was held and description of any unusual circumstances encountered;

   10.   Any other relevant comments/information CSHOs believe may be helpful, based on his/her professional judgment;

   11.   Names, Addresses and Phone Numbers of other persons contacted during the inspection, such as the police, coroner, attorney, etc.;

   12.   Names and Job Titles of any individuals who accompanied the CSHO on the inspection;

13. Calculation of the DART rate (at least three full calendar years and the current year);
14. Discussion clearly addressing all items on the Complaint or Referral;
15. Type of Legal Entity [Indicate whether the employer is a corporation, partnership, sole proprietorship, etc. (Do not use the word "owner.") If the employer named is a subsidiary of another firm, indicate that.]; and
16. Coverage Information.

C. **OSHA-1B.**

1. A separate OSHA-1B should normally be completed for each alleged violation. Describe the observed hazardous conditions or practices, including all relevant facts, and all information pertaining to how and/or why a standard is violated. Specifically identify the hazard to which employees have been or could be exposed. Describe the type of injury or illness which the violated standard was designed to prevent in this situation, or note the name and exposure level of any contaminant or harmful physical agent to which employees are, have been, or could be potentially exposed. If employee exposure was not actually observed during the inspection, state the facts on which the determination was made (i.e., tools left inside an unprotected trench) that an employee has been or could have been exposed to a safety or health hazard.

2. The following information shall be documented:

   a. Explanation of the hazard(s) or hazardous condition(s);
   b. Identification of the machinery or equipment (such as equipment type, manufacturer, model number, serial number);
   c. Specific location of the hazard and employee exposure to the hazard;
   d. Injury or illness likely to result from exposure to the hazard;
   e. Employee proximity to the hazard and specific measurements taken, (describe how measurements were taken, identify the measuring techniques and equipment used, identify those who were present and observed the measurements being made, include calibration dates of equipment used);
   f. For contaminants and physical agents, any additional facts that clarify the nature of employee exposure. A representative number of Material Safety Data Sheets should be collected for hazardous chemicals that employees may potentially be exposed to;
   g. Names, addresses, phone numbers, and job titles for exposed employees;
   h. Approximate duration of time the hazard has existed and frequency of exposure to the hazard;
   i. Employer knowledge;
   j. Any and all facts which establish that the employer actually knew of the hazardous condition, or what reasonable steps the employer failed to take (including regular inspections of the worksite) that could have revealed the presence of the hazardous condition. The mere presence of the employer in the workplace is not sufficient evidence of knowledge. There must be evidence that demonstrates why the employer reasonably could have recognized the presence of the hazardous condition. Avoid relying on conclusory statements such as "reasonable diligence" to establish employer knowledge. See Chapter 4,
   Paragraph II.C.4., *Knowledge of the Hazardous Condition*, for additional information.
   - In order to establish that a violation may be potentially classified as willful, facts shall be documented to show either that the employer knew of the applicable legal requirements and intentionally violated them or that the employer showed plain indifference to employee safety or health (See Section V of Chapter 4, *Willful Violations*). For example, document facts that the employer knew that the condition existed and that the employer was required to take additional steps to abate the hazard. Such evidence could include prior OSHA citations, previous warnings by a CSHO, insurance company or city/state inspector regarding the requirements of the standard(s), the employer's familiarity with the standard(s), contract specifications requiring compliance with applicable standards, or warnings by employees or employee safety representatives of the presence of a hazardous condition and what protections are required by OSHA standards.
   - Also include facts showing that even if the employer was not consciously or intentionally violating the Act, the employer acted with such plain indifference for employee safety that had the employer known of the standard, it probably would not have complied anyway. This type of evidence would include instances where an employer was aware of an employee exposure to an obviously hazardous condition(s) and made no reasonable effort to eliminate it.
   - Any relevant comments made by the employer or employee during the walkaround or closing conference, including any employer comments regarding why it violated the standard, which may be characterized as admissions of the specific violations described; and
   k. Include any other facts, which may assist in evaluating the situation or in reconstructing the total inspection picture in preparation for testimony in possible legal actions.
   l. Appropriate and consistent abatement dates should be assigned and documented for abatement periods longer than 30 days. The abatement period shall be the shortest interval within which the employer can reasonably be expected to correct the violation. An abatement period should be indicated in the citation as a specific date, not a number of days. When abatement is witnessed by the CSHO during an inspection, the abatement period shall be listed on the citation as "Corrected During Inspection."
   m. The establishment of the shortest practicable abatement date requires the exercise of professional judgment on the part of the CSHO. Abatement periods exceeding 30 days shall not normally be offered, particularly for simple safety violations. Situations may arise, however, especially for complex health or program violations, where abatement cannot be completed within 30 days (e.g., ventilation equipment needs to be installed, new parts or equipment need to be ordered, delivered and installed or a process hazard analysis needs to be performed as part of a PSM program). When an initial abatement date is granted that is in excess of 30 calendar days, the reason should be documented in the case file.

3. Records obtained during the course of the inspection which the CSHO determines are necessary to support the violations.

4.   For violations classified as repeated, the file shall include a copy of the previous citation(s) on which the repeat classification is based and documentation of the final order date of the original citation.

III. **Inspection Conducted But No Citations Issued.** For inspections that do not result in citations being issued, a lesser amount of documentation may be included in the case file. At a minimum, the case file shall include the OSHA-1, the OSHA-1A, and a general narrative/statement that at the time of the inspection no conditions were observed in violation of any standard, and a complaint/referral response letter, if appropriate shall clearly address all of the item(s).

IV.   **No Inspection.** For "No Inspections," the CSHO shall include in the case file an OSHA-1, which indicates the reason why no inspection was conducted. If there was a denial of entry, the information necessary to obtain a warrant or an explanation of why a warrant is not being sought shall be included. The case file shall also include a complaint/referral response letter, if appropriate, which explains why an inspection was not conducted.

V.   Health Inspections.

A.   **Document Potential Exposure.** In addition to the documentation indicated above, CSHOs shall document all relevant information concerning potential exposure(s) to chemical substances or physical agents (including, as appropriate, collection and evaluation of applicable Material Safety Data Sheets), such as symptoms experienced by employees, duration and frequency of exposures to the hazard, employee interviews, sources of potential health hazards, types of engineering or administrative controls implemented by the employer, and personal protective equipment being provided by the employer and used by employees.

B.   **Employer's Occupational Safety and Health System.** CSHOs shall request and evaluate information on the following aspects of the employer's occupational safety and health system as it relates to the scope of the inspection:

1.   **Monitoring.** The employer's system for monitoring safety and health hazards in the establishment should include a program for self-inspection. CSHOs shall discuss the employer's maintenance schedules and inspection records. Additional information shall be obtained concerning activities such as sampling and calibration procedures, ventilation measurements, preventive maintenance procedures for engineering controls, and laboratory services. Compliance with the monitoring requirements of any applicable substance-specific health standards shall be determined.

2.   **Medical.** CSHOs shall determine whether the employer provides the employees with pre-placement and peri-odic medical examinations. The medical examination protocol shall be requested to determine the extent of the medical examinations and, if applicable, compliance with the medical surveillance requirements of any applicable substance-specific health standards.

3.   **Records Program.** CSHOs shall determine the extent of the employer's records program, such as whether records pertaining to employee exposure and medical records are being maintained in accordance with §1910.1020.

4.   **Engineering Controls.** CSHOs shall identify any engineering controls present, including substitution, isolation, general dilution and local exhaust ventilation, and equipment modification.

5.   **Work Practice and Administrative Controls.** CSHOs shall identify any control techniques, including personal hygiene, housekeeping practices, employee job rotation, employee training and education. Rotation of employees as an administrative control requires employer knowledge of the extent and duration of exposure.
      NOTE: *Employee rotation is not permitted as a control under some standards.*

6.   **Personal Protective Equipment.** An effective personal protective equipment program should exist in the plant. A detailed evaluation of the program shall be documented to determine compliance with specific standards, such as, §§1910.95, 1910.134, and 1910.132.

7.   **Regulated Areas.** CSHOs shall investigate compliance with the requirements for regulated areas as specified by certain standards. Regulated areas must be clearly identified and known to all appropriate employees. The regulated area designation must be maintained according to the prescribed criteria of the applicable standard.

8.   **Emergency Action Plan.** CSHOs shall evaluate the employer's emergency action plan when such a plan is required by a specific standard. When standards provide that specific emergency procedures be developed where certain hazardous substances are handled, CSHO's evaluation shall determine if: potential emergency conditions are included in the written plan, emergency conditions are explained to employees and there is a training program for the protection of affected employees, including use and maintenance of personal protective equipment.

VI.   **Affirmative Defenses.** An affirmative defense is a claim which, if established by the employer and found to exist by the CSHO, will excuse the employer from a citation that has otherwise been documented.

A.   **Burden of Proof.** Although employers have the burden of proving any affirmative defenses at the time of a hearing, CSHOs must anticipate when an employer is likely to raise an argument supporting such a defense. CSHOs shall keep in mind all potential affirmative defenses and attempt to gather contrary evidence, particularly when an employer makes an assertion that would indicate raising a defense/excuse against the violation(s). CSHOs shall bring all documentation of hazards and facts related to possible affirmative defenses to the attention of the Area Director or designee.

B.   **Explanations.** The following are explanations of common affirmative defenses.

1.   **Unpreventable Employee or Supervisory Misconduct or "Isolated Event."**

a.   To establish this defense in most jurisdictions, employers must show all the following elements:
■   A work rule adequate to prevent the violation;
■   Effective communication of the rule to employees;
■   Methods for discovering violations of work rules; and
■   Effective enforcement of rules when violations are discovered.

b.   CSHOs shall document whether these elements are present, including if the work rule at issue tracks the requirements of the standard addressing the hazardous condition.

EXAMPLE 5-1: An unguarded table saw is observed. The saw, however, has a guard which is reattached while the CSHO watches. Facts to be documented include:

■   Who removed the guard and why?
■   Did the employer know that the guard had been removed?
■   How long or how often had the saw been used without the guard?

- Were there any supervisors in the area while the saw was operated without a guard?
- Did the employer have a work rule that the saw only be operated with the guard on?
- How was the work rule communicated to employees?
- Did the employer monitor compliance with the rule?
- How was the work rule enforced by the employer when it found noncompliance?

2. **Impossibility/Infeasibility of Compliance.** Compliance with the requirements of a standard is impossible or would prevent performance of required work **and the employer took reasonable alternative steps to protect employees or there are no alternative means of employee protection available**.

EXAMPLE 5-2: An unguarded table saw is observed. The employer states that a guard would interfere with the nature of the work. Facts to be documented include:

- Would a guard make performance of the work impossible or merely more difficult?
- Could a guard be used some of the time or for some of the operations?
- Has the employer attempted to use a guard?
- Has the employer considered any alternative means of avoiding or reducing the hazard?

3. **Greater Hazard.** Compliance with a standard would result in a greater hazard(s) to employees than would non-compliance and the employer took reasonable alternative protective measures, or there are no alternative means of employee protection. Additionally, an application for a variance would be inappropriate.

EXAMPLE 5-3: The employer indicates that a saw guard had been removed because it caused the operator to be struck in the face by particles thrown from the saw. Facts to be documented include:

- Was the guard initially properly installed and used?
- Would a different type of guard eliminate the problem?
- How often was the operator struck by particles and what kind of injuries resulted?
- Would personal protective equipment such as safety glasses or a face shield worn by the employee solve the problem?
- Was the operator's work practice causing the problem and did the employer attempt to correct the problem?
- Was a variance requested?

VII. **Interview Statements.**
  A. **Generally.** Interview statements of employees or other individuals shall be obtained to adequately document a potential violation. Statements shall normally be in writing and the individual shall be encouraged to sign and date the statement. During management interviews, CSHOs are encouraged to take verbatim, contemporaneous notes whenever possible as these tend to be more credible than later general recollections.
  B. **CSHOs shall obtain written statements when:**
    1. There is an actual or potential controversy as to any material facts concerning a violation;
    2. A conflict or difference among employee statements as to the facts arises;
    3. There is a potential willful or repeated violation; and
    4. In accident investigations, when attempting to determine if potential violations existed at the time of the accident.
  C. **Language and Wording of Statement.** Interview statements shall normally be written in the first person and in the language of the individual when feasible. (Statements taken in a language other than English shall be subsequently translated.) The wording of the statement shall be understandable to the individual and reflect only the information that has been brought out in the interview. The individual shall initial any changes or corrections to the statement; otherwise, the statement shall not be modified, added to or altered in any way. The statement shall end with the wording: "I have read the above, or the statement has been read to me, and it is true to the best of my knowledge." Where appropriate, the statement shall also include the following: "I request that my statement be held confidential to the extent allowed by law." Only the individual interviewed may later waive the confidentiality of the statement. The individual shall sign and date the interview statement and the CSHO shall sign it as a witness.
  D. **Refusal to Sign Statement.** If the individual refuses to sign the statement, the CSHO shall note such refusal on the statement. Statements shall be read to the individual and an attempt made to obtain an agreement. A note to this effect shall be documented in the case file. Recorded statements shall be transcribed whenever possible.
  E. **Video and Audiotaped Statements.** Interview statements may be videotaped or audiotaped, with the consent of the person being interviewed. The statement shall be reduced to writing in egregious, fatality/catastrophe, willful, repeated, failure to abate, and other significant cases so that it may be signed. CSHOs are encouraged to produce the written statement for correction and signature as soon as possible, and identify the transcriber.
  F. **Administrative Depositions.** When necessary to document or develop investigative facts, a management official or other individual may be administratively deposed.
    NOTE: See Chapter 3, Paragraph VII.I.4., Interviews of Non-Managerial Employees, for additional guidance regarding interviews of non-managerial employees.

VIII. **Paperwork and Written Program Requirements.** In certain cases, violations of standards requiring employers to have a written program to address a hazard or make a written certification (e. g., hazard communication, personal protective equipment, permit required confined spaces and others) are considered paperwork deficiencies. However, in some circumstances, violations of such standards may have an adverse impact on employee safety and health. See CPL 02-00-111, Citation Policy for Paperwork and Written Program Requirement Violations.

IX. **Guidelines for Case File Documentation for Use with Videotapes and Audiotapes.** The use of videotaping as a method of documenting violations and of gathering evidence for inspection case files is encouraged. Certain types of inspections, such as fatalities, imminent danger and ergonomics shall include videotaping. Other methods of documentation, such as handwritten notes, audiotaping, and photographs, continue to be acceptable and are encouraged to be used whenever they add to the quality of the evidence and whenever videotaping equipment is not available. See CPL 02-00-098, Guidelines for Case File Documentation for use with Videotapes and Audiotapes, dated October 12, 1993.

X. **Case File Activity Diary Sheet.** All case files shall contain an activity diary sheet, which is designed to provide a ready record and summary of all actions relating to a case. It will be used to document important events or actions related to the case, especially those not noted elsewhere in the case file. Diary entries should be clear, concise and legible and should be dated in chronological order to reflect a timeline of the case development. Information provided should include, at a minimum, the date of the action or event, a brief description of the action or event and the initials of the person making the entry. When a case file is completed, the CSHO must ensure that it is properly organized. See ADM 03-01-005, OSHA Compliance Records, dated August 3, 1998.

XI. **Citations.** Section 9 of the OSH Act addresses the form and issuance of citations.

Section 9(a) provides: "... Each citation shall be in writing and shall describe with particularity the nature of the violation including a reference to the provision of the Act, standard, rule, regulation, or order alleged to have been violated. In addition, the citation shall fix a reasonable time for the abatement of the violation...."

A. **Statute of Limitations.** Section 9(c) provides. "...No citation may be issued under this Section after the expiration of six months following the occurrence of any violation." Accordingly, a citation shall not be issued where any alleged violation last occurred six months or more prior to the date on which the citation is actually signed, dated and served by certified mail as provided by Section 10(a) of the Act. Where the actions or omissions of the employer concealed the existence of the violation, the six-month issuance limitation is tolled until such time that OSHA learns or could have learned of the violation. The RSOL shall be consulted in such cases. In some cases, particularly those involving fatalities or accidents, the six-month period begins to run from the date of the incident, not from the opening conference date.

B. **Issuing Citations.**
1. Citations shall be sent by certified mail. Hand delivery of citations to the employer or an appropriate agent of the employer, or use of a mail delivery service other than the United States Postal Service, may be used **in addition** to certified mail if it is believed that these methods would effectively give the employer notice of the citation. A signed receipt shall be obtained whenever possible. The circumstances of delivery shall be documented in the diary sheet.
2. Citations shall be mailed to employee representatives after the Certified Mail Receipt card is received by the Area Office. Citations shall also be mailed to any employee upon request and without the need to make a written request under the Freedom of Information Act (FOIA). In the case of a fatality, the family of the victim shall be provided with a copy of the citations without charge or the need to make a written request.

C. **Amending/Withdrawing Citations and Notification of Penalties.**
1. **Amendment Justification.** Amendments to, or withdrawal of, a citation shall be made when information is presented to the Area Director or designee, which indicates a need for such action and may include administrative or technical errors such as:
   a. Citation of an incorrect standard;
   b. Incorrect or incomplete description of the alleged violation;
   c. Additional facts not available to the CSHO at the time of the inspection establish a valid affirmative defense;
   d. Additional facts not available to the CSHO at the time of the inspection establish that there was no employee exposure to the hazard; or
   e. Additional facts establish a need for modification of the abatement date or the penalty, or reclassification of citation items.
2. **When Amendment is not Appropriate.** Amendments to, or withdrawal of, a citation shall not be made by the Area Director or designee for any of the following:
   a. Timely Notice of Contest received;
   b. The 15 working days for filing a Notice of Contest has expired and the citation has become a Final Order; or
   c. Employee representatives were not given the opportunity to present their views (unless the revision involves only an administrative or technical error).

D. **Procedures for Amending or Withdrawing Citations.** The following procedures apply whenever amending or withdrawing citations.
   NOTE: *The instructions contained in this section, with appropriate modifications, are also applicable to the amendment of the OSHA-2B, Notification of Failure to Abate Alleged Violation.*
1. Withdrawal of, or modifications to, the citation and notification of penalty, shall normally be accomplished by means of Informal or Formal Settlement Agreements.
2. In exceptional circumstances, the Area Director or designee may initiate a change to a citation and notification of penalty without an informal conference. If proposed amendments to citation items (individual violations) change the original classification of the items, such as willful to repeated, the original items shall be withdrawn and the new, appropriate items will be issued. The amended Citation and Notification of Penalty Form (OSHA-2) shall clearly indicate that the employer is obligated under the Act to post the amendment to the citation along with the original citation, until the amended violation has been corrected, or for three working days, whichever is longer.
3. The 15 working day contest period for the amended portions of the citation will begin on the day following the day of receipt of the amended Citation and Notification of Penalty.
4. The contest period is not extended for the unamended portions of the original citation. A copy of the original citation shall be attached to the amended Citation and Notification of Penalty Form when the amended form is forwarded to the employer.
5. When circumstances warrant, the Area Director or designee may withdraw a citation and notification of penalty in its entirety. Justification for the withdrawal must be noted in the case file. A letter withdrawing the Citation and Notification of Penalty shall be sent to the employer. The letter, signed by the Area Director or designee, shall refer to the original citation and notification of penalty, state that they are withdrawn and direct that the employer post the letter for three working days in the same location(s) where the original citation was posted. When applicable, a copy of the letter shall also be sent to the employee representative(s) and/or complainant.

XII. Inspection Records.

A. **Generally.**

1. Inspection records are any record made by a CSHO that concern, relate to, or are part of, any inspection, or are a part of the performance of any official duty.

2. All official forms and notes constituting the basic documentation of a case must be part of the case file. All original field notes are part of the inspection record and shall be maintained in the file. Inspection records also include photographs (including digital photographs), negatives of photographs, videotapes, DVDs and audiotapes. Inspection records are the property of the United States Government and not the property of the CSHO and are not to be retained or used for any private purpose.

B. **Release of Inspection Information.** The information obtained during inspections is confidential, but may be disclosable or non-disclosable based on criteria established in the Freedom of Information Act. Requests for release of inspection information shall be directed to the Area director or designee.

C. **Classified and Trade Secret Information.**

1. Any classified or trade secret information and/or personal knowledge of such information by agency personnel shall be handled in accordance with OSHA regulations. Trade Secrets are matters that are not of public or general knowledge. A trade secret, as referenced in Section 15 of the Act, includes information concerning or related to processes, operations, style of work, or apparatus, or to the identity, confidential statistical data, amount or source of any income, profits, losses, or expenditures of any person, firm, partnership, corporation, or association. See 18 USC 1905. The collection of such information and the number of personnel with access to it shall be limited to the minimum necessary for the conduct of investigative activities. CSHOs shall specifically identify any classified and trade secret information in the case file. Title 18 USC 1905, as referenced by Section 15 of the OSH Act, provides for criminal penalties in the event of improper disclosure.

2. It is essential to the effective enforcement of the Act that CSHOs and all OSHA personnel preserve the confidentiality of all information and investigations which might reveal a trade secret. When the employer identifies an operation or condition as a trade secret, it shall be treated as such (unless, after following proper procedures, including consulting with the Solicitor's Office, the agency determines that the matter is not a trade secret). Information obtained in such areas, including all negatives, photographs, videotapes and documentation forms shall be labeled: "ADMINISTRATIVELY CONTROLLED INFORMATION" "RESTRICTED TRADE INFORMATION"

3. Under Section 15 of the Act, all information reported to or obtained by CSHOs in connection with any inspection or other activity which contains or may reveal a trade secret shall be kept confidential. Such information shall not be disclosed except to other OSHA officials concerned with the enforcement of the Act or, when relevant, in any proceeding under the Act.

4. Title 18 USC 1905, provides criminal penalties for Federal employees who disclose such information. These penalties include fines up to $1,000 or imprisonment of up to one year, or both, and removal from office or employment.

5. Trade secret materials shall not be labeled as "Top Secret," "Secret," or "Confidential," nor shall these security classification designations be used in conjunction with other words, unless the trade secrets are also classified by an agency of the U. S. Government in the interest of national security.

6. If the employer objects to the taking of photographs and/or videotapes because trade secrets would or may be disclosed, CSHOs should advise employers of the protection against such disclosure afforded by Section 15 of the Act and § 1903.9. If the employer still objects, CSHOs shall contact the RSOLs office, Area Director or designee for guidance.

Chapter 6 — Penalties and Debt Collection

I. **General Penalty Policy.** The penalty structure in Section 17 of the OSH Act is designed primarily to provide an incentive for preventing or correcting violations voluntarily, not only to the cited employer, but to other employers. While penalties are not designed as punishment for violations, Congress has made clear its intent that penalty amounts should be sufficient to serve as an effective deterrent to violations.

Proposed penalties, therefore, serve the public policy purpose intended under the Act; and criteria approved for such penalties by the Assistant Secretary are based on effectuating this purpose.

The penalty structure described in this chapter is part of OSHA's general enforcement policy and shall normally be applied as set forth below. If, in a specific case, the Area Director determines that it is warranted to depart from the general policy in order to achieve the appropriate deterrent effect, the extent of the departure and the reasons for doing so should be fully explained in the case file.

II. **Civil Penalties.**

A. **Statutory Authority for Civil Penalties.** Section 17 provides the Secretary with the statutory authority to propose civil penalties for violations of the Act. Civil penalties advance the purposes of the Act by encouraging compliance and deterring violations. **Proposed penalties** are the penalty amounts OSHA issues with citation(s).

1. Section 17(a) of the Act provides that any employer who willfully or repeatedly violates the Act may be assessed a civil penalty of not more than $70,000 for each violation, but not less than $5,000 for each willful violation.

2. Section 17(b) provides that any employer who has received a citation for an alleged violation of the Act which is determined to be of a serious nature shall be assessed a civil penalty of up to $7,000 for each violation.

3. Section 17(c) provides that, when the violation is specifically determined not to be of a serious nature, a proposed civil penalty of up to $7,000 may be assessed for each violation.

4. Section 17(d) provides that any employer who fails to correct a violation for which a citation has been issued, may be assessed a civil penalty of not more than $7,000 for each day during which such failure or violation continues.

5. Section 17(i) provides that, when a violation of a posting requirement is cited, a civil penalty of up to $7,000 shall be assessed for each violation.

   NOTE: *While OSHA proposes penalties, the Occupational Safety and Health Review Commission assesses penalties.*

B. **Appropriation Act Restrictions.** In providing funding for OSHA, Congress has placed restrictions on enforcement activities regarding two categories of employers: small farming operations and small employers in low-hazard industries. The Appropriations Act contains limits for OSH Act activities on a year-by-year basis.

C.	**Minimum Penalties.** The following policies apply:
1.	The proposed penalty for any willful violation shall not be less than $5,000. The $5,000 penalty is a statutory minimum and not subject to administrative discretion. This minimum penalty applies to all willful violations, whether serious or other-than-serious.
2.	When the proposed penalty for a serious violation (citation item) would amount to less than $100, a $100 penalty shall be proposed for that violation.
3.	When the proposed penalty for an other-than-serious violation (citation item), or a regulatory violation other than a posting violation, would amount to less than $100, no penalty shall be proposed for that violation.
4.	If, however, there is a citation for a posting violation, a penalty shall be proposed even if less than $100 since penalties for such violations are mandatory under the Act.

D.	**Maximum Penalties.** The civil penalty amounts included in Section 17 are generally maximum amounts before any permissible reductions are taken. Table 6-1 below summarizes the maximum amounts for proposed civil penalties:

Table 6-1: Maximum Amounts for Civil Penalties

Type of Violation	Penalty Maximum
Serious	$7,000 per violation
Other-Than-Serious	$7,000 per violation
Willful or Repeated	$70,000 per violation
Posting	$7,000 per violation
Requirements	
Failure to Abate	$7,000 per day unabated beyond the abatement date [generally limited to 30 days maximum]

III.	**Penalty Factors.** Section 17(j) of the Act provides that penalties shall be assessed giving due consideration to four factors:
- The **gravity** of the violation;
- **Size** of the employer's business;
- The **good faith** of the employer; and
- The employer's **history** of previous violations.

A.	**Gravity of Violation.** The gravity of the violation is the **primary consideration** in determining penalty amounts. It shall be the basis for calculating the basic penalty for serious and other-than-serious violations. To determine the gravity of a violation, the following two assessments shall be made:
- The **severity** of the injury or illness which could result from the alleged violation.
- The **probability** that an injury or illness could occur as a result of the alleged violation.

1.	**Severity Assessment.** The classification of an alleged violation as serious or other-than-serious is based on the severity of the potential injury or illness and is the first step. The following categories shall be considered in assessing the severity of potential injuries or illnesses:

a.	**For Serious:**
- **High Severity:** Death from injury or illness; injuries involving permanent disability; or chronic, irreversible illnesses.
- **Medium Severity:** Injuries or temporary, reversible illnesses resulting in hospitalization or a variable but limited period of disability.
- **Low Severity:** Injuries or temporary, reversible illnesses not resulting in hospitalization and requiring only minor supportive treatment.

b.	**For Other-Than-Serious:**
Minimal Severity: Although such violations reflect conditions which have a direct and immediate relationship to the safety and health of employees, the most serious injury or illness that could reasonably be expected to result from an employee's exposure would not be low, medium or high severity and would not cause death or serious physical harm.

2.	**Probability Assessment.** The probability that an injury or illness will result from a hazard has no role in determining the classification of a violation, but does affect the amount of the proposed penalty.

a.	Probability shall be categorized either as greater or as lesser.
- **Greater Probability:** Results when the likelihood that an injury or illness will occur is judged to be relatively high.
- **Lesser Probability:** Results when the likelihood that an injury or illness will occur is judged to be relatively low.

b.	**How to Determine Probability.** The following factors shall be considered, as appropriate, when violations are likely to result in injury or illness:
- Number of employees exposed;
- Frequency of exposure or duration of employee overexposure to contaminants;
- Employee proximity to the hazardous conditions;
- Use of appropriate personal protective equipment;
- Medical surveillance program;
- Youth and inexperience of employees, especially those under 18 years old; and
- Other pertinent working conditions.

EXAMPLE 6-1: Greater probability may include an employee exposed to the identified hazard for four hours a day, five days a week. Lesser probability may be present when an employee is performing a non-routine task with two previous exposures within the previous year and no injuries or illnesses are associated with the identified hazard.

Field Operations Manual

   c.   **Final Probability Assessment.** All of the factors outlined above shall be considered in determining a final probability assessment.

      When adherence to the probability assessment procedures would result in an unreasonably high or low gravity, the assessment may be adjusted at the discretion of the Area Director as appropriate. Such decisions shall be fully explained in the case file.

3.   **Gravity-Based Penalty (GBP).**

   a.   The gravity-based penalty (GBP) for each violation shall be determined by combining the severity assessment and the final probability assessment.

   b.   GBP is an unreduced penalty and is calculated in accordance with the procedures below.

   NOTE: *Throughout the FOM when the term "unreduced penalty" is used, it is the same as GBP.*

4.   **Serious Violation & GBP.**

   a.   The gravity of a violation is defined by the GBP:
- A **high gravity** violation is one with a GBP of $5,000 or greater.
- A **moderate gravity** violation is one with a GBP of $2,000, $2,500 or $3,500.
- A **low gravity** violation is one with a GBP of $1,500.

   b.   The highest gravity classification (high severity and greater probability) shall normally be reserved for the most serious violative conditions, such as those situations involving danger of death or extremely serious injury or illness.

   c.   If the Area Director determines that it is appropriate to achieve the necessary deterrent effect, a GBP of $7,000 may be proposed instead of $5,000. Such discretion should be exercised based on the facts of the case. The reasons for this determination shall be fully explained in the case file.

   d.   For serious violations, the GBP shall be assigned on the basis of the following scale in Table 6-2:

Severity + Probability = GBP

Table 6-2: Serious Violations

Severity	Probability	GBP	Gravity	IMIS Code
High	Greater	$5,000 (or $7,000)	High	10
Medium	Greater	$3,500	Moderate	5
Low	Greater	$2,500	Moderate	5
High	Lesser	$2,500	Moderate	5
Medium	Lesser	$2,000	Moderate	5
Low	Lesser	$1,500	Low	1

5.   **Other-Than-Serious Violations & GBP.**

   a.   For other-than-serious safety and health violations, there is only minimal severity.

   b.   If the Area Director determines that it is appropriate to achieve the necessary deterrent effect, a GBP of $7,000 may be proposed. Such discretion should be exercised based on the facts of the specific case. The reasons for this determination shall be fully explained in the case file.

Table 6-3: Other-Than-Serious Violations

Severity	Probability	GBP
Minimal	Greater	$1,000 - $7,000
Minimal	Lesser	$0

6.   **Exception to GBP Calculations.** For some cases, a GBP may be assigned without using the severity and the probability assessment procedures outlined in this section when these procedures cannot appropriately be used. In such cases, the assessment assigned and the reasons for doing so shall be fully explained in the case file.

7.   **Egregious Cases.** In egregious cases, violation-by-violation penalties are applied. Such cases shall be handled in accordance with CPL 02-00-080, *Handling of Cases to be Proposed for Violation-By-Violation Penalties*, dated October 21, 1990. Penalties calculated under this policy shall not be proposed without the concurrence of the Assistant Secretary and NSOL.

8.   **Gravity Calculations for Combined or Grouped Violations.** Combined or grouped violations will be considered as one violation with one GBP. The following procedures apply to the calculation of penalties for combined and grouped violations:

   NOTE: *Multiple violations of a single standard may be combined into one citation item. When a hazard is identified which involves interrelated violations of different standards, the violations may be grouped into a single item.*

   a.   **Combined Violations.** The severity and probability assessments for combined violations shall be based on the instance with the highest gravity. It is not necessary to complete the penalty calculations for each instance or sub item of a combined or grouped violation once the instance with the highest gravity is identified.

   b.   **Grouped Violations.** The following shall be adhered to:

- **Grouped Severity Assessment.** There are two considerations for calculating the severity of grouped violations:
  - a. The severity assigned to the grouped violation shall be no less than the severity of the most serious reasonably predictable injury or illness that could result from the violation of any single item; AND
  - b. If the injury or illness that is reasonably predictable from the grouped items is more serious than that from any single violation item, the more serious injury or illness shall serve as the basis for the calculation of the severity factor.
- **Grouped Probability Assessment.** There are two factors for calculating the probability of grouped violations:
  - a. The probability assigned to the grouped violation shall be no less than the probability of the item which is most likely to result in an injury or illness; AND
  - b. If the overall probability of injury or illness is greater with the grouped violation than with any single violation item, the greater probability of injury or illness shall serve as the basis for the calculation of the probability assessment.

B. **Penalty Reduction Factors.**

1. **General.**
   a. Penalty reductions may exceed 100 percent, depending upon the employer's "size" (number of employees), "good faith," and "history of previous violations."
      - A maximum of 60 percent (80 percent for serious willful violations) reduction is permitted for **size**;
      - A maximum of 35 percent reduction for **good faith**; and
      - 10 percent reduction may be given for **history**.
   b. However, no penalty reduction can be more than 100 percent of the initial assessment. Since these reduction factors are based on the general character of an employer's safety and health performance, they shall be calculated only once for each employer.
   c. After the classification (as serious or other-than-serious) and the gravity-based penalty have been determined for each violation, the penalty reduction factors (for size, good faith, history) shall be applied subject to the following limitations:
      - Penalties proposed for violations classified as **repeated** shall be reduced only for size.
      - Penalties proposed for violations classified as **willful**, shall be reduced only for size and history.
      - Penalties proposed for **serious** violations classified as high severity/greater probability **shall be reduced only for size and history**.

2. **Size Reduction.**
   a. A maximum penalty reduction of 60 percent is permitted for small employers (80 percent for serious willful violations, see Table 6-6). "Size of employer" shall be calculated on the basis of the maximum number of employees of an employer at all workplaces nationwide, including State Plan States, at any one time during the previous 12 months.
   b. The rates of reduction to be applied are as follows.
      - Employees Percent reduction
      - 1-25 60
        26-100 40
        101-250 20
        251 or more None
   c. When an employer with 1-25 employees has one or more serious violations of high gravity or a number of serious violations of moderate gravity indicating a lack of concern for employee safety and health, the CSHO may recommend that only a partial reduction in penalty shall be permitted for size. If the Area Director approves the partial reduction, the justification is to be fully explained in the case file.

3. **Good Faith Reduction.** A penalty reduction is permitted in recognition of an employer's effort to implement an effective safety and health management system in the workplace. The following apply to reductions for good faith:
   a. **Reduction Not Permitted.**
      - No reduction shall be given for **high gravity serious violations**.
      - No reduction shall be given if a **willful violation** is found. Additionally, where a willful violation has been documented, no reduction for good faith can be applied to any of the violations found during the same inspection.
      - No reduction shall be given for **repeated violations**. If a repeated violation is found, no reduction for good faith can be applied to any of the violations found during the same inspection.
      - No reduction shall be given if a **failure to abate violation** is found during an inspection. No good faith reduction shall be given for any violation in the inspection in which the FTA was found.
      - No reduction shall be given to employers being cited under abatement verification for **failure to certify abatement**.
      - No reduction shall be given to employers being cited under abatement verification for **failure to notify employees and tagging movable equipment**.
      - No reduction shall be given if the employer has **no safety and health management system**, or if there are **major deficiencies** in the program.
   b. **Twenty-Five Percent Reduction.** A 25 percent reduction for "good faith" normally requires a written safety and health management system. In exceptional cases, CSHOs may recommend a full 25 percent reduction for employers with 1-25 employees who have implemented an effective safety and health management system, but has not reduced it to writing.

   To qualify for this reduction, the employer's safety and health management system must provide for:

- Appropriate management commitment and employee involvement;
- Worksite analysis for the purpose of hazard identification;
- Hazard prevention and control measures;
- Safety and health training; and
- Where **young persons** (i.e., less than 18 years old) are employed, the CSHO's evaluation must consider whether the employer's safety and health management system appropriately addresses the particular needs of such employees, relative to the types of work they perform and the potential hazards to which they may be exposed.
- Where **persons who speak limited or no English** are employed, the CSHO's evaluation must consider whether the employer's safety and health management system appropriately addresses the particular needs of such employees, relative to the types of work they perform and the potential hazards to which they may be exposed.
- **Fifteen Percent Reduction.** A 15 percent reduction for good faith shall normally be given if the employer has a documented and effective safety and health management system, with only incidental deficiencies.

EXAMPLE 6-2: An acceptable program should include minutes of employee safety and health meetings, documented employee safety and health training sessions, or any other evidence of measures advancing safety and health in the workplace.

    d.   **Ten Percent Additional Reduction for OSHA Strategic Partnership Participation.**
- OSHA may provide an additional 10 percent reduction for good faith **in addition to the normal available reductions** where the employer is an OSHA Strategic Partnership (OSP) site.
- Employers in OSP sites, must have taken specific significant steps beyond those mentioned in the Twenty-Five Percent Reduction, and has achieved a high level of employee protection.
- This benefit must be specified in the partnership (not all partnerships offer this benefit), and the employer must also be working toward the goals of the partnership in a demonstrable fashion, which would be observed through the verification process.
- In cases where the total penalty reduction is 100 percent or more, the minimum penalty provisions shall apply.
- This is an additional good faith reduction; it will not apply unless the employer first qualifies for the 25 percent reduction.

    e.   **Allowable Percentages.** Only these percentages (15%, 25% or 35%) may be used to reduce penalties due to the employer's good faith; this includes the possible additional 10 percent reduction for qualifying participants in OSHA's OSP program.

4.   **History Reduction.**
    a.   **Allowable Percent.** A reduction of 10 percent shall be given to employers who have not been cited by OSHA nationwide, or by any State Plan state for any serious, willful, or repeated violations in the prior three years.
    b.   **Time Limitation and Final Order.** The three-year history of no prior citations (both Federal and State) shall be calculated from the opening conference date of the current inspection. Only citations that have become a final order of the Commission within the three years immediately before the opening conference date shall be considered.
    c.   **Reduction Will Not be Given.**
- For a repeated violation, or
- To employers being cited for failure to certify abatement, or
- To employers being cited for failure to notify employees and tagging movable equipment.

5.   **Total Reduction.** The total reduction will normally be the sum of the reductions for each factor. Table 6-4 provides an overview of the percent of penalty reductions applicable to serious, other-than-serious, and repeated violations.

6.   **Penalty Table.** Table 6-4 may be used for determining appropriate reduced penalties for serious and other-than-serious violations.

Table 6-4: Penalty Table

Percent Reduction	Penalty in Dollars							
0	$1,000	$1,500	$2,000	$2,500	$3,000	$3,500	$5,000	$7,000
10	$900	$1,350	$1,800	$2,250	$2,700	$3,150	$4,500	$6,300
15	$850	$1,275	$1,700	$2,125	$2,550	$2,975	$4,250*	$5,950*
20	$800	$1,200	$1,600	$2,000	$2,400	$2,800	$4,000	$5,600
25	$750	$1,125	$1,500	$1,875	$2,250	$2,625	$3,750*	$5,250*
30	$700	$1,050	$1,400	$1,750	$2,100	$2,450	$3,500	$7,900
35	$650	$975	$1,300	$1,625	$1,950	$2,275	$3,250*	$4,550*
40	$600	$900	$1,200	$1,500	$1,800	$2,100	$3,000	$4,200
45	$550	$825	$1,100	$1,375	$1,650	$1,925	$2,750*	$3,850*
50	$500	$750	$1,000	$1,250	$1,500	$1,750	$2,500	$3,500
55	$450	$675	$900	$1,125	$1,350	$1,575	$2,250*	$3,150*
60	$400	$600	$800	$1,000	$1,200	$1,400	$2,000	$2,800
65	$350	$525	$700	$875	$1,050	$14,225	$1,750*	$2,450*
70	$300	$450	$600	$750	$900	$1,050	$1,500	$2,100
75	$250	$375	$500	$625	$750	$875	$1,250*	$1,750*
85	$150	$225	$300	$375	$450	$525	$750*	$1,050*
95	$100	$100	$100	$125	$150	$175	$250*	$350*

* Starred figures represent penalty amounts that would not normally be proposed for high gravity serious violations because no reduction for good faith is made in such cases. They may occasionally be applicable for other-than-serious violations where the Area Director has determined a high unreduced penalty amount to be warranted.

IV. **Effect on Penalties if Employer Immediately Corrects.** Appropriate penalties will be proposed with respect to an alleged violation even though, after being informed of the violation by the CSHO, the employer immediately corrects or initiates steps to abate the hazard. In limited circumstances, this prompt abatement of a hazardous condition may be taken into account in determining the amount of the proposed penalties under the Quick-Fix penalty reduction.

A. **Quick-Fix Penalty Reduction.** Quick-Fix is an abatement incentive program meant to encourage employers to immediately abate hazards found during an OSHA inspection and thereby quickly prevent potential employee injury, illness, and death. Quick-Fix does not apply to all violations. However, penalty reductions are permitted in certain circumstances where OSHA has determined that immediate abatement reduces the gravity of the violation.

B. **Quick-Fix Reduction Shall Apply to:**
1. All general industry, construction, maritime and agriculture employers.
2. All sizes of employers in all Standard Industrial Classification (SIC) codes and North American Industry Classification System (NAICS) codes.
3. Both safety and health violations, provided hazards are immediately abated during the inspection, once identified by the CSHO (e.g., on the day the condition was pointed out to the employer, or within 24 hours of being discovered by the CSHO).
4. Violations classified as other-than-serious, "low gravity serious" or "medium gravity serious."
5. Individual violations, i.e., not to the citation or penalty as a whole.
6. Corrective actions that are permanent and substantial, not temporary or cosmetic (e.g., installing a guard on a machine rather than removing an employee from the zone of danger, including administrative controls, or other specific measures to abate a violation).

C. **Quick-Fix Reductions Shall Not Apply to:**
1. Violations classified as "high gravity serious," "willful," "repeated," or "failure-to-abate."
2. Violations related either to a fatal injury or illness, or to any incidents resulting in serious injuries to employees.
3. Blatant violations that are easily corrected (e.g., turning on a ventilation system to reduce employee exposure to a hazardous atmosphere, or putting on hard hats that are readily available at the workplace).

D. **Reduction Amount.**
1. A Quick-Fix penalty reduction of 15 percent shall be applied to an individual violation's GBP.
2. After the 15 percent Quick-Fix reduction is applied, the reductions for size, good faith, and history will then be applied. Table 6-5, below, provides an overview of the program.

Table 6-5: Quick-Fix Penalty Reduction Factor

Reduction Factor	Restrictions	Application	Percent Reduction	Comments

Quick-Fix	No Reduction Factor for:
	• Violations classified as:
	  – High gravity serious
	  – Willful
	  – Repeated
	  – Failure to Abate penalty
	• Violations related to a fatal injury or illness, or a serious incident resulting in serious injuries
	• Blatant violations that are easily corrected
		• All general industry, construction, maritime & agriculture employers
		• All sizes of employers in all SIC/NAICS codes
		• Safety & health violations, provided hazards are immediately abated during the inspection
		• Violations classified as:
		  – Other-than serious
		  – Low gravity serious
		  – Medium gravity serious
		• Only to individual violations
		• Only to a corrective action that is permanent and substantial
			After the GBP has been calculated, a 15% reduction is applied. **After the 15% Quick-Fix reduction is applied, the reductions for size, good faith, and history are applied.**	No penalty for a serious violation shall be less than $100

V. Repeated Violations.

  A. **General.**

    1. Each repeated violation shall be evaluated as serious or other-than-serious, based on current workplace conditions, and not on hazards found in the prior case.

    2. A Gravity-Based Penalty (GBP) shall then be calculated for repeated violations based on facts noted during the current inspection.

    3. Only the reduction factor for size, appropriate to the facts at the time of the reinspection, shall be applied.

    NOTE: *Section 17(a) of the Act provides that an employer who repeatedly violates the Act may be assessed a civil penalty of not more than $70,000 for each violation.*

  B. **Penalty Increase Factors.** The amount of any increase to a proposed penalty for repeated violations shall be determined by the size of the employer's business.

    1. **Small Employers.** For employers with 250 or fewer employees nationwide, the GBP shall be multiplied by a factor of 2 for the first repeated violation and multiplied by 5 for the second repeated violation. The GBP may be multiplied by 10 in cases where the Area Director determines that it is necessary to achieve the deterrent effect. The reasons for imposing a high multiplier factor shall be explained in the file.

    2. **Large Employers.** For employers with more than 250 employees nationwide, the GBP shall be multiplied by a factor of 5 for the first repeated violation and, by 10 for the second repeated violation.

  C. **Other-than-Serious, No Initial Penalty.** For a repeated other-than-serious violation that otherwise would have no initial penalty, a GBP penalty of $200 shall be proposed for the first repeated violation, $500 for the second repeated violation, and $1,000 for a third repetition.

  NOTE: *These penalties shall not be subject to the Penalty Increase factors as discussed in Paragraph V.B. of this chapter.*

  D. **Regulatory Violations.**

    1. For calculating the GBP for regulatory violations, see Paragraph III.A.5. and Section X.

    2. For repeated instances of regulatory violations, the initial penalty shall be multiplied by 2 for the first repeated violation and multiplied by 5 for the second repeated violation. If the Area Director determines that it is necessary to achieve the proper deterrent effect, the initial penalty may be multiplied by 10.

VI. Willful Violations. Section 17(a) of the Act provides that an employer who willfully violates the Act may be assessed a civil penalty of not more than $70,000 for each violation, but not less than $5,000 for each violation. See *Minimum Penalties* at Paragraph II.C. of this chapter.

  A. **General.**

    1. Each willful violation shall be classified as serious or other-than-serious.

    2. There shall be no reduction for good faith.

    3. In no case shall the proposed penalty for a willful violation (serious or other-than-serious) after reductions be less than $5,000.

  B. **Serious Willful Penalty Reductions.** The reduction factors for size for serious willful violations shall be applied as shown in the following chart. This chart helps minimize the impact of large penalties for small employers with 50 or fewer employees. However, in no case shall the proposed penalty be less than the statutory minimum, i.e., $5,000 for these employers.

  NOTE: *For violations that are not serious willful, use the size chart in Paragraph III.B.2.*

Employees	Percent reduction
10 or fewer	80
11-20	60
21-30	50
31-40	40
41-50	30
51-100	20
101-250	10
251 or more	0

The reduction factor for history shall be applied.
The proposed penalty shall then be determined from Table 6-6.

Table 6-6: Penalties to be Proposed for Serious Willful

Violations Total percent reduction for size and/or history	High Gravity	Moderate Gravity	Low Gravity
0%	$70,000	$55,000	$40,000
10%	$63,000	$49,500	$36,000
20%	$56,000	$44,000	$32,000
30%	$49,000	$38,500	$28,000
40%	$42,000	$33,000	$24,000
50%	$35,000	$27,500	$20,000
60%	$28,000	$22,000	$16,000
70%	$21,000	$16,500	$12,000
80%	$14,000	$11,000	$8,000
90%	$7,000	$5,500	$5,000

C. **Willful Regulatory Violations.**
   1. For calculating the GBP for regulatory violations, see Paragraph III.A.5. and Section X for other-than-serious violations.
   2. In the case of regulatory violations that are determined to be willful, the GBP penalty shall be multiplied by 10. In no event shall the penalty, after reduction for size and history, be less than $5,000.

VII. **Penalties for Failure to Abate.**
   A. **General.**
      1. Failure to Abate penalties shall be proposed when:
         a. A previous citation issued to an employer has become a final order of the Commission; and
         b. The condition, hazard or practice found upon re-inspection is the same for which the employer was originally cited and has never been corrected by the employer (i.e., the violation was continuous).
      2. The citation has to have become a final order of the Review Commission. Citations become a final order of the Review Commission when the abatement date for that item passes, if the employer has not filed a notice of contest prior to that abatement date.
      3. See Chapter 15, *Legal Issues*, for information on determining final dates of uncontested citations, settlements and Review Commission decisions.
   B. **Calculation of Additional Penalties.**
      1. **Unabated Violations.** A GBP for unabated violations is to be calculated for failure to abate a serious or other-than-serious violation on the basis of the facts noted upon reinspection. This recalculated GBP, however, shall not be less than that proposed for the item when originally cited.
         a. EXCEPTION: When the CSHO believes and documents in the case file that the employer has made a good faith effort to correct the violation and had an objective reasonable belief that it was fully abated, the Area Director may reduce or eliminate the daily proposed penalty.
         b. For egregious cases see CPL 02-00-080
      2. **No Initial Proposed Penalty.** In instances where no penalty was initially proposed, an appropriate penalty shall be determined after consulting with the Area Director. In no case shall the GBP be less than $1,000 per day.
      3. **Size Only Permissible Reduction Factor.** Only the reduction factor for size – based upon the circumstances noted during the reinspection – shall be applied to arrive at the daily proposed penalty.
      4. **Daily Penalty Multiplier.** The daily proposed penalty shall be multiplied by the number of calendar days that the violation has continued unabated, except as provided below:
         a. The number of days unabated shall be counted from the day following the abatement date specified in the citation or the final order. It will include all calendar days between that date and the date of reinspection, excluding the date of reinspection.
         b. Normally the maximum total proposed penalty for failure to abate a particular violation shall not exceed 30 times the amount of the daily proposed penalty.

c. At the discretion of the Area Director, a lesser penalty may be proposed. The reasoning for the lesser penalty shall be fully explained (e.g., achievement of an appropriate deterrent effect) in the case file.

d. If a penalty in excess of the normal maximum amount of 30 times the amount of the daily proposed penalty is deemed necessary by the Area Director to deter continued non-abatement, the case shall be treated pursuant to the violation-by-violation (egregious) penalty procedures established in CPL 02-00-080, *Handling of Cases to be Proposed for Violation-By-Violation Penalties*, dated October 21, 1990.

C. **Partial Abatement.**

1. When a citation has been partially abated, the Area Director may authorize a reduction of 25 to 75 percent to the amount of the proposed penalty calculated as outlined above.

2. When a violation consists of a number of instances and the follow-up inspection reveals that only some instances of the violation have been corrected, the additional daily proposed penalty shall take into consideration the extent of the abatement efforts.

EXAMPLE 6-3: Where three out of five instances have been corrected, the daily proposed penalty (calculated as outlined above, without regard to any partial abatement) may be reduced by 60 percent.

VIII. Violation-by-Violation (Egregious) Penalty Policy.

A. **Penalty Procedure.** Each instance of noncompliance shall be considered a separate violation with individual proposed penalties for each violation. This procedure is known as the egregious or violation-by-violation penalty procedure.

B. **Case Handling.** Such cases shall be handled in accordance with CPL 02-00-080, *Handling of Cases to be Proposed for Violation-By-Violation Penalties*, dated October 21, 1990.

C. **Calculation of Penalties.** Penalties calculated using the violation-by-violation policy shall not be proposed without the concurrence of the Assistant Secretary.

IX. Significant Enforcement Actions.

A. **Definition.** A significant enforcement action (aka significant case) is one which results from an investigation in which the total proposed penalty is $100,000 or more.

B. **Multi-employer Worksites.** Several related inspections involving the same employer, or involving more than one employer in the same location (such as multi-employer worksites) and submitted together, may also be considered to be a significant enforcement action if the total aggregate penalty is $100,000 or more.

C. **Federal Agency Significant Cases.** For Federal Agencies, the action is considered significant if penalties of $100,000 or more would have been applied if it were a private sector employer.

1. Significant Federal Agency cases shall be developed, documented, and reviewed with the same rigorousness required for private sector cases.

2. In addition, Notices of Unsafe or Unhealthful Working Conditions in Federal Agency cases shall be issued no later than six months from the date of the opening conference, thereby paralleling the six month statutory limit in private sector cases set by the OSH Act.

D. **Assistant Secretary Concurrence.** The Assistant Secretary's concurrence is normally required for issuing citations in significant enforcement cases.

X. Penalty and Citation Policy for Part 1903 and 1904 Regulatory Requirements.
Section 17(i) of the Act provides that any employer who violates any of the posting requirements shall be assessed a civil penalty of up to $7,000 for each violation (this includes recordkeeping violations). The following policy and procedure document must also be consulted for an in-depth review of these policies: CPL 02-00-111, *Citation Policy for Paperwork and Written Program Requirement Violations*, issued November 27, 1995. Gravity-Based Penalties (GBPs) for regulatory violations, including posting requirements, shall be reduced for size and history (excluding willful violations, see Chapter 4, Section V, *Willful Violations*).

A. **Posting Requirements Under Part 1903.** Penalties for violation of posting requirements shall be proposed as follows:

1. **Failure to Post the OSHA Notice (Poster) – §1903.2(a).** A citation for failure to post the OSHA Notice is warranted if:

   a. The pattern of violative conditions for a particular establishment demonstrates a consistent disregard for the employer's responsibilities under the Occupational Safety and Health Act of 1970 (Act); AND

   b. Interviews show that employees are unaware of their rights under the Act; OR

   c. The employer has been previously cited or advised by OSHA of the posting requirement.

   If the criteria above are met and the employer has not displayed (posted) the notice furnished by the Occupational Safety and Health Administration as prescribed in §1903.2(a), an other-than-serious citation shall normally be issued. The GBP for this alleged violation shall be $1,000.

2. **Failure to Post a Citation - §1903.16.**

   a. If an employer received a citation that was not posted as prescribed in §1903.16, an other-than-serious citation shall normally be issued. The GBP shall be $3,000.

   b. For information regarding the OSHA-300A form, see CPL 02-00-135, *Recordkeeping Policies and Procedures Manual*, December 30, 2004.

B. **Advance Notice of Inspection – §1903.6.** When an employer has received advance notice of an inspection and fails to notify the authorized employee representative as required by §1903.6, an other-than-serious citation shall be issued. The violation shall have a GBP of $2,000.

C. **Abatement Verification Regulation Violations – §1903.19.**

1. **General.**

   a. The penalty provisions of Section 9 and Section 17 of the OSH Act apply to all citations issued under this regulation. Only the reduction factor for size shall apply when assessing penalties.

   b. See Chapter 7, *Post-Citation Inspection Procedures and Abatement Verification*, for detailed guidance.

2. **Penalty for Failing to Certify Abatement.**

   a. A penalty for failing to submit abatement certification documents, §1903.19(c)(1), shall be $1,000, reduced only for size.

   b. A penalty for failure to submit abatement verification documents will not exceed the penalty for the entire original citation.

    c. No "Good Faith" or "History" reductions shall be given to employers cited for failure to certify abatement.

3. **Penalty for Failing to Notify and Tagging.**

    a. Penalties for not notifying employees and tagging movable equipment §1903.19 [paragraphs (g)(1), (g)(2), (g)(4), (i)(1), (i)(2), (i)(3), (i)(5) and (i)(6)] will follow the same penalty structure (GBP of $3,000) as for Failure to Post a Citation.

    b. No "Good Faith" or "History" reductions shall be given to employers for failure to notify employees and tagging movable equipment.

D. **Injury and Illness Records and Reporting under Part 1904.**

1. Part 1904 violations are always other-than-serious.

2. Repeated and Willful penalty policies in paragraphs V.D. and VI.C., respectively, of this Chapter, may be applied to recordkeeping violations.

3. OSHA's egregious penalty policy may be applied to recordkeeping violations. See CPL 02-00-080, *Handling of Cases to be Proposed for Violation-By-Violation Penalties*, October 21, 1990.

4. See CPL 02-00-135, *Recordkeeping Policies and Procedures Manual*, dated December 30, 2004; specifically Chapter 2, Section II, *Inspection and Citation Procedures*.

XI. **Failure to Provide Access to Medical and Exposure Records – §1910.1020.**

A. **Proposed Penalties.** If an employer is cited for failing to provide access to records as required under §1910.1020 for inspection and copying by any employee, former employee, or authorized representative of employees, a GBP of $1,000 shall normally be proposed for each record (i.e., either medical record or exposure record, on an individual employee basis). A maximum GBP of $7,000 may be proposed for such violations. See CPL 02-02-072, *Rules of Agency Practice and Procedure Concerning OSHA Access to Employee Medical Records*, dated August 22, 2007.

EXAMPLE 6-4: If the evidence demonstrates that an authorized employee representative requests both exposure and medical records for three employees and the request was denied by the employer, a citation would be issued for six instances (i.e., one medical record and one exposure record (total two) for each of three employees) of a violation of §1910.1020, with a GBP of $6,000.

B. **Use of Violation-by-Violation Penalties.** The above policy does not preclude the use of violation-by-violation or per employee penalties where higher penalties are appropriate. See CPL 02-00-080, *Handling of Cases to be Proposed for Violation-By-Violation Penalties*, October 21, 1990.

XII. **Criminal Penalties.**

A. **OSH Act and U.S. Code.** The Act and the U.S. Code provide for criminal penalties in the following cases:

1. Willful violation of an OSHA standard, rule, or order causing the death of an employee; Section 17(e);

2. Giving unauthorized advance notice; Section 17(f);

3. Knowingly giving false information; Section 17(g); and

4. Killing of a CSHO while engaged in the performance of investigative, inspection or law enforcement functions; Section 17(h)(2).

B. **Courts.** Criminal penalties are imposed by the courts after trials and not OSHA or the Occupational Safety and Health Review Commission.

XIII. **Handling Monies Received from Employers.**

A. **Responsibility of the Area Director.** Pursuant to its statutory authority, it is OSHA policy to collect all penalties owed to the government. The Area Director is responsible for:

1. Informing employers of OSHA's debt collection procedures;

2. Collecting assessed penalties from employers;

3. Reporting penalty amounts collected and those due;

4. Calculating interest and other charges on overdue penalty amounts;

5. Referring cases with uncollected penalties to the Office of Financial Management Debt Collection Accountability Team (DCAT);

6. Transferring selected cases to the RSOL for legal action and subsequently tracking such cases;

7. Mailing collected monies in accordance with the procedures set forth in this chapter and in other OSHA Instructions; and

8. Reviewing the DOL bankruptcy logs emailed by DCAT.

B. **Receiving Payments.** The Area Director shall be guided by the following with regard to penalty payments:

1. **Methods of Payment.** Employers assessed penalties shall remit the total payment to the Area Office by certified check, personal check, company check, postal money order, bank draft or bank money order, payable to the **DOL-OSHA**. Payment in cash shall not be accepted. Upon request of the employer and for good cause, alternate methods of payment are permissible, such as payments in installments.

2. **Identifying Payment.** The Reporting I.D. of the Area Office, along with the Inspection Number(s), **MUST BE PLACED** in the upper left or lower left hand corner of the face of the payment instrument. The date of receipt **MUST BE STAMPED** on the face of the check and in the upper right corner if possible.

3. **Adjustment to Payments.** The following adjustments shall be made prior to transmitting the payment instrument to the Lockbox Depository. See Paragraph XIII.B.6. of this chapter, *Depositing Payments.*

    a. If the payment instrument is not dated, the date received shall be entered as the date of payment.

    b. If the payment instrument has differing numeric and written amounts, the written amount shall be credited and the instrument deposited. If the written amount is obviously incorrect or differs from the amount referenced in the accompanying correspondence, the payment instrument shall be returned to the employer via certified mail for correction.

    c. If the payment instrument does not include the establishment name, the name shall be inserted on the face of the payment instrument.

    d. If the payment instrument includes the notation, "Payment in Full," whether or not the notation is incorrect, the payment shall be deposited.

e.   If the payment instrument is unsigned, the payment shall be deposited.

f.   If an employer mistakenly makes the payment payable to an official of OSHA by name, it shall be endorsed as follows:
- Postal Money Orders – follow instruction on reverse of the money order.
- All others – enter on reverse:

Pay to the order of the U.S. Department of Labor – OSHA

(Signature) (Typewritten name of payee)

4.   **Incorrect, Unhonored, or Foreign Payments.**
a.   Incorrectly dated payments shall be handled as follows:
- If the payment instrument is dated 10 days or more after the date of receipt, it is to be returned to the employer.
- If the payment instrument is dated less than 10 but more than 3 days after the date of receipt, it is to be held for deposit on the day it is dated.
- Payment instruments dated 3 or fewer days after the date of receipt are to be mailed to the Lockbox.
- If the payment instrument is dated more than six months prior to the current date, it is to be returned to the employer via certified mail.

b.   Payment instruments which have been returned to the Office of Financial Management (OFM) without payment, due to insufficient funds, shall be forwarded to the Area Office for return to the employer via certified mail.

c.   Payments drawn on non-U.S. banks **MUST BE SENT** directly to OFM (without using the "Lockbox" procedures described in Paragraph XIII.B.6. of. of this chapter, *Depositing Payments*) at the following address:

Office of Financial Management

U.S. Department of Labor – OSHA Post Office Box 2422 Washington, D.C. 20013

5.   **Endorsing Payments.** All payment instruments shall be endorsed as follows:

16-01-2012 Payment FRB or BR Credit Treasury U.S, Payment on an Obligation to U.S. and must be paid at Par DO NOT WIRE NON PAYMENT U.S. DEPT. OF LABOR Occupational Safety and Health Administration DOL OSHA Washington DC

6.   **Depositing Payments.** All payments shall be kept in a safe place and, unless otherwise indicated, transmitted daily in accordance with current IMIS procedures to the Lockbox Depository at the following address: U.S. Department of Labor - OSHA Post Office Box 70964 Charlotte, NC 28272-0964

7.   **Records.** A copy of the penalty payment instrument shall be included in the case file. Additional accounting records shall also be included in the case file in accordance with current procedures.

C.   **Refunds.** In cases of later penalty modifications by OSHA or by the Commission or a court, refunds to the employer shall be made by the Department of Labor through DCAT. The Area Director shall notify DCAT in accordance with current instructions.

XIV. Debt Collection Procedures.

A.   **Policy.** The *Debt Collection Improvement Act of 1996* (DCIA) provides for the assessment of interest, administrative charges, and additional costs for nonpayment of debts arising under the OSHA program. Under the regulations of the Department of Labor implementing the DCIA, penalties assessed by OSHA are considered as debts. It is OSHA policy to exercise the authority provided under the DCIA to assess additional charges on delinquent debts. It is also OSHA policy to forbear collection of penalties until the employer has exhausted its right to challenge them administratively, as well as in all legal forums.

B.   **Time Allowed for Payment of Penalties.** The date when penalties become due and payable depends on whether or not the employer contests.

1.   **Uncontested Penalties.** When citations and/or proposed penalties are uncontested, the penalties are due and payable 15 working days following the employer's receipt of the Citation and Notification of Penalty or, in the case of Informal Settlement Agreements, 15 working days after the date of the last signature unless a later due date for payment of penalties is agreed upon in the settlement.

2.   **Contested Penalties.** When citations and/or proposed penalties are contested, the date penalties are due and payable will depend upon whether the case is resolved by a settlement agreement, an administrative law judge decision, a Commission decision, or a court judgment. See Chapter 15, Section XIII., *Citation Final Order Dates*, for additional information.)

NOTE: *The Area Director shall forward the notice of contest and the case file to the RSOL with a transmittal letter informing the Solicitor that any resulting penalty must be directed to the Area Office for payment.*

3.   **Partially Contested Penalties.** When only part of a citation and/or a proposed penalty is contested, the due date for payment as stated in paragraph XIV.B.1., *Uncontested Penalties*, shall be used for the uncontested items and the due date stated in Paragraph XIV.B.2., *Contested Penalties*, for the contested items.

NOTE: *This provision notwithstanding, formal debt collection procedures will not be initiated in partially contested cases until a final order for the outstanding citation items has been issued.*

C. **Notification Procedures.** It is OSHA policy to notify employers (the "Notice") that debts are payable and due, and to inform them of OSHA's debt collection procedures prior to assessing any applicable delinquent charges. A copy of the "Notice" stating OSHA's debt collection policy, including assessment of interest, additional charges for nonpayment and administrative costs, shall be included with each Citation and Notification of Proposed Penalty, OSHA-2 Form, sent to employers. Interest rates and administrative costs are published annually and may be revised quarterly by the Secretary of the Treasury. DCAT shall advise Area Directors of any changes in the interest rate as they occur. A copy of the "Notice" shall be retained in the case file.

D. **Notification of Overdue Debt.** The Area Director shall send a demand letter to the employer when the debt has become delinquent and shall retain a copy of the demand letter in the case file. A debt becomes delinquent **30 calendar days after the due date**, which is the same as the **final order date** as stated in Chapter 15, Section XIII., *Citation Final Order Dates*.

1. **Uncontested Case with Penalties.** If payment of any applicable penalty is not received within 30 calendar days after the date of the expiration of the 15 working day contest period, or 15 working days after the date of the last signature (unless a later due date for payment of penalties is agreed upon in the settlement) if an Informal Settlement Agreement has been signed, a demand letter shall be mailed.

2. **Contested Case with Penalties.** If payment of any applicable penalty is not received within 30 calendar days after the Review Commission's **Order** approving a Formal Settlement Agreement, 60 calendar days after the **Notice of Docketing**, 90 calendar days after the **Notice of Commission Decision**, or 120 calendar days after date of the judgment of a U.S. Court of Appeals, and no appeal of the case has been filed by either OSHA or the employer, the Area Director shall either send a demand letter or a letter notifying the employer that the OSHA fine is past due (without assessing late fees and updating the IMIS as if a default letter had been sent).

3. **Exceptions to Sending the Demand Letter.** The demand letter will not be sent in the following circumstances:
   a. The employer is currently making payments under an approved installment plan or other satisfactory payment arrangement. Such plan or arrangement shall be set forth in writing and signed by the employer and the Area Director.
      NOTE: *If the employer enters into a written plan establishing a set payment schedule within one calendar month of the due date, but subsequently fails to make a payment within one calendar month of its scheduled due date, a payment default letter shall be sent to the employer. If the employer fails to respond satisfactorily to that letter within one month, the unpaid portion of the debt shall be handled in accordance with Paragraph XIV.F., Assessment Procedures.*
   b. The employer has partially contested the case (even if the penalty has not been contested). In such circumstances a demand letter shall not be sent until a final order has been issued.

E. **Assessment of Additional Charges.** Additional charges shall be assessed in accordance with the Debt Collection Improvement Act (31 USC 3717) and Department of Labor Regulations (29 CFR 20).

1. **Interest.** Interest on the unpaid principal amount shall be assessed on a monthly basis at the current annual rate if the debt has not been paid within one calendar month of the date on which the debt (penalty) became due and payable (i.e., the date of the final order). Interest is not assessed if an acceptable repayment schedule has been established in a written plan by the due date.
   NOTE: *Interest and delinquent charges are not compounded; only the unpaid balance of the penalty amount is used to calculate these additional charges.*

2. **Delinquent Charges.** Delinquent charges shall be assessed on a monthly basis if the debt has not been paid within 3 calendar months of the delinquent date (which is one calendar month after the due date). Debts paid in full within 3 calendar months of the delinquent date shall not be assessed a delinquent charge. Delinquent charges accrue at the annual rate of 6 percent (0.5 percent per month).
   NOTE: *Although the delinquent charge is not initially assessed until 3 calendar months after the debt became delinquent (4 calendar months after the due date), it is nevertheless calculated from the delinquent date. Thus, the first assessment of a delinquent charge will amount to a 3-month charge or 1.5 percent of the outstanding principal amount. Each month after that, the additional delinquent charge will be 0.5 percent of the unpaid principal.*

3. **Administrative Costs.** Administrative costs shall be assessed for each demand letter sent in an attempt to collect the unpaid debt. Costs are not assessed for payment default letters.

F. **Assessment Procedures.** If the penalty has not been paid by the delinquent date (i.e., within one calendar month of the due date), the Area Director shall implement the following procedures:

1. Interest shall be assessed at the current interest rate on the unpaid balance of the debt. The rate of interest shall remain fixed for the duration of the debt.
   NOTE: *Interest is to be calculated for one month and shall be assessed on the date on which such charges become payable. Any later additional charges will not be assessed until the first of the month following the date on which the charge becomes payable. For example, if interest becomes payable on the twentieth of the month and the second demand letter is not sent out until the eighth of the following month, only one month's interest is assessed.*

2. The demand letter shall be sent to the employer requesting immediate payment of the debt. The demand letter shall show the total amount of the debt, including the unpaid penalty amount, interest and administrative costs.

3. Employers may respond to the demand letter in several ways:
   a. The entire debt may be paid. In such cases no further collection action is necessary.
   b. A repayment plan may be submitted or offered; after a set payment schedule has been approved by the Area Director, no additional charges shall be levied against the debt as long as payments are timely made in accordance with the approved schedule. See note under Paragraph XIV.D.3.a. of this chapter, *Exceptions to Sending Demand Letter*. If payments are not made on schedule, the unpaid portion of the debt shall be treated in accordance with Paragraph XIV.F..
   c. A partial payment may be made; the unpaid portion of the debt shall be treated in accordance with Paragraph XIV.F. of this chapter.

4. If any portion of the debt remains unpaid after one calendar month from the time the demand letter was sent to the employer, the Area Director shall institute one of the following:
   a. Outstanding debts less than $100 may be written off.

b. If the employer made a payment after receiving the demand, letter the area office may:
- Send a receipt letter or contact the employer to request the balance due on the debt
- Refer the case to DCAT

c. Outstanding debts with a current debt of $100 or more shall be referred to DCAT.

5. After a case has been referred to DCAT for collection, the Area Director has no further responsibilities with regard to penalty collection related to that case.

6. If, after a case has been referred to DCAT, the employer mistakenly sends a payment to the Area Office, the case is subsequently contested, or new information regarding the debt or employer is obtained, the Area Director shall contact DCAT immediately.

7. DCAT shall update the host database to reflect all penalty collection actions taken by the National Office. Detailed information on subsequent debt collection activity on each case is available on the OSHA Intranet website. A written communication outlining collection actions taken for each case referred to DCAT shall be sent to the Area Office upon completion of National Office and Treasury debt collection procedures for that case.

8. The responsibility for closing the case remains with the Area Director. Once final collection action has been completed, the case may be closed whenever appropriate.

G. **Application of Payments.** Payments that are for less than the full amount of the debt shall be applied to satisfy the following categories in order of priority:
1. Administrative charges;
2. Delinquent charges;
3. Interest;
4. Outstanding principal.

H. **Uncollectible Penalties.** There may be cases where a penalty cannot be collected, regardless of any action that has been or may be undertaken. Examples might be when a demand letter is not deliverable, a company is no longer in business and has no successor, or the employer is bankrupt. In such cases, the Area Director **shall notify** DCAT by phone or email prior to referring the case to the National Office. DCAT will then advise what further collection action is appropriate. The database shall be updated following current IMIS procedures to reflect the most recent action. In bankruptcy cases, the Area Director may also seek the advice of the RSOL to determine whether to file as a creditor under the Bankruptcy Act.

I. **National Office Debt Collection Procedures.** Upon receipt of a case from an Area Director, DCAT shall verify the amount of the outstanding debt and proceed to implement National Office debt collection procedures.

1. **Demand Letter.** In accordance with the *Debt Collection Improvement Act of 1996* (DCIA), unless a debt meets certain exemption criteria, it must be referred to the Department of Treasury within 180 days after the debt becomes delinquent. The DCIA also requires that the debtor be notified that the debt may be referred to Treasury and what debt collection actions Treasury may take regarding the debt. This information is included in the demand letter DCAT sends to the employer, notifying him/her of the overdue debt and requesting immediate payment to DCAT.

2. **Exemptions Criteria for Referral to Treasury.** Debts may be exempt from the DCIA requirement if the case is in litigation by the Solicitor, in bankruptcy, in contest or on appeal.

3. **Referral to the Department of Treasury.** In accordance with the DCIA, if the debt remains uncollected sixty days from the date the DCAT demand letter was sent, the case may be referred to the Department of Treasury. Treasury actions include: referral to private debt collection firms; reporting to commercial credit reporting agencies; referral to the Internal Revenue Service for collection by offset; referral to the Department of Treasury Offset Program where collection is done by offset from payments due the debtor by any Federal agency; and/or litigation. In addition, Treasury will add their collection fees to the debt.
   a. Any penalty settlement offer received by Treasury shall be referred to the Area Director for approval.
   b. All penalty amounts collected by Treasury beyond their collection fees will be applied to the employer's penalty account.
   c. Any disputes received by Treasury will be forwarded to DCAT and may be sent to the Area Director for response.

4. **Updating the Database.** DCAT shall update the database to reflect all specific debt collection actions taken since referral to the National Office and indicate if the case has been returned to the Area Office.

5. **Compromise of Debts over $100,000.** Debts of $100,000 or more, exclusive of interest, delinquent charges, and administrative costs, cannot be waived by OSHA without Justice or Treasury approval. DCAT will obtain this approval before returning the debt to the Area Office.

6. **Return to the Area Office.** Once it has been decided to return the collection action, DCAT shall prepare a written transmittal memorandum to the Area Director stating the final status of the debt and what actions should be taken. Included with the memo will be copies of the DCAT case documents or correspondence. Electronic copies of each National Office Letter will also be maintained by DCAT. Information on each closed case remains available on the OSHA Intranet website.

Chapter 7 — Post-Citation Procedures And Abatement Verification

I. **Contesting Citations, Notifications of Penalty or Abatement Dates.** CSHOs shall advise the employer that the citation, the penalty and/or the abatement date may be contested in cases where the employer does not agree to the citation, penalty or abatement date or any combination of these.

A. **Notice of Contest.** CSHOs shall inform employers that if they intend to contest, the Area Director must be notified in writing and such notification must be postmarked no later than the 15th working day after receipt of the citation and notification of penalty (working days are Monday through Friday, excluding Federal holidays), otherwise the citation becomes a final order of the Commission. See §1903.17. The agency has no authority to modify the contest period. Employers may also be apprised that their notice of contest can be sent electronically via email to the Area Director within the 15 working day period and provide employers the email address(es). It shall be emphasized that oral notices of contest do not satisfy the requirement to give written notification.

NOTE: *Upon receipt of all electronic notices of contest, the Assistant Area Director or Area Director shall print copies of the email notice and include it in the documents and files to be transmitted to the Review Commission and the RSOL's office. Contest emails are not to be electronically forwarded to the Commission or RSOL. Area Offices are encouraged to establish procedures to ensure ready access to email accounts designated to receive notices of contest to ensure the timely transmission of copies to the Commission and RSOL. OSHA's acceptance of notices of contest via email shall not be interpreted to mean that the agency has consented to, or accepted, the electronic service of documents in litigation pursuant to Commission Rule §2200.7.*

1. An employer's Notice of Intent to Contest must clearly state what is specifically being contested. It must identify which item(s) of the citation, penalty, the abatement date, or any combination of these is being objected to. CSHOs shall ask the employer to read the OSHA-3000 pamphlet accompanying the citation for additional details.
   a. If the employer only requests a later abatement date and there are valid grounds to consider the request, the Area Director should be contacted. The Area Director may issue an amended citation changing an abatement date prior to the expiration of the 15 working day period.
   b. If the employer contests only the penalty or some of the citation items, all uncontested items must still be abated by the dates indicated on the citation and the corresponding penalties paid within 15 days of notification.
2. CSHOs shall inform the employer that the Act provides that employees or their authorized representative(s) have the right to contest in writing any or all of the abatement dates set for a violation if they believe the date(s) to be unreasonable.

B. **Contest Process.** The CSHO shall explain that when a Notice of Intent to Contest is properly filed (i.e., received in the Area Office and postmarked as described in the note to A.1. of this chapter), the Area Director is required to forward the case to an independent adjudicatory agency, (Review Commission) at which time the case is considered to be in litigation.
1. OSHA will normally cease all investigatory activities once an employer has filed a notice of contest. Any action relating to a contested case must first have the concurrence of the RSOL.
2. Upon receipt of the Notice of Intent to Contest, the Review Commission assigns the case to an administrative law judge, who will schedule a hearing in a public place close to the workplace.

II. **Informal Conferences.**
A. **General.**
1. Pursuant to §1903.20, the employer, any affected employee, or the employee representative may request an informal conference for the purpose of discussing any issues raised by an inspection, citation, notice of proposed penalty, or notice of intention to contest.
2. The informal conference will be conducted within the 15 working day contest period. The conference or any request for such a conference shall not operate as a stay of the 15 working day contest period.
3. If the employer's intent to contest is not clear, the Area Director or designated representative will make an effort contact the employer for clarification.
4. Informal conferences may be held by any means practical, but meeting in person is preferred.

B. **Assistance of Counsel.** In the event that an employer is bringing its attorney to an informal conference, the Area Director or his or her designee may contact the RSOL's Office and ask for the assistance of counsel.

C. **Opportunity to Participate.**
1. If an informal conference is requested by the employer, an affected employee or his representative shall be afforded the opportunity to participate. If the conference is requested by an employee or an employee representative, the employer shall be afforded an opportunity to participate.
2. If the affected employee or employee representative chooses not to participate in the informal conference, an attempt will be made to contact that party and to solicit their input prior to the informal conference. Attempts to contact the party should be noted in the case file.
   NOTE: *In the event of a settlement, it is not necessary to have the employee representative sign the informal settlement agreement.*
3. If any party objects to the attendance of another party or the Area Director believes that a joint informal conference would not be productive, separate informal conferences may be held.
4. During the conduct of a joint informal conference, separate or private discussions will be permitted if either party so requests.

D. **Notice of Informal Conferences.** Area Director shall document in the case file notification to the parties of the date, time and location of the informal conference. In addition, the Case File Diary Sheet shall indicate the date of the informal conference.

E. **Posting Requirement.**
1. The Area Director will ask the employer at the beginning of the informal conference whether the form in the citation package indicating the date, time, and location of the conference has been posted as required.
2. If the employer has not posted the form, the Area Director may postpone the informal conference until such action is taken.

F. **Conduct of the Informal Conference.** The informal conference will be conducted in accordance with the following guidelines:
1. **Conference Subjects.**
   a. Purpose of the informal conference;
   b. Rights of participants;
   c. Contest rights and time constraints;
   d. Limitations, if any;
   e. Potential for settlements of citations; and
   f. Other relevant information (e.g., if no employee or employee representative has responded, whether the employer has posted the notification form regarding the informal conference, etc.).
2. **Subjects Not to be Addressed.**
   a. No opinions regarding the legal merits of an employer's case shall be expressed during the informal conference.
   b. There should be no discussion with employers or employee representatives concerning the potential for referral of fatality inspections to the Department of Justice for criminal prosecution under the Act.

3. **Closing Remarks.**

 a. At the conclusion of the conference, all main issues and potential courses of action will be summarized and documented.

 b. A copy of the summary, together with any other relevant notes of the discussion made by the Area Director, will be placed in the case file.

III. **Petition for Modification of Abatement Date (PMA).** An employer may file a petition for modification of abatement date when it has made a good faith effort to comply with abatement requirements, but such abatement has not been completed due to circumstances beyond its control. See §1903.14a. If the employer requests additional abatement time after the 15 working-day contest period has passed, the following procedures for PMAs are to be observed:

 A. **Filing.** A PMA must be filed in writing with the Area Director who issued the citation no later than the close of the next working day following the date on which abatement was originally required.

  1. If a PMA is submitted orally, the employer shall be informed that OSHA cannot accept an oral PMA and that a written petition must be mailed by the end of the next working day after the abatement date. If there is not sufficient time to file a written petition, the employer shall be informed of the requirements below for late filing of the petition.

  2. A late petition may be accepted only if accompanied by the employer's statement of exceptional circumstances explaining the delay.

 B. **Where Filing Requirements Are Not Met.** If the employer's written PMA does not meet all the requirements of §1903.14a(b)(1)-(5), the employer shall be contacted within 10 working days and notified of the missing elements. A reasonable amount of time for the employer to respond shall be specified during this contact.

  1. If no response is received or if the information returned is still insufficient, a second attempt (by telephone or in writing) shall be made. The employer shall be informed that if it fails to respond in a timely or adequate manner, the PMA will not be granted and the employer may be found to not have abated.

  2. If the employer responds satisfactorily by telephone and the Area Director determines that the requirements for a PMA have been met, that finding shall be documented in the case file.

  3. Although OSHA policy is to handle PMAs as expeditiously as possible, there may be cases where the Area Director's decision on may be delayed because of deficiencies in the PMA, the need to conduct a monitoring inspection and/or a request for Regional Office or National Office involvement. Requests for additional time (e.g., 45 days) for the Area Director to reach a decision shall be sent to the Review Commission through the RSOL. A letter conveying this request shall be simultaneously sent to the employer and the employee representatives.

 C. **Approval of PMA.** After the expiration of 15 working days following the posting of a PMA, the Area Director shall agree with or objecting to the request within 10 working days, if additional time has not been requested from the Review Commission. In the absence of a timely objection, the PMA shall be deemed granted even if not explicitly approved. The following action shall be taken:

  1. If the PMA requests an abatement date that is two years or less from the issuance date of the citation, the Area Director has the authority to approve or object to the petition.

  2. Any PMA requesting an abatement date that is more than two years from the issuance date of the citation requires the approval of the Regional Administrator as well as the Area Director.

  3. If the PMA is approved, the Area Director shall notify the employer and the employee representatives by letter.

  4. The Area Director or Regional Administrator (as appropriate) after consultation with the RSOL, shall object to a PMA where the evidence supports non-approval (e.g., employer has taken no meaningful abatement action at all or has otherwise exhibited bad faith). In such cases, all relevant documentation shall be sent to the Review Commission in accordance with §1903.14a(d). Both the employer and the employee representatives shall be notified of this action by letter, with return receipt requested.

   a. Letters notifying the employer or employee representative of the objection shall be mailed on the same date that the agency objection to the PMA is sent to the Review Commission.

   b. When appropriate, after consultation with the RSOL, a failure to abate notification may be issued in conjunction with the objection to the PMA.

 D. **Objection to PMA.** Affected employees or their representatives may file a written objection to an employer's PMA with the Area Director within 10 working days of the date of posting of the PMA by the employer or its service upon an authorized employee representative.

  1. Failure to file such a written objection with the 10 working day period constitutes a waiver of any further right to object to the PMA.

  2. If an employee or an employee representative objects to the extension of the abatement date, all relevant documentation shall be sent to the Review Commission.

   a. Confirmation of this action shall be mailed (return receipt requested) to the objecting party as soon as it is accomplished.

   b. Notification of the employee objection shall be mailed (return receipt requested) to the employer on the same day that the case file is forwarded to the Commission.

IV. **OSHA's Abatement Verification Regulation, §1903.19.**

 A. **Important Terms and Concepts.**

  1. **Abatement.**

   a. Abatement means action by an employer to comply with a cited standard or regulation or to eliminate a recognized hazard identified by OSHA during an inspection.

   b. For each inspection, except follow-up inspections, OSHA shall open an employer-specific case file. The case file remains open throughout the inspection process and is not closed until the Agency is satisfied that abatement has occurred. If abatement was not completed, annotate the circumstances or reasons in the case file and enter the proper code in the IMIS.

   c. Employers are required to verify in writing that they have abated cited conditions, in accordance with §1903.19.

2. **Abatement Verification.** Abatement verification includes abatement certification, documents, plans, and progress reports.

3. **Abatement Certification.** Employers must certify that abatement is complete for each cited violation. The written certification must include: the employer's name and address; the inspection number; the citation and item numbers; a statement that the information submitted is accurate; signature of the employer or employer's authorized representative; the date and method of abatement for each cited violation; and a statement that affected employees and their representatives have been informed of the abatement.

4. **Abatement Documents.** Documentation submitted must establish that abatement has been completed, and include evidence such as the purchase or repair of equipment, photographic or video evidence of abatement or other written records verifying correction of the violative condition.

5. **Affected Employee.** Affected employee means those employees who are exposed to the hazards(s) identified as violations(s) in a citation.

6. **Final Order Dates.**
   a. **Uncontested Citation Item.** For an uncontested citation item, the final order date is the day following the fifteenth working day after the employer's receipt of the citation.
   b. **Contested Citation Item.** For a contested citation item, the final order date is as follows:
      - The thirtieth day after the date on which a decision or order of a Review Commission administrative law judge has been docketed with the Commission, unless a member of the Commission has directed review; or
      - Where review has been directed, the thirtieth day after the date on which the Commission issues its decision or order disposing of all or pertinent part of a case; or
      - The date on which a federal appeals court issues a decision affirming the violation in a case in which a final order of Review Commission has been stayed.
   c. **Informal Settlement Dates.** The final order date is when, within the 15 working days to contest a citation, the ISA is signed by **both** parties. See also Chapter 15, Section XIII, *Citation Final Order Dates.*

7. **Abatement Dates.**
   a. **Uncontested Citations.** For uncontested citations, the abatement date is the later of the following dates:
      - The abatement date identified in the citation;
      - The extended date established as a result of an employer's filing for a Petition for Modification of Abatement (PMA) (see Review Commission Rule 37, §2200.37); or
      - The date established by an informal settlement agreement.
   b. **Contested Citations.** For contested citations for which the Review Commission has issued a final order, the abatement date is the later of the following dates:
      - The date identified in the final order for abatement;
      - Where there has been a contest of a violation or abatement date (not penalty), the date computed by adding the period allowed in the citation for abatement to the final order date; or
      - The date established by a formal settlement agreement.
   c. **Contested Penalty Only.** Where an employer has contested only the proposed penalty, the abatement period continues to run unaffected by the contest. The abatement period is subject to the time periods set forth above.

8. **Movable Equipment.**
   a. Movable equipment means a hand-held or non-hand-held machine or device, powered or non-powered, that is used to do work and is moved within or between worksites.
   b. Hand-held equipment is equipment that is hand-held when operated and can generally be picked up and operated with one or two hands, such as a hand grinder, skill saw, portable electric drill, nail gun, etc.

9. **Worksite.**
   a. For the purpose of enforcing the Abatement Verification regulation, the worksite is the physical location specified within the "Alleged Violation Description" of the citation.
   b. If no location is specified, the worksite shall be the inspection site where the cited violation occurred.

B. **Written Certification.** The Abatement Verification Regulation, §1903.19, requires those employers who have received a citation(s) for violation(s) of the Act to certify in writing that they have abated the hazardous condition for which they were cited and to inform affected employees of their abatement actions.

C. **Verification Procedures.** The verification procedures to be followed by an employer depend on the nature of the violation(s) identified and the employer's abatement actions. The abatement verification regulation establishes requirements for the following:
   1. Abatement Certification
   2. Abatement Documentation
   3. Abatement Plans
   4. Progress Reports
   5. Tagging for Movable Equipment

D. **Supplemental Procedures.** Where necessary, OSHA supplements these procedures with follow-up inspections and onsite monitoring inspections. For additional information see Section XII of this chapter, *OnSite Visits: Procedures for Abatement Verification and Monitoring.*

E. **Requirements.** Except for the application of warning tags or citations on movable equipment (§1903.19(i)), the abatement verification regulation does not impose any requirements on the employer until a citation item has become a final order of the Review Commission. For moveable hand-held equipment, the warning tag or citation must be attached immediately after the employer receives the citation. For other moveable equipment, the warning tag or citation must be attached prior to moving the equipment within or between worksites.

V. Abatement Certification.

A. **Minimum Level.** Abatement certification is the minimum level of abatement verification and is required for all violations once they become Review Commission final orders. An exception exists where the CSHO observed abatement during the onsite portion of the inspection and the violation is listed on the citation as "Corrected During Inspection (CDI)" or "Quick-Fix." See Paragraph VI.D. of this chapter, CSHO *Observed Abatement*.

B. **Certification Requirements.** The employer's written certification that abatement is complete must include the following information for each cited violation:

1. The date and method of abatement and a statement that affected employees and their representatives have been informed of the abatement;
2. The employer's name and address;
3. The inspection number to which the submission relates;
4. The citation and item numbers to which the submission relates;
5. A statement that the information submitted is accurate; and
6. The signature of the employer or the employer's authorized representative.

   A non-mandatory example of an abatement certification letter is available in Appendix A of the Abatement Verification Regulation (§1903.19).

C. **Certification Timeframe.**

1. All citation items which have become final orders, regardless of their characterizations, require written abatement certification within 10 calendar days of the abatement date.
2. A PMA received and processed in accordance with the guidance of the FOM will suspend the 10-day time period for receipt of the abatement certification for the item for which the PMA is requested.
   a. Thus, no citation will be issued for failure to submit the certification within 10 days of the abatement date.
   b. If the PMA is denied, the 10-day time period for submission to OSHA begins on the day the employer receives notice of the denial.

VI. Abatement Documentation.
More extensive documentation of abatement is required for the most serious violations. When a violation requires abatement documentation, in addition to certifying abatement, the employer must submit documents demonstrating that abatement is complete.

A. **Required Abatement Documentation.** Pursuant to §1903.19, documentation of abatement is required for the following:

1. Willful violations;
2. Repeat violations; and
3. Serious violations where OSHA determines that such documentation is necessary as indicated on the citation. For further information see Paragraph VI.C. of this chapter, *Abatement Documentation for Serious Violations*.

B. **Adequacy of Abatement Documentation.**

1. Abatement documentation must be accurate and describe or portray the abated condition adequately. It may be submitted in electronic form, if approved by the Area Director.
2. The abatement regulation does not mandate a particular type of documentary evidence for any specific cited conditions.
3. The adequacy of the abatement documentation submitted by the employer will be assessed by OSHA using the information available in the citation and the Agency's knowledge of the employer's workplace and history.
4. Examples of documents that demonstrate that abatement is complete include, but are not limited to:
   a. Photographic or video evidence of abatement;
   b. Evidence of the purchase or repair of equipment;
   c. Evidence of actions taken to abate;
   d. Bills from repair services;
   e. Reports or evaluations by safety and health professionals describing the abatement of the hazard or a report of analytical testing;
   f. Documentation from the manufacturer that the article repaired is within the manufacturer's specifications;
   g. Records of training completed by employees if the citation is related to inadequate employee training; and
   h. A copy of program documents if the citation was related to a missing or inadequate program, such as a deficiency in the employer's respirator or hazard communication program.
5. Abatement documentation (photos, employer programs, etc.) shall be retained in accordance with ADM 03-01-005, OSHA *Compliance Records*, dated August 3, 1998.

C. **Abatement Documentation for Serious Violations.**

1. **High Gravity Serious Violations.**
   a. OSHA policy is generally that all high gravity serious violations will require abatement documentation.
   b. Where, in the opinion of the Area Director, abatement documentation is not required for a high gravity serious violation, the reasons for this must be set forth in the case file.
2. **Moderate or Low Gravity Serious Violations.** Moderate or low gravity serious violations should not normally require abatement documentation, except that the Area Director will require evidence of abatement for moderate and low gravity serious violations under the following circumstances:
   a. If the establishment has been issued a citation for a willful violation or a failure-to-abate notice for any standard which has become final order in the previous three years; or
   b. If the employer has any history of a violation that resulted in a fatality or an OSHA-300 log entry indicating serious physical harm to an employee in the past three years. The standard being cited must be similar to the standard cited in connection with the fatality or serious injury or illness.

D. **CSHO Observed Abatement.**

1. Employers are not required to certify abatement for violations which they promptly abate during the onsite portion of the inspection and observed by the CSHO.
   a. Area Directors may use their discretion in extending the "24 hour" time limit to document abated conditions during the inspection.

     b.   Observed abatement will be documented on the Violations Summary Form (OSHA-1B and/or OSHA-1B(IH)), for each violation and must include the date and method of abatement.

    2.   If the observed abatement is for a violation that would normally require abatement documentation by the employer, the documentation in the case file must also indicate that abatement is complete. Where suitable, the CSHO may use photographs or video evidence. For additional information regarding adequacy of abatement documentation, see Paragraph VI.B. of this chapter, *Adequacy of Abatement Documentation*.

    3.   When the abatement has been witnessed and documented by the CSHO, a notation reading "Corrected During Inspection" shall be made on the citation. Immediate abatement of some violations may qualify for penalty reductions under OSHA's "Quick-Fix" incentive program. These incentives are discussed with the employer during the opening conference. See Chapter 6, Paragraph IV.A., *Quick-Fix Penalty Adjustment*.

    4.   Notations stating "Corrected during inspection" or "Employer has abated all hazards" shall not be made on the citation in cases where there is evidence of a continuing violative practice by an employer that may be subject to a summary enforcement order under Section 11(b) of the Act (i.e., failure to provide fall protection is a recurring condition based on citation history or other indications suggesting widespread violations of the same or similar standards at other establishments or construction worksites).

VII. Monitoring Information for Abatement Periods Greater than 90 Days.

  A.   **Abatement Periods Greater that 90 Days.** For abatement periods greater than 90 calendar days, the regulation allows the Area Director flexibility in either requiring or not requiring monitoring information.

    1.   The requirement for abatement plans and progress reports must be specifically associated to the citation item to which they relate.

    2.   Progress reports may not be required unless abatement plans are specifically required.

    3.   Note that Paragraphs (e) and (f) of §1903.19 have limits: the Area Director is not allowed to require an abatement plan for abatement periods less than 91 days or for citations characterized as other-than-serious.

    4.   The regulation places an obligation on employers, where necessary, to identify how employees are to be protected from exposure to the violative condition during the abatement period. One way of ensuring that interim protection is included in the abatement plan is to note this requirement on the citation. See §1903.19, Non-Mandatory Appendix B, for a sample of an Abatement Plan and Progress Report.

  B.   **Abatement Plans.**

    1.   The Area Director may require an employer to submit an abatement plan for each qualifying cited violation.

        a.   The requirement for an abatement plan must be indicated in the citation.

        b.   The citation may also call for the abatement plan to include interim measures.

    2.   Within 25 calendar days from the final order date, the employer must submit an abatement plan for each violation that identifies the violation and the steps to be taken to achieve abatement. The abatement plan must include a schedule for completing the abatement and, where necessary, the methods for protecting employees from exposure to the hazardous conditions in the interim until the abatement is complete (§1903.19(e)(2)).

    3.   In cases where the employer can not prepare an abatement plan within the allotted time, a PMA must be submitted by the employer to amend the abatement date.

  C.   **Progress Reports.**

    1.   An employer that is required to submit an abatement plan may also be required to submit periodic progress reports for each cited violation. In such cases, the citation must indicate:

        a.   That periodic progress reports are required and the citation items for which they are required;

        b.   The date on which an initial progress report must be submitted, which may be no sooner than 30 calendar days after the due date of an abatement plan;

        c.   Whether additional progress reports are required; and

        d.   The date(s) on which additional progress reports must be submitted.

    2.   For each violation, the progress report must identify in a single sentence if possible, the action taken to achieve abatement and the date the action was taken. There is nothing in this policy or the regulation prohibiting progress reports as a result of settlement agreements.

  D.   **Special Requirements for Long-Term Abatement.**

    1.   Long-term abatement is abatement which will be completed more than one year from the citation issuance date.

    2.   The Area Director must require the employer to submit an abatement plan for every violation with an abatement date in excess of one year.

    3.   Progress reports are mandatory and must be required at a minimum every six months. More frequent reporting may be required at the discretion of the area director.

VIII. Employer Failure to Submit Required Abatement Certification.

  A.   **Actions Preceding Citation for Failure to Certify Abatement.**

    1.   If abatement certification, or any required documentation, is not received within 13 calendar days after the abatement date (the regulation requires filing within 10 calendar days after the abatement date; and another 3 calendar days is added for mailing), the following procedures should be followed:

        a.   Remind the employer by telephone of the requirement to submit the material and tell the employer that a citation will be issued if the required documents are not received within 7 calendar days after the telephone call.

        b.   During the conversation with the employer, determine why it has not complied and document all communication efforts in the case file. Discuss OSHA's PMA policy and explain that a late petition to modify the abatement date can be accepted only if accompanied by the employer's statement of exceptional circumstances explaining the delay.

        c.   Issue a follow-up letter to the employer the same day as the telephone call.

        d.   The employer may be allowed to respond via fax or email where appropriate.

    2.   If the certification and/or documentation are not received within the next 7 calendar days, a single other-than-serious citation will be issued.

3. Normally citations for failure to submit abatement certification for violations of §1903.19(c) shall not be issued until the above procedures have been followed and the employer has been provided additional opportunity to comply. These pre-citation procedures also apply when abatement plans or progress reports are not received within 13 days of the due date.

B. **Citation for Failure to Certify.**

1. Citations for failure to submit abatement verification (certification, documentation, abatement plans or progress reports) can be issued without formal follow-up activities by following the procedures identified below.

2. A single other-than-serious citation will be issued combining all the individual instances where the employer has not submitted abatement certification and/or abatement documentation.

   a. This "other" citation will be issued under the same inspection number which contained the original violations cited.

   b. The abatement date for this citation shall be set 30 days from the date of issuance.

   NOTE: *Each violation of §1903.19(c), (d), (e), or (f) with respect to each original citation item is a separate item.*

3. For those situations where the abatement date falls within the 15 day informal conference time period, and an informal conference request is likely, enforcement activities should be delayed for these citations until it is known if the citation's characterization or abatement period is to be modified.

4. For those rare instances where the reminder letter is returned to the Area Office by the Post Office as undeliverable and telephone contact efforts fail, the Area Director has the discretion to stop further efforts to locate the employer and document in the case file the reason for no abatement certification.

C. **Certification Omissions.**

1. An initial minor or non-substantive omission in an abatement certification (e.g., lack of a definitive statement stating that the information being submitted is accurate) should be considered a de minimis condition of the regulation.

2. If there are minor deficiencies, such as omitting the inspection number, signature or date, the employer should be contacted by telephone to verify that the documents received were the ones they intended to submit. If so, the date stamp of the Area Office can serve as the date on the document.

3. A certification with an omitted signature should be returned to the employer to be signed.

D. **Penalty Assessment for Failure to Certify.** The penalty provisions of Sections 9 and 17 of the OSH Act apply to all citations issued under this regulation. See Chapter 6, *Penalties and Debt Collection*, for additional information.

IX. **Tagging for Movable Equipment.**

A. **Tag-Related Citations.** Tag-related citations must be observed by CSHOs prior to the issuance of a citation for failure to initially tag cited movable equipment.

1. See §1903.19, Non-mandatory Appendix C, for a sample warning tag. OSHA must be able to prove the employer's initial failure to act (tag the movable equipment upon receipt of the citation).

2. Where there is insufficient evidence to support a violation of the employer's initial failure to tag or post the citation on the cited movable equipment, a citation may be issued for failure to maintain the tag or copy of the citation using §1903.19(i)(6).

B. **Equipment Which is Moved.** Tags are intended to provide an interim form of protection to employees through notification for those who may not know of the citation or the hazardous condition.

1. For non hand-held equipment, CSHOs should make every effort to be as detailed as possible when documenting the initial location where the violation occurred. This documentation is critical to the enforcement of the tagging requirement (§1903.19(i)) because the tagging provision is triggered upon *movement of* the equipment.

2. For hand-held equipment, employers must attach a warning tag or copy of the citation *immediately* after the employer's receipt of the citation. The attachment of the tag is not dependent on any *subsequent* movement of the equipment.

X. **Failure to Notify Employees by Posting.**

A. **Evidence.** Like tag-related citations, CSHOs shall investigate an employer's failure to notify employees by posting.

B. **Location of Posting.** Where an employer claims that posting at the location where the violation occurred would ineffectively inform employees (§1903.19(g)(2)) the employer may post the document or a summary of the document in a location where it will be readily observable by affected employees and their representatives. Employers may also communicate by other means with affected employees and their representatives regarding abatement activities.

C. **Other Communication.** The CSHO must determine not only whether the documents or summaries were appropriately posted, but also whether, as an alternative, other communication methods, such as meetings or employee publications, were used.

XI. **Abatement Verification for Special Enforcement Situations.**

A. **Construction Activity Considerations.**

1. Construction activities pose situations requiring special consideration.

   a. Construction site closure or hazard removal due to completing of the structure or project will only be accepted as abatement without certification where the area office CSHO verifies the site closure/completion and where closure/completion effectively abates the condition cited.

   b. In all other circumstances, the employer must certify to OSHA that the hazards have been abated by the submission of an abatement certification. In rare cases the verification may have to cease and the abatement action closed through cessation of work or verification with the general contractor of the site to verify abatement.

2. Equipment-related and all program-related (e.g., crane inspection, hazard communication, respirator, training, competent person, qualified persons, etc.) violations *will always* require employer certification of abatement regardless of construction site closure.

3. Where the violation specified in a citation is the employer's general practice of failing to comply with a requirement (e.g., the employer routinely fails to provide fall protection at its worksites), closure/completion of the individual worksite will not be accepted as abatement.

4. For situations where the main office of the employer being cited is physically located in another Regional jurisdiction, the Area Director having the jurisdiction over the work site will proceed as if the employer's main office were in the Area Director's own jurisdiction, and notify the affected Regional Office of the communication with the employer.

5. Where a follow-up inspection to verify abatement is deemed necessary, the affected Regions and Area Offices will determine the most efficient and mutually beneficial approach to conducting the inspection.

B. **Field Sanitation and Temporary Labor Camps.** Under Secretary's Order 3-2000, the authority to conduct inspections and issue citations for field sanitation and most temporary labor camps in agricultural employment has been delegated to the Employment Standards Administration (ESA).

1. An employer's obligation under the abatement verification regulation still applies. However, OSHA's delegation of authority to ESA does not extend to other OSHA regulations or standards, including §1903.19.

2. In situations where ESA determines employers are in violation of §1903.19, the following procedures are to be followed:

   a. Wage and Hour District Directors, after following the procedures outlined in Section VIII. of this chapter, *Employer Failure to Submit Required Abatement Certification*, will send a copy of the inspection case file or a summary memorandum to the OSHA Regional Administrator's Office for referral following established practice.

   b. The OSHA Regional Office shall forward appropriate case files to the Area Office having jurisdiction to open a NEW inspection (coded as a Referral) and process citation(s) for failure to comply with §1903.19. Upon receipt of the abatement verification documents related to the ESA inspection, OSHA will fax them to ESA. **NOTE:** *All field sanitation and temporary labor camp cases will automatically comply with the Appropriations Act rider because the field sanitation standard does not apply to employers with 10 or fewer employees and the rider does not apply to temporary labor camps.*

   c. Penalties will be collected and processed following normal procedures. Upon receipt of penalties for the OSHA-issued §1903.19 citations, OSHA's case file will be closed.

   d. In situations where an employer does not respond to OSHA's issuance of violations of §1903.19 and dunning efforts fail, ESA shall be informed through memorandum and the OSHA case file closed with the penalties referred for debt collection. **NOTE:** *See also to Chapter 10, Industry Sectors, and Chapter 12, Specialized Inspection Procedures, for additional information.*

C. **Follow-Up Policy for Employer Failure to Verify Abatement under §1903.19.** Follow-up or monitoring inspections would not normally be conducted when evidence of abatement is provided by the employer or employee representatives. For further information on exceptions for Enhanced Enforcement Program (EEP) cases, see CPL 02-00-145, *Enhanced Enforcement Program (EEP) Directive*, dated January 1, 2008. **NOTE:** *For further information on extended abatement periods, see Section VII, Monitoring Information for Abatement Periods Greater than 90 Days, and Section XIII, Monitoring Inspections, both of this chapter.*

1. Where the employer has not submitted the required abatement certification or documentation within the time permitted by the regulation, the Area Director has discretion to conduct a follow-up inspection.

2. Submission of inadequate documents may also be the basis for a follow-up inspection.

3. This inspection should not generally occur before the end of the original 15 day contest period except in unusual circumstances.

XII. OnSite Visits: Procedures for Abatement Verification and Monitoring.

A. **Follow-Up Inspections.** The primary purpose of a follow-up inspection is to determine if the previously cited violations have been corrected.

B. **Enhanced Enforcement Program (EEP) Follow-Up.**

1. For any inspection opened after October 1, 2003, which results in an EEP case, an enhanced follow-up inspection will normally be conducted even if abatement of the cited violations has been verified. The primary purpose of follow-up inspections is to assess both whether the cited violation(s) were abated and whether the employer is committing similar violations.

2. If there is a compelling reason not to conduct a follow-up inspection, the reason must be documented in the file. The Region shall also report these cases to the Director of Enforcement Programs, along with the reason why a follow-up was not initiated.

3. Grouped and combined violations from the original inspection will be counted as one violation for EEP purposes.

4. For further information on exceptions for Enhanced Enforcement Program (EEP) cases, see CPL 02-00-145, *Enhanced Enforcement Program (EEP) Directive*, dated January 1, 2008, for more information on the Enhanced Enforcement Program.

C. **Initial Follow-Up.**

1. The initial follow-up is the first follow-up inspection after issuance of the citation.

2. If a violation is found not to have been abated, the CSHO shall inform the employer that the employer is subject to a Notification of Failure to Abate Alleged Violation and proposed additional daily penalties while such failure or violation continues.

3. Failure to comply with enforceable interim abatement dates involving multi-step abatement shall be subject to a Notification of Failure to Abate Alleged Violation.

4. Where the employer has implemented some controls, but the control measures were inadequate during follow-up monitoring, and other technology was available which would have brought the process into compliance, a Notification of Failure to Abate Alleged Violation normally shall be issued. If the employer has exhibited good faith, a late PMA for extenuating circumstances may be considered.

5. Where an apparent failure to abate by means of engineering controls is found to be due to technical infeasibility, no failure to abate notice shall be issued; however, if proper administrative controls, work practices or personal protective equipment are not utilized, a Notification of Failure to Abate Alleged Violation shall be issued.

D. **Second Follow-Up.**

1. Any subsequent follow-up after the initial follow-up inspection dealing with the same violations is considered a second follow-up.

    a.   After the Notification of Failure to Abate Alleged Violation has been issued, the Area Director shall allow a reasonable time for abatement of the violation before conducting a second follow-up. The employer must ensure that employees are adequately protected by other means until the violations are corrected.

    b.   If the employer contests the proposed additional daily penalties, a follow-up inspection shall still be scheduled to ensure correction of the original violation.

2. If a second follow-up inspection reveals the employer still has not corrected the original violations, a second Notification of Failure to Abate Alleged Violation with additional daily penalties shall be issued if the Area Director, after consultation with the Regional Administrator and RSOL, believes it to be appropriate.

3. If a Notification of Failure to Abate Alleged Violation and additional daily penalties are not to be proposed because of an employer's flagrant disregard of a citation or an item on a citation, the Area Director shall immediately contact the Regional Administrator, in writing, detailing the circumstances so the matter can be referred to the RSOL for action, as appropriate, in the U.S. Court of Appeals in accordance with Section 11(b) of the Act.

E. **OSH Act Section 11(b).** There may be times during the initial follow-up when, because of an employer's flagrant disregard of a citation or other factors, it will be apparent that traditional enforcement actions would be inappropriate or ineffective. In such cases, a summary enforcement action shall be initiated under Section 11(b) of the Act in the U.S. Court of Appeals. The Area Director shall notify the Regional Administrator, in writing, of all the particular circumstances of the case for referral to the RSOL.

F. **Follow-Up Inspection Reports.**

1. Follow-up inspection reports shall be included with the original initial inspection case file. The applicable identification and description sections of the OSHA-1B/1B(IH) Form shall be used for documenting correction of willful, repeated, and serious violations and failure to correct items during follow-up inspections.

2. If Serious, Willful, or Repeat violation items were appropriately grouped in the OSHA-1B/1B(IH) in the original case file, they may be grouped on the follow-up OSHA-1B; otherwise, individual OSHA-1B/1B(IH) forms shall be used for each item. The correction of other-than-serious violations may be documented in the narrative portion of the case file.

3. **Documentation of Hazard Abatement by Employer.**

    a.   The hazard abatement observed by the CSHO shall be specifically described in the OSHA-1B/1B(IH) form, including any applicable dimensions, materials, specifications, personal protective equipment, engineering controls, measurements or readings, or other conditions.

    b.   Brief terms such as "corrected" or "in compliance" will not be accepted as proper documentation for violations having been corrected.

    c.   When appropriate, this written description shall be supplemented by a photograph and/or a videotape to illustrate correction circumstances.

    d.   Only the item description and identification blocks need be completed on the follow-up OSHA-1B/1B(IH) with an occasional inclusion of an applicable employer statement concerning correction under the employer knowledge section, if appropriate.

4. **Sampling.**

    a.   CSHOs conducting a follow-up inspection to determine abatement of violations of air contaminant or noise standards, shall decide whether sampling is necessary and if so, what kind (i.e., spot sampling, short-term sampling, or full-shift sampling).

    b.   If there is reasonable probability that a Notification of Failure to Abate Alleged Violation will be issued, full-shift sampling is required to verify exposure limits based on an 8-hour time-weighted average.

5. **Narrative.** The CSHO must include in the narrative the findings pursuant to the inspection, along with recommendations for action. In order to make a valid recommendation, it is important to have all the pertinent factors available in an organized manner.

6. **Failure to Abate.** In the event that any item has not been abated, complete documentation shall be included on an OSHA-1B.

XIII. Monitoring Inspections.

A. **General.** Monitoring inspections are conducted to ensure that hazards are being corrected and employees are being protected, whenever a long period of time is needed for an establishment to come into compliance. Such inspections may be scheduled, among other reasons, as a result of:

- Abatement dates in excess of one year.
- A petition for modification of abatement date (PMA).
- A Corporate Wide Settlement Agreement. See CPL 02-00-090, *Guidelines for Administration of Corporate-Wide Settlement Agreements*, dated June 3, 1991.
- To ensure that terms of a permanent variance are being carried out.
- At the request of an employer requesting technical assistance granted by the Area director.

B. **Conduct of Monitoring Inspection (PMAs and Long-Term Abatement).** Monitoring inspections shall be conducted in the same manner as follow-up inspections. An inspection shall be classified as a monitoring inspection when a safety/health inspection is conducted for one or more of the following purposes:

- Determine the progress an employer is making toward final correction.
- Ensure that the target dates of a multi-step abatement plan are being met.
- Ensure that an employer's petition for the modification of abatement dates is made in good faith and that the employer has attempted to implement necessary controls as expeditiously as possible.
- Ensure that the employees are being properly protected until final controls are implemented.
- Ensure that the terms of a permanent variance are being carried out.
- Provide abatement assistance for items under citation.

C. **Abatement Dates in Excess of One Year.**

1. Monitoring visits shall be scheduled to check on progress made whenever abatement dates extend beyond one year from the issuance date of the citation.

2. These inspections shall be conducted approximately every six months, counted from the citation date, until final abatement has been achieved for all cited violations.
   a. If the case has been contested, the final order date shall be used as a starting point, instead of the citation date.
   b. A settlement agreement may specify an alternative monitoring schedule.
3. If the employer is submitting satisfactory quarterly progress reports and the Area Director agrees after careful review, that these reports reflect adequate progress on implementation of control measures and adequate interim protection for employees, a monitoring inspection may be conducted every twelve months.
4. Such inspections shall have priority equal to that of serious formal complaints. The seriousness of the hazards requiring abatement shall determine the priority among monitoring inspections.

D. **Monitoring Abatement Efforts.**
   1. The Area Director shall take the steps necessary to ensure that the employer is making a good faith attempt to bring about abatement as expeditiously as possible.
   2. Where engineering controls have been cited or required for abatement, a monitoring inspection shall be scheduled to evaluate the employer's abatement efforts. Failure to conduct a monitoring inspection shall be fully explained in the case file.
   3. Where no engineering controls have been cited but more time is needed for other reasons not requiring assistance from OSHA, such as delays in receiving equipment, a monitoring visit need not normally be scheduled.
   4. Monitoring inspections shall be scheduled as soon as possible after the initial contact with the employer and shall not be delayed until actual receipt of the PMA.
   5. CSHOs shall decide during the monitoring inspection whether sampling is necessary and, if so, to what extent; i.e., spot sampling, short-term sampling, or full-shift sampling.
   6. CSHOs shall include pertinent findings in the narrative along with recommendations for action. To reach a valid conclusion when recommending action, it is important to have all the relevant factors available in an organized manner. The factors to be considered may include, but are not limited to the following:
      a. Progress reports or other indications of the employer's good faith, demonstrating effective use of technical expertise and/or management skills, accuracy of information reported by the employer, and timeliness of progress reports.
      b. The employer's assessment of the hazards by means of surveys performed by in-house personnel, consultants, and/or the employer's insurance agency.
      c. Other documentation collected by Area Office personnel including verification of progress reports, success and/or failure of abatement efforts, and assessment of current exposure levels of employees.
      d. Employer and employee interviews.
      e. Specific reasons for requesting additional time including specific plans for controlling exposure and specific calendar dates.
      f. Personal protective equipment.
      g. Medical programs.
      h. Emergency action plans.

E. **Monitoring Corporate-Wide Settlement Agreements.** Corporate-wide Settlement Agreements (CSA) extend abatement requirements to all covered locations of the company. These agreements may require baseline, periodic and follow-up monitoring. Additional information regarding abatement related to CSA may be found in CPL 02-00-090, *Guidelines for Administrating of Corporate-Wide Settlement Agreements*, dated June 3, 1991.

XIV. Notification of Failure to Abatement.

A. **Violation.** A Notification of Failure to Abate an Alleged Violation (OSHA-2B) shall be issued in cases where violations have not been corrected as required, as verified by an onsite inspection or follow-up inspection.

B. **Penalties.** Failure to abate penalties shall be applied when an employer has not corrected a previously cited violation which had become a final order of the Commission.

C. **Calculation of Additional Penalties.**
   1. A Gravity Based Penalty (GBP) for unabated violations is to be calculated for failure to abate a serious or other-than-serious violation on the basis of the facts noted upon re-inspection.
   2. Detailed information on calculating failure to abate (FTA) penalties is included in Chapter 6, *Penalties and Debt Collection*.

XV. Case File Management.

A. **Closing of Case File Without Abatement Certification.** The closing of a case file without abatement certification(s) must be justified through a statement in the case file by the Area Director or his/her designee, addressing the reason for accepting each uncertified violation as an abated citation.

B. **Review of Employer-Submitted Abatement.** Area Offices are encouraged to review employer-submitted abatement verification materials as soon as possible but no later than 30 days after receipt. If the review will be delayed, notify the employer that the material will be reviewed by a certain date, and that the case will be closed if appropriate, after that time.

C. **Whether to Keep Abatement Documentation.** Abatement documentation (photos, employer programs, etc.) shall be retained in accordance with OSHA Instruction ADM 03-01-005, OSHA *Compliance Records*, dated August 3, 1998.

XVI. Abatement Services Available to Employers.
Employers requesting abatement assistance shall be informed that OSHA is willing to work with them even after citations have been issued and provides incentives for immediate onsite abatement of certain types of violations. For further information see Chapter 6, Section IV, *Effect on Penalties if Employer Immediately Corrects*.

Chapter 8 — Settlements

I. Settlement of Cases by Area Directors. Area Directors are granted settlement authority and shall follow these instructions when negotiating settlement agreements.

A. **General.**

1. Except for egregious cases, or cases that affect other jurisdictions, Area Directors may enter into Informal Settlement Agreements with employers prior to the employer filing a written notice of contest.

   NOTE: *After the employer has filed a written notice of contest, the Area Director may proceed toward a Formal Settlement Agreement with the concurrence and participation of the RSOL.*

2. Area Directors may amend abatement dates, reclassify violations (e.g., willful to serious, serious to other-than-serious), and modify or withdraw a penalty, a citation, or a citation item, where evidence establishes during the informal conference that the changes are justified.

3. Area Directors may actively negotiate the amount of proposed penalties, depending on the circumstances of the case and the particular improvements in employee safety and health that can be obtained.

4. Employers shall be informed that they are required by §1903.19 to post copies of all amendments or changes to citations resulting from informal conferences. Employee representatives must also be provided with copies of any agreements.

5. Cases or issues relating to potential Section 17 settlements shall be handled in accordance with established agency procedures, including approval by the National Office.

B. **Pre-Contest Settlement (Informal Settlement Agreement).** Pre-contest settlement discussions will generally occur during or immediately following the information conference and prior to the expiration of the 15 working day contest period.

1. In the event that an employer is bringing an attorney to an informal conference, Area Directors or their designees are encouraged to contact the RSOL and ask for the assistance of counsel.

2. If a settlement is reached during the informal conference, an Informal Settlement Agreement (ISA) shall be prepared and the employer will be asked to sign it. It will be effective upon signature of both the employer and the Area Director (**who shall sign last**), provided the contest period has not expired. Both parties will date the documents on the day of actual signature.

3. If the employer is not present to sign the ISA, the Area Director shall send the agreement to the employer for signature. After signing, the employer must return the agreement to the Area Director by and delivery or via facsimile within the 15 day contest period.

   a. In every case, Area Directors shall give employers notice in writing that the citation will become final and unreviewable at the end of the contest period, unless the employer signs the proposed agreement or files a written notice of contest.

   b. If an employer wishes to make any changes to the text of the agreement, the Area Director must agree to and authorize the proposed changes prior to the expiration of the contest period.
      - If the changes proposed by the employer are acceptable to the Area Director, the exact language written into the agreement shall be mutually agreed upon. Employers shall be instructed to incorporate the agreed-upon language into the agreement, sign it, and return to the Area Office by hand delivery or via facsimile.
      - Annotations incorporating the exact language of any changes authorized shall be made to the retained copy of the agreement and signed and dated by the Area Director.

   c. Upon receipt of the ISA signed by the employer, the Area Director will ensure, prior to his/her signature, that any modifications to the agreement are consistent with the notations made in the case file.
      - In these cases, the citation record will then be updated in IMIS in accordance with current procedures.
      - If an employer's changes substantially alter the original terms, the agreement signed by the employer will be treated as a notice of contest and handled accordingly. The employer will be informed of this as soon as possible.

   d. A reasonable time will be allowed for return of the agreement from the employer.
      - If an agreement is not received within the 15 day contest period, the Area Director will presume the employer did not sign the agreement, and the citation will be treated as a final order.
      - The employer will be required to certify that the informal settlement agreement was signed prior to the expiration of the contest period.

4. If settlement efforts are unsuccessful and the employer contests the citation, the Area Director will state the terms of the final settlement offer in the case file.

C. **Procedures for Preparing the Informal Settlement Agreement.** The ISA shall be prepared and processed in accordance with current OSHA policies and practices. For guidance in determining final dates of settlement and Review Commission orders, see Chapter 15, Section XIII, *Citation Final Order Dates.*

D. **Post-Contest Settlement (Formal Settlement Agreement).** Post-contest settlements will normally occur before the complaint is filed with the Review Commission.

1. Following the filing of a notice of contest, the Area Director shall (unless other procedures have been agreed upon) notify the RSOL when it appears that negotiations with the employer may produce a settlement. This notification shall occur at the time the notice of contest transmittal memorandum is sent to the RSOL.

2. If a settlement is later requested by the employer, the Area Director will communicate the proposed terms to the RSOL, who will then draft and execute the agreement.

E. **Corporate-Wide Settlement Agreement.** Corporate-wide Settlement Agreements (CSAs) may be entered into under special circumstances to obtain formal recognition by the employer of cited hazards and formal acceptance of the obligation to seek out and abate those hazards throughout all workplaces under its control. See CPL 02-00-090, *Guidelines for Administration of Corporate-Wide Settlement Agreements*, dated June 3, 1991, for additional information.

Chapter 9 — Complaint and Referral Processing

I. **Safety and Health Complaints and Referrals.**

  A. **Definitions.**

    1. **Complaint.** Notice of an alleged safety or health hazard (over which OSHA has jurisdiction), or a violation of the Act, submitted by a current employee or representative of employees.

    2. **Formal Complaint.** Complaint made by a current employee or a representative of employees that meets all of the following requirements:

      a. Asserts that an imminent danger, a violation of the Act, or a violation of an OSHA standard exposes employees to a potential physical or health harm in the workplace;

      b. Is reduced to writing or submitted on an OSHA-7 form; and

      c. Is signed by at least one current employee or employee representative.

    3. **Non-formal Complaint.** Any complaint alleging safety or health violations that does not meet all of the requirements of a formal complaint identified above and does not come from one of the sources identified under the definition of Referral, below.

    4. **Inspection.** An onsite examination of an employer's worksite conducted by an OSHA compliance officer, initiated as the result of a complaint or referral, and meeting at least one of the criteria identified in the section on Criteria Warranting an Inspection, below.

    5. **Inquiry.** A process conducted in response to a complaint or a referral that does not meet one of the identified inspection criteria. It does not involve an onsite inspection of the workplace, but rather the employer is notified of the alleged hazard(s) or violation(s) by telephone, fax, email, or by letter if necessary. The employer is then requested to provide a response, and OSHA will notify the complainant of that response via appropriate means.

    6. **Electronic Complaint.** A complaint submitted via OSHA's public website. All complaints submitted via OSHA's public website are considered non-formal.

    7. **Permanently Disabling Injury or Illness.** An injury or illness that has resulted in permanent disability or an illness that is chronic or irreversible. Permanently disabling injuries or illnesses include, but are not limited to amputation, blindness, a standard threshold shift in hearing, lead or mercury poisoning, paralysis or third-degree burns.

    8. **Referral.** An allegation of a potential workplace hazard or violation received from one of the sources listed below.

      a. **CSHO referral** – information based on the direct observation of a CSHO. (On the OSHA-90, code 14A – A. CSHO (*Within Office*).)

      b. **Safety and health agency referral** – from sources including, but not limited to: NIOSH, state programs, consultation, and state or local health departments, as well as safety and/or health professionals in other Federal agencies. (As appropriate, code 14A – B. *Federal OSHA; C. State OSH; F. Consultation; G. State/Local Government; or I. Other.*)

      c. **11(c) complaint referral** – made by a whistleblower investigator when an employee alleges that he or she was retaliated against for complaining about safety or health conditions in the workplace, refusing to do an allegedly imminently dangerous task, or engaging in other activities related to occupational safety or health (Code 14A – D. *Discrimination.*)

      d. **Other government agency referral** – made by other Federal, State, or local government agencies or their employees, including local police and fire departments. (As appropriate, code 14A – E. *Other Federal Agency*, or G. *State/Local Government.*)

      e. **Media report** – either news items reported in the media or information reported directly to OSHA by a media source. (Code 14A – H. *Media.*)

      f. **Employer report** - of accidents other than fatalities and catastrophes. (Code 14A – I. *Other.*)

    9. **Representative of Employees.** Any of the following:

      a. An authorized representative of the employee bargaining unit, such as a certified or recognized labor organization.

      b. An attorney acting for an employee.

      c. Any other person acting in a bona fide representative capacity, including, but not limited to, members of the clergy, social workers, spouses and other family members, and government officials or nonprofit groups and organizations acting upon specific complaints and injuries from individuals who are employees.

      NOTE: *The representative capacity of the person filing complaints on behalf of another should be ascertained unless it is already clear. In general, the affected employee should have requested, or at least approved, the filing of the complaint on his or her behalf.*

  B. **Classifying as a Complaint or a Referral.** Whether the information received is classified as a complaint or a referral, an inspection of a workplace is normally warranted if **at least one** of the conditions in the section *Criteria Warranting an Inspection* is met.

  C. **Criteria Warranting an Inspection.** An inspection is normally warranted if **at least one** of the conditions below is met (but see also Paragraph I.D. of this chapter, *Scheduling an Inspection of an Employer in an Exempt Industry*):

    1. A valid formal complaint is submitted. Specifically, the complaint must be reduced to writing or submitted on an OSHA-7 form, be signed by a current employee or representative of employees, and state the reason for the inspection request with reasonable particularity. Additionally, there must be reasonable grounds to believe either that a violation of the Act or OSHA standard that exposes employees to physical harm exists, or that an imminent danger of death or serious injury exists, as provided in Section 8(f)(1) of the Act.

    2. The information alleges that a permanently disabling injury or illness has occurred as a result of the complained of hazard(s), and there is reason to believe that the hazard or related hazards still exist.

    3. The information alleges that an imminent danger situation exists.

    4. The information concerns an establishment and an alleged hazard covered by a local, regional, or national emphasis program, the Site-Specific Targeting Plan.

    5. The employer fails to provide an adequate response to an inquiry, or the individual who provided the original information provides further evidence that the employer's response is false or does not adequately address the hazard(s).

6.   The establishment that is the subject of the information has a history of egregious, willful, failure-to-abate, or repeated citations within the Area Office's jurisdiction during the past three years, or is an establishment or related establishment in the Enhanced Enforcement Program. However, if the employer has previously submitted adequate documentation for these violations demonstrating that they were corrected and that programs have been implemented to prevent a recurrence of hazards, the Area Director will normally determine that an inspection is not necessary.

7.   A whistleblower investigator or Regional Supervisory Investigator requests that an inspection be conducted in response to an employee's allegation that the employee was discriminated against for complaining about safety or health conditions in the workplace, refusing to perform an allegedly dangerous job or task, or engaging in other activities related to occupational safety or health.

8.   If an inspection is scheduled or has begun at an establishment and a complaint or referral that would normally be handled via inquiry is received, that complaint or referral may, at the Area Director's discretion, be incorporated into the scheduled or ongoing inspection. If such a complaint is formal, the complainant must receive a written response addressing the complaint items.

9.   If the information gives reasonable grounds to believe that an employee under 18 years of age is exposed to a serious violation of a safety or health standard or a serious hazard, an onsite inspection will be initiated if the information relates to construction, manufacturing, agriculture, or other industries as determined by the Area Director. Limitations placed on OSHA's activities in agriculture by Appropriations Act provisions will be observed. See CPL 02-00-051, *Enforcement Exemptions and Limitations under the Appropriations Act*, dated May 28, 1998. A referral to Wage and Hour should also be initiated.

    NOTE: *The information does not need to allege that a child labor law has been violated.*

10.   The information received is a signed, written complaint from a current employee or employee representative that alleges a recordkeeping deficiency that indicates the existence of a serious safety or health violation.

D.   **Scheduling an Inspection of an Employer in an Exempt Industry.** In order to schedule an inspection of an employer in an exempt industry classification as specified by Appropriations Act provisions:

    NOTE: See CPL 02-00-051, *Enforcement Exemptions and Limitations under the Appropriations Act*, dated May 28, 1998.

1.   The information must come directly from a current employee; OR

2.   It must be determined and documented in the case file that the information came from a representative of the employee (see Paragraph I.A.9. of this chapter, *Representative of Employees*), with the employee's knowledge of the representative's intended action.

E.   **Electronic Complaints Received via the OSHA Public Website.**

1.   Electronic complaints submitted via the OSHA public website are automatically forwarded via email to a designated Area Office in the appropriate state. That Office then forwards the electronic complaints to the appropriate Area Office in the state.

2.   Each Area Office manages a "Complaints" mailbox and processes electronic complaints according to internal complaint processing procedures. The complaints mailbox is monitored daily and every incoming complaint is reviewed for jurisdiction.

    a.   If the complaint falls within the jurisdiction of the Area Office, the complaint is entered into IMIS and processed as usual.

    b.   If the complaint falls within the jurisdiction of another Area Office, the complaint is forwarded appropriately.

3.   Area Offices will coordinate with State Plan States to establish procedures to process electronic complaints. The State establishes its own internal procedures for responding to such complaints. These procedures may be the State's usual procedures for handling unsigned complaints or they may include some further coordination with the complainant prior to action. In State Plan states, the Federal Monitoring office will screen the complaints unless there is another arrangement. If the complaint falls within the individual State Plan's jurisdiction, the Screening Office will follow the procedures developed with the State Plan for processing the complaint.

4.   Complete an OSHA-7 form for all complaint information received. In order to facilitate the tracking of electronic complaints, enter the following code in the Optional Information field:

    N-11-LOGXXXXXX

      ▪ Where N-11 indicates that the complaint was filed electronically; and

      ▪ The digits following LOG are the unique complaint ID/log numbers assigned to the electronic complaint when processed by the Salt Lake Technical Center. The log number may vary and does not have to be exactly six digits. In entering the code, there is no space between the word LOG and the digits that follow.

5.   Information received electronically from a current employee is considered a non-formal complaint until that individual provides a signed copy of the information. The employee can send or fax a signed copy of the information, request that an OSHA-7 form be sent, or sign the information in person at the Area Office. Normally a complainant has five working days to formalize an electronic complaint. The Area Office must actively follow up on information received electronically in order to provide the employee with the opportunity to formalize the complaint.

6.   All complaint-related material received electronically should be printed and date stamped with the date the material was submitted and received. When these dates are not the same, the Area Director will determine the appropriate date for the incoming material.

F.   **Information Received by Telephone.**

1.   While speaking with the caller, OSHA personnel will attempt to obtain the following information:

    a.   Whether the caller is a current employee or an employee representative.

    b.   The exact nature of the alleged hazard(s) and the basis of the caller's knowledge. The individual receiving the information must determine, to the extent possible, whether the information received describes an apparent violation of OSHA standards or the OSH Act.

    c.   The employer's name, address, email address, telephone and fax numbers, as well as the name of a contact person at the worksite.

        d.   The name, address, telephone number, and email address of any union and/or employee representative at the worksite.

  2.   As appropriate, OSHA will provide the caller with the following information:

      a.   Describe the complaint process, and if appropriate, the concepts of "inquiry" and "inspection," as well as the relative advantages of each.

      b.   If the caller is a current employee or a representative of employees, explain the distinction between a formal complaint and a non-formal complaint, and the rights and protections that accompany filing a formal complaint. These rights and protections include:

- The right to request an onsite inspection.
- Notification in writing if an inspection is deemed unnecessary because there are no reasonable grounds to believe that a violation or danger exists.
- The right to obtain review of a decision not to inspect by submitting a request for review in writing.

  3.   Information received by telephone from a current employee is considered a non-formal complaint until that individual provides a signed copy of the information. The employee can send or fax a signed copy of the information, request that an OSHA-7 form be sent, or sign the information in person at the Area Office. Normally a complainant has five working days to formalize an electronic complaint.

  4.   If appropriate, inform the complainant of rights to confidentiality in accordance with Section 8(f)(1) of the Act for private sector employees, and Executive Order 12196 ,dated February 26, 1980, for Federal employees, and ask whether the complainant wishes to exercise this right. When confidentiality is requested, the identity of the complainant is protected regardless of the formality of the complaint.

  5.   Explain Section 11(c) rights to private sector employees and employees of the U.S. Postal Service, or reprisal and discrimination protection provided by Executive Order 12196, §1960.46 and the Whistleblowers Protection Act of 1989 to Federal employees. See FAP 01-00-003, *Federal Agency Safety and Health Programs*, dated May 17, 1996, for reports of reprisal or discrimination from Federal employees.

G.   **Procedures for Handling Complaints Filed in Multiple Area Offices or Regions.**

  1.   When a Regional Office determines that multiple offices within the Region have received the same complaint or, if the Regional Office suspects the same complaint has been filed in multiple Regions, the Regional Office should contact the Director or Deputy Director of the Directorate of Enforcement Programs (DEP).

  2.   DEP will query all 10 Regions and coordinate with the Directorate of Cooperative and State Programs to query the State Plan States in order to determine whether similar complaints were filed in multiple offices.

      a.   If multiple Regions have received the same complaint, the National Office will address the complaint with the employer.

      b.   Area Offices should indicate in IMIS that these complaints have been transferred to the National Office. On the OSHA-7, in field 45a., select A. *Federal OSHA*; in field 45b., select 00 – *National Office*. The complaint should then be closed using field 48.

H.   **Procedures for an Inspection.**

  1.   Upon receipt of a complaint or referral, the Area Director (or his or her designee) will evaluate all available information to determine whether there are reasonable grounds to believe that a violation or hazard exists.

      a.   If necessary, reasonable attempts will be made to contact the individual who provided the information in order to obtain additional details or to clarify issues raised in the complaint or referral. See the Complaint Questionnaire beginning on page 9-17.

      b.   The Area Director may determine not to inspect a facility if he/she has a substantial reason to believe that the condition complained of is being or has been abated.

  2.   Despite the existence of a complaint, if the Area Director, believes there is no reasonable grounds that a violation or hazard exists, no inspection or inquiry will be conducted.

      a.   Where a formal complaint has been submitted, the complainant will be notified in writing of OSHA's intent not to conduct an inspection, the reasoning behind the determination, and the right to have the determination reviewed under §1903.12. The justification for not inspecting will be noted in the case file.

      b.   In the event of a non-formal complaint or referral, if possible, the individual providing the information will be notified by appropriate means of OSHA's intent not to conduct an inquiry or inspection. The justification for not inspecting will be noted in the case file.

  3.   If the information contained in the complaint or referral meets at least one of the inspection criteria listed in Paragraph I.C. of this chapter, *Criteria Warranting an Inspection*, and there are reasonable grounds to believe that a violation or hazard exists, the Area Office is authorized to conduct an inspection.

      a.   If appropriate, the Area Office will inform the individual providing the information that an inspection will be scheduled and that he or she will be advised of the results.

      b.   After the inspection, the Area Office will send the individual a letter addressing each information item, with reference to the citation(s) or a sufficiently detailed explanation for why a citation was not issued.

  4.   If an inspection is warranted, it will be initiated as soon as resources permit. Inspections resulting from formal complaints of serious hazards will normally be initiated within five working days of formalizing.

I.   **Procedures for an Inquiry.**

  1.   If the complaint or referral does not meet the criteria for initiating an onsite inspection, an inquiry will be conducted. OSHA will promptly contact the employer to notify it of the complaint or referral and its allegation(s), and fax or email a confirming letter.

  2.   If a non-formal complaint is submitted by a current employee or a representative of employees that does not meet any of the inspection criteria, the complainant may be given five working days to make the complaint formal.

      a.   The complainant may come into the Area Office and sign the complaint, or mail or fax a signed complaint letter to OSHA. Additionally, an OSHA-7 form can be mailed or faxed to the complainant, if appropriate.

      b.   If the complaint is not made formal after five working days, after making a reasonable attempt to inform the complainant of the decision, OSHA will proceed with the inquiry process.

3.   The employer will be advised of what information is needed to answer the inquiry and encouraged to respond by fax or email. See FAP 01-00-003, *Federal Agency Safety and Health Programs*, dated May 17, 1996, for differing Federal Agency procedures. Employers are encouraged to do the following:

    a.   Immediately investigate and determine whether the complaint or referral information is valid and make any necessary corrections or modifications.

    b.   Advise the Area Director either in writing or via email within five working days of the results of the investigation into the alleged complaint or referral information. At the discretion of the Area Director, the response time may be longer or shorter than five working days, depending on the circumstances. Additionally, although the employer is requested to respond within the above time frame, the employer may not be able to complete abatement action during that time, but is encouraged to do so.

    c.   Provide the Area Director with supporting documentation of the findings, including any applicable measurements or monitoring results, and photographs and/or videos that the employer believes would be helpful, as well as a description of any corrective action the employer has taken or is in the process of taking.

    d.   Post a copy of the letter from OSHA where it is readily accessible for review by all employees.

    e.   Return a copy of the signed Certificate of Posting to the Area Office.

    f.   If there is a recognized employee union or safety and health committee in the facility, provide it with a copy of OSHA's letter and the employer's response.

4.   As soon as possible after contacting the employer, a notification letter will be faxed to the employer, or mailed where no fax is available. Sample letters to complainants and employers are provided on the NCR. Note that some of these letters are for private sector use and some are for Federal Agency use. If email is an acceptable means of responding, this should be indicated in the notification letter and the proper email address should be provided.

5.   If no employer response or an inadequate employer response is received after the allotted five working days, additional contact with the employer may be made before an inspection is scheduled. If the employer provides no response or an inadequate response, or if OSHA determines from other information that the condition has not been or is not being corrected, an inspection will be scheduled.

6.   The complainant will be advised of the employer's response, as well as the complainant's rights to dispute that response, and if the alleged hazard persists, of the right to request an inspection. When OSHA receives an adequate response from the employer and the complainant does not dispute or object to the response, an onsite inspection normally will not be conducted.

7.   If the complainant is a current employee or a representative of employees and wishes to dispute the employer's response, the disagreement must be submitted in writing and signed, thereby making the complaint formal.

    a.   If the employee disagreement takes the form of a written and signed formal complaint, see Paragraph I.H. of this chapter, *Procedures for an Inspection*.

    b.   If the employee disagreement does not take the form of a written and signed formal complaint, some discretion is allowed in situations where the information does not justify an onsite inspection. In such situations, the complainant will be notified of OSHA's intent not to conduct an inspection and the reasoning behind the determination. This decision should be thoroughly documented in the case file.

8.   If a signed complaint is received after the complaint inquiry process has begun, the Area Director will determine whether the alleged hazard is likely to exist based on the employer's response and by contacting the complainant. The complainant will be informed that the inquiry has begun and that the complainant retains the right to request an onsite inspection if he/she disputes the results and believes the hazard still exists.

9.   The complaint must not be closed until OSHA verifies that the hazard has been abated.

J.   **Complainant Protection.**

1.   **Identity of the Complainant.** Upon request of the complainant, his or her identity will be withheld from the employer in accordance with Section 8(f)(1) of the Act. No information will be given to the employer that would allow the employer to identify the complainant.

2.   **Whistleblower Protection.**

    a.   Section 11(c) of the Act provides protection for employees who believe that they have been the subject of an adverse employment action in retaliation for engaging in activities related to workplace safety or health. Any employee who believes that he or she has been discharged or otherwise retaliated against by any person as a result of engaging in such activities may file a whistleblower complaint. The complaint must be filed within thirty days of the discharge or other retaliation.

    b.   Complainants should always be advised of their Section 11(c) rights and protections upon initial contact with OSHA and whenever appropriate in subsequent communications.

K.   **Recording in IMIS.** Information about complaint inspections or inquiries must be recorded in IMIS following current instructions given in the IMIS manual. See OSHA Instruction IRT 01-00-007, *The IMIS Enforcement Data Processing Manual for Use with the NCR Computer System* (Table of Contents and Chapters 1 through 7), dated September 20, 1993.

II.   Whistleblower Complaints.

A.   OSHA enforces the whistleblower or anti-retaliation provisions of the OSH Act and sixteen other federal statutes. A desk reference summarizing these statutes can be found in the Whistleblower Investigations Manual on OSHA's Web site. These statutes generally provide that employers may not discharge or otherwise retaliate against an employee because the employee has reported an alleged violation related to the statute to an employer or a government agency, or otherwise exercised any rights provided to employees by the various statutes.

B.   When a retaliation complaint is made under any of the sixteen federal whistleblower statutes enforced by OSHA other than the OSH Act, the complainant should be referred promptly to the Regional Supervisory Investigator or Team Leader because the requirements for filing complaints under those statutes vary from those of the OSH Act. They should also be advised that there are statutory deadlines for filing these complaints.

C.   In the context of an OSHA enforcement action or a consultation activity, the complainant will be advised of the protection against retaliation afforded by Section 11(c) of the Act. A Section 11(c) complaint may be in any form, including an oral complaint made to a CSHO. Thus, if a person alleges that he has suffered an adverse action because of activity protected under Section 11(c), CSHOs will record that person's identifying information and the date and time of this initial contact on an OSHA-87 form and forward it to the Regional Supervisory Investigator or Team Leader for processing.

D.   In State Plan States, employees may file occupational safety and health retaliation complaints with Federal OSHA, the State, or both. Federal OSHA normally refers such complaints to the State Plan States for investigation. OSHA's Whistleblower Manual outlines the Agency's referral/deferral policies for such complaints.

III. Decision Trees.

A.   See tree on page 9-15 for OSHA enforcement action or consultation activity when information is obtained in writing.

B.   See tree on page 9-16 for OSHA enforcement action or consultation activity when information is obtained orally.

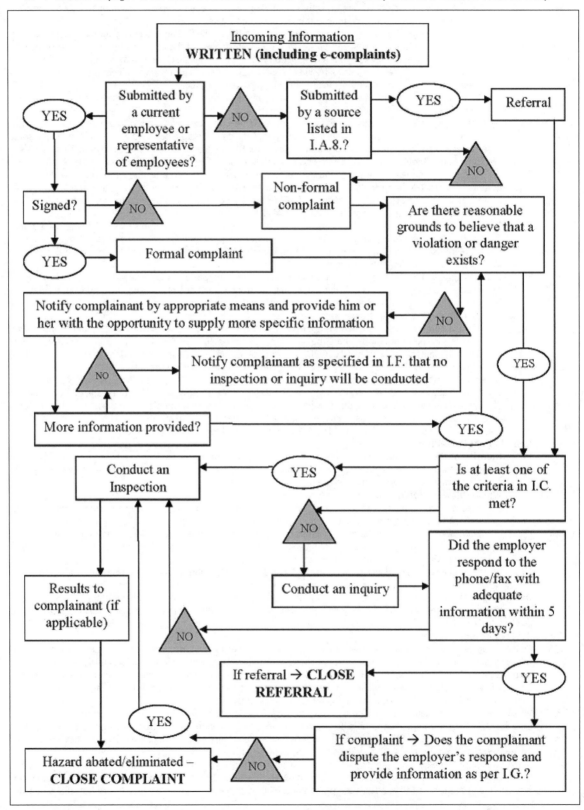

INCOMING INFORMATION

TELEPHONE

Complaint Questionnaire

Obtain information from the caller by asking the following questions, where relevant.

For All Complaints:
1. What is the specific safety or health hazard?
2. Has the hazardous condition been brought to the employer's attention? If so, when? How?
3. How are employees exposed to this hazard? Describe the unsafe or unhealthful working conditions; identify the location.
4. What work is done in the unsafe/unhealthful area? Identify, as well as possible, the type and condition of equipment in use, the materials (e.g., chemicals) being used, the process/operation involved, and the kinds of work being done near the hazardous area. Have there been any recent chemical spills, releases, or accidents?
5. With what frequency are employees doing the task that leads to the exposure? Continuously? Every day? Every week? Rarely? For how long at one time? How long has the condition existed (so far as can be determined)? Has it been brought to the employer's attention? Have any attempts been made to correct the condition, and, if so, who took these actions? What were the results?
6. How many shifts are there? What time do they start? On which shift does the hazardous condition exist?
7. What personal protective equipment (e.g., hearing protection, gloves or respirators) is required by the employer relevant to the alleged exposure? Is it used by employees? Include all PPE and describe it as specifically as possible. Include the manufacturer's name and any identifying numbers.
8. How many people work in the establishment? How many are exposed to the hazardous conditions? How near do they get to the hazard?
9. Is there an employee representative or a union in the establishment? Include the name, address, and telephone number of the union and/or the employee representative(s).

For Health Hazards
10. Has the employer administered any tests to determine employee exposure levels to the hazardous conditions or substance? Describe these tests. Can the employees get the results (as required by the standard)? What were the results?
11. What engineering controls are in place in the area(s) in which the exposed employees work? For instance, are there any fans or acoustical insulation in the area which may reduce exposure to the hazard?
12. What administrative or work practice controls has the employer put in place?
13. Do any employees have any symptoms that may have been caused by exposure to hazardous substances? Have any employees ever been treated by a physician for a work-related disease or condition? What was it?
14. Have there been any "near-miss" incidents?
15. Are respirators worn to protect against health hazards? If so, what kind? What exposures are they protecting against?
16. If the complaint is related to noise, what, if any, hearing protection is provided to and worn by the employees?
17. Do employees receive audiograms on a regular basis?

For Safety Hazards:
18. Under what adverse or hazardous conditions are employees required to work? This should include conditions contributing to stress and "other" probability factors.
19. Have any employees been injured as a result of this hazardous condition? Have there been any "near-miss" incidents?

Chapter 10 — Industry Sectors

I. **Agriculture.**

A. **Introduction.** Special situations arising in the agriculture industry, which is regulated under 29 CFR Part 1928 and the General Duty Clause, are discussed in this section. Part 1928 covers "agricultural operations," which include, but are not limited to, egg farms, poultry farms, livestock grain and feed lot operations, dairy farms, horse farms, hog farms, fish farms, and fur-bearing animal farms. OSHA has very few standards that are applicable to this industry. Part 1928 sets forth a few standards in full and lists particular Part 1910 standards which apply to agricultural operations. Part 1910 standards not listed do not apply. The General Duty Clause may be used to address hazards not covered by these standards.

B. **Definitions.**

1. **Agricultural Operations.** This term is not defined in 29 CFR Part 1928. Generally, agricultural operations would include any activities involved in the growing and harvesting of crops, plants, vines, fruit trees, nut trees, ornamental plants, egg production, the raising of livestock (including poultry and fish), as well as livestock products. The Occupational Safety and Health Review Commission has ruled that activities integrally related to these core "agricultural operations" are also included within that term. *Darragh Company*, 9 BNA OSHC 1205, (Nos. 77-2555, 77-3074, and 77-3075, 1980) (delivery of feed to chicken farmer by integrator of poultry products is agricultural operation); *Marion Stevens dba Chapman & Stephens Company*, 5 BNA OSHC 1395 (No. 13535, 1977) (removal of pipe to maintain irrigation system in citrus grove is agricultural operation). Post-harvest activities not on a farm, such as receiving, cleaning, sorting, sizing, weighing, inspecting, stacking, packaging and shipping produce, are not "agricultural operations." J. C. Watson Company, 22 BNA OSHC 1235 (Nos. 05-0175 and 05-0176, 2008).

2. **Agricultural Employee.** OSHA regulation § 1975.4(b)(2) states that members of the immediate family of the farm employer **are not** regarded as employees.

3. **Farming Operation.** This term is used in OSHA's Appropriations Act, and has been defined in CPL 02-00-051, *Enforcement Exemptions and Limitations under the Appropriations Act*, dated May 28, 1998, to mean any operation involved in the growing or harvesting of crops, the raising of livestock or poultry, or related activities conducted by a farmer on sites such as farms, ranches, orchards, dairy farms or similar farming operations.

   These are employers engaged in businesses that have a two digit Standard Indstrial Classification (SIC) of 01 and three digit North American Industry Classification System (NAICS) of 111 (Agricultural Production - Crops); SIC 02 and NAICS 112 (Agricultural Production - Livestock and Animal Specialties); four digit SIC 0711 and six digit NAICS 115112 (Soil Preparation Services); SIC 0721 and NAICS 115112 (Crop Planting, Cultivating, and Protecting); SIC 0722 and NAICS 115113 (Crop Harvesting, Primarily by Machine); SIC 0761 and NAICS 115115 (Farm Labor Contractors and Crew Leaders); and SIC 0762 and NAICS 115116 (Farm Management Services).

4. **Post-Harvesting Processing.** This is a term that is used in CPL 02-00-051, *Enforcement Exemptions and Limitations under the Appropriations Act*, dated May 28, 1998, in discussing enforcement guidance for small farming operations. Generally, post-harvest processing can be thought of as changing the character of the product (canning, making cider or sauces, etc.) or a higher degree of packaging versus field sorting in a shed for size.

C. **Appropriations Act Exemptions for Farming Operations.**

1. **Exempt Farming Operations.** OSHA is limited by provisions in its Appropriations Act as to which employers it may inspect. Some of the Appropriations Act exemptions and limitations apply to small farming operations. Specifically, OSHA shall not inspect farming operations that have 10 or fewer employees and have had no temporary labor camp (TLC) activity within the prior 12 months.

2. **Non-Exempt Farming Operations.** A farming operation with 10 or fewer employees that maintains a temporary labor camp or has maintained a temporary labor camp within the last twelve months is not exempt from inspection.

3. **State Plans States.** States with OSHA-approved State Plans may enforce on small farms and provide consultation or training, provided that 100% state funds are used and the state has an accounting system in place to assure that no federal or matching state funds are expended on these activities.

4. **Enforcement Guidance for Small Farming Operations.** OSHA's Appropriations Act exempts qualifying small farming operations from enforcement or administration of all rules, regulations, standards or orders under the Occupational Safety and Health Act, including rules affecting consultation and technical assistance or education and training services..

   Table 10-1, below, provides an at-a-glance reference to OSHA activities under its funding legislation.

Table 10-1: OSHA's Appropriation Act Exemptions for Farming Operations

OSHA Activity	Farming operations with 10 or fewer employees (EEs) and no TLC activity within 12 months.	Farming operations with more than 10 EEs or a farming operation with an active TLC within 12 months.
Programmed Safety Inspections	Not Permitted	Permitted
Programmed Health Inspections	Not Permitted	Permitted
Employee Complaint	Not Permitted	Permitted
Fatality and/or two or more Hospitalizations	Not Permitted	Permitted
Imminent Danger	Not Permitted	Permitted
11(c) (whistleblower investigation)	Not Permitted	Permitted
Consultation & Technical Assistance	Not Permitted	Permitted
Education & Training	Not Permitted	Permitted
Conduct Surveys & Studies	Not Permitted	Permitted

NOTE: *See CPL 02-00-051, Enforcement Exemptions and Limitations under the Appropriations Act, May 28, 1998, for additional information.*

D. **Standards Applicable to Agriculture.** OSHA has very few standards that apply to employers engaged in agricultural operations. Activities that take place after harvesting are considered general industry operations and are covered by OSHA's general industry standards.

    1. **Agricultural Standards (Part 1928).**

        a. Roll-over Protective Structures (ROPS) for Tractors (§§1928.51, 1928.52, and 1928.53).

        b. Guarding of Moving Machinery Parts of Farm Field Equipment, Farmstead Equipment, and Cotton Gins (§1928.57).

        c. Field Sanitation (§1928.110). See Paragraph I.F. of this chapter, *Wage & Hour/OSHA Shared Authority under Secretary's Order*, regarding Wage & Hour authority. OSHA has no authority to issue any citations under this standard.

    2. **General Industry Standards (Part 1910).**

        a. Temporary Labor Camps (§1910.142). See Chapter 12, Section II, *Temporary Labor Camps*.

        b. Storage and Handling of Anhydrous Ammonia (§1910.111(a) and (b)).

        c. Logging Operations (§1910.266).

        d. Specifications for Accident Prevention Signs and Tags – Slow-Moving Vehicle Emblem (§1910.145(d)(10)).

        e. Hazard Communication (§1910.1200).

        f. Cadmium (§1910.1027).

        g. Retention of Department of Transportation Markings, Placards and Labels (§1910.1201).

        Except to the extent specified above, the standards contained in subparts B through T and subpart Z of Part 1910 of Title 29 do not apply to agricultural operations.

    3. **General Duty Clause.** As in any situation where no standard is applicable, Section 5(a)(1) of the OSH Act may be used; all the elements for a Section 5(a)(1) citation must be met. See Chapter 4, Section III, *General Duty Clause*.

E. **Pesticides.**

    1. **Coverage.**

        a. Pursuant to the Federal Insecticide, Fungicide and Rodenticide Act (FIFRA), the Environmental Protection Agency (EPA) has jurisdiction over employee protection relating to pesticides (which also includes herbicides, fungicides and rodenticides). The EPA Worker Protection Standard (WPS) protects employees on farms, forests, nurseries, and greenhouses from occupational exposure to agricultural pesticides. The WPS includes provisions for personal protective equipment, labeling, employee notification, safety training, safety posters, decontamination supplies, emergency assistance, and restricted field entry. See 40 CFR Part 170, Worker Protection Standard.

        b. The regulation covers two types of employees:

            ■ **Pesticide Handlers.** Those who mix, load, or apply agricultural pesticides; clean or repair pesticide application equipment; or assist with the application of pesticides in any way.

            ■ **Agricultural Workers.** Those who perform tasks related to the cultivation and harvesting of plants on farms or in greenhouses, nurseries, or forests – such as carrying nursery stock, repotting plants, or watering – related to the production of agricultural plants on an agricultural establishment.

        c. For all pesticide use, including uses not covered by 40 CFR Part 170, it is a violation of FIFRA to use a registered pesticide in a manner inconsistent with its labeling. Thus, OSHA has no authority to issue any citations related to pesticide exposures, pursuant to Section 4(b)(1) of the OSH Act. In the event that a CSHO should encounter any cases of pesticide exposure or the lack of an appropriate pesticide label on containers, a referral shall be made to the local EPA office or to state agencies administering pesticide laws.

        d. EPA also has jurisdiction in non-agriculture situations where pesticides are being applied by pest control companies. This would include, but not be limited to, applications in and around factories, warehouses, office buildings, and personal residences. OSHA may not cite its Hazard Communication standard in such situations.

    2. **OSHA's Hazard Communication Standard.** Although OSHA will not cite employers covered under EPA's WPS with regard to hazard communication requirements for pesticides, agricultural employers otherwise covered by OSHA are still responsible for having a hazard communication program for all hazardous chemicals that are not considered pesticides.

F. **Wage & Hour/OSHA Shared authority under Secretary's Order.** Since 1997, the Wage & Hour Division (WHD) of the Employment Standards Administration (ESA) has had shared authority with OSHA over two standards: the Field Sanitation standard (1928.110), and the Temporary Labor Camp standard (1910.142). See Delegation of Authorities and Assignment of Responsibilities to the Assistant Secretary for Employment Standards and Other Officials in the Employment Standards Administration (*Federal Register*, January 2, 1997 (62 FR 107)) and Secretary's Order 5-2002: Delegation of Authority and Assignment of Responsibility to the Assistant Secretary for Occupational Safety and Health, *Federal Register*, October 22, 2002 (67 FR 65007).

    1. **Field Sanitation Standard.**

        a. The WHD has sole federal enforcement authority for this standard, including the issuing of citations.

        b. OSHA, therefore, shall not issue citations under this standard.

        c. The provisions of the Field Sanitation standard are also applicable to reforestation activities involving "hand-labor operations" as defined by the standard. This position regarding reforestation activities was developed through extensive intra-agency discussions and was intended to provide, in the absence of a clear and un-ambiguous exemption of this activity from the provisions of the standard, the broadest possible coverage for these employees.

    2. **Temporary Labor Camp (TLC) Standard.** Under the Secretary's Order, enforcement authority for the TLC standard is split between the WHD and OSHA. See Chapter 12, Section II, *Temporary Labor Camps*, for a detailed discussion on Temporary Labor Camps.

3. **Compliance Interpretation Authority.** WHD has sole interpretation authority for both the Field Sanitation and the Temporary Labor Camp standards, even over those temporary labor camp areas for which OSHA has enforcement authority.

4. **Standard Revision and Variance Authority.** OSHA retains all authority for revisions of both the Field Sanitation and the Temporary Labor Camp standards, as well as the evaluation and granting of temporary and permanent variances.

5. **State Plan States.**
   a. Eight of the twenty-two jurisdictions (21 states and Puerto Rico) that have OSHA-approved state plans covering private sector employment elected not to enforce the Field Sanitation standard in agriculture and the Temporary Labor Camp standard, except with respect to egg, poultry, red meat production, and post-harvesting processing of agricultural and horticultural commodities. Thus, WHD enforces these standards, except as noted above, in the following states: Alaska, Indiana, Iowa, Kentucky, Minnesota, South Carolina, Utah and Wyoming.
   b. The 14 other jurisdictions with OSHA-approved state plans covering private sector employment have retained enforcement authority for the Field Sanitation and Temporary Labor Camp standards in agriculture. They are Arizona, California, Hawaii, Maryland, Michigan, Nevada, New Mexico, North Carolina, Oregon, Puerto Rico, Tennessee, Vermont, Virginia and Washington.

II. **Construction [Reserved].**
III. **Maritime [Reserved].**

Chapter 11 — Imminent Danger, Fatality, Catastrophe, and Emergency Response

I. **Imminent Danger Situations.**
   A. **General.**
      1. **Definition of Imminent Danger.** Section 13(a) of the Act defines imminent danger as "...any conditions or practices in any place of employment which are such that a danger exists which could reasonably be expected to cause death or serious physical harm immediately or before the imminence of such danger can be eliminated through the enforcement procedures otherwise provided by this Act."
      2. **Conditions of Imminent Danger.** The following conditions must be present in order for a hazard to be considered an imminent danger:
         a. Death or serious harm must be threatened; AND .
         b. It must be reasonably likely that a serious accident could occur immediately OR, if not immediately, then before abatement would otherwise be implemented.
         NOTE: *For a health hazard, exposure to the toxic substance or other hazard must cause harm to such a degree as to shorten life or be immediately dangerous to life and health (IDLH) or cause substantial reduction in physical or mental efficiency or health, even though the resulting harm may not manifest itself immediately.*
   B. **Pre-Inspection Procedures.**
      1. **Imminent Danger Report Received by the Field.**
         a. After the Area Director or designee receives a report of imminent danger, he or she will evaluate the inspection requirements and assign a CSHO to conduct the inspection.
         b. Every effort will be made to conduct the imminent danger inspection on the same day that the report is received. In any case, the inspection will be conducted no later than the day after the report is received.
         c. When an immediate inspection cannot be made, the Area Director or designee will contact the employer immediately, obtain as many pertinent details as possible about the situation, and attempt to have any employee(s) affected by the imminent danger voluntarily removed, if necessary.
            - A record of what steps, if any, the employer intends to take in order to eliminate the danger will be included in the case file.
            - This notification is considered an advance notice of inspection to be handled in accordance with the advance notice procedures described below.
      2. **Advance Notice.**
         a. §1903.6 authorizes advance notice of an inspection of potential imminent danger situations in order to encourage employers to eliminate dangerous conditions as quickly as possible.
         b. Where an immediate inspection cannot be made after the Area Office is alerted to an imminent danger condition and advance notice will speed the elimination of the hazard, the Team Leader or CSHO, at the direction of the Area Director, will give notice of an impending inspection to the employer.
         c. Where advance notice of an inspection is given to an employer, it shall also be given to the authorized employee representative, if present. If the inspection is in response to a formal Section 8(f)(1) complaint, the complainant will be informed of the inspection unless this will cause a delay in speeding the elimination of the hazard.
   C. **Imminent Danger Inspection Procedures.** All alleged imminent danger situations brought to the attention of or discovered by CSHOs while conducting any inspection will be inspected immediately. Additional inspection activity will take place only after the imminent danger condition has been resolved.
      1. **Scope of Inspection.** CSHOs may consider expanding the scope of an imminent danger inspection based on additional hazards discovered or brought to their attention during the inspection.
      2. **Procedures for Inspection.**
         a. Every imminent danger inspection will be conducted as expeditiously as possible.
         b. CSHOs will offer the employer and employee representatives the opportunity to participate in the worksite inspection, unless the immediacy of the hazard makes it impractical to delay the inspection in order to afford time to reach the area of the alleged imminent danger.
         c. As soon as reasonably practicable after discovery of existing conditions or practices constituting an imminent danger, the employer shall be informed of such hazards. The employer shall be asked to notify affected

employees and to remove them from exposure to the imminent danger hazard. The employer should be encouraged to voluntarily take appropriate abatement measures to promptly eliminate the danger.

D. **Elimination of the Imminent Danger.**

1. **Voluntary Elimination of the Imminent Danger.**

    a. **How to Voluntarily Eliminate a Hazard.**

    - Voluntary elimination of the hazard has been accomplished when the employer:
        a. Immediately removes affected employees from the danger area;
        b. Immediately removes or abates the hazardous condition; and
        c. Gives satisfactory assurance that the dangerous condition will remain abated before permitting employees to work in the area.
    - Satisfactory assurance can be evidenced by:
        a. After removing the affected employees, immediate corrective action is initiated, designed to bring the dangerous condition, practice, means or method of operation, or process into compliance, which, when completed, would permanently eliminate the dangerous condition; or
        b. A good faith representation by the employer that permanent corrective action will be taken as soon as possible, and that affected employees will not be permitted to work in the area of the imminent danger until the condition is permanently corrected; or
        c. A good faith representation by the employer that permanent corrective action will be instituted as soon as possible. Where personal protective equipment can eliminate the imminent danger, such equipment will be issued and its use strictly enforced until the condition is permanently corrected.

        NOTE: *Through onsite observations, CSHOs shall ensure that any/all representations from the employer that an imminent danger has been abated are accurate.*

    b. **Where a Hazard is Voluntarily Eliminated.** If an employer voluntarily and completely eliminates the imminent danger without unreasonable delay:

    - No imminent danger legal proceeding shall be instituted;
    - The OSHA-8, Notice of an Alleged Imminent Danger, does not need to be completed;
    - An appropriate citation(s) and notice(s) of penalty will be proposed for issuance with an appropriate notation on the OSHA-1B to document corrective actions; and
    - CSHOs will inform the affected employees or their authorized representative(s) that, although an imminent danger had existed, danger has been eliminated. They will also be informed of any steps taken by the employer to eliminate the hazardous condition.

2. **Refusal to Eliminate an Imminent Danger.**

    a. If the employer does not or cannot voluntarily eliminate the hazard or remove affected employees from the exposure and the danger is immediate, CSHOs will immediately consult with the Area Director or designee and obtain permission to post an OSHA-8, Notice of an Alleged Imminent Danger.

    b. Area Directors or designees will then contact the Regional Administrator and determine whether to consult with the RSOL to obtain a Temporary Restraining Order (TRO).

    c. The employer will be advised that Section 13 of the Act gives United States district courts the authority to restrain any condition or practice that poses an imminent danger to employees.

    NOTE: *The Agency has no authority to order the closing of a worksite or to order affected employees to leave the area of the imminent danger or the workplace.*

    d. CSHOs will notify affected employees and the employee representative that an OSHA-8 has been posted and will advise them of the Section 11(c) discrimination protections under the OSH Act. Employees will be advised that they have the right to refuse to perform work in the area where the imminent danger exists.

    e. The Area Director or designee and the Regional Administrator, in consultation with the RSOL, will assess the situation and, if warranted, make arrangements for the expedited initiation of court action, or instruct the CSHO to remove the OSHA-8.

3. **When Harm Will Occur Before Abatement is Required.**

    a. If CSHOs have clear evidence that harm will occur before abatement is required (i.e., before a final order of the Commission in a contested case or before a TRO can be obtained), they will confer with the Area Director or designee to determine a course of action.

    NOTE: *In some cases, the evidence may not support the finding of an imminent danger at the time of the physical inspection, but rather after further evaluation of the case file or presence of additional evidence.*

    b. As appropriate, an imminent danger notice may be posted at the time citations are delivered or even after the notice of contest is filed.

II. Fatality and Catastrophe Investigations.

A. **Definitions.**

1. **Fatality.** An employee death resulting from a work-related incident or exposure; in general, from an accident or an illness caused by or related to a workplace hazard.

2. **Catastrophe.** The hospitalization of three or more employees resulting from a work-related incident or exposure; in general, from an accident or an illness caused by a workplace hazard.

3. **Hospitalization.** Being admitted as an **inpatient** to a hospital or equivalent medical facility for examination, observation or treatment.

4. **Incident Requiring a Coordinated Federal Response.** An incident involving multiple fatalities, extensive injuries, massive toxic exposures, extensive property damage, or one that presents potential employee injury and generates widespread media interest.

B. **Initial Report.**

1. The Fatality/Catastrophe Report Form (OSHA-36) is a pre-inspection form that must be completed for all fatalities or catastrophes unless knowledge of the event occurs during the course of an inspection at the establishment involved. The purpose of the OSHA-36 is to provide OSHA with enough information to determine whether or not to investigate the event. It is also used as a research tool by OSHA and other agencies.

2. If, after the initial report, the Area Office becomes aware of information that affects the decision to investigate, the OSHA-36 should be updated. If the additional information does not affect the decision to investigate, or the investigation has been initiated or completed, the OSHA-36 need not be updated. After updating the OSHA-36, it should be resubmitted to the National Office.

3. See additional details on completing the OSHA-36 in Paragraph II.I. of this chapter, *Recording and Tracking for Fatality/ Catastrophe Inspections.*

C. **Investigation Procedures.**

1. All fatalities and catastrophes will be thoroughly investigated in an attempt to determine the cause of the event, whether a violation of OSHA safety and health standards, regulations, or the general duty clause occurred, and any effect the violation had on the accident. Each Regional Administrator will establish a procedure to ensure that each fatality or catastrophe is thoroughly investigated and processed in accordance with established policy.

2. The investigation should be initiated as soon as possible after receiving an initial report of the incident, ideally within one working day, by an appropriately trained and experienced compliance officer assigned by the Area Director or designee. The Area Director or designee determines the scope of the fatality/catastrophe investigation. All investigations must be completed in an expeditious manner.

3. Inspections following fatalities or catastrophes should include videotaping as a method of documentation and gathering evidence when appropriate. The use of photography is also encouraged in documenting and evidence gathering.

4. As in all inspections, under no circumstances should OSHA personnel conducting fatality/catastrophe investigations be unprotected against a hazard encountered during the course of an investigation. OSHA personnel must use appropriate personal protective equipment and take all necessary precautions to avoid and/or prevent occupational exposure to potential hazards that may be encountered.

D. **Interview Procedures.**

1. **Identify and Interview Persons.**

    a. Identify and interview all persons with firsthand knowledge of the incident, including first responders, police officers, medical responders, and management, as early as possible in the investigation. The sooner a witness is interviewed, the more accurate and candid the witness statement will be.

    b. If an employee representative is actively involved in the inspection, he or she can serve as a valuable resource by assisting in identifying employees who might have information relevant to the investigation.

    c. Conduct employee interviews privately, outside the presence of the employer. Employees are not required to inform their employer that they provided a statement to OSHA.

    d. When interviewing:
    - Properly document the contact information of all parties because follow-up interviews with a witness are sometimes necessary.
    - When appropriate, reduce interviews to writing and have the witness sign the document. Transcribe video- and audio-taped interviews and have the witness sign the transcription.
    - Read the statement to the witness and attempt to obtain agreement. Note any witnesses' refusal to sign or initial his/her statement.
    - Ask the interviewee to initial any changes or corrections made to his/her statement.
    - Advise interviewee of OSHA whistleblower protections.

    e. See Chapter 3, *Inspection Procedures*, for additional information on conducting interviews.

2. **Informer's Privilege.**

    a. The informer's privilege allows the government to withhold the **identity** of individuals who provide information about the violation of laws, including OSHA rules and regulations. The identity of witnesses will remain confidential to the extent possible. However, inform each witness that disclosure of his/her identity may be necessary in connection with enforcement or court actions.

    b. The informer's privilege also protects the contents of statements to the extent that disclosure would reveal the witness' identity. When the contents of a statement will not disclose the identity of the informant (i.e., statements that do not reveal the witness' job title, work area, job duties, or other information that would tend to reveal the individual's identity), the privilege does not apply and such statements may be released.

    c. Inform each witness that his/her interview statements may be released if he or she authorizes such a release or if he or she voluntarily discloses the statement to others, resulting in a waiver of the privilege.

    d. Inform witnesses in a tactful and nonthreatening manner that making a false statement to a CSHO during the course of an investigation could be a criminal offense. Making a false statement, upon conviction, is punishable by up to $10,000 or six months in jail, or both.

E. **Investigation Documentation.** Document all fatality and catastrophe investigations thoroughly.

1. **Personal Data – Victim.** Potential items to be documented include: Name; Address; Email address; Telephone; Age; Sex; Nationality; Job Title; Date of Employment; Time in Position; Job being done at the time of the incident; Training for job being performed at time of the incident; Employee deceased/injured; Nature of injury – fracture, amputation, etc.; and Prognosis of injured employee.

2. **Incident Data.** Potential items to be documented include: How and why did the incident occur; the physical layout of the worksite; sketches/drawings; measurements; video/audio/photos to identify sources, and whether the accident was work-related.

3. **Equipment or Process Involved.** Potential items to be documented include: Equipment type; Manufacturer; Model; Manufacturer's instructions; Kind of process; Condition; Misuse; Maintenance program; Equipment inspection (logs, reports); Warning devices (detectors); Tasks performed; How often equipment is used; Energy sources and disconnecting means identified; and Supervision or instruction provided to employees involved in the accident.

4. **Witness Statements.** Potential witnesses include: the Public; Fellow employees; Management; Emergency responders (e.g., police department, fire department); and Medical personnel (e.g., medical examiner).

5. **Safety and Health Program.** Potential questions include: Does the employer have a safety and/or health program? Does the program address the type of hazard that resulted in the fatality/catastrophe? How are the elements of the program specifically implemented at the worksite?

6. **Multi-Employer Worksite.** Describe the contractual and in practice relationships of the employer with the other employers involved with the work being performed at the worksite.

7. **Records Request.** Potential records include: Disciplinary Records; Training Records; and Next of Kin information.
   NOTE: *Next of kin information should be gathered as soon as possible to ensure that condolence letters can be sent in a timely manner.*

F. **Potential Criminal Penalties in Fatality and Catastrophe Cases.**

   1. **Criminal Penalties.**
      a. Section 17(e) of the Act provides criminal penalties for an employer who is convicted of having willfully violated an OSHA standard, rule or order when the violation results in the death of an employee. However, Section 17(e) does not apply to violations of the general duty clause. When there are violations of an OSHA standard, rule or order, or a violation of the general duty clause, criminal provisions relating to false statements and obstruction of justice may also be relevant.

      b. The circumstances surrounding all occupationally-related fatalities will be evaluated to determine whether the fatality was caused by a willful violation of a standard, thus creating the basis for a possible criminal referral. The evidence obtained during a fatality investigation is of paramount importance and must be carefully gathered and considered.

      c. Early in the investigation, the Area Director or designee, in consultation with the investigator, should make an initial determination as to whether there is potential for a criminal violation. The decision will be based on consideration of the following:
         - A fatality has occurred.
         - There is evidence that an OSHA standard has been violated and that the violation contributed to the death.
         - There is reason to believe that the employer was aware of the requirements of the standard and knew it was in violation of the standard, or that the employer was plainly indifferent to employee safety.
         - If the Regional Administrator agrees with the Area Director or designee's assessment of the case, the Regional Administrator will notify the RSOL. At the discretion of the Regional Administrator and the Area Director or designee, and dependent upon Regional procedures in place, a Regional team or trained criminal investigator may assist in or perform portions of an investigation.
         - When there is a potential criminal referral in a case, it is essential that the Regional Administrator and/or the Area Director involve the RSOL's Office in the early stages of the investigation during the evidence gathering process.

   2. **Additional Prosecution.** In addition to criminal prosecution under Section 17(e) of the OSH Act, employers may potentially face prosecution under a number of other sections of the United States Code, including, but not limited to:
      a. Crimes and Criminal Procedures, for actions such as conspiracy, making false statements, fraud, obstruction of justice, and destruction, alteration or falsification of records during a federal investigation.
      b. The Clean Water Act.
      c. The Clean Air Act.
      d. The Resource Recovery and Conservation Act (RCRA).
      e. The Comprehensive Environmental Response, Compensation, and Liability Act (CERCLA).

   3. **Procedures for Criminal Referral.** When a case is forwarded from the Regional Office to the RSOL for criminal review, advise the Director of Enforcement Programs (or, when appropriate, the Director of Construction Programs). Provide follow-up reports to indicate any subsequent actions.

G. **Families of Victims.**

   1. **Contacting Family Members.** Family members of employees involved in fatal or catastrophic occupational accidents or illnesses shall be contacted early in the investigation and given the opportunity to discuss the circumstances of the accident or illness. OSHA staff contacting family members must exercise tact and good judgment in their discussions.

   2. **Information Letter.** The standard information letter will normally be sent to the individual(s) listed as the emergency contact on the victim's employment records (if available) and/or the otherwise determined next of kin within 5 working days of determining the victim's identity and verifying the proper address where communications should be sent.
      NOTE: *In some circumstances, it may not be appropriate to follow these exact procedures; i.e., in the case of a small business, the owner or supervisor may be a relative of the victim. Modify the form letter to take any special circumstances into account or do not send the letter, as appropriate.*

   3. **Letter to Victim's Emergency Contact.** In addition to the standard information letter sent by the Area Director or designee, the Assistant Secretary also sends a letter to the victim's emergency contact or otherwise verifiable next of kin.

   4. **Interviewing the Family.**
      a. When taking a statement from families of the victim(s), explain that the interview will be handled following the same procedures as those in effect for witness interviews. Sensitivity and professionalism are required during these interviews. Carefully evaluate the information received and attempt to corroborate it during the investigation.

      b. Maintain follow-up contact with key family members or other contact persons so that these parties can be kept up-to-date on the status of the investigation. Provide family members or their legal representatives with a copy of all citations, subsequent settlement agreements or Review Commission decisions as these are issued, or as soon thereafter as possible. However, such information will only be provided to family members after it has been provided to the employer.

      c. The releasable portions of the case file will not be made available to family members until after the contest period has passed and no contest has been filed. If a contest is filed, the case file will not be made available until after the litigation is completed. Additionally, if a criminal referral is under consideration or has been made, the case file may not be released to the family. Notify the family of these policies and inform them that this is necessary so that any potential litigation is not compromised.

H. **Public Information Policy.** OSHA's public information policy regarding response to fatalities and catastrophes is to explain Federal presence to the news media. It is not to issue periodic updates on the progress of the investigation. The Area Director and his or her designee will normally handle response to media inquiries.

I. **Recording and Tracking for Fatality/Catastrophe Investigations.**

1. **Fatality/Catastrophe Report Form (OSHA-36).** The OSHA-36 is a pre-inspection form that must be completed for all fatalities and catastrophes unless knowledge of the event occurs during the course of an inspection at the establishment involved. Processing of the OSHA-36 shall be as follows:

a. The Area Office will complete and enter into IMIS an OSHA36 for all fatalities and catastrophes as soon as possible after learning of the event. As much information as is known at the time of the initial report should be provided; however, all items on the OSHA-36 need not be completed at the time of this initial report. Wherever possible, the age of the victim(s) should be provided, because this information is used for research by OSHA and other agencies.

b. The Regional Office or Area Office will fax an OSHA-36 for each event that will be investigated to the Director of Enforcement Programs (or, as appropriate, the Director of Construction) within 48 hours of receipt.

c. If additional information relating to the event becomes available that affects the decision to investigate, the OSHA-36 is to be updated and resubmitted via fax to the National Office.

d. In addition, the Regional Administrator will contact the Deputy Director of Enforcement Programs (or Construction, as appropriate) to ensure prompt notification of the National Office of major events, such as those likely to generate significant public or congressional interest.

2. **Investigation Summary Report (OSHA-170).**

a. The OSHA-170 is used to summarize the results of investigations of all events that involve fatalities, catastrophes, amputations, hospitalizations of two or more days, have generated significant publicity, and/or have resulted in significant property damage. An OSHA-170 must be opened, logged into IMIS, and saved as final as soon as the agency becomes aware of a workplace fatality and determines that it is within its jurisdiction, even if most of the data fields are left blank. The information on this form enables the Agency to track fatalities and summarizes circumstances surrounding the event.

NOTE: *The two-day hospitalization criterion is an cutoff to preclude completing an OSHA-170 for events that may not be serious. There is no relationship between this criterion and the definition of hospitalization in Section II. A. of this chapter, Definitions.*

b. For fatality/catastrophe investigations, the OSHA-170 will be:

- Opened in IMIS at the beginning of the investigation and saved as *final*, even if most of the data fields are left blank, so that the Agency can track fatality/catastrophe investigations in a close to "real time" fashion.
- Modified as needed during the investigation to account for updated information.
- Updated with all data fields completely and accurately completed at the conclusion of the investigation, including a thorough narrative description of the incident.

c. The OSHA-170 narrative should not be a copy of the summary provided on the OSHA-36 pre-inspection form. The narrative must comprehensively describe the characteristics of the worksite; the employer and its relationship with other employers, if relevant; the employee task/activity being performed; the related equipment used; and other pertinent information in enough detail to provide a third party reader of the narrative with a mental picture of the fatal incident and the factual circumstances surrounding the event.

d. Only one OSHA-170 should be submitted for an event, regardless of how many inspections take place. If a subsequent event occurs during the course of an inspection, a new OSHA170 for that event should be submitted.

EXAMPLE 11-1: A fatality occurs in employer's facility in August. Both a safety and health inspection are initiated. One OSHA-170 should be filed to summarize the results of the inspections that resulted from the August fatality. However, in September, while the employer's facility is still undergoing the inspections, a second fatality occurs. In this case, a *second* OSHA170 should be submitted for the second fatality and an additional inspection should be opened.

3. **Immigrant Language Questionnaire (IMMLANG).**

a. The IMMLANG Questionnaire is designed to allow the Agency to track fatalities among Hispanic and immigrant employees and to assess the impact of potential language barriers and training deficiencies on fatal accidents. Information for this questionnaire should be collected as early in the investigation as possible, as the availability of immigrants for questioning later in the process is often uncertain.

b. The IMMLANG Questionnaire shall be completed before the conclusion of a fatality investigation according to the procedures outlined in the December 16, 2003, memorandum from Deputy Assistant Secretary R. Davis Layne to the Regional Administrators, It should be completed only if "IMMLANG-Y" is indicated on the OSHA-1 (N-10 Optional Information Code). The Questionnaire is not to be completed if "IMMLANG-N" is indicated on the OSHA-1.

c. The IMMLANG Questionnaire shall be submitted via the intranet. A copy of the completed questionnaire should be printed and placed in the case file.

4. **Related Event Code (REC).** The OSHA-1B provides specific supplemental information documenting hazards and violations. If any item cited is directly related to the occurrence of the fatality or catastrophe, the related event code "A" shall be entered in block 13. If multiple related event codes apply, the only code that has priority over relation to a fatality/catastrophe ("A") is relation to an imminent danger ("I").

J. **Pre-Citation Review.**

1. Because cases involving a fatality may result in civil or criminal enforcement actions, the Area Director is responsible for reviewing all fatality and catastrophe investigation case files to ensure that the case has been properly developed and documented in accordance with the procedures outlined here.

2. The Area Director is responsible for ensuring that an OSHA-170 is reported to IMIS for each incident (see Paragraph II.I.2. of this chapter, *Investigation Summary Report* (OSHA-170)).

3. Review all proposed violation-by-violation penalties in accordance with CPL 02-00-080, *Handling of Cases to be Proposed for Violation-by-Violation Penalties*, dated October 21, 1990.

4. Review citations covered by Regional OSHA/SOL workload agreements in accordance with those agreements.

5. Each Regional Administrator should establish a procedure to ensure that each fatality or catastrophe is thoroughly investigated and processed in accordance with established policy.

K. **Post-Citation Procedures/Abatement Verification.** The regulation governing abatement verification is found at § 1903.19, and OSHA's enforcement policies and procedures for this regulation are outlined in Chapter 7, *Post-Citation Procedures and Abatement Verification*.

1. Due to the transient nature of many of the worksites where fatalities occur and because the worksite may be destroyed by the catastrophic event, it is frequently impossible to conduct follow-up inspections. In such cases, the Area Director should obtain abatement verification from the employer, along with an assurance that appropriate safety and health programs have been implemented to prevent the hazard(s) from recurring.

2. While site closure due to the completion of the cited project is an acceptable method of abatement, it can only be accepted as abatement without certification where a CSHO directly verifies that closure; otherwise, certification by the employer is required. Follow-up inspections need not be conducted if the CSHO has verified abatement during the inspection or if the employer has provided other proof of abatement.

3. Where the worksite continues to exist, OSHA will normally conduct a follow-up inspection if serious citations have been issued.

4. Include abatement language and safety and health system implementation language in any subsequent settlement agreement.

5. If there is a violation that requires abatement verification, field 22 on the OSHA1-B must be completed with the date of abatement verified.

6. If the case is an Enhanced Enforcement Program (EEP) case, follow-up inspections will be conducted in accordance with paragraph XII.A. of the *Enhanced Enhancement Program* (EEP) Directive, CPL 02-00-145, dated January 1, 2008. Follow-up inspections will normally be conducted even if abatement of cited violations have been verified through abatement verification.

L. **Audit Procedures.** The following procedures will be implemented to evaluate compliance with, and the effectiveness of, fatality/catastrophe investigation procedures:

1. Regional Offices will incorporate the review and analysis of fatality/catastrophe files into their audit functions and include their findings in the regular audit reports to the National Office. The review and analysis will utilize random case files to address the following:

   a. *Inspection Findings.* Ensure that hazards have been appropriately addressed and violations have been properly classified. Also ensure that criminal referrals are made when appropriate.

   b. *Documentation.* Ensure that the OSHA-170 narrative and data fields and the OSHA-1B narrative have been completed accurately and detailed enough to allow for analysis at the national level of the circumstances of fatal incidents. Ensure that the IMMLANG Questionnaire is completed, if relevant.

   c. *Construction Fatalities.* Ensure that the case file has been copied and forwarded to the University of Tennessee in accordance with the memoranda to the Regional Administrators from H. Berrien Zettler, Deputy Director, Directorate of Construction, dated September 12 and 13, 2000 (via email) and from Deputy Assistant Secretary R. Davis Layne dated May 14, 2003 and February 18, 2004.

   d. *Settlement Terms.* Ensure that settlement terms are appropriate, including violation reclassification, penalty reductions, and additional abatement language.

   e. *Abatement Verification.* Ensure that abatement verification has been obtained.

   f. Review IMIS reports to identify any trends or cases that may indicate that a further review of those cases may be necessary.

M. **Relationship of Fatality and Catastrophe Investigations to Other Programs and Activities.**

1. **Homeland Security.** OSHA's *National Emergency Management Plan* (NEMP), as contained in HSO 01-00-001, dated December 18, 2003, clarifies the procedures and policies for OSHA's National Office and Regional Offices during responses to incidents of national significance. Generally, OSHA will provide technical assistance and consultation in coordinating the protection of response worker and recovery worker safety and health. When the President makes an emergency declaration under the Stafford Act, the National Response Framework (NRF) is activated. The NEMP can then be activated by the Assistant Secretary, the Deputy Assistant Secretary, or by request from a Regional Administrator. Whether OSHA will conduct a formal fatality or catastrophe investigation in such a situation will be determined on a case-by-case basis.

2. **Enhanced Enforcement Program.**

   a. Inspections that result in citations being issued for at least one of the following are considered Enhanced Enforcement cases:

   b. A fatality inspection in which there is at least one serious violation that is also classified as a repeated or a willful, related to the death;

   c. A fatality inspection in which there is at least one serious violation related to the death, and the employer has an OSHA history of violations similar to the violation that led to the current fatality that consisted of at least one serious, willful, or repeated violation within the last three years;

   d. A fatality inspection in which there is at least one serious violation related to the death, and another fatality has occurred within the last three years;

   e. An inspection that results in three or more serious violations that are also classified as willful or repeated, and the employer has an OSHA history of violations similar in kind to one or more of the violations found in the current inspection consisting of at least one serious, willful, or repeated violation within the last three years;

   f. An inspection that results in at least one failure-to-abate penalty notice where the underlying violation was classified as serious;

   g. Any egregious case.

   h. In such cases, the instructions outlined in CPL 02-00-145, *Enhanced Enforcement Program* (EEP), dated January 1, 2008, shall be followed to ensure that the proper measures are taken regarding classification, coding and treatment of the case.

3. **Significant Enforcement Cases.**
   a. Significant enforcement cases are defined as inspection cases with initial proposed penalties over $100,000. An inspection resulting from an employee fatality or a workplace catastrophe may well be a significant enforcement case and, therefore, particularly thorough documentation is necessary to sustain legal sufficiency.
   b. In cases involving a fatality or catastrophe, the procedures outlined in the memorandum dated March 24, 2004, to Regional Administrators from Deputy Assistant Secretary R. Davis Layne regarding Procedures for Significant Enforcement Cases should be closely followed.
4. **Special Emphasis Programs.** If a fatality or catastrophe investigation arises with respect to an establishment that is also in the current inspection cycle to receive a programmed inspection under any Site Specific Targeting program, the investigation and the inspection may be conducted either concurrently or separately.
5. **Cooperative Programs.** If a fatality or catastrophe occurs at a Voluntary Protection Program (VPP), OSHA Strategic Partnership Program (OSPP) site, or OSHA's Safety and Health Achievement Recognition Program (SHARP), the Regional VPP Manager, OSPP Coordinator, or Consultation Project Manager, as well as the Director of the Directorate of Cooperative and State Programs, should be notified. When enforcement activity has concluded, the Regional VPP Manager, OSPP Coordinator, or Consultation Project Manager should be informed so that the site can be reviewed for program issues.

N. **Special Issues Related to Workplace Fatalities.**
   1. **Death by Natural Causes.** Workplace fatalities caused by natural causes, including heart attacks, must be reported by the employer. The Area Director will then decide whether to investigate the incident.
   2. **Workplace Violence.** As with heart attacks, fatalities caused by incidents of workplace violence must be reported to OSHA by the employer. The Area Director or designee will determine whether or not the incident will be investigated.
   3. **Motor Vehicle Accidents.**
      a. OSHA does not require reporting motor vehicle accidents that occur on public roads or highways, unless the accident occurs in a construction work zone.
      b. Although employers who are required to keep records must record vehicle accidents in their OSHA-300 Log of Work-Related Injuries and Illnesses, OSHA does not investigate such accidents. See §1904.39(b)(3).

III. **Rescue Operations and Emergency Response.**
   A. **OSHA's Authority to Direct Rescue Operations.**
      1. **Direction of Rescue Operations.** OSHA has no authority to direct rescue operations. These are the responsibility of the employer and/or local political subdivisions or state agencies.
      2. **Monitoring and Inspecting Working Conditions of Rescue Operations.** OSHA may monitor and inspect working conditions of covered employees engaged in rescue operations to ensure compliance with standards that protect rescuers, and to provide technical assistance where appropriate.
   B. **Voluntary Rescue Operations Performed by Employees.** OSHA recognizes that an employee may choose to place himself/herself at risk to save the life of another person. The following provides guidance on OSHA citation policy toward employers whose employees perform, or attempt to perform, rescues of individuals in life-threatening danger.
      1. **Imminent Danger.** Section 1903.14(f) provides that no citation may be issued to an employer because of a rescue activity undertaken by an employee of that employer with respect to an individual in imminent danger [i.e., the existence of any condition or practice that could reasonably be expected to cause death or serious physical harm before such condition or practice can be abated] unless:
         a. Such employee is designated or assigned by the employer to have responsibility to perform or assist in rescue operations, AND the employer fails to provide protection of the safety and health of such employee, including failing to provide appropriate training and rescue equipment; or
         b. Such employee is directed by the employer to perform rescue activities in the course of carrying out the employee's job duties, AND the employer fails to provide protection of the safety and health of such employee, including failing to provide appropriate training and rescue equipment; or
         c. Such employee is employed in a workplace that requires the employee to carry out duties that are directly related to a workplace operation where the likelihood of life-threatening accidents is foreseeable, such as operations where employees are located in confined spaces or trenches, handle hazardous waste, respond to emergency situations, perform excavations, or perform construction over water; AND such employee has not been designated or assigned to perform or assist in rescue operations and voluntarily elects to rescue such an individual; AND the employer has failed to instruct employees not designated or assigned to perform or assist in rescue operations of the arrangements for rescue, not to attempt rescue, and of the hazards of attempting rescue without adequate training or equipment.
      2. **Citation for Voluntary Actions.** If an employer has trained his or her employees in accordance with §1903.14, no citation will be issued for an employee's voluntary rescue actions, regardless of whether they are successful.
   C. **Emergency Response.**
      1. **Role in Emergency Operations.** While it is OSHA's policy to respond as quickly as possible to significant events that may affect the health or safety of employees, the agency does not have authority to direct emergency operations.
      2. **Response to Catastrophic Events (Note: these are not OSH Act requirements).** OSHA responds to catastrophic events promptly and acts as an active and forceful protector of employee safety and health during the response, cleanup, removal, storage, and investigation phases of these incidents, while maintaining a visible but limited role during the initial response phase.
      3. **OSHA's Role.**
         a. For inspections of an ongoing emergency response or post-emergency response operation where there has been a catastrophic event, or where OSHA is acting under the National Emergency Management Plan (NEMP), Regional Administrators will determine the overall role that OSHA will play. See CPL 02-02-073, *Inspection Procedures for 29 CFR 1910.120 and 1926.65, Paragraph (q): Emergency Response to Hazardous Substance Releases*, dated August 27, 2007.

      b.   During an event that is covered by the NEMP, OSHA has a responsibility and authority to both enforce its regulations and provide technical advice and assistance to the Federal on-scene coordinator. If such an event occurs in a State Plan State, OSHA will coordinate with the State Plan agency to ensure their involvement in the response.

      c.   For details on OSHA's response to occupationally-related incidents involving multiple fatalities, extensive injuries, massive toxic exposures, extensive property damage, or potential employee injury that generates widespread media interest. See CPL 02-00-094, OSHA's *Response to Significant Events of Potentially Catastrophic Consequences*, dated July 22, 1991.

    4.   **Incidents of National Significance.** For detailed procedures on how to proceed during incidents of national significance when OSHA has been designated as the primary Federal agency for the coordination of technical assistance and consultation for emergency response and recovery worker health and safety, and the Assistant Secretary has activated the National Emergency Response Plan, see HSO 01-00-001 *National Emergency Management Plan*, dated December 18, 2003, and the National Response Framework (Worker Safety and Health Support Annex).
Note: *These documents apply when activated.*

Chapter 12 — Specialized Inspection Procedures

I.   **Multi-Employer Workplace/Worksite [Reserved].** See CPL 02-00-124, *Multi-Employer Citation Policy*, dated December 10, 1999.

II.   **Temporary Labor Camps.**

    A.   **Introduction.** 29 CFR 1910.142, the Temporary Labor Camp standard, is applicable to both agricultural and non-agricultural workplaces.

    B.   **Definitions.**
    NOTE: *Section 1910.142 does not contain a definition section. The following definitions reflect OSHA's interpretation of the standard.*

      1.   **Temporary.** The term *temporary* in §1910.142 refers to employees who enter into an employment relationship for a discrete or defined time period. As a result, the term *temporary* refers to the length of employment, and not to the physical structures housing employees.

      2.   **Temporary Labor Camp Housing.** Temporary labor camp housing is required employer-provided housing that, due to company policy or practice, necessarily renders such housing a term or condition of employment. See *Frank Diehl Farms v. Secretary of Labor*, 696 F.2d 1325 (11th Cir. 1983).

      3.   **New Construction.** All agriculture housing construction started on or after April 3, 1980, including totally new structures and additions to existing structures, will be considered new construction. Cosmetic remodeling work on pre-1980 structures will not be considered new construction and should be treated as existing housing.

    C.   **Wage & Hour/OSHA Shared Authority Under Secretary's Order.** Pursuant to a Secretary's Order, the Wage & Hour Division (WHD) of the Employment Standards Administration (ESA) has shared authority with OSHA over the Temporary Labor Camp standard (§1910.142). See Delegation of Authorities and Assignment of Responsibilities to the Assistant Secretary for Employment Standards and Other Officials in the Employment Standards Administration (*Federal Register*, January 2, 1997 (62 FR 107)) and Secretary's Order 5-2002: Delegation of Authority and Assignment of Responsibility to the Assistant Secretary for Occupational Safety and Health, *Federal Register*, October 22, 2002 (67 FR 65007).

      1.   **Enforcement Authority.**

        a.   **WHD Responsibility.** WHD has enforcement authority with respect to any agricultural establishment where employees are engaged in "agricultural employment" within the meaning of the Migrant and Seasonal Agricultural Worker Protection Act, 29 U.S.C. 1802(3), regardless of the number of employees, including employees engaged in hand packing of produce into containers, whether done on the ground, on a moving machine, or in a temporary packing shed. See Appendix A, Paragraph 4.a.2. of ADM 01-00-003, *Redelegation of Authority and Responsibility of the Assistant Secretary for Occupational Safety and Health*, dated March 6, 2003.

        b.   **OSHA Responsibility.** OSHA retains enforcement authority over temporary labor camps for egg, poultry, red meat production, post-harvesting processing of agricultural and horticultural commodities, and any non-agricultural TLCs. See Appendix A, Paragraph 4.a.2.b. of, ADM 01-00-003, *Redelegation of Authority and Responsibility of the Assistant Secretary for Occupational Safety and Health*, dated March 6, 2003.

      2.   **Compliance Interpretation Authority.** WHD has sole interpretation authority for the Temporary Labor Camp standard, even over those temporary labor camp areas for which OSHA has enforcement authority.

      3.   **Standard Revision and Variance Authority.** OSHA retains all authority for revisions of the Temporary Labor Camp standard, as well as the evaluation and granting of temporary and permanent variances.

      4.   **State Plan States.**

        a.   Eight of the twenty-two jurisdictions (21 states and Puerto Rico) that have OSHA-approved state plans covering private sector employment elected not to enforce the Temporary Labor Camp standards, except with respect to egg, poultry, red meat production, post-harvesting processing of agricultural and horticultural commodities, and any non-agricultural TLCs. Thus, WHD enforces these standards, except as noted above, in the following states: Alaska, Indiana, Iowa, Kentucky, Minnesota, South Carolina, Utah and Wyoming.

        b.   The 14 other jurisdictions with OSHA-approved state plans covering private sector employment have retained enforcement authority for the Temporary Labor Camp standards in agriculture. They are Arizona, California, Hawaii, Maryland, Michigan, Nevada, New Mexico, North Carolina, Oregon, Puerto Rico, Tennessee, Vermont, Virginia and Washington.

    D.   **Enforcement of Temporary Labor Camp Standards for Agriculture.**

      1.   **Choice of Standards on Construction Prior to April 3, 1980.** Prior to walkaround inspections of temporary labor camps built before April 3, 1980, employers providing the housing will be asked to specify their preference of applicable departmental standards. Choices shall be limited to Subpart E of 29 CFR Part 654, or §1910.142, or provisions contained in variances from these standards. If an employer has been issued a variance, it shall produce copies upon request. See Housing for Agricultural Employees, 29 CFR 500.132.

        a.   In instances where Subpart E of Part 654 is specified as the governing standard for existing housing, hazardous conditions violating both the Employment and Training Administration (ETA) and OSHA requirements shall be cited under the OSHA standard. Hazardous conditions found in violation of ETA standards, but in compliance with §1910.142 shall not be cited.

    b.   In instances where conditions are deemed in violation of the ETA standard and not covered by the OSHA standard, either Section 5(a)(1) shall be cited (only serious violations) or such deficiencies shall be brought to the employer's attention and correction shall be encouraged.

    c.   In instances where §1910.142 is selected by the employer as the governing standard for the existing facility or is applicable in the case of "new construction," all requirements of that standard shall apply and shall be cited when violations are found.

    d.   Under no circumstances shall Subpart E of Part 654 be cited by CSHOs, since no authority exists within the Act to cite standards not adopted under the Act.

2.   **Informing Employers.** Prior to the inspection of an agriculture housing facility, employers shall be made aware of the foregoing policy and procedures during the opening conference. This policy applies to all employment-related agriculture housing covered by OSHA, regardless of whether or not employees housed in the facility are recruited through the U.S. Employment Service's inter-intrastate clearance system.

3.   **Agriculture Worksites Under OSHA Responsibility.** For agriculture worksites that OSHA has responsibility for, §1928.21 lists which Part 1910 standards apply.

E.   **OSHA Enforcement for Non-Agriculture Worksites.**

1.   For non-agriculture worksites other Part 1910 standards may be cited for hazards which are not covered under §1910.142. For non-agriculture worksites, the TLC standard has no provisions that specifically apply to fire protection, so those standards are not explicitly pre-empted by the TLC standard. The same is true for §§1910.36 and 37 (exit routes). However, §1910.38 (emergency action plans) applies only where an emergency action plan is required by a particular OSHA standard, so it cannot be used with TLCs.

2.   Examples of temporary labor camp housing for non-agriculture worksites would be for the construction industry and garment industry in the Pacific territories. Such housing for these industries may also be found in large cities and rural areas in various parts of the United States.

3.   The choice of standards issue, discussed in Paragraph D.1., *Choice of Standards on Construction Prior to April 3, 1980*, does not apply to non-agriculture temporary housing.

F.   **Employee Occupied Housing.** Generally, inspections shall be conducted when housing facilities are occupied and as soon as feasible so that any hazards identified may be corrected early in the work season.

1.   Since employees may not speak English, or may only speak English as a second language, every effort shall be made to send a bilingual CSHO on the inspection or have a bi-lingual person accompany the CSHO to translate conversations with employees.

2.   CSHOs shall conduct inspections in a way that minimizes disruptions to those living in the housing facilities. If an occupant of a dwelling unit refuses entry for inspection purposes, CSHOs shall not insist on entry and shall continue the rest of the inspection unless the lack of access to the dwelling unit involved would substantially reduce the effectiveness of the inspection. In that case, valid consent should be obtained from the owner of the unit. If the owner also refuses entry, the procedures for refusal of entry shall be followed. See Chapter 15, *Legal Issues*. The same shall apply in cases where employers refuse entry to the housing facility and/or to the entire worksite.

3.   During inspections, CSHOs shall encourage employers to correct hazards as quickly as possible. Particular attention shall be paid to identifying instances of failure to abate and repeated violations from season to season or past occupancy. These violations shall be cited in accordance with normal procedures.

G.   **Primary Concerns.** When conducting a housing inspection, CSHOs shall be primarily concerned with those facilities or conditions that most directly relate to employee safety and health. Accordingly, all housing inspections shall address at least the following:

1.   **Site.**

    a.   Review the location of the site for adequate drainage in relation to periodic flooding, swamps, pools, sinkholes, and other surfaces where water may collect and remain for extended periods.

    b.   Determine whether the site is adequate in size to prevent overcrowding and whether it is located near (within 500 feet of) livestock.

    c.   Evaluate the site for cleanliness and sanitation; i.e., free from rubbish, debris, wastepaper, garbage, and other refuse.

2.   **Shelter.**

    a.   Determine whether the shelter provides protection against the elements; has the proper floor elevation and floor space; whether rooms are used for combined purposes of sleeping, cooking and eating; and whether all rooms have proper ventilation and screening.

    b.   Determine which rooms are used for sleeping purposes, the number of occupants, size of the rooms, and whether beds, cots, or bunks and lockers are provided.

    c.   Determine what kind of cooking arrangements or facilities are provided, and whether all heating, cooking and water heating equipment are installed in accordance with state and local codes.

3.   **Water Supply.** Determine whether the water supply for drinking, cooking, bathing and laundry is adequate and convenient, and has been approved by the appropriate local health authority.

4.   **Toilet Facilities.** Determine the type, number, location, lighting, and sanitary conditions of toilet facilities.

5.   **Sewage Disposal.**

6.   **Laundry, Handwashing and Bathing Facilities.**

    a.   Determine the number, kind, locations and conditions of these facilities, and whether there is an adequate supply of hot and cold running water.

    b.   Determine also whether such facilities have appropriate floors, walls, partitions and drains. Determine, in camps where public sewers are available, whether all sewer lines and floor drains are connected.

7.   **Lighting.**

    a.   Determine whether electric service is available, and if so, if appropriate light levels, number of ceiling-type light fixtures, and separate floor- or wall-type convenience outlets are provided.

b.   Determine also whether the light fixtures, floor and wall outlets are properly grounded and covered.

8. **Refuse Disposal and Insect and Rodent Control.** Determine the type, number, locations and conditions of refuse disposal containers, and whether there are any infestations of animal or insect vectors or pests.

9. **First-Aid Facilities.** Determine whether adequate first-aid facilities are available and maintained for emergency treatment.

H. **Dimensions.** The relevant dimensions and ratios specified in §1910.142 are mandatory; however, CSHOs may exercise discretion to not cite minor variations from specific dimensions and ratios when such violations do not have an immediate or direct effect on safety and health. In those cases in which the standard itself does not make reference to specific dimensions or ratios but instead uses adequacy as the test for the cited conditions and facilities, the Area Director shall make the determination as to whether a violation exists on a case-by-case basis considering all relevant factors.

I. **Documentation for Housing Inspections.** The following facts shall be carefully documented:

1. The age of the dwelling unit, including any additions. For recently built housing, date the construction was started.

2. Number of dwelling units, number of occupants in each unit.

3. Approximate size of area in which the housing is located and the distance between dwelling units and water supply, toilets, livestock and service building.

J. **Condition of Employment.** The Act covers only housing that is a term and condition of employment. Factors in determining whether housing is a term and condition of employment include situations where:

1. Employers require employees to live in the housing.

2. The housing is in an isolated location or the lack of economically comparable alternative housing makes it a practical necessity to live there.

3. Additional factors to consider in determining whether the housing is a term and condition of employment include, but are not limited to:

a.   Cost of the housing to the employee – is it provided free or at a low rent?

b.   Ownership or control of the housing – is the housing owned or controlled or provided by the employer?

c.   Distance to the worksite from the camp, distance to the work-site from other non-camp residences – is alternative housing reasonably accessible (distance, travel, cost, etc.) to the worksite?

d.   Benefit to the employer – does the employer make the camp available in order to ensure that the business is provided with an adequate supply of labor?

e.   Relationship of the camp occupants to the employer – are those living in the camp required to work for the employer upon demand?

Chapter 13 — Federal Agency Safety and Health Programs
I.   **Federal Agency Programs [Reserved]**

Chapter 14 — Health Inspection Enforcement Programs
I.   **Health Enforcement Programs [Reserved]**

Chapter 15 — Legal Issues
I.   **Administrative Subpoenas.**

A. **When to Issue.** An Administrative Subpoena may be issued whenever there is a need for records, documents, testimony or other supporting evidence necessary for completing an inspection or an investigation of any matter falling within OSHA's authority.

1. Regional Administrators have authority to issue subpoenas, and are also authorized and encouraged to delegate to Area Directors the authority to issue routine administrative subpoenas.

2. The issuance of an administrative subpoena requires the Area Director's or Regional Administrator's signature.

B. **Two Types of Subpoenas.** There are two types of subpoenas used to obtain evidence during an OSHA investigation:

1. A Subpoena Duces Tecum is used to obtain documents. It orders a person or organization to appear at a specified time and place and produce certain documents, and to testify to their authenticity. Employers are not required to create a new record in order to respond to these types of subpoenas.

2. A Subpoena Ad Testificandum commands a named individual or corporation to appear at a specified time and place, such as the Area Office, to provide testimony under oath. A verbatim transcript is made of this testimony.

C. **Area Director Delegated Authority to Issue Administrative Subpoenas.** Although authority to issue some types of subpoenas is reserved to the Regional Administrator, Area Directors may be authorized to issue routine administrative subpoenas.

1. Area Directors may be delegated authority to issue administrative subpoenas for any record or document relevant to an inspection or investigation under the Act, including:

a.   Injury and illness records such as the OSHA-301 and the OSHA-300 See CPL 02-02-072, *Rules of Agency Practice and Procedure Concerning OSHA Access to Employee Medical Records*, dated August 22, 2007, and 29 CFR 1913.10(b)(6);

b.   Hazard communication program;

c.   Lockout/tagout program; and

d.   Safety and health program.

2. Information shall be requested from the employer or holder of records, documents, or other information-containing materials.

a.   If this person/entity refuses to provide requested information or evidence, the OSHA representative serving the subpoena shall explain the reason for the request.

b.   If there is still a refusal to produce the information or evidence requested, the OSHA representative shall inform the person/entity that the agency may take further legal action.

3. The official issuing the subpoena is responsible for evaluating the circumstances and deciding whether to issue a subpoena. In cases with potential national implications or involving extraordinary circumstances, the Regional Administrator shall be contacted for concurrence or to determine whether the subpoena should be issued by the Regional Administrator.

D. **Regional Administrator Authority to Issue Administrative Subpoenas.**
1. Regional Administrators have independent authority to issue subpoenas for any appropriate purpose. Unless delegated to an Area Director, the following authority shall be reserved to Regional Administrators:
    a. Issuance of a *Subpoena Ad Testificandum* to require the testimony of any company official, employee, or other witness;
    b. Issuance of a subpoena for the production of personally identifiable medical records for which a medical access order has been obtained See CPL 02-02-072, *Rules of Agency Practice and Procedure Concerning OSHA Access to Employee Medical Records*, dated August 22, 2007, and §1913.10(b)(6); and
    c. Issuance of a subpoena for the production of physical evidence, such as samples of materials.
2. Although this authority may not routinely be delegated to Area Directors, in a few cases such delegation may be appropriate.

E. **Administrative Subpoena Content and Service.**
1. Model administrative subpoenas for use by the Area Offices are provided at the end of this chapter. If the Area Director believes that there is reason for any departure from the models due to circumstances of the case, the RSOL shall be consulted.
2. The subpoena shall be prepared for the appropriate party and will normally be served by personal service (delivery to the party named in person). Leaving a copy at a place of business or residence is not personal service.
    a. In exceptional circumstances, service may be by certified mail with return receipt requested.
    b. Where no individual's name is available, the subpoena can be addressed to a business' or organization's "Custodian(s) of Records."
3. Examples of language for a routine *Subpoena Duces Tecum* are provided below. This language should be expanded when requesting additional or more detailed information for accident, catastrophe, referral or fatality investigations.
    a. "Copies of any and all documents, including information stored electronically, which reflect training procedures for the lockout/tagout procedures and hazard communication program in effect at the [insert site name}in [insert city, state], during the period [insert month/day/year], to present."
    b. "Copies of the OSHA-300 and the OSHA-301 forms, for the entire site, during calendar years [insert year] and [insert year]."
    c. "Copies of any and all documents, including information stored electronically, such as safety and health program handbooks, minutes of safety and health meetings, training certification records, audits and reprimands for violations of safety and health rules by employees of the [insert site name] in [insert city, state], that show [insert employer's name] had and enforced safety rules relating to the use of trench boxes during the period [insert month/day/year], to present."
    NOTE: *Where particular information is being sought, a subpoena's description should be narrow and specific in order to increase the likelihood for prompt compliance with the request.*
4. A copy of the subpoena, signed by the Area Director, shall be forwarded as soon as possible to the Regional Administrator and shall also be maintained at the Area Office.
    a. Copies of subpoenas may be forwarded to the RSOL as practicable.
    b. Regional Administrators and Area Directors shall establish procedures to track all administrative subpoenas issued. These procedures shall include instructions for completing the return of service.

F. **Compliance with the Subpoena.** The person/entity served may comply with the subpoena by making the information or evidence available to the compliance officer immediately upon service, or at the time and place specified in the subpoena.
1. With respect to any record required to be made or kept pursuant to any statute or regulation, the subpoena shall normally allow **three days** from the date of service for production of the required information although a shorter period may be appropriate.
2. With respect to other types of records or information, such as safety programs or incident reports, the subpoena shall normally allow at least **five working days** from the date of service for production of the required information.
3. Separate subpoenas for items 1 and 2 above may be necessary.
4. Any witness fees or mileage costs potentially associated with administrative subpoenas should be discussed with the RSOL prior to the issuance.

G. **Refusal to Honor Subpoena.**
1. If the person/entity served refuses to comply with (or only partially honors) the subpoena, the compliance officer shall document all relevant facts and advise the Area Director before taking further action.
2. To enforce a subpoena, the Area Director shall follow the procedures outlined for obtaining warrants, and shall refer the matter, through the Regional Administrator, to the RSOL for appropriate action.

H. **Anticipatory Subpoena.** Generally, agency policy is to seek voluntary production of evidence before an administrative subpoena is issued. However, a subpoena may be executed and served without making a prior request where there is reason to believe that the corporate entity and/or person from whom information is sought will not voluntarily comply, or where there is an urgent need for the information. Anticipatory subpoenas require consultation with RSOL.
    NOTE: *For example, pre-inspection preparation of subpoenas for issuance at the opening conference is appropriate in cases where the employer has previously denied access to records or where complex inspections, involving extensive review of records, are planned.*

II. **Service of Subpoena on OSHA Personnel.**
A. **Proceedings to which the Secretary of Labor is a Party.** If any, OSHA personnel is served with a subpoena or order either to appear or to provide testimony in, or information for, a proceeding where the Secretary of Labor is a party, they shall immediately contact the RSOL for instructions regarding the manner in which to respond. If a CSHO is served with a subpoena, they shall notify the Area Director immediately who shall then refer the matter to the RSOL.

NOTE: *Review Commission rules provide that any person served with a subpoena, whether to testify in any Commission hearing or to produce records and testify in such hearing shall, within five days after date of service, move to revoke the subpoena if the person does not intend to comply with its terms. See §2200.57(c). Therefore, expeditious handling of any subpoena served on OSHA employees is essential. When any such subpoena is served, the RSOL must immediately be notified by telephone or email.*

B. **Proceedings to which the Secretary of Labor is Not a Party.**

1. If any OSHA personnel is served with a subpoena or order either to appear or to provide testimony in, or information for, a proceeding to which the Secretary of Labor is not a party (e.g., a private third party tort suit for damages associated with a workplace injury), they shall immediately contact the RSOL.

2. U.S. Department of Labor regulations prohibit Department employees from participating in, or from providing information for, proceedings in which the Secretary of Labor is not a party without explicit permission from the designated Deputy Solicitor of Labor. See 29 CFR 2.21 and 29 CFR 2.22. These regulations apply to demands to disclose or provide:

   a. Any material contained in the files of the Department;

   b. Any information relating to material contained in the files of the Department; or

   c. Any information or material acquired by any person while such person was an employee of the Department as a part of the performance of his/her official duties or because of his/her official status.

3. The Office of the Solicitor is responsible for responding to such requests and will take appropriate steps to have the subpoena quashed or provide the necessary permission, as appropriate, to allow an employee to comply with an issued order.

III. **Obtaining Warrants.**

A. **Warrant Applications.**

1. Upon refusal of entry, of if there is reason to believe an employer will refuse entry, the Area Director shall proceed according to guidelines and procedures established in the region for warrant applications. The Area Director may initiate the compulsory process with approval of the RSOL.

2. Warrant applications for establishments where consent has been denied for a limited scope inspection (i.e., complaint, referral, accident investigation) shall normally be limited to the specific working conditions or practices forming the basis of the inspection. However, a broad scope warrant may be sought if there is evidence of potentially pervasive violative conditions or if the establishment is on a current list of establishments targeted for a comprehensive inspection.

B. **General Information Necessary to Obtain a Warrant.** If the warrant is to be obtained by the RSOL, the Area Director shall inform the RSOL in writing within **48 hours** after the determination is made and provide all information necessary to obtain a warrant, including:

1. Area/District Office, telephone number, and name of Area Director or designee involved;

2. Name of CSHO attempting inspection and inspection number, if assigned. Identify whether the inspection to be conducted will include safety items, health items or both;

3. Legal name(s) of establishment and address, including City, State and County. Include site location if different from mailing address;

4. Estimated number of employees at inspection site;

5. Standard Industrial Classification (SIC) or North American Industry Classification System (NAICS) Code and high hazard ranking for that specific industry within the State, as obtained from statistics provided by the National Office;

6. Summary of all facts leading to the refusal of entry or limitation of inspection, including:

   a. Date and time of entry/attempted entry;

   b. Date and time of denial;

   c. Stage of denial (entry, opening conference, walkaround, etc.);

7. A narrative of all actions taken by the CSHO leading up to, during, and after refusal, including:

   a. Full name and title of the person(s) to whom CSHO presented credentials;

   b. Full name and title of person(s) who refused entry;

   c. Reasons stated for the denial by person(s) refusing entry;

   d. Response, if any, by CSHO to the denial name and address (if known) of any witnesses to denial of entry.

8. Any information related to past inspections, including copies of previous citations.

9. Any previous requests for warrants. Attach details, if applicable.

10. All completed information related to the current inspection report, including documentation of any observations of violations in plain view discovered prior to denial.

11. If a construction site involving work under contract from any agency of the Federal Government, the name of the agency, the date of the contract, and the type of work involved.

12. Other pertinent information, such as: description of the workplace; the work processes; machinery, tools and materials used; known hazards and injuries associated with the specific manufacturing process or industry.

13. Investigative procedures that may be required during the proposed inspection, e.g., interviewing of employees/witnesses, personal sampling, photographs, audio/videotapes, examination of records, access to medical records, etc.

C. **Specific Warrant Information Based on Inspection Type.** Document all specific reasons for the selection of the establishment to be inspected, including proposed scope of the inspection:

1. **Imminent Danger.**

   a. Description of alleged imminent danger situation;

   b. Date information received and source of information;

   c. Original allegation and copy of typed report, including basis for reasonable expectation of death or serious physical harm and immediacy of danger; and

   d. Whether all current imminent danger investigative procedures have been followed.

2. **Fatality/Catastrophe.** The OSHA-36 Form should be completed with as much detail as possible.

3. **Complaint or Referral.**

a. Original complaint or referral and copy of typed complaint or referral;

b. Reasons OSHA believes that a violation threatening physical harm or imminent danger exists, including possible standards that could be violated if the complaint or referral is credible and representative of workplace conditions;

c. Whether all current complaint or referral processing procedures have been followed; and

d. Any additional information pertaining to the evaluation of the complaint or referral.

4. **Programmed.**

a. Targeted safety – general industry, maritime, construction;

b. Targeted health; and/or

c. Special emphasis program–Special Programs, Local Emphasis Program, Migrant Housing Inspection, etc.

5. **Follow-up.**

a. Date of initial inspection;

b. Details and reasons follow-up was conducted;

c. Copies of previous citations which served as the basis for initiating the follow-up;

d. Copies of settlement agreements and final orders, if applicable; and/or

e. Previous history of failure to correct, if any.

6. **Monitoring.**

a. Date of original inspection;

b. Details and reasons monitoring inspection is to be conducted;

c. Copies of previous citations and/or settlement agreements that serve as the basis for the monitoring inspection; and/or

d. Petition for Modification of Abatement Date (PMA) request, if applicable.

D. **Warrant Procedures.** Where a warrant has been obtained, CSHOs are authorized to conduct the inspection in accordance with the terms of the warrant. All questions from employers concerning the reasonableness of a compulsory process inspection shall be referred to the Area Director and the RSOL.

1. **Action Taken Upon Receipt of Warrant (Compulsory Process).**

a. The inspection will normally begin within 24 hours of receipt of a warrant or from the date authorized by the warrant for initiating the inspection.

b. Upon completion of the inspection, if the warrant includes a return of service space for entering inspection dates, CSHOs shall complete the return of service on the original warrant, sign and forward it to the Area Director or designee for appropriate action.

2. **Serving a Subpoena for Production of Records.** Where appropriate, even where the scope of an inspection is limited by a warrant or an employer's consent to specific conditions or practices, any subpoena for production of records shall be served in accordance with the section on administrative subpoenas in this chapter.

E. **Second Warrant.** Under certain circumstances, a second warrant may be sought to expand an inspection based on a records review or "plain view" observations of other potential violations discovered during a limited scope walkaround.

F. **Refused Entry or Interference.**

1. When an apparent refusal to permit entry or inspection is encountered upon presenting the warrant, CSHOs shall specifically inquire whether the employer is refusing to comply with the warrant.

2. If the employer refuses to comply or if consent is not clearly given, CSHOs shall not attempt to conduct the inspection at that time, and shall leave the premises and contact the Area Director or designee regarding further action.

a. CSHOs shall fully document all facts relevant to the refusal (including noting all witnesses to the denial of entry or interference).

b. Area Directors shall then contact the RSOL and the Regional Administrator, who shall jointly decide the action to be taken.

G. **Federal Marshal Assistance.** In unusual circumstances, a U.S. Marshal may be asked to accompany a CSHO when a warrant is presented. A request for a U.S. Marshal's assistance shall be made only by an Area Director after consultation with the Regional Administrator and the RSOL, and only when there is a potential for violence, harassment and/or interference with the inspection, or reason to believe that the presence of a U.S. Marshall will assist with compliance with the warrant.

IV. **Equal Access to Justice Act (EAJA).**

A. **Prevailing Party May be Awarded Fees.** The Equal Access to Justice Act (EAJA) provides that a party prevailing against the United States in litigation may be awarded fees payable by an agency of the United States if the agency's position in litigation was not "substantially justified" or if the agency proposed a penalty that was reduced as a result of litigation and subsequently determined to be "unreasonable." EAJA awards are statutorily limited to certain small entity parties, generally those with a designated net worth and/or number of employees. See 28 U.S.C. § 2412(d)(2)(B).

B. **OSHA's Position Must be Substantially Justified.** Pursuant to the EAJA, the Commission or a federal court may award an employer fees if OSHA proceeds in litigation on a position that is not substantially justified or proposes a penalty that subsequently is found to be unreasonable in light of the statutory penalty assessment provisions and the circumstances relevant to the particular case. If an EAJA award is assessed by the Commission or a court following an OSHA proceeding and the award becomes a final order, OSHA is responsible for paying the award.

C. **EAJA Should Not Affect How the Agency Operates.** EAJA should not affect the manner in which the agency operates, as citations are issued only after OSHA determines that there is adequate evidence that a violation exists, and proposed penalty amounts are determined based on established statutory and administrative criteria, and facts derived during the inspection/ investigation. However, the potential for incurring EAJA costs underscores the importance of thoroughly documenting each element of a violation with evidence supporting the violative condition and characterization. In addition, because the Secretary generally bears the burden of proof in litigation, it is important that CSHOs promptly discuss with the RSOL during the early stages of an investigation any factors affecting the Secretary's ability to support an alleged violation or penalty proposal (e.g., the likely unavailability of a critical witness or the need for an expert).

V. **Notice of Contest.** OSHRC is an independent Federal agency created to decide contests of citations or penalties resulting from OSHA inspections. The Review Commission, therefore, functions as an administrative court, with established procedures for conducting hearings, receiving evidence and rendering decisions by its Administrative Law Judges (ALJs). The Act states that the Review Commission operate as an independent agency (i.e., not part of another Federal department) to ensure that parties to agency cases receive impartial hearings.

A. **Time Limit for Filing a Notice of Contest.**
1. The Act provides employers fifteen working days following its receipt of a notice of a citation to notify OSHA of the employer's desire to contest a citation and/or proposed assessment of penalty.
2. Where a notice of contest was not mailed, i.e., postmarked, within the 15 working day period allowed for contest, the Area Director shall follow the instructions for Late Notices of Contest. A copy of any untimely notice of contest shall be retained in the case file.

B. **Contest of Abatement Period Only.** If the notice of contest is submitted to the Area Director after the 15 working day period, but contests only the reasonableness of the abatement period, it shall be treated as a Petition for Modification of Abatement and handled in accordance with PMA procedures.

C. **Communication Where the Intent to Contest is Unclear.**
1. If a written communication is received from an employer containing an objection, criticism or other adverse comment as to a citation or proposed penalty, but which does not clearly appear to contest the citations, the Area Director shall contact the employer to clarify the intent of the communication.
   a. After receipt of the communication, any clarification should be obtained within the 15 working day contest period, so that if a determination is made that it is a notice of contest, the file may be timely forwarded to the Review Commission.
   b. In cases where the Area Office receives a written communication from an employer requesting *an informal conference that also states an intent to contest*, the employer must be informed that there can be no informal conference unless the notice of contest is withdrawn. If the employer still wants to pursue an informal conference, it must first present or send a letter expressing that intent and rescinding the contest. All documents pertaining to such communications shall be retained in the case file.
2. If an Area Director determines that the employer intends the document to be a notice of contest, it shall be transmitted to the OSHRC. If contact with the employer reveals a desire for an informal conference, the employer shall be informed that the conference does not stay the running of the 15 working day contest period.
   NOTE: *Settlement is permitted at any stage of Commission proceedings. See §2200.100(a).*

VI. Late Notice of Contest.

A. **Failure to Notify OSHA of Intent to Contest.** If the employer fails to notify OSHA of its intent to contest a citation or penalty within fifteen working days following the receipt of a citation, the citation and proposed penalties become final orders of the Review Commission.

B. **Notice Received after the Contest Period.**
1. In every case where OSHA receives notice of an employer's intent to contest a citation and/or proposed assessment of penalty beyond the 15 working day period, Area Directors shall inform employers in writing that OSHA will not accept the untimely notice of contest, but that the it may transmit the late filed notice of contest to the Commission.
2. **The letter from the Area Director will also indicate the following:**
   a. Inspection number;
   b. Citation number(s);
   c. Corresponding proposed penalties;
   d. Date on which OSHA believes the employer received the notice of a violation (and proposed penalty, if applicable);
   e. Date on which OSHA received the employer's notice of contest, as well as any additional information the Area Director believes to be pertinent.
      NOTE: *The postmarked envelope containing the late filed notice of contest date is to be retained. A copy of the letter and envelope shall be sent to RSOL.*

C. **Retention of Documents.**
1. Area Offices shall maintain all documents reflecting the date on which the employer received the notice of a violation (and proposed penalty, if applicable), and the employer's notice of contest was received, as well as any additional information pertinent to demonstrating failure to file a timely notice of contest.
2. Written or oral statements from the employer or its representative explaining the employer's reason for missing the filing deadline shall also be maintained (notes shall be taken to memorialize oral communications).

VII. Contested Case Processing Procedures.
The notice of contest and related documents must be sent to the OSHRC within 15 working days of receipt of the employer's notification. See §2200.33. The RSOL shall be consulted in any questionable cases.

A. **Transmittal of Notice of Contest to Commission.**
1. **Documents to Executive Secretary.** In most cases, the envelope sent to the OSHRC Executive Secretary will contain the following three documents:
   a. Employer's original letter contesting OSHA's action;
   b. One copy of the Citation and Notification of Penalty Form (OSHA-2) or of the Notice of Failure to Abate Form (OSHA-2B); and
   c. Certification form.
2. **Notices of Contest.** The original notice of contest shall be transmitted to the Commission and a copy retained in the case file. The envelope containing the notice of contest shall be retained in the case file with the postmark intact.
3. **Contested Citations and Notice of Proposed Penalty or Notice of Failure to Abate.** A signed copy of each of these documents shall be sent to the Commission and a copy retained in the case file.
4. **Certification Form.**
   a. The certification form shall be used for all contested cases and a copy retained in the case file. It is essential that the original of the certification form, properly executed, be transmitted to the Commission.
      ■ When listing the Region number in the heading, do not use Roman numerals. Use 1, 2, 3, 4, 5, 6, 7, 8, 9, or 10. Insert "C" in the CSHO Job Title block if a safety CSHO or "I," if a health CSHO.

- Item 3 of the form shall be filled by inserting only the word "employer" or "employee" in the space provided. This shall be done even where the notice of contest is filed by an attorney for the party contesting the action. An item "4" shall be added where other documents, such as additional notices of contest, are sent to the Commission.
- Insert the correct date for each item in the document list in the column headed "Date."
- Insert the name and address of the RSOL attorney who will handle the case, in the box containing the printed words "FOR THE SECRETARY OF LABOR." The Commission notifies this person of the hearing date and other official actions on the case.

   b. The documents are to be transmitted within the 15 working day time limit to: Executive Secretary Occupational Safety and Health Review Commission 1120 20th Street, N.W., 9th floor Washington, DC 20036-3419

B. **Transmittal of File to Regional Solicitor.**
   1. Under the Commission's Rules of Procedure, the Secretary of Labor is required to file a complaint with the Commission within **20 calendar days** after the Secretary's receipt of a notice of contest.
   2. Immediately after receiving a notice of contest, the Area Director shall send to the RSOL by U.S. mail (or other mutually agreeable manner) the notice of contest, which the Area Director or designee will later transmit to the Commission, along with the complete investigative file (including photos and video).

VIII. Communications while Proceedings are Pending before the Commission.
A. **Consultation with Regional Solicitor.**
   1. After a notice of contest is filed and the case is within the jurisdiction of the Commission, there shall be no subsequent investigations of, or conferences with, the employer or employee representatives that have sought party status relating to any issues underlying the contested citations, without prior clearance from the RSOL.
   2. Once a notice of contest has been filed, all inquiries relating to the Citation and Notification of Penalty shall be referred promptly to the RSOL. This includes inquiries from the employer, affected employees, employee representatives, prospective witnesses, insurance carriers, other Government agencies, attorneys, and any other party.
B. **Communications with Commission Representatives while Proceedings are Pending before the Commission.** CSHOs, Area Directors, Regional Administrators, or other field personnel shall not have any direct or indirect communication relevant to the merits of any open case with Administrative Law Judges, employees of the Commission, or any of the parties or interveners. All inquiries and communications shall be handled through the RSOL.

IX. Commission Procedures.
A. **Two Levels of Adjudication.** OSHRC's Rules of Procedure provide for two levels of adjudication. The first level is before an Administrative Law Judge. The second level is review of ALJ decisions by the agency's Commissioners if one of the Commissioners directs review.
B. **Rules of Procedure.**
   1. The OSHRC Rules of Procedure are found in Part 2200 of Title 29 of the Code of Federal Regulations. These rules govern two types of ALJ proceedings.
       a. The more conventional proceeding involves the use of pleadings, discovery, a hearing and post-hearing briefs.
       b. Simplified Proceedings are less formal hearings that employ fewer legal procedures and are used in less complex cases (few citation items, no willful or repeat violation or fatality) and can be requested by either party or by the ALJ. In Simplified Proceedings, pleadings are generally not required and early discussion among the parties to narrow the disputed issues is required.
   2. **Receipt of Case.** Upon receipt of a case by the assigned ALJ, a hearing date is set and a site selected as close as possible to where the alleged violation(s) occurred. The hearing is an administrative trial conducted in accordance with the Commission's Rules of Procedure.
   3. **Hearing Evidence.**
       a. Review includes a new examination of all of the evidence, as well as briefs submitted by the parties.
       b. Upon hearing all of the evidence, the judge will issue a written decision, including both findings of fact and conclusions of law.
       c. The OSHRC then issues a decision affirming, modifying or vacating the citations and penalties proposed by OSHA.
       d. The decision becomes final in **30 days** unless, within that period, one of the Commissioners directs that the case be reviewed.
   4. **Review of ALJ's Decision.** If one of the parties requests review of the ALJ's decision, but review is not directed by the Commission, the petitioning party may request review by the appropriate U.S. Circuit Court of Appeals. Review by a Court of Appeals must be sought within **60 days** after the Commission's decision becomes final.
   5. **Availability of Commission Decisions.** Commission decisions, including Administrative Law Judge decisions, are available from the Review Commission website, www.oshrc.gov.

X. Discovery Methods.
Once a legal proceeding has been initiated, each party has the opportunity to "discover" evidence in the possession of an opposing party. Traditionally, discovery methods include:
- Request for Admissions,
- Interrogatories,
- Requests for Production of Documents, and
- Depositions.

An attorney from the Solicitor's Office will represent the agency in responding to discovery requests. It is essential that all OSHA personnel coordinate and cooperate with the assigned attorney to ensure that such responses are accurate, complete, and filed in a timely manner.
A. **Interrogatories.** CSHOs shall draft and sign answers to interrogatories, with RSOL assistance. It is the responsibility of the CSHO to answer each interrogatory separately and fully. The RSOL attorney shall sign any objections to the interrogatories. CSHOs should be aware that they may be deposed and/or examined at hearing on the interrogatory answers provided.

B. **Production of Documents.**

    1. If a request for production of documents is served on RSOL and that request is forwarded to the Area Office CSHOs, or staff member, they should immediately make all documents relevant to that discovery demand available to the RSOL attorney.

    2. While portions of those materials may be later withheld based on governmental privileges or doctrine (e.g., statements that would reveal the identity of an informer), CSHOs must not withhold any information from the RSOL attorney.

    3. It is RSOL's responsibility to review all material and to assert any applicable privileges that may justify withholding documents/materials that would otherwise be discoverable.

C. **Depositions.** Depositions permit an opposing party to take a potential witness' pre-hearing statement under oath in order to better understand the witness's potential testimony if the matter later proceeds to a hearing. CSHOs or other OSHA personnel may be required to offer testimony during a deposition. In such cases, an RSOL attorney will be present with the witness.

XI. Testifying in Hearings. While instructions provided by RSOL attorneys take precedence, particularly during trial preparation, the following considerations will generally enhance the hearing testimony of CSHOs:

A. **Review Documents and Evidence.** In consultation with RSOL, CSHOs should review documents and evidence relevant to the inspection or investigation before the proceeding so that when testifying, they are very familiar with the evidence and need not regularly refer to the file or other documents.

B. **Attire.** Wear appropriate clothing that reflects the agency's respect for the court or other tribunal before which you are testifying. This also applies when appearing before a magistrate to seek an administrative warrant.

C. **Responses to Questions.** Answer all questions directly and honestly. If you do not understand a question, indicate that and ask that the question be repeated or clarified.

D. **Judge's Instruction(s).** Listen carefully to any instruction provided by the judge and, unless instructed to the contrary by RSOL counsel, follow the judge's instruction.

XII. Commission Simplified Proceedings. Simplified Proceedings (formerly known as "E-Z Trials") are the Commission's attempt to simplify the resolution of some contested citations.

A. **Proposed Penalty Threshold.** Because the Commission has raised the proposed penalty threshold for cases that are eligible for simplified proceedings, a greater number of cases will be eligible for this type of proceeding. These include most cases with aggregate proposed penalties of less than $20,000 and, at the discretion of the Chief ALJ, some cases with aggregate proposed penalties of up to $30,000.

B. **Prompt Disclosure of Inspection Documents.** Simplified proceedings contemplate the prompt disclosure of inspection documents. Pursuant to the Commission's rules [29 CFR 2200.206], the Secretary must provide the employer within prescribed time periods, the following documents:

    1. Within **12 working days** after the case is designated for simplified proceedings, copies of the OSHA-1A and -1B forms (or their equivalents);

    2. Within **30 calendar days** after the case is designated for simplified proceedings, copies of photographs or videotapes expected to be used at the hearing; and

    3. Within **30 calendar days** after the case is designated for simplified proceedings, any evidence in OSHA's possession that may support the employer's defense to the citation.

    NOTE: *Simplified proceedings provide fewer opportunities for the Secretary's counsel to obtain information concerning the employer's positions and defenses prior to a hearing. Therefore, it is particularly important for CSHOs to promptly provide SOL counsel with all information regarding potential affirmative defenses that an employer may raise and/or arguments the employer may use to refute a violation(s) or the propriety of a proposed penalty.*

XIII. Citation Final Order Dates.

A. **Citation/Notice of Penalty Not Contested.** The Citation/Notice of Penalty and abatement date becomes a final order of the Commission **on the date the 15 working day contest period expires**. For purposes of computing the 15 working day period, the day the employer receives the citation is not counted.

    Example 15-1: An employer receives the Citation/Notice of Penalty on Monday, August 4th. The day the employer receives the Citation/Notice of Penalty is not counted. Therefore, the final order date would be Monday, August 25th.

B. **Citation/Notice of Penalty Resolved by Informal Settlement Agreement (ISA).** Because there is no contest of the citation, an ISA becomes final, with penalties due and payable, **on the date of the last signature of the parties**. See also Chapter 8, Paragraph I.B.2. (An ISA is effective upon signature by both the Area Director and the employer representative as long as the contest period has not expired).

    NOTE: *A later due date for payment of penalties may be set by the terms of the ISA.*

C. **Citation/Notice of Penalty Resolved by Formal Settlement Agreement (FSA).** The Citation/Notice of Penalty **becomes final 30 days after docketing of the Administrative Law Judge's (ALJ's) Order approving the parties' stipulation and settlement agreement**, assuming there is no direction for review. The Commission's Notice of Docketing specifies the date upon which the decision becomes a final order. If the FSA is approved by an order of the full Commission, **it will become final after 60 days**.

D. **Cases Resolved by an ALJ Decision.** The ALJ's decision **becomes a final order of the Commission 30 days after docketing, unless the Commission directs review of the case**. The Commission's Notice of Docketing specifies the date upon which the decision becomes a final order.

E. **ALJ Decision Reviewed by Commission.** Pursuant to Section 11 of the Act, **the Commission's decision becomes final 60 days after the Notice of Commission Decision**. The Notice of Commission Decision specifies the date the Commission decision was issued. As a matter of policy, OSHA does not attempt to collect civil penalties while a case is being appealed. However, unless the employer requests a "stay" of the Commission's decision, court of appeals review does not delay the abatement obligation.

F. **Commission Decision Review by the U.S. Court of Appeals.** The U.S. Court of Appeals' decision becomes final when the court issues its mandate.

XIV. Federal Court Enforcement under Section 11(b) of the OSH Act. An employer's obligation to abate a cited violation arises when there is a final order of the Review Commission upholding the citation.

A.   **Section 11(b) Summary Enforcement Orders.** Section 11(b) of the OSH Act authorizes OSHA to obtain a summary enforcement order from the appropriate Circuit Court of Appeals enforcing final Review Commission orders. An employer who violates such a court order can be found in contempt of court. Potential sanctions for contempt include daily penalties and other fines, recovery of the Secretary's costs of bringing the action, incarceration of an individual company officer who flouts the Court's order, and any other sanction which the court deems necessary to secure compliance. Employers who ignore ordinary enforcement actions may be induced to comply by the severity of these potential contempt sanctions.

Section 11(b) orders can be an effective and speedier alternative to failure-to-abate notices that are typically issued when an employer does not abate a violation within the allowed time. They can be requested from the Court whether the final order results from a Review Commission or ALJ decision, a settlement agreement, or an uncontested citation.

B.   **Selection of Cases for Section 11(b) Action.** All final orders issued in enhanced enforcement cases must be considered for Section 11(b) enforcement. In addition, a petition for 11(b) enforcement is to be considered in cases where final orders do not meet the enhanced enforcement case criteria but where the following factors suggest that an 11(b) petition should be filed:

1.   Employer's citation history and/or other indications suggest serious compliance problems, such as widespread violations of the same or similar standards at multiple establishments or construction worksites. The OSHA IMIS database should be searched for the employer's history of violations;

2.   Employer statements or actions indicating reluctance or refusal to abate significant hazards, or behavior that demonstrates indifference to employee safety;

3.   Repeated violations of the Act, particularly of the same standard, which continue undeterred by the traditional remedies of civil monetary penalties and Review Commission orders to abate;

4.   Repeated refusal to pay penalties;

5.   Filing false or inadequate abatement verification reports;

6.   Disregard of a previous settlement agreement, particularly one that includes a specific or company-wide abatement plan.

C.   **Drafting of Citations and Settlements to Facilitate Section 11(b) Enforcement.** Proper drafting of citations and settlement agreements can facilitate obtaining a Section 11(b) order and maximize its deterrent effect.

Notations stating "Corrected during inspection" or "Employer has abated all hazards" shall not be made on the citation in cases where there is evidence of a continuing violative practice by an employer that may be subject to a summary enforcement order under Section 11(b) of the Act (i.e., failure to provide fall protection is a recurring condition based on citation history or other indications suggesting widespread violations of the same or similar standards at other establishments or construction worksites).

Where possible, OSHA should attempt to identify cases that may warrant Section 11(b) enforcement at least a month before issuing the citation. When OSHA identifies such a case, it will contact the RSOL to discuss citation language that is in accord with Section 11(b) enforcement. If a case identified for potential 11(b) action is being resolved through a settlement agreement, whether formal or informal, language should be sought in the agreement that commits the employer to specific ongoing abatement duties.

Language in a settlement agreement that imposes a specific duty on the employer, such as a requirement that the employer hire a consultant to develop a safety program or provide OSHA with a list of other worksites, can be enforced under Section 11(b).

D.   **Follow-up Inspections.** The OSH Division in the National Office of the Solicitor's Office will notify the RSOL and the Directorate of Enforcement Programs (and, where the order pertains to a construction employer, the Directorate of Construction), when a court has entered an 11(b) order. OSHA will then promptly schedule an inspection or investigation to determine whether the employer is complying with the court order. The Regional Administrator, in consultation with the RSOL, will determine the nature and extent of the inspection or investigation. The RSOL will advise on the kind of "clear and convincing" evidence that would be needed to support a contempt petition in the event of the employer's noncompliance with the order of the court.

E.   **Conduct of Verification Inspections.** Whenever an enforcement order is issued by a Court of Appeals, an inspection shall be scheduled within six months to determine whether the company is complying with the court order. If serious violations of the standard(s) subject to the enforcement order are found, the RSOL shall be contacted immediately for guidance on what evidence will be needed for submission to the court.

APPENDIX A

United States of America

DEPARTMENT OF LABOR Occupational Safety and Health Administration

Subpoena Duces Tecum

TO : _____

Pursuant to Section 8(b) of the Occupational Safety and Health Act (29 U.S.C. §657(b)) you are hereby required to appear before of the OCCUPATIONAL SAFETY AND HEALTH ADMINISTRATION, UNITED STATES DEPARTMENT OF LABOR, at

_____, in the city of _____, on the

_____ day of _____, 20____, at _____ o'clock am/pm of that day, to testify regarding the working conditions maintained by

_____ And you are hereby required to bring with you and produce at said time and place the following books, papers, and documents, including information stored electronically:

FAIL NOT AT YOUR PERIL

IN TESTIMONY WHEREOF *I have hereunto affixed my signature and the seal of the* UNITED STATES DEPARTMENT OF LABOR at *(Insert Location) this*

_____ day of _____ *(insert month and year).*

(Insert name of Regional Administrator), Occupational Safety and Health Administration, United States Department of Labor

---

APPENDIX B

United States of America

DEPARTMENT OF LABOR Occupational Safety and Health Administration

Subpoena Duces Tecum

I hereby certify that a duplicate original of the attached subpoena was duly served as follows:
in person_____
by leaving at principal office or place of business ___
by registered mail_____ :

(Indicate by check method used.)

_____

on the person named herein on

_____
(Month, day, year) (Name of person making service)

_____
(Official title)
I certify that the person named herein was in attendance as a witness at

_____ _____
on _____
(Month, day or days, and year)

_____
(Name of person certifying)

_____
(Official title 15-26)

Chapter 16 — Disclosure Under The Freedom Of Information Act (FOIA)
I.   **Disclosure [Reserved]**

Appendix I — Answers to Test and Workshops

Answers to General Pre-Test

1. **What are the two basic purposes of the OSH Act of 1970?**
   a. f and h
   b. g and i
   c. g and h
   d. f and I
   f. To eliminate or minimize occupational hazards in the workplace.
   g. To provide a safe and healthful workplace.
   h. To recognize, avoid and control hazards in the workplace.
   i. To conserve human resources.

2. **What is one important effect that Executive Order 12196 has on Federal Agencies?**
   a. Mandates compliance with all standards applicable to private industry, except where alternative standards are approved by the Secretary of Labor.
   b. Mandates that Federal Agencies' programs be consistent with private industry.
   c. Provides for OSHA response to reports of hazardous conditions from employees of any Federal Agency.
   d. Mandates the establishment of Occupational Safety and Health Committees at the national and other appropriate levels.

3. **A confined space supervisor must ensure the following before allowing entry into a confined space.**
   a. Employee's are trained and qualified
   b. The atmosphere has been tested and is safe for entry
   c. A standby attendant is present
   d. All of the above

4. **OSHA regulates the use of compressed air for cleaning purposes. What is the main reason for this and how is it regulated?**
   a. Compressed air can cause increased noise exposure, and this is controlled by the use of sound-dampening nozzles.
   b. Air hoses can rupture causing the hose to "whip" and strike workers. Airlines must be equipped with pressure loss closure valves.
   c. Compressed air blows particles and dust causing eye and pressure with guarding.
   d. Gases in compressed air can be toxic. Filters and gas absorbents must be used on air compressors.

5. **Air purifying respirators are:**
   a. Permitted in oxygen deficient atmospheres
   b. Not permitted in oxygen deficient atmospheres

c. Worn with full beards if the employee will not shave
d. Designed to cool the respirator user

6. **Arc welding refers to the use of an electrical current to produce the weld.**
    a. True
    b. False

7. **What is the purpose of ring-testing abrasive grinding wheels?**
    a. A method of detecting cracks in the wheels.
    b. Checks the wheel diameter to assure proper size and mounting.
    c. Tests the rated capacity (in rpm) for the compatibility of the wheel and grinder.
    d. Checks the abrasive action to assure that older wheels are not overworked.

8. **The 29 CFR 19 10, Subpart N addresses storage and handling of materials. Which of the following does Subpart N not address?**
    a. Flammable storage
    b. Fork lift trucks
    c. Hoisting equipment
    d. Railroad cars

9. **Doors, passageways, and stairways, which are not a means of egress, shall be:**
    a. Clearly marked "NOT AN EXIT"
    b. Locked to prevent entry
    c. Removed to prevent confusion
    d. No action required

10. **The most important factor in the use of hearing protectors is:**
    a. The Noise Reduction Factor published by the vendor
    b. The case hardened shell
    c. The polymeric expanded foam adhesive
    d. The fitting to an employee

11. **The permissible exposure limit set by OSHA for lead is:**
    a. 200 ugh/m3
    b. 20 ugh/m3
    c. 50 ugh/m3
    d. 100 ugh/m3

12. **What is a safety can?**
    a. A tightly sealed metal container used to store corrosive material.
    b. A spring-loaded, self-closing container of 10 gallons or less which will not allow the escape of vapor when heated.
    c. A glass container used to store materials that are corrosive to metal containers.
    d. A spring-loaded, self-closing metal container, 5 gallons or less, that will allow the escape of vapor when heated.

13. **Rolling scaffolds must have guardrails at what height?**
    a. 4 feet
    b. 6 feet
    c. 10 feet
    d. 12 feet

14. **Flammable materials have a flash point of less than _____ degrees F.**
    a. 200
    b. 110
    c. 160
    d. 100

15. **Guardrails must be 42" high with a midrail between the top rail and floor.**
    a. True
    b. False

16. **A spreader must be used whenever cross cutting stock.**
    a. True
    b. False

17. **High pressure compressed gas cylinders can be handled by their protective caps:**
    a. Anytime, that's what the caps are made for
    b. Only when lifting vertically
    c. During transportation and storage
    d. Never, the cap is only designed to protect the valve.

18. **Which of the following is not one of the storage requirement flammable and combustible liquids?**
    a. The quantity of material stored
    b. The types of containers

c. The stacking and arrangement of containers

d. Continuous monitoring for vapor concentration

19. OSHA makes only three basic requirements of employers with regard to Medical and First Aid. What are they?
a. f, g, and h
b. f, g, and j
c. g, h, and j
d. g, h, and I
e. h, 1, and j
f. Availability of ambulance service
g. First Aid
h. Availability of medical personnel
i. Availability of drenching & flushing
j. Personal Protection Equipment

20. A chemical with a skin designation indicates:
a. The chemical may be absorbed into the bloodstream through the skin, the mucous membranes, and/or the eye. This absorption contributes to overall exposure.
b. Skin absorption is the only significant route of exposure; inhalation potential is minimal.
c. All chemicals are readily absorbed through the skin; those chemicals with a skin designation are corrosive or irritating to the skin.
d. All of the above

21. Reverse polarity would be a serious OSHA citation.
a. True
b. False

22. A class "A" GFCI trips at 5 mA plus or minus 1 mA.
a. True
b. False

23. "Medical personnel" as defined by OSHA, may be physicians, nurses, or trained (Red Cross or equivalent) First Aid personnel.
a. True
b. False

24. Which of the following is not a function of foot protection?
a. Protect the foot from crushing
b. Protect the sole of the foot from puncture by nails
c. Electrical protection
d. High visibility with reflective footwear

25. A good disinfectant mixture is 1 part chlorine bleach to _ part(s) water:
a. 1
b. 7
c. 5
d. 10

26. A "Point of Operation" can be described as:
a. The area where a belt and pulley create a nip point
b. The location where the operator stands.
c. The point at which cutting, shaping, boring, or forming is accomplished upon the stock
d. The area of the press where material is actually positioned and work is being performed during any process such as shearing, punching, forming, or assembling.

27. Which of the following devices may be used for overcurrent protection?
a. Circuit Breaker
b. Main Disconnect
c. Fuse
d. GFCI
e. Both A and C

28. Which of the following best describes the term egress as applied by OSHA?
a. The way to, through, and away from an exit.
b. A specially designated exit or escape.
c. A function of the fire protection requirements of a building.
d. Non-portable fire protection, such as a sprinkling system.

29. Water is a good extinguishing agent but should never be used on a Class___ fire.
   a. A
   b. B
   c. C
   d. It can be used on all fires

30. 29 CFR 19 10, Subpart D, covers the safe use of walking and working surfaces. Which of the following is not considered under Subpart D?
   a. Stairways
   b. Ladders
   c. Handrails
   d. Slippery floors
   e. Workbenches

31. Egress (emergency exiting) fundamentals include:
   a. Sufficient exits for occupant load
   b. Illuminated exit markings
   C. Exits not locked or obstructed
   d. All of the above

32. The Hazard Communication standard requires which of the following:
   a. Employees must be provided with a comprehensive medical examination.
   b. Employees must receive training on the hazardous chemicals in their work area.
   c. Each employee must be provided with his/her own set of MSDSs.
   d. All of the above

33. Tongue guards on bench grinders must be adjusted within:
   a. 1/8"
   b. 1/4"
   c. 3/8"
   d. 1/2"

34. Which of the following are not points of operation guards or devices
   a. Photoelectric light curtain
   b. Pullbacks
   c. Emergency pull cord
   d. Two hand controls

35. A worker is using a ladder improperly. Which of the following situations constitutes improper use of a ladder?
   a. An extension ladder is being used in place of a single ladder.
   b. An employee is using a ten-foot stepladder and standing on the next to-the-top step,
   c. A single ladder is leaning against a roof, extending one foot above the roof surface.
   d. An extension ladder is extended to a length of forty feet and the footing is about ten feet from the supporting wall.

Answers to Hazard Violation Search Workshop #1

Description of Hazard	Standard
1. Exit access blocked by pallet. Less than 20 inches width.	1910.36(g)(2)
2. Fire extinguisher (charged) found lying on floor.	1910.157(c)(1)
3. Type BC fire extinguisher used near bales of shredded paper - no type A available	1910.157(d)(1)
4. At some locations in large facility, directions of travel to exit are not apparent.	1910.37(b)(4)
5. No portable fire extinguisher inspection/maintenance program.	1910.157(e)(1)
6. Fixed carbon dioxide extinguishing system not being inspected and tested annually.	1910.160(b)(6)
7. No exit signs anywhere in plant employing 50 employees.	1910.37(b)(2)
8. Exit door blocked from outside.	1910.37(a)(3)

9. Sprinkler heads in storage area -blocked by stacked bags ....1910.159(c)(10)
10. Fire extinguishers obstructed by containers. ....1910,157(c)(1)
11. Exit access door swings against exit travel; ....1910.37(e)(2)
12. No eyewash facility in battery charging area-.. 1910.151(c)
13. Employee observed smoking in a flammable storage area. ....1910.106(d)(7)(iii)
14. Eye protection -items do not meet ANSI requirements. .... 1910.133(a)(6)
15. Respirators required - no training program for users. ....1910.134(e)(5)(i-iii)
16. Baseball caps being worn by maintenance employees replacing take-up
    roller bearing on conveyor while standing on a maintenance catwalk. .... 1910.132(a)
17. Equipment ground prong broken off. ....1910.304(0(5)(v)(C)(3)
18. Forklift being used as a man lift using a standard pallet. 1910.178(m)(12)(i)
19. Permanent aisles in container storage area not marked. .... 1910.176(a)
20. Containers being used for storing flammable liquids -
    not of the approved type. ....1910.106(d)(2)(i)
21. Paint spray booth with electric motor and fan placed inside exhaust duct. ...... 1910.107(d)(5)
22. End attachments on a wire rope sling are cracked and deformed. 1910.184(f)(5)(v)
23. General industrial plant: 150 gallons of toluene (Flashpoint = 45 degrees F, B.P. =
    232 degrees F) stored outside of an inside storage room. ....1910.106(e)(2)(ii)(b)(2)
24. Welding operation being done in paint spray booth. ....1910.107(c)(2)
25. Forklift purchased in 1966, without overhead guard. ....1910.178(e)(1)
26. LP gas dispensing area without "No Smoking " signs. ....1910. 110(h)(1) 2)
27. 150 gallons of Class I liquid stored in a storage cabinet. ....1910.106(d)(3)(i)
28. Forklift operator giving a ride to two personnel on a pallet. ....1910,178(m)(3)
29. The dry filter spray booth had an exhaust of less than 50 L.F.M.......................1910.107(b)(5)(i)
30. Containers used to transfer flammables were not
    bonded to the dispensing drum. ....1910.106(e)(6)(iii)
31. Safety cans containing flammable liquids not
    in red can nor contents identified. ....1910.144(a)(1)(ii); 1910.1200(f)(5)
32. Stairway - 6 risers - no handrail...1910.23(d)(1)
33. Hospital 20 miles away, no employee trained in first aid..1910.151(b)
34. Open-sided floor - 6-foot drop; no guardrails...1910.23(c)(1)
35. Fixed ladder - 30 feet high with no cage guard..1910.27(d)(1)(ii)
36. Wooden extension ladder – ladder safety shoes broken. ....1910.25 (d)(1)(iv)
37. Stairway more than 44 inches wide does not
    have stair rails on open sides. ....1910.23(d)(1)(iv)
38. Opened-sided work platform (less than adjacent to dangerous equipment, not
    guarded with standard railing and toeboard. ....1910.23 (c)(3)
39. Elevated area used for storage has no approved floor loading signs posted
    in a conspicuous place...1910.22(d)(1)
40. Portable dockboard without any securing device to prevent slipping. ....1910.30(a)(2)
41. Stairways with steam pipe 6 feet above stair tread causing overhead obstruction. ..... 1910.24(i)
42. Defective portable wooden ladder with split side rail being used
    in building maintenance operation. ....1910.25(d)(2)(viii)
43. Compressed gas cylinders in storage -no valve protection caps. ....1910.253(b)(2)(iv)
44. Oxygen and fuel-gas cylinders stored together. ....1910.253(b)(4)(i)
45. Respirators not stored in a clean, sanitary location. ....1910.134(b)(6)
46. Arc welding area - work area personnel exposed to rays.   1910.252(b)(2)(iii)
47. Welding electrode cable lead is exposing bare wire.   1910.254(d)(9)(iii)
48. Air receiver not equipped with indicating pressure gage. ....1910.169(b)(3)(i)
49. There is a loose conduit feeding into a fuse box. ....1910.305(a)(1)(i)

50. A powered industrial truck is sitting and idling while its
    operator drinks coffee 200 feet away. .... 1910.178(m)(5)(i)
51. Steel frame of sorter machine not grounded.
    Machine located 3 feet from water pipe.
      1910.304(f)(5)(iv)(A)
52. Hand-held portable electric grinder with no guard. .... 1910.243(c)(3) & (4)
53. Hand-held electric circular saw equipped with a lock-on control switch. .... 1910.243(a)(2)(1)
54. 150 psi air being used for cleaning purposes in machine shop. .... 1910.242(b)
55. Hand-held circular saw being used -no lower blade guard. .... 1910.243(a)(1)(i)
56. Portable electric drill owned by employee had defective switch. .... 1910.242(a)
57. Radial arm saw has lower portion of blade unguarded. .... 1910.213(h)(1)
58. Explosive-actuated fastening tool without a protective shield. .... 1910.243(d)(2)(i)(a)
59. Work rest on bench grinder has ½ inch space between wheel and rest .... 1910.215(a)(4)
60. Employee working in a mechanical equipment room daily
    for eight hours is exposed to 92 dBA. .... 1910.95(a-e)
61. Employer had no energy control (lockout/tagout) procedures. .... 1910.147(c)(1)
62. No guarding provided to protect employees
    from flying chips of a metal lathe .... 1910.133(a)(1) 1910.212(a)(1)

Answers to Hazard Violation Search Workshop #2

(The purpose of the workshop is to stimulate discussion among the students. There is more than one correct answer and some answers are provided here. The student must determine which solution best fits the needs of their organization)

Photo #1

Discrepancy: Workers are exposed to a hazard of falling. In this case one of the companies workers and one of the contractors were conducting a weekly inspection of the cables and antenna system. They would then climb down the ladder, walk across the top of the breezeway, then climb up the other side and inspect on the other building. Temporary ladders are installed incorrectly.

Cited Regulation: Subpart D, Walking and Working Surfaces (see 1910.26(c) (use of ladders) 1910.23(c)(1) protection of open sided floors

Corrective Action: Employee should be retrained on fall hazards Contractor should be advised by the contracting officer that they are in violation of OSHA rules and the terms of the contract which requires them to comply with Federal, state and local regulations and to retrain their workers.

Install guardrails on the roof and a permanent ladder system by using a work order. OR- Simply retrain the workers and have them use each buildings rooftop access system, instead of taking a shortcut across the roof of the breezeway.

Photo #2

Discrepancy: Men standing in the doorway of a loading dock, exposed to a fall of 4 feet.

Cited Regulation: Subpart D, Walking and Working Surfaces 1910.23(c)(1) protection of open sided floors

Corrective Action: Install a guardrail, chain or other approved guard. OR..... close the door.

Photo #3

Discrepancy: At the loading dock the trailer is not chocked.

Cited Regulation: Subpart N, material Handling 1910.178(k)(1)

Corrective Action: Chock the wheel (OSHA letter of interpretation states that chocking one wheel to prevent the vehicle from moving is sufficient)

Photo #4

Discrepancy: Container is labeled gasoline, but is being used as a waste oil or ink receptacle. This is an unlabeled container.

Cited Regulation: Subpart Z, Hazard Communications 1910.1200(f)(5)

Corrective Action: Label container, replace container if necessary

Photo #5

Discrepancy: Blocked egress from the office behind the two workers. Warehouse personnel had stacked material and supplies on pallets in such a way that 28 inches of access was not provided to the office.

Cited Regulation: Subpart E, Exit Routes, Emergency Action Plans and Fire Prevention Plans, 1910.36(g)(2)

Corrective Action: Have warehouse workers move the materials and stack them appropriately.

Photo #6

Discrepancy: Incorrect use of ladders. This self made ladder does not meet the criteria established by OSHA.

Cited Regulation: Subpart D, Walking and Working Surfaces (see 1910.26(c) (use of ladders)

Corrective Action: Have worker disassemble the ladder and remove it from the job site.

Photo #7

Discrepancy: Incorrect use of ladders. This aluminum ladder is in a swimming pool and the man is using a powered drill to drill a hole. The ladder, water and his pants are wet and conductive.

Cited Regulation: (see 1910.26(c) (use of ladders) General Duty Clause

Corrective Action: Retrain the worker, remove the ladder, possibly use battery powered drill.

Photo #8

Discrepancy: Trash and garbage outside the dumpster area. Housekeeping violation.

Cited Regulation: Subpart D, Walking and Working Surfaces 1910.22(a)

Corrective Action: Have workers clean up trash

APPENDIX II —

FEDERAL AGENCY PROGRAMS

COURSE OBJECTIVES

For Federal Supervisor and Collateral Duty Training

The course materials are designed to allow participants to accomplish the following objectives:

- Become familiar with the Occupational Safety and Health Act, 29 CFR 1960, 1910 and relevant Agency policy, interpretations and applications.
- Describe major provisions of the Executive Order 12196.
- Identify selected safety and health hazards and corresponding OSHA Standards.
- Describe abatement methods for selected safety and health hazards.
- Explain and apply workplace inspection procedures consistent with established policies, procedures and directives.

This version of the course material has been revised based upon comments from instructors and students in the field. The original material provided by the OSHA Training Institute in Arlington Heights, Illinois, was of sufficient quality that only minor changes and updates were required. Wherever possible the original intent and content of the 1995 manual has been retained to allow current instructors to remain familiar with the manual that they have been using, as well as to keep the material in the public domain. The material has been field tested with federal employees.

The text is designed to create a flow of educational topics that can enhance the learning process as opposed to requiring participants to page back and forth from one section to another in the book. For example, following a discussion of industrial hygiene in which the student learns about PELs and TWAs, the discussion leads to asbestos, lead and hearing conservation programs to reinforce the use of those industrial hygiene terms. The book begins with an explanation of OSHA, discusses OSHA regulations and builds to industrial hygiene terms and practices. Then the book discusses specific OSHA regulations, how to conduct inspections and how the student would conduct an inspection. Additional information requested by federal workers has been included:

- A discussion of construction versus industrial standards has been inserted.
- A discussion of safety committees has been added to the manual.
- The most frequently cited violations for the most current year available are included.
- Content relating to the Federal Employee Compensation Act is included.
- Risk Management, a practice adopted by most federal agencies, has been added.
- 29CFR1960 is included in the book.
- The OSHA Field Operations Manual has been included.

What Every Federal Manager Needs to Know About OSHA
Supervisor Safety Training for Federal Agencies

Suggested Curriculum
(meets requirements for 29CFR 1960-Collateral Duty for Other Federal Agencies)

TIME	MONDAY	TUESDAY	WEDNESDAY	THURSDAY
8:00 8:50	Opening Remarks Bio Sheets Objectives	Hazard Violation workshop	Hazard Violation workshop	accident investigation and reporting
9:00 9:50	Intro to OSHA, Inspections, Penalties Intro. to OSHA Standards	Subpart Z Hazard Communication 1910.1200	Subpart S: Electrical 29CFR1910.301	Federal Employee compensation act recordkeeping
10:00 10:50	Federal Programs 29CFR1960	Subpart H Hazardous Materials 29CFR1910.101	Subpart S: Electrical (Concluded)	Inspection techniques
11:00 11:45	Introduction to Safety Committees	Subpart L/E Fire Protection 29CFR1910.155 Means of Egress 29cFR1910.36	Subpart O Machine Guarding 29CFR1910.211	Preparation for facility inspection Group work
11:45 12:45	Lunch	Lunch	Lunch	Lunch
12:45 1:35	Subpart D Walking & Working Surfaces 29CFR1910.21	Subpart J Confined Space entry 29CFR1910.146	Subpart J Control of Hazardous Energy 29CFR1910.147	Facility Inspection
1:45 2:35	Subpart Z Introduction to Industrial Hygiene	Welding & Cutting Subpart Q 29CFR1910.252	Subpart P Portable and powered hand tools 29CFR1910.241	Facility Inspection
2:45 3:35	Subpart Z Bloodborne Pathogens 29CFR1910.1030	Subpart I Personal Protective Equipment 29CFR1910.132	Subpart N Material Handling Forklift s 29CFR1910.176	Inspection Write-up & report
3:45 4:30	Subpart G Hearing conservation 29CFR1910.95	Risk Management for federal agencies	Office Safety	Q & A OSHA Rep. Certificate Awards Course Closes

Appendix III —

Federal Agency Safety and Health Programs

The Occupational Safety and Health Act of 1970 was designed "to assure so far as possible every working man and woman in the Nation safe and healthful working conditions and to preserve our human resources."

Section 19 of the Act specifically charges the head of each federal agency with the responsibility to "establish and maintain an effective and comprehensive occupational safety and health program which is consistent with the standards" set by OSHA for private sector employees. This broad mandate is further defined by Presidential Executive Order 12196, which identifies the responsibilities of the agencies and the role of the Secretary of Labor in developing, implementing and evaluating such programs.

The Secretary of Labor also has been assigned broad responsibilities under Section 19 of the Act. Department of Labor regulations (Title 29 Code of Federal Regulations, Part 1960) spell out in detail the responsibilities of the Secretary of Labor and of the heads of other federal agencies under the Act and the Executive Order.

This discussion will provide an overview of Section 19 of the Act, Executive Order 12196, and Part 1960 of Title 29 so that federal employees and managers may be informed of their rights and responsibilities under the Act.

OSHA Act – Section 19

In requiring an effective and comprehensive occupational safety and health program, Section 19 of the OSH Act places a much broader requirement on Federal agency heads than that required of employers in the private sector. Private sector employers must: (1) provide a workplace free of recognized hazards; and, (2) comply with the OSHA standards. However, under Section 19, Federal agency programs must include all aspects of a comprehensive program, not just compliance with the standards. Federal programs must deal with the human element, the workplace environment, training, motivation and attitudes.

Section 19 of the Act further requires agency heads, after consultation with employee representatives, to:

- Provide safe and healthful places and conditions of employment;
- Acquire, maintain and require the use of safety equipment, devices and personal protective equipment;
- Keep appropriate injury and illness records and file an annual report of injuries and illnesses with the Secretary of Labor.

Executive Order 12196

The requirement to have a program "consistent" with OSHA standards (as required by Section 19) was expanded upon by Executive Order 12196 (February 26, 1980), which requires the Agency head to:

- Comply with all standards issued under Section 6 of the Act except where the Secretary approves compliance with alternative standards;
- Provide procedures for adoption of alternative standards.

Additional elements of the Executive Order apply to all agencies of the Executive Branch except unique military equipment and systems. The Executive Order does not apply to the judicial or legislative branches of government. However, since Section 19 of the Act covers all Federal employees, the Secretary of Labor cooperates and consults with the agency heads of these branches to help them adopt safety and health programs.

Executive Order 12196 also:

- Incorporates a General Duty Clause similar to the one in effect in the private sector.

(Two previous Executive Orders did not include this.)

- Requires an Occupational Safety and Health Program, including elements promulgated by the Secretary of Labor (i.e., 29 CFR 1960).
- Requires designation of an official with authority to represent the interest and support of the agency head to be responsible for the management and administration of the agency program.
- Necessitates prompt abatement (or an abatement plan) for unsafe or unhealthy working conditions.
- Establishes a discrimination clause (similar to Section 11(c) in the private sector). This prohibits retribution against employees who file complaints regarding unsafe or unhealthful working conditions.

Under the Executive Order, agency heads must:

- Assure periodic inspection of workplaces.
- Assure prompt response to employee reports of hazardous conditions.
- Assure employee representation during inspections.
- Operate an occupational safety and health management information system.
- Provide safety and health training for supervisors, inspectors, committee members and other employees.

Most of these requirements are similar to those set forth in earlier Executive Orders. However, an area that was not covered previously was that of occupational safety and health committees.

Agency heads may establish certified occupational safety and health committees. If committees are established, they must be at both the national and other appropriate (e.g., regional or local) levels. The committees are to be joint labor-management committees. Agencies with certified committees do not generally receive unannounced OSHA inspections, unless half the members of the committee requests OSHA action.

Committees shall:

- Have access to agency information relative to their duties.
- Monitor performance of agency programs.
- Consult and advise the agency on the operation of the program.

Under the Executive Order, the Secretary of Labor has specific responsibilities, including coordination with other agencies having responsibilities related to Federal employee safety and health and the issuance of a set of basic program elements (29 CFR 1960, October 21, 1980). The Secretary is also required to:

- Prescribe recordkeeping and recording requirements.
- Provide training materials and conduct training.
- Provide technical services.
- Evaluate programs.
- Conduct inspections: when necessary if the agency does not have a certified committee; upon request of a committee; or when a committee fails to respond to an employee's imminent danger report. Inspection results are reported to agency heads and to the safety and health committee.

Executive Order 12196 includes special provisions related to the General Services Administration (GSA). GSA responsibilities include:

- Establishing procedures for resolving conflicting standards for space leased by GSA.
- Requiring GSA personnel to accompany the OSHA inspector on inspections of facilities subject to GSA authority
- Assuring prompt attention to reports of unsafe or unhealthy conditions in facilities subject to the authority of GSA.
- Providing safe supplies, devices and equipment to other agencies and maintaining a product safety program.

29 CFR 1960

The third major reference concerning Federal Agency safety and health programs is 29 CFR 1960 — Basic Program Elements for Federal Employee OSH Programs and Related Matters. Agency heads are required to operate their programs in accordance with the basic elements. However, there is flexibility so that agencies can implement their programs in a manner consistent with their mission, size and organization. There are 11 subparts in Part 1960, Subparts A–K:

Subpart A — General
Subpart B — Administration
Subpart C — Standards
Subpart D — Inspection and Abatement

Subpart E — General Services Administration and Other Federal Agencies

Subpart F — Occupational Safety and Health Committees

Subpart G — Allegations of Reprisal

Subpart H — Training

Subpart I — Recordkeeping and Reporting Requirements

Subpart J — Evaluation of Federal Occupational Safety & Health Programs

Subpart K — Field Federal Safety and Health Councils

In Subpart B, Agency Responsibilities (1960.8) states that each agency head is required to comply with the governmental equivalent of Sections 5(a)(1) and 5(a)(2) (the General Duty Clause and standards) and, as noted in Section 19 of the Act, develop, implement and evaluate a comprehensive program. The Federal program specifically extends the General Duty Clause and standards requirements to supervisors "to the extent of their authority" (1960.9). The 5(b) requirement in the private sector (regarding employee responsibilities) has its counterpart in 1960.10, with a specific addition relating to use of safety equipment.

Subpart C, Standards, requires compliance with OSHA standards or approved alternative standards.

Subpart D covers Inspection and Abatement. 1960.25 contains the important requirement relating to frequency of inspections. All areas and operations of each workplace, including offices, must be inspected annually. Where there is an increased risk of accident or illness due to the work performed, more frequent inspections are required. The conduct of inspections, covering preparation, inspection procedures and the written report is dealt with in 1960.26. The guidelines for employee reporting of hazards are found in 1960.28. Section 1960.31 outlines the situations where OSHA would conduct an unannounced inspection.

Special provisions concerning GSA and NIOSH are covered in Subpart E, 1960.34 and 35.

Subpart F deals with Occupational Safety and Health Committees, their purpose and functions. Ideally, such committees can perform a valuable function by maintaining an open channel of communication between employees and management concerning safety and health matters.

An important provision related to reprisals is contained in Subpart G. This Subpart incorporates the Federal equivalent of Section 11(c) of the OSH Act. It provides that employees not be subject to restraint, interference, coercion, discrimination or reprisal for their participation in the agency's safety and health program.

Subpart H deals with safety and health training. The type of training required for top management, supervisors, safety and health specialists, inspectors, employees with collateral duties, committee members and employee representatives are spelled out in this Subpart.

Subpart I covers Recordkeeping and Reporting Requirements. Federal agency recordkeeping and posting requirements differ from private sector requirements. The Federal agency requirements are outlined in "Recordkeeping and Reporting Guidelines for Federal Agencies," OSHA Publication 2014.

Evaluation of Federal Occupational Safety and Health Programs is outlined in Subpart J. Agency heads are responsible for conducting self-evaluations of their safety and health programs and the Secretary of Labor - OSHA is responsible for evaluating the extent to which each agency head has developed and implemented agency programs.

The final subpart of 29 CFR 1960, Subpart K, covers Field Federal Safety and Health Councils. Guidelines for establishing councils, membership and participation, and operating procedures are provided.

Executive Order 12196, signed by President Carter, requires federal agencies to:
- Comply with the Act
- Assure periodic inspections
- Provide safety training for employees
- Operate a safety management information system.

U.S. Department of Labor Program Highlights
Fact Sheet No. OSHA 89-20
OCCUPATIONAL SAFETY AND HEALTH FOR FEDERAL EMPLOYEES

The Occupational Safety and Health Act of 1970 was designed "to assure so far as possible every working man and woman in the Nation safe and healthful working conditions and to preserve our human resources."

There are more than 3.1 million federal civilian employees in more than 100 departments and agencies across the country. Each year thousands of these employees are injured, made ill, or die in work-related incidents.

For example, in fiscal 1988, more than 165,000 occupational injuries and illnesses occurred, involving civilian federal employees. Beyond the human implications of these statistics, this takes its toll on the American taxpayer. Chargeback billings of federal agencies arising from the injuries and illnesses suffered by federal employees totaled more than $1.1 billion in 1988.

To focus on this problem, Section 19 of the Act specifically charges the head of each federal agency with the responsibility to "establish and maintain an effective and comprehensive occupational safety and health program which is consistent with the standards" set by OSHA for private sector employees.

Presidential Executive Order 12196 that identifies the responsibilities of the agencies and the role of the Secretary of Labor in developing, implementing and evaluating such programs further defines that broad mandate.

The Secretary of Labor also has been assigned broad responsibilities under Section 19 of the Act. Department of Labor regulations (Title 29 Code of Federal Regulations Part 1960) spell out in detail the responsibilities of the Secretary of Labor and of the heads of other federal agencies under the Act and the Executive Order.

Agency Responsibilities:
- To furnish to employees places and conditions of employment that are free from recognized hazards that are causing or are likely to cause death or serious physical harm.
- To set up procedures for responding to employee reports of unsafe and unhealthful working conditions.
- To acquire, maintain, and require the use of approved personal protective equipment and safety equipment.
- To inspect all workplaces at least annually with participation by representatives of employees.
- To establish procedures to assure that no employee is subject to restraint, coercion, discrimination, or reprisal for exercising his/her rights under the safety and health program.
- To post notices of unsafe or unhealthful working conditions found during Inspections
- To assure prompt abatement of hazardous conditions. Employees exposed to the conditions shall be informed of the abatement plan. Imminent danger corrections must be made immediately.
- To set up a management information system to keep records of occupational accidents, injuries, illnesses, and their causes; and to post annual summaries of injuries and illnesses for a minimum of 30 days at each establishment.
- To conduct occupational safety and health training programs for top management, supervisors, safety and health personnel, employees and employee representatives.

Employee Responsibilities:
- To comply with all OSHA and approved agency occupational safety and health standards.
- To comply with agency policies and directives relative to the safety and health program.
- To use personal protective equipment and safety equipment provided by the agency.

Rights of Employees and their Representatives:
- To participate in their agency's safety and health program. Employees shall be authorized official time to participate in the activities provided by Executive Order 12196, 29 CFR Part 1960 and the agency's safety and health program.

- To have access to agency safety and health information including data on hazardous substances in agency workplaces.
- To comment on standards their agency proposes that differ from OSHA standards.
- To report and request inspections of unsafe or unhealthful working conditions to the appropriate officials, including the Secretary of Labor. However, the Secretary of Labor encourages employees to use agency procedures for reporting hazardous conditions as the most expeditious means to achieve abatement.

For more information, call OSHA's Office of Federal Agency Programs at (202) 523-8081.

---

29 CFR Part 1960
BASIC PROGRAM ELEMENTS FOR FEDERAL EMPLOYEE OCCUPATIONAL SAFETY AND HEALTH PROGRAMS AND RELATED MATTERS

Subpart A — General
1960.1 Purpose and scope.
1960.2 Definitions.

Subpart B — Administration
1960.6 Designation of agency safety and health officials.
1960.7 Financial management.
1960.8 Agency responsibilities.
1960.9 Supervisory responsibilities.
1960.10 Employee responsibilities and rights.
1960.11 Evaluation of occupational safety and health performance.
1960.12 Dissemination of occupational safety and health program information.

Subpart C — Standards
1960.16 Compliance with OSHA standards.
1960.17 Alternate standards.
1960.18 Supplementary standards.
1960.19 Other Federal agency standards affecting occupational safety and health.

Subpart D — Inspection and Abatement
1960.25 Qualifications of safety and health inspectors and agency inspections.
1960.26 Conduct of inspections.
1960.27 Representatives of officials in charge and representatives of employees.
1960.28 Employee reports of unsafe or unhealthful working conditions.
1960.29 Accident investigation.
1960.30 Abatement of unsafe or unhealthful working conditions.
1960.31 Inspections by OSHA.

Subpart E — General Services Administration and Other Federal Agencies
1960.34 General provisions.
1960.35 National Institute for Occupational Safety and Health.

Subpart F — Occupational Safety and Health Committees
1960.36 General provisions.
1960.37 Committee organization.
1960.38 Committee formation.
1960.39 Agency responsibilities.
1960.40 Establishment committee duties.
1960.41 National committee duties.

Subpart G — Allegations of Reprisal
1960.46 Agency responsibility.
1960.47 Results of investigation.

Subpart H — Training
1960.54 Training of top management officials.
1960.55 Training of supervisors.
1960.56 Training of safety and health specialists.
1960.57 Training of safety and health inspectors.
1960.58 Training of collateral duty safety and health personnel and committee members.
1960.59 Training of employees and employee representative.
1960.60 Training assistance.

Subpart I — Recordkeeping and Reporting Requirements
1960.66 Purpose, scope and general provisions.
1960.67 Log of occupational injuries and illnesses.
1960.68 Supplementary record of occupational injuries and illnesses.

1960.69 Annual summaries of Federal occupational injuries and illnesses.
1960.70 Reporting of serious Accidents.
1960.71 Location and utilization of records and reports.
1960.72 Access to records by Secretary.
1960.73 Retention of records.
1960.74 Agency annual reports.
1960.75 – 1960.77 [Reserved]

Subpart J — Evaluation of Federal Occupational Safety and Health Programs
1960.78 Purpose and scope.
1960.79 Self-evaluations of occupational safety and health programs.
1960.80 Secretary's evaluations of agency occupational safety and health programs.

Subpart K — Field Federal Safety and Health Councils
1960.84 Purpose.
1960.85 Role of Secretary.
1960.86 Establishing councils.
1960.87 Objectives.
1960.88 Membership and participation.
1960.89 Organization.
1960.90 Operating procedures.

Subpart A—General
§ 1960.1 Purpose and scope.
(a) Section 19 of the Occupational Safety and Health Act (the Act) contains special provisions to assure safe and healthful working conditions for Federal employees. Under that section, it is the responsibility of the head of each Federal agency to establish and maintain an effective and comprehensive occupational safety and health program which is consistent with the standards promulgated under section 6 of the Act. The Secretary of Labor (the Secretary), under section 19, is to report to the President certain evaluations and recommendations with respect to the programs of the various agencies, and the duties which section 24 of the Act imposes on the Secretary of Labor necessarily extend to the collection, compilation and analysis of occupational safety and health statistics from the Federal Government. The role of the General Services Administration in this area stems from its duties as the Government's principal landlord and from its specific safety and health responsibilities under 41 CFR part 101, subchapter D, Federal Property Management Regulations.

(b) Executive Order 12196, Occupational Safety and Health Programs for Federal Employees, issued February 26, 1980, prescribes additional responsibilities for the heads of agencies, the Secretary, and the General Services Administrator. Among other duties, the Secretary is required to issue basic program elements in accordance with which the heads of agencies shall operate their safety and health programs. The purpose of this part is to issue these basic program elements. Although agency heads are required to operate a program in accordance with the basic program elements, those elements contain numerous provisions which, by their terms, permit agency heads the flexibility necessary to implement their programs in a manner consistent with their respective missions, sizes, and organizations. Moreover, an agency head, after consultation with agency employees or their representatives and with appropriate safety and health committees may request the Secretary to consider approval of alternate program elements; the Secretary, after consultation with the Federal Advisory Council on Occupational Safety and Health, may approve such alternate program elements.

(c) Under Executive Order 12196, the Secretary is required to perform various services for the agencies, including consultation, training, recordkeeping, inspections, and evaluations. Agencies are encouraged to seek such assistance from the Secretary as well as advice on how to comply with the basic program elements and operate effective occupational safety and health programs. Upon the request of an Agency, the Office of Federal Agency Safety and Health Programs will review proposed agency plans for the implementation of program elements.

(d) Section 19 of the Act and the Executive Order require specific opportunities for employee participation in the operation of agency safety and health programs. The manner of fulfilling these requirements is set forth in part in these program elements. These requirements are separate from but consistent with the Federal Service Labor Management Relations

Statute (5 U.S.C. 71) and regulations dealing with labor-management relations within the Federal Government.

(e) Executive Order 12196 and these basic program elements apply to all agencies of the Executive Branch. They apply to all Federal employees. They apply to all working conditions of Federal employees except those involving uniquely military equipment, systems, and operations.

(f) No provision of the Executive Order or this part shall be construed in any manner to relieve any private employer, including Federal contractors, or their employees of any rights or responsibilities under the provisions of the Act, including compliance activities conducted by the Department of Labor or other appropriate authority.

(g) Federal employees who work in establishments of private employers are covered by their agencies' occupational safety and health programs. Although an agency may not have the authority to require abatement of hazardous conditions in a private sector workplace, the agency head must assure safe and healthful working conditions for his/her employees. This shall be accomplished by administrative controls, personal protective equipment, or withdrawal of Federal employees from the private sector facility to the extent necessary to assure that the employees are protected.

[45 FR 69798, Oct. 21, 1980, as amended at 60 FR 34852, July 5, 1995]

§ 1960.2 Definitions.

(a) The term *Act* means the Occupational Safety and Health Act of 1970 (84 Stat. 1590 *et seq.*, 29 U.S.C. 651 et seq.).

(b) The term *agency* for the purposes of this part means an Executive Department, as defined in 5 U.S.C. 101, or any employing unit or authority of the Executive Branch of the Government. For the purposes of this part to the extent it implements section 19 of the Act, the term *agency* includes the United States Postal Service. By agreement between the Secretary of Labor and the head of an agency of the Legislative or Judicial Branches of the Government, these regulations may be applicable to such agencies.

(c) The term *agency liaison* means an agency person appointed with full authority and responsibility to represent the occupant agency management with the official in charge of a facility or installation such as a GSA Building Manager.

(d) The term *building manager* means the person who manages one or several buildings under the authority of a Federal agency. For example, a building manager may be the GSA person who manages building(s) for GSA.

(e) As used in Executive Order 12196, the term *consultation with representatives of the employees thereof* shall include such consultation, conference, or negotiation with representatives of agency employees as is consistent with the Federal Service Labor Management Relations Statute (5 U.S.C. 71), or collective bargaining or other labor-management arrangements. As used in this part, the term *representative of employees* shall be interpreted with due regard for any obligation imposed by the aforementioned statute and any other labor-management arrangement that may cover the employees involved.

(f) The term *Designated Agency Safety and Health Official* means the individual who is responsible for the management of the safety and health program within an agency, and is so designated or appointed by the head of the agency pursuant to §1960.6 and the provisions of Executive Order 12196.

(g) The term *employee* as used in this part means any person, other than members of the Armed Forces, employed or otherwise suffered, permitted, or required to work by an *agency* as the latter term is defined in paragraph (b) of this section.

(h) The term *establishment* means a single physical location where business is conducted or where services or operations are performed. Where distinctly separate activities are performed at a single physical location, each activity shall be treated as a separate *establishment*. Typically, an *establishment* as used in this part refers to a field activity, regional office, area office, installation, or facility.

(i) The term *uniquely military equipment, systems, and operations* excludes from the scope of the order the design of Department of Defense equipment and systems that are unique to the national defense mission, such as military aircraft, ships, submarines, missiles, and missile sites, early warning systems, military space systems, artillery, tanks, and tactical vehicles; and excludes operations that are uniquely military such as field maneuvers, naval operations, military flight operations, associated research test and development activities, and actions required under emergency conditions. The term includes within the scope of the Order Department of Defense workplaces and operations comparable to those of industry in the private sector such as: Vessel, aircraft, and vehicle repair, overhaul, and modification (except for equipment trials); construction; supply services; civil engineering or public works; medical services; and office work.

(j) The term *incidence rates* means the number of injuries and illnesses, or lost workdays, per 100 full-time workers. Rates are calculated as

$N \times 200,000 \div EH$ N = number of injuries and illnesses, or number of lost workdays. EH = total hours worked by all employees during a month, a quarter, or fiscal year. 200,000 = base for 100 full-time equivalent workers (working 40 hours per week, 50 weeks per year).

(k) The term *inspection* means a comprehensive survey of all or part of a workplace in order to detect safety and health hazards. Inspections are normally performed during the regular work hours of the agency, except as special circumstances may require. Inspections do not include routine, day-to-day visits by agency occupational safety and health personnel, or routine workplace surveillance of occupational health conditions.

(l) *Categories of injuries/illnesses/fatalities*—(1) *Injury (Traumatic)*. A wound or other condition of the body caused by external force, including stress or strain. The injury is identifiable as to time and place of occurrence and member or function of the body affected, and is caused by a specific event or incident or series of events or incidents within a single day or work shift.

(2) *Illness/disease (occupational)*. A physiological harm or loss of capacity produced by systemic infection; continued or repeated stress or strain; exposure to toxins, poisons, fumes, etc.; or other continued and repeated exposures to conditions of the work environment over a long period of time. For practical purposes, an occupational illness/disease is any reported condition which does not meet the definition of injury (traumatic).

(3) *Fatality*. Death resulting from an injury (traumatic) or illness/disease (occupational).

(4) The term *lost time case* means a nonfatal traumatic injury that causes any loss of time from work beyond the day or shift it occurred; or a nonfatal nontraumatic illness/disease that causes disability at any time.

(5) *No-lost time case*. A nonfatal injury (traumatic) or illness/disease (occupational) that does not meet the definition of lost time case.

(6) *Catastrophe*. An accident resulting in five or more agency and/or nonagency people being hospitalized for inpatient care.

(m) The term *representative of management* means a supervisor or management official as defined in the applicable labor-management relations program covering the affected employees.

(n)–(p) [Reserved]

(q) The term *Safety and Health Inspector* means a safety and/or occupational health specialist or other person authorized pursuant to Executive Order 12196, section 1–201(g), to carry out inspections for the purpose of subpart D of this part, a person having equipment and competence to recognize safety and/or health hazards in the workplace.

(r) The term *Safety and Health Official* means an individual who manages the occupational safety and/or occupational health program at organizational levels below the Designated Agency Safety and Health Official.

(s) The term *Safety and Health Specialist* means a person or persons meeting the Office of Personnel Management standards for such occupations, which include but are not limited to:

Safety and Occupational Health Manager/Specialist GS–018 Safety Engineer GS–803 Fire Prevention Engineer GS–804 Industrial Hygienist GS–690 Fire Protection and Prevention Specialist/Marshal GS–081 Health Physicist GS–1306 Occupational Medicine Physician GS–602 Occupational Health Nurse GS–610 Safety Technician GS–019 Physical Science Technician GS–1311 Environmental Health Technician GS–699 Air Safety Investigation Officer GS–1815 Aviation Safety Specialist GS–1825 Chemist GS–1320 Health Technician GS–645 Highway Safety Manager GS–2125 or equally qualified military, agency, or non-government personnel. The agency head shall be responsible for determination and certification of equally qualified personnel.

(t) The term *workplace* means a physical location where the agency's work or operations are performed.

(u) The term *imminent danger* means any conditions or practices in any workplace which are such that a danger exists which could reasonably be expected to cause death or serious physical harm immediately or before the imminence of such danger can be eliminated through normal procedures.

(v) The word *serious* as used in *serious hazard, serious violation* or *serious condition* means a hazard, violation or condition such that there is a substantial probability that death or serious physical harm could result.

(w) The term *certified safety and health committee* means an agency safety and health committee that meets the provisions of section 1-3 of Executive Order 12196 and of this part, as listed and attested to by the head of each agency in writing to the Secretary.

(x) The term *reprisal* as used in this part means any act of restraint, interference, coercion or discrimination against an employee for exercising his or her rights under Executive Order 12196 and this part, or for participating in the agency's safety and health program.

[45 FR 69798, Oct. 21, 1980, as amended at 49 FR 3078, Jan. 25, 1984; 50 FR 40269, Oct. 2, 1985; 51 FR 28378, Aug. 7, 1986]

Subpart B—Administration

§ 1960.6 Designation of agency safety and health officials.

(a) The head of each agency shall designate an official with sufficient authority and responsibility to represent effectively the interest and support of the agency head in the management and administration of the agency occupational safety and health program. This Designated Agency Safety and Health Official should be of the rank of Assistant Secretary, or of equivalent rank, or equivalent degree of responsibility, and shall have sufficient headquarters staff with the necessary training and experience. The headquarters staff should report directly to, or have appropriate access to, the Designated Agency Safety and Health Official, in order to carry out the responsibilities under this part.

(b) The Designated Agency Safety and Health Official shall assist the agency head in establishing:

(1) An agency occupational safety and health policy and program to carry out the provisions of section 19 of the Act, Executive Order 12196, and this part;

(2) An organization, including provision for the designation of safety and health officials at appropriate levels, with adequate budgets and staffs to implement the occupational safety and health program at all operational levels;

(3) A set of procedures that ensures effective implementation of the agency policy and program as required by section 19 of the Act, Executive Order 12196, and the program elements of this part, considering the mission, size, and organization of the agency;

(4) Goals and objectives for reducing and eliminating occupational accidents, injuries, and illnesses;

(5) Plans and procedures for evaluating the agency's occupational safety and health program effectiveness at all operational levels; and

(6) Priorities with respect to the factors which cause occupational accidents, injuries, and illnesses in the agency's workplaces so that appropriate corrective actions can be taken.

(c) The agency head shall assure that safety and health officials are designated at each appropriate level with sufficient authority and responsibility to plan for and assure funds for necessary safety and health staff, equipment, materials, and training required to ensure implementation of an effective occupational safety and health program.

§ 1960.7 Financial management.

(a) The head of each agency shall ensure that the agency budget submission includes appropriate financial and other resources to effectively implement and administer the agency's occupational safety and health program.

(b) The Designated Agency Safety and Health Official, management officials in charge of each establishment, safety and health officials at all appropriate levels, and other management officials shall be responsible for planning, requesting resources, implementing, and evaluating the occupational safety and health program budget in accordance with the regulations of the Office of Management and Budget Circular A–11 (sections 13.2(f) and 13.5(f)) and other relevant documents.

(c) Appropriate resources for an agency's occupational safety and health program shall include, but not be limited to:

(1) Sufficient personnel to implement and administer the program at all levels, including necessary administrative costs such as training, travel, and personal protective equipment;

(2) Abatement of unsafe or unhealthful working conditions related to agency operations or facilities;

(3) Safety and health sampling, testing, and diagnostic and analytical tools and equipment, including laboratory analyses;

(4) Any necessary contracts to identify, analyze, or evaluate unsafe or unhealthful working conditions and operations;

(5) Program promotional costs such as publications, posters, or films;

(6) Technical information, documents, books, standards, codes, periodicals, and publications; and

(7) Medical surveillance programs for employees.

§ 1960.8 Agency responsibilities.

(a) The head of each agency shall furnish to each employee employment and a place of employment which are free from recognized hazards that are causing or are likely to cause death or serious physical harm.

(b) The head of each agency shall comply with the Occupational Safety and Health Administration standards applicable to the agency.

(c) The head of each agency shall develop, implement, and evaluate an occupational safety and health program in accordance with the requirements of section 19 of the Act, Executive Order 12196, and the basic program elements prescribed in this part, or approved alternate program elements.

(d) The head of each agency shall acquire, maintain, and require the use of approved personal protective equipment, approved safety equipment, and other devices necessary to protect employees.

(e) In order to provide essential specialized expertise, agency heads shall authorize safety and health personnel to utilize such expertise from whatever source available, including but not limited to other agencies, professional groups, consultants, universities, labor organizations, and safety and health committees.

§ 1960.9 Supervisory responsibilities.

Employees who exercise supervisory functions shall, to the extent of their authority, furnish employees employment and a place of employment which are free from recognized hazards that are causing or are likely to cause death or serious physical harm. They shall also comply with the occupational safety and health standards applicable to their agency and with all rules, regulations, and orders issued by the head of the agency with respect to the agency occupational safety and health program.

§ 1960.10 Employee responsibilities and rights.

(a) Each employee shall comply with the standards, rules, regulations, and orders issued by his/her agency in accordance with section 19 of the Act, Executive Order 12196, and this part which are applicable to his/her own actions and conduct.

(b) Employees shall use safety equipment, personal protective equipment, and other devices and procedures provided or directed by the agency and necessary for their protection.

(c) Employees shall have the right to report unsafe and unhealthful working conditions to appropriate officials.

(d) Employees shall be authorized official time to participate in the activities provided for in section 19 of the Act, Executive Order 12196, this part, and the agency occupational safety and health program.

§ 1960.11 Evaluation of occupational safety and health performance.

Each agency head shall ensure that any performance evaluation of any management official in charge of an establishment, any supervisory employee, or other appropriate management official, measures that employee's performance in meeting requirements of the agency occupational safety and health program, consistent with the employee's assigned responsibilities and authority, and taking into consideration any applicable regulations of the Office of Personnel Management or other appropriate authority. The recognition of superior performance in discharging safety and health responsibilities by an individual or group should be encouraged and noted.

§ 1960.12 Dissemination of occupational safety and health program information.

(a) Copies of the Act, Executive Order 12196, program elements published in this part, details of the agency's occupational safety and health program, and applicable safety and health standards shall be made available upon request to employees or employee representatives for review.

(b) A copy of the agency's written occupational safety and health program applicable to the establishment shall be made available to each supervisor, each occupational safety and health committee member, and to employee representatives.

(c) Each agency shall post conspicuously in each establishment, and keep posted, a poster informing employees of the provisions of the Act, Executive Order 12196, and the agency occupational safety and health program under this part. The Department of Labor will furnish the core text of a poster to agencies. Each agency shall add the following items:

(1) Details of the agency's procedures for responding to reports by employees of unsafe or unhealthful working conditions, and to allegations of discrimination or reprisal due to participation in safety and/or health activities;

(2) The location where employees may obtain information about the agency's occupational safety and health program, including the full text of agency occupational safety and health standards, and

(3) Relevant information about any agency safety and health committees.

Such posters and additions shall not be altered, defaced, or covered by other material.

(d) A copy of the agency's poster shall be provided to the Secretary. If the agency needs assistance and advice on the content and development of the poster, such shall be requested of the Secretary prior to printing and distribution.

(e) Agency heads shall promote employee awareness of occupational safety and health matters through their ordinary information channels, such as newsletters, bulletins and handbooks.

Subpart C—Standards
§ 1960.16 Compliance with OSHA standards.

Each agency head shall comply with all occupational safety and health standards issued under section 6 of the Act, or with alternate standards issued pursuant to this subpart. In complying with section 6 standards, an agency may, upon prior notification to the Secretary, prescribe and enforce more stringent permissible exposure levels or threshold limit values and may require more frequent monitoring of exposures without recourse to the approval procedures for alternate standards described in § 1960.17. In addition, after consultation with employees and safety and health committees and prior notification to the Secretary, an agency may utilize the latest edition of a reference standard if it is more stringent than the section 6 standard. After notification, the Secretary may require the use of the approval procedures for alternate standards for any of the situations described in this paragraph.

§ 1960.17 Alternate standards.

An agency head may apply an alternate standard where deemed necessary, and shall, after consultation with employees or their representatives, including appropriate occupational safety and health committees, notify the Secretary and request approval of such alternate standards.

(a) Any request by the head of the agency for an alternate standard shall be transmitted to the Secretary.

(b) Any such request for an alternate standard shall not be approved by the Secretary unless it provides equivalent or greater protection for affected employees. Any such request shall include:

(1) A statement of why the agency cannot comply with the OSHA standard or wants to adopt an alternate standard;

(2) A description of the alternate standard;

(3) An explanation of how the alternate standard provides equivalent or greater protection for the affected employees;

(4) A description of interim protective measures afforded employees until a decision is rendered by the Secretary of Labor; and

(5) A summary of written comments, if any, from interested employees, employee

representatives, and occupational safety and health committees.

§ 1960.18 Supplementary standards.

(a) In addition to complying with emergency temporary standards issued under section 6 of the Act, an agency head shall adopt such emergency temporary and permanent supplementary standards as necessary and appropriate for application to working conditions of agency employees for which there exists no appropriate OSHA standards. In order to avoid any possible duplication of effort, the agency head should notify the Secretary of the subject matter of such standard when the development of the standard begins.

(b) The agency head shall send a copy of the final draft of the permanent supplementary standard to the Secretary prior to official adoption by the agency, along with any written comments on the standard from interested employees, employee representatives, and occupational safety and health committees. If the Secretary finds the permanent supplementary standard to be adopted inconsistent with OSHA standards, or inconsistent with OSHA enforcement practices under section 5(a)(1) of the Act, the Secretary shall have 15 working days in which to notify the head of the agency of this finding. In such a case, the supplementary standard shall not be adopted, but the agency will be afforded an opportunity to resubmit a revised standard that is designed to provide adequate protection and is consistent with OSHA standards. Upon request of the agency head, the Secretary shall offer to the agency technical assistance in the development of the supplemental standard.

§ 1960.19 Other Federal agency standards affecting occupational safety and health.

(a) Where employees of different agencies engage in joint operations, and/or primarily report to work or carry out operations in the same establishment, the standards adopted under § 1960.17 or § 1960.18 of the host agency shall govern.

(b) There are situations in which the head of an agency is required to comply with standards affecting occupational safety and health issued by a Federal agency other than OSHA. For example, standards issued by the Federal Aviation Administration, the Department of Energy, or the General Services Administration may be applicable to certain Federal workplaces. Nothing in this subpart affects the duty of any agency head to comply with such standards. In addition, agency heads should comply with other standards issued by Federal agencies which deal with hazardous working conditions, but for which OSHA has no standards.

(c) Although it is not anticipated that standards of other Federal agencies will conflict with OSHA standards, should such conflict occur, the head of the agency shall inform the other Federal agency and the Secretary so that joint efforts to resolve the issues may be undertaken. However, until conflicts are resolved, agencies shall comply with the more protective of the conflicting standards.

Subpart D—Inspection and Abatement
§ 1960.25 Qualifications of safety and health inspectors and agency inspections.

(a) Executive Order 12196 requires that each agency utilize as inspectors "personnel with equipment and competence to recognize hazards." Inspections shall be conducted by inspectors qualified to recognize and evaluate hazards of the working environment and to suggest general abatement procedures. Safety and health specialists as defined in § 1960.2(s), with experience and/or up-to-date training in occupational safety and health hazard recognition and evaluation are considered as meeting the qualifications of safety and health inspectors. For those working environments where there are less complex hazards, such safety and health specializations as cited above may not be required, but inspectors in such environments shall have sufficient documented training and/or experience in the safety and health hazards of the workplace involved to recognize and evaluate those particular hazards and to suggest general abatement procedures. All inspection personnel must be provided the equipment necessary to conduct a thorough inspection of the workplace involved.

(b) Each agency which has workplaces containing information classified in the interest of national security shall provide access to safety and health inspectors who have obtained the appropriate security clearance.

(c) All areas and operations of each workplace, including office operations, shall be inspected at least annually. More frequent inspections shall be conducted in all workplaces where there is an increased risk of accident, injury, or illness due to the nature of the work performed. Sufficient unannounced inspections and unannounced follow-up inspections should be conducted by the agency to ensure the identification and abatement of hazardous conditions.

(d) When situations arise involving multiple agencies' responsibilities for conditions affecting employee safety and health, coordination of inspection functions is encouraged.

§ 1960.26 Conduct of inspections.

(a) *Preparation.* (1) Prior to commencement of the inspection, the Safety and Health Inspector shall be provided all available relevant information which pertains to the occupational safety and health of the workplace to be inspected, including safety and health hazard reports, injury and illness records, previous inspection reports, and reports of unsafe and unhealthful working conditions.

(2) The Safety and Health Inspector shall determine in advance, where possible, the actual work procedures and conditions to be inspected, in order to have the proper equipment available to conduct an effective inspection.

(b) *Inspection.* (1) For the purpose of assuring safe and healthful working conditions for employees of agencies, the head of the agency shall authorize safety and/or health inspectors: To enter without delay, and at reasonable times, any building, installation, facility, construction site, or other area, workplace, or environment where work is performed by employees of the agency; to inspect and investigate during regular working hours and at other reasonable times, and within reasonable limits and in a reasonable manner, any such place of employment and all pertinent conditions, structures, machines, apparatus, devices, equipment, and materials therein, and to question privately any agency employee, and/or any agency supervisory employee, and/or any official in charge of an establishment.

(2) If there are no authorized representatives of employees, the inspector shall consult with a reasonable number of employees during the walkaround.

(3) When, in the opinion of the inspector, it is necessary to conduct personal monitoring (sampling) of employee's work environments,

the inspector may request employees to wear reasonable and necessary personal monitoring devices, e.g., noise dosimeters and air sampling pumps, for periods determined by the inspector to be necessary for complete and effective sampling of the environment.

(4) Upon request of the inspector, the employer shall encourage employees to wear the personal environmental monitoring devices during an inspection.

(5) Whenever and as soon as it is concluded on the basis of an inspection that a danger exists which could reasonably be expected to cause death or serious physical harm immediately, the inspector shall inform the affected employees and official in charge of the workplace of the danger. The official in charge of the workplace, or a person empowered to act for that official, shall undertake immediate abatement and the withdrawal of employees who are not necessary for abatement of the dangerous conditions. In the event the official in charge of the workplace needs assistance to undertake full abatement, that official shall promptly contact the Designated Agency Safety and Health Official and other responsible agency officials, who shall assist the abatement effort. Safety and health committees shall be informed of all relevant actions and representatives of the employees shall be so informed.

(6) At the conclusion of an inspection, the Safety and Health Inspector shall confer with the official in charge of the workplace or that official's representative, and with an appropriate representative of the employees of the establishment, and informally advise them of any apparent unsafe or unhealthful working conditions disclosed by the inspection. During any such conference, the official in charge of the workplace and the employee representative shall be afforded an opportunity to bring to the attention of the Safety and Health Inspector any pertinent information regarding conditions in the workplace.

(c) *Written reports and notices of unsafe or unhealthful working conditions.* (1) The inspector shall, in writing, describe with particularity the procedures followed in the inspection and the findings which form the basis for the issuance of any Notice of Unsafe or Unhealthful Working Conditions.

(2) Each agency shall establish a procedure for the prompt issuance of a Notice of Unsafe or Unhealthful Working Conditions. Such notices shall be issued not later than 15 days after completion of the inspection for safety violations or not later than 30 days for health violations. If there are compelling reasons why such notice cannot be issued within the 15 days or 30 days indicated, the persons described in paragraph (c)(2)(iii) of this section shall be informed of the reasons for the delay. Such procedure shall include the following:

(i) Notices shall be in writing and shall describe with particularity the nature and degree of seriousness of the unsafe or unhealthful working condition, including a reference to the standard or other requirement involved;

(ii) The notice shall fix a reasonable time for the abatement of the unsafe or unhealthful working condition; and

(iii) A copy of the notice shall be sent to the official in charge of the workplace, the employee representative who participated in the closing conference, and/or the safety and health committee of the workplace, if any.

(3) Upon receipt of any notice of an unsafe or unhealthful working condition, the official in charge of a workplace shall immediately post such notice, or copy thereof, unedited, except for reason of national security, at or near each place an unsafe or unhealthful working condition referred to in the notice exists or existed. In addition, a notice shall be posted if any special procedures are in effect. Where, because of the nature of the workplace operations, it is not practicable to post the notice at or near each such place, such notice shall be posted, unedited, except for reason of national security, in a prominent place where it will be readily observable by all affected employees. For example, where workplace activities are physically dispersed, the notice may be posted at the location to which employees report each day. Where employees do not primarily work at or report to a single location, the notice may be posted at the location from which the employees operate to carry out their activities.

(4) Each notice of an unsafe or unhealthful working condition, or a copy thereof, shall remain posted until the unsafe or unhealthful working condition has been abated or for 3 working days whichever is later. A copy of the notice will be filed and maintained for a period of five years after abatement at the establishment and made available to the Secretary upon request.

[45 FR 69798, Oct. 21, 1980; 45 FR 77003, Nov. 21, 1980]

§ 1960.27 Representatives of officials in charge and representatives of employees.

(a) Safety and health inspectors shall be in charge of inspections and may interview any employee in private if the inspector deems it necessary. A representative of the official in charge of a workplace and a representative of employees shall be given an opportunity to accompany Safety and Health Inspectors during the physical inspection of any workplace, both to aid the inspection and to provide such representatives with more detailed knowledge of any existing or potential unsafe or unhealthful working conditions. The representative of employees shall be selected by the employees. Additional representatives of the official in charge and additional representatives of employees may accompany the Safety and Health Inspectors if it is determined by the inspector that such additional representatives will further aid the inspection. Different representatives of the employer and employees may be allowed to accompany the Inspector during each different phase of an inspection.

(b) Safety and health inspectors shall be authorized to deny the right of accompaniment under this section to any person whose participation interferes with a fair and orderly inspection.

(c) With regard to facilities classified in the interest of national security, only persons authorized to have access to such facilities shall be allowed to accompany a Safety and Health Inspector in such areas.

(d) Safety and health inspectors shall consult with employees concerning matters of occupational safety and health to the extent deemed necessary for the conduct of an effective and thorough inspection. During the course of an inspection, any employee shall be afforded an opportunity to bring to the attention of the Safety and Health Inspector any unsafe or unhealthful working condition which the employee has reason to believe exists in the workplace.

§ 1960.28 Employee reports of unsafe or unhealthful working conditions.

(a) The purpose of employee reports is to inform agencies of the existence of, or potential for, unsafe or unhealthful working conditions. A report under this part is not a grievance.

(b) This section provides guidance in establishing a channel of communication between agency employees and those with responsibilities for safety and health matters, e.g., their supervisor, the agency safety and health officials, safety and health committees, safety and health inspectors, the head of the agency, or the Secretary. These channels of communication are intended to assure prompt analysis and response to reports of unsafe or unhealthful working conditions in accordance with the requirements of Executive Order 12196. Since many safety and health problems can be eliminated as soon as they are identified, the existence of a formal channel of communication shall not preclude immediate corrective action by an employee's supervisor in response to oral reports of unsafe or unhealthful working conditions where such action is possible. Nor should an employee be required to await the outcome of such an oral report before filing a written report pursuant to the provisions of this section.

(c) Any employee or representative of employees, who believes that an unsafe or unhealthful working condition exists in any workplace where such employee is employed, shall have the right and is encouraged to make a report of the unsafe or unhealthful working condition to an appropriate agency safety and health official and request an inspection of such workplace for this purpose. The report shall be reduced to writing either by the individual submitting the report or, in the case of an oral notification, by the above official or other person designated to receive the reports in the workplace. Any such report shall set forth the grounds for the report and shall contain the name of the employee or representative of employees. Upon the request of the individual making such report, no person shall disclose the name of the individual making the report or the names of individual employees referred to in the report, to anyone other than authorized representatives of the Secretary. In the case of imminent danger situations, employees shall make reports by the most expeditious means available.

(d) *Reports received by the agency.* (1) Each report of an existing or potential unsafe or unhealthful working condition should be recorded on a log maintained at the establishment. If an agency finds it inappropriate to maintain a log of written reports at the establishment level, it may avail itself of procedures set forth in § 1960.71. A copy of each report received shall be sent to the appropriate establishment safety and health committee.

(2) A sequentially numbered case file, coded for identification, should be assigned for purposes of maintaining an accurate record of the report and the response thereto. As a minimum, each establishment's log should contain the following information: date, time, code/reference/file number, location of condition, brief description of the condition, classification (imminent danger, serious or other), and date and nature of action taken.

(3) Executive Order 12196 requires that agency inspections be conducted within 24 hours for employee reports of imminent danger conditions, within three working days for potentially serious conditions, and within 20 working days for other than serious safety and health conditions. However, an inspection may not be necessary if, through normal management action and with prompt notification to employees and safety and health committees, the hazardous condition(s) identified can be abated immediately.

(4) An employee submitting a report of unsafe or unhealthful conditions shall be notified in writing within 15 days if the official receiving the report determines there are not reasonable grounds to believe such a hazard exists and does not plan to make an inspection based on such report. A copy of each such notification shall be provided by the agency to the appropriate certified safety and health committee, where established under Executive Order 12196. An agency's inspection or investigation report, if any, shall be made available to the employee making the report within 15 days after completion of the inspection, for safety violations or within 30 days for health violations, unless there are compelling reasons,

and shall be made available to the Secretary or the Secretary's authorized representative on request.

(e) *Reports received by the Secretary of Labor.* (1) Agency safety and health programs must have provisions for responding to employees' reports of unsafe or unhealthful working conditions and the Secretary encourages employees to use agency procedures as the most expeditious means of achieving abatement of hazardous conditions. It is recognized, however, that employee reports may be received directly by the Secretary.

(2) When such reports are received directly from an employee or employee representative, the Secretary shall, where a certified safety and health committee exists, forward the report to the agency for handling in accordance with procedures outlined in §1960.28(d). A copy of the response to the originator shall be sent to the Secretary.

(3) Where there is no certified safety and health committee, or when requested by half the members of a committee, the Secretary may initiate an inspection or other appropriate action. When the Secretary determines that an inspection is warranted, the Secretary shall observe the same response times as required of the agencies under the Executive Order and §1960.28(d)(3). When the Secretary determines not to make an inspection, the report shall be forwarded to the agency for handling in accordance with procedures outlined in §1960.28(d). A copy of the response to the originator shall be sent to the Secretary.

§ 1960.29 Accident investigation.

(a) While all accidents should be investigated, including accidents involving property damage only, the extent of such investigation shall be reflective of the seriousness of the accident.

(b) In any case, each accident which results in a fatality or the hospitalization of five or more employees shall be investigated to determine the causal factors involved. Except to the extent necessary to protect employees and the public, evidence at the scene of an accident shall be left untouched until inspectors have an opportunity to examine it.

(c) Any information or evidence uncovered during accident investigations which would be of benefit in developing a new OSHA standard or in modifying or revoking an existing standard should be promptly transmitted to the Secretary.

(d) The investigative report of the accident shall include appropriate documentation on date, time, location, description of operations, description of accident, photographs, interviews of employees and witnesses, measurements, and other pertinent information. A copy of the investigative report required by this section shall be forwarded to the official in charge of the workplace, the appropriate safety and health committee, and the exclusive employee representative, if any. The investigative report shall be made available to the Secretary or his authorized representative on request.

§ 1960.30 Abatement of unsafe or unhealthful working conditions.

(a) The agency shall ensure the prompt abatement of unsafe and unhealthful conditions. Where a Notice of an Unsafe or Unhealthful Working Condition has been issued, abatement shall be within the time set forth in the notice, or in accordance with the established abatement plan.

(b) The procedures for correcting unsafe or unhealthful working conditions shall include a follow-up, to the extent necessary, to determine whether the correction was made. If, upon the follow-up, it appears that the correction was not made, or was not carried out in accordance with an abatement plan prepared pursuant to paragraph (c) of this section, the official in charge of the establishment and the appropriate safety and health committee shall be notified of the failure to abate.

(c) The official in charge of the establishment shall promptly prepare an abatement plan with the appropriate participation of the establishment's Safety and Health Official or a designee, if in the judgment of the establishment official the abatement of an unsafe or unhealthful working condition will not be possible within 30 calendar days. Such plan shall contain an explanation of the circumstances of the delay in abatement, a proposed timetable for the abatement, and a summary of steps being taken in the interim to protect employees from being injured as a result of the unsafe or unhealthful working condition. A copy of the plan shall be sent to the safety and health committee, and, if no committee exists, to the representative of the employees. Any changes in an abatement plan will require the preparation of a new plan in accordance with the provisions of this section.

(d) When a hazard cannot be abated within the authority and resources of the official in charge of the establishment, that official shall request assistance from appropriate higher authority. The local safety and health official, any established committee and/or employee representatives, and all personnel subject to the hazard shall be advised of this action and of interim protective measures in effect, and shall be kept informed of subsequent progress on the abatement plan.

(e) When a hazard cannot be abated without assistance of the General Services Administration or other Federal lessor agency, the occupant agency shall act with the lessor agency to secure abatement. Procedures for coordination with the General Services Administration are contained in subpart E of this part.

§ 1960.31 Inspections by OSHA.

(a) The Secretary or the Secretary's representatives are authorized to conduct, when the Secretary deems necessary, announced or unannounced inspections in the following situations:

(1) Where an agency has not established occupational safety and health committees or where committees no longer operate in conformance to the requirements of subpart F of this part;

(2) In response to a request from half the membership of record of any certified safety and health committee; and

(3) In response to an employee's report of an imminent danger situation, where there is a certified committee, but where the Secretary determines that neither the agency nor the committee has responded to the employee.

(b) The Secretary's inspectors or evaluators are authorized: to enter without delay, and at reasonable times, any building, installation, facility, construction site, or other area, workplace, or environment where work is performed by employees of the agency; to inspect and investigate during regular working hours and at other reasonable times, and within reasonable limits and in a reasonable manner, any such place of employment, and all pertinent conditions, structures, machines, apparatus, devices, equipment, and materials therein, and to question privately any employee, any supervisory employee, and/or any official in charge of an establishment.

(c) The Secretary may also make scheduled inspections as an integral part of OSHA's evaluation of an agency's safety and health program in accordance with subpart J of this part.

(d) OSHA inspections shall follow the general format set forth for agency inspections in other applicable parts of this subpart.

Subpart E—General Services Administration and Other Federal Agencies
§ 1960.34 General provisions.

Within six months of the effective date of this part, the Secretary of Labor and the Administrator of the General Services Administration (GSA) shall initiate a study of conflicts that may exist in their standards concerning Federal buildings, leased space, products purchased or supplied, and other requirements affecting Federal employee safety and health. Both agencies shall establish and publish a joint procedure for resolving conflicting standards. All other Federal agencies that have authority for purchasing equipment, supplies, and materials, and for controlling Government space, as well as the leasing of space, shall also be subject to the requirements of this subpart, including publication of a procedure for resolving conflicting standards.

(a) In order to assist agencies in carrying out their duties under section 19 of the Act, Executive Order 12196, and this part, the Administrator or the Administrator's designee shall:

(1) Upon an agency's request, furnish for any owned or leased space offered to a Federal agency for occupancy:

(i) A report of a recent pre-occupancy inspection to identify serious hazards or serious violations of OSHA standards or approved alternate standards, and

(ii) A plan for abatement of the hazards and violations discovered;

(2) Provide space which:

(i) Meets any special safety and health requirements submitted by the requesting agency, and

(ii) Does not contain either serious hazards or serious violations of OSHA standards or approved alternate standards which cannot be abated;

(3) Repair, renovate, or alter, upon an agency's request, owned or leased space in a planned and controlled manner to reduce or eliminate, whenever possible, any hazardous exposure to the occupant agency's employees;

(4) Accompany, upon request, the Secretary or the Secretary's designee on any inspection or investigation of a facility subject to the authority of the General Services Administration. Requests made for this purpose shall, whenever possible, be made at the GSA regional level in order to facilitate prompt assistance;

(5) Investigate, upon an official agency request, reports of unsafe or unhealthful conditions within the scope of GSA's responsibility. Such investigation, when requiring an on-site inspection, shall be completed within 24 hours for imminent danger situations, within three working days for potentially serious conditions, and within 20 working days for other safety and health risk conditions;

(6) Abate unsafe or unhealthful conditions disclosed by reports, investigation or inspection within 30 calendar days or submit to the occupant agency's designated liaison official an abatement plan. Such abatement plan shall give priority to the allocation of resources to bring about prompt abatement of the conditions. (GSA shall publish procedures for abatement of hazards in the Federal Property Management Regulations—41 CFR part 101);

(7) Establish an occupancy permit program which will regulate the types of activities and occupancies in facilities in order to avoid incompatible groupings, e.g., chemical or biological laboratories in office space. GSA shall seek to consolidate Federal laboratory operations in facilities designed for such purposes;

(8) Ensure, insofar as possible, that agency safety and health problems still outstanding are resolved, or otherwise answered by acceptable alternatives prior to renegotiation of leases; and

(9) Ensure that GSA or other Federal lessor agencies' building managers maintain a log of reports of unsafe or unhealthful conditions submitted by tenants to include: date of receipt of report, action taken, and final resolution.

(b) *Product safety.* Agencies such as GSA, DOD, and others which procure and provide supplies, equipment, devices, and material for their own use or use by other agencies, except for the design of uniquely military products as set forth in § 1960.2(i), shall establish and maintain a product safety program which:

(1) Ensures that items procured will allow user agencies to use such products safely for their designed purpose and will facilitate user compliance with all applicable standards.

(2) Requires that products meet the applicable safety and health requirements of Federal law and regulations issued thereunder;

(3) Ensures that hazardous material will be labeled in accordance with current law or regulation to alert users, shippers, occupational safety and health, and emergency action personnel, and others, to basic information concerning flammability, toxicity, compatibility, first aid procedures, and normal as well as emergency handling and disposal procedures;

(4) Ensures availability of appropriate safety rescue and personal protective equipment to supply user agencies. The writing of Federal procurement specifications will be coordinated by GSA with OSHA/NIOSH as needed to assure purchase of approved products;

(5) Ensures that products recalled by the manufacturer, either voluntarily or by order from a regulatory authority, are removed from inventory. Each recall notice or order shall be forwarded to all agencies which have ordered such product from or through the procuring/supplying Federal agency, e.g., GSA, DOD, etc.;

(6) Includes preparation of FEDSTD 313, Material Safety Data Sheets (MSDS), involving all interested agencies in review to keep the standard current. MSDS provided by agencies or contractors shall meet the requirements of FEDSTD 313 and be furnished to DOD for filing and distribution.

(c) In order to assist agencies in carrying out their duties under section 19 of the Act, Executive Order 12196, and this part, the DOD operates and maintains an automated system to receive, file, reproduce, and make available MSDS data to other Federal agencies through the Government Printing Office or the National Technical Information Services.

(d) All Federal agencies shall use MSDS either provided by DOD, or acquired directly from suppliers, when purchasing hazardous materials (as defined in FEDSTD 313) for local use. These data will be used to develop detailed procedures to advise employees in the workplace of the hazards involved with the materials and to protect them therefrom.

(e) *Safety and health services.* GSA will operate and maintain for user agencies the following services:

(1) Listings in the "Federal Supply Schedule" of safety and health services and equipment which are approved for use by agencies when needed. Examples of such services are: Workplace inspections, training, industrial hygiene surveys, asbestos bulk sampling, and mobile health testing; examples of such equipment are: personal protective equipment and apparel, safety devices, and environmental monitoring equipment;

(2) Rules for assistance in the preparation of agency "Occupant Emergency Plans" (formerly called "Facility Self-Protection Plans"), to be published by GSA at 41 CFR part 101;

(3) An effective maintenance program in the Interagency Motorpool System which will ensure the safety and health of Federal employees utilizing the vehicles. Critical items to be included are: Exhaust systems, brakes, tires, lights, steering, and passenger restraint or other crash protection systems; and

(4) A rapid response system whereby agencies can alert GSA to unsafe or unhealthful items purchased or contracted for by GSA, which in turn will evaluate the reports, initiate corrective action, as appropriate, and advise use agencies of interim protective measures.

§ 1960.35 National Institute for Occupational Safety and Health.

(a) The Director of the National Institute for Occupational Safety and Health (NIOSH) shall, upon request by the Secretary, assist in:

(1) Evaluations of Federal agency safety and health programs;

(2) Investigations of possible safety and health hazards and

(3) Inspections resulting from employee or committee reports of unsafe or unhealthful working conditions.

(b) The Director of NIOSH shall provide a Hazard Evaluation (HE) program for Federal agencies. This program shall be designed to respond to requests for assistance in determining whether or not safety or health hazards are present in a Federal workplace. Requests for such Hazard Evaluations may be submitted to the Director by:

(1) The Secretary of Labor;

(2) The Head of a Federal agency;

(3) An agency safety and health committee if half the committee requests such service; and

(4) Employees who are not covered by a certified safety and health committee.

(c) The Director of NIOSH may assist agencies by providing hazard alerts, technical services, training materials and conducting training programs upon request by an agency and with reimbursement.

Subpart F—Occupational Safety and Health Committees
§ 1960.36 General provisions.

(a) The occupational safety and health committees described in this subpart are organized and maintained basically to monitor and assist an agency's safety and health program. These committees assist agencies to maintain an open channel of communication between employees and management concerning safety and health matters in agency workplaces. The committees provide a method by which employees can utilize their knowledge of workplace operations to assist agency management to improve policies, conditions, and practices.

(b) Agencies may elect to establish safety and health committees meeting the minimum requirements contained in this subpart. Where such committees are not established or fail to meet the minimum requirements established by the Secretary, the Secretary is authorized by section 1–401(i) of Executive Order 12196 to conduct unannounced inspections of agency workplaces when the Secretary determines them necessary.

§ 1960.37 Committee organization.

(a) For agencies which elect to utilize the committee concept, safety and health committees shall be formed at both the national level and, for agencies with field or regional offices, at appropriate levels within the agency. To realize exemption from unannounced OSHA inspections, an agency must form a committee at the national level and at any establishment or grouping of establishments that is to be exempt, keeping the Secretary advised of the locations and activities where such committees are functioning.

(1) The principal function of the national level committee shall be to consult and provide policy advice on, and monitor the performance of, the agency-wide safety and health program.

(2) Committees at other appropriate levels shall be established at agency establishments or groupings of establishments consistent with the mission, size and organization of the agency and its collective bargaining configuration. The agency shall form committees at the lowest practicable local level. The principal function of the establishment (or local) committees is to monitor and assist in the execution of the agency's safety and health policies and program at the workplaces within their jurisdiction. Any dispute over the meaning of the term "appropriate levels" shall be resolved by the Secretary.

(b) Committees shall have equal representation of management and nonmanagement employees, who shall be members of record.

(1) Management members of both national level and establishment level committees shall be appointed in writing by the person empowered to make such appointments.

(2) Nonmanagement members of establishment level committees shall represent all employees of the establishment and shall be determined according to the following rules:

(i) Where employees are represented under collective bargaining arrangements, members shall be appointed from among those recommended by the exclusive bargaining representative;

(ii) Where employees are not represented under collective bargaining arrangements, members shall be determined through procedures devised by the agency which provide for effective representation of all employees; and

(iii) Where some employees of an establishment are covered under collective bargaining arrangements and others are not, members shall be representative of both groups.

(3) Nonmanagement members of national level committees shall be determined according to the following rules:

(i) Where employees are represented by organizations having exclusive recognition on an agency basis or by organizations having national consultation rights, some members

shall be determined in accordance with the terms of collective bargaining agreements and some members shall be selected from those organizations having consultation rights, and

(ii) Where employees are not represented by organizations meeting the criteria of paragraph (b)(3)(i) of this section, members shall be determined through procedures devised by the agency which provide for effective representation of all employees.

(c) Committee members should serve overlapping terms. Such terms should be of at least two years duration, except when the committee is initially organized.

(d) The committee chairperson shall be nominated from among the committee's members and shall be elected by the committee members. Management and nonmanagement members should alternate in this position. Maximum service time as chairperson should be two consecutive years.

(e) Committees shall establish a regular schedule of meetings and special meetings shall be held as necessary; establishment level committees shall meet at least quarterly and national committees shall meet at least annually.

(f) Adequate advance notice of committee meetings shall be furnished to employees and each meeting shall be conducted pursuant to a prepared agenda.

(g) Written minutes of each committee meeting shall be maintained and distributed to each committee member, and upon request, shall be made available to employees and to the Secretary.

§ 1960.38 Committee formation.

(a) Upon forming such committees, heads of agencies shall submit information to the Secretary concerning the existence, location, and coverage, in terms of establishments and population, of such committees, certifying to the Secretary that such committees meet the requirements of this subpart. The information submitted should include the name and telephone numbers of the chairperson of each committee, and should be updated annually as part of the annual report required by § 1960.74 to reflect any changes that may have occurred.

(b) If, upon evaluation, the Secretary determines that the operations of a committee do not meet the requirements of this subpart, the

Secretary shall notify the agency and identify the deficiencies to be remedied. If the agency does not satisfy the Secretary within 90 days that the committee meets the requirements of this subpart, the committee shall not be deemed a committee under Executive Order 12196 and this part.

[45 FR 69798, Oct. 21, 1980; 45 FR 77003, Nov. 21, 1980, as amended at 49 FR 3080, Jan. 24, 1984]

§ 1960.39 Agency responsibilities.

(a) Agencies shall make available to committees all agency information relevant and necessary to their duties, except where prohibited by law. Examples of such information include, but are not limited to: The agency's safety and health policies and program; human and financial resources available to implement the program; accident, injury, and illness data; epidemiological data; employee exposure monitoring data; Material Safety Data Sheets; inspection reports; reprisal investigation reports; abatement plans; NIOSH hazard evaluation reports; and internal and external evaluation reports.

(b) Agencies shall provide all committee members appropriate training as required by subpart H of this part.

§ 1960.40 Establishment committee duties.

(a) The safety and health committee is an integral part of the safety and health program, and helps ensure effective implementation of the program at the establishment level.

(b) An establishment committee formed under this subpart shall, except where prohibited by law:

(1) Monitor and assist the safety and health program at establishments under its jurisdiction and make recommendations to the official in charge on the operation of the program;

(2) Monitor findings and reports of workplace inspections to confirm that appropriate corrective measures are implemented;

(3) When requested by the agency Safety and Health Official, or when the committee deems it necessary for effective monitoring of agency establishment inspection procedures, participate in inspections of the establishment;

(4) Review internal and external evaluation reports and make recommendations concerning the establishment safety and health program;

(5) Review, and recommend changes, as appropriate, to procedures for handling safety and health suggestions and recommendations from employees;

(6) When requested by the Designated Agency Safety and Health Official, or when the committee deems it necessary, comment on standards proposed pursuant to the provisions of subpart C of this part;

(7) Monitor and recommend changes, as required, in the level of resources allocated and spent on the establishment safety and health program;

(8) Review agency responses to reports of hazardous conditions, safety and health program deficiencies, and allegations of reprisal;

(9) Report their dissatisfaction to the Secretary if half a committee determines there are deficiencies in the establishment's safety and health program or is not satisfied with the agency's reports of reprisal investigations; and

(10) Request the Secretary to conduct an evaluation or inspection if half the members of record are not satisfied with an agency's response to a report of hazardous working conditions.

§ 1960.41 National committee duties.

National committees established under this subpart shall, except where prohibited by law:

(a) Monitor performance of the agency safety and health program and make policy recommendations to the head of the agency on the operation of the program;

(b) Monitor and assist in the development and operation of the agency's establishment committees. As the committee deems appropriate, monitor and review: Reports of inspections; internal and external evaluation reports; agency safety and health training programs; proposed agency standards; agency plans for abating hazards; and responses to reports of hazardous conditions; safety and health program deficiencies; and allegations of reprisal;

(c) Monitor and recommend changes in the resources allocated to the entire agency safety and health program;

(d) Report their dissatisfaction to the Secretary if half a committee determines there are deficiencies in the agency's safety and health program or is not satisfied with the agency's reports of reprisal investigations; and

Appendix

(e) Request the Secretary to conduct an evaluation or inspection if half the members of record are not satisfied with an agency's response to a report of hazardous working conditions.

Subpart G—Allegations of Reprisal
§ 1960.46 Agency responsibility.

(a) The head of each agency shall establish procedures to assure that no employee is subject to restraint, interference, coercion, discrimination or reprisal for filing a report of an unsafe or unhealthful working condition, or other participation in agency occupational safety and health program activities, or because of the exercise by such employee on behalf of himself or herself or others of any right afforded by section 19 of the Act, Executive Order 12196, or this part. These rights include, among other, the right of an employee to decline to perform his or her assigned task because of a reasonable belief that, under the circumstances the task poses an imminent risk of death or serious bodily harm coupled with a reasonable belief that there is insufficient time to seek effective redress through normal hazard reporting and abatement procedures established in accordance with this part.

(b) Based on the Secretary's evaluation of agencies' procedures for protecting employees from reprisal, the Secretary shall report to the President by September 30, 1982 his findings and recommendations for improvements in procedures for the investigation and resolution of allegations of reprisal.

§ 1960.47 Results of investigations.

Each agency shall keep occupational safety and health committees advised of agency activity regarding allegations of reprisal and any agency determinations thereof. Agency officials shall provide copies of reprisal investigation findings, if any, to the Secretary and to the appropriate safety and health committee.

Subpart H—Training
§ 1960.54 Training of top management officials.

Each agency shall provide top management officials with orientation and other learning experiences which will enable them to manage the occupational safety and health programs of their agencies. Such orientation should include coverage of section 19 of the Act, Executive Order 12196, the requirements of this part, and the agency safety and health program.

§ 1960.55 Training of supervisors.

(a) Each agency shall provide occupational safety and health training for supervisory employees that includes: supervisory responsibility for providing and maintaining safe and healthful working conditions for employees, the agency occupational safety and health program, section 19 of the Act, Executive Order 12196, this part, occupational safety and health standards applicable to the assigned workplaces, agency procedures for reporting hazards, agency procedures for reporting and investigating allegations of reprisal, and agency procedures for the abatement of hazards, as well as other appropriate rules and regulations.

(b) This supervisory training should include introductory and specialized courses and materials which will enable supervisors to recognize and eliminate, or reduce, occupational safety and health hazards in their working units. Such training shall also include the development of requisite skills in managing the agency's safety and health program within the work unit, including the training and motivation of subordinates toward assuring safe and healthful work practices.

§ 1960.56 Training of safety and health specialists.

(a) Each agency shall provide occupational safety and health training for safety and health specialists through courses, laboratory experiences, field study, and other formal learning experiences to prepare them to perform the necessary technical monitoring, consulting, testing, inspecting, designing, and other tasks related to program development and implementation, as well as hazard recognition, evaluation and control, equipment and facility design, standards, analysis of accident, injury, and illness data, and other related tasks.

(b) Each agency shall implement career development programs for their occupational safety and health specialists to enable the staff to meet present and future program needs of the agency.

§ 1960.57 Training of safety and health inspectors.

Each agency shall provide training for safety and health inspectors with respect to appropriate standards, and the use of appropriate equipment and testing procedures necessary to identify and evaluate hazards and suggest general abatement procedures during or following their assigned inspections, as well as preparation of reports and other documentation to support the inspection findings.

§ 1960.58 Training of collateral duty safety and health personnel and committee members.

Within six months after October 1, 1980, or on appointment of an employee to a collateral duty position or to a committee, each agency shall provide training for collateral duty safety and health personnel and all members of certified occupational safety and health committees commensurate with the scope of their assigned responsibilities. Such training shall include: The agency occupational safety and health program; section 19 of the Act; Executive Order 12196; this part; agency procedures for the reporting, evaluation and abatement of hazards; agency procedures for reporting and investigating allegations of reprisal, the recognition of hazardous conditions and environments; identification and use of occupational safety and health standards, and other appropriate rules and regulations.

§ 1960.59 Training of employees and employee representatives.

(a) Each agency shall provide appropriate safety and health training for employees including specialized job safety and health training appropriate to the work performed by the employee, for example: Clerical; printing; welding; crane operation; chemical analysis, and computer operations. Such training also shall inform employees of the agency occupational safety and health program, with emphasis on their rights and responsibilities.

(b) Occupational safety and health training for employees of the agency who are representatives of employee groups, such as labor organizations which are recognized by the agency, shall include both introductory and specialized courses and materials that will enable such groups to function appropriately in ensuring safe and healthful working conditions and practices in the workplace and enable them to effectively assist in conducting workplace safety and health inspections. Nothing in this paragraph shall be construed to alter training provisions provided by law, Executive Order, or collective bargaining arrangements.

§ 1960.60 Training assistance.

(a) Agency heads may seek training assistance from the Secretary of Labor, the National Institute for Occupational Safety and Health and other appropriate sources.

(b) After the effective date of Executive Order 12196, the Secretary shall, upon request and with reimbursement, conduct orientation for Designated Agency Safety and Health Officials and/or their designees which will enable them to manage the occupational safety and health programs of their agencies. Such orientation shall include coverage of section 19 of the Act, Executive Order 12196, and the requirements of this part.

(c) Upon request and with reimbursement, the Department of Labor shall provide each agency with training materials to assist in fulfilling the training needs of this subpart, including resident and field training courses designed to meet selected training needs of agency safety and health specialists, safety and health inspectors, and collateral duty safety and health personnel. These materials and courses in no way reduce each agency's responsibility to provide whatever specialized training is required by the unique characteristics of its work.

(d) In cooperation with OPM, the Secretary will develop guidelines and/or provide materials for the safety and health training programs for high-level managers, supervisors, members of committees, and employee representatives.

Subpart I—Recordkeeping and Reporting Requirements

Source: 50 FR 40269, Oct. 2, 1985, unless otherwise noted.

§ 1960.66 Purpose, scope and general provisions.

(a) The purpose of this subpart is to establish uniform requirements for the collection and compilation by agencies of occupational safety and health data, for proper evaluation and necessary corrective action and to assist the Secretary in meeting the requirement to develop and maintain an effective program of collection, compilation, and analysis of occupational safety and health statistics. The term "incident" as hereinafter used in this subpart shall include all occupational injuries and illnesses.

(b) In order to perform his duties under section 19 of the Act and Executive Order 12196, particularly with respect to providing the President with current information about the Federal agency safety and health program, it is necessary that the Secretary be promptly informed of serious incidents involving agency employees as provided in § 1960.70. Assistance to agencies in the investigation of such incidents is available pursuant to the provisions of Executive Order 12196 and this subpart.

(c) Each agency shall utilize the information collected through its management information system to identify unsafe and unhealthful working conditions, and to establish program priorities.

(d) The Department of Labor shall provide Federal agencies with the OSHA Form 101, when requested, to meet the recordkeeping specified in § 1960.68.

(e) The provisions of this subpart are not intended to discourage agencies from utilizing recordkeeping and reporting forms which contain a more detailed breakdown of information than the form provided by the Department of Labor.

(f) Retention and access of employee record shall be in accordance with 29 CFR 1910.20.

(g) Information concerning occupational injuries and illnesses or accidents which, pursuant to statute or Executive Order, must be kept secret in the interest of national defense or foreign policy shall be recorded on separate forms. Such records shall not be submitted to the Department of Labor, but may be used by the appropriate Federal agency in evaluating the agency's program to reduce occupational injuries, illnesses and accidents.

[50 FR 40269, Oct. 2, 1985, as amended at 60 FR 34852, July 5, 1995]

§ 1960.67 Log of occupational injuries and illnesses.

(a) Each Federal agency shall maintain a log of all occupational injuries and illnesses specified in § 1960.67(c) for each establishment. Except as provided in § 1960.71 (b) and (c), the log is to be maintained at the establishment.

(b) Within six working days after receiving information of an occupational injury or illness, appropriate information concerning such injury or illness shall be entered on the log. The format printed in OSHA publication 2014 or an agency form with at least the same 12 data elements shall be used for the log.

(c) Any occupational injury, illness or fatality reported on a CA-1, CA-2, or CA-6 to OWCP shall be reported on the log.

[51 FR 28378, Aug. 7, 1986]

§ 1960.68 Supplementary record of occupational injuries and illnesses.

In addition to the log of occupational injuries and illnesses provided for under § 1960.67, each Federal agency shall maintain a supplementary record for each occupational injury and illness. The record shall be completed within six working days after the receipt of information that an occupational injury or illness has occurred. Each Federal agency shall complete OWCP Forms CA-1, CA-2, and CA-6 in the detail required by the forms and instructions provided by the Secretary (OSHA-2014), and may be used as the supplementary record. OSHA Form No. 101 or an agency equivalent may be used as a supplementary record. Where OWCP forms are used as supplementary records, copies shall be maintained in the occupational safety and/or health office.

[51 FR 28379, Aug. 7, 1986]

§ 1960.69 Annual summaries of Federal occupational injuries and illnesses.

(a) Each Federal agency, on a fiscal year basis, shall compile an annual summary of occupational injuries and illnesses as prescribed in OSHA publication 2014. The summaries shall be based on the log of occupational injuries and illnesses maintained pursuant to § 1960.67.

(b) At the agency's option, and consistent with the Privacy Act considerations and applicable collective bargaining agreements, the last page of the log of occupational injuries and illnesses may be posted as the annual summary of Federal occupational injuries and illnesses.

[51 FR 28379, Aug. 7, 1986]

§ 1960.70 Reporting of serious accidents.

(a) Within 8 hours after the death of any employee from a work-related incident or the in-patient hospitalization of three or more employees as a result of a work-related incident, the Federal Agency head or his/her designee shall orally report the fatality/multiple hospitalization by telephone or in person to the Area Office of the Occupational Safety and Health

Administration (OSHA), U.S. Department of Labor, that is nearest to the site of the incident, or by using the OSHA toll-free central telephone number.

(b) This requirement applies to each such fatality or hospitalization of three or more employees which occurs within thirty (30) days of an incident.

(c) Exception: If the Federal Agency Head or designee does not learn of a reportable incident at the time it occurs and the incident would otherwise be reportable under paragraphs (a) and (b) of this section, the Federal Agency Head or designee shall make the report within 8 hours of the time the incident is reported to any agent or employee of the employer.

(d) Each report required by this section shall relate the following information: Establishment name; location of incident; time of the incident; number of fatalities or hospitalized employees; contact person; phone number; and a brief description of the incident.

(e) Agencies shall provide the Office of Federal Agency Programs with a summary report of each fatal and catastrophic accident investigation. The summaries shall address the date/time of accident, agency/establishment name and location, and consequences, description of operation and the accident, causal factors, applicable standards and their effectiveness, and agency corrective/preventive actions.

[60 FR 18994, Apr. 14, 1995]

§ 1960.71 Location and utilization of records and reports.

(a) The provisions of the section, dealing with the availability of information compiled pursuant to this subpart, are designed to guide agencies in providing agency employees and their representatives with the basic information necessary to assure that they can actively participate in an agency safety and health program. The provisions of this section are also designed to encourage agencies to allow agency safety and health inspectors to have direct access to the accident, injury and illness records of the establishments they are inspecting in order that they may better carry out their duties pursuant to subpart D of this part.

(b) The log and supplementary record required by § 1960.67 and § 1960.68 shall be maintained at each establishment. Where, for reasons of efficient administration or practicality, an agency must maintain this record at a place other than at each establishment, such agency shall ensure that there is available at each establishment a copy of this record. This record shall be complete and as current as possible; in no case shall more than 3 months elapse between the recording of an illness or injury occurring in an establishment and the availability of records reflecting that injury or illness at that establishment.

(c)(1) For agencies engaged in activities such as agriculture, construction, transportation, communication, and electric, gas and sanitary services, which may be physically dispersed, the log and supplementary records, or copies thereof, may be maintained at a place to which employees report each day.

(2) For personnel who do not primarily report or work at a single establishment, and who are generally not supervised in their daily work, such as traveling employees, technicians, engineers, etc., the log and supplementary records, or copies thereof, may be maintained at the base from which personnel operate to carry out their activities.

(d) Each Federal agency shall post a copy of its agency annual summary of Federal occupational injuries and illnesses for an establishment, as compiled pursuant to § 1960.67 or 1960.69, at such establishment, not later than 45 calendar days after the close of the fiscal year or otherwise disseminate a copy of the annual summary for an establishment in written form to all employees of the establishment. Copies of the annual summary shall be posted for a minimum of 30 consecutive days in a conspicuous place or places in the establishment where notices to employees are customarily posted. Where establishment activities are physically dispersed, the notice may be posted at the location to which employees report each day. Where employees do not primarily work at or report to a single location, the notice may be posted at the location from which the employees operate to carry out their activities. Each Federal agency shall take necessary steps to ensure that such summary is not altered, defaced, or covered by other material.

(e) The head of each agency shall ensure access to establishment logs and annual summaries by the establishment's Occupational Safety and Health Committees, employees, former employees and employee representatives.

[50 FR 40269, Oct. 2, 1985, as amended at 51 FR 28379, Aug. 7, 1986]

§ 1960.72 Access to records by Secretary.

The records required to be maintained under the provisions of this subpart shall also be available and made accessible to the Secretary of Labor, Secretary of Health and Human Services and their authorized representative.

§ 1960.73 Retention of records.

The records and reports required to be maintained under the provisions of this subpart shall be retained by each agency for five years following the end of the fiscal year to which they relate, and any location including a Federal record retention center, to which the Secretary or his authorized representative would have reasonable access. In addition, records required by OSHA standards shall be retained in accordance with those standards.

§ 1960.74 Agency annual reports.

(a) The Act and E.O. 12196 require all Federal agency heads to submit to the Secretary an annual report on their agency's occupational safety and health program, containing such information as the Secretary prescribes.

(1) Each agency shall submit to the Secretary by January 1 of each year a report describing the agency occupational safety and health program of the previous fiscal year and objectives for the current year. The report shall include a summary of the agency's self-evaluation findings as required by § 1960.78(b).

(2) Guidelines for agency annual reports to OSHA are prescribed in OSHA publication 2014. The Secretary shall notify agencies by January 1 of any changes to the guidelines for the subsequent year's report.

(3) The agency reports shall be used in the preparation of the Secretary's report to the President.

(b) The Secretary shall submit to the President by October 1 of each year a summary report of the status of the occupational safety and health of Federal employees, based on agency reports, evaluations of individual agency progress and problems in correcting unsafe or unhealthful working conditions, and recommendations for improving their performance.

§§ 1960.75-1960.77 [Reserved]
Subpart J—Evaluation of Federal Occupational Safety and Health Programs
§ 1960.78 Purpose and scope.

(a) The purpose of this subpart is to establish a comprehensive program for the evaluation of Federal employee occupational safety and health programs. This subpart includes the responsibilities of agency heads in conducting self-evaluations of the effectiveness of their occupational safety and health programs, and the responsibilities of the Secretary in evaluating the extent to which each agency head has developed and implemented agency programs in accordance with the requirements of Executive Order 12196 and this part.

(b) Agency heads shall develop and implement a program for evaluating the effectiveness of their agency's occupational safety and health program. An annual summary report shall be submitted to the Secretary covering self-evaluations conducted during the previous year.

(c) The Secretary shall conduct a comprehensive evaluation of each Federal agency's occupational safety and health program. Evaluations shall be conducted on a regular schedule to determine the performance levels of each agency's program. The Secretary shall submit to the President each year: A summary report of the status of the occupational safety and health of Federal employees; Department of Labor evaluations, together with agency responses, of individual agency progress and problems in correcting unsafe and unhealthful working conditions, and recommendations for improving agency's performance.

§ 1960.79 Self-evaluations of occupational safety and health programs.

Agency heads shall develop and implement a program of self-evaluations to determine the effectiveness of their occupational safety and health programs. The self-evaluations are to include qualitative assessments of the extent to which their agency safety and health programs are:

(a) Developed in accordance with the requirements set forth in Executive Order 12196 and this part and,

(b) Implemented effectively in all agency field activities.

Agencies needing assistance in developing a self-evaluation program should contact the Secretary.

§ 1960.80 Secretary's evaluations of agency occupational safety and health programs.

(a) In accordance with section 1–401(h), the Secretary shall develop a comprehensive program for evaluating an agency's occupational safety and health program. To accomplish this, the Secretary shall conduct:

(1) A complete and extensive evaluation of all elements of an agency's occupational safety and health program on a regular basis;

(2) Special studies of limited areas of an agency's occupational safety and health program as deemed necessary by the Secretary; and

(3) Field reviews and scheduled inspections of agency workplaces as deemed necessary by the Secretary.

(b) The Secretary shall develop and distribute to Federal agencies detailed information on the Department of Labor's evaluation program. The information shall include, but is not limited to:

(1) The major program elements included in a complete and extensive evaluation of an agency's occupational safety and health program;

(2) The methods and factors used to determine the effectiveness of each element of an agency's program;

(3) The factors used to define "large" or "more hazardous" Federal agencies, establishments, or operations;

(4) The procedures for conducting evaluations including field visits and scheduled inspections; and

(5) The reporting format for agency heads in submitting annual summaries of their self-evaluation programs.

(c) Prior to the initiation of an agency evaluation, the Department of Labor will review the annual agency self-evaluation summary report. The Secretary will then develop a program evaluation plan before the initiation of an agency evaluation. A copy of the plan shall be furnished to the agency to be evaluated at the time of the notification of the evaluation.

(d) To facilitate the evaluation process and to insure full understanding of the procedures to be followed and the support required from the agency, the Secretary, or the Secretary's representative, shall conduct an opening conference with the agency head or designee. At the opening conference, the Secretary's authority and evaluation plan will be explained.

(e) The agency evaluation should be completed within 90 calendar days of the date of the opening conference.

(f) A report of the evaluation shall be submitted to the agency head by the Secretary within 90 calendar days from the date of the closing conference.

(g) Agency heads shall respond to the evaluation report within 60 calendar days of receipt of the report.

[45 FR 69798, Oct. 21, 1980; 45 FR 77003, Nov. 21, 1980]

Subpart K—Field Federal Safety and Health Councils

§ 1960.84 Purpose.

(a) Executive Order 12196 provides that the Secretary shall "facilitate the exchange of ideas and information throughout the Government about occupational safety and health."

(b) Consistent with this objective, the Secretary will continue to sponsor and/or provide guidance for those Field Federal Safety and Health Councils now established and in operation, and establish new field councils as necessary. The field councils will consist primarily of qualified representatives of local area Federal field activities whose duties pertain to occupational safety and health, and also of representatives of recognized local labor organizations, or other civilian employee organizations, at local area Federal field activities. For the purpose of this subpart the definition of field activity will be provided by each agency.

§ 1960.85 Role of the Secretary.

(a) The Secretary shall maintain liaison with agency heads to ensure that they encourage their field activities to participate actively in field council programs. To ensure maximum participation, the field councils' annual reports to the Secretary shall provide descriptions of the degree of management and employee participation by the defined Federal field activities. The Secretary shall annually furnish each agency head with a report consolidating the information received as to the participation of the agency's several field installations in field council activities.

(b) The Secretary shall provide leadership and guidance and make available necessary equipment, supplies, and staff services to the Field Federal Safety and Health Councils to assist them in carrying out their responsibilities. The Secretary shall also provide consultative and technical services to field councils. These services shall involve aid in any phase of developing and planning programs; and in sponsoring, conducting or supporting safety and health training courses.

§ 1960.86 Establishing councils.

(a) Those field councils established and in operation prior to the effective date of this subpart will continue to function without interruption provided they are operating in accordance with the provision of their charter and this subpart.

(b) The Secretary may establish a council in any area where ten or more Federal establishments totaling 300 or more employees are located within an area having a radius of 50 miles, and there is substantial agreement among the agencies that such a council would be useful. In any such area where there is no council already established, a field representative of the Secretary may, upon his own initiative or at the request of any establishment within the area, contact representatives of all establishments within the area and encourage the organization of a field council.

(c) After a new council has been organized, officers elected, and articles of organization drafted and accepted by the council membership, a formal request for recognition as a field council shall be sent to the Secretary. Upon approval of the Articles of Organization, a charter will be issued.

(d) At the first general meeting of the council, committees should be appointed and the cooperation of all participants should be solicited to aid the functioning of committees and the successful accomplishment of the council's objectives.

§ 1960.87 Objectives.

The basic objective of field councils is to facilitate the exchange of ideas and information to assist agencies to reduce the incidence, severity and cost of occupational accidents, injuries, and illnesses. Field councils shall act on behalf of the Secretary or his designees on occupational safety and health activities in carrying out within their respective geographic areas the following functions:

(a) To act as a clearinghouse on information and data on occupational accidents, injuries, and illnesses and their prevention.

(b) To plan, organize and conduct field council meetings or programs which will give technical advice and information on occupational safety and health to representatives of participating agencies and employee organizations.

(c) To promote improvement of safety and health programs and organizations in each Federal agency represented or participating in council activities.

(d) To promote coordination, cooperation, and sharing of resources and expertise to aid agencies with inadequate or limited resources. These objectives can be accomplished in a variety of ways. For example, field councils could organize and conduct training programs for employee representatives, collateral duty and professional safety and health personnel, coordinate or promote programs for inspections, or, on request, conduct inspections and evaluations of the agencies' safety and health programs.

(e) To provide Federal Executive Boards, Federal Executive Associations, labor union organizations and other employee representatives with information on the administrative and technical aspects of safety and health programs.

(f) To evaluate the safety and health problems peculiar to local conditions and facilitate solutions to these problems through council activities.

(g) To develop a cooperative relationship with local community leaders by informing them of the existing functions and objectives of the council and by calling on them for support and participation in council meetings and activities.

§ 1960.88 Membership and participation.

(a) Each field council shall consist of the designated representatives of local Federal activities appointed by their respective activity heads, after consultation with appropriate employee representatives and appropriate certified safety and health committees.

(b) Federal agency heads should encourage each field activity having responsibility for the safety and health of agency employees to participate in the programs of these councils.

(c) Each activity head shall appoint an equal number of officially designated representatives (with designated alternates), from management and from nonmanagement employees, consistent with applicable collective bargaining arrangements.

(d) Representatives shall be selected from individuals in the following categories:

(1) Federal occupational safety and health professionals.

(2) Related Federal professionals, or collateral duty personnel. This includes persons employed in professions or occupations related to or concerned with safety and health of employees.

(3) Line management officials.

(4) Representatives of recognized Federal labor or other employee organizations.

(i) Where certified occupational safety and health committees exist, nonmanagement members of the committees shall be given the opportunity to select one individual for official appointment to field councils by the activity head.

(ii) Where employees are represented by collective bargaining arrangements, but no committee exists, nonmanagement members of field councils shall be selected from among those recommended by the exclusive bargaining representatives for official appointment to field councils by the activity head.

(iii) Where some employees in an activity are represented by collective bargaining arrangements and others are not, the agency head should solicit nominations for the agency's designated nonmanagement representative and alternate both from lawful labor organization(s) with collective bargaining status and from employees not represented through collective bargaining and should select from the nominees for official appointment as designated employee representatives on the field council.

(e) Representatives from non-Federal organizations. Associate membership may be granted to any non-Federally employed person who demonstrated interest in occupational safety and health. An associate member has no voting rights and may not hold any office.

(f) No maximum limitation shall be imposed by a council on itself, in regard to the numbers of personnel in any of the above categories

that may attend meetings and/or participate in field council activities. An agency is free to have any number of individuals, in addition to the officially designated representatives participate in council activities.

(g) Only officially designated agency representatives or their alternates shall have voting privileges. All representatives and participants shall serve without additional compensation.

(h) Travel funds shall be made available equally to management and nonmanagement employee representatives.

§ 1960.89 Organization.

(a) Field council officers shall include, as a minimum, a chairperson, vice chairperson, and secretary. Officers shall be elected for a one or two-year term on a calendar year basis by a majority vote of the designated representatives. Election of officers shall be held at least 60 days before the beginning of a calendar year. The election may be conducted at a regularly scheduled meeting or by letter ballot.

(b) Each council shall notify the appropriate OSHA Regional Office and the Office of Federal Agency Safety and Health Programs of the name, agency address, and telephone number of each newly elected official.

(c) Each council shall have an Executive Committee consisting of all elected officers, chairpersons of appointed committees and the immediate past chairperson of the field council.

(d) In addition to the Executive Committee, each council shall have either a membership committee, a program committee and a finance committee, or a council official designated responsibility in these areas. Additional committees may be appointed by the chairperson for specific purposes as warranted.

§ 1960.90 Operating procedures.

(a) The Executive Committee of each council shall meet at least 45 days before the beginning of each calendar year to approve an annual program for the council designed to accomplish the objectives and functions stated in §1960.87. In addition, the Executive Committee shall meet periodically to ensure that the meetings and other activities of the council are being conducted as outlined in the council schedule.

(b) The council program shall include at least four meetings or activities per year dealing with occupational safety and health issues.

(c) Each field council shall submit to the Secretary or his designee by March 15 of each year a report describing the activities and programs of the previous calendar year and plans for the current year. In addition, the report shall address the participation and attendance of designated representatives of the council. The Office of Federal Agency Safety and Health Programs, OSHA, shall furnish guidelines to field councils concerning the preparation of this report.

(d) Upon determination that a council is not operating in accordance with its charter and the provisions of this subpart, and after consultation with appropriate OSHA regional officials, the Secretary shall revoke the council's charter. Upon revocation of a charter, the council shall surrender all its government property to the appropriate OSHA regional official. Any continuing or future organization in the same geographical area shall not use the title Field Federal Safety and Health Council, or any derivation thereof, unless formally rechartered by the Secretary. Notification of revocation of a council's charter shall be sent to the chairperson, where identifiable, and to the appropriate OSHA Regional Office.

Material Safety Data Sheets for Federal Agencies

Chemical manufacturers and importers must develop an MSDS for each hazardous chemical they produce or import, and must automatically provide the MSDS with the initial shipment of a hazardous chemical to a downstream distributor or user. Distributors must also ensure that downstream employers are provided an MSDS. Each MSDS must be in English and include information regarding the specific chemical identity of the hazardous chemicals involved as well as their common names. In addition, information must be provided on:

- the physical and chemical characteristics of the hazardous chemical;
- known acute and chronic health effects and related health information;
- exposure limits;
- whether the chemical is considered to be a carcinogen by the NTP, IARC, or OSHA;
- precautionary measures;
- emergency and first-aid procedures; and
- the identification of the organization responsible for preparing the sheet.

Copies of the MSDS for hazardous chemicals in a given work site are to be readily accessible to employees in that area. As a source of detailed information on hazards, they must be located close to workers and readily available to them during each work shift. A copy of the non-mandatory MSDS form (OSHA 174) can be obtained from OSHA field offices.

Federal agencies may obtain MSDS information on CD through the Department of the Navy, which has responsibility for maintaining this information. Send official requests for this subscription (a two-CD set of all MSDSs used by the federal government) to:

Commanding Officer
ATTN: CD-ROM TEAM CODE N911
NCTAMS LANT
9625 Moffett Ave
Norfolk, VA 23511-2784
(757) 445-9192

Most Frequently Cited Standards

Manufacturing Citations

Listed below are the standards which were cited by **Federal OSHA** for the specified SIC during the period October 2007 through September 2008.

Standard	Cited	Insp	Penalty ($)	Description
Total	38060	6082	38054020	
19100147	3469	1795	3488668	The control of hazardous energy (lockout/tagout).
19101200	2757	1494	789734	Hazard Communication.
19100212	2403	1954	3074319	General requirements for all machines.
19100134	2301	965	769938	Respiratory Protection.
19100305	2153	1271	1296022	Wiring methods, components, and equipment for general use.
19100178	1878	1224	1462565	Powered industrial trucks.
19100303	1643	1155	1108481	General requirements.
19100219	1640	890	1065985	Mechanical power-transmission apparatus.
19100215	1148	702	463726	Abrasive wheel machinery.
19100132	1005	756	598124	General requirements.
19100023	913	697	1185741	Guarding floor and wall openings and holes.
19100095	819	394	582507	Occupational noise exposure.
19100022	805	640	2221852	General requirements.
19100119	753	89	2852799	Process safety management of highly hazardous chemicals.
19100213	742	404	461846	Woodworking machinery requirements.
19100157	713	568	204579	Portable fire extinguishers.
19100179	595	258	493996	Overhead and gantry cranes.
19100217	594	225	656526	Mechanical power presses.
19100107	575	237	295865	Spray finishing using flammable and combustible materials.
19100037	547	431	261353	Maintenance, safeguards, and operational features for exit routes.
19040029	524	483	163403	Forms.
5A0001	508	412	1460288	
19100242	482	475	317540	Hand and portable powered tools and equipment, general.
19100304	458	386	326609	Wiring design and protection.
19100106	457	275	335601	Flammable and combustible liquids.
19100146	457	194	483432	Permit-required confined spaces
19100253	413	319	222827	Oxygen-fuel gas welding and cutting.
19100151	401	392	306304	Medical services and first aid.
19100133	354	335	294471	Eye and face protection.
19100266	342	79	148578	Logging operations.
19100184	338	182	236103	Slings.
19101025	319	96	347794	Lead.
19101000	282	138	248576	Air contaminants.
19040032	267	213	36567	Annual summary.
19100335	248	140	237748	Safeguards for personnel protection.
19101026	245	109	135969	
19100036	210	188	193973	Design and construction requirements for exit routes.
19100307	205	121	5697279	Hazardous (classified) locations.
19100252	197	161	150595	General requirements.
19101030	185	99	63462	Bloodborne pathogens.
19100334	183	156	91052	Use of equipment.
19100024	166	138	138073	Fixed industrial stairs.
19100176	162	151	175106	Handling materials - general.
19100333	160	137	190903	Selection and use of work practices
19100141	153	109	51083	Sanitation.
19100110	118	98	74801	Storage and handling of liquefied petroleum gases.
19101052	117	40	66673	Methylene Chloride.
19100138	115	110	50653	Hand Protection.
19100265	101	48	88708	Sawmills.
19100243	97	92	86124	Guarding of portable powered tools.
19100038	94	88	45008	Emergency action plans.
19100332	90	83	117020	Training
19100101	86	83	36522	Compressed gases (general requirements).
19100027	78	51	94262	Fixed ladders.
19101027	77	13	36814	Cadmium
19100120	71	41	84190	Hazardous waste operations and emergency response.
19101048	69	30	26698	Formaldehyde.
19100254	56	50	52137	Arc welding and cutting.
19100067	55	49	58208	Vehicle-mounted elevating and rotating work platforms.
19040007	53	38	12390	General recording criteria.
19040041	53	53	13820	
19100094	52	38	20353	Ventilation.
19100145	51	48	34940	Specifications for accident prevention signs and tags.

United States Postal Service

Listed below are the standards which were cited by **Federal OSHA** for the specified SIC during the period October 2007 through September 2008.

Standard	Cited	Insp	Penalty ($)	Description
Total	143	75	89753	
19100037	14	9	18850	Maintenance, safeguards, and operational features for exit routes.
19100303	11	9	4581	General requirements.
5A0001	11	10	22800	
19101200	9	7	655	Hazard Communication.
19100022	8	8	4650	General requirements.
19100178	8	7	4575	Powered industrial trucks.
19100305	7	6	1500	Wiring methods, components, and equipment for general use.
19100212	6	6	3400	General requirements for all machines.
19100157	5	4	0	Portable fire extinguishers.
19100036	4	4	4092	Design and construction requirements for exit routes.
19100120	4	2	0	Hazardous waste operations and emergency response.
19100141	4	3	0	Sanitation.
19100147	4	4	1700	The control of hazardous energy (lockout/tagout).
19101025	4	2	0	Lead.
19040032	3	3	0	Annual summary.
19040040	3	3	500	
19100132	3	2	500	General requirements.
19100133	3	3	1500	Eye and face protection.
19100151	3	3	1700	Medical services and first aid.
19100176	3	2	5425	Handling materials - general.
19100219	3	3	0	Mechanical power-transmission apparatus.
19101001	3	3	3763	Asbestos.
19040029	2	1	5000	Forms.
19100038	2	2	0	Emergency action plans.
19100138	2	2	500	Hand Protection.
19100304	2	2	0	Wiring design and protection.
19100334	2	2	0	Use of equipment.
19101030	2	1	0	Bloodborne pathogens.
19100024	1	1	500	Fixed industrial stairs.
19100025	1	1	975	Portable wood ladders.
19100029	1	1	562	Manually propelled mobile ladder stands and scaffolds (towers).
19100067	1	1	0	Vehicle-mounted elevating and rotating work platforms.
19100136	1	1	1275	Occupational foot protection.
19100179	1	1	0	Overhead and gantry cranes.
19100242	1	1	750	Hand and portable powered tools and equipment, general.
19100333	1	1	0	Selection and use of work practices

OSHA Instruction FAP 1.3 May 17, 1996 Office of Federal Agency Programs
Subject: Federal Agency Safety and Health Programs

A. **Purpose**. The purpose of this instruction is to transmit policies that are unique to Federal Agency Safety and Health Programs. This directive was developed by the Field Operations Manual (FOM) Chapter XIII Revision Team to provide the field offices a reference document for identifying the responsibilities associated with Federal Agency Inspections and Evaluations.

B. **Scope**. This instruction applies OSHA-wide.

C. **References**.
   1. Occupational Safety and Health Act of 1970, Sections 19 and 24.
   2. Executive Order 12196, February 26, 1980, Occupational Safety and Health Programs for Federal Employees.
   3. 29 CFR Part 1960, Basic Program Elements for Federal Employee Occupational Safety and Health Programs and Related Matters, October 21, 1980.
   4. OSHA Publication 2014, revised 1986, Recordkeeping and Reporting Guidelines for Federal Agencies.
   5. OSHA Instruction ADM 1-1.32, July 19, 1993, The Enforcement User Skills Manual for use with the NCR Computer System.
   6. OSHA Instruction FAP 1.2A, April 10, 1995, Federal Agency Safety and Health Programs with Bureau of Prisons, U.S. Department of Justice.
   7. OSHA Instruction CPL 2.102, March 28, 1994, Procedures for Approval of Local Emphasis Programs (LEPs) and Experimental Programs.
   8. OSHA Instruction CPL 2.103, September 26, 1994, Field Inspection Reference Manual (FIRM).

D. **Action**. Policies and procedures for Federal agencies are to be the same as those followed in the private sector, except as specified in this instruction. This instruction supersedes Chapter XIII, Federal Agency Programs of the FOM, CPL 2.45B. Until Chapter XIII is removed from the FOM, FAP 1.3 will take precedence. Area Office questions should be directed to the Regional Federal Agency Program Officer (FAPO).

E. **Federal Agencies**. This instruction describes a change that affects Federal agencies. Federal Agencies are subject to the enforcement policy and procedures contained in this instruction which are consistent with the Executive Order 12196, Section 1-201, and 29 CFR 1960.16.

F. **Jurisdiction**. The Occupational Safety and Health Administration's (OSHA's) Federal agency jurisdiction varies according to the activity being performed. Further information may be obtained from the Directorate for Policy, Office of Intra-Governmental Affairs at 202-219-8021.
   NOTE: A list of Federal agencies that are excluded from OSHA jurisdiction is found in Appendix E. NOTE: A list of Interagency agreements with DOL is found in Appendix F.

   1. **Federal Agency Compliance**. OSHA is authorized to conduct **unannounced** inspections in Executive Branch Federal agency establishments unless:
      a. Inspections are to be conducted at Federal prisons.
         NOTE: OSHA can conduct **announced** inspections at Federal Prisons following guidelines found in OSHA Instruction FAP 1.2A.
      b. The agency has Certified Safety and Health Committees (Certified Committees).
         NOTE: OSHA can conduct **announced** inspections in agencies with Certified Committees.
      c. The work is performed by military personnel or involves "uniquely military equipment, systems and operations." NOTE: Workplaces and operations similar to those of industry are not excluded from OSHA coverage.
      d. Another Federal agency has occupational safety and health standards and exercises jurisdiction under Section 4(b)(1) of the Occupational Safety and Health Act (OSH Act). (See Appendix F.)

2. **Private Sector Compliance on Federal Property**. a. Employees of private contractors performing work under Government contracts are not covered under Section 19 of the OSH Act, the Executive Order, and 29 CFR Part 1960 program elements, but are covered by private sector procedures under the OSH Act. b. Where an authorized State program is in existence, the State program shall have jurisdiction over private sector contractors unless the work being performed is at a location of "exclusive Federal jurisdiction" within the Federal property. The Regional Administrator shall refer to State Plan Operational agreements to determine "exclusive Federal jurisdiction." If the agreement is not clear, the legal staff having management authority over the Federal property shall be consulted.

3. **Government-Owned Contractor-Operated Facilities (GOCO's)**. OSHA compliance policies concerning GOCO operations are described in separate Memoranda of Understanding (MOU) applicable to specific agencies. (See Appendix F.)

G. **Definitions**. The following definitions apply to Federal agencies:

1. **Establishment**. A single physical location where business is conducted or services or operations are performed. Where distinctly separate activities are performed at a single physical location, each activity shall be treated as a separate "establishment." Typically, an "establishment" refers to a field activity, Regional Office, Area Office, installation, or facility. Examples are as follows:
   a. Major organizational units with distinct lines of authority shall be counted as separate establishments.
   b. Agencies or bureaus in an agency would be separate establishments even if they occupied the same building.
   c. Each component of the Department of Defense (Army, Navy, etc.) and each major command located at an installation would be a separate establishment.
   d. Lower organizational units such as offices or divisions within a bureau or shops within a command are **not** considered separate establishments.

2. **Evaluation**. A Department-wide (comprehensive) assessment of a Federal agency's occupational safety and health program. Includes document reviews and interviews at various organizational levels from the top down to track the flow and implementation of the program, and includes information from visits to Agency sites (field reviews).

3. **Field Review**. A "mini-evaluation" of an agency's occupational safety and health program at a specific site. Includes document reviews and interviews at various organization levels at the site, and information obtained from a walkaround inspection to assess implementation of the program at the site.

4. **OSHA Notice**. The Federal agency equivalent of a "citation" is the Notice of Unsafe and Unhealthful Working Conditions, OSHA-2H Form, (OSHA Notice) which is the agency's report as required by 29 CFR Part 1960. Instructions for completing the OSHA Notice are found in OSHA Instruction ADM 1-1.32, Chapter VII and XI.

5. **Citable Program Elements**. Specific program elements in 29 CFR Part 1960 that are to be cited when found not in compliance during inspections or evaluations.

6. **General Duty Clause**. Executive Order 12196, Section 201(a), and 29 CFR 1960.8(a) mandate the head of each agency to furnish to each employee a workplace free from recognized hazards. OSHA Notices shall refer to 29 CFR 1960.8(a) to enforce serious violations that are not addressed by a specific OSHA standard or program element. NOTE: Section 5(a)(1) of the OSH Act is the "general duty clause" for the private sector and does not apply to Federal agencies.

7. **Uniquely Military**. Equipment and systems designed by The Department of Defense that are unique to the national defense mission, such as military aircraft, ships, submarines, missiles, and missile sites, early warning systems, military space systems, artillery, tanks, and tactical vehicles. Also operations such as field maneuvers, naval operations, military

flight operations, associated research test and development activities, and actions required under emergency conditions.

H. **Compliance**.

1. **Targeted Inspections**. Targeted inspections are equivalent to the private sector programmed inspections. Federal agency establishments are targeted using the Office of Workers Compensation Program's (OWCP) data. a. Area Directors shall schedule all targeted Federal agency inspections within the fiscal year. b. OSHA targeted inspections shall identify violations of OSHA standards and citable program elements. (See Appendix A.)

2. **Special Emphasis Inspections**. Area Directors, in concurrence with the FAPO, may develop Federal agency special emphasis programs following OSHA Instruction CPL 2.102. The FAPO shall obtain concurrence from the Director, Office of Federal Agency Programs (OFAP), before any special emphasis inspection programs are implemented.

3. **Fatality/Catastrophe Investigations**. Executive Order 12196, Section 1-401(i) and 29 CFR 1960.31 authorizes OSHA to investigate fatal or catastrophic incidents to Federal employees in agencies subject to OSHA inspections. NOTE: A catastrophe is a work-related incident that results in the inpatient hospitalization of three or more employees within 30 days of an incident.

   a. **Agency Investigation**. Agencies are required to conduct an investigation of each fatal or catastrophic incident and, upon request, to provide OSHA with a report of findings upon completion of the investigation.

   b. **OSHA Investigation Decision**. The Area Director shall determine whether OSHA will conduct an investigation of the incident. OSHA may conduct an independent investigation or participate in the agency's investigation.
   NOTE: When OSHA joins an agency investigation, the compliance safety and health officer (CSHO) shall participate fully with the investigation and not be subject to "observer status" by the agency.

   c. **Excluded Agencies**. If an incident report is received concerning a Federal agency not under OSHA's jurisdiction, the person reporting the incident shall be referred to that agency's safety and health staff. (See Appendix E for list of excluded agencies.)

4. **Complaint Handling**. Unsafe or Unhealthful Working Conditions (complaints) referred to Federal agencies for investigation shall be handled in accordance with 29 CFR 1960.28. Use complaint form letters in Appendix D, Section I for transmittal of the complaint to the agency. OSHA investigations of complaints shall be handled the same as private sector complaints except for the following:

   a. **Certified Committees**.

      (1) If OSHA determines not to make an announced inspection, any complaints received shall be forwarded to the agency Designated Agency Safety and Health Official (DASHO) for investigation.

      (2) The agency shall handle the complaint in accordance with procedures outlined in 29 CFR 1960.28(d).

      (3) If half the members of record of an agency's Certified Committee are not satisfied with the agency's response to complaints of hazardous working conditions, a request can be made for OSHA to evaluate or inspect the condition.

      (4) If OSHA determines that an inspection is necessary, the establishment official shall be notified at least one day in advance of the scheduled inspection.

      (5) The results of the inspection will be provided to the establishment official who will be requested to share the results with the Certified Committee. A copy of the inspection results shall also be forwarded to the agency DASHO.

      (6) The following agencies have Certified Committees: * Panama Canal Commission * Central Intelligence Agency * Securities and Exchange Commission * Interstate

Commerce Commission * General Services Administration * Department of Labor * Tennessee Valley Authority * U.S. International Trade Commission

  b. **Reports of Safety and Health Program Violations**. When complaints allege violations of program elements of 29 CFR Part 1960, the Area Director may schedule an inspection or respond by letter. Any program deficiency trends noticed in a Federal agency shall be reported to the FAPO and forwarded to OFAP for review. OFAP shall determine if an evaluation of the agency's program should be conducted.

  c. **Responding to Complaints When OSHA Does Not Have Authority**. If OSHA does not have compliance authority over the complainant's agency, the complainant shall be advised to contact his/her employer's safety and health staff. Every effort shall be made to assist in identifying the proper person to be contacted. (See Appendix E for excluded agencies.)

5. **Reports of Reprisal or Discrimination**. Section 11(c) of the OSH Act does not apply to Federal employees. The Executive Order 12196 and 29 CFR Part 1960.46 and the Whistle-blower Protection Act of 1989 require agency heads to assure that no employee is subject to restraint, interference, coercion, discrimination or reprisal for exercising any right under these laws.

  a. **Covered Employees**. The Whistleblower Protection Act of 1989 is enforced by the Office of Special Counsel. Whenever a covered employee believes that reprisal actions are taken against him/her for reporting a violation of a law, rule or regulation, reporting OSHA will refer covered Federal employees or former employees directly to the Office of Special Counsel, Complaints Examining Unit, 3rd Floor, 1730 M. Street, N.W., Washington D.C. 20036, telephone #1-800-872-9855. There are no time limitations for filing a reprisal complaint with the Special Counsel.

  b. **Noncovered Employees**. Employees of a government corporation such as the Tennessee Valley Authority; the U.S. Postal Service or Postal Rate Commission; the Central Intelligence Agency, Defense Intelligence Agency, National Security Agency or certain other intelligence agencies excluded by the President; the General Accounting Office; and the Federal Bureau of Investigation are not covered by the Whistleblower Protection Act. Inmates at Federal prisons have their own reprisal program through the Bureau of Prisons and are not covered by the Special Counsel (See OSHA Instruction FAP 1.2). Reports of reprisal or discrimination from Federal employees who are not covered by e Special Counsel, should be sent to the agency DASHO. Contact OFAP for further assistance, if needed.

6. **Alternate Standards**. If an agency has been approved for an alternate standard in lieu of an OSHA standard, the CSHO shall determine if the agency is in compliance with the alternate standard.

   NOTE: An alternate standard is the Federal agency equivalent to a variance from OSHA standards that private sector employers may obtain.

7. **Refusal of Entry**. If a Federal agency scheduled for an inspection refuses entry, the Area Director shall attempt to resolve the issue with the establishment official.

  a. If a resolution cannot be worked out, the Area Director shall contact the FAPO. The FAPO shall contact the equivalent agency organizational level with responsibility and authority for the establishment's working conditions to discuss the refusal. If agreement cannot be reached, the FAPO shall contact the Director, OFAP, for resolution with the DASHO.

  b. A written record of all actions taken to resolve the issue shall be kept in the case file.

8. **Warrants/Subpoenas**. Administrative subpoenas or warrants will not be used for Federal agencies. Issues unresolved at the Area or Regional Office level shall be transferred to the Director, OFAP, for resolution with the DASHO.

9. **Recordkeeping and Reporting Requirements**. Federal agency recordkeeping and reporting requirements are outlined in 29 CFR Part 1960 program elements, Subpart I, and in Appendix B "Recordkeeping and Reporting Guidelines for Federal Agencies" (OSHA Publication 2014). NOTE: The lost workday injury (LWDI) rate (Item 33) and the

occupational injury/illness cases (Item 34) are not to be completed for Federal agency activity on the OSHA-1.

a. **Reports of Fatality/Catastrophes**. Agencies must notify OSHA within 8 hours of each work related fatality or inpatient hospitalization of three or more employees. This requirement applies to each such fatality or hospitalization of three or more employees which occurs within thirty (30) days of an incident. Notification can be made by telephone or in person to the OSHA area office nearest the site of the incident or by using the OSHA toll-free central phone number 1-800-321-OSHA.

b. **Occupational Injury/Illness Logs (OSHA Logs)**. Where, for reasons of efficient administration or practicality, an agency must maintain these records at a place other than at each establishment, these records **may** be maintained at Regional or Area levels **if** quarterly updated copies are available at the establishment. (See Appendix B.)

(1) Agencies may use their own forms to log injuries and illnesses, but the forms **must** include all data elements listed in OSHA Publication 2014. Cases reported to OWCP which do not involve lost time or cost are "First Aid" cases and must appear on the log. First aid cases may be displayed under a column labeled "First Aid" or may be listed under the "No lost time case" column.

(2) As new OSHA standards are published under Section 6(b) of the OSH Act that require certain injuries/illnesses to be recorded on the OSHA Log, Federal agencies will also be required to enter this information on their injury/illness log. For example, needle sticks, carpel tunnel syndrome, and threshold shifts in hearing loss are now required to be recorded.

c. **OSHA Supplementary Record of Occupational Injuries and Illnesses (OSHA-101)**. Agencies may use the OSHA-101, or OWCP Forms CA-1, CA-2, CA-6, or an equivalent agency form, as its supplementary record. The supplementary record is to be completed in the detail required by the form.

d. **Annual Summaries of Federal Occupational Injuries and Illnesses**. An annual summary of Federal occupational injuries and illnesses for an establishment based on the OSHA Log shall be compiled not later than 45 calendar days after the close of the fiscal year. The summary shall then be posted for 30 consecutive days in a conspicuous place or places in the establishment where notices to employees are customarily posted. (See 29 CFR 1960.71(d)).

e. **OWCP Compensation Claim Forms**. Agencies are required to complete OSHA-related items on OWCP compensation claim forms CA-1, CA-2, and CA-6. NOTE: OWCP forms printed since 1986 include specific blocks for Type, Source, and Duty Station Zip Codes which are OSHA-required information.

f. **Access to Federal Employee Exposure and Medical Records**. The authority for obtaining Federal employee exposure and medical records is Section 19(d) of the OSH Act, the Executive Order 12196, and 29 CFR Part 1960, Subpart I. Specifically, 29 CFR 1960.66(f) requires Federal agencies to comply with 29 CFR 1910.20, Access to Employee Exposure and Medical Records as published in the Federal Register, Vol. 60, No. 128, July 5, 1995.

I. **Evaluation**. Compliance officers may be asked to participate in field reviews for evaluations of Federal agency programs. They will receive guidance from the FAPO. Evaluation procedures are contained in Appendix C.

1. **Agency Selection**. OFAP will annually provide the Regional Administrators with a rolling two-year listing of agencies to be evaluated over the following two years. FAPOs, in consultation with Area Office Directors, will use this information to select the Federal agency sites where they plan to conduct field reviews.

2. **Frequency of Field Reviews**. In order to ensure that Federal agencies receive more regular feedback on their occupational safety and health programs, each FAPO will be expected to conduct at least four field reviews annually at the Federal agency sites of their choice. These sites may be at one agency or divided among different agencies. The goal is to distribute

the four field reviews evenly throughout the year, although the scheduling is at the discretion of the FAPO.

3. **Report Format**. A site report will be written by the FAPO. FAPOs will forward the report to the top manager at the site, with copies to the Agency Safety and Health Manager and OFAP.

J. **Agency Technical Assistance Request (ATAR)**. An ATAR is a request by a Federal agency for onsite assistance. Assistance provided onsite shall be recorded on an OSHA-1.

1. An ATAR may include hazard abatement advice, training, a partial or comprehensive inspection, and program assistance.

2. While many ATARs for hazard abatement advice or for an assistance visit will be submitted by telephone, the requesting agency normally shall be required to reduce the ATAR to writing before an onsite visit can be scheduled. If special circumstances arise that make it impractical to wait for a written request, the ATAR visit may be performed.

3. Agencies requesting assistance shall be informed that the agency is expected to correct any violations of citable program elements or OSHA standards observed by CSHOs.

4. At Area Office discretion the decision of whether to conduct an ATAR can include considerations such as:

   a. Site commitment to safety and health,
   b. Willingness by the requesting agency to assign necessary staff and resources to implement safety and health programs,
   c. Abatement of previous violations and hazards, and
   d. Willingness by the requesting agency to pay CSHO travel and per diem while an ATAR is conducted.

5. Assistance visit procedures will vary according to the scope of the visit, as prescribed by the Area Director.

   a. If the ATAR has resulted in a partial or a comprehensive inspection, all violations of citable program elements or OSHA standards observed shall be discussed with the establishment official at the closing conference.
   b. For serious violations that are unabated prior to the closing conference, abatement dates and an abatement plan shall be discussed. Abatement dates shall be based on the shortest interval within which the agency can reasonably be expected to correct the violation.
   c. For other-than-serious violations that are unabated prior to the closing conference, abatement advice shall be provided when appropriate.
   d. The Area Director shall inform the establishment official using inspection form letter "e" ("Notification to Employer-ATAR Results") in Appendix D, Section II, of the results of the visit. The letter shall describe OSHA's action taken in response to the ATAR and provide findings and recommendations, as appropriate.
      (1) If any violations were uncorrected at the end of the visit, the letter shall:
          (a) Discuss in sufficient detail all apparent violations observed by the assistance team.
          (b) Indicate abatement dates for serious violations as discussed with the establishment official.
          (c) Request abatement plans for any serious violation that cannot be eliminated within 30 calendar days. Abatement plans must be submitted within 30 calendar days of receipt of the letter.
          (d) Request that the establishment official notify OSHA in writing of abatement action taken upon expiration of the established abatement period.
      (2) If no violations were observed or if all hazards were eliminated prior to the completion of the closing conference, the Area Director shall so inform the establishment official.
   e. If, after 30 calendar days, the Area Director has not received an abatement plan and has not been notified that violations have been abated, the Area Director shall check on abatement status by telephone or onsite visit. If any violations are unabated, an OSHA

Notice shall be issued with a copy sent to the agency's Designated Agency Safety and Health Official (DASHO). NOTE: Where onsite assistance is provided for those agencies excluded from OSHA jurisdiction, a **recommendation letter shall be sent** instead of an OSHA Notice.

K. **Application for an Alternate Standard**. An agency may apply for an exception from an OSHA standard by applying for an alternate standard. Application procedures are found at 29 CFR 1960.17.

L. **Notice of Unsafe or Unhealthful Working Conditions, OSHA-2H Form, (OSHA Notice)**.

1. **Issuance of the OSHA Notice**. The OSHA Notice shall be used to inform establishment officials of violations of OSHA standards, alternate standards, and 29 CFR Part 1960 citable program elements.

   a. When violations are observed during an OSHA inspection of, evaluation of, or assistance visit to a Federal agency establishment, the private sector procedures shall be followed, except as otherwise indicated in this document:

      (1) 29 CFR 1960.8(a) (the Federal equivalent of the general duty clause) shall be used in the notification of serious hazards that are not addressed by a specific OSHA standard. For other-than-serious hazards the establishment shall be notified using the inspection form letter "g" ("Letter for a Hazard Not Covered by Standard or General Duty Clause") in Appendix D, Section II.
      NOTE: Executive Order 12196, Section 1-201(a), will no longer be used to cite hazards not addressed by a specific OSHA standard or program element.

      (2) 29 CFR Part 1960, Subpart I, shall be used to enforce recordkeeping violations.
      NOTE: Executive Order 12196, Section 1-201(j), will no longer be used to cite record-keeping violations.

      (3) Violations of citable program elements of 29 CFR Part 1960 will normally be classified as "other-than-serious" unless they are considered a contributing factor to a serious safety or health standard violation (e.g., where lack of supervisory training contributed to an unshored trench, both the trenching standard and 29 CFR 1960.55 would be cited as "serious").

      (4) A Repeat OSHA Notice may be issued to a Federal agency establishment for repeat violations if the agency had been cited previously for the same or a substantially similar condition **and** the following conditions are present:
         (a) For serious violations, if OSHA regionwide inspection history for the agency lists a previous OSHA Notice issued within the past 3 years to an agency establishment within the same two-digit SIC code. (See Appendix G for map of OSHA Regions.)
         (b) For other-than-serious violations if the establishment being inspected received a previous OSHA Notice issued within the past 3 years.
         (c) There is documentary evidence that the previous OSHA Notice had been abated.
         NOTE: Include the inspection identification number, date, and location of the previous inspection on the OSHA Notice.

   b. An OSHA Notice shall be completed in accordance with current IMIS instructions.

   c. The multiemployer worksite policy described in the FIRM, at III-28 and 29, applies to both construction and nonconstruction, with both private and Federal employers.

   d. The Area Office shall send the OSHA Notice to the establishment official.
      (1) When violations are classified as willful or repeated, a copy shall also be sent to the DASHO. NOTE: For U.S. Army only send to: U.S. Army Safety Center, Fort Rucker, Alabama 36362-5363, with a copy to: ODUSD (ES) SH, Suite 110, 400 Army Navy Drive, Arlington, Virginia 22202.
      (2) The DASHO list is available from the FAPO.

   d. If violations cannot be corrected within 30 days, Area Directors may assign abatement dates up to 6 months in 90-day increments for violations of 29 CFR Part 1960 authorized program elements. Justification for abatement in excess of 30 days must be documented in the case file.

2. **Cover Letter**. If the laser OSHA Notice is not used, each OSHA Notice shall be accompanied with inspection form letter "a" ("Notification to Employer —Inspection Results") in Appendix D, Section II, which may also contain a general summary of what penalty amounts would have been proposed in the private sector.

   a. Request that the establishment official post a copy of the OSHA Notice at or near each place the violation exists or existed.

   b. Inform the establishment official that an informal conference may be requested in writing or by telephone with a confirming letter within 15 working days of receipt of the OSHA Notice. The letter must identify the items to be discussed.

   c. Enclose the OSHA Publication, "Federal Employer Rights & Responsibilities Following an OSHA Inspection."

M. **Informal Conference Procedures**. Informal conference procedures will be the same as in the private sector. The Area Director shall make every effort to resolve any disagreements at an informal conference with the establishment official.

N. **Appeal Procedures**. If an issue is not resolved by the Area Director, a summary of the discussion together with the agency's position on the unresolved issues shall be forwarded to the FAPO within 5 working days of the informal conference.

1. The FAPO/Regional Administrator shall confer with the appropriate Regional agency official before making a decision on the unresolved issues.

2. If the FAPO/Regional Administrator, in consultation with the Area Director, decides that the item in question should remain unchanged on the OSHA Notice, the appropriate agency officials shall be advised.

3. If there is still an unresolved issue after the Regional review, the agency may send a letter of appeal to OSHA's Office of Federal Agency Programs (OFAP).

4. Upon receipt of the letter of appeal, the Director, OFAP, shall request pertinent portions of the investigation file and informal conference notes from the Area Director.

5. OFAP shall review the disputed issues and discuss these with top agency officials, as appropriate, to obtain resolution. The decision at the National Office level, in consultation with the Regional Administrator, FAPO, and Area Director, is final.

6. Any changes to the OSHA Notice resulting from agreement during the informal conference procedures or subsequent appeal to OFAP will be made in accordance with private sector procedures.

   NOTE: Contest procedures before the OSHA Review Commission do not apply to Federal agencies.

O. **Verification of Abatement**. Follow private sector guidelines to verify abatement. Notify Certified Committee, if appropriate, of the abatement plan.

P. **Petitions for Modification of Abatement Dates (PMAs)**. When Area Offices receive Federal agency requests for additional abatement time, they shall follow 29 CFR 1903.14(a) and 29 CFR 2200.37, which prescribe PMA procedures for private sector. Since the Occupational Safety and Health Review Commission has no jurisdiction over Federal agencies, and if the Area Director does not agree to extend the abatement date, the agency may bring unresolved issues to the Regional Administrator/FAPO for resolution with his counterpart in the agency. Issues not resolved at the regional level shall be forwarded to the Director, OFAP, for resolution with agency headquarters in consultation with the Regional Administrator, the FAPO, and the Area Director.

Q. **Failure to Abate**. Area Directors shall work with local Federal agency managers in developing an acceptable abatement plan. When this cannot be achieved within 30 calendar days of the abatement date, the following steps shall apply:

1. The Area Director shall send a Notification of Failure-to-Abate Alleged Violation, OSHA-2C Form, (FTA Notice) with inspection form letter "h" ("Notification of Failure to Abate

Alleged Violation") in Appendix D, Section II, to the establishment official. This letter may also contain a general summary of what penalty amounts would have been proposed had they been a private sector employer.

2. The Area Director shall send a copy of the FTA Notice and inspection form letter to the DASHO and representative of employees (a transmittal letter is not required).

   NOTE: For U.S. Army address refer to paragraph L.1.d.(1) NOTE.

3. If the inspection was initiated because of a complaint, the Area Director shall send a copy of the FTA Notice to the complainant with complaint form letter "o" ("Notification to Complainant —Failure to Abate Issued") in Appendix D, Section I.

4. The Area Director shall forward a copy of pertinent portions of the **complete case file** to the FAPO, if the Area Director cannot resolve the issue at the local level.

5. The FAPO shall immediately contact the Federal agency official at the equivalent organizational level with responsibility and authority for the establishment's working conditions, and request the manager to abate the violation(s) or to develop an acceptable abatement plan. If no solution is reached within 60 calendar days, the Regional Administrator shall forward the Area Office case file and written documentation showing the dates, contacts, and results of discussions undertaken at the Regional level to the Director, OFAP.

6. The Director, OFAP, shall, within 30 calendar days, determine which Directorate within OSHA is the most appropriate to review the case file. The Director, Directorate of Compliance Programs (DCP) shall then forward the case file to the appropriate Directorate.

   a. The reviewing Directorate shall have 30 calendar days in which to review the case file and return it to DCP with appropriate recommendations.

   b. If DCP upholds the citation, the Director shall, within 30 calendar days, schedule a meeting with his or her counterpart in the cited Federal agency to discuss OSHA's findings and request an abatement schedule.

   c. If a satisfactory abatement schedule is not received within 60 calendar days, the Assistant Secretary shall schedule a meeting with the DASHO.

   d. If no solution is reached, the Assistant Secretary shall request the Secretary of Labor's involvement.

7. DCP shall provide the Regional Office with a status report every 60 calendar days until the case is resolved.

Joseph A. Dear Assistant Secretary

DISTRIBUTION: National, Regional, and Area Offices Compliance Officers Designated Agency Safety and Health Officials

---

OSHA Instruction FAP 1.3
APPENDIX A
CITABLE ELEMENTS OF 29 CFR PART 1960

PROGRAM ELEMENT EXPLANATION

1960.8(a) This section is the "general duty clause" element, that will replace the Executive Order 201(a) for enforcing serious hazards that are not covered by a standard.

1960.8(b) This element gives specific directions for all agencies to comply with applicable OSHA standards.

1960.8(c) This element gives specific directions to all agencies to develop, implement, and evaluate an occupational safety and health program.

1960.8(d) This element gives specific directions to all agencies to acquire, maintain, and require employee use of approved personal protective equipment (PPE) and other safety equipment.

1960.11 This element provides for accountability of managers and supervisors and can apply equally to all agencies.

1960.12(c) This element directs all agencies to post an agency occupational safety and health poster informing employees of the agency safety and health program.

1960.25(a) The last sentence requiring that necessary equipment to conduct inspections be provided can be enforced in all agencies; the first part of the paragraph is general guidance that may not apply.

1960.25(c) The first sentence requires that each agency inspect each workplace annually. The remaining part of the element is general guidance that may not apply to all agencies.

1960.26(b)(5) The first sentence gives specific imminent danger instructions to the inspector that can apply uniformly. The rest of the paragraph gives guidance dealing with imminent danger that may not apply at all locations.

1960.26(c)(1-4) These elements direct how agencies should handle agency inspection reports and notices of unsafe or unhealthful conditions.

1960.27(a) The first sentence gives specific instructions that the safety and health inspector is in charge of an agency inspection. The rest of the paragraph is general instruction that would be difficult to enforce.

1960.28(d)(3) This element gives specific time frames for an agency to inspect employee reports of hazards.

1960.29(b) This element directs all agencies to investigate accidents resulting in a fatality or hospitalization of five or more employees.

1960.29(d) This element requires agencies to include specific information on all investigative reports of accidents.

1960.30(a-e) This section gives specific abatement directions that apply to all agencies.

1960.34(a-d) This section gives specific directions to General Services Administration (GSA) and other agencies that affect the safety and health programs of agencies in federally owned or leased buildings.

1960.37(b) This section requires equal representation of management and non-management employees for those agencies who choose to have a Certified Safety and Health Committee.

1960.37(d) This element directs that the safety and health committee chairperson alternate between management and non-management and applies equally for those agencies who choose to have a Certified Safety and Health Committee.

1960.37(e) This element requires that safety and health committees meet on a regular schedule and applies to those agencies who choose to have a Certified Safety and Health Committee.

1960.55(a) This element requires agencies to train all supervisory employees on the Act, E.O. 12196, the agency safety and health program, etc.

1960.56(a) This element gives specific directions for training agency safety and health specialists.

1960.57 This section directs agencies to train safety and health inspectors.

1960.58 This section directs agencies to train collateral duty safety and health personnel and committee members.

1960.59(a-b) This section directs agencies to train employees and employee representatives in safety and health appropriate to the work performed.

1960.67(a-c) This section directs all agencies to maintain a record or log of occupational injuries and illnesses.

1960.68 This section directs all agencies to maintain a record or log of occupational injuries and illnesses.

1960.69(a) This element directs all agencies to compile an annual summary of Federal occupational injuries and illnesses.

1960.70(a-c) This section gives directions to all agencies when to report serious accidents to OSHA.

1960.71(b) This element directs the agency to have a copy of the injury and illness log and supplementary records at each establishment.

1960.71(d) This element directs all agencies where and when to post the annual summary.

1960.71(e) This element directs agencies to ensure safety and health committees, employees, former employees and employee representatives have access to the records and reports.

1960.72 This section directs all agencies to make their records available to the Secretary of Labor.

1960.73 This section directs all agencies to retain records for 5 years.

OSHA Instruction FAP 1.3
APPENDIX B
RECORDKEEPING AND REPORTING GUIDELINES FOR FEDERAL AGENCIES
(OSHA Publication 2014)

Under the Williams-Steiger Occupational Safety and Health Act of 1970
U.S. Department of Labor William E. Brock, Secretary
Occupational Safety and Health Administration John A. Pendergrass, Assistant Secretary
Revised 1986
Includes Federal Register Amendments to 29 CFR 1960.70, Vol. 60, No. 72 Friday, April 14, 1995
OSHA 2014

TABLE OF CONTENTS

DEFINITIONS

The following definitions apply to terms used in this booklet:

* **Catastrophe** - A work related incident resulting in three or more employees being hospitalized for inpatient care within 30 days of an incident.

* **Compensation Claims** - Forms submitted to the Department of Labor's office or workers' compensation programs to record and report injured, illnesses, and fatalities arising out of or in the course of employment. Three forms contain items OSHA requires agencies to complete:

    Form CA-1 - Federal Employee's Notice of Traumatic Injury and Claim for Continuation of Pay/Compensation (Appendix G):

    Form CA-2 - Notice of Occupational Disease and Claim for Compensation (Appendix H); and,

    Form CA-6 - Official Superior's Report of Employee's Death (Appendix I).

* **Establishment** - A single physical location where business is conducted or where services or operations are performed. Typically, an "Establishment" refers to a field activity, regional office, and area office, installation or facility.

* **Illness/Disease** - A nontraumatic physiological harm or loss of capacity produced by systemic infection; continued or repeated stress or strain; exposure to toxins, poisons, fumes, etc.; or other continued and repeated exposures to conditions of the work environment over a long period of time. For practical purposes, an occupational illness/disease is any reported condition which does not meet the definition of injury.

* **Incident** - Used to refer to an injury or illness/disease.

* **Injury** - A traumatic wound or other condition of the body caused by external force, including stress or strain. The injury is identifiable as to the time and place of occurrence and member or function of the body affected, and is caused by a specific event or Incident or series of events or incidents within a single day or work shift.

* **Lost Time Case** - A nonfatal traumatic injury that causes any loss of time from work beyond the day or shift on which it occurred; or a nonfatal nontraumatic illness that causes loss of time from work or disability at any time.

* **No Lost Time Case** - A nonfatal incident that does not meet the definition of a lost time case. (Usually created by a compensation claim for medical expense.)

INTRODUCTION

This booklet summarizes Federal Accident Reporting and Recordkeeping requirements of the Occupational Safety and Health Administration (OSHA). It addresses provisions of the Occupational Safety and Health Act of 1970 (PL 91-596), Executive Order 12196, Occupational Safety and Health Programs for Federal Employee, and 29 CFR Part 1960, Basic Program Elements for Federal Employee Occupational Safety and Health Programs.

Federal agencies are required to collect occupational injury and illness data, to analyze this data to identify unsafe and unhealthful working conditions: and to establish program priorities based on their analyses. OSHA is to have access to agency records of occupational injuries and illnesses unless they are specifically required by Executive Order to be kept secret in the Interest of national defense or foreign policy.

OSHA uses injury/illness data from compensation claim forms submitted under the Federal Employees' Compensation Act and provided by the U.S. Department of Labor, Employment Standards Administration, Office of Workers' Compensation Programs (OWCP). OSHA uses the data to set program priorities, identify Federal worksites for OSHA inspections; monitor agencies' progress in reducing occupational injured, illness, and fatalities, and to report on the status of Federal civilian employees' safety and health.

Agencies are required to complete OSHA related items on OWCP compensation claim forms. In 1986 OWCP revised forms CA-1 and CA-2 to accommodate agencies' coding and OWCP's entry of data. The revised forms include labeled blocks for the codes; codes are to be placed n existed blocks on previous forms.

The recordkeeping and reporting provisions described in this booklet cover the basic requirements for all Occupational Safety and Health Programs. Agencies should augment these requirements to design accident prevention programs tailored to their missions, organizations and operations.

Log of Occupational Injuries and Illnesses (1960.67, .69, and .71)

Each establishment must maintain a log of occupational injuries and illnesses to provide a quick and current view of workplace safety and health throughout the establishment. The format shown in Appendix A, or one with the same 12 data items, is to be used for the log. The log is to be completed with six working days after receiving information on an incident. All injuries, illnesses and fatalities for which a CA-1, 2 or 6 is filed **with OWCP** shall be logged. CA-1's submitted to document an injury or exposure are to be placed in the employee's official personnel or medical folder, not sent to OWCP, there is no lost time or medical reimbursement required.

Claims controverted or otherwise challenged shall be logged but may be deleted if OWCP denies the legitimacy of the claims. Claims resulting in permanent transfer, termination of employment or subsequent granting of Continuation of Pay (COP) shall be recorded as lost time cases. Maintenance of logs at area or regional levels is permitted if there is quarterly feedback of data to each establishment for access by management, employee representatives, employees and OSHA.

Yearly totals of all injuries/illnesses/fatalities shall be posted in each establishment within 45 days of the close of the fiscal year and shall remain posted for 30 consecutive days. The log format (Appendix A) with the right lower part completed may be used for this posting requirement.

Supplementary Records (1960.68)

An incident resulting in a fatality, a lost time case, or medical expense, including termination and permanent transfer, warrants investigation, analysis and documentation on a supplementary record. The supplementary record should identify the personnel, equipment, and activities involved, as well as the causes and contributing factors. OSHA Form 131 (Appendix B), OWCP Form CA-1, 2 and 6, or equivalent agency forms, may be used for supplementary records.

Supplementary records shall be completed within six working days after receipt of information that an accident has occurred. If OWCP forms are use to meet OSHA's requirement for supplementary records, copies shall be maintained in the occupational safety and/or health office.

Regardless of the form used as a supplementary record, agencies shall complete OWCP forms CA-1, CA-2 and CA-6 as described in this publication. Privacy Act restrictions applicable to OWCP records shall be maintained for OWCP forms and data when they are used in relation to accident prevention.

Agency Coding of Forms CA-1, CA-2 and CA-6 (1960.68)

OSHA required agencies to code items on the CA-1, CA-2 and CA-6 prior to their submission to OWCP. Appendix C summarizes where the codes are to be placed on the new (CA-1 and CA-2, revised 1986) and old versions of the forms. New forms have coding blocks for the OSHA-related items. On old forms, the codes are to be **added to** information required by the title of the block.

Occupation Code

Identify the occupation by writing the two letters of the employee's Pay Plan (i.e. "GS," "GM," "WG," etc.) and the four numbers of the occupational series, as listed on the employee's most recent "Notification of Personnel Action", (OPM Standard Form 50). Occupational series are listed in the Federal Personnel Manual Supplement 292-1, "Personnel Data Standards." For U.S. Postal Service employees, write "PS", followed by the first four number of the occupation code. For employees who perform service for the Federal government, but do not have job titles that fall under the usual job classification systems, see Appendix D, Nonstandard Occupation Codes.

Type and Source Codes

Type and Source Codes are used to described what caused the incident. The type code stands for an **action** and the Source Code for an **object or substance**. Together, they form a brief description of how the incident occurred. Where there are two different sources, code the initiating source of the incident (see example 1, below). Type and Source codes are given in Appendix

E. Example are:
   1. An employee tripped on carpet Type: 210 (fell on same level) and struck his head on a desk. Source: 0110 (walking/working surface) **NOTE**: This example would NOT be coded 120 (struck against) and 0140 (furniture).
   2. A letter carrier was bitten. Type: 440 (bitten by) by dog. Source: 0911 (dog)
   3. A forest ranger contracted Type: 510 (contact) dermatitis from poison ivy. Source: 0920 (plant)
   4. A nurse contracted hepatitis Type: 410 (punctured by) after being punctured by a Source: 0831 (needle) contaminated needle.
   5. An employee was driving a Type: 800 (traveling in) government vehicle when it Source: 0421 (government-owned was struck by another vehicle. vehicle, as driver)
      NOTE: The type code 800, "traveling in" is different from the other type codes in that its function is not to identify factors contributing to the injury or fatality, but rather to collect data on the type of vehicle the employee was operating or traveling in at the time of the incident.

Agencies desiring additional codes to cover hazards of their operations should contact the Office of Federal Agency Programs, telephone 202-219-9329.

OWCP Agency Code

The OWCP Agency Code ("chargeback code") is a four-digit (or four-digit plus two letter) code used to identify the employee's agency. Agencies wishing to expand from a four digit to a six-digit Code must contact the Office of Workers' Compensation Programs, telephone 202-219-8463.

Duty Station Zip Code

Duty Station Zip Codes should be entered in the blocks indicated in Appendix C. For an employee officially detailed to another duty station, use the Zip Code for the temporary duty station. **DO NOT** enter the zip code of a central office processing compensation forms in these blocks.

OSHA Site Code

If OSHA finds that the OWCP Codes and the Duty Station Zip Code do not effectively identify an agency's establishments, OSHA will require the agency to develop OSHA Site Codes. In most cases the agency will be able to use existing codes - financial management codes or unit identification codes, for example. Agencies wishing to establish OSHA Site Code may contact the Office of Federal Agency Programs, telephone: 202-219-9329.

Fatality and Catastrophe Notification (1960.70)

Agencies must notify OSHA within 8 hours of each work related fatality or inpatient hospitalization of three or more employees. This requirement applies to each such fatality or hospitalization of three or more employees which occurs within thirty (30) days of an incident.

Notification can be made by telephone or in person to the OSHA area office nearest the site of the incident or by using the OSHA toll-free central phone number 1-800-321-OSHA.

Notification to OSHA shall include:
* Establishment Name
* Number of fatalities and/or hospitalized employees
* Time, date, location and brief description of the incident
* Contact person and phone number.

Agencies shall provide the Office of Federal Agency Programs with a summary report of each fatal and catastrophic accident investigation. The summary should include the information listed above, causal factors, the effectiveness of applicable standards, and proposed corrective/preventive actions.

Access to and Retention of Records and Reports (1960.71, .72 and .73)

Agencies shall publicize the availability of and provide access to establishment logs and annual injury/illness summaries. Access to these documents shall be provided to establishment agency safety and health personnel, establishment occupational safety and health committees, employees, employee representatives and former employees with a need to know, and to the Secretary of Labor, Secretary of Health and Human Services and their authorized representatives. Records and reports shall be maintained by the agency for five years following the end of the fiscal year to which they relate.

Agency Annual Report (1960.74)

By January 1st of each year, agencies shall submit a report to the Secretary of Labor describing the previous fiscal year's occupational safety and health program. Guidelines for the report are provided in Appendix F.

[Editor's note Appendix A and B omitted.]

Appendix C

Summary of OSHA Items Agencies Must Code on Compensation Forms

---

FORM CA-1 FORM CA-2 FORM CA-6

ITEM OLD NEW OLD NEW OLD (REVISED (REVISED (REVISED (REVISED (REVISED 1983) 1986) 1985) 1986) 1976)

OCCUPA- BLOCK 12. SHADED BLOCK 7. SHADED BLOCK 13. TION EMPLOYEE'S BOX "a" OCCUPATION BOX "a" WAS EMPLOYEE CODE OCCUPATION OCCUPATION OCCUPATION IN PERFORMANCE CODE CODE OF DUTY WHEN INJURY OCCURRED?

TYPE OF BLOCK 13. SHADED BLOCK 15. SHADED BLOCK 12. INJURY CAUSE OF BOX "b" NATURE BOX "b" DESCRIBE HOW ILLNESS INJURY TYPE OF THE TYPE INJURY CODE CODE DISEASE CODE OCCURRED

SOURCE BLOCK 13. SHADED BLOCK 15. SHADED BLOCK 12. OF CAUSE OF BOX "c" NATURE BOX "c" DESCRIBE HOW INJURY INJURY SOURCE OF THE SOURCE INJURY ILLNESS CODE DISEASE CODE OCCURRED CODE

OWCP. BLOCK 22. BLOCK 17. BLOCK 23. BLOCK 19. BLOCK 6. AGENCY BUREAU OR OWCP BU- REAU OR OWCP BUREAU OR CODE OFFICE AGENCY OFFICE AGNECY OFFICE CODE CODE

OSHA BLOCK 17. BLOCK 19. SITE ---- OSHA SITE ---- OSHA SITE ---- CODE CODE (AS CODE (AS NECESSARY) NECESSARY)

DUTY BLOCK 7. BLOCK 18. BLOCK 8. BLOCK 20 BLOCK 5. STATION NAME AND DUTY NAME AND DUTY DEPARTMENT ZIP ADDRESS STATION ADDRESS STATION OR CODE OF OF AGENCY EMPLOYING EMPLOYING AGENCY AGENCY

Appendix D
Nonstandard Occupation Code
"Nonemployees" covered by OWCP:

| | | CODE | TITLE | CODE | TITLE

?0136 | PEACE CORPS VOLUNTEER | ?0060 | CHAPLAIN ?0083 | NON-FED. LAW ENF. OFF. | ?1863 | STATE/LOCAL AGRI INSP. ?0021 | VISTA VOLUNTEER | ?0030 | SPORTS CLINIC PERFORM. ?0243 | NEIGHBORHOOD YC ENROLL | ?0188 | ENTERTAINER/ARMED FORCES ?0243 | JOB CORPS ENROLLEE | ?0243 | VOCATIONAL TRAINEE ?0302 | MAIL MESSENGER | ?0460 | FOREST SERVICE COOPERATOR ?3501 | CONTRACT JOB CLEANER | ?1316 | GAGE READER, CORPS ENGRS ?0621 | STUDENT NURSE | ?4701 | MAINTENANCE WORKERS, HUD ?0462 | FOREST SRVC VOLUNTEER | ?0026 | NAT'L PARK SRVC VOLUNTR ?1341 | VOL. WEATHER OBSERVER | ?0204 | NAT'L DEFENS EXEC RESERV ?0099 | STATE MARTME ACAD CADT | ?1740 | NAT'L TEACHRS CORPS MBR ?0099 | ROTC CADET | ?0610 | CONTRACT NURSE ?0930 | FEDERAL JUROR | ?0602 | CONTRACT PHYSICIAN ?2181 | CIVIL AIR PATROL VOL. | ?0630 | NUTRITIONAL-AIDE, USDA ?0685 | VOL. HOSPITAL WORKER | ?1740 | READER FOR THE BLIND ?0243 | YOUTH CONS. CORPS VOL. | ?1016 | TRUST EMPL SMITHSONIAN ?0475 | CNTY AGWT, DEPT. AGRI. | ?0457 | SOIL/WATER CONS DIST EMPL ?3506 | STUDENT AIDE | ?0243 | YTH/ADLT CONS CORPS ENRLL ?9825 | SEAMAN | ?0099 | MILITARY ACAD CADET ?0204 | COAST GUARD RES MEMBR | ?0006 | VOL TRAINEE PROBATION OFF ?0204 | COAST GUARD AUX MEMBR | ?0006 | URBAN CRIME PREV PROG VOL ?0023 | NAT'L PARK SRVC COLLAB | ?0345 | CONGRESSIONAL STAFF MBR ?0099 | COLLEGE WK/STDY PARTIC. | |

[Editor's note: Appendix E omitted.]
Appendix F
Guidelines for Agency's Annual
Occupational Safety and Health Report to the Secretary of Labor

Fiscal Year: _____

Name of Agency (Department): _____

Name of Component: _____

Address: _____

Number of employees covered by this report: _____

Name of individual responsible for the occupational safety and health program of the agency or component covered by this report: _____

Title: _____ Telephone number: _____

Each agency shall:

1.a. Use agency injury/illness data to display the annual statistics for fatalities and lost time disabilities for the report year and, if possible, compare these fatalities and disabilities with similar statistics for the previous three-year period. Data based on agency claims submitted to OWCP is preferred, but internal accident or incident reporting data (FARS) is acceptable, if OWCP data is not available to the agency. The data should be displayed in charts or tables so that changes can be easily seen or demonstrated.

b. Use agency data to display the most recent OWCP chargeback and COP costs and, if possible, compare these costs with similar statistics for the previous three-year period. The data should be displayed in charts or tables so that changes can be easily seen or demonstrated.

c. Use agency accident or incident reporting system or supplemental reports to the OSHA logs or the OWCP reports for details which will help explain any significant trends and major causes or sources of fatalities and lost time disabilities which occurred last year(s).

2. Describe safety and occupational health program accomplishments and initiatives implemented last fiscal year to control the trends and major causes or sources of fatalities and lost time disabilities in your agency and to improve your agency's overall safety and occupational health programs. Discuss your successes and/or failures as a result of your agency's implementation of these initiatives. Explain any significant onetime or additional permanent resources allocated to the safety and occupational health program last year for areas such as: workplace hazard abatement, research and development, data systems, staffing, training, etc. Attach a copy of any significant safety and occupational health policy or proclamation related to those initiatives.

In describing your accomplishments and initiatives, please try to explain your agency's efforts in the following areas:

- Accomplishments for assuring that workers, supervisors and committee members received appropriate job health and safety awareness and hazard recognition information and training.
- Accomplishments for assessing the effectiveness of your safety and occupational health programs.
- Accomplishments in the identification, assessment and resolution of safety and health problems, including your agency's system of (a) providing recognition to outstanding achievers and (b) establishing accountability and performance standards for managers, supervisors and employees. - Unique or significant accomplishments that your agency made last year to enhance employee participation, involvement and consultation in the safety and occupational health program.

3. Identify your annual OSH plans, goals and objectives, and significant OSH initiatives planned and programmed for the coming year(s).

4. Provide comments, requests and recommendations for consideration by OSHA's Office of Federal Agency Programs (OFAP) in Government-wide occupational safety and health programs or report any items of special interest concerning occupational safety and health activities or programs. (Optional)

It is suggested that the report be in executive summary format and be limited to ten pages exclusive of attachments.

[Editor's note: Appendix G—J omitted.]

OSHA Instruction FAP 1.3
APPENDIX C
EVALUATION OF FEDERAL AGENCY OCCUPATIONAL
SAFETY AND HEALTH PROGRAMS

A. **Purpose and Scope**. This Appendix describes the Occupational Safety and Health Program Evaluation guidelines for evaluation of Federal Agency occupational safety and health programs as required by the regulations at 29 CFR Part 1960. OSHA field staff most directly affected are the Federal Agency Program Officers (FAPOs).

B. **Background.** A task force consisting primarily of Federal Agency Program Officers (FAPOs) was appointed in November 1992 to develop new procedures for conducting Federal agency safety and health program evaluations. These procedures are based on their recommendations.

1. These procedures are intended to provide FAPOs increased latitude in that they:

a. Give FAPOs an opportunity to plan and schedule Federal agency field reviews in their Regions.

     b. Give FAPOs an opportunity to select the particular sites for review at those Federal agencies in their Regions whose safety and health programs are to be evaluated.

2. This Appendix establishes the overall objectives for the field review activity carried out by the FAPOs:

     a. To conduct at least four field reviews per Region per year.

     b. To conduct as many field reviews in conjunction with targeted inspections as possible. In so doing, to de-emphasize the additional use of Area Office personnel for evaluation field reviews.

     c. To provide the Federal agency sites and the nation wide evaluation program with high quality field reviews based on the following indicators:

        (1) Time frames set forth in this Appendix are met;

        (2) Well documented, thorough analysis and review of the site; and.

        (3) Significant findings which can be implemented at the site.

3. These procedures will provide more timely feedback to the Federal agencies and speed up the Agency-wide evaluation process.

C. **Regional Field Reviews**.

1. **Agency Selection.** The Director, Office of Federal Agency Programs, will annually provide the Regional Administrators with a rolling two-year listing of agencies to be evaluated over the following two years. Federal Agency Program Officers (FAPOs), in consultation with Area Office Directors, will use this information to select the Federal agency sites where they plan to conduct field reviews.

2. **Field Reviews.** In order to ensure that Federal agencies receive more regular feedback on their occupational safety and health programs, each FAPO will be expected to conduct at least four field reviews annually at the Federal agency sites of their choice. These sites may be at one agency or divided among deferent agencies.

3. **Notification of OFAP.** In order to assure a coordinated range of sites, the Regions should notify OFAP of the sites they have selected for review.

4. **Field Review Frequency.** The goal for each FAPO is to distribute the four field reviews evenly throughout the year. Although the scheduling is at the discretion of the FAPO, the field review reports are needed for input into the Agency-wide evaluations and effort should be made to avoid creating a last quarter logjam.

5. **Procedures**. FAPOs should use the field review procedures described in Attachment I. When conducting field reviews in conjunction with targeted inspections, the field review procedures will take precedence.

6. **Report Format**. A site report will be written by the FAPO, using a simplified format, with a cover narrative summary and with recommendations for corrective action. The grid format will be provided, on computer disk, to each FAPO. FAPOs are encouraged to load this format on the laptop computer which they will use onsite to prepare the report. FAPOs will forward the report to the top manager at the site, with copies to the Agency Safety and Health Official and OFAP.

D. **Agency-Wide Evaluations.**

1. **Agencies to be Evaluated**. The Assistant Secretary for OSHA will identify the agencies to be evaluated over the following two years. The Office of Federal Agency Programs (OFAP) will annually provide the Regional Administrators with an updated list of these agencies.

2. **Components of the Agency-Wide Evaluations**. OFAP will develop the report of the agency-wide evaluations based on: (1) a two-year history of the Regional field review reports and workplace compliance inspections, (2) written program information provided by the agency, including its annual report and (3) interviews of agency personnel, including headquarters personnel.

3. **Role of OFAP**.

     a. **Interface with Regional Administrators.** OFAP will provide FAPOs with periodic reports on the progress nationwide in completing needed field review reports for the agencies to be evaluated. This information will be provided in order for the FAPOs to select Agency sites for review.

b. **Interface with Federal Agencies.** OFAP will request detailed information on Agencies' safety and health programs from the Agencies. Agencies being evaluated will be asked to complete a "baseline questionnaire" consisting of key information on their plans and procedures for administering their nationwide occupational safety and health program.

c. **Evaluation Steps.** OFAP will review agency program documents, interview managers, and travel to subagency or command headquarters levels, as necessary. OFAP will conduct the opening and closing conferences and prepare the written report in accordance with the regulations at 29 CFR Part 1960. d. **Reports.** The Federal Agency evaluation reports will consist of an Executive Summary and appropriate appendices including, at a minimum, a chart comparing the Federal agency safety and health program with the requirements at 29 CFR Part 1960, analysis of statistics, and major recommendations.

ATTACHMENT I
FIELD REVIEW PROCEDURES

A. **Purpose:** These procedures are based on practices in wide-spread use in the field

B. **Obtain Site Documentation Before the Scheduled Field Review**. Before the scheduled field review, the Federal Agency Program Officer shall contact the top manager at the site concerning the following information. In order to shorten the time Federal reviewers are on site, the site should be requested to provide as many of these documents as possible in advance. The others should be assembled and available at the start of the review. At a minimum the basic written program and the injury and illness logs should be provided in advance.

1. **TOP MANAGEMENT SUPPORT**
   a. **Policy Statements**.
      - Sample policy statement received from agency head. - Any policy statements issued by facility manager.
   b. **Program Documentation**.
      - Written safety and health program documentation transmitted from the agency to the facility.
      - Written program documentation developed at the facility.
   c. **Personal Participation**
      - Any memos on safety and health issues from the facility manager during the past year.
   d. **Accountability**.
      - Sample (blank) performance standards for managers.
   e. **Resources**.
      - List of occupational safety and health staff by job titles.
      - Training and experience of Occupational Safety and Health staff.

2. **PROGRAM PLANNING**
   a. **Goals and Objectives**.
      - Any documentation showing Agency safety and health goals.
      - Any documentation showing facility safety and health goals.
   b. **Management Information System.**
      - Copies of the log of injuries and illnesses.
      - Any feedback from agency on injury/illness statistics.

3. **PROGRAM IMPLEMENTATION**
   a. **Employee Rights and Involvement**.
      - Copy of the safety and health poster.
      - Written procedures for employees to report hazards anonymously.
      - Copy of log of employee reports of hazardous conditions going back one year.

- Copy of safety and health provisions in the collective bargaining agreement.
  b. **Reprisal Policy and Procedures**.
  - Copies of most recent investigations of reprisals (if any).
  c. **Occupational Safety and Health Committees.**
  - Minutes of last two safety and health committee meetings, if any.
  d. **Federal Safety and Health Councils**.
  - Names of facility personnel who are members of Councils, if any.
  e. **Training.**
  - List any facility-wide occupational safety and health training courses that have been provided within the past year, with class roster.
  f. **Recordkeeping**.
  - Attach the facilities' log of injuries and illnesses for the past two years.
  g. **Inspections.**
  - Attach the most recent facility inspection report(s) (both safety and health if they are separate).
  h. **Hazard Abatement**.
  - Attach the facility's written abatement procedures.
  - Attach the facility's written hazard abatement log.
  i. **Standards Compliance and Adoption.**
  - Identify any standards other than OSHA standards which are being followed.
4. **PROGRAM EVALUATION**
  - Attach the safety and health site evaluation report, if any.
C. **Field Review Procedures.**
  1. **Review Written Materials.** Review of written materials provided by the site will establish the basis for the field review. The purpose of the field review will be to determine the extent of program implementation and effectiveness at the facility.
  2. **Telephone Contact**. The FAPO should telephone the site manager, discuss the list of materials needed, and come to agreement on a time for the field review. (The FAPO can communicate that this is an opportunity for the site to demonstrate their program. If they do not produce the requested documentation, we will assume it does not exist.) The telephone call should be followed by a letter for clarification and accountability. The FAPO should request that the site manager invite union representative(s) to the opening conference. Upon request, a separate opening and closing conference will be held for union representatives.
  3. **Onsite Review**. The onsite review will usually be carried out by a team consisting of the FAPO, a safety specialist and an industrial hygienist. Depending on the complexity of the site, and at the discretion of the FAPO, the FAPO may sometimes conduct the review alone. When field reviews are conducted in conjunction with a targeted inspection, the safety specialist and health specialist shall be CSHOs from the Area Office scheduled to conduct the targeted inspection.
  4. **Pre-Review Planning.** If the field review is not conducted in conjunction with a targeted inspection, a field review team consisting of the FAPO and any necessary support must be appointed.
    a. The FAPO will make all necessary arrangements with the site manager.
    b. The team members will review the written program documentation well in advance and prepare for the onsite review.
    c. The FAPO will conduct a team strategy meeting prior to the onsite review. This meeting may be held by teleconference for convenience.
  5. **Onsite Review**. The onsite review consists of the following sections:
    a. **Opening Conference.** Hold with facility officials and employee representatives, or schedule separate opening conference with employee representatives.

b. **Document Review.** Verify the information submitted with the application.

c. **Site Walkthrough**. Assess whether the program is operating as described.

d. **Employee interviews.** Conduct to determine level of involvement in and perceptions of the site safety and health program.

e. **Presentation of Findings.** Site representatives will conduct a closing conference at the conclusion of the field review, and give the site manager a draft report of the findings.

D. **Field Review Preparation.**

1. **The Team.** The size will depend upon the site and the complexity of the potential hazards. Field review teams should be composed of:

   a. The Federal Agency Program Officer is responsible for the onsite review. For the FAPO to lead the review he or she should have a thorough knowledge of the regulations at 29 CFR Part 1960, good knowledge of safety and health program management, and prior experience in previous onsite reviews.

   b. A safety specialist c. An industrial hygienist

2. **Arrangements.** Arrangements for the field review will be coordinated by the FAPO.

   a. **Schedule.** The FAPO will contact the site manager by phone to determine a convenient time for the onsite field review and explain the purpose and general activities of this review. A follow-up letter should be sent to confirm arrangements if time allows.

      (1) The FAPO should ascertain several dates convenient for the field review team and suggest these dates to the site manager.

      (2) The duration of the field review will depend upon the size of the site and the complexity of the operations. Usually the visit will take about one week.

      (3) In the case of the Department of Defense sites, let the site manager know which command(s) will be included in the review.

   b. **Documentation**. To save time during the field review the FAPO should review as much documentation as possible in advance. A suggested list of these items is included in paragraph B of this attachment. If other items will be needed at the site, provide the site representative with a suggested list of items to have ready for the team's review.

   c. **Room Arrangements**. Arrange the use of a room for document reviews and interviews. If it appears that a word processor will be helpful and can conveniently be made available, arrange during this call.

   d. Determine whether any special security clearances are required for admission to the buildings and areas of this facility that need to be visited. If they are required, ensure that the team has such clearances, adjusting the team membership as necessary.

3. **Advance Planning Responsibilities for Team Members.**

   a. **Review of Written Information**. Team members should review the site's written documentation carefully well in advance of the field review visit.

   b. **Information Needed Onsite.** Team members should make notes concurring any other data which must be obtained during the onsite portion of the field review.

   c. **Checklist.** Team members should carefully review the safety and health program documentation and compile a checklist to use during the documentation review and walkthrough. The training program should be included on that list.

   d. **Onsite Questions**. The FAPO should carefully review the written documentation, compile the list of additional documents to be reviewed and questions to be asked, and provide the list to team members during the strategy meeting. The list can be augmented with questions suggested by the other team members.

4. **Strategy Meeting**. Shortly before the scheduled field review, the FAPO will hold a strategy meeting with all the team members to plan the details and to assign specific tasks.

   a. **Timing**. The FAPO should carefully plan the time onsite because there is much to accomplish in a short time.

    b. **Briefing.** The FAPO should ascertain whether the team members are familiar with both onsite procedures and the written documentation for the site, and if not, provide a quick review.

    c. **Program Evidence.** The FAPO should discuss the various signs of an effective safety and health program in action, for example:

      (1) Conditions are good,

      (2) Employees are aware of hazards and what management has done to control them, and knowledgeable about how to protect themselves and how to notify management about safety and health concerns; and

      (3) Management is fully involved in hazard prevention and control, and these efforts are thoroughly tracked.

      (4) Accident experience is being systematically and programmatically addressed.

    d. **Assignments**. The FAPO should make specific onsite assignments to utilize each team member's expertise most effectively. The FAPO may assign responsibility for various sections of the report to other team members. This should be done at the strategy meeting so they are aware of this responsibility while conducting the field review.

E. **Opening Conference**. The opening conference with the top management and employee representatives will set the stage for the onsite review, letting everyone know what to expect and what assistance will be needed. During this session, the team should be able to get a sense of the extent that commitment exists for workplace safety and health.

  1. **Discussion Topics**. The FAPO should convey the following information.

    a. **Goals.** Clearly state that the goals of the field review visit are to assess the adequacy of the safety and health program at the site.

    b. **Schedule**. Briefly cover what activities the field review will entail and the appropriate timing of each stage.

    c. **Interviews**. Indicate that some private interviews of supervisors and employees will be required and request cooperation. Explain that these individuals will be selected randomly. In addition, there will be some brief conversations with employees during the walkthrough.

    d. **Handling Hazards.** Explain what will happen during the site walkthrough, and explain abatement requirements for any hazards identified.

      (1) Immediate correction is expected.

      (2) For any hazards that cannot be corrected before the team leaves the site, a **Notice of Unsafe or Unhealthful Working Conditions** will be issued.

      (3) If the hazards are abated before the team leaves the site, a **Notice of Unsafe or Unhealthful Working Conditions** will be issued, but marked "abated."

    e. **Status.** Explain that when the field review is over, the team will discuss its findings with management and appropriate employee representatives to clarify any misconceptions. Explain that they will be given an opportunity to review the draft copy of the report prior to the final report being issued. Offer to provide a brief status update at the end of each day.

F. **Documentation.** To the extent possible, all documents should be reviewed prior to beginning the onsite review.

  1. **Safety and Health Program.** Review documentation of all aspects of the safety and health program for compliance with 29 CFR Part 1960. This will include inspections, training, hazard abatement, accountability, complaint and reprisal procedure, PPE, and other Part 1960 requirements.

  2. **Recordkeeping**. Review of the injury and illness records is important in determining which are the more hazardous work areas, and whether the site is maintaining accurate and appropriate records.

    a. The team should review the log and a sample of CA-1, CA-2, and CA-6 Office of Workers' Compensation Program forms to see if injuries and illnesses were properly recorded.

b. Discrepancies should be discussed with the recordkeeper.

3. **Health Program Documentation.** Review documentation of potential health hazards, such as basic industrial hygiene survey and monitoring records which are required by relevant health standards. Documentation of the hazard communication system should be checked to ensure that worksite personnel have been properly trained and are aware of chemical products brought onto the worksite.

4. **Committee Records.** If there are certified safety and health committees, minutes and other records should be reviewed to determine if the committees are properly structured and are fulfilling the requirements of Part 1960.

G. **Site Walkthrough.**

1. **Purpose.** The site walkthrough is intended to determine whether the safety and health program is being appropriately implemented at the site.

2. **Scope**.

a. All team members should walk through enough of the site to verify their findings from the review of the written program, and to see the program as it is implemented at the site.

b. The safety and health specialists must see enough of the site to understand the types of hazards that might exist and to determine that they are being addressed systematically by the site safety and health program.

c. If the site being assessed is a targeted site, the team should follow standard targeted inspection procedures.

3. **Problem Areas**. If the previous inspection record or the log shows repeated problems of certain types or in certain areas, special attention should be given to them.

4. **Interviews**. During the walkthrough, safety and health specialists shall talk briefly to randomly selected employees at their work stations and ask **them to** explain the work procedures and the use of (and the maintenance of, where applicable) any personal protective equipment being used. (Additional questions are included in Attachment 11.)

5. **Safety Specialist Review**. The safety specialist shall:

a. Follow the process flow where possible.

b. Look for evidence that categories of hazards such as walking-working surfaces, fire safety, storage and handling of general materials, machine guarding, powered tools, and welding are appropriately managed.

c. Make notes concerning those categories that need unproved attention and management.

d. Relate the problems which are visible in the work areas to documents reviewed concerning work procedures; emergency planning; self-inspection procedures and reports; complaints or reports of hazards from employees; and make notes concerning program improvements needed to provide the management systems which would prevent these problems, if any.

6. **Industrial Hygiene Review**. The industrial hygienist shall:

a. Follow the process flow where possible.

b. Based on review of monitoring records and material data sheets, check known potential hazard areas for possible problems in work practices; ventilation; storage, handling and use of toxic materials; emergency equipment; respirator usage and maintenance; and noise and radiation protective measures where applicable.

c. Look for evidence that hazards are appropriately managed.

d. Make notes concerning any areas that need improvement.

e. Relate these problems to documents reviewed concerning safe work practices and training, the respirator program, industrial hygiene sampling and analysis, hazard communication systems, etc., and make notes concerning program improvements needed to provide the management systems to prevent these problems, if any.

H. **Interviews.**
   1. **Purpose.** Employee interviews are conducted to ascertain the extent of involvement and the awareness of employees in the safety and health program.
   2. **Guidelines.** Private employee interviews (supervisors, maintenance personnel, committee members, and/or other employees can be conducted simultaneously with the site walkthrough. In this case the team member will select employees at random who can be spared from the work station for a few minutes and send them back for interviews with the FAPO and backup leader, when applicable, on a staggered schedule. Interviews should be conducted in a manner which keeps work disruption at a minimum. Interview questions are provided in Attachment II for formal interviews with supervisors, employees, and employee representatives.
      a. **Supervisors.** A few supervisors, the number depending on the size of the facility, should be interviewed using the interview questions in Attachment II.
      b. **Maintenance Personnel.** It is often a good idea to interview a few maintenance personnel. This would be especially important in work situations where high hazard chemicals or biological wastes are present.
      c. **Committee Members.** In the agencies with certified committees, at least one management member and one employee member should be interviewed.
      d. **Other employees.** It is helpful to interview other employees during the field review. They may be able to offer additional insights on program implementation. Employees should be informed that the interview is voluntary.
         (1) **Kinds of Employee Interviews.** The following two kinds of interviews can be conducted:
            (a) Informal, brief chats with employees at their work stations.
            (b) More formal interviews in a private area away from the work station.
         (2) **Selecting the Employees.** The number of employees formally interviewed is constrained by the time allowed for the whole field review.
            (a) Time for each formal interview should be estimated as approximately 15-25 minutes.
            (b) Total time for formal employee interviews should take no longer than the time needed for team members to walk through the work areas.
            (c) One method of selection involves going to areas where most hazards are expected to occur and selecting employees at random.
            (d) The team must be flexible in choosing the most sensible method of selection given the characteristics of the site and any concerns expressed by the employer. Where possible a representative sample based on grade levels, gender, and racial composition of the agency should be sought.
            (e) Some first line supervisors must be interviewed to document the results of training and accountability.
      e. **Use of Interview Questions.** The team members shall assure each interviewee that responses will be treated confidentially and that the answers they give will not by themselves be responsible for the findings of the team. Discuss reprisal rights in the event of harassment or other types of discrimination for participating in the interviews.
         (1) **Record Responses.** The interviewer will use the list of questions to guide the interview and to note the employee response.
         (2) **Suitability.** Not every question listed need be asked and others may be substituted or added. The interviewer must use judgement as to which are most relevant at any given site or for any given interviewee.
         (3) **Other Relevant Information.** The interviewer's perception and discussion of any relevant matter not indicated on the list of questions should also be recorded.
      f. **Evaluating Responses.** Professional judgement is essential in assessing the implementation of a safety and health program. In evaluating employee perceptions of worksite

conditions and the safety and health program, it is important to be mindful that the small number of interviews that time permits only enables the team to obtain general impressions rather than draw conclusions which carry the weight of a valid statistical sample.

    (1) **Factors Impacting Responses.** Many factors may enter into the response that an individual employee may give, for example:

        (a) Individual employees may have personal agendas to follow in supplying answers to questions.

        (b) Factors affecting employee morale, including reductions-in-force or furloughs, may be causing temporary antagonism between the employer and employees.

    (2) **Pattern**. The team should look for an overall pattern. Employee responses which are supported by information obtained by other employee interviews, document review or observation should carry the most weight.

I. **Preparation for Briefing on Findings.**

1. When the documentation review, the employee interviews, and the walkthrough have been completed, the FAPO should ascertain that the team has seen everything that the site representative believes is relevant and that the representative is satisfied that the team has a good "picture" of the safety and health program in action. The FAPO should specifically address any unresolved issues noted by the team.

2. **Briefing Schedule.** The briefing(s) should then be scheduled to give time to get on appropriate calendars.

    a. The briefing(s) should be scheduled at least 24 hours after the end of the field review in order to allow time to prepare a draft report.

    b. The number of briefings will depend on whether the employee representatives attend the management closing briefing or a separate briefing is held for them.

    c. A preliminary meeting may be scheduled with the site safety and health staff to discuss general findings before writing begins.

J. **Preparation of Findings.**

1. **Findings Meeting.** The team should meet privately (off-site if possible) to review and summarize their findings.

    a. Discussion of Findings and Conclusion. Allow time for complete discussion of issues and reaching consensus prior to the oral presentation of findings and drafting the report.

    b. **Discussion Guide**. The grid report format provided to the FAPO may be useful as a discussion guide.

2. **Responsibility**. The FAPO is responsible for organizing the findings from team input.

    a. **Organization of Findings**. The findings should be organized for the briefing presentation as a comparison to the program requirements contained in 29 CFR Part 1960.

    b. **Hazard Correction.** Safety and health specialists should state, both during this meeting and at the presentation of findings which allows, the apparent violations, if any, that they have noted, any **Notices of Unsafe or** Unhealthful Working, Conditions that may be issued, and the correction plans they have discussed with management.

    c. **Examples of Problems.** Where more general problems have been detected, the team should be prepared to give examples.

    d. **Confidentiality.** Care should be taken to protect the confidentiality of information provided by employees, specifically or in general, whether negative or positive. On one hand, the sample of employees could be small enough to make identification fairly supple. On the other hand, the sample may be too small to provide anything more than confirmation of what the team has gathered from other sources

    e. **Consensus**. The team should come to consensus on the major findings and recommendations that will be presented to management at the closing briefing.

3. **Guidelines**. In summarizing the findings, the team must consider the following information in relation to the program requirements contained in 29 CFR Part 1960.

a. What has been observed in the work areas.
b. The kind of accidents or illnesses in the log and in the workers' compensation data in terms of what documentation has been seen.
c. What employees, their representatives, and, where applicable, committee members have said about the program and conditions.
d. The degree to which the written program is implemented and adequately covers the potential hazards of the facility.

   EXAMPLE: If the log and workers' compensation data indicate few head, foot and eye injuries; the team has seen documentation of training and enforcement of safety rules concerning the wearing of hard hats, safety shoes and safety glasses; all employees in areas requiring such equipment were wearing them and at least some show signs of wear; and information gathered by the team confirms that they wear the equipment and that management enforces the wearing of equipment; then the team can say without hesitation that the personal protective equipment program for safety is working well.

K. **Presentation of Findings**. The major findings and recommendations of the team must be presented before leaving the site.

   1. **Purpose**. The purpose of this briefing is to inform management and employee representatives of the major findings of the field review. Findings and recommendations will be presented in terms of the site safety and health program's compliance with the requirements of 29 CFR Part 1960.
   2. **Measures.** Presentation of the findings should give the applicant a clear idea of how the site measures up to the 29 CFR Part 1960 requirements for the program. This includes:
      (1) Rates and recordkeeping.
      (2) Employee involvement in the safety and health program to the extent of having an impact on safety and health decisions.
      (3) A qualitative review of the site safety and health program in relation to the basic minimum requirements contained in 29 CFR Part 1960 and in relation to the potential hazards of the facility.
   3. **Hazards**. If serious hazards have been noted, they must be discussed along with the agreed-upon time and means of abatement. Any **Notices of Unsafe or Unhealthful Working Conditions** which are expected to be issued should be discussed.
   4. **Federal Safety and Health Councils**. Encourage the site to participate in the local Federal Safety and Health Council as a cost-effective way of networking and expanding their training and problem-solving capability. Be prepared to give them information on the local Council.
   5. **Positive Approach**. Always express appreciation to the site representatives for their cooperation in the field review and make it clear that the OSHA contact person will be available to assist with their safety and health program.

L. **Draft Report.** The FAPO is responsible for preparing a report following the grid report format provided to the FAPO.

   1. **Report Assignments**. The FAPO is responsible for the preparation of the report and will be the coordinator if sections of the report have been assigned to team members.
      a. **Deadlines**. Each writer must meet established deadlines.
      b. **Team Review.** Each team member will review the draft report.
      c. **Team Consensus**. The draft report should reflect the consensus of the team, but the FAPO is more familiar with the specific requirements which 29 CFR Part 1960 places on Federal agencies, and the FAPO should take a leadership role in the discussions.
   2. **Location and Timing.** The draft report shall be prepared as quickly as possible, and not later than two weeks after the closing briefing. In the interest of speed and efficiency, the report might be drafted prior to the closing briefing at the site. If this is done, it is preferable that the team meet off site (at the motel, for example), but, if necessary, the team can make arrangements for a work area at the site.

3. **Review of the Draft Report**. The FAPO shall provide an opportunity for the site management to review the draft report and suggest changes. The draft report shall be given to site management for review not later than two weeks after the closing briefing.
   a. A follow-up meeting for review and discussion may be scheduled, or minor changes can be handled by telephone.
   b. A one week deadline should be established for the site to provide any comments on the draft report.
M. **Final Report**. After comments are received from the site management, the final report will be prepared by the FAPO.
   1. After the comments have been received from the site, or any follow-up meetings have been held to discuss changes in the draft report, the FAPO should prepare the final report.
   2. The FAPO should use professional judgement as to what changes, if any, should be made in the report based on the comments received from the site management.
   3. The final report should be sent from the Regional Administrator to the top manager at the site not more than 30 days after the closing briefing. Copies of the report should be sent to:
      a. the Agency's top safety and health manager.
      b. OSHA's Office of Federal Agency Programs.

ATTACHMENT II
FIELD REVIEW QUESTIONS

During field reviews, safety specialists and industrial hygienists will review working conditions to determine if the facility complies with OSHA standards, and, if not, why not. (For example, lack of training, failure to conduct inspections, lack of funds for correction, etc.) Safety and health hazards should be pointed out to management and labor representatives mentioned in the closing conference and in the field review report.

The attached questions have been supplied as a guide to safety specialists and industrial hygienists for their interviews of supervisors, employee representatives and employees.

SAMPLE INTERVIEW QUESTIONS
SUPERVISORS

1. Have you seen any policy statements on occupational safety and health? From whom?
2. Does your performance evaluation have an element for occupational safety and health? In what way does it measure your safety and health performance (i.e., reduction in injuries, training courses, etc.)?
3. Do employees report unsafe or unhealthful conditions to you? How do you get the condition corrected?
4. Who selects your employees' personal protective equipment? Does it have to be approved by the safety office before it is purchased?
5. Have you received any safety and health training? When? From whom? What was the subject?

SAMPLE INTERVIEW QUESTIONS
EMPLOYEE REPRESENTATIVES

1. Have you ever seen any policy statements on occupational safety and health? From whom?
2. What type of personal protective equipment are you issued? Do you feel you need any other type?
3. Does management consult with employee representatives about the occupational safety and health program?
4. Do employee representatives accompany inspectors during inspection? Do inspectors question employees privately?
5. Have you received any occupational safety and health training? When? From whom? What was the subject, and how long was the training?

6. Are there any unresolved occupational safety and health concerns that have been raised to management?

SAMPLE INTERVIEW QUESTIONS
EMPLOYEES

1. Have you ever seen any information about occupational safety and health at this facility? Where? What was it?
2. Do you know of anyone who has gotten into trouble for making a safety or health complaint?
3. Do you know what you can do if you see an unsafe condition?
4. Have you ever reported a safety or health hazard? Who did you report it to? Was it taken care of? How long did it take?
5. Have you received any training about your agency's occupational safety and health program, or about the hazards of your job? When? Who gave it? What subjects were covered?
6. Are there any unresolved occupational safety and health concerns that have been raised to management?

OSHA Instruction FAP 1.3
APPENDIX D
FEDERAL SECTOR STANDARD FORM LETTERS

I. **COMPLAINT FORM LETTERS**
    a. **No Inspection - Invalid Complaint**
.dfcomplaint.drcmp_first_name .drcmp_last_name .drcmp_street .drcmp city, .drcmp_state. drcmp_zip

Dear .drcmp_first_name .drcmp_last_name:

We have received your report of alleged hazardous working conditions and/or violations of 29 CFR Part 1960 citable program elements in your workplace. After careful review, we have decided not to conduct an inspection because:

[Choose One]

1. More information is needed about the complaint item(s). Please contact the area office as soon as possible to complete the report.
2. As a result of a recent inspection [give date] or on the basis of other objective evidence [describe], I believe that the hazard which you brought to our attention [is not present] [has been corrected] [will shortly be corrected].
3. The hazard does not fall within OSHA's jurisdiction because:

[Choose One]

a. It involves conditions covered by [name other Federal agency].
b. OSHA only has inspection authority for non-military work operations in Executive Branch agencies. Under the Occupational Safety and Health Act of 1970, however, your agency is required to have a safety and health program. You may wish to contact your agency's safety and health staff. [If known, provide name and address.]
c. Your agency has certified that it has established safety and health committees that comply with Department of Labor regulations 29 CFR Part 1960. Your report, therefore, has been transferred to [name and address] for investigation.
   [**Note:** Use only if statement applies.]

Since you have requested anonymity, we will provide you a copy of your establishment's investigation findings. Enclosed is a copy of the letter for your information.

If you can provide additional information concerning this report which you think we should consider, please contact us.

Your interest in workplace health and safety is appreciated.

Sincerely,
.dftabsite.drsite_director Area Director
Enclosure

b. No Inspection - Referred to Agency
.dfcomplaint.drcmp_last_name, .drcmp_first_name .drcmp_street .drcmp_city, .drcmp_state. drcmp_zip

Dear .drcmp_last_name:

In response to your report of alleged hazardous working conditions and/or violations of 29 CFR Part 1960 citable program elements in your workplace, the Occupational Safety and Health Administration (OSHA) has sent a letter to your establishment requesting that appropriate action be taken to correct the situation. Enclosed is a copy of that letter for your information.

[Choose one or more]
1. Your report was sent to your Agency because it is OSHA policy to refer certain reports of hazards to the agency for investigation and action, if necessary.
2. We have requested that your Agency provide you with a copy of the investigation findings and actions taken.
3. Since you have requested anonymity, we will provide you with a copy of your establishment's investigation findings.

Please let me know if the violation(s) have not been corrected in the time allowed as shown in the enclosed letter to your agency.

Your continued interest in workplace safety and health is appreciated.

Sincerely,
.dftabsite.drsite_director Area Director
Enclosure

c. OSHA-7 for Signature
.dfcomplaint.drcmp_first_name .drcmp_last_name .drcmp_street .drcmp_city, .drcmp_state. drcmp_zip

Dear .drcmp_first_name .drcmp_last_name:

This letter is in response to your recent report of alleged hazardous working conditions and/or violations of 29 CFR Part 1960 citable program elements in your workplace and your desire to have an on site inspection conducted by OSHA. The information you provided has been entered on the enclosed Notice of Alleged Safety or Health Hazards, OSHA-7 Form.

Please sign your name on the "signature" line provided on the back of the form and return the signed form to us within 10 days. If a signed copy is received within 10 days, and the condition(s) you describe provides reasonable grounds to believe that a violation exists, an OSHA inspection of your workplace will be scheduled. If the signed copy of the form is not received in 10 days a letter will be sent to the appropriate Federal agency establishment official (without revealing your identity), requesting that the hazardous condition(s) be corrected.

[Choose one]

(1)Since you have requested anonymity, we will provide you with a copy of your establishment's investigation findings.

(2)We will request that your agency provide you with a copy of the investigation findings.

Sincerely,

.dftabsite.drsite_director Area Director

d. **Deleted**

d1. **Notification to Employer Without Certified Committee - No inspection**

.dfestablish.drest_name .drest_m_street .drest_m city, .drest_m_state .drest_m_zip

Dear .keemployer_name:

On .kedate_received_rpt, the Occupational Safety and Health Administration (OSHA) received a report of alleged hazardous working conditions and/or violations of 29 CFR Part 1960 citable program elements in your workplace at [establishment and address]. The specific nature of the report involves [describe the reported condition(s) in detail].

OSHA has decided not to conduct an inspection in response to this report. However, since allegations of the violation of standards have been made, you should investigate the alleged violation(s). Department of Labor regulation 29 CFR 1960.28 requires that your inspection be conducted within 3 working days for potentially serious conditions and within 20 working days for other-than-serious hazards. Any necessary correction(s) should be made within 30 calendar days after completion of the inspection. If correction(s) cannot be made within 30 calendar days, please provide me with a detailed abatement plan. Your plan should include.

(1)All steps taken and the dates of such action to achieve compliance during the prescribed abatement period.

(2)The specific additional abatement time estimated to achieve compliance.

(3)The reasons such additional time is necessary, including the unavailability of professional or technical personnel or of materials and equipment, or because necessary construction or alteration of facilities cannot be completed by the original abatement date.

(4)Interim steps being taken to safeguard the employees against the cited violation(s) during the abatement period.

[Choose One]

1. [Anonymous] - Since the complainant has requested to remain anonymous, please advise me in writing, within 30 calendar days after completion of inspection, of your finding(s) and of any action you have taken. Your response should be detailed, stating specifically what corrective action(s), if any, were taken. If it is determined that, based on the report, no violation(s) exist and an inspection will not be conducted, please notify me in writing within 15 calendar days of receipt of this letter. We have notified the complainant that the complaint has been forwarded to you for action, and, if the violation(s) are not corrected, to notify us. We will forward a copy of your report to the complainant.

2. [Anonymity not requested] - The complainant has been advised of this preliminary response to the report and given a copy of this letter. Please advise the complainant, in writing, within 30 calendar days after completion of the inspection, of the findings and of the action you have taken. Your response should be detailed, stating specifically what corrective action(s), if any, were taker. If it is determined that, based on the report, no violation(s) exist and an inspection will not be conducted, the complainant shall be notified in writing within 15 calendar days of receipt of this letter. Please provide me with a copy of your response to the complainant.

You should enclose any supporting documentation on the action(s) taken, such as monitoring results, new equipment orders, or photograph(s) of corrected condition.

If we do not receive a response from you within 30 calendar days, indicating that appropriate action has been taken or that no violation(s) exist, an OSHA inspection may be scheduled.

If you have any questions or need assistance concerning this matter, please contact our office.

Sincerely,

.dftabsite.drsite_director Area Director

Enclosure

d2. **Notification to Employer With Certified Committee - No Inspection**

.dfestablish.drest_name .drest_m_street .drest_m_city, .drest_m_state .drest_m_zip

Dear .keemployer_name:

On .kedate_received_rpt, the Occupational Safety and Health Administration (OSHA) received a report of alleged hazardous working conditions and/or violations of 29 CFR Part 1960 citable program elements in your workplace at [establishment and address]. The specific nature of the report involves [describe the reported condition(s) in detail].

Since your agency exercises the option of using Certified Safety and Health Committees, OSHA expects you to notify the Committee(s) of this complaint and to take action(s) that may be required to protect employees.

[Choose One]

(1) [Imminent Danger] - This letter is to confirm that you were notified of the report by telephone. Since the report was of an imminent danger, you were reminded that your investigation was required within 24 hours and that since your agency has Certified Committees, OSHA was required by Section 1-401(i) of Executive Order 12196 to respond if your investigation did not begin within 24 hours. You are also reminded that if an imminent danger exists, employees exposed to it must immediately be removed from danger and corrective action taken as soon as possible.

(2) [Serious/Other-than-Serious] - The Department of Labor regulation 29 CFR 1960.28, requires that your investigation be conducted within 3 working days for potentially serious conditions and within 20 working days for other-than-serious conditions.

Please review the operation of your establishment's safety and health program in light of the reported deficiencies. If corrective action(s) are deemed necessary we request that you implement them. Please advise us of the findings of your review and any corrective actions taken.

[Choose One]

1. [Anonymous] - Since the complainant has requested to remain anonymous, please advise me in writing, within 30 calendar days after completing the inspection, of your finding(s) and of any action you have taken. Your response should be detailed, stating specifically what corrective action(s), if any, were taken. If it is determined that, based on the report, no violation(s) exist and an inspection will not be conducted, please notify me in writing within 15 calendar days of receipt of this letter. We have notified the complainant that the complaint has been forwarded to you for action, and, upon receipt of your report, we will provide him/her with a copy.

2. [Anonymity not requested] - The complainant has been advised of this preliminary response to the report and given a copy of this letter. Please advise the complainant, in writing, within 30 calendar days after completion of the inspection, of the findings and of the action you have taken. Your response should be detailed, stating specifically what corrective action(s), if any, were taken. If it is determined that, based on the report, no violation(s) exist and an inspection will not be conducted, the complainant shall be notified in writing within 15 calendar days of receipt of this letter. Please provide me with a copy of your response to the complainant.

If you have any questions or need assistance concerning this matter, please contact our office.

Sincerely,

.dftabsite.drsite_director Area Director

Enclosure

d3. **Notification to Employer With Certified Committee - Announced Inspection**
.dfestablish.drest_name .drest_m_street .drest_m_city, .drest_m state .drest_m_zip

Dear .keemployer_name:

On .kedate_received_rpt, the Occupational Safety and Health Administration (OSHA) received a report of alleged hazardous working conditions and for violations of 29 CFR Part 1960 citable program elements occurring in your workplace at [establishment name and address]. Pursuant to Executive Order 1-401(i) we are announcing our plans to conduct a complaint inspection at your worksite.

Since your agency exercises the option of using Certified Safety and Health Committees, OSHA expects you to keep the Committee(s) informed of OSHA's inspection plans and subsequent actions.

If you have any questions concerning this matter, please contact our office.

Sincerely,
.dftabsite.drsite_director Area Director

e. **Acknowledgement to Complainant - Referral to Complainant's Agency**
.dfcomplaint.drcmp_first_name .drcmp_last_name .drcmp_street .drcmp_city, .drcmp_state .drcmp zip

Dear .drcmp_first_name .drcmp_last_name:

In response to your report alleging hazardous working conditions and/or violations of 29 CFR Part 1960 citable program elements in your workplace, the Occupational Safety and Health Administration (OSHA) has sent a letter to your establishment requesting that appropriate action be taken to correct the situation. Enclosed is a copy of that letter for your information.

[Choose One or More]

1. Your report was sent to your Agency to investigate because OSHA does not have jurisdiction over your agency.
2. We have requested that your Agency provide you with a copy of the investigation findings and actions taken.
3. Since you have requested anonymity, we will provide you with a copy of your establishment's investigation findings.

Please let me know if the hazard(s) have not been corrected in the time allowed as shown in the enclosed letter to your agency.

Your continued interest in workplace safety and health is appreciated.

Sincerely,
.dftabsite.drsite_director Area Director
Enclosure

f1. **Acknowledgement to Complainant - With Inspection**
.dfcomplaint.drcmp_first name.drcmp_last_name .drcmp_street .drcmp_city, .drcmp_state .drcmp_zip

Dear .drcmp_first_name .drcmp_last_name:

The purpose of this letter is to acknowledge receipt of your report of hazardous working conditions and/or violations of 29 CFR Part 1960 citable program elements, and to inform you that an inspection of the workplace will be scheduled as soon as possible. You will be informed of the results of our inspection when they are available.

Thank you for your interest in workplace safety and health.

Sincerely,
.dftabsite.drsite_director Area Director

f2. **Acknowledgement to Complainant - Referral to Another OSHA Office to Another OSHA Office**

.dfcomplaint.drcmp_first name.drcmp last_name .drcmp_street .drcmp city,.drcmp state .drcmp ZiP

Dear.drcmp first_name.drcmp_last name:

This letter is to acknowledge receipt of your report of hazardous working conditions and/or violations of 29 CPR Part 1960 citable program elements at [establishment name and address]. The Occupational Safety and Health Administration (OSHA) office in .drcmp city, .drcmp_state has jurisdiction over the above named establishment so we sent your report to that office for appropriate action. You may also contact the area office listed below.

.dftabsite.drsite_director Area Director U.S. Department of Labor .kestreet_address .kecity, .kestate .kezip .keoffice_telephone

That office will inform you as to what action is being taken on your report.

Sincerely
.dftabsite.drsite_director Area Director

g. **Notification to Complainant - Satisfactory Employer Response**

.dfcomplaint.drcmp_first_name .drcmp_last name .drcmp_street .drcmp_city,.drcmp state .drcmp zip

Dear.drcmp_first_name .drcmp_last_name:

As the enclosed letter indicates, we have been advised by your establishment official that the hazardous working conditions and/or violations of 29 CFR Part 1960 citable program elements you reported to the Occupational Safety and Health Administration (OSHA) on .drcmp_cmp_rec_dt, have been investigated and that corrective action has been taken.

With this information, OSHA feels the case can be closed on the grounds that the hazardous condition(s) no longer exist(s). If you do not agree that the condition(s) you reported have been satisfactorily corrected, please contact us within 10 calendar days. If we do not hear from you within that time period, we will assume that the condition(s) have been eliminated and we will close our case file.

Your action on behalf of safety and health in the workplace is appreciated.

Sincerely,
.dftabsite.drsite_director Area Director
Enclosure: Copy of the Federal establishment official's response.

h. **Notification to Complainant with Inspection Results**

.dfcomplaint.drcmp_first_name .drcmp_last_name .drcmp_street .drcmp_city, .drcmp_state .drcmp_zip

Dear .drcmp_first_name .drcmp_last_name:

In response to your report of alleged hazardous working conditions and/or violations of 29 CFR Part 1960 citable program elements at .dfestablish.drest_name, .drest_m_street, .drest_m_city, .drest_m_state .drest_m_zip, the Occupational Safety and Health Administration (OSHA) has conducted a workplace inspection. The inspection was completed on .kedate_insp_cmpl.

We found that [list reported conditions)] did not violate OSHA standards and/or citable program elements [describe findings in detail].

We also found that [list condition(s)] violated OSHA standards and/or citable program elements. Therefore, a Notice of Unsafe and Unhealthful Working Conditions (Notice) was sent to your establishment official stating that violations identified by OSHA must be corrected. The

Notice (enclosed) reflects the dates by which the violations must be corrected. The contents of the Notice must be posted near the violation(s) for three working days or until the violation(s) are abated, whichever is later.

If you do not agree that the condition(s) you reported have been satisfactorily investigated or cited, please contact us within 10 calendar days and request a review of the complaint handling process.

Thank you for your concern about workplace safety and health.

Sincerely,
.dftabsite.drsite_director Area Director
Enclosure

i. Request for Employer's Response to Complaint Letter - No Inspection
.dfestablish.drest_name .drest_m_street .drest_m_city, .drest_m_state .drest_m_zip

Dear .keemployer_name:

On .kedate_of_notification, this office sent a letter to you concerning alleged hazardous working conditions and/or violations of 29 CFR Part 1960 citable program elements at your establishment. A copy of the letter is enclosed.

We have not received a reply from you concerning these allegations. Please advise this office of your findings and of any corrective actions you have taken within 10 days. If we do not hear from you, an inspection may be scheduled.

A copy of this letter is being sent to the complainant.

Your cooperation in this matter is appreciated.

Sincerely,
.dftabsite.drsite_director Area Director
Enclosure
cc: Complainant

j. Correcting But Additional Information Needed
.dfestablish.drest_name .drest_m_street .drest_m_city, .drest_m_state .drest_m_zip

Dear.keemployer name:

Thank you for your response to our letter of .kedate. Your letter stated that you were making progress toward correcting the conditions but did not provide sufficient information. The additional information needed is: [described information needed, i.e., abatement dates, interim measures to protect employees, etc.]

Please advise this office of the time which will be required to correct the conditions. Further, when final corrective action has been completed, please notify this office in detail of the abatement steps taken to remove the hazard.

A copy of this letter is being sent to the complainant.

Your interest in the safety and health of your employees is appreciated.

Sincerely,
.dftabsite.drsite_director Area Director

k. Deleted

l. Notification to Complainant - Unsatisfactory Employer Response
.dfcomplaint.drcmp_first_name .drcmp_last_name .drcmp_street .drcmp_city, .drcmp_state .drcmp_zip

Dear .drcmp_first_name .drcmp_last_name:

On .kedate_of_notification, this office notified you that your report of alleged hazardous working conditions and/or violations of 29 CFR Part 1960 citable program elements was sent to your establish-

ment requesting that appropriate action be taken. We have not received a satisfactory response.
[Choose One.]
1. Therefore, this office will schedule an inspection as OSHA priorities allow. You will be informed of the inspection results.
2. Therefore, I have requested additional information from your establishment official. I will keep you informed of the progress of your report of alleged hazard

Sincerely,
. dftabsite. drsite_director Area Director

m.Deleted
m1.Notification To Reprisal Complainant - Cover Federal Employee
.dfcomplaint.drcmp_first_name .dremp_last_name .drcmp_street .drcmp_city, .drcmp_state .drcmp_zip

Dear .drcmp_first_name .drcmp_last_name:

The Occupational Safety And Health Administration (OSHA) has received your report of alleged reprisal against you for your occupational safety and health activities. Executive Order 12196 and 29 CFR Part 1960, which establish safety and health programs for Federal employees, do not give OSHA authority to take remedial action on behalf of Federal employees who believe that they have suffered reprisal.

We are forwarding your report to the Office of Special Counsel, which may have jurisdiction to investigate your allegation of reprisal under the Whistleblower Protection Act of 1989.

If you have further questions you may contact:
Office of Special Counsel Complaints Examining Unit 1730 M Street, N. W.
3rd Floor Washington, D.C. 20036
Telephone: 1-800-872-9855

Sincerely,
.dftabsite.drsite_director Area Director

m2. Notification To Reprisal Complainant - NonCovered Federal Employee
.dfcomplaint.drcmp first_name .dremp_last_name .drcmp_street .drcmp_city, .drcmp_state .drcmp_zip

Dear .drcmp_first_name .drcmp_last_name:

The Occupational Safety And Health Administration (OSHA) has received your report of alleged reprisal against you for your occupational safety and health activities.

The options available to [Insert specific agency name, e.g. Postal] employees who believe they have been discriminated against for reporting unsafe or unhealthful working conditions are:
1. To have an investigation conducted by their agency.
2. To follow agency grievance and arbitration procedures which have been established to resolve disputes, differences, disagreements or complaints between parties concurring conditions of employment.

Pursuant to item number one, above, we have requested your agency to conduct an investigation and take appropriate action. You should be aware that under Executive Order 12196 and 29 CFR Part 1960, which establish safety and health programs for Federal employees, OSHA's authority is limited. Specifically, OSHA does not have the authority to take remedial action on behalf of Federal employees who believe that they have suffered reprisal for reporting unsafe or unhealthful working conditions. That authority is vested with their employing agency.

Sincerely,
.dftabsite.drsite_director Area Director
m3. Notification To DASHO - NonCovered Federal Employee

.keofficialname Designated Agency Safety and Health Official .kestreet_address .kecity, .kestate .kezip

Dear .kDASHO_name:

The Occupational Safety and Health Administration (OSHA) is forwarding to you the enclosed employee's allegation of reprisal for reporting unsafe or unhealthful working conditions.

Executive Order 12196 and 29 CFR Part 1960, which establish safety and health programs for Federal employees, requires each agency to establish a reprisal plan. Since OSHA does not have the authority to take remedial action on behalf of Federal employees who believe that they have suffered reprisal for reporting unsafe or unhealthful working conditions, we ask that you investigate this allegation and take appropriate action.

Sincerely,
.dftabsite.drsite_director Area Director
Enclosure

n. Deleted

o. **Notification to Complainant - Failure-to-Abate Issued**

.dfcomplaint.drcmp_first_name .drcmp last_name .drcmp_street .drcmp_city, .drcmp_state .drcmp_zip

Dear .drcmp_first_name .drcmp_last_name:

In my letter of .kedate_letter sent you were informed that the Occupational Safety and Health Administration (OSHA) had conducted an inspection and issued a Notice of Unsafe or Unhealthful Working Conditions to your establishment. OSHA has conducted a followup inspection and determined that item(s) was/were not abated.

Enclosed for your information is a copy of the Notice of Failure-to-Abate Alleged Violations which was sent to your establishment.

Sincerely,
.dftabsite.drsite_director Area Director

P. Deleted

II. **INSPECTION FORM LETTERS**

a. **Notification to Employer - Inspection Results**

NOTE: Do not use if the Laser Notice of Unsafe or Unhealthful Working Conditions is being used.

.dfestablish.drest_name .drest_m_street .drest_m_city, .drest_m_state .drest_m_zip

Dear. keemployer_name:

On .kedate_of_insp, representatives of this office conducted an inspection at your establishment.

[Choose One]

1. Violations of OSHA standards and/or violations of 29 CFR Part 1960 citable program elements were found during the inspection which are described on the enclosed Notice of Unsafe or Unhealthful Working Conditions (Notice). Included are the correction date(s), discussed for each condition. Although the Notice is normally issued only to the establishment official, in the case of repeated or willful violations a copy of the Notice is also sent to the Designated Agency Safety and Health Official (DASHO).

Copies of the Notice or your Agency's form on which you have reproduced the information shown on the Notice, must be posted at or near the area where the violation occurred for three working days or until the violation(s) are corrected, whichever is longer.

[If the inspection was for an imminent danger, conclude the letter here.]

Please advise me promptly, in writing, of the abatement actions you have taken. Since we need to assess the effectiveness of the corrective measures, please describe them in detail, and include any pertinent information; e.g., photographs, monitoring results, measurements and equipment requisitions. If correction of any listed violation cannot be achieved within the time period, please provide me with an abatement plan which includes:

(1) A timetable of the steps to be taken to achieve compliance during the prescribed abatement period.

(2) The specific additional abatement time estimated to achieve compliance.

(3) The reasons such additional time is necessary, including the unavailability of professional or technical personnel or of materials and equipment, or because necessary construction or alteration of facilities cannot be completed by the original abatement date.

(4) Interim steps being taken to safeguard the employees against the cited hazard during the abatement period.

You may request an informal conference with me within 15 working days of receipt of this Notice. The request must be in writing or by telephone with a confirming letter that identifies the items on the Notice you wish to discuss. During the informal conference, you may present any evidence or views which you believe would support an adjustment to the violation(s) listed on the Notice.

Any violation which is not corrected within the agreed upon time frame will be subject to a Notice of Failure to Abate Alleged Violations, a copy of which will be sent to your DASHO.

2. As we discussed at the closing conference, no violations of OSHA standards or citable program elements were found during the inspection. Thank you for you cooperation during our inspection. If this office can be of assistance in the future, please contact us.

Sincerely,

.dftabsite.drsite_director Area Director

Enclosure

cc: Complainant [If complaint inspection and anonymity not requested] Employee Representative DASHO

b. Deleted

c. **Notification to Employer - Evaluation Results**

.dfestablish.drest_name .drest_m_street .drest_m_city, .drest_m_state .drest_m_zip

Dear .keemployer_name:

Federal agency heads are required to operate effective occupation safety and health programs. The Occupational Safety and Health Administration (OSHA) is required to evaluate the effectiveness of Federal agency occupational safety and health programs. Effectiveness is determined by analyzing injury/illness statistics, by comparing the agency's written program with 29 CFR Part 1960, and by conducting field reviews at agency establishments.

On .kedate_conducted_review, OSHA personnel conducted a field review at your establishment as part of an evaluation of your Agency's safety and health program. The purpose of the review was to evaluate program implementation at the workplace. As explained in the opening conference the field review may or may not be part of an OSHA inspection. If violations of OSHA standards and/or citable program elements are observed during the review, a Notice of Unsafe and Unhealthful Working Conditions (Notice) will be issued.

[Choose One]

1. Violation(s) were found during the evaluation and are described on the enclosed Notice. Included are the correction date(s) discussed for (the/each) violation. A copy of the Notice or Agency's form on which you have reproduced the information shown on the Notice, must be posted near the violations for three working days or until the violation(s) are corrected, whichever is longer.

Please advise me promptly, in writing, of the abatement actions you have taken. Since we need to assess the effectiveness of the corrective measures, please describe them in detail, and include any pertinent information; e.g., photographs, monitoring results, measurements and equipment requisitions. If correction of any violation(s) listed cannot be achieved within the time period, please provide me an abatement plan which includes:

(1) A timetable of the steps to be taken to achieve compliance during the prescribed abatement period.

(2) The specific additional abatement time estimated to achieve compliance.

(3) The reasons such additional time is necessary, including the unavailability of professional or technical personnel or of materials and equipment, or because necessary construction or alteration of facilities cannot be completed by the original abatement date.

(4) Interim steps being taken to safeguard the employees against the cited hazard during the abatement period.

You may request an informal conference with me within 15 working days of receipt of the Notice. The request must be in writing, or by telephone with confirming letter, and identify the items on the Notice you may wish to discuss. During the informal conference, you may present any evidence or views which you believe would support an adjustment to the violation(s) listed on the Notice.

Any violation(s) which is not corrected within the agreed upon time frame will be subject to a Notice of Failure to Abate Alleged Violation. A copy will also be sent to your Designated Agency Safety and Health Official.

If you have any questions or need assistance concerning this matter, please contact our office.

2. As we discussed at the closing conference, no violations of OSHA standards or citable program elements were found during the evaluation. Thank you for your cooperation during our evaluation.

If this office can be of assistance in the future, please contact us.

Sincerely,

.dftabsite.drsite_director Area Director

Enclosure

cc: Employee Representative (who participated in the Closing Conference)

d. **Notification to Employer - ATAR Scheduled**

.dfestablish.drest_name .drest_m_street .drest_m_city, .drest_m_state .drest_m_zip

Dear .keemployer_name:

The purpose of this letter is to acknowledge receipt of your request for technical assistance. An Agency Technical Assistance Request (ATAR) visit is scheduled at your establishment for .kedate_ATAR_scheduled. Someone from this office will contact you to make the necessary arrangements.

During the opening conference of the visit, ATAR procedures will be explained in detail by the Occupational Safety and Health Administration (OSHA) team. If serious violations of OSHA standards and/or citable program elements are observed, we will work with you to develop a reasonable abatement plan and will assist you in their abatement. If serious violation(s) are abated within the agreed upon time frames, no further OSHA action will be necessary. However, uncorrected serious violation(s) may result in a Notice of Unsafe or Unhealthful Working Conditions being issued to you and to your Designated Agency Safety and Health Official.

Upon completion of the ATAR visit, you will be advised of OSHA's action taken in response to your request and provided OSHA's findings and recommendations.

If you have any questions, please feel free to contact me.

Sincerely,

.dftabsite.drsite_director Area Director

e. **Notification to Employer - ATAR Results**

.dfestablish.drest_name .drest_m_street .drest_m_city, .drest_m_state .drest_m_zip

Dear .keemployer name:

In response to your request for technical assistance, the Occupational Safety and Health Administration (OSHA) conducted an Agency Technical Assistance Request (ATAR) visit on .kedate_ATAR_visit.

[Choose one or more as applicable.]

1. The following violation(s) of OSHA standards or citable program elements were observed during the visit by the OSHA team. The violation(s) were eliminated prior to the completion of the closing conference. [List observed violation(s) and describe findings in detail.]

2. We have determined that the violation(s) of OSHA standards or citable program elements observed during the visit by the OSHA team listed below do not appear to present a threat of serious physical harm (other-than-serious hazard).

   [List observed violation(s) and describe findings in detail, including recommended corrective action.]

   Since these violation(s) were not corrected prior to the closing conference, you should take the necessary action to correct them within 30 calendar days.

3. The violation(s) of OSHA standards or citable program elements observed during the visit by the OSHA team appear(s) to present a threat of serious physical harm (serious violation) and were not corrected prior to the closing conference. The violation(s) are described below including the agreed upon correction date(s) for each violation.

   [List observed violations) and describe findings in detail, including abatement dates and agreed upon corrective action.]

   For the serious violation(s) described above which cannot be corrected within 30 calendar days of receipt of this letter, please provide me with an abatement plan which includes:

   (1) All steps taken and the dates of such action to achieve compliance during the prescribed abatement period.

   (2) The specific additional abatement time estimated to achieve compliance.

   (3) The reasons such additional time is necessary, including the availability of professional or technical personnel or of materials and equipment, or because necessary construction or alteration of facilities cannot be completed by the original abatement date.

   (4) Interim steps being taken to safeguard the employees against the cited hazard during the abatement periods.

   Please advise me in writing of the actions taken to correct the violation(s) identified as serious. Since we need to assess the effectiveness of the corrective measures, please describe them in detail. If correction of any serious violation listed cannot be achieved within the agreed upon time period, please contact this office so that we can provide further assistance and discuss new abatement dates if necessary.

4. As we discussed at the closing conference, OSHA can provide technical assistance to help you correct the violation(s). Any violation(s) which is not corrected within the agreed upon timeframe will be subject to a Notice of Unsafe or Unhealthful Working Conditions (OSHA Notice). A copy will also be sent to your Designated Agency Safety and Health Official.

5. As we discussed at the closing conference, no violations of OSHA standards or citable program elements were observed during the visit.

6. The following [technical/program] assistance was provided during our visit: [List services rendered.]

   (**NOTE:** Use if no partial or comprehensive inspection was conducted.)

If this office can be of assistance in the future, please contact me.

Sincerely,

.dftabsite.drsite_director Area Director

f. **Agency Technical Assistance Request (ATAR) - Issuance of Notice**
.dfestablish.drest_name .drest_m_street .drest_m_city, .drest_m_state .drest_m_zip

Dear .keemployer_name:

In response to your request for technical assistance, the Occupational Safety and Health Administration (OSHA) conducted an Agency Technical Assistance Request (ATAR) visit on .kedate_of_visit.

On .kedate_of_ATAR_letter a letter was sent to you in which the serious violation(s) of OSHA standards and/or citable program elements observed by the OSHA team were listed along with the agreed upon abatement date(s).

We found that the necessary action to correct the violation(s) were not taken within the agreed upon time frame. Therefore, a Notice of Unsafe or Unhealthful Working Conditions (Notice) is being issued.

Please advise me promptly, in writing, that you have taken appropriate corrective action within the time frame set forth on the Notice.

Any violation which is not corrected will be subject to a Notice of Failure to Abate Alleged Violation. A copy will be sent to your Designated Agency Safety and Health Official.

Sincerely,
.dftabsite.drsite_director Area Director
Enclosure

g. **Letter for a Hazard Not Covered by Standard - General Duty Clause**
.dfestablish.drest_name .drest_m_street .drest_m_city, .drest_m_state .drest_m_zip

Dear .keemployer_name:

An inspection of your workplace at .dfestablish.drest_name on .kedate disclosed the following hazards:

[Describe Hazards]

OSHA does not have a specific standard that applies to these hazards and it is not considered appropriate at this time to issue a Notice of Unsafe and Unhealthful Working Conditions for violation(s) of 29 CFR 1960.8a, the general duty clause for Federal agencies.

In the interest of workplace safety and health, however, I recommend that you take the following steps voluntarily to eliminate or reduce your employees exposure to the hazards described above:

[Described recommended abatement methods]

Sincerely,
.dftabsite.drsite_director Area Director

h. **Notification of Failure to Abate Alleged Violation**
.dfestablish.drest_name .drest_m_street .drest_m_city, .drest_m_state .drest_m_zip

Dear .keemployer name:

A Notice of Unsafe and Unhealthful Working Conditions (Notice) was issued to you on .kedate. A reinspection conducted on .kedate noted that you had failed to abate the violation(s) listed on the Notice within the time prescribed. Therefore, you are now being issued the enclosed Notification of Failure to Abate Alleged Violation. The Designated Agency Safety and Health Official for your agency has been furnished a copy of this Notification.

If I have not been notified, in writing, within .kenumber days that the violation(s) have been abated, I will forward the necessary information to the Occupational Safety and Health Administration's Regional Administrator for resolution at a higher organizational

Sincerely,
.dftabsite.drsite_director Area Director
Enclosure

cc: Employer Representative Complainant if appropriate

i. **Informal Conference Scheduled**
.dfestablish.drest_name .drest_m_street .drest_m_city, .drest_m_state .drest_m_zip

Dear .keemployer_name:

This is in response to your letter of .kedate_of_letter requesting an informal conference to discuss the Notice of Unsafe or Unhealthful Working Conditions issued to you on .kedate_notice_issued. An informal conference has been scheduled for .kedate, .ketime, .kelocation.

[Use if applicable.]

Please notify the appropriate employee representative(s) that they have the right to attend the conference.

If you have any questions, please call me at .ketelephone_name.

Sincerely,
.dftabsite. drsite_director Area Director

III. **PMA FORM LETTERS**

a. **Notification of Modification of the Abatement Dates**
.dfestablish.drest_name .drest_m_street .drest_m_city, .drest_m_state .drest_m_zip
RE: Inspection No. .dfinspection .drins_ins_nr Notice: .dfvioiation.drvio_cit_nr Issuance Date: .drvio_issue_dt

Dear .keemployer_name:

Your request for a modification of the abatement dates contained in the above captioned Notice(s) is acknowledged. However, it fails to fully meet the requirements for filing a Petition for Modification of Abatement (PMA). The deficiencies are highlighted in the rules which follow:

You, as an employer, may file a PMA when you have made a good faith effort to comply with the abatement requirements of a Notice, but such abatement dates have not been completed because of factors beyond your reasonable control.

A PMA must be in writing and must include the following information:

1. All steps taken by you and the dates of such action, in an effort to achieve compliance during the prescribed abatement period.
2. The specific additional abatement time estimated to achieve compliance.
3. The reasons such additional time is necessary, including the unavailability of professional or technical personnel or of the materials and equipment, or because necessary construction or alteration of facilities cannot be completed by the original abatement period.
4. Interim steps being taken to safeguard the employees against the cited hazard during the abatement period.
5. A certification that a copy of the petition has been posted and, if appropriate served on the authorized representative of affected employees in accordance with the rules setforth below and a certification of the date upon which such posting service was made.

[Enclosure a copy of the certification form letter d.]

If you have any questions concerning this matter, please do not hesitate to contact this office.

Sincerely,
.dftabsite.drsite_director Area Director
Enclosure

b. **Notification of Amended Abatement Date**
.dfestablish.drest_name .drest_m_street .drest_m_city, .drest_m_state .drest_m_zip
RE: Inspection No. .dfinspection .drins_ins_nr Notice: .dfviolation.drvio_cit_nr Issuance Date: .drvio_issue_dt

Dear .keemployer name:

This will serve to advise you that this office has received your Petition for Modification of Abatement Date (PMA).

Within 10 days after the expiration of 15 working days from the date the PMA was posted and if no objection was received from an employee or representative of employees, we shall issue the amended abatement date.

Sincerely,

.dftabsite.drsite_director Area Director

c. Notification to Employer - Approval - No Objections

.dfestablish. drest_name .drest_m_street .drest_m_city, .drest_m_state .drest_m_zip

RE: Inspection No: .dfinspection.drins_ins_nr Notice: .dfviolation.drvio_cit_nr Issuance Date: .drvio_issue_dt

Dear .keemployer_name:

Your Petition for Modification of Abatement date(s) (PMA) .dfviolation.drvio_issue_dt, for the violation(s) alleged by Item(s): .drvio_item_nr of above captioned Notice has been approved:

Inspection No. Notice No. Item No. New Abatement Date

_____ _____ _____ _____

Our records are being adjusted according to the new abatement dates. This letter should be posted next to the original Notice(s).

Since all Notices are subject to follow-up inspection, timely abatement responses with adequate supporting documentation, i.e., photographs, purchase orders, air sampling results, etc. may allow us to administratively close the case without such follow-up action.

If you have any further questions do not hesitate to contact this office.

Sincerely,

.dftabsite.drsite_director Area Director
Enclosure

cc: Employee Representative

d. Petition for Modification of Abatement Date(s)

Inspection No: _____

Date of Posting: _____

Date of Service: _____

on Employee Representative

Notice Item Abatement Date No. No. Standard From To

On behalf of the employer, I hereby certify that a copy of our Petition for Modification of Abatement date(s) have been posted on the above indicated date, in a conspicuous place, where all affected employees will have access to, or near such location where the violation(s) occurred. In addition, the petition has been served upon each authorized representative of affective employees, if any.

Affected employees or their representatives may file an objection in writing to the above mentioned petition with the Area Director of the United States Department of Labor who issued the Notice. This objection must be filed within ten (10) working days of the date of posting of the petition or of service upon an authorized representative.

_____

Signature

_____

Title
Enclosures

e. **Notification to Employer - Review of Request**
.dfestablish.drest_name .drest m_street .drest_m_city, .drest_m_state .drest_m_zip
RE: Inspection No: .dfinspection.drins_ins_nr Notice Number: .dfviolation.drvio_cit_nr Issuance Date: .drvio issue_dt

Dear .keemployer_name:
This is in reference to your Petition for Modification of Abatement date(s), dated .kedate_of_letter, for the violation(s) alleged by item(s) .keitem_nr, of the above captioned Notice.
Our office is undertaking a detailed review of your request and anticipates being able to respond to your petition by .kedate of response.
If you have any questions concerning this matter, please do not hesitate to contact this office.
Sincerely,
.dftabsite.drsite_director Area Director

cc: Employee Representative
f. Deleted

g. **Notification to Employer - Object to Petition**
.dfestablish.drest_name .drest_m_street .drest_m_city, .drest_m_state .drest_m_zip
RE: Inspection No: .dfinspection.drins_ins_nr Notice No: .dfviolation.drvio_cit_nr Issuance Date: .drvio_issue_dt

Dear .keemployer_name:
After our review of your Petition for Modification of Abatement date(s), dated .keletter_date, with regard to Item(s) .keitem_nr, of the above captioned Notice, we have decided to object to your petition with regard to Item(s) .keitem nr.
Further correspondence concerning this matter will be forthcoming.
Sincerely,
.dftabsite.drsite_director Area Director

cc: Employee Representative

h. **Processing Petition for Modification of Abatement**
SUBJECT: Information Required for Processing Petition for Modification of Abatement (PMA)
COMPANY NAME: _____
ADDRESS: _____
_____
_____

Original Abatement CSHO Inspection Notice Item Notice Abatement Date Number Number Number Number Date Number Number
_____ Monitoring visit conducted on _____.
_____ PPE violations were found on monitoring inspection.
_____ Regional approval on _____ by _____.
Rationale for granting/denying PMA:
Supervisors
Signature _____ Date _____.

i. **Notification to Employer - Objection by the Union**
.dfestablish.drest_name .drest m_street .drest_m_city, .drest_m_state .drest_m_zip
RE: Inspection No: .dfinspection.drins_ins_nr Notice No: .dfviolation.drvio_cit_nr Issuance Date: .dfviolation.drvio_issue_dt

Dear .keemployer_name:

This office has advised the Occupational Safety and Health Administration (OSHA) Regional Administrator that .keunion_name has objected to your Petition for Modification of Abatement. If the objection cannot be resolved at the regional level this may be referred to the Occupational Safety and Health National Office for handling.

If you have any further questions do not hesitate to contact this office.

Sincerely,
.dftabsite.drsite_director Area Director

j. **Notification to Employer - Objection by OSHA**

.dfestablish.drest_name .drest_m_street .drest_m_city, . drest_m_state .drest_m_zip

RE: Inspection No: .dfinspection.drins_ins_nr Notice No: .dfviolation.drvio_cit_nr Issuance Date: .dfviolation.drvio issue dt

Dear.keemployer name:

This is to notify you that the Occupational Safety and Health Administration (OSHA) objects to your Petition for Modification of the Abatement date(s) for the item(s) outlined below.

Notice No. Item No. Standard No.

Your petition is being forwarded to the OSHA Regional Administrator as to the merits of the petition and objections.

If you have any questions, please feel free to contact this office.

Sincerely,
.dftabsite.drsite_director Area Director

cc: Employee Representative

OSHA Instruction FAP 1.3
APPENDIX E
FEDERAL AGENCIES NOT COVERED BY OSHA

I.   LEGISLATIVE BRANCH
   a. Congress
      Senate
      House of Representatives
   b. Architect of the Capitol
      Incl. Botanic Garden
   c. Congressional Budget Office
   d. General Accounting Office
   e. Government Printing Office
   f. Library of Congress
   g. Office of Technological Assessment
   h. U.S. Tax Court
II. JUDICIAL BRANCH
   a. Supreme Court
   b. U.S. Court
III. EXECUTIVE BRANCH
   a. Military Personnel
   b. niquely military equipment, systems and operations

OSHA Instruction FAP 1.3
APPENDIX F
DOL INTERAGENCY AGREEMENTS AFFECTING FEDERAL AGENCY
SAFETY AND HEALTH PROGRAMS

FEDERAL TYPE OF DATE OF SUBJECT OF AGREEMENT AGENCY AGREEMENT AGREEMENT

USDA/FSIS MOU 9/13/82 FSIS and OSHA to coordinate OSHA job safety and health standards and FSIS sanitation and health standards.

DOD/Army Letter of 7/2/73 Application of OSHA's standards to Agreement the procurement mission of the Army Material Command.

DOD/Army MOU 11/6/78 Establish procedures for entry of GOCO OSHA Compliance Officers to Army Ammunition GOCO ammunition plants and to Plants establish procedures for mutual resolution of any conflicts.

DOE Letter of 2/4/74 Letter of Agreement with AEC, Agreement (DOE's predecessor agency) clarifying applicability of section 4(b)(1) of the OSH Act to working condition for private AEC contractors performing contractual operations in facilities owned or leased by AEC.

DOT/Coast MOU 12/19/79 To coordinate enforcement Guard activities for occupational safety and health on the Outer Continental Shelf.

DOT/Coast MOU 3/8/83 To set clear boundaries of the Guard authority to prescribe and enforce regulations affecting the safety and health of seamen aboard USCG-inspected vessels.

EPA Letter of 2/14/86 Provides for OSHA consultants to Agreement respond to requests from arsenical wood treatment plant employees.

EPA Letter of 11/8/79 Allows EPA enforcement of wood Agreement preservations.

GSA MOU 11/4/83 Cooperative efforts between GSA and OSHA for addressing occupational safety and health concerns in Federal agencies under GSA authority

HHS/NIOSH MOU 12/18/80 Provided guidelines for worker protection at hazardous waste sites.

HHS/NIOSH MOU 12/18/80 Provide guidance to workers who /EPA/DOE/ investigate and/or clean up waste CG/NASA/ sites and respond to hazards Army R&D/ substance emergencies.

Navy SWC/ Sub-agreement 1/7/86 provides for additional coordination of activities regarding chemical protection clothing.

NRA MOU 10/21/88 To delineate OSHA and NRC responsibilities at NRC-licensed facilities and to establish cooperative measure to increase worker protection at such facilities.

Treasury MOU 7/5/74 Letter explaining the jurisdictional authority between OSHA and the BATF regarding standards for the storage and handling of explosives.

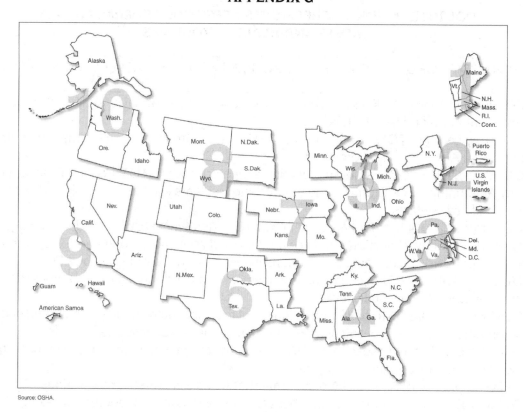

Source: OSHA.

MAP SHOWING OSHA REGIONS

A Handbook for Employing Agency Personnel

Publication CA-810
(Rev. Feb. 1994)

This material was prepared by the Office of Workers' Compensation Programs (OWCP), Employment Standards Administration, U.S. Department of Labor. It is meant to serve as a handbook for Federal agency personnel specialists, compensation specialists, and supervisors (the term "supervisor" is used generically to refer to individuals in all of these roles).

This handbook replaces FPM Chapter 810, and it incorporates all material published through the OPM issuance system which specifically addresses the Federal employees' compensation program through FPM Letter 810-22.

For information concerning any aspect of the program which is not addressed in this manual, contact the OWCP district office which serves your agency

[Editor's Note: Appendices A, B and C, which list basic forms, illness type and source codes, and occupational disease checklists have been omitted from this manual.]

TABLE OF CONTENTS

Chapter 1. Overview

This chapter provides basic information concerning the administration of the Federal Employees' Compensation Act (FECA).

1-1. Purpose

The FECA provides compensation benefits to civilian employees of the United States for disability due to personal injury or disease sustained while in the performance of duty. The FECA also provides for the payment of benefits to dependents if a work-related injury or disease causes an employee's death. The FECA is intended to be remedial in nature, and proceedings under it are non-adversarial.

1-2. Exclusiveness of remedy

Benefits provided under the FECA constitute the sole remedy against the United States for work-related injury or death. A Federal employee or surviving dependent is not entitled to sue the United States or recover damages for such injury or death under any other statute.

1-3. OWCP Structure

The Division of Federal Employees' Compensation (DFEC) administers the FECA. The Director of the program, in conjunction with regional managers, has authority over the operations of the 12 district offices. Each of these offices is headed by a District Director, who has overall responsibility for office functions.

In each district office are two or more Supervisory Claims Examiners, who are responsible for the operation of individual claims units, and a number of Senior Claims Examiners and Claims Examiners, who have primary responsibility for handling claims. Individuals at each level of authority from Claims Examiner to District Director have been delegated specific responsibilities for issuing decisions on claims.

1-4. Jurisdiction

The jurisdictions of the 12 district offices are as follows:

District 1 — Boston, MA: Connecticut, Maine, Massachusetts, New Hampshire, Rhode Island, and Vermont.

District 2 — New York, NY: New Jersey, New York, Puerto Rico, and the Virgin Islands.

District 3 — Philadelphia, PA: Delaware, Pennsylvania, and West Virginia.

District 6 — Jacksonville, FL: Alabama, Florida, Georgia, Kentucky, Mississippi, North Carolina, South Carolina, and Tennessee.

District 9 — Cleveland, OH: Indiana, Michigan, and Ohio.

District 10 — Chicago, IL: Illinois, Minnesota, and Wisconsin.

District 11 — Kansas City, MO: Iowa, Kansas, Missouri, and Nebraska; Department of Labor employees.

District 12 — Denver, CO: Colorado, Montana, North Dakota, South Dakota, Utah, and Wyoming.

District 13 — San Francisco, CA: Arizona, California, Hawaii, and Nevada; Pacific territories and possessions.

District 14 — Seattle, WA: Alaska, Idaho, Oregon, and Washington.

District 16 — Dallas, TX: Arkansas, Louisiana, New Mexico, Oklahoma, and Texas.

District 25 — Washington, DC: Maryland, Virginia, the District of Columbia; employees injured overseas; employees claiming injury due to radiation, Agent Orange, or HIV infection; Peace Corps and VISTA volunteers; Members of Congress and their staffs; White House officials and employees; Reserve Officer Training Corps (ROTC) Cadets; members of the Coast Guard Auxiliary and temporary members of the Coast Guard Reserve; employees whose cases involve security considerations; and certain non-Federal claims.

1-5. Information and Records

Individual case files are protected under the Privacy Act, and only the employee, his or her representative (if any), and agency personnel may routinely have access to the file. Any of these parties may inspect the file at the district office which has custody of the file; an appointment should be requested ahead of time. If it is not possible to inspect the record at the district office, arrangements may be made to have the case sent to another Department of Labor office for review.

Employees and their representatives may have access to records (including medical reports) which OWCP has released to the agency from the case file. The records must, however, be safeguarded in the same manner as other personnel material. Each agency is responsible for determining whether such information may properly be released in accordance with the regulations contained in 29 CFR 70 (a).

1-6. Penalties

The regulations at 20 CFR 10.23 provide that:

a. Any person who knowingly makes, or knowingly certifies to, any false statement, misrepresentation, concealment of fact, or any other act of fraud with respect to a claim under the FECA or who knowingly accepts compensation to which that person is not entitled, is subject to criminal prosecution and may, under appropriate U.S. Criminal Code provisions (e.g., 18 USC 287 and 1001), be punished by a fine of not more than $10,000 or imprisonment for not more than five years, or both.

b. Any person who, with respect to a claim under the FECA, enters into any agreement, combination, or conspiracy to defraud the United States by obtaining or aiding to obtain the payment or allowance of any false, fictitious or fraudulent claim is subject to criminal prosecution and may, under appropriate U.S. Criminal Code provisions (e.g., 18 USC 286), be punished by a fine of not more than $10,000 or imprisonment for not more than 10 years, or both.

c. Any person charged with the responsibility of making reports in connection with an injury who willfully fails, neglects, or refuses to do so; induces, compels, or directs an injured employee to forego filing a claim; or willfully retains any notice, report, or paper required in connection with an injury, is subject to a fine of not more than $500 or imprisonment for not more than one year, or both.

Moreover, claimants convicted of fraudulently claiming or obtaining benefits under the Federal Employees' Compensation Act (FECA) on or after October 21, 1993, the effective date of Public Law 103-112, will lose entitlement to medical benefits, compensation for wage loss, and any other benefits payable under the FECA.

1-7. Forms

Agencies should maintain an adequate supply of the basic forms needed to process claims, as follows:

Form .... Title
CA-1 .... Federal Employee's Notice of Traumatic Injury and Claim for Continuation of Pay
CA-2 .... Federal Employee's Notice of Occupational Disease and Claim for Compensation
CA-2a .... Notice of Employee's Recurrence of Disability and Claim for Pay
CA-3 .... Report of Termination of Disability and/or Payment
CA-5 .... Claim for Compensation by Widow, Widower and/or Children
CA-5b .... Claim for Compensation by Parents, Brothers, Sisters, Grandparents/children
CA-6 .... Official Superior's Report of Employee's Death
CA-7 .... Claim for Compensation on Account of Traumatic Injury/Occupational Disease
CA-8 .... Claim for Continuing Compensation on Account of Disability
CA-16 .... Authorization for Examination and/or Treatment
CA-17 .... Duty Status Report
CA-20 .... Attending Physician's Report (attached to Form CA-7; also available separately)
CA-20a .... Attending Physician's Supplemental Report (attached to Form CA-8)
CA-35, a-h .... Occupational Disease Checklists
OWCP-1500a .... Health Insurance Claim Form

A chart showing the use of each form is found in Appendix A. Forms may be ordered from the Superintendent of Documents, U.S. Government Printing Office, Washington, D. C. 20402. The purchase order must include the agency appropriation symbol and the requestor's signature. Forms may also be ordered by telephone at 202-783-3238.

1-8. References

Several resources describing the provisions of the law and how they are applied are available.

a. **The Federal Employees' Compensation Act** as amended, 5 USC 8101 et seq., is the source of entitlement to compensation benefits for Federal workers. Because virtually all of the provisions of the FECA have been interpreted and more fully described through OWCP directives and decisions of the Employees' Compensation Appeals Board, other resources will usually prove more helpful than the FECA itself except in locating citations found in OWCP decisions. Copies may be obtained at no charge from the district offices.

b. The Code of Federal Regulations, 20 CFR Chapter 10, Part A, more fully describes the provisions of the law and contains additional information concerning administration of the program. References to the regulations may occasionally be found in letters and decisions of OWCP. Copies may be obtained free of charge from the district offices.

c. **The Federal (FECA) Procedure Manual** describes in detail the procedures used by OWCP personnel in processing claims. It is divided into several sections by subject area; the section most likely to be of use to agency personnel is Part 2, Claims. One copy of this volume may be provided free of charge to each agency's National headquarters. Other interested parties may obtain it for $35 per copy. It may be ordered from:

> Division of Federal Employees' Compensation
> Office of Workers' Compensation Programs
> 200 Constitution Avenue N. W., Room S-3229
> Washington, D. C. 20210

d. Questions and Answers About the Federal Employees' Compensation Act (Pamphlet CA-550) describes in non-technical language the basic provisions of the law and includes information concerning the most common issues about entitlement and claims processing. It is intended for use primarily by employees, who may obtain single copies by contacting the district office. Agencies may order copies from GPO at the address shown in Chapter 1-7.

e. **Decisions of the Employees' Compensation Appeals Board** may be found in bound volumes in most law libraries. The most recent issues can also be purchased from GPO.

1-9. Training

OWCP has developed several kinds of instructional materials to assist agencies in processing compensation claims. The following courses are provided in response to requests from agency personnel:

a. **The FECA Seminar** provides an overview of the law for first line supervisors as well as middle and senior level managers. The seminar, which is comprised of lectures and visual aids, may range from one to six hours, and it may be given for either small or large groups. The seminar is usually held at the requesting agency and may be given to single or multi-agency groups as well as to Federal labor unions.

b. **The Basic Compensation Specialist Workshop** provides a three day formal training session in a classroom setting. It is intended for agency personnel who are primarily responsible for processing OWCP claims and for those who spend at least 50% of their time handling OWCP claims. The training stresses skills needed to counsel injured employees, review claim forms for accuracy, document continuation of pay, and develop a record-keeping system.

c. **The Advanced Compensation Specialist Training** is a self-instructional unit requiring approximately 12 hours to complete. It is primarily intended for compensation specialists who have attended the basic course and who have nine to twelve months of experience. The course stresses management of agency compensation case files with regard to third party matters, review of chargeback reports and billings, light duty assignments, and reemployment of the long-term disabled.

d. **The FECA Supervisors Workshop** is tailored to meet the needs of the agency requesting training. The training generally covers supervisory responsibilities to employees who are injured at work. It includes reviewing initial reporting forms; counseling employees about continuation of pay; determining whether the claim should be controverted; and offering light duty assignments for injured employees. The length of this course varies according to the kind and amount of material presented.

Arrangements for delivery of these courses may be made with the Technical Assistant of the district office which serves your agency.

Chapter 2. Initiating Claims

This chapter describes the difference between exposure to an infectious agent, which is not compensable, and actual injury. The forms and procedures to be used by employees and agency personnel in initiating claims for traumatic injury, occupational disease, recurrence of disability, and death are then outlined. Agency personnel are cautioned never to prevent employees from filing claims under any circumstances.

2-1. Exposure to Infectious Agents

The FECA does not provide for payment of any expenses associated with simple exposure to an infectious disease, without the occurrence of a work-related injury. Such infectious disease may include tuberculosis, hepatitis, and HIV (human immunodeficiency virus).

Under regulations published by the Occupational Safety and Health Administration addressing the health risks posed by bloodborne pathogens in the workplace, an "exposure incident" is defined as a "specific eye, mouth, other mucous membrane, non-intact skin, or parenteral contact with blood or other potentially infectious materials that results from the performance of an employee's duties" (29 CFR 1910.1030).

Both a work-related injury and exposure to a known carrier must occur before OWCP can pay for diagnostic testing. A puncture wound from a needle used to draw blood from a patient not known to be infected with HIV would entitle the worker to benefits only for the effects of the puncture wound, and the supervisor would not issue Form CA-16 to authorize precautionary testing since no indication exists that a communicable disease has been contracted on duty. However, a puncture wound from a needle used to draw blood from a patient who was known to be infected with HIV would entitle the worker to benefits for the effects of the puncture wound and to payment for diagnostic studies to rule out the presence of a more serious condition, because exposure to a known carrier would be involved.

Similarly, fear of exposure to an infectious agent does not entitle the worker to benefits under the FECA since no definable injury has occurred. For instance, the act of searching an individual known to have hepatitis, or an individual who is believed to belong to a high-risk group for HIV infection, would not entitle an employee to benefits. In these situations, the supervisor should not issue Form CA-16 as no injury or exposure has occurred.

However, employees who have encountered persons with HIV infection may suffer anxiety for their health, and employing agencies should take these concerns seriously when actual exposure (as opposed to fear of exposure) has occurred. In such cases, the supervisor may use the authority provided by 5 USC 7901 to authorize testing or counseling. This section of the law allows agencies to provide screening and associated health services to their own employees, and the services offered may be geared to the particular occupational hazards to which an agency's employees are commonly exposed.

It may also be useful to consider performance of surveillance testing, which monitors a population at risk for a certain condition (as opposed to diagnostic testing, which is performed to assess the specific nature of an individual's illness when a medical condition is known to exist). To arrange for HIV testing or employee counseling, you may wish to contact the appropriate regional office of the Public Health Service.

2-2. Traumatic Injury

A traumatic injury is defined as a wound or other condition of the body caused by external force, including stress or strain. The injury must be identifiable by time and place of occurrence and member of the body affected; it must be caused by a specific event or incident or series of events or incidents within a single day or work shift. Traumatic injuries also include damage to or destruction of prosthetic devices or appliances, including eyeglasses and hearing aids if they were damaged incidental to a personal injury requiring medical services. (Personal property claims can be made only under the Military Personnel and Civilian Employees' Claims Act, 31 USC 240.)

   a. **Notice of Injury**—*Form* CA-1. When an employee sustains a traumatic injury in the performance of duty, he or she should give a written report on Form CA-1 to the supervisor as soon as possible but not later than 30 days from the date of injury. If the employee is incapacitated, this action may be taken by someone acting on his or her behalf, including a family member, union official, representative, or agency official. The form must contain the original signature of the person giving notice. The supervisor should:

(1) Review the front of the form for completeness and accuracy, and assist the employee in correcting any deficiencies found;

(2) Complete and sign the reverse of Form CA-1, including a telephone number in case OWCP personnel have questions about the injury. Also, insert the appropriate codes on both the front and back of the form. Codes should be included for occupation, type and source of injury, agency identification, and location of duty station by zip code (Appendix B of this publication describes the type and source of injury codes and their use).

(3) Sign and return to the employee the receipt attached to Form CA-1 and give a copy of the form to the employee if requested;

(4) Authorize medical care if needed in accordance with paragraph (b) below;

(5) Inform the employee of the right to elect continuation of regular pay (COP) (discussed in detail in Chapter 5), or annual or sick leave if time loss will occur;

(6) Advise the employee whether COP will be controverted, and if so, whether pay will be terminated. The basis for the action must be explained to the employee. (Controversion is discussed in Chapter 5-3; the reason for controverting a claim must always be shown on Form CA-1.)

(7) Advise the employee of his or her responsibility to submit prima facie medical evidence of disability within 10 working days or risk termination of COP (see Chapter 5-8).

If the employee incurs medical expense or loses time from work beyond the date of injury, the supervisor should submit Form CA-1 to the district office with supporting information as soon as possible but no later than 10 working days after receipt of Form CA-1 from the employee. If one or more visits for medical care are required during duty hours after the date of injury, or if two or more such visits are required during non-duty hours after the date of injury, the case should be submitted to OWCP as a first aid injury. If no medical expense will be incurred and no time will be lost from work beyond the date of injury, the notice of injury should be retained in the Employee Medical Folder.

b. **Medical Treatment—Form CA-16.** If an employee requires medical treatment because of the injury, the supervisor should promptly complete the front of Form CA-16 within four hours of the request whenever possible. If the supervisor doubts whether the employee's condition is related to the employment, he or she should so indicate on the form. In an emergency, where there is no time to complete a Form CA-16, the supervisor may authorize medical treatment by telephone and then forward the completed form to the medical facility within 48 hours. Retroactive issuance of Form CA-16 is usually not permitted under other circumstance.

(1) **Delayed Report of Injury.** If an employee has reported an injury several days after the fact, or did not request medical treatment within 24 hours of the injury, the supervisor may still authorize medical care using Form CA-16. Agency personnel are encouraged to use discretion in issuing authorizations for medical care under such circumstances, but employees should not be penalized for short delays in reporting injuries. The supervisor may, however, refuse to issue a CA-16 if more than a week has passed since the injury on the basis that the need for immediate treatment would normally have become apparent in that period of time. An employee may not use Form CA-16 to authorize his or her own medical treatment.

(2) **Choice of Physician.** The employee is entitled to select the physician or facility which is to provide treatment. The provider must meet the definition of "physician" under the FECA and must not have been excluded from payment under the program (refer to Chapter 6 for guidance in authorizing providers). An agency may make its own facilities available for examination and treatment of injured employees, but may not mandate use of its facilities

to the exclusion of the employee's choice. Physicians employed by or under contract to the agency may examine the employee at the agency's facility in accordance with OPM regulations, but the employee's choice of physician must be honored, and treatment by the employee's physician must not be delayed.

(3) **Obtaining Treatment.** Along with Form CA-16, the supervisor should give the employee Form OWCP-1500, which is used for billing (this form is discussed in Chapter 6). The physician should complete the reverse of Form CA-16 and the OWCP-1500 and forward them to OWCP; the supervisor may ask the physician for a copy of the report as well. The employee may be furnished transportation and/or reimbursed for travel and incidental expenses. OWCP generally considers 25 miles from the agency or the employee's home a reasonable distance to travel for medical care unless appropriate care is not available within that radius.

(4) **Referral.** The original treating physician may wish to refer the employee for specialized treatment or for further testing. He or she may do so on the basis of the Form CA-16 already issued; it is not necessary to issue additional authorizations for treatment. Both the original physician and any physician to whom the employee is referred is guaranteed payment for 60 days from the date of issue of Form CA-16 unless OWCP terminates this authority at an earlier date. Treatment may continue at OWCP expense if the claim is approved.

Should the employee wish to change physicians after the initial choice, he or she must contact OWCP in writing for approval and include the reasons for requesting the change.

c. **Medical Reports—Forms** CA-20, CA-20a, and CA-17. In cases sent to OWCP, a medical report from the attending physician is required. This report may be made on Form CA-16 or on Forms CA-20 or CA-20a, which are attached to compensation claim forms. It may also be made by narrative report on the physician's letterhead stationery, or in the form of an emergency room summary. In all instances, however, the physician's original signature must appear on the report. The supervisor should supply medical report forms to the employee for completion by the physician as often as needed. These reports should be submitted in original form to OWCP.

Agency personnel should use Form CA-17, Duty Status Report, to obtain interim medical reports concerning the employee's fitness for duty; it may be issued initially with Form CA-16. The supervisor should complete the agency's portion of the form by describing the physical requirements of the employee's job and noting the availability of any light duty. The physician should forward the original Form CA-17 to the agency and a copy to the district office. The supervisor may send Form CA-17 to the physician at reasonable intervals (but not more often than once a week) to monitor the employee's medical status and ability to return to light or full duty. (Agency offers of light duty during the COP period are discussed in Chapter 5.)

d. **Wage Loss/Permanent Impairment—Form** CA-7. If disability is anticipated at the time of injury, the employee may elect to use leave or COP (which is discussed in Chapter 5) on Form CA-1. An employee who cannot return to work when COP terminates, or who is not entitled to receive COP, may claim compensation for wage loss on Form CA-7. In controverted cases where pay is terminated, Form CA-7 should be submitted with Form CA-1.

(1) **When to File.** If disability is expected to continue beyond the period of entitlement to COP, the employee may claim compensation or use leave to cover his or her absence from work. If it is not clear whether the employee will remain disabled after the 45 days of COP are used, claim for compensation should be initiated. Employees who have filed claims should be carried in LWOP status. If an employee returns to work after Form CA-7 has been filed, however, the supervisor should notify OWCP by telephone to avoid overpayments, and later provide written confirmation of return to duty.

(2) **Completion.** If compensation is to be claimed, the supervisor should give Form CA-7 to the employee on the 30th day of COP with instructions to complete the front and return the form to the agency within one week. (If the employee has not returned it by the 40th day of COP,

the supervisor should contact him or her by telephone and request that it be submitted as soon as possible). The supervisor should also indicate the address of the district office in the box on the reverse of the Form CA-20 which is attached to the claim form.

When the form is returned, the supervisor should complete the reverse of the form, including the name and the telephone number of an agency official with direct knowledge of the claim. The employee should arrange to provide medical evidence to support the period of disability claimed; this evidence may be submitted with the Form CA-7 or sent to OWCP separately.

(3) **Submission.** After completing the form, the supervisor should submit it to OWCP along with any new medical evidence in the agency's possession. OWCP will use the pay data supplied by agency personnel to determine the rate at which compensation is to be paid. (Submission should not be delayed for computation of shift differential, Sunday or holiday pay, or other incremental pay; these elements, which are discussed in Chapter 8, may be computed and submitted separately). The dates of compensation claimed should represent the period of disability supported by the medical evidence or the interval until the employee's next medical appointment.

(4) **Leave Repurchase.** An employee who uses sick or annual leave to avoid possible interruption of income may repurchase that leave, subject to agency concurrence, if the claim is approved. Form CA-7 may be used for this purpose as well. The employee and supervisor should supply the factual and medical evidence described above, and the supervisor should also provide a detailed breakdown of leave used, showing the number of hours charged for each day claimed and whether sick or annual leave was used. (The relationship between COP use and leave use is discussed in Chapter 5-2.)

(5) **Lost Wages for Medical Treatment.** An employee who has returned to work but continues to require medical treatment during work hours may claim compensation for lost wages while undergoing or traveling to and from the treatment. Such a claim may be made on Form CA-7, and it should be accompanied by a statement from the supervisor showing the exact period of time and the total amount of wages lost due to the treatment, the rate of pay and the number of hours or days the employee would have worked if available.

Form CA-7 may also be used to claim a schedule award for permanent impairment as a result of traumatic injury (entitlement to such awards is discussed in Chapter 7-1).

e. **Continuing Wage Loss—Form CA-8.** If disability is expected to continue, the supervisor should give the injured employee Form CA-8 ten days before the period claimed on Form CA-7 expires. The supervisor should indicate the address of the OWCP district office in the box on the back of CA-20a which is attached to the form. The employee should complete the front and return it to the supervisor, which should complete the reverse of the form. As with the Form CA-7, the employee is responsible for obtaining medical support for the period claimed, and the dates of compensation claimed should represent the period of disability supported by the medical evidence or the interval until the employee's next medical appointment.

The completed form should be sent to OWCP at least five days before the end of the period claimed on Form CA-7. During the period of disability a Form CA-8 should be submitted every two weeks absent other instructions from OWCP. Form CA-8 may also be used to claim additional periods of leave repurchase; an itemized breakdown of leave used should be provided as described in paragraph (d) above. Here again, if the employee returns to work after a claim has been submitted, the supervisor should notify the district office by telephone immediately so that an overpayment can be avoided. Written confirmation of return to duty should also be supplied to the district office.

If the employee is examined or treated at the agency's medical facilities or by medical providers under contract to the agency, and this examina-tion or treatment occurs during working hours beyond the date of injury, the supervisor should submit Form CA-1 to OWCP. In doing so, the supervisor should add the words "first aid" to the upper right corner of the agency's portion of Form CA-1. "First aid" injuries also include those requiring two or more visits to a medical facility for examination or treatment during non-duty hours beyond the date of injury, as long as no leave or continuation of pay is charged and no medical expense is incurred.

If the employee obtains no medical care, or obtains only agency-sponsored care on the date of injury, and no time loss is charged to either leave or continuation of pay, the supervisor should place Form CA-1 in the worker's Employee Medical Folder (EMF) instead of sending it to OWCP.

2-3. Occupational Disease

An occupational disease is defined as a condition produced in the work environment over a period longer than one work day or shift. It may result from systemic infection, repeated stress or strain, exposure to toxins, poisons, or fumes, or other continuing conditions of the work environment.

a. **Notice of Occupational Disease—Form CA-2.** The injured employee, or someone acting on his or her behalf, should give notice of occupational disease on Form CA-2. The supervisor should issue to the employee two copies of the appropriate checklist, Form CA-35a-h, for the disease claimed. (Specific checklists have been devised for various conditions in order to facilitate submission of evidence—see Appendix C.) The supervisor should also explain the need for detailed information to the employee and advise him or her to furnish supporting medical and factual information requested on the checklist. If possible, this information should accompany the form when it is submitted. Upon receiving Form CA-2, the supervisor should:

   (1) Review the front of the form for completeness and accuracy, and assist the employee in correcting any deficiencies found;

   (2) Complete and sign the reverse of Form CA-2, including a telephone number in case OWCP personnel have questions about the claim. Also, show the appropriate codes for occupation, type and source of injury, agency identification, and location of duty station by zip code. (Appendix B describes the type and source of injury codes and their use.)

   (3) Sign and return to the employee the receipt attached to Form CA-2 and give a copy of the form to the employee if requested;

   (4) Review the employee's portion of the form and provide comments on the employee's statement requested in (5);

   (5) Prepare a supporting statement to include exposure data, test results, copies of reports of previous medical examinations, and/or witness statements, depending on the nature of the case. The checklist may be used to coordinate compilation of material by agency personnel, including compensation specialists and safety and health officers;

   (6) Advise the employee of the right to elect sick or annual leave or leave without pay, pending adjudication of the claim.

The supervisor should submit completed Form CA-2 to the district office within 10 working days of receipt from the employee. It should not be held for receipt of supporting documentation.

b. **Medical Treatment—Form CA-16.** Only rarely do employing agency personnel authorize medical care in occupational disease claims. The supervisor must contact OWCP before issuing a Form CA-16 in such a claim.

c. **Wage Loss—Form CA-7.** Form CA-7 is used to file an original claim for compensation because of pay loss resulting from an occupational disease. The claim should be filed within 10 days after pay stops or when the employee returns to work, whichever occurs first.

   (1) **Leave Repurchase.** The employee may wish to use sick or annual leave pending adjudication of the claim. If so, the employee may initiate repurchase of this leave, subject to agency concurrence, using Form CA-7. The supervisor should certify the amount and kind of leave used for each day claimed, and the employee should arrange for submission of medical evidence supporting the period of repurchase requested.

(2) **Lost Wages for Medical Treatment.** An employee who has returned to work but con-tin-ues to require medical treatment during work hours may claim compensation for lost wages while undergoing or traveling to and from the treatment. Such a claim may be made on Form CA-7, and it should be accompanied by a statement from the supervisor showing the exact period of time and the total amount of wages lost due to the treatment, the rate of pay and the number of hours or days the employee would have worked if available.

Form CA-7 may also be used to initiate a claim for schedule award for permanent impairment resulting from occupational disease. Chapter 7-1 addresses entitlement to such awards.

d. **Continued Wage Loss—Form CA-8.** Form CA-8 may be used to claim continuing compensation after the initial period claimed on Form CA-7, or to claim additional periods of leave repurchase.

2-4. Recurrences

A recurrence is defined as a spontaneous return or increase of disability due to a previous injury or occupational disease without intervening cause, or a return or increase of disability due to a consequential injury (defined in Chapter 3-5). A recurrence differs from a new injury in that with a recurrence, no event other than the previous injury accounts for the disability. Follow-up medical care for an injury or disease which causes time loss is considered part of the original injury rather than a recurrence unless the employee was previously released from treatment.

a. **Claim for Recurrence—Form CA-2a.** If a recurrence develops, the employee and supervisor should complete Form CA-2a and submit it to OWCP. If the employee was entitled to use COP and the 45 calendar days of COP have not been exhausted, he or she may elect to use the remaining days if 90 days have not elapsed since first return to duty (see Chapter 5-7 for detailed information). Otherwise, the employee may elect to use sick or annual leave pending adjudication of the claim for recurrence. The employee should arrange for submission of the factual and medical evidence described in the instructions attached to the form, paying particular attention to the need for "bridging" information which describes his or her condition and job duties between the original injury and the recurrence.

b. **Medical Treatment—Form CA-16.** The supervisor, at his or her discretion, may issue Form CA-16 to authorize examination or treatment for a recurrence of disability if it resulted from an injury previously recognized as compensable by the OWCP. The supervisor may not authorize examination or treatment when OWCP has disallowed the original claim or when more than six months have elapsed since the employee last returned to work.

c. **Claim for Wage Loss—Forms CA-7 and CA-8.** If an employee wishes to claim compensation because of a recurrence, Form CA-7 is required if one was not previously submitted. If a Form CA-7 was submitted, then the employee is to complete a Form CA-8 and submit it to the supervisor along with supporting medical evidence. A Form CA-8 is to be completed and submitted every two weeks until OWCP notifies the employee otherwise.

2-5. Death

When an employee dies because of an injury incurred while in performance of duty, the supervisor should immediately notify the district office by telephone or facsimile message. The supervisor should also contact any survivors, provide them with claim forms, and assist them in preparing the claim as much as possible. The forms should be submitted even if a disability claim had previously been filed and benefits were paid. Continuation of benefits is not automatic, as it must be shown that the death resulted from the same condition for which the disability claim was accepted.

a. **Claims for Death Benefits—Forms CA-5 and CA-5b.** The survivors of a deceased employee should use Form CA-5 or CA-5b to submit claims for death benefits. The survivor should complete the front of the appropriate form, while the attending physician should complete the medical report on the reverse and forward it to OWCP. The submission should include a copy of the death certificate which has been certified by the issuing authority. It should also include a certified marriage certificate if a spouse is making claim, and a copy of any divorce or annulment decree if the decedent or spouse was formerly married. The submission should include certified copies of birth certificates of any children for whom claim is made.

b. **Agency Notice—Form CA-6.** The supervisor uses this form to report the work-related death of an employee.

Chapter 3. Conditions of Coverage

Each claim for compensation must meet certain requirements before it can be accepted. This is true whether the claim is for traumatic injury, occupational disease, or death. While the requirements are examined somewhat differently according to the type of claim, they are always considered in the same order. This chapter will describe these requirements as well as the three statutory prohibitions to payment of compensation. It will also describe the kind of information which should be submitted by the supervisor and employee for each issue.

3-1. Time

All cases must first satisfy the statutory time requirements of the FECA.

a. **Provisions of the Law.** For injuries and deaths on or after September 7, 1974, the law provides that a claim for compensation must be filed within three years of the injury or death. Even if claim is not filed within three years, however, compensation may still be allowed if written notice of injury was given in 30 days or the immediate superior had actual knowledge of the injury or death within 30 days after occurrence. This knowledge may consist of written records or verbal notification; an entry into an employee's medical record may also satisfy this requirement if it is sufficient to place the agency on notice of a possible work-related injury or illness.

   The law also provides that the filing of a disability claim because of injury will satisfy the time requirements for a death claim based on the same injury. OWCP may excuse failure to comply with the three year time requirement because of exceptional circumstances (for example, being held prisoner of war).

   For injuries occurring before September 7, 1974, different provisions apply with respect to timeliness. Contact the district office concerning any case in this category.

b. **When Time Begins to Run.** For traumatic injury, the statutory time limitation begins to run from the date of injury. For a latent condition, it begins to run when an injured employee who has a compensable disability becomes aware, or reasonably should have been aware, of a possible relationship between the condition and the employment. In situations where the exposure to possibly injurious employment-related conditions continues after this knowledge, the time for filing begins to run on the date of the employee's last exposure to the implicated conditions.

   In death cases resulting from traumatic injury, time begins to run from the date of death. Where death is due to disease, time begins to run when the beneficiary is aware, or reasonably should have been aware, of causal relationship between the death and the factors of employment. For a minor, the time limitations do not begin to run until the person reaches the age of 21 or has a legal representative. For a person who is mentally incompetent, the time limitations do not begin to run until the person has a legal representative.

c. **Written Notice.** Form CA-1 or CA-2 constitutes notice of injury. A claim for compensation (Form CA-7 in disability cases, CA-5 or CA-5b in death cases) may also constitute notice of injury. Moreover, OWCP will accept as a notice of injury or death any written statement which is signed by the person claiming benefits or someone acting on his or her behalf and which states the name of the employee; the name and address of the person claiming benefits; the time and location of the injury or death; and the cause and nature of the injury or death.

d. **Actual Knowledge.** An agency official may acquire actual knowledge through firsthand observation of the incident, from another employee, or from medical personnel at the agency's medical facility. This knowledge must place the employing establishment reasonably on notice of an on-the-job injury or death. An entry into the employee's medical records may be considered actual knowledge, as may the results of tests conducted by agency personnel in connection with known occupational hazards. The date on which the agency or OWCP receives written notice will be considered the date of filing. Information addressing the issue of actual knowledge is needed only when the agency did not receive written notice within three years.

3-2. Civil Employee

If the claim is timely filed, it must be determined whether the injured or deceased individual was an "employee" within the meaning of the law. This is always the second requirement considered.

a. **Provisions of the Law.** The FECA covers all civilian Federal employees except for non-appropriated fund employees. In addition, special legislation provides coverage to Peace Corps and Vista volunteers; Federal petit or grand jurors; volunteer members of the Civil Air Patrol; Reserve Officer Training Corps Cadets; Job Corps and Youth Conservation Corps enrollees; and non-Federal law enforcement officers under certain circumstances involving crimes against the U.S.

b. **Other Considerations.** Temporary employees are covered on the same basis as permanent employees. Contract employees, volunteers, and loaned employees are covered under some circumstances; such determinations must be made on a case by case basis once a claim is filed. Federal employees who are not citizens or residents of the U.S. or Canada are covered subject to certain special provisions governing their pay rates and computation of compensation payments.

3-3. Fact of Injury

If the issues of "time" and "civil employee" have been resolved affirmatively, it must be established whether the employee in fact sustained an injury or disease. Two factors are involved in this determination:

a. **Occurrence of Event.** Whether the employee actually experienced the accident, event, or employment factor which is alleged to have occurred. This is resolved on the basis of factual evidence, including statements from the employee, the supervisor, and any witnesses. An injury need not be witnessed in order to be compensable. A supervisor who believes, however, that the employee's testimony is contrary to the facts should supply pertinent information to support this belief.

b. **Medical Condition.** Whether the accident or employment factor resulted in an injury or disease; this is determined on the basis of the attending physician's statement that a medical condition is present which may be related to the incident. Simple exposure, for instance to a contagious condition or dusty environment, does not constitute an injury.

3-4. Performance of Duty

If the first three criteria have been accepted, it must be determined whether the employee was in the performance of duty when the injury occurred.

a. **Agency Premises.** An employee who is injured on agency premises during working hours has the protection of the FECA unless engaged in an activity which removes him or her from the scope of employment. Coverage includes injuries which occur while the employee was performing assigned duties or engaging in an activity which was reasonably associated with the employment. Such activities include use of facilities for the employee's comfort, health, and convenience as well as eating meals and snacks provided on the premises. The premises include areas immediately outside the building, such as steps or sidewalks, if these are Federally owned or maintained. The supervisor should document an injury occurring in such an area by submitting a diagram showing where it happened.

(1)**Outside Working Hours.** Coverage is extended to employees who are on the premises for a reasonable time before or after working hours. It is not extended, however, to employees who are visiting the premises for non-workrelated reasons. The supervisor should verify the time of the injury and provide any information in its possession about the employee's purpose in being on the premises at the time of injury.

(2)**Representational Functions.** Injuries to employees performing representational functions entitling them to official time are covered. Injuries to employees engaged in the internal business of a labor organization, such as soliciting new members or collecting dues, are not covered. The supervisor should advise whether the employee was entitled to official time when injured.

(3)**Parking Facilities.** The agency's premises include the parking facilities which it owns, controls, or manages. An employee will usually be covered if injured on such parking facilities. Information submitted by the supervisor should include a statement indicating whether it owns or leases the parking lot, and if the latter, the name and address of the owner (this information may be needed for purposes of developing the third-party aspect of the claim, which is described in Chapter 4-1). If the parking lot is not immediately adjacent to the building, the supervisor should also supply a diagram showing where the injury took place in relation to the parking lot and building.

(4)**Agency Housing.** An employee is covered if injured during the reasonable use of premises which he or she is required or expected to occupy, and which are furnished or made available by the agency. (Employees using such housing include firefighters and Job Corps enrollees.) Any claim for injury occurring under such circumstances should be accompanied by a full description of the living arrangements and the requirements and expectations surrounding their use.

b. **Off-Premises Injuries.** Coverage is extended to workers such as letter carriers, chauffeurs, and messengers who perform service away from the agency's premises. It is also extended to workers who are sent on errands or special missions and workers who perform services at home.

(1)**To and From Work.** Employees do not have the protection of the FECA when injured en route between work and home, except where the agency furnishes transportation to and from work, the employee is required to travel during a curfew or an emergency, or the employee is required to use his or her vehicle during the work day. Such claims should be accompanied by a description of the circumstances.

(2)**Lunch Hour.** Injuries which occur during lunch hour off the premises are not ordinarily covered unless the employee is in travel status or is performing regular duties off premises.

(3)**Travel Status.** Employees in travel status are covered 24 hours a day for all reasonable incidents of their TDY. Thus, an employee injured on a sightseeing trip in the city to which he or she was assigned may not be covered, while an employee injured in the hotel shower would be covered. All claims for injuries occurring in travel status should be accompanied by a copy of the travel authorization.

(4)**Vehicular Accidents.** Any claim involving a traffic accident should be accompanied by a copy of the police report, if any, and a diagram or map showing the location of the accident in relation to the places where official duty was last performed and next scheduled.

c. **Other Factors.** Some injuries occur under circumstances which are not governed, or not completely governed, by the premises rules. Injuries involving any of the circumstances indicated below must be determined on a case-by-case basis.

(1)**Recreation.** An employee is covered while engaged in formal recreation for which he or she is paid or is required to perform as a part of training or assigned duties. Also covered are employees engaged in informal recreation, such as jogging, while on the agency premises. Under other circumstances, the agency must explain what benefit it derived from the employee's participation, the extent to which the agency sponsored or directed the activity, and whether the employee's participation was mandatory or optional.

(2)**Horseplay.** An employee who is injured during horseplay is covered if the activity was one which could reasonably be expected where a group of workers is thrown into personal association for extended periods of time. In this kind of case, it must be determined whether the particular activity was a reasonable incident of the employment or was an isolated event which could not reasonably have been expected to result from close association.

(3) **Assault.** An injury or death caused by the assault of another person may be covered if it is established that the assault was accidental and arose out of an activity directly related to the work or work environment. Coverage may also be extended if the injury arose out of a personal matter having no connection with the employment if it was materially and substantially aggravated by the work association. The supervisor should submit copies of any internal or external investigation to which the agency has access as well as witness statements from parties having knowledge of the incident.

(4) **Emergencies.** Coverage is extended to employees who momentarily step outside the sphere of employment to assist in an emergency, such as to extinguish a fire or assist a person in imminent danger.

3-5. Causal Relationship

After the four factors described above have been considered, causal relationship between the condition claimed and the injury or disease sustained is examined. Unlike fact of injury, which is discussed in paragraph (3) above and which involves the determination that a medical condition is present, causal relationship involves establishment of a connection between the injury and the condition found. This factor is based entirely on medical evidence provided by physicians who have examined and treated the employee. Opinions of the employee, supervisor or witness are not considered, nor is general medical information contained in published articles.

a. *Kinds of Causal Relationship.* An injury or disease may be related to employment factors in any one of four ways:

(1) **Direct Causation.** This term refers to situations where the injury or factors of employment result in the condition claimed through a natural and unbroken sequence.

(2) **Aggravation.** If a pre-existing condition is worsened, either temporarily or permanently, by a work-related injury, that condition is said to be aggravated.

(a) Temporary aggravation involves a limited period of medical treatment and/or disability, after which the employee returns to his or her previous physical status. Compensation is payable only for the period of aggravation established by the medical evidence, and not for any disability caused by the underlying disease. This is true even if the employee cannot return to the job held at time of injury because the pre-existing condition may be aggravated again. For example, if exposure to dust at work temporarily aggravates an employee's pre-existing allergy, compensation will be payable for the period of work-related disability but not for any subsequent period, even though further exposure in the work place may cause another aggravation.

(b) Permanent aggravation occurs when a condition will persist indefinitely due to the effects of the work-related injury or when a condition is materially worsened by a factor of employment such that it will not return to the pre-injury state.

(3) **Acceleration.** A work-related injury or disease may hasten the development of an underlying condition, and acceleration is said to occur when the ordinary course of the disease does not account for the speed with which a condition develops.

(4) **Precipitation.** This term refers to a latent condition which would not have manifested itself on this occasion but for the employment. For example, an employee's latent tuberculosis may be precipitated by work-related exposure.

b. **Medical Evidence.** The issue of causal relationship almost always requires reasoned medical opinion for resolution. This opinion must be obtained from a physician who has examined or treated the employee for the condition claimed. In any case where a pre-existing condition involving the same part of the body is present, the physician must provide rationalized medical opinion which differentiates between the effects of the employment-related injury or disease and the pre-existing condition. Such evidence will permit the proper kind of acceptance (temporary vs. permanent aggravation, for instance).

To establish causal relationship, additional medical opinion may be requested of OWCP's District Medical Director/Adviser or from a specialist in the medical field pertinent to the injury or disease. In a claim for a psychiatric condition, a report from a psychiatrist or licensed clinical psychologist will be required to meet this criterion. In claims for occupational hearing loss and pulmonary disease, the OWCP will refer the employee for examination by an appropriate specialist after exposure to the hazardous substance or condition has been established. Chapter 6 may be consulted for further information concerning medical examinations.

c. **Consequential and Intervening Injuries.** Sometimes an injury occurring outside performance of duty may affect the compensability of a work-related injury.

(1) A consequential injury is a new injury which occurs as the result of a work-related injury; for example, it occurs because of weakness or impairment caused by a work-related injury. Included in this definition are injuries sustained while obtaining medical care for a work-related injury. Consequential injuries are compensable.

(2) An intervening injury is one which occurs outside the performance of duty to the same part of the body originally injured. The resulting condition will be considered related to the original injury unless the second injury alone is established as its cause.

3-6. Statutory Exclusions

Sometimes the circumstances of a case raise the issues of willful misconduct, intention to bring about the injury or death of oneself or another, or intoxication. If any of these factors is established as the cause of the injury or death, benefits must be denied. Agency or OWCP personnel must assert and prove these factors.

a. **Willful Misconduct.** The question of deliberate willful misconduct may arise when the employee violated a safety rule, disobeyed other orders of the employer, or violated a law. Because safety rules have been established for the protection of the worker rather than the employer, simple negligent disregard of such rules is not sufficient to deprive an employee or beneficiary of entitlement to compensation. Disobedience of such orders may destroy the right to compensation only if the disobedience is deliberate and intentional as distinguished from careless and heedless.

b. **Intoxication.** In any case involving intoxication (whether by alcohol or any other drug) the record must establish both the extent to which the employee was intoxicated at the time of the injury and the particular manner in which the intoxication caused the injury. It is not sufficient just to show that the employee was intoxicated; it must be shown that the intoxication proximately caused the injury. This requirement does not, however, provide agency personnel with any additional authority to test employees for drug use beyond that which may exist under other statutes or regulations.

c. **Intention to Bring About Injury or Death to Oneself or Another.** Where it appears that the employee brought about his or her own injury or death, or that of another, intention must be established. If the factual and medical evidence shows that the employee was not in full possession of his or her faculties, the injury may be compensable. Thus, suicide may be compensable if the injury and its consequences directly caused a mental disturbance or physical condition which produced a compulsion to commit suicide and prevented the employee from exercising sound discretion or judgment so as to control that compulsion.

Chapter 4. Processing Claims

This chapter describes general procedures and responsibilities for case handling once the proper forms and information have been filed with OWCP. It also describes the steps which agency personnel should take if it believes a claim to be questionable.

4-1. Administrative Matters

a. **Initial Handling.** The notice of traumatic injury, occupational disease or death should be filed with the district office with jurisdiction over the location of the employing agency. (After adjudication, the claim may be transferred to the district office with jurisdiction over the location of the employee's residence, if different.) When possible, the notice should be accompanied by supporting documents such as medical reports and statements from the employee, the supervisor, and witnesses. When the notice is received, OWCP will send the employee and the supervisor a postcard (Form CA-801) advising the claim number assigned to the case.

Uncontroverted claims with medical bills totalling less than $1000, no claim for compensation benefits, and no potential third-party liability will be administratively closed after payment of any outstanding medical bills. Claims not meeting these criteria will be assigned to a Claims Examiner for formal adjudication, as will those which pass the $1000 threshold for medical bill payment.

The Claims Examiner will determine if information in addition to the initial submission is required to adjudicate the claim. If so, the information will be requested of the employee and/or the supervisor with a copy to all parties to the claim. While the requirements for accepting a claim are considered in the order shown in the previous chapter,

OWCP will attempt to request information on all unresolved aspects of the claim simultaneously in the interests of efficient case handling.

b. **Obtaining Information.** Agencies and employees usually communicate with OWCP in writing. Most district offices have a contact office which can provide information on the status of a claim and answer general questions. When more detailed information is needed, the Claims Examiner responsible for the case file can often satisfy the inquiry. A supervisor with questions about common themes identified in a number of claims should contact the Assistant District Director or District Director for clarification of the procedure in question. Only inquiries which cannot be resolved in this manner should be referred to OWCP's National Office, and any such matter should be referred through the agency's headquarters. Policy questions may also be referred to OWCP's National Office.

Under the Privacy Act, the employee or representative is entitled to receive one copy of the case file from OWCP free of charge; additional copies will be sent at a cost of $.10 per page. It is not necessary to request the records under the Freedom of Information Act. Ordinarily, a complete copy of the record is sent directly to the requestor; occasionally, if sensitive medical information is involved, the district office will choose to forward the medical reports to a physician of the employee's choice so that the contents may be properly interpreted to the employee. Sensitive medical information may be released to the employee's representative, with the proviso that it not be disclosed to the employee, without the attending physician's permission.

c. **Conferencing.** Telephone conferences conducted by a Senior Claims Examiner are often held in cases involving complicated adjudicatory and case management issues. Conferences may be used to address the agency's controversion; the occurrence of an injury as claimed; the occurrence of an injury in performance of duty; occupational disease cases involving voluminous factual evidence or complex determinations; overpayments; and return to work efforts. Conferences may also be held where the employee is not able to express himself or herself well in writing. A representative of the employing agency may be asked to participate in such a conference, either with the Senior Claims Examiner alone or together with other parties to the claim. After the conference, the Senior Claims Examiner completes a Memorandum of Conference which describes what each party said, then asks the participant to provide any comments on this document within 15 days. The Senior Claims Examiner then makes findings on the issue for resolution and issues a decision accordingly.

d. **Representation.** The FECA provides that an employee may be represented if he or she so desires, but it is not required. A representative need not be an attorney; a union representative or friend, for example, may act in this capacity. The employee must designate any representative in writing before OWCP will recognize him or her. The law contains no provision for OWCP to pay representatives' fees. It does require, however, that OWCP approve such fees prior to payment. OWCP does not honor contingency fee agreements, and the employee should not pay any fee prior to approval by OWCP, unless the fee is paid into a true escrow account.

e. **Third Party.** When a party other than the employee or agency personnel appears to be responsible for an injury or death, the employee may be asked to seek damages from that party, which may be an individual or product manufacturer. Agency personnel are encouraged to investigate the third party aspect of any claim and submit all information gathered to OWCP. The employee will be contacted with specific instructions concerning this aspect of the claim; he or she should not attempt to settle such a claim without first obtaining advice and approval from the Solicitor of Labor through OWCP.

While a claim is pending against the third party, OWCP will pay medical and compensation benefits to which the beneficiary is entitled. If a recovery is made, the beneficiary must first pay outstanding legal fees and costs. He or she is then entitled to retain 20 percent of the remaining amount, plus an amount equivalent to a reasonable attorney's fee in proportion to the sum which will be owed to OWCP. The latter amount generally includes the total medical and compensation payments made by OWCP up to the time of settlement. Any money remaining is retained by the beneficiary and credited against future claims for benefits. OWCP will resume payment of compensation benefits and medical bills only after the beneficiary has submitted claims which equal the amount of money remaining.

4-2. Burden of Proof

The employee is responsible for establishing the essential elements of the claim as described in Chapter 3. OWCP will assist the employee in meeting this responsibility, which is also termed burden of proof, by requesting evidence needed to fulfill the requirements of the claim if such information is not included with the original submission.

OWCP will attempt to obtain any pertinent medical evidence in the possession of another Federal facility, including the employing agency, but this assistance does not relieve the employee of his or her burden of proof. Agencies are required by law to provide medical and factual evidence requested by OWCP in order to adjudicate a claim. Agencies and employees alike are always entitled to present information not specifically requested by OWCP.

When information is not submitted in a timely manner, delays in adjudicating cases and paying claims often result. To minimize such delays, OWCP will ask the employee and supervisor to submit the required evidence within a specific period, usually 30 days from the date of the request. A copy of any request to the supervisor for information will be sent to the employee, and vice versa. Following is a description of the procedures which OWCP uses with respect to requests for information from agencies.

a. **Traumatic Injury Cases (Including Recurrence and Death).**
  (1) The factual evidence required from an employer in a traumatic case will often concern the circumstances surrounding the injury. By anticipating the information which OWCP will need, as described in the preceding chapter, agency personnel will often be able to avoid handling correspondence which would otherwise be generated. Each submission of forms should contain a clear description of how the injury occurred, including the time and place, whether it happened during working hours, the presence of witnesses, etc.

  If this information is not included in the original submission, OWCP will request it. If a second request for such information is needed, OWCP will advise that absent a response the case will be processed on the basis of the evidence submitted by the employee as follows:
    (a) If the employee's statement is sufficiently detailed and/or credible, OWCP will accept the statement and adjudicate the claim accordingly.
    (b) If the employee's statement is not sufficient and/or credible, the claim will be denied for the reason that one or more of the five basic elements required to approve a claim has not been established.
  (2) Medical evidence in possession of the agency may also be requested.

(a) In an unadjudicated claim, the supervisor should submit copies of medical records pertaining to the injury and any relevant pre-existing condition at the time of initial submission to OWCP. This evidence will be requested of the agency if it is not sent with the original submission.

(b) In an accepted case, if the employee receives continuing care from an agency physician (or its contract provider), the supervisor should include supporting medical evidence for disability with claims submitted. Otherwise, the agency will be asked to submit the relevant medical evidence if the file does not support disability for the claimed period.

   If the file contains prima facie medical evidence of disability for the period claimed but additional support is needed, OWCP will authorize payment for a reasonable period and request the evidence from the employer. If another claim is received and the previously requested evidence has not been submitted, OWCP will again authorize payment of compensation for a reasonable period and refer the employee to a medical specialist for examination.

(3) Payment information needed will usually involve the employee's salary or the days of LWOP claimed or leave used during the period involved. Agencies can speed the payment process by advising OWCP of any elements of the pay rate which should be included, such as night and Sunday differential, and whether the employee has received these increments regularly (in which case the biweekly amount should be indicated) or sporadically (in which case the employee's entire earnings in the relevant pay category for the year preceding the injury should be provided).

   Where the pay rate is in question, OWCP will begin paying compensation using the lower salary and request clarification from the supervisor. If a second request is necessary, the employee will be advised that documentation is necessary to support the higher pay rate and asked to submit any documentation in his or her possession. If the agency fails to reply and the employee submits adequate documentation (e.g., pay stubs), OWCP will adjust compensation. Until sufficient documentation is received from either the supervisor or the employee, compensation will be paid at the lower rate.

   Where the days and hours of LWOP or leave status during a claimed period are in question, OWCP will request clarification from the supervisor. Any follow-up request needed will also advise the employee of the need for documentation and invite him or her to submit a detailed account for the period in question. If the employee provides such an account, OWCP will send a copy to the supervisor for review and advise that unless OWCP is notified of any inaccuracies in a timely manner, the employee's accounting will be used to compute the payment.

b. **Occupational Disease Claims (Including Recurrence and Death).**

(1) OWCP will require factual information from the employer according to the type and severity of the medical condition involved. (Simple occupational disease claims, for example a claim for poison ivy where the job duties involved exposure to the plant, and the medical evidence confirmed the diagnosis, require less evidence to adjudicate.) The information specified in the instructions for completing Form CA-2 and on the evidence checklist appropriate to the disease in question should be forwarded with the initial submission. If sufficiently detailed descriptions of the circumstances surrounding development of the claimed condition are not received, OWCP will request whatever additional information is considered necessary for adjudication.

   If a second request is necessary, the agency will be advised that if timely response is not received the OWCP will process the claim based on the evidence submitted by the employee. As with traumatic injury cases, if that evidence is sufficient and/or credible, the employee's statements will be accepted and the claim will be adjudicated accordingly.

If the evidence is not sufficient and/or credible, the claim will be denied because one or more of the five basic elements required to approve a claim has not been established.

(2) Medical examination and treatment will generally not have been provided solely by an agency medical facility. An employee who has also been seen by a private physician must submit supporting medical evidence from that physician. If additional evidence from the agency is needed, the employee will be advised that OWCP is attempting to obtain it but that the burden of proof still rests upon the employee and that he or she should also try to obtain that evidence.

(3) As with traumatic injury cases, wage loss information needed from the agency will probably involve the employee's pay rate or the days on LWOP or leave during the period claimed, and the procedures described for obtaining such information in traumatic injury cases will apply. The extensive development of medical evidence during the initial adjudication process should provide sufficient information concerning the nature and extent of disability to permit adjudication of the wage loss claim. If not, OWCP will follow the procedures for developing medical evidence in a traumatic wage loss claim.

Once OWCP accepts a claim, the burden of proof shifts from the employee to the OWCP. To rescind the acceptance of a condition or to make a retroactive determination that an employee was not disabled for a period during which compensation was paid, OWCP must demonstrate not only that an error was made but that the weight of the evidence supports its new conclusion concerning the merits of the claim.

4-3. Questionable Claims

If the supervisor questions the validity of a claim, he or she should investigate the circumstances and report the results to OWCP. All such allegations must be supported by specific factual evidence before OWCP can consider them. Situations which may prompt the supervisor to conduct such an investigation, and actions which the agency may take, are as follows:

a. **Differing Versions.** If the employee has given differing versions of the incident to different people, or several witnesses give differing accounts of the facts surrounding the injury, the supervisor should request a written statement from each person which details his or her knowledge of the situation.

b. **Previous Injury.** If the employee reported to work on the date of the claimed injury with the appearance of a pre-existing condition or injury, the agency should obtain statements detailing the relevant observations from witnesses.

c. **Time Lags.** If a lengthy period elapses between the alleged injury and the time it is reported, and the employee appears to be able to perform normal duties, a written statement detailing the situation should be composed.

d. **Other Employment.** If an employee who has claimed injury is reported to be working at another job, the supervisor should first ask him or her about the requirements of the other employment. Depending on the reply, the supervisor may wish to ask the employee for permission to contact the other employer for information concerning duties and periods of employment.

OWCP will consider all information submitted and correspond further with the parties involved if necessary. Also, OWCP may investigate the claim on its own authority, whether or not the agency has conducted an investigation. The authority to determine any aspect of a claim rests with OWCP, however, and while the agency is entitled to an explanation of the basis of OWCP's action, it must accept the determination rendered.

4-4. Decisions and Notification

The employee will be notified by letter of the acceptance of his or her case if disability is expected to ensue or continue. The letter will state the condition for which the claim is accepted and advise how to claim compensation benefits and payment or reimbursement of medical bills. In cases involving potential long-term disability, OWCP will notify the employee of his or her obligation to seek work when disability is no longer total. The supervisor will receive a copy of this notification to the employee and will also be asked to submit a copy of the employee's job description and SF-171 in order to prepare for eventual reemployment (this process is described in Chapter 8).

During the life of a claim, decisions may be rendered on various issues. Employees are usually notified by letter about such matters as approval or denial of surgical procedures and other forms of medical care, and payment of medical bills by OWCP. Appeal rights are not usually included in such determinations, but formal decisions may be issued on such matters if requested.

Any determination, whether affirmative or negative, which sets forth OWCP's findings with respect to the case and which includes a description of the employee's appeal rights is known as a formal decision. When a beneficiary is placed on the compensation rolls for schedule award, loss of wage-earning capacity, or death, he or she will receive a formal decision. Likewise, a formal decision is issued any time an adverse decision involving entitlement is reached, such as denial of an initial claim or denial of continuing benefits. Three avenues of appeal are provided for employees; the agency is not entitled to appeal. The employee may request only one form of appeal at a time.

a. **Hearing.** The employee is entitled to either an oral hearing before an office representative or a review of the written record (but not both), as long as written request is made within 30 days of the formal decision, and a reconsideration has not already been requested. The employee may change his or her hearing request in writing within 30 days of OWCP's acknowledgement of the initial request. The request should be sent to the Branch of Hearings and Review at the address included with the appeal rights; no special form is needed. If an oral hearing is requested, it will be held within 100 miles of the employee's home, and he or she may present written evidence or oral testimony in support of the claim. If a review of the written record is selected, the employee may not present oral testimony, but may submit written evidence or argument.

If an oral hearing is requested, the agency will be notified when it is scheduled and advised that it may request a copy of the transcript and/or send a representative to the hearing. The agency representative may not participate in the proceed-ings, however, unless specifically invited to do so by the employee or the OWCP representative. If a review of the written record is requested, the agency representative will be given 15 days to submit comments and/or additional documents, which will be subject to review and comment by the employee within an additional 15 days.

After the hearing is held or the review of the written record is completed, OWCP will issue a formal decision, including a description of the employee's further appeal rights.

b. **Reconsideration.** The employee may ask OWCP to reconsider a formal decision made by the district office. The request should be addressed to the district office handling the claim; no special form is required, but the request should clearly state the ground on which it is based. It must also be accompanied by relevant evidence not previously submitted or arguments for error in fact or law in reaching the contested decision. A reconsideration must be requested within one year of the date the contested formal decision was issued.

For any request which meets these criteria, OWCP will provide the agency representative with a copy of the employee's request, and allow 15 days for submission of comments and/or documents, which will in turn be subject to employee review and comment within 15 days. Following OWCP reconsideration, a new formal decision, which includes a description of the employee's further appeal rights, will be issued.

c. **Review by Employees' Compensation Appeals Board (ECAB).** An employee may request review by the ECAB, which is the highest authority in Federal workers' compensation claims. The employee should file for such review directly with the ECAB at the address included with the formal decision. The ECAB's review is based solely upon the case record at the time of the formal decision; new evidence is not considered. Employees residing within the continental United States or Canada should file application for review within 90 days of the date of the decision. Employees residing elsewhere should file within 180 days of the date of the decision. For good cause shown the ECAB may excuse failure to timely file an application for review if it is filed within one year of the date of the decision.

Chapter 5. Continuation of Pay (COP)

This chapter describes the employee's entitlement to continuation of his or her regular pay for periods of disability or medical care which occur shortly after a traumatic injury.

5-1. Definition and Entitlement

The FECA provides that an employee's regular pay may be continued for up to 45 calendar days of wage loss due to disability and/or medical treatment following a traumatic injury. The intent of this provision is to eliminate interruption in the employee's income while the claim is being adjudicated. COP is not considered compensation and is therefore subject to income tax, retirement and other deductions. After entitlement to COP is exhausted, the employee may apply for compensation or use leave.

An employee is entitled to receive COP when he or she is absent from work due to disability or medical treatment or when he or she is reassigned by formal personnel action to a position with a lower rate of pay due to partial disability. Because informal assignment of light or restricted duties without a personnel action does not result in pay loss, time worked in such a position may not be charged to COP. An employee whose work schedule is changed, however, so that a loss of salary or premium pay (e.g., Sunday pay or night differential) results, is entitled to COP for such wage loss whether or not the change in schedule was accomplished by a formal personnel action.

Temporary employees are entitled to COP on the same basis as permanent employees. If a termination date has been set for an employee prior to the injury, however, COP need not be continued past the date of termination as long as Form SF-52 showing the date of termination has been completed. Compensation will be paid after employment has ceased, regardless of how many days of COP have been used. Like any other employee, a temporary worker who first reports a traumatic injury after the employment is terminated is not entitled to COP.

5-2. Use of Leave Instead of COP

An employee may use annual or sick leave to cover all or part of an absence due to injury. If an employee elects to use leave, each full or partial day for which leave is taken will be counted against the 45 days of entitlement. Therefore, while an employee may use COP intermittently along with sick or annual leave, entitlement is not extended beyond 45 days of combined absences.

An election of sick or annual leave during the 45-day period is not irrevocable. If an employee who has elected leave for the period wishes to elect COP, the supervisor must make such a change on a prospective basis from the date of the employee's request. Where the employee wishes to have leave restored retroactively, the supervisor must honor the request, provided he or she receives prima facie medical evidence of injury-related disability for the period.

5-3. Controversion

Sometimes a supervisor objects to paying a claim for continuation of pay, either for one of the reasons provided by regulation or for some other reason. This action is called controversion. The supervisor may controvert a claim by completing the indicated portion of Form CA-1 and submitting detailed information in support of the controversion to OWCP. Even though a claim is controverted, the agency must continue the employee's regular pay unless at least one of the conditions set forth below applies:

a. The disability is a result of an occupational disease or illness;

b. The employee comes within the exclusions of 5 USC 8101 (1) (B) or (E) (which refer to persons serving without pay or nominal pay, and to persons appointed to the staff of a former President);

c. The employee is neither a citizen nor a resident of the United States, Canada, or the territory under the administration of the Panama Canal Commission (i.e., a foreign national employed outside the areas indicated);

d. The injury occurred off the employing agency's premises and the employee was not engaged in official "off-premises" duties;

e. The employee caused the injury by his or her willful misconduct, or intended to bring about his or her injury or death or that of another person, or the employee's intoxication was the proximate cause of the injury;

f. The injury was not reported on a form approved by OWCP (usually Form CA-1) within 30 days following the injury;

g. Work stoppage first occurred more than 90 days following the injury;

h. The employee initially reported the injury after employment was terminated;

i. The employee is enrolled in the Civil Air Patrol, Peace Corps, Job Corps, Youth Conservation Corps, work study program, or other group covered by special legislation.

The agency may not continue pay under any of the above circumstances.

The agency may dispute an employee's right to receive COP (and/or the validity of the claim as a whole) on other grounds, for instance on the basis that the employee was not performing assigned duty when the injury occurred, or that the condition claimed is not the result of a workrelated injury. Any such objection should be supported by objective evidence such as witness statements, pictures, accident investigations, or time sheets. If the validity of a claim is disputed for reasons other than the nine conditions listed above, regular pay must be continued for up to 45 calendar days and may not be interrupted during the 45-day period unless one of the conditions in Chapter 5-6 or 5-8 is met.

5-4. Pay Rate for COP

An employee's regular pay is his or her average weekly earnings, including premium pay, night or shift differential, Sunday or holiday pay, and other extra pay, including pay authorized by the Fair Labor Standards Act for employees who receive annual premium pay for standby duty and who also earn and use leave on the basis of their entire tour of duty, including periods of standby duty. Overtime pay should not be included, however, except for administratively uncontrollable work covered under 5 USC 5545(c)(2).

a. **Standard Number of Hours.** For a full-time or part-time worker, either permanent or temporary, who works the same number of hours per week, the weekly pay rate equals the number of hours regularly worked each week times the hourly pay rate on the date of injury, excluding overtime.

b. **Non-standard Number of Hours.** For a part-time worker, either permanent or temporary, who does not work the same number of hours per week, the weekly pay rate equals the average weekly earnings for the one-year period prior to the date of injury, excluding overtime.

c. **Intermittent Work.** For an intermittent or part time worker, either permanent or temporary, who does not work each week of the year (or the period of appointment), the weekly pay rate equals the average of the employee's weekly earnings during the one year before the injury.

It is computed on the basis of the total earnings divided by the number of weeks worked (partial weeks worked are counted as whole weeks). The annual earnings used for this computation must not, however, be less than 150 times the average daily wage earned within one year before the date of injury (the daily wage is the hourly rate times eight).

d. **Increments of Pay.** Premium, night, or shift differential as well as Sunday, holiday, or other extra pay should be included, but overtime pay may not be considered.

e. **Changes in Pay.** Within-grade increases or promotions, demotions, terminations of temporary details, etc. which the employee would have received but for the injury are included in COP since this payment represents salary and not compensation. Moreover, an employee who does not exhaust his or her entitlement to COP at the time of injury and who is later entitled to use COP while employed at a higher paying job than the one held at the time of injury is entitled to receive COP at the higher rate of pay. Where the weekly COP rate is based on the employee's average weekly earnings over the one-year period prior to the date of injury, the COP rate should be changed by the same percentage as the change in hourly pay or salary.

f. **Lost Elements of Pay.** The effects of the injury sometimes result in loss of elements of pay such as night or Sunday differential (e.g., a night shift worker is reassigned to the day shift to perform prescribed light duty). In such situations COP should be granted for the lost elements of pay (e.g., the night differential). Each day for which COP is granted to cover lost elements of pay will count as one full day of COP toward the 45-day limit.

5-5. Computation

Unless the injury occurs before the beginning of the work day, time loss on the day of injury should be charged to administrative leave. The period to be charged to COP begins with the first day or shift of disability or medical treatment following the date of injury, provided that the absence began within 90 days after the injury. COP should be charged for weekends and holidays if the medical evidence shows the employee was disabled on the days in question; for example, if the physician indicates that disability will continue only through Saturday for an individual who has Saturday and Sunday off, COP will be charged only through Saturday.

If work stoppage occurs for only a portion of a day or shift, a full day of COP will be counted against the 45 calendar day entitlement, even though the employee is not entitled to COP for the entire day or shift. For example, if an employee who has returned to work must lose three hours in order to receive physical therapy for the effects of the injury, he or she is entitled to only three hours of COP even though one full calendar day will be charged against the 45 day limit. If the employee is absent for all or part of the remaining work day, the time loss should be covered by leave, LWOP, AWOL, etc., as appropriate, since absence beyond the time needed to obtain the physical therapy cannot be charged to COP.

If the employee is only partially disabled following the injury, and continues to work several hours each work day, each day or partial day of absence from work is chargeable against the 45-day period.

5-6. Light Duty Assignments

When the physician's report indicates that the employee is no longer totally disabled, he or she is required to accept any reasonable offer of suitable light or limited duty. Such an offer may be made by telephone but must be confirmed in writing in order to be valid; it should include a description of the duties and requirements of the offered position. If a personnel action is involved, the employee must be furnished with a copy of it prior to the effective date.

COP should be paid if the employee has been assigned light duty by formal personnel action and pay loss results (e. g., the employee is placed in a light duty position at lower pay). COP should also be paid if the light duty consists of work at regular duties for fewer than the usually scheduled number of hours. The dollar amount of COP will be the difference between the pay rates of the job held on date of injury and the light duty position. One full day of COP should be charged for each day of light duty, even though the employee is working a full shift.

If the employee refuses to accept the work offered, COP should be terminated as of the date of the employee's refusal or after five workdays from the date of the offer, whichever is earlier. OWCP will then determine entitlement based on the medical reports and the duties of the offered position and issue a formal decision concerning payment of COP. A discussion of the criteria used in making such determinations is contained in Chapter 8-4.

5-7. Recurrences

In many cases, an employee will return to work without using all 45 days of entitlement of COP. Should such an employee suffer a recurrence of disability, he or she may use COP if no more than 90 days have elapsed since the date of first return to work, including part-time work and light duty, following the first work stoppage. If the recurrence begins later than 90 days after the first return to work, the agency should not pay COP even though some days of entitlement remain unused. A period which begins before the 90 day deadline and continues beyond it may be charged to COP as long as the period of time is uninterrupted. If a third-party credit has been established, the supervisor should contact OWCP before paying COP.

5-8. Terminating COP

COP should not be stopped except under the following circumstances:

a. **Medical Evidence is Not Submitted Within 10 Workdays.** This period should be counted from the date the employee claims COP or the disability begins (or recurs), whichever is later. If the agency has not received prima facie medical evidence of injury-related disability within that period, COP may be discontinued. However, the agency may not wait 10 days to request such evidence, which is defined as medical evidence showing that the employee is disabled for the job held at the time of injury because of an employment injury. Pay may be continued without such evidence if the supervisor is satisfied that the employee sustained a disabling traumatic injury. For the purposes of this provision:

(1) The 10-workday period begins the workday after the employee claims COP or the disability begins (or recurs).

(2) A "workday" means the business day of the office or facility where the employee works or reports such that the medical evidence could be submitted by the employee to an authorized agency official.

b. **The Employee is No Longer Disabled.** The agency should terminate COP if it receives medical information from the attending physician stating that the employee is no longer disabled for regular work, if a partially disabled employee returns to full-time light duty with no pay loss, or if the employee refuses a suitable offer of light duty.

c. **OWCP Notifies the Agency That Pay Should be Terminated.**

d. **The 45 Calendar Day Period Expires.**

An employee who is scheduled to be separated and reports a traumatic injury on or before the separation date should still be separated; he or she is entitled to COP up to the date of termination and to compensation thereafter.

5-9. Reporting COP—Form CA-3

a. **Time Cards.** Time loss for an employee who is receiving COP should be recorded as "COP" on the Time and Attendance Report. A diminishing record of the 45 day limitation is to be maintained in the "Remarks" block.

b. **Completion of Form CA-3.** Sometimes, return to duty information is shown on Form CA-1 when the injury is first reported. If not, the agency may (but is not required to) complete Form CA-3 and submit it to OWCP when entitlement to COP ends, the employee returns to work, or the disability ceases. The CA-3 should state the specific days and hours charged to COP and/or leave, and attachments may be used if necessary. The amount of money shown should reflect only the amount paid for COP; it should not include wages paid for light duty or for parts of days actually worked. In cases of intermittent or delayed disability, time charged to COP may be reported by narrative letter instead of by Form CA-3.

If the disability ends before the expiration of the 45 day period, the agency should terminate COP. An employee who is no longer disabled must return to work upon notification by the attending physician that he or she is able to perform full regular duty or suitable and available light duty. If the employee does not return to duty, an overpayment may result which is subject to collection by the agency.

c. **Formal Decision.** In all cases OWCP has the final authority to determine whether the agency's action in paying or terminating COP is correct. If entitlement is denied, OWCP will inform the employee and the supervisor by formal decision (Form CA-1050 is usually used for this purpose). Payment made may then be charged, at the employee's option, to sick or annual leave or be deemed an overpayment subject to collection by the agency.

Chapter 6. Medical Benefits and Care

This chapter addresses the employee's entitlement to medical benefits under the FECA.

6-1. Entitlement

The FECA at 5 USC 8103 authorizes medical services needed to provide treatment or to counteract or minimize the effects of any condition which is causally related to factors of Federal employment. No limit is imposed on the amount of medical expenses paid or on the length of time for which they are paid, as long as the charges represent the reasonable and customary fees for the services involved and the need for the treatment can be demonstrated.

Federal employees are entitled to all services, appliances, and supplies prescribed or recommended by qualified physicians which, in the opinion of OWCP, are likely to cure, give relief, reduce the degree or the period of disability, or aid in lessening the amount of monthly compensation. Medical care includes examination, treatment, and related services such as hospitalization, medications, appliances, supplies, and transportation incident to securing them. Preventive care may not be authorized, however.

6-2. Definition of Physician

The term "physician" includes surgeons, osteopathic practitioners, podiatrists, dentists, clinical psychologists, optometrists, and chiropractors within the scope of their practice as defined by State law. Naturopaths, faith healers, and other practitioners of the healing arts are not recognized as physicians within the meaning of the law.

a. **Chiropractors.** Under the FECA, the services of chiropractors may be reimbursed only for treatment consisting of manual manipulation of the spine to correct a subluxation as demonstrated by X-ray to exist. The term "subluxation" is defined as an incomplete dislocation, off-centering, misalignment, fixation or abnormal spacing of the vertebrae anatomically which must be demonstrable on any X-ray film to individuals trained in the reading of X-rays. Chiropractors may interpret their own X-rays, and if a subluxation is diagnosed the chiropractor's assessment of any disability caused by it will be accepted. If a Form CA-16 is issued to a chiropractor for emergency care and the condition diagnosed is other than a subluxation, charges will be honored until OWCP terminates the authority of Form CA-16. In this situation the employee is entitled to select another attending physician, who will need to submit a report substantiating the condition found and addressing any disability for work in order for the claim to be accepted.

b. **Excluded Physicians.** The term "qualified physician" does not include those whose licenses to practice medicine have been suspended or revoked by a state licensing or regulatory authority or who have been excluded from payment under the FECA (see paragraph (5) below).

6-3. Choice of Physician

a. **Initial Choice.** An employee is entitled to initial selection of physician for treatment of an injury. He or she may choose any licensed physician in private practice who is not excluded, or he or she may choose to be treated at a government facility where one is available. Such facilities include medical officers and hospitals of the Army, Navy, Air Force, and Department of Veterans Affairs.

Agency personnel may not interfere with the employee's right to choose a physician, nor may they require an employee who claims an injury to go to a physician who is employed by or under contract to the agency before going to the physician of the employee's choice. Agency personnel may contact the attending physician by telephone only to obtain additional information about or clarify the employee's duty status or medical progress.

b. **Referral by Attending Physician.** The attending physician may engage the services of other facilities which provide X-ray or laboratory services or of specialists whom the physician feels it necessary to consult. Charges for such services will usually be paid if they were requested by the attending physician.

c. **Change of Physician.** Except for referral by the attending physician, any change in treating physician after the initial choice must be authorized by OWCP. Otherwise, OWCP will not be liable for the expenses of treatment. The employee should request any such change in writing with an explanation of the reasons for the request. If a physician initially selected by an employee is later excluded from participation under the regulations, the employee should choose another physician. Otherwise, and upon notification by OWCP, he or she will be liable for payment of the bills from the excluded provider.

d. **Transfer of Medical Care.** The agency does not have authority to transfer medical care from one physician to another. If adequate medical care is not available locally or agency personnel believe that transfer of medical care is advisable for other reasons, OWCP must be contacted for instructions.

6-4. Medical Treatment and Evaluation

a. **Employee Requests.** Some forms of medical treatment should be approved by OWCP in advance in order to guarantee payment. Among such services are:

(1) Non-emergency surgery; a second opinion examination may be included in the approval process. (OWCP may not require an employee to undergo surgery or any other invasive procedure, such as a myelogram);

(2) Private hospital room accommodations (only semi-private rooms will be authorized unless the employee's condition necessitates private accommodations;

(3) Hospital beds, traction apparatus, wheelchairs, and similar equipment;

(4) Orthopedic appliances and shoes;

(5) Nursing home care;

(6) Courses of physical therapy;

(7) Hearing aids and lip reading services;

(8) The services of hearing and seeing eye dogs;

(9) Membership in health clubs.

Request for any of these services should be made by the attending physician, who should include his or her reasons for believing the services to be necessary. Prior authorization need not be obtained to purchase minor appliances such as a sacroiliac belt or an ankle strap, or for such items as crutches and canes if prescribed by the attending physician.

b. **OWCP Requests.** In addition to the attending physician, other medical personnel may be asked to evaluate an employee and/or file. Evaluations may be requested in connection with original or continuing entitlement to benefits, the percentage of the employee's permanent impairment or ability to return to full or light duty, or other issues. Physicians who may be asked to examine the employee and/or file are as follows:

(1) **District Medical Director/Advisor (DMD/DMA).** Each district office has one or more physicians on staff or under contract who respond to questions raised by OWCP staff. Issues include interpretation of medical issues posed by the treating physician and provision of the DMD/DMA's own opinion on medical questions. The DMD/DMA also considers requests for surgery and other modalities of treatment requiring OWCP approval. The DMD/DMA does not, however, examine employees except where a claim for disfigurement of the face, head or neck is involved.

(2) **Medical Specialist (Second Opinion Referral).** Medical issues sometimes arise which cannot be resolved on the basis of opinions given by the attending physician and the DMD/DMA. Opinion will then be requested from a physician who specializes in the field of medicine pertinent to the issue. The appointment for examination may be made by OWCP, or the employee may be asked to make the appointment. In either case, OWCP will pay for the examination, reasonable travel expenses, and wage loss incurred in connection with it. The employee may bring a physician paid by him or her to the examination if desired. The compensation of an employee who fails to attend an OWCP-scheduled examination without good reason will be suspended until the employee reports for examination.

(3) **Referee Medical Specialist.** A conflict of medical opinion may be created when differing opinions of approximately equal weight appear in the file. Medical opinion from a referee specialist will then be arranged to resolve the conflict of opinion, which may concern the relationship of a condition to factors of employment, or the extent of disability, for example. The physician is chosen on the basis of rotation among the available specialists within a given geographical area who practice the pertinent area of medicine. OWCP will arrange the appointment and advise the employee of the arrangements. As with second opinion referral, OWCP will pay the cost of the examination, reasonable travel expenses, and the amount of lost wages. Here again, the compensation of an employee who fails

to attend the examination without good reason will be suspended until the employee reports for examination.

c. **Agency Requests.** The FECA does not address the issue of medical examinations desired by the agency. Parts 339 and 353 of OPM's regulations grant broad authority to agencies to arrange for examination of any employee who files a compensation claim by a physician of the agency's choice, at the agency's expense. However, the purpose of such examinations is solely to determine if the individual is able to work in some capacity, thereby facilitating return to work.

Examinations may not be used to intimidate employees. While agencies must send the results of such examinations to OWCP and notify OWCP if the individual refuses to be examined, and the results of such examinations *per se* do not affect entitlement to compensation.

6-5. Exclusion of Providers

Certain providers may be excluded from participation in the Federal employees' compensation program. The services of such providers may not be reimbursed by OWCP during the period of exclusion.

a. **Fraud.** Providers who have been convicted under a criminal statute for fraudulent activities in connection with a Federal or state program which makes payments to providers for medical services are automatically excluded from participation in the FECA program. This means that OWCP will not honor their bills for services. Providers who are excluded or suspended from similar Federal or state programs, including Medicare, are also automatically excluded from participation in the FECA program.

b. **Other Grounds.** OWCP will initiate exclusion procedures upon receipt of information that a provider has knowingly made a false statement or misrepresented a fact in connection with a claim for reimbursement or request for payment; charged more than the provider's customary fee for similar services without good cause; failed to reimburse an employee who has paid a bill for treatment which was also paid by OWCP; repeatedly failed to submit full and accurate medical reports or failed to respond to requests for medical information; or furnished treatment substantially beyond the employee's needs, or which fails to meet professionally recognized standards.

c. **Due Process.** The regulations appearing at 20 CFR 10.450-457 include due process at every step to protect the rights of providers. These rights include administrative review of decisions and consideration of reinstatement after a period of exclusion if reasonable assurances exist that the action which led to the exclusion will not be repeated. Providers reinstated to participation in Medicare by the Health Care Financing Administration are automatically reinstated by OWCP.

d. **Notification.** OWCP will periodically distribute to agencies the names and addresses of excluded medical providers along with those who have been reinstated. Before authorizing medical services on Form CA-16, the supervisor should ensure that the medical provider selected by the employee is not among those excluded. An excluded physician may be reimbursed only for services rendered in a medical emergency. Designated agency officials should report instances of fraud or abuse coming to their attention to the district office.

e. **Medical Charges.** On receipt of a bill from an excluded provider, OWCP will determine whether either the agency or OWCP notified the employee that the provider was excluded from the program. If not, OWCP will honor the bill and advise both the provider and the employee that further treatment may not be paid in accordance with the regulations. An employee whose initially chosen attending physician is excluded will be given the opportunity to choose a new physician.

6-6. Payment of Bills

Medical support is required to substantiate that services for which payment or reimbursement is requested were required for the accepted, workrelated injury. Documentation usually takes the form of a report or clinical notes from the physician. Hospital bills should be supported by a copy of the discharge summary.

a. *Forms.* Most providers must submit their bills on the American Medical Association Standard Health Insurance Claim Form (HCFA-1500). A version of the form which includes instructions for submitting bills to OWCP carries the form number OWCP-1500. In some states the local version of the form may not be designated "HCFA-1500" or may differ from the standard AMA form in other ways. Such local variations are acceptable if they are otherwise complete.

The following providers are *required* to use Form HCFA-1500 to submit bills: physicians; nursing services; laboratories and X-ray facilities; chiropractors; therapists; and suppliers of medical equipment and goods.

The following providers are *encouraged*, though not required, to use the HCFA-1500: dentists (may use standard ADA form); and pharmacists (may use standard pharmacy billing form).

Hospitals must use Form UB-82 or UB-92, and nursing homes are encouraged to use these forms as well.

Bills rendered by ambulance services may be submitted on billhead, as may bills from foreign providers. VA facilities may submit bills using Form VA-10-9014.

b. **Requirements.** To be accepted for payment, the bill must include the following information:
(1) Employee's name;
(2) Provider's name and address;
(3) Diagnosis;
(4) Itemized list of services, with charges; and
(5) Tax identification number (the provider's Employer Identification Number or Social Security Number).

c. **Itemization.** All bills must be sufficiently itemized to allow for evaluation of the charges. The Current Procedural Terminology (CPT) code for each medical, surgical, X-ray or laboratory service should be shown on the HCFA-1500, and bills should show the dates when the services or supplies were furnished. Individual dates are not necessary if the bill is for repetitive charges over a period of time. In such cases the billing should show the beginning and ending dates of service, and the number of units of service.

d. **Time Limitation on the Payment of Bills.** No bill will be paid unless it is submitted to OWCP on or before December 31st of the year following the calendar year in which the expense was incurred or the claim (or specific condition, as appropriate) was first accepted as compensable by OWCP, whichever is later. This provision applies to any bill for which the later of the two dates falls on or after January 1, 1987.

e. **Disallowance of Charges.** Unless the amount involved is minor, OWCP will advise the payee fully of any adjustments to the bill by letter which explains the amount of the deletion or reduction, the particular charge affected, the reasons for the action, and the amount for which the bill is being approved. If a bill is reduced because the charges exceed the amount allowed by the OWCP fee schedule, a separate notice will be provided.

f. **Reimbursement.** An employee who has paid a provider may request reimbursement by submitting either receipted bills from the provider or a completed HCFA-1500 signed by the provider. Hospital bills must be stamped paid or otherwise certified to indicate that payment was made. Cash sales receipts that bear imprints of mechanical cash registers may be accepted if the nature of sale is identified. Photocopies of cancelled checks may be accepted in lieu of receipts but must be accompanied by itemized bills or other evidence of the charge for which payment was made. Prescription receipts must include the name of the drug and the date the prescription was filled.

g. **Insurance Companies.** The employee should advise medical providers to submit bills for services to OWCP. In some cases, however, bills are submitted to the employee's health insurance carrier. The carrier may request reimbursement for such charges by submitting a completed HCFA-1500 or similar OWCP-approved form. The form should list procedures and charges for each provider, and copies of paid bills and cancelled checks should be attached. It should also include the carrier's Tax Identification Number.

h. ***Transportation Expenses.*** When transportation to obtain medical care is not furnished by the government, the employee may be reimbursed for travel expenses. Travel should be undertaken by the shortest route and by public conveyance such as bus or subway unless the employee's medical condition requires the use of a taxicab or specially equipped vehicle. An employee who uses his or her automobile will be reimbursed at the standard mileage rate for government travel.

    Standard Form 1012 should be used to claim reimbursement for travel expenses. All items will be reimbursed on the basis of actual expense; a per diem allowance is not payable. Wages and travel expenses of an attendant to accompany the employee may be approved if his or her condition is such that travel cannot be accomplished otherwise. Authorization for this expense should be obtained in advance of the travel if possible.

i. ***Incorrect Payments.*** An employee who receives a reimbursement for medical expense which he or she knows to be incorrect, either partially or totally, should return the check to OWCP immediately. If an overpayment occurs, OWCP will determine whether the beneficiary is with fault in creation of the overpayment. Only if a beneficiary is determined to be without fault may waiver of the overpayment be considered.

Chapter 7. Compensation Benefits

This chapter describes the various forms of compensation benefits which are available to injured employees and survivors in death claims. It also includes a section on computation of compensation benefits.

7-1. Disability Benefits

An employee who suffers employment-related disability may be eligible for one or more types of wage loss compensation. Such benefits are classified according to the nature and extent of disability incurred.

a. ***Temporary Total Disability.*** Compensation based on loss of wages is payable after the end of continuation of pay where entitlement exists (see Chapter 5) or from the beginning of pay loss. An employee without dependents is entitled to compensation at the rate of 66 2/3% of his or her salary. With dependents, he or she is entitled to 75% of the salary.

  (1)**Dependents.** The following are considered dependents for compensation purposes:

    (a) A wife or husband residing with the employee or receiving regular support payments from him/her, either court-ordered or otherwise;

    (b) An unmarried child who lives with the employee or who receives regular contributions of support from him or her, and who is under the age of 18, or over the age of 18 and incapable of self-support due to physical or mental disability;

    (c) A student between 18 and 23 years of age who has not completed four years of post-high school education and who is regularly pursuing a full time course of study.

    (d) A parent who is wholly dependent upon and supported by the employee.

  (2)**Waiting Days.** A three-day waiting period, for which no compensation is payable, applies except in cases where disability extends more than 14 days or permanent disability results. In these cases compensation will be paid for the three days.

    An employee who receives long-term disability payments will be notified by letter of the amount of compensation to be paid, including the pay rate and compensation rate. Compensation payments for total disability may continue as long as the medical evidence substantiates total disability. Only rarely is an employee declared permanently and totally disabled; benefits provided to such an employee are the same as those provided for temporary total disability.

b. ***Schedule Awards.*** Compensation is provided for specified periods of time for the permanent loss, or loss of use, of certain parts and functions of the body. Partial loss or loss of use of these parts and functions is compensated on a proportional basis.

  (1)**Compensation Schedule.** Following is a table which shows the number of weeks payable for each schedule member if the loss or loss of use of the function or part of the body is total:

Member	Weeks	Member	Weeks
Arm	312	Loss of hearing—monaural	52
Leg	288	binaural	200
Hand	244	Breast	52
Foot	205	Kidney	156
Eye	160	Larynx	160
Thumb	75	Lung	156
First finger	46	Penis	205
Great toe	38	Testicle	52
Second finger	30	Tongue	160
Third finger	25	Ovary(including Fallopian tube)	52
Toe other than great toe	16	Uterus/cervix	205
Fourth finger	15	Vulva/vagina	205

Compensation for loss of binocular vision or for loss of 80 percent or more of the vision of an eye is the same as for loss of the eye. The degree of loss of vision or hearing for a schedule award is determined without regard to correction; that is, improvements obtainable with use of eyeglasses and hearing aids are not considered in establishing the percentage of impairment. The law contains no provision for payment of a schedule award on account of permanent impairment to the back, heart or brain.

(2) **Medical Evidence Required.** Before payment of a schedule award can be considered, the condition of the affected part of the body must reach maximum improvement. This determination involves a medical judgment that the condition has permanently stabilized. In most cases the percentage of impairment is determined in accordance with the American Medical Association's Guides to the Evaluation of Permanent Impairment, and the evaluation on which the award is based must conform to the guidelines set forth in that publication.

(3) **Claim and Payment.** If a claim for wage loss has not previously been submitted, Form CA-7 may be used to initiate a claim for schedule award. Otherwise, consideration may be requested by narrative letter. Compensation for schedule awards is computed by multiplying the indicated number of weeks times 66 2/3 percent (without dependents) or 75 percent (with dependents) of the pay rate (see paragraph (1) above for more information concerning dependents).

(4) **Decision.** When a schedule award is issued, the employee and agency will be notified of the length of the award (in number of weeks or days), the starting date of the award (the date of maximum medical improvement), the pay rate on which benefits are computed, and the compensation rate. The decision will include a description of the employee's appeal rights should he or she disagree with any element of the decision.

Schedule awards can be paid even if the employee returns to work. Employees may not, however, receive wage loss compensation and schedule awards benefits concurrently for the same injury. If an employee sustains a period of temporary total disability during the course of the award, it may be interrupted to pay the period of disability; the schedule award will resume afterwards. If an employee dies during the course of a schedule award from causes unrelated to the compensable injury, his or her dependents are entitled to the balance of the award at the rate of 66 2/3 percent.

c. *Loss of Wage-Earning Capacity.* When the medical evidence shows that the employee is no longer totally disabled, OWCP will take steps to effect reemployment of the employee, either with the original agency or with another employer (this process is described in

Chapter 8). If the employee is reemployed at a job paying less than the original position, or if it is otherwise determined that he or she can perform the duties of a specific job that is deemed suitable, medically and otherwise, compensation will be payable based on this loss of wage-earning capacity.

(1)**Payment.** The FECA provides that employees who are partially disabled by an illness or injury causally related to Federal employment shall be compensated at a rate equal to 66 2/3 (without dependents) or 75 (with dependents) percent of the wage loss incurred as a result of the disability (see paragraph (1) above concerning dependents). Benefits are paid for the duration of the wage loss due to the work- related disability.

(2)**Decision.** A formal decision containing the basis for OWCP's determination that the employee can perform the duties indicated and that the position is otherwise suitable is issued before benefits are reduced. The decision also shows the formula used to compute the new level of benefits and contains a description of the employee's appeal rights should he or she disagree with any element of the decision.

d. **Disfigurement.** In cases where the employee suffers injury to the face, neck, or head, and disfigurement results, the FECA provides for payment of an award of compensation not to exceed $3500 if the disfigurement will likely prove to be a handicap in securing or maintaining employment. As with schedule awards, payment of an award for disfigurement cannot be considered until maximum medical improvement has occurred. It should be noted that such awards can be considered only for seriously disfiguring scars and deformities.

e. **Attendant's Allowance.** If an injury is so severe that the employee is unable to care for his or her physical needs, such as feeding, bathing, or dressing, an attendant's allowance of up to $1500 per month may be paid in addition to compensation for loss of wages. The assistance required must be personal in nature; an attendant's allowance cannot be paid for housekeeping services. An employee who believes he or she is entitled to such an allowance should contact the district office by letter for instructions on how to apply for this benefit.

f. **House and Vehicle Modifications.** An employee whose injury severely restricts mobility and independence in the normal functions of living, either permanently or for a prolonged period, may be entitled to house or vehicle modifications. Examples of such conditions include blindness, profound bilateral deafness, and total loss of use of limbs such that a prosthesis, wheelchair, or leg brace is required. An employee may apply for such modifications by narrative letter. They must be recommended by the attending physician and must be consistent with the employee's pre-injury standard of living.

7-2. Death Benefits

The survivors of a Federal employee whose death is causally related to employment are entitled to benefits in the form of compensation payments, funeral expenses, transportation expenses for the remains, if necessary, and payment for termination of the deceased's status as a Federal employee.

a. **Entitlement.** The following individuals are entitled to compensation:

(1)A widow or widower;

(2)An unmarried child under the age of 18, or over the age of 18 who is incapable of self-support due to mental or physical disability;

(3)A child between 18 and 23 years of age who has not completed four years of post high school education and is regularly pursuing a full-time course of study;

(4)A parent, brother, sister, grandparent, or grandchild who was wholly or partially dependent on the deceased.

b. **Compensation Payments.** Compensation is paid at the following rates:

(1)A surviving spouse with no eligible children is entitled to compensation at the rate of 50% of the deceased employee's salary. Benefits are paid to the spouse until death or remarriage if he or she is under age 55. If a spouse under age 55 remarries, OWCP makes a lumpsum payment equal to 24 times the monthly compensation at the time of remarriage. The benefits of a spouse who remarries after the age of 55 will not be affected by the marriage.

(2) If children are eligible in addition to the spouse, he or she may receive compensation equal to 45 percent of the employee's regular pay, plus an additional 15 percent for each child, to a maximum of 75 percent of the deceased employee's regular pay. The children's portion is paid on a share and share alike basis.

(3) If the deceased employee leaves no spouse, the first child is entitled to 40 percent and each additional child is entitled to 15 percent of the employee's salary, up to a maximum of 75 percent, payable on a share and share alike basis.

(4) Other surviving dependents may be entitled to compensation benefits at various percentages specified by the FECA according to the degree of dependence. Contact the district office for information concerning claims in this category.

c. **Funeral and Burial Expenses.** Up to $800 will be paid for funeral and burial expenses. If the employee dies away from his or her area of residence, the cost of transporting the body to the place of burial will be paid in full. Itemized funeral bills should be submitted to OWCP for consideration of payment or reimbursement. In addition, a $200 allowance will be paid in consideration of the expense of terminating the deceased's status as a Federal employee.

7-3. Dual Benefits

The FECA prohibits payment of compensation and certain other Federal benefits at the same time. This prohibition does not, however, prevent an individual from filing for benefits from more than one government program at the same time. For instance, a claimant for disability benefits may file for a retirement annuity, either regular or disability, while his or her claim with OWCP is pending. Similarly, a claimant for death benefits may file for retirement benefits while his or her claim with OWCP is pending. Only if both benefits are approved will the rules governing dual benefits be invoked.

a. **Office of Personnel Management (OPM).** Except for schedule awards, a person may not receive disability benefits from OWCP concurrently with a regular or disability annuity (either CSC or FERS), nor may a person receive death benefits from OWCP concurrently with a survivor's annuity (either CSC or FERS). Therefore, a beneficiary who is entitled to both benefits must elect between them. The election may be offered by either OWCP or OPM depending on the order in which entitlement is determined. An individual may, however, receive disability benefits from OWCP or an annuity from OPM on his or her own behalf along with death benefits from the other agency which are payable on account of a spouse's death.

The beneficiary may change his or her election for different periods of time based on the benefits which are more advantageous. In either case, however, the beneficiary must be fully advised of the amount which will be forthcoming and the nature and frequency of any increases which will accrue so that he or she can make an informed election.

b. **Department of Veterans Affairs (VA).** Beneficiaries who receive compensation from the VA may also be required to elect between the benefits paid by that agency and those paid by OWCP. Such an election is required when the disability or death resulted from an injury sustained in civilian Federal employment and the VA has held that it was caused by military service, or when the VA increases a service-connected disability award due to an injury sustained in Federal civilian employment (in the latter case the election involves only the increase in VA benefits due to disability incurred during civilian employment). No election is required between OWCP benefits and those granted by the VA for strictly service-related disability. In death claims, any payment made by the VA for funeral or burial expenses may not be duplicated by OWCP, and the total payable by both agencies may not exceed $800.

c. **Social Security Administration.** An employee may receive Social Security payments payable on account of non-Federal employment and OWCP benefits at the same time, subject to income limitations imposed by the Social Security Administration. OWCP will offset Social Security benefits earned on account of Federal service.

d. **Other Federal Income.** An employee may receive compensation concurrently with military retired pay, retirement pay, retainer pay or equivalent pay for service in the armed forces or other uniformed services subject to reduction of such pay in accordance with 5 USC 5532 (b).

An employee may receive severance pay concurrently with compensation for a schedule award or for loss of wage-earning capacity, but not with compensation for temporary total disability. Separation pay may constitute a dual benefit, and an agency which is offering such payments should contact OWCP for further guidance.

Finally, an employee may receive unemployment compensation benefits concurrently with OWCP benefits.

7-4. Computing Compensation

While compensation is usually claimed in two-week increments to conform to standard Federal pay periods, compensation checks are issued on a weekly or four-weekly basis, depending on the kind of benefit and the length of time benefits are paid. Payments of compensation for very brief periods of temporary total disability or schedule impairment are issued on a weekly basis, while longer-term payments for disability and death are made every four weeks. Checks may be sent to the beneficiary or to a financial institution designated by him or her to receive the funds, but they may not be sent in care of the employee's representative unless guardianship or conservatorship is established.

Compensation payments for wage loss are based on a percentage of the employee's salary (or a statutory pay rate). Payments are computed by multiplying the applicable percentage by the wage rate and increasing the result by any cost-of-living increases to which the beneficiary is entitled.

a. **Pay Rate.** For both disability and death claims, the pay rate used to compute compensation payments is the one in effect on the date of injury, date of recurrence, or date disability began, whichever is higher. Thus, the pay rate for compensation purposes may change over the life of a claim. The salary used to compute compensation is not affected, however, by general increases in the rate paid for the employee's grade and step. Moreover, the pay rate is not affected by any promotion or raise the employee might have received but for the injury.

b. **Additional Elements of Pay.** Included in the salary are: night shift; Sunday differential; holiday pay; hazard pay; dirty work pay; quarters allowance and post differential for overseas employees; and extra pay authorized by the Fair Labor Standards Act (FLSA) for employees who receive annual premium pay for standby duty and who also earn and use leave on the basis of their entire of tour of duty, including periods of standby duty. Overtime pay is not included, however, except for administratively uncontrollable work covered under 5 USC 5545(c)(2).

In reporting these elements of pay, the supervisor should indicate the weekly or biweekly amount if the employee has a regular schedule. If not, the supervisor should compute and submit to OWCP the dollar amount paid in each category for the calendar year preceding the effective date of the pay rate.

c. **Compensation Rate.** The compensation rate is the percentage applied to the salary in order to determine the monetary amount of the compensation payment. These rates are described in Chapters 7-1 for disability cases and 7-2 for death cases.

d. **Cost-of-Living Increases.** Each March 1 the increase in the cost of living for the preceding calendar year is determined. If the beneficiary has been entitled to compensation for at least one year prior to March 1, a cost-of-living increase is applied to the benefits.

e. **Minimum and Maximum Rates.** The law provides for minimum and maximum payments of compensation.

(1)**Disability.** Compensation for temporary total disability or schedule awards may not exceed 75 percent of the monthly salary of an employee at the highest step of the GS-15 level. For total disability, it may not be less than 75 percent of the monthly salary of an employee at the first step of the GS-2 level or actual pay, whichever is less.

(2) **Death.** Compensation for death may not exceed 75 percent of the highest step of the GS-15 level, and it may not be less than the minimum pay of the first step of the GS-2 salary. In no case may it exceed the employee's salary except when the excess is created by cost-of-living increases.

f. **Buy-back of Leave.** Compensation entitlement for leave repurchase is computed in the same way as compensation for temporary total disability. Because leave is paid at 100% of the usual wage rate and compensation is paid as a percentage, the employee will generally owe the agency money for the leave repurchase. When OWCP advises the employee and the agency of the amount payable, the employee should consult with the agency to determine how much money he or she will need to repay.

The amount to be recovered by the agency should be the value of the salary or wages paid to the employee while in a leave status. If the employee wishes to complete the transaction, the agency and employee will decide whether the compensation should be paid directly to the employee or refunded to the agency. The agency will be asked to state the amount paid to the employee for the leave to be repurchased; this amount may be either net or gross.

g. **Lump Sum Payments.** The FECA was designed to provide for the periodic payment of compensation in order to ensure that beneficiaries have a continuing source of income to offset wage loss. With few exceptions such benefits are free from speculation, fluctuation, and attachment by creditors, and they are also generally free from taxes. Lump sum payments of compensation will be considered only for payments of schedule awards or survivors' benefits to widows or widowers who remarry before age 55.

h. **Incorrect Payments.** An employee who receives a compensation payment which he or she knows to be incorrect, either partially or totally, should return the check to OWCP immediately. If an overpayment occurs, OWCP will determine whether the beneficiary is with fault in creation of the overpayment. Only if a beneficiary is determined to be without fault may waiver of the overpayment be considered.

i. **Health Benefits.** OWCP will make deductions for health benefits coverage for beneficiaries who are entitled to continue their enrollment. Deductions cannot be made for periods less than 14 days, and compensation must be paid for at least 28 days in order for deductions to be made.

(1) **Criteria.** The following requirements must be met to continue enrollment:

(a) **Disability.** An employee may continue enrollment if he or she was enrolled (or covered as a family member) in a health benefits plan during the five years of service immediately preceding the start of compensation; during all service since his or her first opportunity to enroll; or continuously for the full period or periods of service beginning with the enrollment which became effective not later than December 31, 1984.

(b) **Death.** A beneficiary in a death case may continue enrollment if the three conditions noted above have been met and, in addition, the deceased employee was enrolled for self and family at time of death and at least one covered family member is receiving compensation from OWCP.

(2) **Transfer.** If the beneficiary will likely be on OWCP rolls for longer than six months, transfer in will be requested from the employing agency. If an employee returns to duty, the enrollment will be transferred back to the agency even if he or she is receiving compensation for loss of wage-earning capacity. If compensation benefits are terminated or if the employee elects an annuity from OPM over benefits from OWCP, OWCP will transfer enrollment to OPM. Similarly, enrollment will be transferred to OPM for a retired employee who is receiving a schedule award.

Beneficiaries are entitled to change health benefits plans during open season in the same manner as other Federal employees.

j. *Optional Life Insurance* (OLI). Basic life insurance is continued at no cost to the employee while he or she is receiving compensation unless the employee has elected Post-Retirement Basic Life Withholdings at 100% or 50% of the original value. An employee may retain OLI while receiving compensation if he or she is eligible to continue regular insurance and has been enrolled for no less than the five years of service immediately preceding the disability, or the full period or periods of service during which OLI was available, if less than five years. Questions about basic life insurance coverage should be referred to OPM, while questions about OLI may be directed to OWCP.

Chapter 8. Managing Disability Claims

This chapter describes how OWCP manages disability claims, including reemployment of partially disabled employees. It also describes the sanctions applied to employees who do not cooperate with this effort.

8-1. Initial Actions by OWCP

Where it appears that disability will continue for at least 60 days, the employee is placed on the short-term roll, advised that payment is being made, and asked when he or she plans to return to work, if this has not already occurred. An employee who has not returned to full duty, or who does not have plans to do so within the immediate future, is referred to an OWCP Staff Nurse.

The employee is advised that compensation will continue only through the date specified by OWCP's medical matrix or other procedural guidance or the attending physician's report; that he or she is expected to return to duty as soon as possible; and that he or she is expected to contact the agency concerning the availability of light duty.

At the same time, the agency is asked to send a copy of the employee's job description, including physical requirements, and a copy of his or her SF-171 or other employment application form. Information concerning the employee's earnings and dependents will be requested periodically during the course of disability.

When the medical evidence shows that total disability has ended, the employee will be advised that he or she is expected to seek work. In accordance with the provisions of 5 USC 8106, which provides for payment of compensation to partially disabled employees, OWCP will make every reasonable effort to arrange for employment of such employees. These efforts will concentrate initially on the agency, and only if reemployment with the agency is not possible will OWCP attempt to place the employee with a new employer.

8-2. Restoration Rights

Federal employees who have fully or partially recovered from an employment-related injury have certain job retention rights. While these rights are provided by the FECA, the pertinent section of the law is actually administered by OPM. An employee who recovers within one year of beginning compensation has mandatory restoration rights to his or her old position or its equivalent, regardless of whether he or she is still on the agency rolls. If full recovery occurs after one year, or the employee is considered partially recovered, he or she is entitled to priority consideration provided that application is made within 30 days of the date compensation ceases.

Such employees incur no loss of benefits which they would have received but for the injury or disease. The regulations on retention rights are contained in 5 CFR 353, 302, and 330.

When an injured employee resumes Federal employment, the agency should verify that the employee had been receiving compensation during the entire period of absence from work whether in LWOP status or separated.

Employees originally hired on or after January 1, 1984 are covered for retirement purposes by the Social Security Act rather than the Civil Service Retirement Act (CSRA). An employee hired before that date will retain CSRA coverage if reemployed by a Federal agency, regardless of the length of time he or she has been receiving compensation, and regardless of whether he or she is in LWOP status or separated.

OWCP's case management procedures emphasize return to work before the expiration of the employee's one-year entitlement to the same or an equivalent job.

8-3. Nurse Services

Independent studies and OWCP's own experience both indicate that the use of nurses may shorten periods of disability and increase the likelihood of return to work. Registered Nurses (RNs) under contract to OWCP meet with employees, physicians, and agency representatives to ensure that proper medical care is being provided and to assist employees in returning to work.

OWCP offers this service to all employees with approved traumatic injury claims who have continuing disability, and on a selective basis to employees with approved occupational illness claims who have continuing disability.

a. **Contacting the Interested Parties.** The RN contacts the employee, attending physician, and supervisor as needed to address the employee's questions about medical care; obtain treatment plans, return to work dates, and descriptions of work limitations; and explore availability of light duty jobs. These contacts, which may be by telephone or in person, generally occur after the 45 day COP period has ended.

b. **Return to Work.** Conference calls may be held to arrange for the employee's return to work. Such a call should always include the agency official who has the authority to offer a light duty job. When an employee returns to work, the RN may accompany him or her on a walk-through of the job to ensure that the duties are within the employee's work limitations and that both the employee and the supervisor understand the duties and limitations.

c. **Agency Nurses.** The RN may occasionally coordinate care with an agency nurse. As a rule, however, agencies should not assign their own nurses to work with employees simultaneously with OWCP RNs.

8-4. Reemployment with the Agency

When the medical evidence shows that total disability has ended, the agency may consider reemployment even if notification from OWCP has not yet been received. The following procedures apply to all employees still on agency rolls, regardless of how long they have received compensation.

a. **Medical Evidence.** To make an appropriate job offer, the agency will need medical evidence pertinent to the employee's work tolerance limitations (in some cases OWCP will provide this information). Medical information which addresses current medical limitations will usually be sufficient for the purpose of making a job offer. If the employee refuses to provide sufficient medical information for the agency to evaluate the propriety of a job offer, the agency should so notify OWCP.

b. **Degree of Recovery.** If the employee is expected to return eventually to the job held at the time of injury, the agency may offer light or modified duty pending full recovery. Any such offer should be made in accordance with the procedures outlined in paragraph d below. If the residuals of the injury will prohibit the employee from returning to the position held at the time of injury and the employee has received compensation for more than one year, the agency should consider reemployment in the following order of preference:

(1) Return to the position held at the time of injury with modifications to accommodate the employee's limitations;

(2) Employment in another position at the same salary as the position held at the time of injury; or

(3) Employment in another position at a lower salary than the position held at the time of injury.

c. **Guidelines for Reemployment.** In identifying potential jobs, the agency should try to minimize any disruption to the employee. The position should be compatible with the employee's medical condition and should take into account any nonwork-related medical condition, which either pre-existed the work-related injury or has developed since it occurred. If a temporary position is offered, it must be at least 90 days in duration.

Generally, an employee who is capable of working four or more hours a day should be offered a position providing at least that much work, since employment of less than four hours a day is regarded as sheltered work and is reserved for the severely disabled. (On the other hand, an offer of less than four hours work a day is suitable for an employee who cannot work longer hours.)

The agency must ensure that any position offered will be available throughout the period required to allow him or her to respond.

d. **Elements of Job Offer.** The agency may contact the employee by telephone to advise that the job is available, but the offer must be confirmed as soon as possible in writing. A copy of the offer must be sent to the OWCP at the same time. The offer should include:

(1) A description of the duties to be performed;

(2) The specific physical requirements of the position and any special demands of the workload or unusual working conditions;

(3) The organizational and geographical location of the job;

(4) The date on which the job will be available;

(5) The date by which a response to the job offer is required.

The agency should not, however, request election of OPM benefits if the employee declines the job offer. Obtaining such an election is solely the responsibility of OWCP.

e. **Advising the Employee.** If the job offer is found to be suitable, and it fairly and reasonably represents the employee's wage-earning capacity, OWCP will so notify the employee in writing and advise that he or she is expected to accept the job or to show reasonable cause for refusal. OWCP will advise the employee that the failure to accept the job or to respond within 30 days will result in termination of compensation payments and allow 30 days for response.

f. **Employee's Response.** The agency should provide a copy of the employee's response to OWCP when it is received.

(1) **Acceptance.** If the employee accepts the job, the agency should notify OWCP as soon as possible of the date of return to duty so as to avoid overpayments of compensation. If the employee accepts the position offered, compensation will be terminated if no loss of pay has resulted, or reduced if the new job pays less than the old, effective the date of return to duty.

(2) **No Response.** If no answer is received, benefits will be terminated and a formal decision will be issued on the basis that the employee has refused suitable work.

(3) **Refusal with No Explanation.** If the employee refuses the offer without explanation, OWCP will issue a formal decision and terminate benefits.

(4) **Refusal with Explanation.** If the employee refuses the offer but provides reasons in support of the refusal, OWCP will evaluate them and determine whether reasonable cause has been shown. If reasonable cause is shown, OWCP will advise the employing agency and compensation will continue at a level reflecting the degree of disability while further attempts at placement are made. If not, the employee will be so advised and allowed an additional 15 days to return to work. If the employee still does not return to work, a formal decision will be issued and benefits will be terminated.

The success of efforts to return employees to gainful employment while providing procedural due process requires close cooperation between employing agencies and OWCP. Early notification of job offers and complete information about the offers will aid OWCP in making its decisions. For its part OWCP recognizes its responsibility to evaluate job offers and to notify employees quickly to avoid undue delays.

8-5. Vocational Rehabilitation Services

The FECA at 5 USC 8104 provides that vocational rehabilitation services may be provided to disabled employees to assist them in returning to gainful employment consistent with their physical, emotional, and educational abilities. An employee with extended disability may be considered for rehabilitation services if requested by the attending physician, the employee, or agency personnel. In addition, OWCP will routinely consider a case for rehabilitation services if the agency cannot reemploy the employee so that placement with another employer may be considered.

a. **Services Provided.** An OWCP Rehabilitation Specialist will contact the employee for an initial interview. The employee will then be referred to a state or private Rehabilitation Counselor for development of a rehabilitation plan. A plan may include one or more of the following services: selective placement with the previous employer, placement with a new employer, counseling, guidance, testing, work evaluations, training, and job follow-up. Each employee is evaluated to provide the most appropriate services to him or her, and not all of the services indicated will be included in any given plan.

b. **Advice to Employee.** When suitable jobs are identified, the employee will be advised that it appears that he or she has a wage-earning capacity of a specific dollar amount which will likely determine future compensation entitlement; that he or she is expected to return to work in a job similar to the one identified, and that only partial compensation based on the wage-earning capacity of the indicated job will probably be paid at the end of this effort; and that when any necessary training or other preparation is completed, OWCP will provide 90 days of placement services.

c. **Benefits Payable.** An employee in an approved vocational rehabilitation program may be paid an allowance in connection with this program not to exceed $200 per month. The employee is also entitled to compensation at the rate for total disability during the rehabilitation program (payment of a schedule award meets this requirement).

When the employee returns to work, compensation will be reduced to reflect his or her wage-earning capacity if the new job pays less than the old. If reemployment is at the same or higher pay rate than the job held at time of injury, compensation benefits will be terminated. Even if the employee does not return to work, his or her compensation will in all likelihood be reduced.

d. **Penalties.** Should an employee involved in a rehabilitation program refuse to cooperate or make a good faith effort to obtain reemployment, OWCP may reduce or terminate compensation depending on the circumstances of the refusal.

e. **Constructed Positions.** In some situations reemployment is not feasible despite the best efforts of both the employee and OWCP. When this happens, the employee's wage-earning capacity may be determined on the basis of a position which the medical evidence indicates the employee can perform and which is available in his or her commuting area. The suitability of the position must be determined in accordance with the following factors:
   (1) The nature of the injury;
   (2) The degree of physical impairment;
   (3) The usual employment;
   (4) The employee's age;
   (5) Qualifications for other employment, including education, previous employment, and training.

A formal decision, including appeal rights, will be issued in any case where the benefit level is affected.

f. **Continued Disability Payments.** Only after aggressive medical and vocational development will OWCP determine that an employee has no current wage-earning capacity, and should therefore be carried on the long-term compensation rolls at the rate for total disability.

8-6. Assisted Reemployment

As part of a demonstration project, the OWCP may reimburse an employer who was not the employer at the time of injury for part of the salary of a reemployed worker. This wage subsidy is intended to assist in reemploying workers who have been difficult to place with their former employers. It is available to other Federal employers as well as to State and local governments and the private sector.

a. **Eligibility.** To be eligible, the agency cannot have been the worker's employer at the time of the injury, as identified by OWCP chargeback billings, appropriations account number and agency hiring authority. Intra-departmental salary reimbursements are limited to agencies with a separate appropriation number from that of the employing agency at the time of injury. It is not proper to use the assisted reemployment approach for transfers within the agency, or where an agency uses more than one appropriation number but hiring is controlled at a higher organizational level.

b. **Conditions of Participation.** The rate of reimbursement may not exceed 75 percent of the employee's gross wage. The actual rate of reimbursement available must therefore be decided on a case-by-case basis by OWCP staff in negotiation with the agency.

Salary reimbursement may extend for up to 36 continuous months, but it may not be interrupted by a recurrence of disability due to the accepted condition. The subsidy may not be transferred from one employer to another.

An agency interested in participating in the Assisted Reemployment project should contact the District Director or a Rehabilitation Specialist at the regional OWCP office. Where a job opening has been identified which may be suitable for a particular worker, the Rehabilitation Counselor assigned to that worker will meet with agency personnel to explain details of the program.

For OWCP to consider reimbursement of salary expenses, the job offer must be found suitable, medically and otherwise (see paragraph 5 above). To make such a finding, OWCP needs several items of information, including a copy of the position description which includes a statement of the physical requirements of the job. With this information, OWCP staff will make a suitability determination.

c. **Elements of Agreement.** When the worker accepts a suitable job offer, the new employing agency and OWCP will enter into an Assisted Reemployment Cooperative Agreement. Each Agreement will include the following elements:

(1) Employee's name and OWCP claim number;

(2) Employer's name and address;

(3) A description of the procedures for claiming reimbursement and the payment schedule, including the method and maximum amount of wage reimbursement payments from OWCP to the employer for each employee hired under the project;

(4) A job description and statement of starting wage rate.

d. **Transfer of Funds.** Once agreement is reached concerning financial and administrative arrangements, OWCP staff will contact the agency to determine the most effective method of payment and transfer of funds. The preferred method of reimbursement by the OWCP is through the U.S. Treasury's GOALS/OPAC (On-Line Payment and Collection) system. Agencies which do not process payments through the U.S. Treasury will be reimbursed by check from OWCP.

OWCP will then advise the agency in writing of the specific accounting procedures for transferring funds. Payment is made after OWCP receives an authorizing document certifying that the employee was actually employed and received wages during the quarter for which reimbursement is requested. Regardless of the method of reimbursement, OWCP will require quarterly submission of records of the wages paid to these reemployed workers and the periods covered by those payments.

8-7. Payment of Relocation Expenses

OWCP's regulations provide at 20 CFR 10.123(f) that an injured employee who relocates to accept a suitable job offer after termination from the agency rolls may receive payment or reimbursement of moving expenses from the compensation fund. This regulation further states that Federal travel regulations (issued by GSA) pertaining to permanent change of duty station moves are to be used as a guideline in determining whether expenses claimed are reasonable and necessary.

a. **Locations of Old and New Jobs.** Relocation expenses may be paid for a former employee who is partially recovered from compensable injury and who is offered a job in either the same or a different commuting area from the former one. OPM regulations governing the restoration rights of injured workers require consideration of partially recovered employees only in the former commuting area. Thus, the extent to which an agency considers partially recovered employees for jobs outside the commuting area is a matter for agency personnel to decide.

Former employees who move voluntarily to other locations and are offered reemployment at their former installations are generally not entitled to payment of relocation expenses. (See GSA's Federal travel regulations and pertinent Comptroller General decisions governing relocation in the Government's interest.) The extent to which relocation expenses are payable when a fully or partially recovered employee is still on the agency's rolls is governed by Federal travel regulations pertaining to permanent change of duty station moves.

However, OWCP's regulations state specifically that "the agency may offer suitable employment at the employee's former duty station or other alternate location" and that relocation expenses will be payable in either case. Therefore, employing agencies should not discourage applications for payment of relocation expenses to the previous duty station. Given the considerable savings in compensation costs which accrue to employing agencies which return their injured workers to the rolls, payment of relocation expenses to the original duty station are considered to be in the interest of the Government.

b. **Eligibility.** The distance between the two locations must be at least 50 miles, and the job must be found medically and vocationally suitable. OWCP will authorize payment of expenses incurred to accept a temporary position as long as it is expected to lead to a permanent assignment. The employee need not demonstrate financial need for relocation expenses to be paid, and payment/reimbursement of relocation expenses may be considered after the fact as long as the move took place after June 1, 1987, the effective date of the provision governing such moves.

OWCP staff will determine whether relocation expenses can be approved and will notify the employee and agency personnel. While payment by the agency with reimbursement by OWCP through the U.S. Treasury's GOALS/OPAC (On-Line Payment and Collection) system is preferred, direct withdrawal from the compensation fund may be authorized where necessary.

c. **Arranging the Move.** Because employing agencies have expertise in arranging PCS moves, OWCP will ask the agencies to calculate the costs and coordinate the activities involved in such moves insofar as possible. OWCP will be responsible for resolving any disputes between the employee and the agency as to allowable costs in accordance with government travel regulations.

d. **RITA Payments.** The IRS considers at least a portion of PCS payments to be reportable as income even though such payments are intended to reflect actual expenses, and employing agencies usually include a Relocation Income Tax Allowance (RITA) to offset the additional income tax liability incurred because of PCS reimbursements. Compensation benefits are not considered taxable, however, and for this reason the RITA should not be included in paying relocation expenses under the FECA.

8-8. Employees in Light Duty Status

Many agencies place both newly injured and long-term disabled employees in light duty jobs. Such placements usually benefit both employers and employees. However, when employees continue to hold light-duty assignments after they are able to return to full duty, the availability of such light duty assignments for more recently injured employees is decreased.

Therefore, it is the policy of OWCP to monitor injured employees who hold light duty jobs until they have returned to full duty, or until the medical evidence firmly establishes that they will never be able to return to full duty. Employing agencies can aid in this effort by identifying employees who have been in light duty status for over three months.

8-9. Separation from Employment

a. **Reductions in Force.** When a formal loss of wage-earning capacity has been determined, the employee has the burden to establish further entitlement to compensation. Therefore, the status of an employee with an established wage-earning capacity who is removed due to an across-the-board reduction in force (RIF) or the closing of an installation (as opposed to the elimination of only light duty jobs) does not change with regard to receipt of FECA benefits unless a formal claim for recurrence is filed. When no formal finding with regard to wage-earning capacity has been made, and the employee has worked in the position for at least 60 days, OWCP may consider a retroactive loss of wage-earning capacity determination.

b. **Removal for Cause.** An employee who is separated for misconduct and whose removal is wholly unconnected to the work-related injury is not entitled to further compensation benefits.

Chapter 9. Agency Management of Compensation Claims

This chapter describes actions agency personnel may take to learn more about individual claims of current and former employees, and to manage their compensation programs.

9-1. Obtaining Information

Claims personnel are instructed to provide agency personnel with copies of all significant correspondence to employees, even when the employees are no longer on the agency's rolls. Under the routine use provisions of the regulations governing release of information under the Privacy Act, agencies are entitled to obtain copies of other materials in their employees' compensation files as well. The use of these copies must, however, be consistent with the reason the information was collected. In practice, this means that the use must generally be connected in some way with the compensation claim.

To safeguard the privacy of information in compensation files, much of which is inherently sensitive, the following procedures are followed:

a. **Making Specific Requests.** Requests from the agency for materials in a case file should include the specific reason for requesting the information (e.g., to verify that the employee actually worked for the agency, or to attempt reemployment of the worker). OWCP will release the requested information either by telephone or in writing once satisfactory identification is presented. (This requirement needs to be met only once if an agency designates a particular individual as a liaison or principal contact with the district office.) Representatives of an investigative body within an agency may also obtain information upon presentation of proper identification as long as the purpose for the request is stated.

b. **Inspecting Files.** An agency representative may ask to inspect files at the district office. All such requests will be accommodated subject to logistical and physical limitations, including reasonable advance notice of the visit and a list of cases to be reviewed. Here again, the purpose should be stated specifically and the identity of the reviewer should be established in advance of the visit. A picture ID must be presented at the time of the visit unless the reviewer is known to the office. Generic requests will be honored when several cases are to be inspected for the same reason.

c. **Penalties Under the Privacy Act.** It is not appropriate for agency personnel to inspect records without a specific and valid purpose for doing so (that is, curiosity is not an acceptable reason for review). Agency personnel who review files should be conversant with the restrictions of the Privacy Act and the penalties stipulated for violations. These penalties include fines and imprisonment. Any individual who improperly uses information from OWCP files will not be given further access to them.

d. **Contractors.** If the agency wishes to designate a private contractor to inspect the records, the agency should contact the OWCP National Office in writing to obtain approval for the arrangement. The agency should ensure that the contractor observes the pertinent regulations governing the privacy of employees' records as they review the files and report their findings to the agency.

9-2. Managing Compensation Programs

Agencies are encouraged to develop comprehensive plans for managing their compensation programs to provide good service to employees while containing costs. Ideally, management of compensation claims should be considered a personnel rather than a safety and health function. Throughout this handbook, numerous suggestions and directives have been provided to help agencies to manage their programs. The following is a summary of the most important actions agencies can take:

a. **Training.** Ensure that sufficient training in technical and managerial skills is provided to those personnel who routinely handle compensation claims and that resource materials are avail-able to those who handle them infrequently. A list of the courses provided and resources for understanding the program is provided in Chapter 1.

b. **Administration.** Establish a record-keeping system which will enable the agency to maintain copies of claim forms, medical reports, correspondence with OWCP, and other materials related to each compensation claim in an orderly fashion. Designate a representative within each organizational unit who will serve as a liaison with OWCP concerning unusually difficult claims.

c. **Documentation.** Ensure that the facts surrounding each injury are adequately investigated at the time of injury. This step will enable OWCP to obtain full documentation and enable agencies to substantiate claims it feels are questionable.

d. **Medical.** Obtain medical information from OWCP or the injured employees as often as necessary within OWCP and OPM regulations to assess the possibility of return to regular or light duty. Advise physicians of any light duty assignments available and their specific requirements to provide the best possible chance for reemployment. This step will also al-low the agency to monitor the medical care provided and notify OWCP if it believes action should be taken in this regard.

e. **Reemployment.** Maintain contact with injured employees while they are receiving compensa-tion, identify jobs suitable for them, and initiate efforts to reemploy recovered or recovering employees as soon as the medical evidence indicates that this is possible.

f. **Financial.** Conscientious application of the above principles will result in savings to the agency and better service to injured employees. Agencies should also pay special atten-tion to chargeback billings and arrange to charge costs to the lowest organizational level practicable to make managers more aware of costs. The chargeback system is discussed in detail in paragraph 9-4.

9-3. Record-Keeping

Employing agencies often retain documents in connection with workers' compensation claims. Rules governing release, retention, and disposal of such records differ according to the nature and source of the document involved.

a. **Documents in Employee Medical Folder (EMF).** A notice of injury not filed with OWCP is to be placed in the employee's EMF and retained in accordance with OPM regulations governing disposal of the EMF.

b. **Documents in OWCP Case File.** These documents include medical reports, copies of let-ters and decisions, and any other material which is part of the case file, regardless of its source. The agency may use and release such material consistent with the provisions of the Privacy Act, and consistent with the reason for which the material was collected. It may not be used in connection with EEO complaints, disciplinary actions, or other administra-tive actions without the employee's consent. Any questions concerning use or release of records should be directed to the district office with jurisdiction over the claim.

These documents should be maintained in folders apart from the EMF or OPF, but such folders are not considered a "system of records" separate from the case file. Rather, they are considered an alternate location for the records, which remain under the jurisdiction of the OWCP. Their retention and disposal is covered by the OWCP Records Retirement

Schedule, which mandates that case file material should be maintained for two years after case closure.

9-4. Chargeback

The FECA program is financed by the Employees' Compensation Fund, which consists of monies appropriated by Congress or contributed from operating revenues. The chargeback system is the mechanism by which the costs of compensation for work-related injuries and deaths are assigned to employing agencies annually at the end of the fiscal accounting period, which runs from July to June for chargeback purposes. Each year OWCP furnishes each agency with a state-ment of payments made from the fund on account of injuries suffered by its employees. The agencies include these amounts in their budget requests to Congress. The resulting sums appropriated or obtained from operating revenues are deposited in the fund.

a. **Identification.** A compensation claim is identified as belonging to a particular agency based on the agency code that is entered into the OWCP data processing system when the case is created. The agency should pre-code all initial notices of injury, disease and death in order to reduce errors in the chargeback system. The agency will receive a postcard (Form CA-801) from OWCP each time a case is created for one of its employees. OWCP also provides each agency quarterly listings of the cases and charges that will appear on the yearly chargeback bill.

b. **Errors.** To prevent incorrect entries from appearing on the quarterly chargeback report and yearly bill, agencies should review Forms CA-801 and report errors to district offices as soon as possible. If no objection is raised upon receipt of the form, OWCP assumes that the chargeback code is correct and charges costs associated with the case to that agency's account.

   If an agency which receives a Form CA-801 which it believes to be incorrect, it should notify OWCP in writing within 60 days. The district office will then review the disputed case to determine whether a keying or coding error occurred and make any necessary corrections to the agency code.

c. **Quarterly Chargeback Report.** Each agency receives a quarterly report which provides a breakdown of cases and costs for which charges will appear on the yearly chargeback bill. This report can be used to identify and correct errors before the agency is billed for them. When an agency believes that a case appearing on its chargeback report does not belong on its account, it should check current personnel and payroll records as well as search the service record file and/or send an inquiry to the Federal Records Center. OWCP also welcomes authorized agency personnel to review case files at the district office to resolve such discrepancies.

d. **Requesting Changes.** Requests for changes based on review of the quarterly chargeback report should be addressed to the District Director of the district office having jurisdiction over the case in question. The request should be made within 90 days of receipt of the report, and it must be accompanied by appropriate documentation such as copies of an SF-50, service record card (SF-7), or response from the Federal Records Center. OWCP will review the case file and supporting evidence to determine whether an incorrect agency code was assigned. If the evidence does not support the agency's request, OWCP will send the agency a copy of the Form CA-1, CA-2, or CA-6 from the case file and explain the basis for its finding.

If the evidence indicates that the disputed case belongs on another agency's account, OWCP will notify the new agency and forward a copy of Form CA-1, CA-2 or CA-6 from the case file. Prior to changing the agency code, OWCP will provide the agency 60 days to respond in the event that it disputes ownership of the case. Due to the time needed for verification and correction, errors brought to the attention of OWCP during the fourth quarter of a fiscal year may not be corrected in time for that year's bill. If incorrect charges appear on the bill, adjustment will be handled as described below.

If the assigned chargeback code represents the wrong organization or command within the agency, the request for change of code must be made by an agency official with the authority to speak for the entire department rather than for a single command or organizational unit.

e. ***Adjustments to the Chargeback* Bill.** When an adjustment to the yearly chargeback bill is desired, the request must be sent directly to the OWCP National Office. It must be accompanied by documentation which shows that the disputed charge did not involve an employee of that agency, or by a complete explanation of the basis for the agency's objection. OWCP will make a determination and correct verified errors by crediting the subsequent year's billing statement.

If another agency should have been charged, OWCP will so notify that agency and a debit will appear on its next bill. Credits or debits will be made only for charges appearing on the agency's most recent bill. Adjustments will be made only if there is an effect on the total for the particular billing entity. Transfers of charges from one organization to another on the same bill will not be made.

APPENDIX IV — FEDERAL AGENCY SAFETY COMMITTEES

The principal function of committees shall be to consult and provide policy advice on and monitor the performance of the safety and health program.

Committee Membership and Activities

Committees shall be established at agency establishments or groupings of establishments consistent with the mission, size and organization of the agency and its collective bargaining configuration. The agency shall form committees at the lowest practicable local level. The principal function of the establishment (or local) committees is to monitor and assist in the execution of the agency's safety and health policies and program at the workplaces.

- Committees shall have equal representation of management and nonmanagement employees, who shall be members of record.
- Management members of both national- and establishment-level committees shall be appointed in writing by the person empowered to make such appointments.
- Nonmanagement members of establishment-level committees shall represent all employees of the establishment and shall be determined according to the following rules:
  - Where employees are represented under collective bargaining arrangements, members shall be appointed from among those recommended by the exclusive bargaining representative;
  - Where employees are not represented under collective bargaining arrangements, members shall be determined through procedures, devised by the agency, that provide for effective representation of all employees; and
  - Where some employees of an establishment are covered under collective bargaining arrangements and others are not, members shall be representative of both groups.

The purpose of safety committees is to find solutions that management can take action on to ensure a safe and healthful workplace for employees. Committees provide a way for workers to use their experience in the workplace to improve conditions and bring issues to the attention of management.

Committees should keep an eye on the safety bulletin board to ensure that it has the federal agency safety poster, a letter of commitment from management and the name of the safety representative posted. OSHA compliance officers will look for these when they visit.

Nonmanagement members of national-level committees shall be determined according to the following rules:

- Where employees are represented by organizations having exclusive recognition on an agency basis or by organizations having national consultation rights, some members shall be determined in accordance with the terms of collective bargaining agreements and some members shall be selected from those organizations having consultation rights.
- Where employees are not represented by organizations meeting the criteria of 1960.37 (b)(3)(i), members shall be determined through procedures, devised by the agency, that provide for effective representation of all employees.
- Committee members should serve overlapping terms. Such terms should be of at least two years' duration, except when the committee is initially organized.
- The committee chairperson shall be nominated from among the committee's members and shall be elected by the committee members. Management and nonmanagement members should alternate in this position. Maximum service time as chairperson should be two consecutive years.
- Committees shall establish a regular schedule of meetings and special meetings shall be held

as necessary; establishment-level committees shall meet at least quarterly and national committees shall meet at least annually.

- Adequate advance notice of committee meetings shall be furnished to employees and each meeting shall be conducted pursuant to a prepared agenda.
- Written minutes of each committee meeting shall be maintained and distributed to each committee member, and upon request, shall be made available to employees and to the Secretary.
- Agencies shall provide all committee members appropriate training as required by subpart H of this part.
- The safety and health committee is an integral part of the safety and health program and helps ensure effective implementation of the program at the establishment level.
- Monitor and assist the safety and health program at establishments under its jurisdiction and make recommendations to the official in charge on the operation of the program;
- Monitor findings and reports of workplace inspections to confirm that appropriate corrective measures are implemented

Injured Workers May Sue Government

A construction worker injured on an Army installation after a contracting officer failed to enforce contractual safety standards may sue the government under the Federal Tort Claims Act, a federal district court ruled June 4, 1999. In *Pelham v. U.S.* (No. 84-1395), the U.S. District Court for the District of New Jersey affirmed its earlier ruling that while a contracting officer's implementation of a safety inspection program is discretionary, once the officer suspects safety deficiency, he or she must act upon it.

The accident occurred when a forklift was used to lift a garbage dumpster in which Jerry Pelham was standing in order to attach cables to a 20-ft. roof-support suspension beam. When the forklift lurched, Pelham lost his balance and caught his hand between the forklift mast chain and pulley, amputating parts of three fingers and severely cutting a fourth.

Shortly before Pelham was injured, the contracting officer observed a worker in a metal container being hoisted by a forklift. The contracting officer testified that he "raised the

issue" with the job superintendent, who told him that it was standard practice.

Under the terms of the contract, the contractor was required to take safety measures prescribed by the government's contracting officer. The contracting officer was required to notify the contractor of any non-compliance with safety provisions and had authority to issue a stop-work order if the contractor failed to comply promptly.

Discretionary Function Exception

Lawsuits against the United States for injuries caused by government employees in situations where a private person, would be liable are authorized by the FTCA. Under an exception to the act, the government is not liable for claims based on a discretionary function, whether or not the discretion involved is abused.

The court distinguished the Pelham case from two other Third Circuit decisions that applied the discretionary function exemption to the government's alleged failure to inspect a radioactive extraction facility and remove asbestos. Negligence in the development of safety provisions or a spot check program is not the kind of conduct at issue here the court stated, where the issue is "ministerial implementation of safety regulations" rather than "the discretionary authority to develop such provisions."

The contracting officer accepted the contractor's response rather than assume his ministerial responsibility under the contract to enforce compliance. The court found that under the contract "there is nothing discretionary about this responsibility." Once the contracting officer suspected a safety violation, his duty to check safety requirements was ministerial and not discretionary under the FTCA, the court ruled. Decisions made at the operational level, as distinguished from the planning level, are not protected by the exception, the court found.

Contractors Working for the Government

Most contracts have an accident prevention clause in them. These contract clauses are written by the government and outlined in the Federal Acquisition Regulation (FAR), which governs contractors working with the U.S. Government. Generally in a section on clauses, the contracting officer lists the clauses included by number. Look in section I or whatever section the contracting officer has listed the clauses. The FAR matrix requires that the accident prevention clause be inserted in contracts for all construction contracts where incorporation by reference is authorized; fixed price construction contracts; and dismantling, demolition and removal contracts. It is an optional clause in simplified acquisition procedure (excluding micropurchase) contracts (See Exhibit 3-1.).

Exhibit 3-1
52.236-13 ACCIDENT PREVENTION.
Accident Prevention (Nov 1991)

(a) The Contractor shall provide and maintain work environments and procedures which will-

(1) Safeguard the public and Government personnel, property, materials, supplies, and equipment exposed to Contractor operations and activities;

(2) Avoid interruptions of Government operations and delays in project completion dates; and

(3) Control costs in the performance of this contract.

(b) For these purposes on contracts for construction or dismantling, demolition, or removal of improvements, the Contractor shall —

(1) Provide appropriate safety barricades, signs, and signal lights;

(2) Comply with the standards issued by the Secretary of Labor at 29 CFR Part 1926 and 29 CFR Part 1910; and

(3) Ensure that any additional measures the Contracting Officer determines to be reasonably necessary for the purposes are taken.

(c) If this contract is for construction or dismantling, demolition or removal of improvements with any Department of Defense agency or component, the Contractor shall comply with all pertinent provisions of the latest version of U.S. Army Corps of Engineers Safety and Health Requirements Manual, EM 385-1-1, in effect on the date of the solicitation.

(d) Whenever the Contracting Officer becomes aware of any noncompliance with these requirements or any condition which poses a serious or imminent danger to the health or safety of the public or Government personnel, the Contracting Officer shall notify the Contractor orally, with written confirmation, and request immediate initiation of corrective action. This notice, when delivered to the Contractor or the Contractor's representative at the work site, shall be deemed sufficient notice of the noncompliance and that corrective action is required. After receiving the notice, the Contractor shall immediately take corrective action. If the Contractor fails or refuses to promptly take corrective action, the Contracting Officer may issue an order stopping all or part of the work until satisfactory corrective action has been taken. The Contractor shall not be entitled to any equitable adjustment of the contract price or extension of the performance schedule on any stop work order issued under this clause.

(e) The Contractor shall insert this clause, including this paragraph (e), with appropriate changes in the designation of the parties, in subcontracts.

Appendix

Your Safety Committee

Name of the Committee (be creative)

```
┌─────────────────────────────────────────────────────────┐
│                                                           │
│                                                           │
└─────────────────────────────────────────────────────────┘
```

Committee Motto:

```
┌─────────────────────────────────────────────────────────┐
│                                                           │
│                                                           │
└─────────────────────────────────────────────────────────┘
```

Measurable Goals For The Committee:

```
┌─────────────────────────────────────────────────────────┐
│                                                           │
│                                                           │
│                                                           │
│                                                           │
│                                                           │
└─────────────────────────────────────────────────────────┘
```

Elected Leader:

```
┌─────────────────────────────────────────────────────────┐
│                                                           │
└─────────────────────────────────────────────────────────┘
```

Recorder:

```
┌─────────────────────────────────────────────────────────┐
│                                                           │
└─────────────────────────────────────────────────────────┘
```

Name of members: _____

Name of members: _____

Name of members: _____

Name of members: _____

Name of members: _____

Name of members: _____

Name of members: _____

Hazard Violation Search Workshop #1
List the Standard Citation and Corrective Action
(See appendix for answers.)

Description of Hazard

1. Exit access blocked by pallet. Less than 20 inches width.
2. Fire extinguisher (charged) found lying on floor.
3. Type BC fire extinguisher used near bales of shredded paper – no type A available.
4. At some locations in large facility, directions of travel to exit are not apparent.
5. No portable fire extinguisher inspection/maintenance program.
6. Fixed carbon dioxide extinguishing system not being inspected and tested annually.
7. No exit signs anywhere in plant employing 50 employees.
8. Exit door blocked from outside.
9. Sprinkler heads in storage area blocked by stacked bags within 5 in. of heads.
10. Fire extinguishers obstructed by containers.
11. Exit access door swings against exit travel; considered high hazard occupancy room.
12. No eyewash facility in battery charging area — battery acid being used.
13. Employee observed smoking in a flammable liquid storage area.
14. Eye protection required — items being used do not meet ANSI requirements.
15. Respirators required — no training program for users.
16. Baseball caps being worn by maintenance employees replacing take-up roller bearing on conveyor while standing on a maintenance catwalk.
17. Equipment ground prong on portable electric drill broken off.
18. Forklift observed being used as a man lift using only standard pallet.
19. Permanent aisles in container storage area not marked.
20. Containers being used for storing flammable liquids — not of the approved type.
21. Paint spray booth with electric motor and fan placed inside exhaust duct.
22. End attachments on a wire rope sling are cracked and deformed.
23. General industrial plant: 150 gallons of toluene stored outside of an inside storage room (Flashpoint = 45°F, B.P. = 232°F).
24. Welding operation being done in paint spray booth.
25. Forklift purchased in 1966 performing high lifts without overhead guard.
26. LP gas service station dispensing area without "No Smoking" signs.
27. 150 gallons of Class I liquid stored in a flammable liquid storage cabinet.
28. Forklift operator giving a ride to two personnel on a standard pallet on forks.
29. The dry filter spray booth had an exhaust of less than 50 LFM.
30. Containers used to transfer flammables were not bonded to the dispensing drum.
31. Safety cans containing flammable liquids not in red can nor contents identified.
32. Stairway — 6 risers — no handrail.
33. Hospital 20 miles away, no employee trained in first aid.
34. Open-sided floor — 6-ft. drop; no guardrails.
35. Fixed ladder — 30 ft. high with no cage guard.
36. Wooden extension ladder – ladder safety shoes broken.
37. Stairway more than 44 in. wide does not have stair rails on open sides.
38. Opened-sided work platform (less than 4 ft. high) adjacent to dangerous equipment not guarded with standard railing and toeboard.
39. Elevated area used for storage has no approved floor-loading signs posted in a conspicuous place.
40. Portable dockboard without any securing device to prevent slipping.
41. Stairway with steam pipe 6 ft. above stair tread causing overhead obstruction.

42. Defective portable wooden ladder with split side rail being used in building maintenance operation.
43. Compressed gas cylinders in storage with no valve protection caps.
44. Oxygen and fuel-gas cylinders stored together.
45. Respirators not stored in a clean, sanitary location.
46. Arc welding area — adjacent work area personnel exposed to welding rays.
47. Welding electrode cable lead is damaged and frayed, exposing bare wire.
48. Air receiver not equipped with indicating pressure gauge.
49. There is a loose conduit feeding into a fuse box.
50. Powered industrial truck idling while its operator drinks coffee 200 ft. away.
51. Steel frame of sorter machine not grounded. Machine located 3 ft. from water pipe.
52. Hand-held portable electric grinder with no guard.
53. Hand-held electric circular saw equipped with a lock-on control switch.
54. 157 psi air being used for cleaning purposes in machine shop.
55. Hand-held circular saw being used with no lower blade guard.
56. Portable electric drill owned by employee had defective switch.
57. Radial arm saw has lower portion of blade unguarded.
58. Explosive-actuated fastening tool without a protective shield.
59. Work rest on bench grinder has ½ in. space between wheel and rest.
60. Employee working in a mechanical equipment room daily for eight hours is exposed to 92 dBA.
61. Employer had no energy control (lockout/tagout) procedures.
62. No guarding to protect employees from flying chips of a metal turning lathe.

Hazard Violation Workshop #2

1. Identify what is wrong in each of the following scenarios.

2. Identify what part of the OSHA regulation has been violated.

3. Propose corrective action.

[Instructor-led discussion.]

Scenario 3.

Scenario 1.

Scenario 4.

Scenario 2.

Scenario 5.

Scenario 7.

Scenario 6.

Scenario 8.

APPENDIX V — FEDERAL AGENCY RISK MANAGEMENT INTEGRATION

The following is a handbook developed by the U.S. Army Safety Center in Ft. Rucker, Ala. Although references are made to military operations and personnel, the majority of the handbook is applicable to the civilian workplace—in both the private and public sectors.

BASE OPERATIONS RISK MANAGEMENT
INTEGRATION HANDBOOK FOR SAFETY PROFESSIONALS

RMI HANDBOOK TABLE OF CONTENTS

INTRODUCTION:

WHY A RISK MANAGEMENT HANDBOOK FOR BASE OPERATION?

The purpose of this handbook is to give the Army Safety professional the foundation and tools to successfully advise and assist Commanders in transitioning Risk Management into the base operations environment. The risk management process and the benefits and opportunities it provides have given the tactical Army an edge, contributing to America's victories on the battlefield. Risk Management enhances the tactical environment by eliminating or controlling hazards before they result in losses, whether personnel or materiel, losses that can degrade or halt the mission. The gains in tactical mission success can now be effectively transferred to the Army's base operations.

WHY RISK MANAGEMENT?

Effective use of Risk Management techniques provides worker, managers and leaders with a workplace for which the risks are acceptable, in fact, a safe workplace. Recognizing this fact, Togo West, Secretary of the Army, signed a letter in May 1997 that directs the integration of Risk Management into everything the Army does, both on and off duty. The Occupational Health and Safety Act also mandates that every workplace be free of recognized hazards. This 'general duty' clause is used when there are no specific standards applicable to a particular hazard.

WHAT IS RISK MANAGEMENT?
Risk Management is a disciplined, organized, and logical decision-making process to identify, evaluate and control hazards. With training and practice, personnel will be better able to spot hazards, analyze risk and make risk decisions at the appropriate level of command. All work and daily routines involve risk. All job tasks and daily living require decisions that include assessing and managing hazards. Each commander and supervisor, along with every individual, is responsible for identifying potential risks and adjusting or compensating appropriately. Decisions must then be made at a level of responsibility that corresponds to the degree of risk and the ability to apply resources, taking into consideration the significance of the task and the timeliness of the required decision. The decision-making techniques apply to all military and civilian operations. The difference is that all workers' health and safety is protected by specific and general standards which work to provide a workplace that is free of recognized hazards, while military may accept risk based on the operational needs and urgency of a specified task. This is particularly true in contingency and combat operations. Risk Management is a privilege. It is not for everyone. It is a privilege earned by the disciplined; for those who know and follow standards, who consider them inviolate. It is a process that gives an added edge to those with a long history of meeting "minimum" requirements, or, of meeting standards. It's an opportunity to go beyond the minimum, to reach greater effectiveness in any task or mission. But, its prerequisite is a firm foundation in standards. One must understand the standards well enough to know the consequences of compromising them, and therefore how to control the task with a new set of 'standards' that provide risk controls or that the decision authority accepts the risk of loss.

Commanders, supervisors and individuals must:
- Take ownership of workplace hazards.
- Not allow uncontrolled hazards.

IS THIS A NEW WAY OF DOING BUSINESS?
Risk management is not a radical new way of doing business. Each of us manages risk on a daily basis, while working, driving, shopping, investing, etc. Most decisions are automatic, guided by years of experience coping with the same or similar situations. In a sense, we are all experienced "Risk Managers".

Simply put, Risk Management is an organized framework for decision-making. The aim is to minimize losses, whether associated with money, equipment or personnel safety, while maximizing mission success. It is the rational decision process: Weigh expected costs against expected benefits; if benefits outweigh costs—go for it; otherwise don't. The dilemma most often is how to quantify expected costs and benefits.

WHAT ABOUT COMPLIANCE?
Meeting OSHA standards is required in the civilian workplace. It's important to understand there is no conflict between standards and the application of Risk Management techniques. The OSHA standards provide a foundation for hazard identification and control. Knowledge of OSHA standards provides valuable insight into understanding and implementing safety programs and systems. Application of OSHA standards provides safe workplaces from recognized hazards. However OSHA standards don't cover all hazards. Risk Management provides a process to make the workplace safer by reviewing and prioritizing tasks and operations either not covered, or not covered effectively, by OSHA standards.

HOW DOES IT WORK?
The basic decision-making principles are applied before any job, action, or mission is executed. As an operation progresses and evolves, risk management controls are continuously reevaluated.

FIGURE 1.
COST AND BENEFIT SCALES

Integrate into planning.
- Risks are more easily assessed and managed in the early planning stages.
- The acceptable plans are in proportion to risks and worth the anticipated cost.
- Mission is accomplished without incurring excessive losses in personnel, equipment, time, or position.

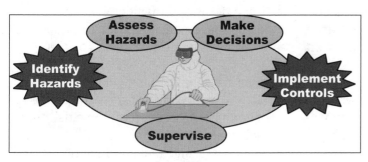

FIGURE 2.
FIVE-STEP PROCESS OF RISK MANAGEMENT

Accept no Unnecessary Risk.
- Unnecessary risk has no payback in terms of real benefits or available opportunities.
- RM provides tools to determine which risk or what level of risk is unnecessary.

Make Risk Decisions at the **Appropriate** *Level.*
- Appropriate level for risk decisions is the one that can allocate the resources to reduce the risk or eliminate the hazard and implement controls.

Accept Risk When Benefits **Outweigh** *the Costs.*
- All identified benefits should be compared to all identified costs.

- Figure 1 depicts this principle. Balancing costs and benefits may be a subjective process and open to interpretation.

Ultimately, the balance may have to be determined by the appropriate decision authority.

Integrate RM into Army Doctrine and Planning at all Levels.
Risks are more easily assessed and managed in the planning stages of an operation. Integrating risk management into planning as early as possible provides the decision maker the greatest opportunity to apply RM principles.

Five-Step Risk Management Process. RM is a continuous process designed to detect, assess, and control risk while enhancing performance and maximizing capabilities. Figure 2 depicts the five-step process.

- **Identify Hazards.** A hazard is any real or potential condition that can cause (mission degradation) injury, illness, death to personnel or damage to or loss of equipment or property. Experience, common sense, and specific risk management tools help identify real or potential hazards.

- **Assess the Hazards.** Risk is the probability and severity of loss from exposure to the hazard. Assessment is the application of quantitative or qualitative measures to determine the level of risk associated with a specific hazard. The assessment step in the process defines the probability and severity of a mishap that could result from the hazard and determines the exposure of personnel or assets to that hazard.

- **Develop Control Measures and Make Risk Decision.** Investigate specific strategies and tools that reduce, mitigate, or eliminate the risk. Effective control measures reduce one or more of the three components (probability, severity, or exposure) of risk. Decision makers at the appropriate level choose controls based on the analysis of overall costs and benefits.

- **Implement Controls.** Once control strategies have been selected, an implementation strategy needs to be developed and then applied by management and the work force. Implementation requires commitment of time and resources.

- **Supervise and Evaluate.** Risk management is a process that continues throughout the life cycle of the system, mission, or activity. Once controls are in place, the process must be scrutinized and reevaluated to determine its effectiveness. Mission performance is periodically evaluated to determine the effectiveness of risk control measures.

WHAT IS RISK?

The following chart depicts risk: as risk is evaluated some emerge as clearly unacceptable. The unacceptable risk will either be controlled or the task will not be performed as planned. Some risk is not identified until later in the planning process or in the actual operation phase. That risk is evaluated as it's identified and additional controls either put into place or the risk is accepted or eliminated. Risk perception, risk tolerance, and risk acceptance play major roles in an individual's definition of "risk". Diversity of age, experience, and training are among the filters individuals use to consider risk. Level of experience with the specific mission or task adds another dimension to each ndividual's concept of "risk".

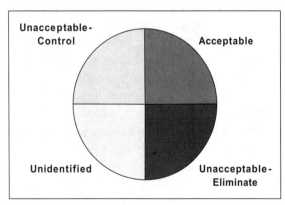

FIGURE 3.
TYPES OF RISK

WHAT ARE THE BENEFITS?

Benefits are not limited to reduced accident rates or decreased injuries, but may be actual increases in efficiency or job effectiveness. Examples of potential benefits include:

- Improved ability to protect the workforce by minimizing accidents—analysis of current processes may reduce risks.
- Enhanced job efficiency—reducing hazards by placing controls may make the task flow decisions are based on a reasoned and repeatable process instead of guess work or intuition.
- Improved confidence in capabilities—adequate risk analysis provides a clear picture of workforce strengths and weaknesses.

WHAT IS UNNECESSARY RISK?

Applying risk management requires a clear understanding of what constitutes "unnecessary risk", when benefits actually outweigh costs, and some guidance as to the appropriate level. Accepting risk is a function of both risk assessment and risk management. Risk acceptance is not as simple a matter as it may first appear. Several points must be kept in mind.

- Some risk is a fundamental reality.
- Risk management is a process of tradeoffs.
- Quantifying risk doesn't ensure safety.

General risk management guidelines are:

- Many activities involving a technical device or complex process entail some risk during their execution.
- Weigh risks and make judgments according to knowledge, experience, and mission requirements.
- Encourage other disciplines to adopt risk management principles. Hazard analysis and risk assessment do not free us from reliance on good judgment.
- It is more important to establish clear objectives and parameters for risk assessment than to find a "cookbook" approach and procedure.
- There may be no "best solution." There are a variety of directions to go. Each of these directions may produce some degree of risk reduction.
- Point out improvements to established controls rather than to say their approach will not work.
- Complete risk control is not the goal; total risk elimination is seldom achieved in a practical manner.

WHO DOES WHAT?

Commanders:

- Set the example both on and off duty.
- Establish, endorse, and enforce established standards.
- Reinforce personal accountability.
- Accept responsibility for effective management of risk.
- Select from risk reduction options provided by the staff.
- Accept or reject risk based on the benefit to be derived.
- Train and motivate leaders to use risk management.
- Elevate to the appropriate decision maker; based on clearly defined risk levels.

Supervisors:

- Apply the risk management process and direct personnel to use it both on and off duty.
- Consistently apply effective risk management concepts and methods to operations and tasks.
- Elevate risk issues beyond their control or authority to superiors for resolution.

Individuals:

- Understand, accept, and implement risk management processes.
- Maintain a constant awareness of the hazards associated with a task.
- Make supervisors immediately aware of any unrealistic risk reduction measures or high risk procedures.

HOW MUCH IS ENOUGH?

Somewhere between the back of an envelope and a multi-year, multi-million dollar, contractor-engineered PERT chart lies the right amount of risk management for the task or mission at hand. How much is enough? How do you advise the Commander as to the most appropriate level of detail for a particular task or mission? What criteria would you use to make your recommendation?

- We've talked about "effective application of the Risk Management process". It means that "hands on", not just following the "fine print", defines an efficient and effective process when it comes to Risk Management. It's easy to fall into using some format that soon becomes a thoughtless process. That road may be efficient; but it's rarely effective and it's full of potholes. We've talked about Risk Management providing insights into balancing cost and benefit. Some, often many, of the costs and benefits are subjective. So, again to the question 'What criteria' would you use to advise the commander on how much Risk Management is enough? There is no easy answer. Yet, at the same time, we all know that the cost benefit of effective Risk Management for a major mobilization would likely be greater than for an everyday delivery of ammunition to a training site. "Enough" Risk Management for a three day holiday weekend for a unit of young soldiers is different than "enough" for a TDA unit of more senior military and civilian personnel facing the same holiday weekend. Some suggested criteria:
- Is hasty or is deliberate decision making underway?
- Is time available to plan?
- What's the Importance of mission success—100% OK? 75%, 50%? What if it fails completely?
- Is the mission or task a new one or an old familiar one?
- Are personnel involved new to the mission or task? Unit? Experienced/Inexperienced?
- What's been their operation tempo recently?

Don't look for a cookbook answer to the question "How much is enough?". You'll only know you're giving the right advise if the spirit of the Risk Management process is not eclipsed by rote compliance with the fine print and filling in blanks on a form.

HOW DO I EVALUATE OUR PROGRAM?

If we use the army performance improvement criteria as a self-assessment tool - where does assessing the level of risk management fit in?

Tools in the appendix of this handbook stress self-assessment in the same manner as the Army Community of Excellence (ACOE). The ACOE Program is a commander's self-assessment process. It is broad enough to accommodate a variety of approaches that can be tailored to any organization, command or installation. Leaders and managers take advantage of the entrepreneurial genius of the people within the community to develop better ways of helping people and getting work done. It is a process which encourages ideas and initiatives to float upward. Embedding the risk management process into organizational processes is one way to help people and get work done better. The idea behind risk management is to identify strengths/weaknesses in planning and execution with emphasis on hazard control. The value of self-assessments is the awakening of self-awareness. With this self-awareness, change is more readily accepted.

Risk management integration as a part of 'Army Communities of Excellence' can help change the thinking from "minimal essential" to "maximum possible" philosophies in providing support to soldiers. Soldiers are deserving of nothing less than excellence; they are entitled to quality of life commensurate with that of the society they are sworn to defend. Authority and responsibility must be pushed down into the organization.

Get to know the ACOE coordinator at your installation. Look at how the APIC is used. Develop strategies that help measure the risk management integration approach; deployment, and results during the APIC self-assessment.

WHERE DOES THE SAFETY OFFICE FIT IN?

The safety professional is the link between the compliance world and the world of uncontrolled risk. The first step the safety professional makes is to help leaders recognize that risks can be controlled, that accidental losses need not be the cost of doing business. Whether an individual views a task or mission as having group or individual risk plays a major role in whether the individual believes he can take action to reduce the risk. The safety professional can facilitate a change of attitude from the idea that warehousemen have back injuries", or group risk about which little can be done; to the reality of individual risk, where worksite redesign, individual work-hardening, or use of manual materials handling equipment and eliminate the hazard. Once leaders believe that losses are unnecessary, the next step is that the safety professional can provide the Risk

Management process as a deliberate, logical decision making methodology to control the hazards that lead to unnecessary losses. Now, the safety professional must advise leaders on how much Risk Management is appropriate to the task at hand and facilitate the process.

Professional safety personnel provide knowledge of Occupational Health and Safety standards, application of safety practices to recognize, avoid/eliminate hazards, and for hazard control and evaluation techniques that provide the foundation of a safe workplace. Safety professionals are investigators when hazardous conditions turn into accidents or incidents related to inadequately controlled hazards. Safety offices assist in training, program management and coordinating with installation Health and Safety related offices; to include Preventive Medicine, Engineers, Provost Marshal, and Logistics.

Appendix A: Risk Management Steps

Tools to accomplish the various steps are explained and examples are given in, The Risk Manager's *Hazard Identification Tool Box*.

Step 1. IDENTIFY THE HAZARDS.

Hazards lead to risk, so the first step is to identify relevant hazards. Consider all aspects of current and future situations, environment, and known historical problems.

In identifying hazards, experience and training cannot be overemphasized; it is the most effective tool available. Those who have experience must use it, if an organization is to effectively use the RM process. Still, everyone is responsible for, and should be involved in finding potential hazards and informing their supervisor.

Visualization is an effective method to identify hazards. Picture the planned operation, think of what could go wrong—**ask yourself what if**? This can be done by an individual or a group, and can also use quality techniques such as brainstorming, "five whys", mental imaging, affinity diagrams, or cause-effect diagrams. The bottom line is: Honestly assess the planned procedure—**Think of what could go wrong, no matter how unlikely**.

Recognize Hazards: The Activity Hazard Analysis and Job Hazard Analysis (JHA) are both excellent tools to help identify risk as you think through a course of action to be

RESOURCE

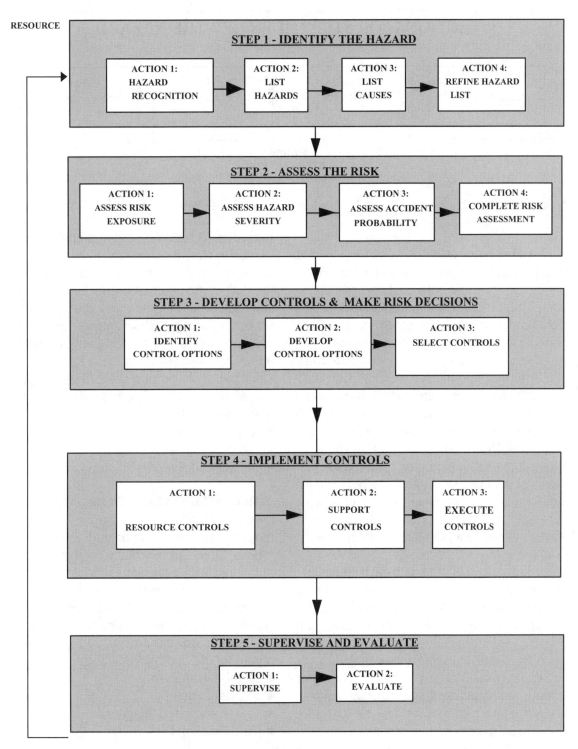

FIGURE 4
RISK MANAGEMENT STEPS

examined. This is accomplished by reviewing current and planned operations describing the task. The supervisor defines what is required to accomplish the tasks and the conditions under which these tasks are to be conducted.

Construct a list or chart depicting the major steps in the job process, normally in time sequence. Break the operation down into 'bite size' chunks.

Some tools that will help perform mission/ task analysis are:

- Activity Hazard Analysis
- Job Hazard Analysis
- Flow Diagram

Appendix

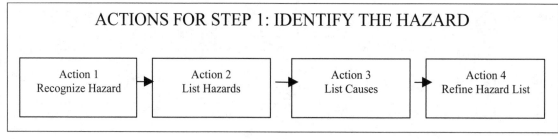

ACTIONS FOR STEP 1: IDENTIFY THE HAZARD

| Action 1 Recognize Hazard | Action 2 List Hazards | Action 3 List Causes | Action 4 Refine Hazard List |

FIGURE 5
STEP 1 ACTIONS

- Multilinear Event Sequence (MES)
- Sequentially Timed Event Plot (STEP)

List Hazards: Hazards, and factors that could generate hazards, are identified based on the deficiency to be corrected and the definition of the task and system requirements. The identification phase produces a listing of hazards or adverse conditions and the accidents which could result. Examples of inherent hazards in any one of the elements include fire, explosion, collision with objects, or electrocution. The analysis must also search for factors that can lead to hazards such as alertness, ambiguity, or escape route. In addition to a hazard list for the elements above, interfaces between or among these elements should be investigated for hazards. An individual required to make critical and delicate adjustment to equipment on a cold, dark night may be at risk to a frost-bite injury, maybe an example of the "interface hazards." Make a list of the hazards associated with each step in the task process. Stay focused on the specific steps in the task being analyzed. Try to limit your list to "big picture" hazards (the final link in the chain of events leading to task degradation, personnel injury, death, or property damage). Hazards should be tracked on paper or in a computer spreadsheet/database system to organize ideas and serve as a record of the analysis for future use. Tools that help list hazards are:

- Preliminary Hazard Analysis.
- Change Analysis.
- Brainstorming.
- "What if" Analysis.

Identify hazards associated with these three categories:

- Task Degradation.
- Personal Injury or Death.
- Property Damage.

List Causes: Make a list of the causes associated with each hazard identified in the hazard list. A hazard may have multiple causes related to man, machine and environments. In each case, try to identify the root cause (the first link in the chain of events leading to mission degradation, personnel injury, death, or property damage). Risk controls can be effectively applied to root causes. Causes should be annotated with the associated hazards in the same paper or computer record mentioned in the previous action. Suggested tools are:

- Change Analysis.
- Brainstorming.
- "What if" Analysis.
- Job Hazard Analysis.

Refine Hazard Lists: If time and resources permit, and additional hazard information is required, use strategic hazard analysis techniques. These are normally used for medium and long term planning, complex tasks, or operations in which the hazards are not well understood. The first step of in-depth analysis should be to examine existing databases or available historical and hazard information regarding the operation. Suggested tools are:

- Database analysis.
- Accident History.
- Cause and effect diagrams.
- Tree Diagrams.

The following tools are particularly useful for complex, coordinated operations in which multiple units, participants, and system components and simultaneous events are involved: Complex operations risk management tools are:

- Sequentially timed event plot.
- Multilinear event sequence.
- Interface analysis.
- Failure mode and effect analysis.

ACTIONS FOR STEP 2: ASSESS HAZARDS

| Action 1 Assess Risk Exposure | Action 2 Assess Hazard Severity | Action 3 Assess Accident Probability | Action 4 Complete Assessment |

FIGURE 6
STEP 2 ACTIONS

There are many additional tools that can help identify hazards. One of the best is through a group process involving representatives directly from the workplace. A simple brainstorming process with a trained facilitator is very productive. The following is a partial list of sources of hazard identification:

- *Accident Reports*: These can come from within the organization, from tenants, within the chain of command, MACOMS, Safety Center, etc. Other sources might be medical reports, maintenance records, and fire and police reports.

- Inspector General (IG) reports: IG visits provide important feedback and written documentation on local process management.

- Accident Databases.

- *Surveys*: These can be unit generated. Target an audience and ask some very simple questions related to such topics as: What will your next accident be? Who will have it? What task will cause it? When will it happen? The survey can be a powerful tool because it pinpoints people in the workplace with first hand knowledge of the job. Often, first line supervisors in the same workplace won't have as good an understanding of risk as those who confront it every day.

- *Inspections*: Safety inspections can consist of spot checks, walk-throughs, checklist inspections, site surveys, and mandatory inspections. Use onsite workers to provide input beyond the standard third-party inspection.

Step 2. ASSESS HAZARDS.

For each hazard identified in the previous step:

Assess Hazards. Once hazards are found, the next step is to analyze the associated risk—how likely and how big a loss is possible? **Recognition and assessment is the core of the Risk Management process.** Risk Management process depends on doing good analyses at each step in the process.

Assess Hazard Exposure: Probability is effected by exposure. Repeated exposure to a hazard greatly increases the total likelihood of an accident. This can be expressed in terms of time, proximity, volume, or repetition. Does it happen often, or near personnel or equipment? Does the event happen to a lot of people or equipment? This level can aid in determining the severity or the probability of the event. Additionally, it may serve as a guide for devising control measures to limit exposure. Another important concept is **interaction**. Interaction occurs when two (or more) hazards are present and their total risk is much greater than simply adding their separate risks. It's more like multiplying than adding. Often it is the combination of several factors that make a situation hazardous, rather than any single factor. Experience and clear thinking are the best ways to consistently assess interaction.

Assess Hazard Severity: Determine the severity of the hazard in terms of its potential impact on the people, equipment, or mission. Cause and effect diagrams, scenarios and "What-If" analysis are some of the best tools for assessing the hazard severity. Severity assessment should be based upon the worst possible outcome that can reasonably be expected. Severity categories are defined to provide a qualitative measure of the worst credible accident resulting from personnel error, environmental FIGURE 7 conditions; design inadequacies; procedural deficiencies; or system, subsystem, or component failure or malfunction. Using

SEVERITY	PROBABILITY				
	Frequent	Likely	Occasional	Seldom	Unlikely
Catastrophic	E	E	H	H	M
Critical	E	H	H	M	L
Marginal	H	M	M	L	L
Negligible	M	L	L	L	L

Risk Level: E-Extremely High, H-High, M-Moderate, L-Low

PROBABILITY - The likelihood that an event will occur.
FREQUENT - Occurs often, continuously experienced.
LIKELY - Occurs several times.
OCCASIONAL - Occurs sporadically.
SELDOM - Unlikely, but could occur at some time.
UNLIKELY - Can assume it will not occur.

SEVERITY - The expected consequence of an event in terms of degree of injury, property damage, or other mission-impairing factors.
CATASTROPHIC - Death or permanent total disability, system loss, major property damage, not able to accomplish mission.
CRITICAL - Permanent partial disability, temporary total disability in excess of 3 months, major system damage, significant property damage, significantly degrades mission capability.
MARGINAL - Minor injury, lost workday accident, minor system damage, minor property damage, some degradation of mission capability.
NEGLIGIBLE - First aid or minor medical treatment, minor system impairment, little/no impact on accomplishment of mission.

FIGURE 7

severity categories provide guidance to a wide variety of missions and systems.

Assess Accident Probability: Determine the probability that the hazard will cause an accident or loss of the severity assessed above. Accident probability is proportional to the cumulative probability of the identified causes for the hazard. Probability may be determined through estimates or actual numbers, if they are available. Assigning a quantitative accident probability to a new mission or system may not be possible early in the planning process.

A qualitative accident probability may be derived from research, analysis, and evaluation of historical safety data from similar missions and systems. The typical accident sequence is much more complicated than a single line of erect dominos where tipping the first domino (hazard) triggers a clearly predictable reaction. Supporting rationale for assigning a accident probability should be documented for future reference.

Complete Risk Assessment: Combine severity and probability estimates to form a risk assessment for each hazard. By combining the probability of occurrence with severity, a matrix is created where intersecting rows and columns define a Risk Assessment Index (RAI), table 3-3, AR 385-10. The Risk Assessment Index forms the basis for judging both the acceptability of a risk and the management level at which the decision of acceptance will be made.

The index may also be used to prioritize resources to resolve risks due to hazards or to standardize hazard notification or response actions. Severity, probability, and risk assessment should be recorded to serve as a record of the analysis for future use. Existing databases, Risk Assessment Index matrix, or a panel of personnel experienced with the mission and hazards can be used to help complete the risk assessment.

The following are some analytical pitfalls that should be avoided in the assessment:

- *Overoptimism*: "It can't happen to us. We're already doing it." This pitfall results from not being totally honest and not looking for root causes of risk.
- *Misrepresentation*: Individual perspectives may distort data.
- *Alarmist*: "The sky's falling" approach, or "worst case" estimates are used.
- *Indiscrimination*: All data is given equal weight.
- *Prejudice*: Subjectivity and/or hidden agendas are used, rather than facts.
- *Inaccuracy*: Bad or misunderstood data nullifies accurate risk assessment.
  - It is difficult to assign a numerical value to human behavior.
  - Numbers may oversimplify real life situations.
  - It may be difficult to get enough applicable data, which could force inaccurate estimates.

ACTIONS FOR STEP 3: DEVELOP CONTROLS AND MAKE RISK DECISION

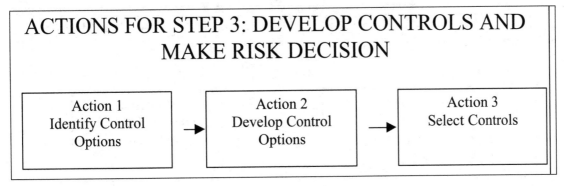

FIGURE 8
STEP 3 ACTIONS

- Oftentimes simple numbers take the place of reasoned judgment.
- Risk can be unrealistically traded off against benefit by relying solely on numbers.

Step 3. DEVELOP CONTROLS & MAKE RISK DECISIONS.

In this area, one must "develop control measures that eliminate the hazard or reduce its risk. As control measures are developed, risks are re-evaluated until all risks are reduced to a level where benefits outweigh potential cost."

Identify Control Options: The process of developing controls starts by taking the risk levels determined in Step 2, then identifying as many risk control options as possible for all hazards which exceed an acceptable level of risk. Refer to the list of possible causes from Step 1 for control ideas. Brainstorming, mission accident analysis and "What-If" analysis are excellent tools to identify control options. Risk control options include: **avoidance, reduction, spreading** and **transference**.

Avoiding risk altogether requires canceling or delaying the job, mission, or operation, but is an option that is rarely exercised due to mission importance. However, it may be possible to avoid specific risks: like wearing proper personal protective equipment can reduce risks in most job areas.

Risk can be **reduced**. The overall goal of risk management is to plan missions or design systems that do not contain uncontrolled hazards. A proven order of precedence for dealing with hazards and reducing the resulting risks is:

- **Plan or Design for Minimum Risk.** From the first, plan the mission or design the system to eliminate hazards. Without a hazard there is no probability, severity or exposure. If an identified hazard cannot be eliminated, reduce the associated risk to an acceptable level.
- **Incorporate Safety Devices.** If identified hazards cannot be eliminated or their associated risk adequately reduced by modifying the mission or system elements or their inputs, that risk should be reduced to an acceptable level through the use of safety design features or devices. Safety devices usually do not effect probability but reduce severity: an automobile seat belt doesn't prevent a collision but reduces the severity of injuries. Nomex gloves and steel toed boots won't prevent the hazardous event, or even change the probability of one occurring, but they prevent, or decrease the severity of, injury. Physical barriers fall into this category.
- **Provide Warning Devices.** When mission planning, system design, and safety devices cannot effectively eliminate identified hazards or adequately reduce associated risk, devices should be used to detect the condition and warn personnel of the hazard. Warning signals and their application should be designed to minimize the probability of the incorrect personnel reaction to the signals and should be standardized. Flashing red lights or sirens are a common warning device that most people understand.
- **Develop Procedures and Training.** Where it is impractical to eliminate hazards through design selection or adequately reduce the associated risk with safety and warning devices, procedures and training should be used. If the system is well designed and the mission well planned, the only remaining risk

FIGURE 9
STEP 4. CONTROL ACTION

reduction strategies may be procedures and training. *Emergency procedure training and disaster preparedness exercises improve human response to hazardous situations.*

Risk is commonly **spread** out by either increasing the exposure distance or by lengthening the time between exposure events. Administratively controlling exposure events, substitution of less hazardous chemicals or re-engineering an operation to reduce exposures to chemicals or toxic agents are examples.

Risk **transference** does not change probability or severity, however, possible losses or costs are shifted to another entity. An example is locating a remote sensing device in a high risk environment instead of risking personnel.

COMMON WAYS TO CONTROL RISK

- Protective equipment, clothing, or safety devices (PPE)
- Highlight hazards for extra care and handling
- Warnings (signs, color coding, audio/visual alarms)
- Repair hazards or build new facilities
- Limit exposure consistent with mission needs
- Train and educate
- Incorporate firm, fail-safe go/no-go criteria
- Select experienced or specialized personnel
- Increase and/or select more highly qualified and experienced supervision
- New policy—formal/informal, written/unwritten
- Develop new procedures

Develop Control Options: Determine the controls for the risk associated with the hazard. A computer spread sheet or data form (Job Hazard Analysis) may be used to list control ideas and indicate control effects. The estimated value(s) for severity and/or probability after implementation of control measures and the change in overall risk assessed from the Risk Assessment Index should be recorded. Scenario building and next accident assessment provide the greatest ability to determine control effects.

Select Controls: For each hazard, select those risk controls that will reduce the risk to an acceptable level.. The decision maker selects the control options after being briefed on all the possible controls. The best controls will be consistent with mission objectives and optimum use of available resources (manpower, material, equipment, money, time. It is not an ad hoc decision, but rather a logical, sequenced part of the risk management process. Decisions are made with awareness of hazards and how important hazard control is to success or failure of the mission (cost versus benefit).

Step 4. IMPLEMENT CONTROLS. The decision maker must allocate resources to control risk. Control decisions must be made at the appropriate level. The standard for risk management is leadership at the appropriate level of authority making informed decisions control hazards or accept risks.

Safety advisors and consultants do not control the necessary resources to implement the control decisions. Appropriate levels of decisions making reflect the ability of the decision maker to resource the controls.

Resource Controls: For each identified hazard, resource controls that will reduce the risk to an acceptable level. The best controls will be

ACTIONS FOR STEP 5: SUPERVISE AND EVALUATE

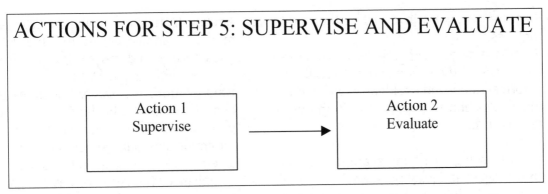

FIGURE 10
STEP 5 ACTIONS

consistent with mission objectives and optimum use of available resources (manpower, material, equipment, money, and time). Record implementation decisions for future reference. Should management determine that the controls require resources beyond their authority, they should elevate the risk decision to higher authority.

Order Controls: To be successful, command must support the control measures put in place. Then, explore appropriate ways to demonstrate command commitment. Provide the personnel and resources necessary to implement the control measures. Design in sustainability from the beginning. Deploy the control measure with a feedback mechanism that provides information on whether the control measure is achieving the intended purpose.

Step 5. SUPERVISE AND EVALUATE.

Supervise: Monitor the operation to ensure:
- The controls are effective and remain in place.
- Changes which require further risk management are identified.
- Action is taken when necessary to correct ineffective risk controls and reinitiate the risk management steps in response to new hazards.

Any time personnel, equipment or mission taskings change or new operations are anticipated in an environment not covered in the initial risk management analysis, the risks and control measures should be reevaluated. The goal of measurement is to answer the question of whether the control measure in fact controlled the associated hazard. The best tool for accomplishing this action of supervision is Change Analysis.

Evaluation: The process review must be systematic. After assets are expended to control risks, then a cost benefit analysis must be accomplished to see if risk and cost are in balance. Any changes in the system (the flow charts from the earlier steps provide convenient benchmarks to compare the present system to the original) are recognized and appropriate risk management controls are applied

To accomplish an effective review:
- Identify whether the actual cost is in line with expectations.
- What effect the control measure has had on mission performance.

Provide mission feedback system to ensure that the corrective or preventive action taken was effective and that any new hazards identified during the mission are analyzed and corrective action taken.

Audits: Measurements are necessary to ensure accurate evaluations of how effectively controls eliminated hazards or reduced risks. After action reports, surveys, and in progress reviews provide great starting places for measurements. To be meaningful, measurements must quantitatively or qualitatively identify reductions of risk, improvements in mission success, or enhancement of capabilities. The Risk Management Evaluation Profile (OSHA's PEP) in appendix B, provides an audit process of a programs overall effectiveness. Benefits of conducting an audit includes:
- Formally going through the internal audit process with managers and employees,
- Formally reviewing the elements of a safety and health program,

- Getting managers involved in the audit process,
- Making managers, supervisors and employees aware of the scope and complexity of a formal safety and health program, and of their roles and responsibilities in the programs success.

After finishing your audit share the results with managers and legal personnel. However the process of doing an audit creates a paper trail of the programs weaknesses. The audit is a formal tool to uncover weak points in the management system that create unsafe work practices and unsafe conditions that can injure workers, diminish their health, interrupt production, or damage products and property.

Conclusion. Risk management provides a logical and systematic means of organizing information for rational decision-making, to identify and control risk. Risk management is a process that requires individuals, supervisors and leaders to support and implement the basic principles, along with the discipline to apply them on a continuing basis. Risk management offers individuals and organizations a powerful tool for eliminating accidents and increasing effectiveness. This process has the unique advantage of being accessible to and usable by everyone in every conceivable setting or scenario. It ensures that all Army personnel will have a voice in the critical decisions that determine success or failure in all our missions and activities, on- and off-duty.

Appendix B: The Risk Management Evaluation Profile (RMEP)

Subject: The Risk Management Evaluation Profile (RMEP)

A. **Purpose.** To establish policies and procedures for the Risk Management Evaluation Profile (RMEP, the RMEP form, which can be used in assessing safety and health programs in general Army workplaces.

B. **Scope.** The RMEP is applicable to all Army workplaces.

C. **References.**
   1. AR 385-10, Army Safety Program.
   2. OSHA Instruction CPL 2.103, September 26, 1994, Field Inspection Reference Manual (FIRM).

D. **Action.** Installation CDRs, directors and managers should ensure that the guidelines and procedures set forth here are followed in using the RMEP.

E. **Background.** Assessment of safety and health conditions in the workplace depends on a clear understanding of the programs and management systems that an employer is using for safety and health compliance. The Army places a high priority on safety and health programs and mandates their implementation.

F. **Application.**
   1. The RMEP should be completed for a general evaluation of workplace safety and health programs.
      a. The RMEP is an educational document for workers and employers, as well as a source of information for use in the inspection process.
      b. In multi-employer workplaces, a RMEP shall be completed for the safety and health program of the host organization. This RMEP will normally apply to all subordinate organizations, and individual RMEPs need not be completed for them.
      c. The RMEP shall be used in experimental programs that require evaluation of an organizations safety and health program, except where other program evaluation methods/tools are specifically approved.
   2. The evaluation of the safety and health program contained in the RMEP shall be shared with the employer and with employee representatives.

G. **Using the RMEP.** The RMEP will be used as a source of safety and health program evaluation for the employer, employees.
   1. **Gathering Information for the RMEP** begins during the opening conference and continues through the inspection process.
      a. The evaluator shall explain the purpose of the RMEP and obtain information about the employer's safety and health program in order to make an initial assessment about the program.
      b. This initial assessment shall be verified—or modified—based on infor-

mation obtained in interviews of an appropriately representative number of employees and by observation of actual safety and health conditions during the inspection process.

2. **Recording the Score.** The program elements in the RMEP correspond generally to the major elements of the Guidelines.

a. **Elements.** The **six** elements to be scored in the RMEP are:
   (1) Management.
   (2) Leadership.
   (3) Employee Participation.
   (4) Hazard Identification.
   (5) Hazard Control.
   (6) Training.

b. **Factors.** These elements will also be scored. The score for an element will be determined by the factor scores. The factors are:
   ■ Management
   ■ Leadership.
      – Employee participation.
      – Contractor safety.
      – Survey and hazard identification.
      – Reporting.
      – Investigation of accidents and near-miss incidents
      – Data analysis.
      – Hazard control. Maintenance.
   ■ Medical program.
   ■ Training (as a whole).

c. **Scoring.** The evaluator shall objectively score the organization on each of the individual factors and elements after obtaining the necessary information to do so. These shall be given a score of 1, 2, 3,4, or 5. If the element or factor does not apply to the worksite being inspected, a notation of **"Not Applicable"** shall be made in the space provided. This shall not affect the score.
   (1) The attachment contains the **RMEP Tables**, which provide verbal descriptors of workplace characteristics for each factor for each of the five levels. Evaluators shall refer to these tables as appropriate to ensure that the score they assign to a factor corresponds to the descriptor that best fits the worksite.
   (2) Determine scores for each of the six elements as follows:

NOTE: The factors of "Management", "Leadership" and "Employee Participation" are given greater weight because they are considered the foundation of a safety and health program.

   (a) For each of the other elements, **average** the scores for the factors.
   (b) In **averaging** factor scores, round to the nearest whole number (1, 2, 3, 4, or 5). Round up from one-half (.5) or greater; round down from less than one-half (.5).

3. **Program Levels.** The Overall Score on the RMEP constitutes the "level" at which the establishment's safety and health program is scored. **Remember: This level is a relatively informal assessment.** The following chart summarizes the levels:

Score	Level of Safety and Health Program
5	Outstanding program
4	Superior program
3	Basic program
2	Developmental program
1	No program or ineffective program

4. **Specific Scoring Guidance.** The following shall be taken into account in assessing specific factors:
a. **Written Programs.** Employer safety and health programs should be in writing in order to be effectively implemented and communicated.

(1) Nevertheless, a program's **effectiveness** is more important than whether it is in writing.

    (a) An employer's failure to comply with a paperwork requirement is normally penalized only when there is a serious hazard related to this requirement.

    (b) An employer's failure to comply with a written program requirement is normally not penalized if the employer is actually taking the actions that are the subject of the requirement.

(2) Thus, evaluators should follow the general principle that "performance counts more than paperwork." In using the RMEP, the evaluator is responsible for evaluating the organizations actual management of safety and health in the workplace, not just the organizations documentation of a safety and health program.

b. **Employee Participation.**

(1) Employee involvement in an establishment's safety and health program is essential to its effectiveness. Thus, evaluation of safety and health programs must include objective assessment of the ways in which workers' rights and responsibilities are addressed in form and practice.

(2) Employee involvement should also include participation walk-around inspections, interviews, informal conferences, and formal settlement discussions, as may be appropriate. Many methods of employee involvement may be encountered in individual workplaces.

c. **Comprehensiveness.** The importance of a safety and health program's comprehensiveness is implicitly addressed in Hazard Identification under both hazard identification and Data analysis. An effective safety and health program shall address all known and potential sources of workplace injuries and illnesses, whether or not they are covered by a specific OSHA standard.

d. **Consistency with Violations/Hazards Found.** The RMEP evaluation and the scores assigned to the individual elements and factors should be consistent with the types and numbers of violations or hazards found during the inspection.

5. **Scope of the RMEP Review.** The duration of the RMEP review will vary depending on the circumstances of the workplace and the inspection. In all cases, however, this review shall include:

a. A review of any appropriate employer documentation relating to the safety and health program.

b. A walk-around inspection of pertinent areas of the workplace.

c. Interviews with an appropriate number of employer and employee representatives.

The RMEP Tables

- The text in each block provides a description of the program element or factor that corresponds to the level of program that the employer has implemented in the workplace.
- To avoid duplicative language, each level should be understood as containing all positive factors included in the level below it.

MANAGEMENT, LEADERSHIP and EMPLOYEE PARTICIPATION	
Management	
Visible management provides the motivating force for an effective safety and health program.	
1	Management demonstrates no policy, goals, objectives, or interest in safety and health issues at this worksite.
2	Management sets and communicates safety and health policy and goals, but remains detached from all other safety and health efforts.
3	Management follows all safety and health rules, and gives | visible support to the safety and health efforts of others.
4	Management participates in significant aspects of the site's safety and health program, such as site inspections, incident reviews, and program reviews. Incentive programs that discourage reporting of accidents, symptoms, injuries, or hazards are absent. Other incentive programs may be present.
5	Site safety and health issues are regularly included on agendas of management operations meetings. Management clearly demonstrates—by involvement, support, and example—the primary importance of safety and health for everyone on the worksite. Performance is consistent and sustained or has improved over time.
Notes:	

Employee Participation
Employee participation provides the means through which workers identify hazards, recommend and monitor abatement, and otherwise participate in their own protection.
1	Worker participation in workplace safety and health concerns is not encouraged. Incentive programs are present which have the effect of discouraging reporting of incidents, injuries, potential hazards or symptoms. Employees/employee representatives are not involved in the safety and health program.
2	Workers and their representatives can participate freely in safety and health activities at the worksite without fear of reprisal. Procedures are in place for communication between employer and workers on safety and health matters. Worker rights under the Occupational Safety and Health Act to refuse or stop work that they reasonably believe involves imminent danger are understood by workers and honored by management. Workers are paid while performing safety activities.
3	Workers and their representatives are involved in the safety and health program, involved in inspection of work area, and are permitted to observe monitoring and receive results. Workers' and representatives' right of access to information is understood by workers and recognized by management. A documented procedure is in place for raising complaints of hazards or discrimination and receiving timely employer responses.
4	Workers and their representatives participate in hazard identification analysis, inspections and investigations, and development of control strategies throughout facility, and have necessary training and education to participate in such activities. Workers and their representatives have access to all pertinent health and safety information, including safety reports and audits. Workers are informed of their right to refuse job assignments that pose serious hazards to themselves pending management response.
5	Workers and their representatives participate fully in development of the safety and health program and conduct of training and education. Workers participate in audits, program reviews conducted by management or third parties, and collection of samples for monitoring purposes, and have necessary training and education to participate in such activities. Employer encourages and authorizes employees to stop activities that present potentially serious safety and health hazards.
Notes:

LEADERSHIP
Implementation
Implementation means tools, provided by management, that include: — budget — information — personnel — assigned responsibility — adequate expertise and authority — means to hold responsible persons accountable (line accountability) — program review procedures.

1	Tools to implement a safety and health program are inadequate or missing.
2	Some tools to implement a safety and health program are adequate and effectively used; others are ineffective or inadequate. Management assigns responsibility for implementing a safety and health program to identified person(s). Management's designated representative has authority to direct abatement of hazards that can be corrected without major capital expenditure.
3	Tools to implement a safety and health program are adequate, but are not all effectively used. Safety representative is knowledgeable in hazard recognition and applicable OSHA requirements. Management keeps or has access to applicable OSHA standards at the facility, and seeks appropriate guidance information for interpretation of OSHA standards. Management representative has authority to order/purchase safety and health equipment.
4	All tools to implement a safety and health program are more than adequate and effectively used. Written safety procedures, policies, and interpretations are updated based on reviews of the safety and health program. Safety and health expenditures, including training costs and personnel, are identified in the facility budget. Hazard abatement is an element in management performance evaluation.
5	All tools necessary to implement a good safety and health program are more than adequate and effectively used. Management safety and health representative has expertise appropriate to facility size and process, and has access to professional advice when needed. Safety and health budgets and funding procedures are reviewed periodically for adequacy.
Notes:	

Appendix

Hazard Identification
Hazard Recognition and Evaluation
Survey and hazard analysis: An effective, proactive safety and health program will seek to identify and evaluate all hazards. In large or complex workplaces, components of such analysis are the **comprehensive survey** and **evaluations of job hazards and changes in conditions**.

1	No system or requirement exists for hazard review of planned/changed/new operations. There is no evidence of a comprehensive survey for safety or health hazards or for routine job hazard analysis.
2	Surveys for violations of standards are conducted by knowledgeable person(s), but only in response to accidents or complaints. The employer has identified principal OSHA standards which apply to the worksite.
3	Process, task, and environmental surveys are conducted by knowledgeable person(s) and updated as needed and as required by applicable standards. Current hazard analyses are written (where appropriate) for all high-hazard jobs and processes; analyses are communicated to and understood by affected employees. Hazard analyses are conducted for jobs/tasks/workstations where injury or illnesses have been recorded.
4	Methodical surveys are conducted periodically and drive appropriate corrective action. Initial surveys are conducted by a qualified professional. Current hazard analyses are documented for all work areas and are communicated and available to all the workforce; knowledgeable persons review all planned/changed/new facilities, processes, materials, or equipment.
5	Regular surveys including documented comprehensive workplace hazard evaluations are conducted by certified safety and health professional or professional engineer, etc. Corrective action is documented and hazard inventories are updated. Hazard analysis is integrated into the design, development, implementation, and changing of all processes and work practices.
	Notes:

	WORKPLACE ANALYSIS
	Hazard Assessment

Inspection: To identify new or previously missed hazards and failures in hazard controls, an effective safety and health program will include regular **site inspections.**

1	No routine physical inspection of the workplace and equipment is conducted.
2	Supervisors dedicate time to observing work practices and other safety and health conditions in work areas where they have responsibility.
3	Competent personnel conduct inspections with appropriate involvement of employees. Items in need of correction are documented. Inspections include compliance with relevant OSHA standards. Time periods for correction are set.
4	Inspections are conducted by specifically trained employees, and all items are corrected promptly and appropriately. Workplace inspections are planned, with key observations or check points defined and results documented. Persons conducting inspections have specific training in hazard identification applicable to the facility. Corrections are documented through follow-up inspections. Results are available to workers.
5	Inspections are planned and overseen by certified safety or health professionals. Statistically valid random audits of compliance with all elements of the safety and health program are conducted. Observations are analyzed to evaluate progress.
	Notes:

WORKPLACE ANALYSIS
Hazard Reporting
A reliable **hazard reporting system** enables employees, without fear of reprisal, to notify management of conditions that appear hazardous and to receive timely and appropriate responses. [Guidelines, (c)(2)(iii)]

1	No formal hazard reporting system exists, or employees are reluctant to report hazards.
2	Employees are instructed to report hazards to management. Supervisors are instructed and are aware of a procedure for evaluating and responding to such reports. Employees use the system with no risk of reprisals.
3	A formal system for hazard reporting exists. Employee reports of hazards are documented, corrective action is scheduled, and records maintained.
4	Employees are periodically instructed in hazard identification and reporting procedures. Management conducts surveys of employee observations of hazards to ensure that the system is working. Results are documented.
5	Management responds to reports of hazards in writing within specified time frames. The workforce readily identifies and self-corrects hazards; they are supported by management when they do so.

Notes:

WORKPLACE ANALYSIS
Accident Investigation
Accident investigation: An effective program will provide for **investigation of accidents and "near miss" incidents**, so that their causes, and the means for their prevention, are identified. [Guidelines, (c)(2)(iv)]

1	No investigation of accidents, injuries, near misses, or other incidents is conducted.
2	Some investigation of incidents takes place, but root cause may not be identified, and correction may be inconsistent. Supervisors prepare injury reports for lost time cases.
3	OSHA-101 is completed for all recordable incidents. Reports are generally prepared with cause identification and corrective measures prescribed.
4	OSHA-recordable incidents are always investigated, and effective prevention is implemented. Reports and recommendations are available to employees. Quality and completeness of investigations are systematically reviewed by trained safety personnel.
5	All loss-producing accidents and "near-misses" are investigated for root causes by teams or individuals that include trained safety personnel and employees.

Notes:

WORKPLACE ANALYSIS	
Data Analysis	
Data analysis: An effective program will **analyze injury and illness records** for indications of sources and locations of hazards, and jobs that experience higher numbers of injuries. By analyzing injury and illness trends over time, patterns with common causes can be identified and prevented.	
1	Little or no analysis of injury/illness records; exposure monitoring) are kept or conducted.
2	Data is collected and analyzed, but not widely used for prevention. Reports are completed for all recordable cases. Exposure records and analyses are organized and are available to safety personnel.
3	Injury/illness logs and exposure records are kept correctly, are audited by facility personnel, and are essentially accurate and complete. Rates are calculated so as to identify high risk areas and jobs. Workers compensation claim records are analyzed and the results used in the program. Significant analytical findings are used for prevention.
4	Employer can identify the frequent and most severe problem areas, the high risk areas and job classifications, and any exposures responsible for OSHA recordable cases. Data are fully analyzed and effectively communicated to employees. Illness/injury data are audited and certified by a responsible person.
5	All levels of management and the workforce are aware of results of data analyses and resulting preventive activity. External audits of accuracy of injury and illness data, including review of all available data sources are conducted. Scientific analysis of health information, including non-occupational data bases is included where appropriate in the program.
Notes:	

HAZARD CONTROL
Hazard Control
Hazard Control: Workforce exposure to all current and potential hazards should be prevented or controlled by using **engineering controls** wherever feasible and appropriate, **work practices** and **administrative controls**, and **personal protective equipment** (PPE).

1	Hazard controls are seriously lacking or absent from the facility.
2	Hazard controls are generally in place, but effectiveness and completeness vary. Serious hazards may still exist. Employer has achieved general compliance with applicable OSHA standards regarding hazards with a significant probability of causing serious physical harm. Hazards that have caused past injuries in the facility have been corrected.
3	Appropriate controls (engineering, work practice, and administrative controls, and PPE) are in place for significant hazards. Some serious hazards may exist. Employer is generally in compliance with voluntary standards, industry practices, and manufacturers, and suppliers' safety recommendations. Documented reviews of needs for machine guarding, energy lockout, ergonomics, materials handling, bloodborne pathogens, confined space, hazard communication, and other generally applicable standards have been conducted. The overall program tolerates occasional deviations.
4	Hazard controls are fully in place, and are known and supported by the workforce. Few serious hazards exist. The employer requires strict and complete compliance with all OSHA, consensus, and industry standards and recommendations. All deviations are identified and causes determined.
5	Hazard controls are fully in place and continually improved upon based on workplace experience and general knowledge. Documented reviews of needs are conducted by certified health and safety professionals or professional engineers, etc.
Notes:	

HAZARD CONTROL
Maintenance
Maintenance: An effective safety and health program will provide for **facility and equipment maintenanc**e, so that hazardous breakdowns are prevented.

1	No preventive maintenance program is in place; break-down maintenance is the rule.
2	There is a preventive maintenance schedule, but it does not cover everything and may be allowed to slide or performance is not documented. Safety devices on machinery and equipment are generally checked before each production shift.
3	A preventive maintenance schedule is implemented for areas where it is most needed; it is followed under normal circumstances. Manufacturers' and industry recommendations and consensus standards for maintenance frequency are complied with. Breakdown repairs for safety related items are expedited. Safety device checks are documented. Ventilation system function is observed periodically.
4	The employer has effectively implemented a preventive maintenance schedule that applies to all equipment. Facility experience is used to improve safety-related preventative maintenance scheduling.
5	There is a comprehensive safety and preventive maintenance program that maximizes equipment reliability.
Notes:	

HAZARD CONTROL
Medical Program

An effective safety and health program will include a suitable **medical program** where it is appropriate for the size and nature of the workplace and its hazards.

1	Employer is unaware of, or unresponsive to medical needs. Required medical surveillance, monitoring, and reporting are absent or inadequate.
2	Required medical surveillance, monitoring, removal, and reporting responsibilities for applicable standards are assigned and carried out, but results may be incomplete or inadequate.
3	Medical surveillance, removal, monitoring, and reporting comply with applicable standards. Employees report early signs/symptoms of job-related injury or illness and receive appropriate treatment.
4	Health care providers provide follow-up on employee treatment protocols and are involved in hazard identification and control in the workplace. Medical surveillance addresses conditions not covered by specific standards. Employee concerns about medical treatment are documented and responded to.
5	Health care providers are on-site for all production shifts and are involved in hazard identification and training. Health care providers periodically observe the work areas and activities and are fully involved in hazard identification and training.

Notes:

TRAINING
Safety and health training should cover the safety and health responsibilities of all personnel who work at the site or affect its operations. It is most effective when incorporated into other training about performance requirements and job practices. It should include all subjects and areas necessary to address the hazards at the site.

1	Facility depends on experience and peer training to meet needs. Managers/supervisors demonstrate little or no involvement in safety and health training responsibilities.
2	Some orientation training is given to new hires. Some safety training materials (e.g., pamphlets, posters, videotapes) are available or are used periodically at safety meetings, but there is little or no documentation of training or assessment of worker knowledge in this area. Managers generally demonstrate awareness of safety and health responsibilities, but have limited training themselves or involvement in the site's training program.
3	Training includes OSHA rights and access to information. Training required by applicable standards is provided to all site employees. Supervisors and managers attend training in all subjects provided to employees under their direction. Employees can generally demonstrate the skills/knowledge necessary to perform their jobs safely. Records of training are kept and training is evaluated to ensure that it is effective.
4	Knowledgeable persons conduct safety and health training that is scheduled, assessed, and documented, and addresses all necessary technical topics. Employees are trained to recognize hazards, violations of OSHA standards, and facility practices. Employees are trained to report violations to management. All site employees—including supervisors and managers—can generally demonstrate preparedness for participation in the overall safety and health program. There are easily retrievable scheduling and record keeping systems.
5	Knowledgeable persons conduct safety and health training that is scheduled, assessed, and documented. Training covers all necessary topics and situations, and includes all persons working at the site (hourly employees, supervisors, managers, contractors, part-time and temporary employees). Employees participate in creating site-specific training methods and materials. Employees are trained to recognize inadequate responses to reported program violations. Retrievable record keeping system provides for appropriate retraining, makeup training, and modifications to training as the result of evaluations.

Notes:

1. Site Location:		2. Page	1	of	1
3. Task:	4. Date Begin:	5. Date End:		6. Date Form Prepared:	

7. Operational Phase in which the Task will be conducted:

8. Prepared by: (Name /Duty Position)

9. Identified Hazards:	10. Assess Hazards: Initial Risk: (Must Be Filled In By Hand)				11. Develop Control Measures for Identified Hazards: (measures to reduce probability and severity of a hazard)	12. Make Risk Decisions: Remaining Risk: (Must Be Filled In By Hand)	13. How to Implement the Controls: (Include SOPs, PPE etc.)	14. Supervision and Evaluation by: (Name of Supervisor, worker, team, etc.)
	L	M	H	E				
(Be Specific)						(Be Specific)		
							L	M	H	E		
						(Be Specific)	(Be Specific)	

15. Remaining Risk Level After Countermeasures Are Implemented: ↑ (CIRCLE HIGHEST REMAINING RISK LEVEL)

LOW	MEDIUM	HIGH	EXTREMELY HIGH
Employee doing the Job	Immediate Supervisor	Site Supervisor	CEO/OWNER

16. RISK AUTHORITY: Signature of the employee accepting the risk and liability for the operation
(Signature indicates only that the appropriate risk decision authority was notified of the initial risk level, control measures taken and appropriate resources requested)

Notes

Notes

Notes

Notes

Notes